OIL RESERVOIR ENGINEERING

Oil Reservoir Engineering

SYLVAIN J. PIRSON

Professor of Petroleum Engineering
The University of Texas

SECOND EDITION

McGRAW-HILL BOOK COMPANY, INC.

New York Toronto London

1958

OIL RESERVOIR ENGINEERING

 Library of Congress Catalog Card Number 57-10917.

IV

50074

PREFACE

The oil reservoir engineer may view with excusable pride the rapid progress which has been achieved at an accelerated rate in his chosen field of applied science. On the theoretical side, notable advances have been made by the derivation of fundamental equations which describe the flow behavior of reservoir fluids in underground reservoirs. On the experimental side, instruments have been developed for the measurement of reservoir rock and fluid properties and of the relative ability of oil, water, and gas to flow simultaneously through such porous media. On the applied side, the reservoir-performance forecasts made by engineers have received recognition and are the basis for the establishment of well-founded production practices which promote conservation of oil and gas reserves. Royalty owners, oil operators, and the public alike are thereby assured of longer-lasting and more abundant supplies of the petroleum fuels and lubricants which have become such an important necessity in our daily activities.

Since publication of the first edition of this volume in 1950, oil reservoir engineering has attained the status of a science, for a science is made up of a body of principles rather than of a mere accumulation of facts, even though in an inductive science such as this it is on these facts that established principles are based. In the development of an inductive science, the interpretation of data is a process by which the gap between the known and the unknown is bridged through vision and imagination. In this process, as in all science, advances were made by eliminating counter hypotheses through carefully controlled experiments. Advances in a particular science are also made by, and depend to a large extent upon, formulation of simple and straightforward statements of hypotheses from which testable deductions are derived. In the present volume such statements have been made, particularly with reference to Petrophysics (Chapter 3) wherein the possibility is indicated of determining relative permeability to two-phase fluid flow from electrical measurements and, therefore, from electric well logs. The hypotheses made in the development of relative-permeability formulas also lead to the testable conclusion that relative-permeability characteristics of porous media should be dependent on the properties of the fluids in motion when the wetting phase is imbibed.

The present volume may be considered as being made up of two sections. The *first section* includes Chapters 1 to 9 inclusive; they are a systematic presentation of the steps by which an *evaluation of the original oil in place* may be made. An oil reservoir, whatever it may be, is made up of two parts, the container and the contained material. Altogether too often, reservoir engineers are prone to forget that the oil containers they deal with are geologic media, variable in unpredictable and unexpected manners in all directions in space, the exact physical properties of which could only be determined by virtually continuous sampling. For practical and economic reasons, the sampling of the reservoir containers and of their fluids is necessarily discrete and limited to a number of wells. It behooves the reservoir engineers to make the most of the well information made available to them, among which well logs of all sorts are by far the most common tools placed in their hands. In view of the important recent advances made since the publication of "Elements of Oil Reservoir Engineering" in 1950 and in view of the increased realization that well logs, and more particularly electric logs, contribute greatly to the delineation of a reservoir, two chapters, 4 and 5, are devoted to the interpretation of such logs in terms of the reservoir-rock characteristics which they reflect. The relative importance attributed to well-log study in this volume is definitely in relation to the time a reservoir engineer generally allocates to this study in making the analysis of a specific field.

Since the first publication of this book, a great many advances have been made also in the laboratory techniques of measuring relative permeabilities. However, the direct applicability of the results of such measurements to the prediction of reservoir performance is yet much in doubt; at this writing it appears that the difficulties stem both from possible inadequate laboratory techniques and from inadequate sampling of the reservoir rock by an insufficient number of wells. Techniques by which uniformity and continuity of reservoir properties may be ascertained are indicated in Chapter 2 as a possible lead by which performance studies may be tempered by reservoir-rock inhomogeneities. The study of reservoir-fluid properties and of reservoir pressure and energy is virtually unchanged from the previous edition; this does not indicate that there has been no advance in these fields of study, but rather that limitation of space rendered impractical a more complete revision.

Chapter 8, devoted to fluid flow in porous media, is an addition to the present volume which introduces in elementary fashion the various practical uses to which Darcy's law may be applied. This includes an elementary treatment of transient single-phase fluid flow and of the tilt of interfaces between immiscible fluids in dynamic equilibrium when one or two of them are in motion.

Chapter 9 is devoted to a study of volumetric evaluation of hydrocarbons in place and illustrates the means by which the reservoir engineer makes use of all available tools—geology, core analysis, log interpretation, and fluid properties—in arriving at the most probable value of the oil in place.

The *second section* of this volume, which includes Chapters 10 to 14 inclusive, is, properly speaking, the section that deals with the *forecast and control of reservoir performance*. Reservoir performance, it is too often forgotten, includes the characteristic variations of pressure, of gas-oil ratio, and of productivity index of the wells as a function of cumulative recovery and/or of time. The above functions are the *essential elements* of reservoir engineering from which *derived elements,* such as cumulative oil and gas production, rate of production, and reserves of both oil and gas, which are more useful perhaps from an economic standpoint, may be obtained. In making these studies in a particular reservoir, it is necessary to match the available past performance history by theory; yet, although the past performance is indeed a guide to the future, it is the prediction of future performance which dominates the thinking and activities of a reservoir engineer. Many methods and techniques have been published for so doing; many more have been devised and have remained unpublished. When reading the literature, the student is generally dismayed by the existence of a maze of conflicting computation techniques.

The reservoir-performance computation methods offered in this volume are based mainly on the use of the *finite-difference form of the material balance equation.* In this manner undergraduate and graduate students, whose investment in computers generally does not exceed the cost of a slide rule, may be introduced to an understanding of the various intricate behavior mechanisms by which oil and gas are recovered from their underground reservoirs. Although calculators are recommended as computing means, accurate reservoir-behavior calculations may indeed be obtained with a slide rule through careful computations by the finite-difference method. In addition, the more sophisticated reservoir engineers will find the finite-difference material balance method highly suitable for programming reservoir analyses on digital high-speed computers.

In the references throughout this volume will be found the names of numerous distinguished authors, associates past and present, and former students who have contributed mostly by their writings but also by personal discussions with the author to the gathering of material for this book. To them, an appreciative acknowledgment is made.

Sylvain J. Pirson

CONTENTS

INTRODUCTION

Reservoir engineering may be defined as the *art of forecasting the future performance of a geologic oil and/or gas reservoir from which production is obtained according to probable and preassumed conditions.* As an *art* dealing with physical conditions occurring in nature, reservoir engineering partakes of many scientific disciplines within the scale of human knowledge. In addition, the forecasting petroleum engineer must accumulate and understand a wealth of knowledge collected by his colleagues, the petroleum geologist and the sedimentary petrographer, on the nature of the reservoir rock, on its granular, textural, and mineral make-up, and on the development of its porosity and permeability. He must further understand the complexity of the reservoir considered at large, such as the type of geologic trap which retains the oil underground, whether the trap is structural or stratigraphic in character, the lateral extension of the reservoir rock, its layering process, its possible outcropping where meteoric water will perhaps infiltrate, its probable dip, connate water-table level, structural closure, etc. In the early stages of development of a reservoir, many of these answers cannot be furnished by the geologist; he must call upon another colleague, the geophysicist, who perhaps can inform him on the probable extent of structural closure. Most certainly, the reservoir engineer will deal with numerous geophysical bore-hole measurements, electric and radiation well logs, temperature and caliper logs, and perhaps even with drill time and drilling mud logs. Owing to the expense and uncertainties of core-analysis results, reservoir-rock data obtainable from geophysical well logs are a welcome addition to the engineer's supply of dependable reservoir data.

Under the temperatures and pressures encountered in modern deep wells, reservoir fluids behave in strange and unexpected ways. A prerequisite to good reservoir performance forecasting is a dependable knowledge of reservoir temperature and pressure in addition to precise information on the physical behavior of gas, oil, and water under reservoir conditions. In general, hydrocarbons may be found in the reservoir in one of the following physical states: undersaturated petroleum, saturated petroleum, distillate petroleum, and dry gas. Each of these requires special handling if maximum recovery is to be achieved.

It is now recognized that the expulsive energy operating on the fluids in a primary reservoir is essentially confined to four sources, namely:

1. *External* driving fluid energy under hydrostatic head, usually edge

and bottom waters. Gas-cap expansion may also be considered as deriving its energy from an external source.

2. *Internal* driving energy, from gases in solution at reservoir pressure.

3. *Potential* energy, or energy of position owing to the action of body forces, usually gravitational pull because of differential densities in the reservoir fluids.

4. *Surface* energy of reservoir fluids as a result of capillary forces.

As in many useful arts where the complexities of a natural medium are dealt with, it is often expedient to substitute a bulk-property measurement for specific microscopic properties even though the constituent properties are amenable to physical reckoning. This is the case for the capillary forces which are controlled by the rock texture, preferential wetting, saturation degree, and interfacial tension. Capillary-pressure determinations of rock samples which lump all the above parameters in one test may be considered as one of the important reservoir-engineering achievements of recent years.

So much for the contact of the reservoir engineer with the natural sciences. He must now call upon the knowledge of his other colleagues, the mathematician and the experimental physicists and chemists. It may be said that there are five known fundamental reservoir-engineering equations with which the engineer must cope in his forecasting computations, namely:

1. The material-balance equation
2. The generalized Darcy law
3. The fractional-flow formula
4. The rate-of-frontal-advance formula
5. The instantaneous reservoir water-oil and gas-oil ratio formula

Although the use of mathematical deductions may give the performance forecasts the appearance of accuracy, one should be aware that inaccuracies in the data are reflected in the results. Errors in the data may be of several kinds: of omission, which result in the necessity of using some assumed values for the missing data; or of commission, as are inevitable in random and unsuspected systematic errors of observation.

With the above mathematical relations at hand, the engineer can make performance predictions with a high degree of dependability for the three fundamental and distinct production processes now recognized, namely:

1. Frontal drives by either water or gas
2. Depletion, or internal gas drive
3. Segregation, or gravity drive

Actual production cases are often a combination, in various degrees, of two and even of all the above processes. For accurate forecasting, their relative importance must be gauged and driving indices computed. Analytical methods, which may include statistical analysis of production data, are used at this point. Because computations may become so involved as to require a mathematical mastermind, the equivalent of electronic computers are then resorted to in the form of electric models, of which there are two types, namely, the potentiometric model for sweep efficiency studies and the performance model for water-drive behavior studies.

Production practices are often designated as primary and secondary recovery operations. Actually, there is no sharp demarcation line between the two, artificial pressuring during primary operations being presently so current as to preclude its future use as secondary recovery practice. In the light of present fundamental studies, secondary recovery is viewed as a particular case of the broader application of reservoir-technology principles to primary recovery.

The above constitutes an outline of "Oil Reservoir Engineering," a subject, which, it may be said, has *come of age* only in very recent years.

CHAPTER 1

THE RESERVOIR ROCKS AND STRUCTURES

Oil reservoirs may be investigated from two points of view, namely, microscopic and megascopic. If we study a core or sample of rock which contains oil and gas in the earth and place it under a magnifying glass (binocular or microscope), we observe the reservoir rock to be made of a framework of minerals (rigid or friable) which fills but part of space. Intercommunicating holes, which can be filled with gas, oil, or water, are interlaced within the mineral framework. A classification of reservoirs can obviously be based upon variations in mineralogy of reservoir rocks, and these variations in turn have an important bearing upon the expected performance of the field. On the other hand, if we look at the oil field as a whole—at the areal extent of its producing pay zone as well as at its barren zone—we study it in its megascopic aspect, namely, from the point of view of the geometric form of its trap configuration. A classification of oil fields may then be based upon variations in reservoir morphology, which variations have again an important bearing upon the recovery of oil and gas.

CLASSIFICATION OF SEDIMENTARY OIL RESERVOIRS ON THE BASIS OF ORIGIN, MINERAL COMPOSITION, AND TEXTURE OF THE RESERVOIR ROCK

Reservoir rocks are mostly sedimentary in origin, but oil and gas are occasionally found in igneous rocks. Sedimentary rocks containing oil and gas may be divided into two main classes: detrital and chemical. Detrital, or clastic, sediments are derived from the disintegration of igneous and metamorphic rocks or other reworked sediments, through a process of weathering, erosion, transport to a basin of sedimentation, and selective precipitation in time and space (sands and shales). Chemical sediments may be formed as a result of two processes: on the one hand, organic growth and precipitation, which is responsible for the formation of most carbonates (limestones and dolomites), and on the other hand, evaporation of sea water in closed basins, which accounts for the formation of evaporites: salt, anhydrite, and gypsum. A genetic classification of reservoir rocks on the basis of their composition and texture, proposed by P. D. Krynine (1943), has proved a useful tool in understanding the make-up of sediments as well as the important bearing which these properties have on oil- and gas-field performance. Krynine's concept will be presented, perhaps in a simplified form, pointing out the relationship between sedimentary characteristics of reservoir rocks and their expected performance in field operating practice. The following passage is quoted with permission from Krynine's original and preliminary work (1943).

Any rock has only two fundamental properties. These two basic properties are composition and texture; the rock is made up of certain minerals put together in a certain way. All other properties, like structure, density, color, electrical properties, porosity, permeability are only second or third order derivatives of these two basic fundamental characteristics—composition and texture.

The most notable of all sedimentary minerals is quartz, or rather the silica group. There are many types of quartz (igneous, metamorphic, sedimentary, chert, etc.), depending upon the mode of its formation. Other major minerals are clays and micas, and locally some feldspars. In addition many new minerals may form during sedimentation—carbonates, sulphates, and iron compounds. Finally a very small but select group is made of accessory minerals, such as tourmaline, zircon, garnet, etc. This mineral assemblage is much more restricted than that found in igneous rocks. As a result, the adequate understanding of the mineral composition of sediments requires extremely thorough investigations. To make matters worse, the texture and apparent composition of sediments are highly variable and may change rapidly from one part of the rock to another. As a result, a systematic petrographic classification of sediments has been thought impossible. In contrast with igneous rocks which are clearly and easily classified on the basis of their mineral composition and texture, the classification of sediments has been either loosely chemical or purely textural (conglomerates, sandstones, shales, limestones). Even then a single formation may pass from a sandstone into a limestone and back within one mile or less, without apparent reason.

A proper understanding of sediments must be both descriptive and genetic; we must know what a sediment is made of and how it was put together showing how the oil got into it and as a result finding the best way of getting this oil out.

In order to produce a sediment, it is necessary to break up an older rock and then put it together again after buffeting it through a series of modifying chemical and physical agencies (weathering, erosion, transport, deposition, lithification, and diagenesis). Obviously a considerable part of the properties of the new sediment will depend upon the character of the parent rock within the source area. But the crust of the earth, like the skin of an onion, is made up (schematically) of several layers: an upper layer of sedimentary rocks, a middle layer of low and medium rank metamorphic rocks (slates, phyllites, schists), and a lowermost crystalline basement complex (gneiss and granite). Since the mineral composition of these layers is entirely different, it follows that the basic mineral make-up of the sediment formed from these three types of source areas will vary greatly. These three typical mineral assemblages are quartz, quartz plus micas, and quartz plus feldspar. As shown in Fig. 1-1 the three rock types resulting from erosion of a sedimentary, metamorphic, or igneous source area will be quartzites, graywackes, and arkoses.

In order to bring up into the zone of erosion the deeper source areas, it is necessary to increase the intensity and extent of the uplift and deformation of the earth's crust. Hence the petrographic character of the source area and consequently the inherited mineral character of the sediment produced from it bear a definite relationship to the amount of deformation (diastrophism) of the earth's crust. This introduces an initial threefold mineralogic division of sediments and serves as the basis of a logical classification. Quartzites, graywackes, and arkoses, since they reflect large-scale earth movements, will be the predominant types of sediments over very large areas at any given time.

A multiplicity of textures may be superimposed upon this large-scale mineral background. In order to understand textural changes and not be hopelessly confused by them, it is necessary to remember that these changes, to a large extent, reflect only purely local changes in the concentration of sedimentary end members.

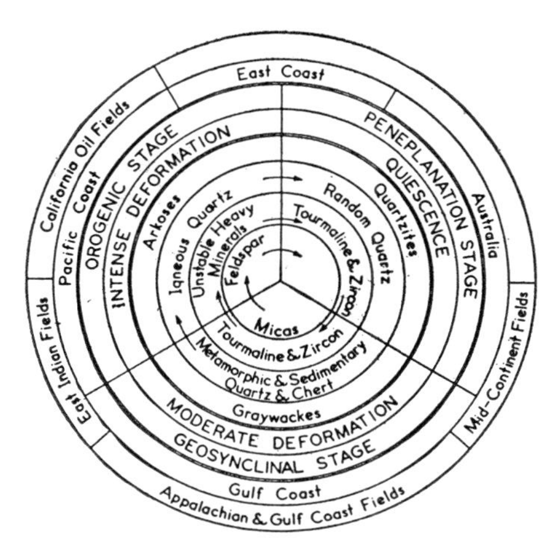

FIG. 1-1. Influence of diastrophism intensity on petrography, structure, and possible oil content of rocks. (*After P. D. Krynine.*)

Most sediments are water laid. As the velocity of a current of water decreases, the larger sand grains carried by the current begin to drop out. Hence, sandstones and shales are due to local changes in current velocity. But at the same time carbonates or silica may be chemically precipitated from the sea water. If this rate of chemical precipitation is high, the amount of formed chemical cements (limestones) may greatly exceed the amount of mechanically deposited sand grains. Water current velocities and rates of chemical precipitation may change rapidly from one place on the sea floor to another and produce an apparently bewildering mixture of sediments. But if sediments are regarded as mechanical mixtures of end members consisting of sand, clay, and chemical cements capable of replacing each other in all proportions according to certain simple laws, these difficulties disappear. Indeed the mineralogical composition of the sand fraction always remains the same, thus giving a clue to the diastrophic history of the region.

Furthermore, different intensities of deformation not only change the character of the source rocks, but also each stage of diastrophism establishes both in the source area and (since all structural forces act in couples) in the basin of deposition a certain type of preferred topographic relief and a certain dominant rate of subsidence. In order to see what this means in terms of modifying processes and in terms of the finished sediment, let us contrast arkoses and quartzites. The powerful structural upward push which brings into the zone of erosion a granite (and as a corollary results in the very rapid sinking of a connected sedimentary basin) also produces a very sharp relief which increases both erosion and mechanical sedimentation and cuts down considerably on the time available for chemical decay, hence almost inhibiting chemical precipitation. Very thick arkoses are the result. The converse is true in the case of very slight deformation which favors lengthy chemical decay on flat surfaces and the precipitation of chemical sediments and clean quartzose sands in shallow seas.

When all of this is considered, it can be seen that, as a whole, each preferred type of mineral composition will be directly related to a certain preferred texture and structure, to a certain preferred type and size of sedimentary body, and to a certain definite type of oil field.

Granular Reservoirs: Consolidated and Unconsolidated. *Quartzose-type Sediments.* In the period of orogenic quiescence, relatively flat coastal plains are bordered by shallow seas, either closed (inland seas), partially closed, or in communication with the ocean (Fig. 1-2). Erosion is at a minimum though weathering, and chemical decay of the relatively flat-

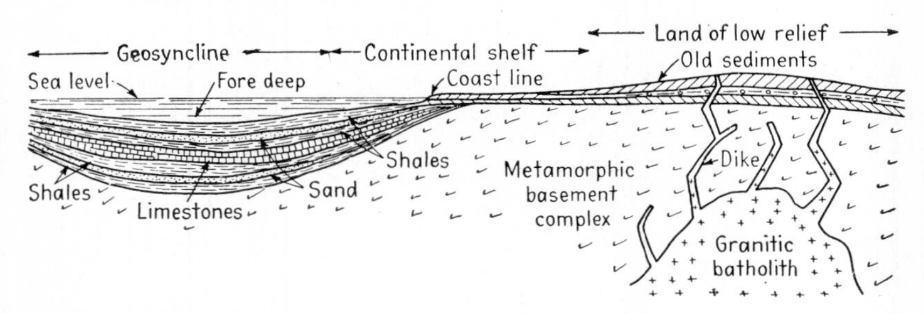

Fig. 1-2. Idealized land and sea conditions which give rise to quartzose-type sediments.

lying land masses, which furnish the clastic sediments, is at a maximum. Only stable minerals (quartz, tourmaline, zircon, etc.) are carried out to sea where they are deposited on the relatively flat but extensive continental shelf in the form of thin but extensive blanketlike sedimentary formations of relatively uniform thickness. Clastic sediments of this type are well sorted in size and shape and are uniform in composition and rounding of grains. Individual grains are usually well rounded and show high sphericity. Rock fragments, as such, from the mother land mass, are absent or very rare. Hence the sediments tend to be uniform in texture and composition over extensive areas. Clean unconsolidated sands as well as clean consolidated sandstones are predominant as reservoir rocks. These sediments have no matrix, and porosity is controlled by the presence or absence of carbonate and silica cement. A small change in sedimentary conditions may bring about the deposition of very thick bodies of shales which act both as source beds for oil and gas and as retainer rock (cap rock) once the hydrocarbons have moved into the reservoir. Shales are mostly of the stable-clay variety. Lensing and wedge edges in these sediments are uncommon, although truncations and angular unconformities resulting from later deformations are by no means absent.

From the reservoir engineer's point of view, clastic sediments present interesting properties. Vertical as well as horizontal permeability is well developed. Owing to the areal extension and lateral continuity of the formations, water drive is the predominant performance, with gas-cap expansion drive a highly probable possibility if poststructural deformations have produced sufficient dip. Oil recovery by primary methods of production reduces the saturation to a low value, which precludes the future use of secondary or tertiary recovery methods. A typical quartzose sediment is pictured in Fig. 1-3, which shows the predominating mineral

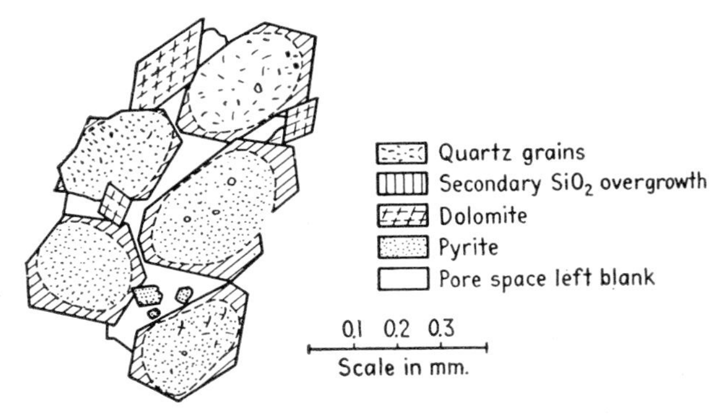

FIG. 1-3. Dolomitic quartzite of the Wilcox, Oklahoma, oil-sand type. *(After P. D. Krynine.)*

grains to be quartz, some of which exhibit secondary growth from the original well-rounded grains. The chemical cement which partially fills the space between sand grains may be amorphous silica: chalcedony and chert, as well as secondary quartz. Calcite and dolomite crystals are most frequent also, and, where present, they act as cement between sand grains. The porosity in these sediments is controlled to a large extent by the presence or absence of carbonate or silica cement. Their removal by acidizing may produce the collapse of the solid framework of the reservoir rock and result in the well sanding up. Barite, glauconite, pyrite, and gypsum may also act as chemical cement. The amount of cement may be highly variable in lateral directions owing to primary depositional differences as well as to postdepositional deformation. Differential cementation may be responsible for porosity and permeability variations with resulting alternation of barren and pay zones.

Examples of clastic quartzose sedimentary reservoirs may be cited, namely: the Oriskany sand and quartzite (eastern Pennsylvania gas fields); the Wilcox sand (Oklahoma City oil field); Tensleep; Wyoming; Dakota; Mid-Continent province; St. Peter (Simpson), Illinois; etc.

Graywacke Sediments. In the period of relatively moderate deformation of the earth's crust (geosynclinal stage), a shorter continental shelf separates the moderately uplifted land areas from the somewhat deeper basins of sedimentation, which are in a process of continuous though not uniform subsidence (Fig. 1-4). Differential balance movements between the loaded geosyncline and the denuded land take place as a result of isostatic adjustments. Erosion and weathering cut deeper into the successive rock shells of the earth, attacking layers which may have suffered little metamorphism into schists and phyllites. The relatively rapid erosion of land areas and the shorter distance of transport do not allow much time for chemical decay and mechanical disintegration to eliminate all the unstable minerals and rock fragments from the transported clastics. Erosion of

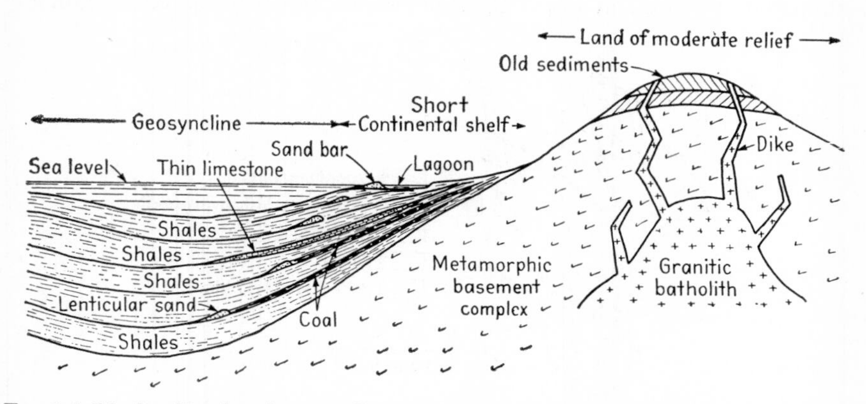

FIG. 1-4. Idealized land and sea conditions which give rise to graywacke-type sediments.

the land area may provide sediments faster than the basin subsides; thus waters may be very shallow, and lagoonal conditions may prevail in which a luxuriant vegetation may ultimately provide abundant material for future coal seams. The deepest part of the basin may oscillate from its median axis, leading to lateral transition from a marine to a continental facies with marked interfingering at the ephemeral shore line. Lenticularity of the sedimentary formations, primarily by lensing and wedge edging, is the rule. The development of transitory sand bars is common, some of which may be buried so quickly, as a result of a rapid shift in the geosynclinal axis, that they remain as fossil witnesses of the nearness of shore-line conditions. They also provide some of the most typical examples of stratigraphic traps. Owing to the rapid subsidence, limestones are rare and, if present, are thin and only of relatively small areal extent, i.e., the Tully limestone of the Appalachian geosyncline, the limestones of the Cherokee section in Oklahoma and Kansas, etc. The individual members of this series of sediments are relatively thin; however, the total thickness of sediments within the geosyncline may be very large, up to 25,000 ft and more. The reservoir rocks of this series of sediments, besides being characterized by their lenticular nature, exhibit poor differentiation. Hence very little difference exists between the reservoir and the cap rock in mineral composition except in terms of grain size. Clay shales, which are characteristic of this group, occur mostly as cap rock and as dilution in the sandier sediments. The typical rock of this series is a *graywacke*, or dirty, clayey sand, containing besides the usual quartz (angular and not too well-rounded in this case) and other stable minerals a large amount of fine mica flakes and nondecayed rock fragments derived from the source area. These sediments may also contain illite, a secondary claylike mineral. The reservoir sands of this series may exhibit high porosities, though relatively low and irregular permeabilities, owing to the fine grains or matrix between the larger ones (since sorting by grain size and shape is relatively poor).

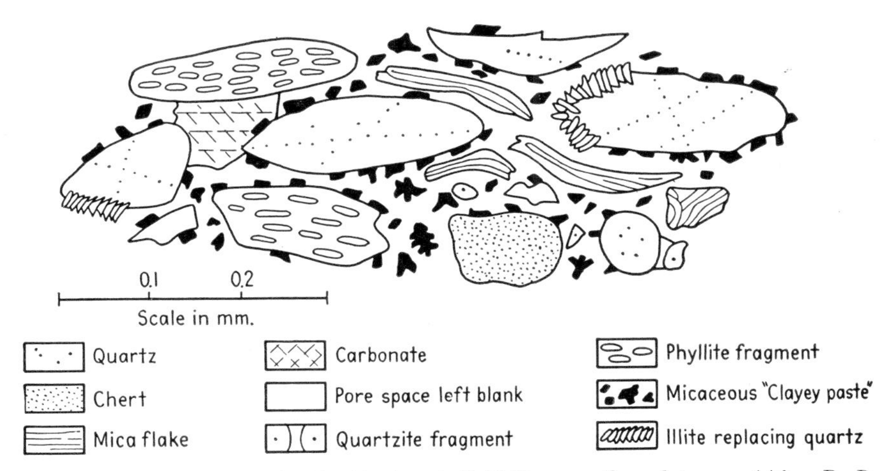

FIG. 1-5. Graywacke of the Bradford and Gulf Eocene oil-sand type. (*After P. D. Krynine.*)

Because of the limited lateral extent of the reservoirs and the lack of vertical permeabilities, water-drive and gravity drainage fields are the exception. Production is primarily by internal depletion gas drive with its attendant low ultimate recovery by primary production methods. Hence, secondary recovery methods are at their best in these reservoirs, especially by means of water flooding but also by external gas and air drive and cycling. A typical graywacke sediment is pictured in Fig. 1-5, which shows quartz grains of metamorphic origin and some relatively unstable mica and phyllite fragments. Clay minerals are abundant, especially as a coating on quartz grains. In the case illustrated, illite or hydromica derived by quartz and kaolin replacement is also shown.

The texture and composition of graywacke reservoirs and cap rocks are responsible for some of their peculiar behavior under artificial water drive and in electric-logging studies, owing to the high reactivity of the clay coating. This subject will be discussed again later. Examples of graywacke reservoirs are the Bradford sand, Pennsylvania, the McLish and Bartlesville sands of Oklahoma, and many Gulf Coast sand reservoirs.

Arkose Sediments. During a period of intense diastrophism of the earth's crust, certain land areas are sharply elevated either above other land masses (a common occurrence) or faulted immediately adjacent to deep depressions in the ocean floor (foredeeps), where the detrital materials removed from the land area are deposited (Fig. 1-6). The distance of detrital transport to sea is very short, with the result that the debris eroded from uplifted lands exhibits a minimum of chemical decay or weathering, and, when deposited, extremely poor sorting of minerals is in evidence. This process of sedimentation results in thick heterogeneous deposits con-

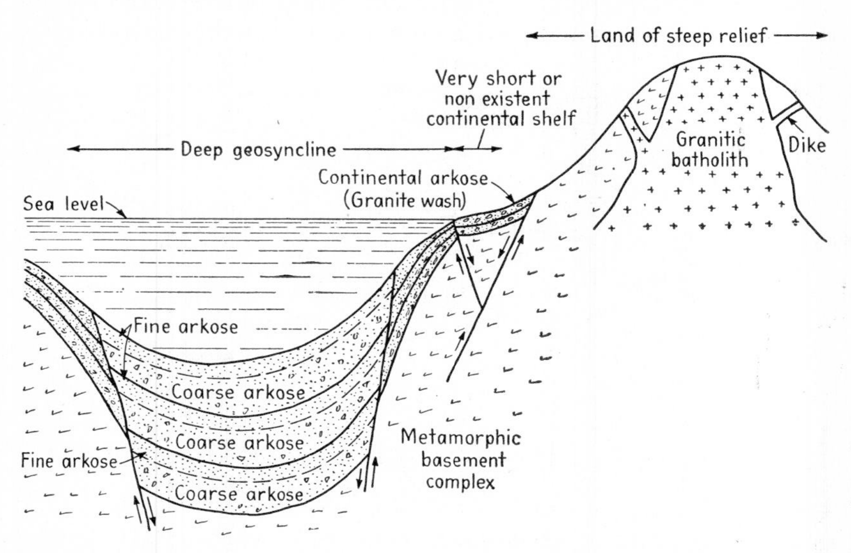

FIG. 1-6. Idealized land and sea conditions which give rise to arkose-type sediments.

taining many unstable minerals which had no chance to decompose during their short period of weathering before transportation over the narrow or possibly nonexistent continental shelf. Unstable minerals such as feldspars are common in typical arkosic sediments. Feldspars and hematite may give arkosic sediments a pink or red color. Grains in arkosic sediments are extremely angular and heterogeneous in size. The matrix which holds the grains together contains a large percentage of kaolinitic clays and sometimes a high proportion of reactive clays, especially montmorillonite formed by volcanic ash precipitations, of frequent occurrence during violent diastrophism. True arkosic sediments are often poorly cemented, as calcite and secondary silica are present only in small amounts or are even totally absent. They may be confused readily with granite or even red beds of continental origin. A rapid deepening of the sedimentary basin as well as a corresponding rapid uplifting of the neighboring land mass is postulated in order to explain the great thicknesses of these sediments. Sedimentation, however, must not be looked upon here as a continuous process but rather as one of successive dumpings into the sea of large heterogeneous loads of clastics followed by a certain degree of size and density sorting, giving rise to successive zones of highly porous (reservoir) rocks and impermeable (cap-rock) shales. This leads to low vertical permeabilities, although there may be considerable ease of fluid transfer parallel to the stratification surfaces. As the basin of sedimentation fills, the sediments tend to get finer. Should the basin fill completely and the sea water be displaced, the marine arkose may be overlain by continental deposits of the same mineral composition but oxidized. During a lull in the orogenic stage, some thin limestones may develop, but this is the exception rather than the rule, owing to the rapidity of the basin's subsidence. A schematic representation of an arkosic texture is represented in Fig. 1-7.

The genetic processes here described for arkose sediments lead us to infer, and rightly so, that stratigraphic traps due to lensing, pinchouts, and

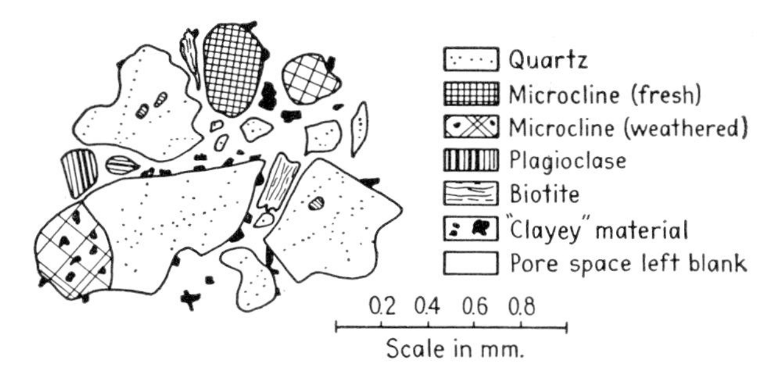

FIG. 1-7. Arkose of the Stevens, California, oil-sand type. (*After P. D. Krynine.*)

unconformities should be prevalent. However, the intense orogenic activity contemporaneous with sedimentation results in a great many possibilities of closed geologic structures: anticlines, faulted blocks, etc.

Arkosic reservoirs offer some peculiar performance problems. In primary production, vertical zoning requires multiple well completion. In addition, the heterogeneous permeabilities are not conducive to very high recoveries, oil remaining trapped in lenses. Those fields should make a fertile ground for the application of secondary recovery methods. However, water flooding is beset by difficulties offered by unstable clays, mainly by montmorillonite which swells tremendously when in contact with fresh water. The use of brine as the flooding agent has partially solved this problem.

Typical examples of arkosic reservoirs are found in California, the Los Angeles basin, the granite wash of the Anadarko basin, Oklahoma, and the Amarillo region, Texas.

Limestones and Dolomites. In the quiescence period of orogeny, erosion and transport of detrital materials may be at a very low ebb, even completely absent. This, coupled with a very slowly sinking, shallow continental shelf, gives an opportunity for abundant development of sea life, particularly of shell sea life—clams, corals, etc.—which have mineral shells of aragonite. When the animals die, the aragonite shell is transformed into calcite. The waters from flat-lying land areas carry in solution mostly salts of calcium and magnesium which are precipitated as calcite and dolomite. The process lasts as long as the continental shelf is covered by shallow waters. A gradual sinking of the shelf permits a prolonged duration of carbonate precipitation, both chemical and biogenic, yielding thick and extensive limestone and dolomite formations. Though dolomite may result from a primary or syngenetic process before consolidation, its origin is ascribed predominantly to a replacement process of calcium by magnesium from sea water after consolidation. The development of porosity and permeability in dolomitic limestones is often explained as resulting from density reduction accompanying the dolomitic replacement, which may attain 12 per cent by weight. However, it is questionable whether or not molecular replacement may account for porosity development by volume shrinkage. Development of porosity in limestones and dolomites which form oil-field reservoirs is mainly through mechanical fissuring and chemical leaching. Once consolidated, a limestone is brittle and has relatively little mechanical resistance to tension and to shear. Under bending stresses, as a result of even slight structural deformations, vertical cracks or joints are readily formed. This provides an easy avenue for the circulation of dissolving meteoric or foreign formation waters. These processes result in the enlargement of fissures, pore development, and even cavern formations, which are very irregular in nature and nonuniform in distribution throughout the reservoir.

Carbonate reservoir rocks include the following *lithological types:*

1. Accretionary limestones. These are formed *in situ* and include *bioherms* (or *reefs*), *biostromes*, and *pelagic* limestones. Each of these consists of a calcareous framework secreted by sea-dwelling organisms. *Reefs* are formed by bottom-dwelling organisms (benthon) which build them from the bottom up near the shore line. These organisms are mostly corals and calcareous algae. The horizontal continuity of reefs is therefore limited in areal extent and their vertical continuity is often interrupted by nonporous zones of more or less horizontal continuity.

Biostromal limestones are the results of mixed conditions favorable to the formation of both bioherms and pelagic limestones and give rise to bedded calcareous accumulations devoid of domelike structure.

2. Clastic limestones. These sediments are formed by mineral grain precipitation resulting from erosion and weathering of limestones originally deposited elsewhere. The precipitate may be partly or wholly fossil debris, carbonate grains, or oöliths, together with sand grains and claylike particles. The pore space is initially an intergranular sand type, but calcite cement later may increase the area of contact between grains.

Clastic limestones include the following common types of rocks: coquina limestones, reef breccia, oölitic limestone, lithographic limestone, etc.

3. Chemical limestones. This type of sediment is formed by the direct chemical precipitation of calcitic grains from carbonate solutions in shallow seas. Deposits such as chalk, caliche, and travertine are so produced, but only chalk has proved to be commerical oil reservoir rock.

4. Dolomite. Dolomitic limestone may be formed with primary porosity through direct precipitation, but it is generally accepted that it is formed by molecular replacement of calcium by magnesium in the original limestone.

We may distinguish the following types of porosity in carbonate reservoirs:

1. Intercrystalline or primary porosity results from interstitial voids between individual crystal or grain and from their arrangement within the rocks.

Primary porosity has a tendency to be discontinuous because of the filling of void spaces by fine material and cement. Primary porosity in limestones seldom gives economical oil reservoirs.

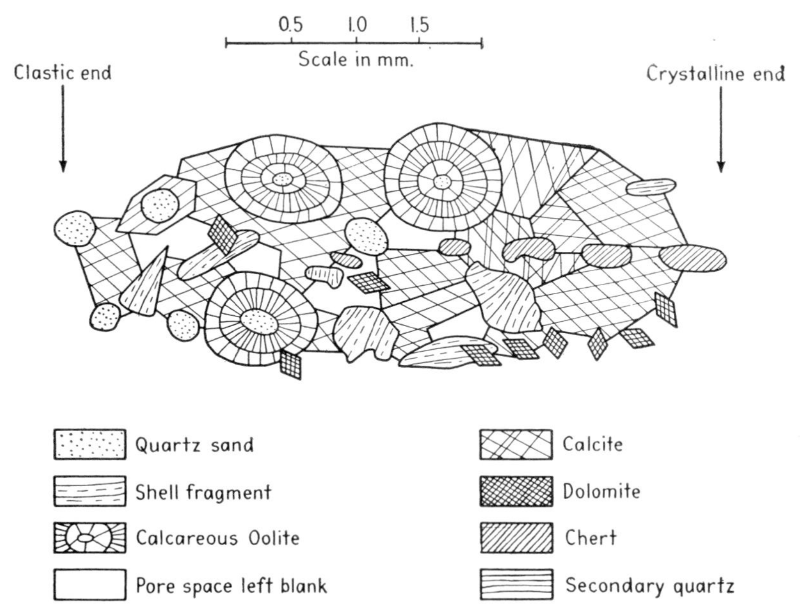

FIG. 1-8. Porosity development in a complex oölitic limestone. (*After P. D. Krynine.*)

2. Oölitic porosity results from the packing of fossil spheres of almost uniform diameter. The original packing usually approaches the hexagonal pattern of 26 per cent porosity. Owing to subsequent leaching or cementation, the porosity may be higher or lower. Clastic grains may, however, be mixed in various degrees with the spherical grains, and cementing crystallization may reduce the available pore space to an appreciable degree. Void space may also exist inside the oöliths themselves which may or may not have any communication with the interconnected pore network. Figure 1-8 gives an idealized picture of porosity development in oölitic limestones.

3. Intergranular porosity in limestones is specifically the pore development in heterogeneously packed clastic sediments. Chalk exhibits a typical intergranular porosity, as the chalk grains constitute but a fine calcareous powder.

4. Vuggy porosity results from leaching of carbonate rocks by solutions or circulating waters and is characterized by channels and large openings

within the rocks. An idea of vuggy-porosity development may be had from Fig. 1-9. This type of porosity is very common in the Permian basin of West Texas and New Mexico.

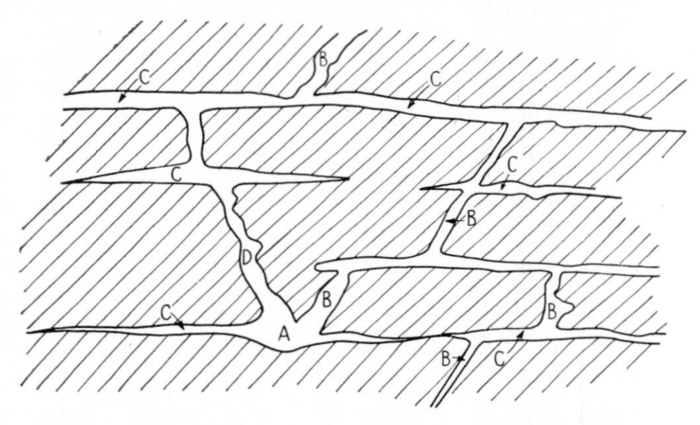

Fig. 1-9. Carbonate rock showing porosity derived from solution along joints and bedding planes. *A*, vugs; *B*, joint channel; *C*, bedding-plane channel; *D*, solution channel.

5. Fracture porosity results from earth movements which create joints and faults through which solution waters may gain easy access throughout the originally massive rock (Fig. 1-10). Mineralizing waters may also

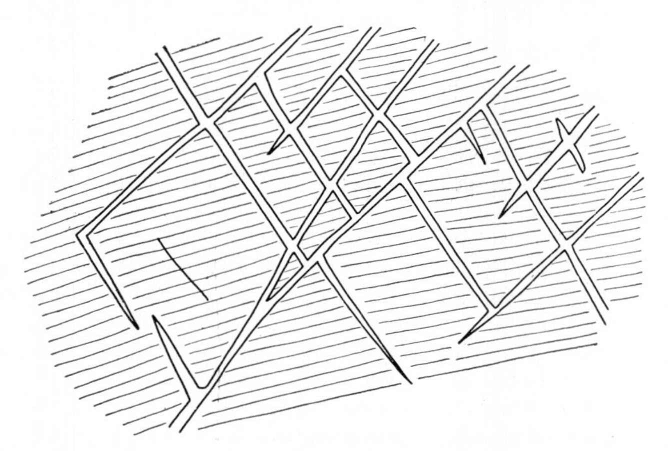

Fig. 1-10. Carbonate rock showing porosity derived from fracturing and fissuring.

circulate through the rocks and be responsible for dolomitic replacement as well as for the filling of previously developed channels and cavities. The development of fracture-porosity patterns is related to the fracturing susceptibility of the formation as a whole under the application of deformational stresses. The structural history of a region may be a clue to the extent of porosity development by fracture.

6. Fossiliferous porosity is developed by leaching when fossil remains within a carbonate rock are more soluble than the rock itself.

7. Reef porosity is a type of fossiliferous porosity which is present in fossil coral and algal reef structures as a result of the decay of organic matter originally filling the openings.

8. Cherty limestones often show fields of porosity development, since fracturing is often responsible for chert mineralization by circulating waters. Weathered cherty limestones may also show high porosity through the removal of carbonates. The ultimate result of weathering may be a highly porous rock of tripoli such as the Mississippi Chat.

Inasmuch as porosity development in carbonate reservoirs is mostly through circulating waters, the latter may also lead to filling of previously existing pores by chert, salt, and sulfates (anhydrite and gypsum).

Examples of carbonate reservoirs are numerous, particularly in the West Texas Permian basin. However, they are not infrequent in other petroliferous provinces. In Oklahoma, the West Edmond field is an outstanding example. The Trenton limestone reservoirs of the Middle West are dolomitic in nature: an example is the Lima-Indiana field. Other outstanding examples are the Madison limestone (Wyoming) and the Edwards limestone (Texas).

Shale Reservoirs. This class of reservoirs is not very important commercially but may be encountered in all series of sedimentary rocks. The development of effective porosity in shales is possible only through fracturing, which presupposes the existence of orogenic deformation. There are but a few instances of shale reservoirs: Florence, Colorado; the gas fields of Kentucky; the basal schist and nodular shale of the San Joaquin basin, California.

Evaporites. Evaporite rocks are either rock salt, anhydrite, or gypsum. Thick deposits of these salts are often formed in sedimentation basins when the latter are cut off from abundant supplies of clastics. Examples of this type of rock in the process of formation are found in the Caspian Sea and the Great Salt Lake of Utah.

Rock salt itself as well as gypsum is seldom a reservoir rock. However, impure anhydrite formations may become good porous formations as a result of leaching of anhydrite by circulating waters which produce vugs and ribbonlike channels. Nevertheless, anhydrite reservoirs are relatively uncommon. One may cite by way of example the gas horizon in the Cotton Valley field and the anhydrite oil horizon in the Upper Comanche formation over the Pine Island structure in Louisiana.

Igneous and Metamorphic Rock Reservoirs. The natural habitat of oil and gas is a low-temperature rock. Rocks formed at high temperature, such as igneous and metamorphic rocks, are not the usual host rock for hydrocarbons. Petroleum, when present in these rocks, must have moved into them after their cooling and consolidation.

Igneous rocks possess originally very little effective porosity, though lavas have considerable absolute porosity in the form of nonconnected bubbles. In order that these rocks may become suitable reservoirs, they must be the object of secondary porosity development, either by fracturing and leaching or weathering of the easily decomposed minerals. Few high-temperature rocks have fulfilled these conditions. The serpentine plugs and laccoliths of Caldwell and Bastrop Counties, Texas, are the best-known oil and gas reservoirs found in igneous rocks, and in particular the Lytton Springs field. The basal metamorphic schist of the western Los Angeles basin, California, is another instance where the porosity was developed by fissuring. Here, production is adjusted to the axis of schist ridges, and oil occurs in fractures within the schistose basement to depths greater than 680 ft.

SELECTED REFERENCES ON RESERVOIR LITHOLOGY

1916

Cayeux, L.: "Introduction à l'étude pétrographique des roches sédimentaires," 2 vols. reprinted 1931, Imprimerie Nationale, Paris.

1929

Milner, H. B.: "Sedimentary Petrography," Thomas Murby & Co., London.

1933

Boswell, P. G. H.: "On the Mineralogy of Sedimentary Rocks," Thomas Murby & Co., London.

1937

Halbouty, M.: "Petrographic and Physical Characteristics of Sands from Seven Gulf Coast Producing Horizons," Houston, Tex.

Krumbein, W. C., and E. Aberdeen: Sediments of Barataria Bay, *J. Sediment. Petrol.*, vol. 7, pp. 3ff.

1938

Black, M., et al.: "The Petrology of Sedimentary Rocks," London.

Krumbein, W. C., and F. J. Pettijohn: "Manual of Sedimentary Rocks," New York.

Waldo, W. A.: The Petrology of the Bradford Sand of the Kane District, *Penn. State Coll. Mineral Ind. Exp. Sta. Bull.* 24.

1939

Grim, R. E.: Properties of Clays in Recent Marine Sediments, "Recent Marine Sediments," American Association of Petroleum Geologists' Symposium, pp. 466ff.

1940

Howard, W. V.: Accumulation of Oil and Gas in Limestone, "Problems of Petroleum Geology," American Association of Petroleum Geologists' Symposium, pp. 365ff.

Krynine, P. D.: Paleozoic Heavy Minerals and Appalachian Structure, *Proc. Penn. Acad. Sci.*, vol. 14.

Krynine, P. D.: Petrology and Genesis of the Third Bradford Sand, *Penn. State Coll. Mineral Ind. Exp. Sta. Bull.* 29.

Moore, P. D.: Origin, Migration and Accumulation of Petroleum in Limestone Reservoirs in the Western United States and Canada, "Problems of Petroleum Geology," American Association of Petroleum Geologists' Symposium, pp. 347ff.

1942

Krynine, P. D.: Petrographic Studies in the Variation in the Cementing Materials in the Oriskany Sand, *Penn. State Coll. Mineral Ind. Exp. Sta. Bull.* 33, 10th Petroleum and Natural Gas Conference, pp. 108ff.

1943

Krynine, P. D.: "Diastrophism and the Evolution of Sedimentary Rocks," Syllabus Outline of Lectures under Distinguished Lecturer Committee, American Association of Petroleum Geologists, 20 pp.

Krynine, P. D.: Sediments and the Search for Oil, *Mineral Ind.*, vol. 13, no. 3.

1944

Ronov, A. B.: Quantitative Method of Study of the Epeirogenic Movements of the Earth's Crust, *Trans. Ins. Th. Geophys. Acad. Sci. U.S.S.R.*, June.

1945

Goodman, A. J.: Limestone Reservoir Conditions in Turner Valley Oil Field, Alberta, Canada, *Bull. Am. Assoc. Petroleum Geol.*, vol. 29, no. 8, pp. 1156ff.

1946

Landes, K. M.: Porosity through Dolomitization, *Bull. Am. Assoc. Petroleum Geol.*, vol. 30, no. 3, pp. 305ff.

Price, W. A., et al.: Algae Reefs in Cap Rock Ogallala Formation of Llana Estacado Plateau, New Mexico and Texas, *Bull. Am. Assoc. Petroleum Geol.*, vol. 30, no. 10, pp. 1742ff.

Ver Wiebe, W. A.: Kinderhook Dolomite of Sedgwick County, Kansas, *Bull. Am. Assoc. Petroleum Geol.*, vol. 30, no. 10, pp. 1747ff.

White, J. L.: The Schist Surface of the Los Angeles Basin, California Oil Fields, *Summary of Operations*, vol. 32, no. 1, January–June, pp. 3ff.

1947

Goldich, S. S., and E. B. Parmelee: Physical and Chemical Properties of Ellenburger Rocks, Llano County, Texas, *Bull. Am. Assoc. Petroleum Geol.*, vol. 31, no. 11, pp. 1982ff.

Imbt, W. C., and S. P. Ellison, Jr.: "Porosity in Limestone and Dolomite Petroleum Reservoirs," American Petroleum Institute, June 7.

Taylor, H.: Middle Ordovician Limestones of Central Kansas, *Bull. Am. Assoc. Petroleum Geol.*, vol. 31, no. 7, pp. 1242ff.

1948

Hohlt, R. B.: The Nature and Origin of Limestone Porosity, *Quart. Colo. School Mines*, vol. 43, no. 4, October.

Krumbein, W. C.: Lithofacies Maps and Regional Sedimentary–Stratigraphic Analysis, *Bull. Am. Assoc. Petroleum Geol.*, vol. 32, no. 10, pp. 1909ff.

Krynine, P. D.: The Megascopic Study and Field Classification of Sedimentary Rocks, *J. Geol.*, vol. 56, no. 2, pp. 130ff.

1951

Griffiths, J. C.: Size versus Sorting in Some Caribbean Sediments, *J. Geol.*, vol. 59, no. 3, pp. 211ff.

Nahin, P. G., et al.: Mineralogical Studies of California Oil-bearing Formations, I, Identification of Clays, AIME *Tech. Pub.* 3059, pp. 151ff.

1952

Archie, G. E.: Classification of Carbonate Reservoir Rocks and Petrophysical Considerations, *Bull. Am. Assoc. Petroleum Geol.*, vol. 36, no. 2, pp. 278ff.

Griffiths, J. C.: Grain Size Distribution and Reservoir Characteristics, *Bull. Am. Assoc. Petroleum Geol.*, vol. 36, no. 2, pp. 205ff.

Krumbein, W. C., and R. M. Garrels: Origin and Classification of Chemical Sediments in Terms of pH and Oxidation-Reduction Potentials, *J. Geol.*, vol. 40, no. 1, pp. 1ff.

1953

Bergenback, R. E., and R. T. Terriere: Petrography of Scurry Reef, Texas, *Bull. Am. Assoc. Petroleum Geol.*, vol. 37, no. 5, pp. 1014ff.

Flawn, P. T.: Petrographic Classification of Argillaceous Sedimentary and Low-grade Metamorphic Rocks in Subsurface, *Bull. Am. Assoc. Petroleum Geol.*, vol. 37, no. 3, pp. 560ff.

1954

Chiligar, G. V., and R. D. Terry: Relationship between Porosity and Chemical Composition of Carbonate Rocks, *Petroleum Engr.*, vol. 26, no. 10, pp. B53ff.

Nanz, R. H.: Nature and Origin of an Oligocene Sandstone Reservoir, *Bull. Am. Assoc. Petroleum Geol.*, vol. 38, no. 1, pp. 96ff.

1955

Jodry, R. L.: Rapid Method for Determining Magnesium-Calcium Ratios of Well Samples and Its Use in Predicting Structure and Secondary Porosity in Calcareous Formations, *Bull. Am. Assoc. Petroleum Geol.*, vol. 39, no. 4, pp. 493ff.

Langenheim, R. L., Jr.: Magnetite in Red Beds and Associated Rocks, *Bull. Am. Assoc. Petroleum Geol.*, vol. 39, no. 7, pp. 1404ff.

1956

Lowry, W. D.: Factors in Loss of Porosity by Quartzose Sandstones of Virginia, *Bull. Am. Assoc. Petroleum Geol.*, vol. 40, no. 3, pp. 489ff.

Waldschmidt, W. A., et al.: Porosity and Fractures in Reservoir Rocks, *Bull. Am. Assoc. Petroleum Geol.*, vol. 40, no. 5, pp. 953ff.

CLASSIFICATION OF RESERVOIRS ON THE BASIS OF GEOLOGIC-TRAP CONFIGURATION

The expected behavior of an oil and gas reservoir is dependent to a high degree upon the geometric configuration of the reservoir-rock body as a whole, as well as upon its relation to the neighboring formations. A classification of oil and gas fields in table form is offered as a ready reference to the main conditions under which the reservoir was formed and the way it can be recognized by its geometry or its external morphology. This classification is of special significance to the reservoir engineer so that he may recognize the particular subsurface conditions with which he is dealing and thereby infer the expected possible and probable performance of the field as a whole. This classification is divided into three parts as follows:

I. Stratigraphic traps
II. Combination stratigraphic and structural traps
III. Structural traps

In the classification tables, it was endeavored to divide each main class genetically into subclasses and each subclass morphologically into subsubclasses. Whenever possible, the geometry of a trap is represented by profile and areal view diagrams with the introduction of as many genetic elements as possible. This is particularly true of some of the stratigraphic-type reservoirs where an understanding of the paleogeography contemporaneous to the formation of the sand body is especially useful. A column describing the main features of the trap is added to the right of the sketches;

in general, they are so selected as to give the diagnostic features recognizable from depth measurements.

The last column gives a series of example pools. This classification makes no claim of being exhaustive and complete. An effort was made to select examples as typical as possible, though it is realized that complex factors played a role in trapping the oil and gas in many of the examples cited.

Stratigraphic Traps. The name "stratigraphic" traps is unfortunately open to objections, as this type of trap does not necessarily result from a process of layering during deposition but is often the result of a reworking and concentration process from previously deposited sediments or of post-depositional changes within the rock (diagenesis). The term "petrologic" trap, as well as its accepted equivalent (stratigraphic trap), is particularly hard to define, and it seems best to define it negatively. Inasmuch as a trap of this nature is never wholly devoid of structural elements, one may say that a stratigraphic trap is one in which later structural deformation plays a subordinate role in the accumulation, migration, and retention of oil and gas.

Traps where late structural effects are at a minimum (Chart I) are primarily associated with shore-line processes. Accordingly, wide use was made of the classical work dealing with this subject, namely, D. W. Johnson's "Shore Processes and Shore Line Development." According to Johnson, shore lines may be classified as follows:

1. Shore lines of emergence, or regressive
2. Shore lines of submergence, or transgressive
3. Fluctuating shore lines
4. Stable shore lines

In the normal process of sedimentation within a geosyncline (where the majority of our present oil and gas fields are located), the predominating type of shore line to be expected is the transgressive shore line. We would expect to find statistically more oil fields in sand bodies having the character of a submerging shore line. However, the greater number of shore-line oil fields have been interpreted as having been formed along regressive shore lines, the most commonly interpreted type being the offshore bar type of reservoir.

Owing to the almost complete absence of structural features, the discovery of fields of this class is almost mere chance, although once they are discovered and the type recognized, a reconstruction of the regional paleogeography permits a more systematic exploration campaign for new fields of the same type.

Combination Stratigraphic-structural Traps. The border line between purely structural traps and stratigraphic traps is diffuse, and, depending on personal opinion, it is possible to make it a very narrow or very broad line as there is hardly a stratigraphic trap where structural elements are absent.

In the group of combination stratigraphic-structural traps (Chart II) are included those reservoirs where structure plays a role substantially equivalent to stratigraphic and lithologic features in controlling the accumulation, migration, and retention of oil and gas.

Two main classes are provided, depending on the operating truncation process, which may be erosional or deformational. Fields associated with erosional truncation have proved to be some of the most prolific pools ever discovered. Because of their association with structure below unconformities, it has been possible to prospect for these fields by ordinary structural means, though the ultimate delineation of the field has to be left largely to random drilling.

Under the term deformational truncation are classed those fields where plastic deformation with stretching and mechanical squeezing of the reservoir formations to their ultimate rupture plays an important part in providing the reservoir closure. Reservoirs of this type are common in regions where compression (not necessarily intense) of unconsolidated or semiconsolidated sediments (Flysch and Molasse) results in their plastic deformation rather than bending and shearing. This type of deformation is usually called "alpine" but is often encountered in a rapidly sinking geosyncline.

Structural Traps. The best known of all oil and gas traps are structural (Chart III), so well known in fact that they have prejudiced oil men and even geologists to the extent that they believe all commercial oil accumulations are primarily structural. The literature of the past is replete with articles where the writers argued at great length to prove that accumulation was controlled by structure, where we now obviously recognize the control to be by stratigraphy and lithology. It is perhaps not unfitting to state that the anticlinal theory of I. C. White has impaired for many years the development of oil geological theory and of oil-discovery efforts. In the words of W. E. Pratt, "Geologists have been so enamoured of anticlines that they have failed really to look for oil."

Notwithstanding the overemphasis placed upon structural traps as reservoirs, they play and have played an important role in building up the known reserves of oil in the earth. For the purpose of this classification, they are divided into four main classes according to deformation, change of dip, faulting, and combination folding and faulting.

The process of strata deformation may be compressional, gravitational, intrusional, or rejuvenated uplifting.

Accumulation within deformed strata may be the result of changes in dip with the formation of terraces, saddles, and plunging anticlines.

Closure by faulting may result in a large number of complex structures, of which only four simple types are represented.

Closure by combination of folding and faulting may exhibit great complexity, and most of the known structural reservoirs show this complexity to varying degrees.

RELATIONS BETWEEN GEOLOGY AND RESERVOIR PERFORMANCE

In order that the influence of geologic configuration on reservoir performance may be understood in its proper perspective, the control that geologic structure may exert on reservoir behavior will be indicated presently.

As will be shown later, there are three principal and fundamentally independent naturally occurring *production processes* by which oil may be obtained from a reservoir: *depletion drive, water drive,* and *segregation drive.*

In truly stratigraphic-type traps, there is absence of extensive lateral continuity in the physical properties of the reservoir rock, especially in lenticular beds where the closure is obtained by fingering out or through facies changes. Under such conditions, it is impossible for the oil to be in communication with a large aquifer and if water influx exists at all it is of limited influence. Stratigraphic traps also are generally associated with relatively moderate structural deformation, and formation dips are small. There is, therefore, little possibility for gravitational segregation of the reservoir fluids. The most common production process in stratigraphic traps is mostly by *depletion* or *solution gas drive* in which the expulsion of oil takes place under the expanding force of dissolved gases. This is inherently an inefficient primary recovery process. As a consequence it is not surprising that secondary recovery operations are more prevalent in such traps.

A *water-drive* performance requires the influx of water into the reservoir in sufficient amount to replace volumetrically the oil and gas produced. Water may encroach into an oil reservoir in two ways, either by *artesian flow* or by *volumetric expansion* attendant to pressure decline in the reservoir and its connecting aquifer. Artesian flow requires a sufficient influx of water at an outcrop of the reservoir rock. Water influx by volumetric expansion of the water contained in the aquifer requires a sufficient areal extension of the reservoir rock to provide the required water volume. In view of the low compressibility of water, the required aquifer volume is very large by comparison to that of the oil pool. Such geologic requirements are found mainly in blanketlike strata of the quartzose series, though occasionally arkosic-type sediments may have sufficient lateral continuity to yield active water-drive fields. Arkosic-type sediments are, however, more likely to contain oil fields associated with aquifers limited in extent because of faulting.

Segregation drives or *gas-cap expansion drives* are encountered mainly in reservoirs of high structural relief, inasmuch as the effective gravitational movement in a down-dip direction requires considerable formation slope. Segregation drives are accordingly found mostly in structural traps of sufficient relief. Structures such as reefs and deltaic reservoirs may show such requirements, but the presence of horizontal shaly barriers, lensing, or cross-bedding within the reservoir rock is a deterrent to segregation. In addition, the true segregation process, which requires counterflow of oil and gas, may take place in an efficient manner only when a good development of permeability exists in the direction of flow.

REFERENCES FOR CHARTS I, II, AND III

1. W. R. Dillard: Olympic Pool, Hughes and Okfuskee Counties, Oklahoma, "Stratigraphic Type Oil Fields," pp. 456–472.
2. C. R. Fettke: Music Mountain Oil Pool, McKean County, Pennsylvania, "Stratigraphic Type Oil Fields," pp. 492–506.
3. J. F. Pepper et al.: Map of Second Berea Sand, Ohio, *USGS Oil and Gas Investigations*, Preliminary Map No. 5, 1944.
4. R. E. Sherrill, P. A. Dickey, and L. S. Matteson: Types of Stratigraphic Oil Pools in Venango Sands of Northwestern Pennsylvania, "Stratigraphic Type Oil Fields," pp. 507–538.
5. R. E. Sherrill et al.: Oil and Gas Geology of the Oil City Quadrangle, Pennsylvania, *Pennsylvania Topographic and Geologic Survey*, 1943.
6. N. W. Bass et al.: Origin and Distribution of Bartlesville and Burbank Shoestring Oil Sands in Parts of Oklahoma and Kansas, *Bull. Am. Assoc. Petroleum Geol.*, vol. 21, pp. 30–66, 1937.
7. M. W. Ball et al.: Shoestring Gas Fields of Michigan, "Stratigraphic Type Oil Fields," pp. 237–266.
8. R. Wright: Red Fork Shoestring Sand Pool, "Stratigraphic Type Oil Fields," pp. 473–491.
9. L. H. White: Subsurface Distribution and Correlation of the Pre-Chattanooga ("Wilcox" sand) Series of Northeastern Oklahoma, *Oklahoma Geological Survey Bull.* 40, p. 22, 1926.
10. F. M. Swain: Personal communication.
11. H. E. McNeil: Wherry Pool, Rice County, Kansas, "Stratigraphic Type Oil Fields," pp. 118–138.
12. H. H. Charles: Bush City Oil Field, Anderson County, Kansas, "Stratigraphic Type Oil Fields," pp. 43–56.
13. Preliminary Oil and Gas Map of Forest and Adjacent Counties, Pennsylvania, *Pennsylvania Topographic and Geologic Survey*, 1942.
14. J. E. Blixt: Cut Bank Oil and Gas Field, Glacier County, Montana, "Stratigraphic Type Oil Fields," pp. 327–381.
15. E. C. Edwards: Kern Front Oil Field, Kern County, California, "Stratigraphic Type Oil Fields," pp. 9–18.
16. E. C. Edwards: Edison Oil Field and Vicinity, Kern County, California, "Stratigraphic Type Oil Fields," pp. 1–8.
17. J. L. Garlough and G. L. Taylor: Hugoton Gas Field (Kansas, Texas, and Oklahoma), "Stratigraphic Type Oil Fields," pp. 78–104.
18. W. B Wilson: Geology of Glenn Pool of Oklahoma, "Structure of Typical American Oil Fields," vol. I, pp. 230–242, 1929.
19. P. D. Krynine: Petrology and Genesis of the Third Bradford Sand, *Penn. State Coll., Mineral Ind. Exp. Sta. Bull.* 29, 1940.
20. J. K. Murphy et al.: Seymour Pool, Baylor County, Texas, "Stratigraphic Type Oil Fields," pp. 760–775.
21. E. R. Lloyd: Capitan Limestone and Associated Formations of New Mexico and Texas, *Bull. Am. Assoc. Petroleum Geol.*, vol. 13, pp. 645–658, 1929.
22. P. D. Krynine: Personal communication.
23. P. D. Krynine: Personal communication.
24. S. B. White: Davenport Field, Lincoln County, Oklahoma, "Stratigraphic Type Oil Fields," pp. 386–407.
25. V. Cotner and H. E. Crum: Geology and Occurrence of Natural Gas in Amarillo District, Texas, *Bull. Am. Assoc. Petroleum Geol.*, vol. 17, no. 8, pp. 877–906, 1933.
26. D. M. Collingwood and R. E. Rettger: The Lytton Springs Oil Field, Caldwell County, Texas, *Bull. Am. Assoc. Petroleum Geol.*, vol. 10, no. 10, pp. 953–975, 1926.
27. D. A. McGee and W. W. Clawson, Jr.: Geology and Development of Oklahoma City Field, Oklahoma County, Oklahoma, *Bull. Am. Assoc. Petroleum Geol.*, vol. 16, no. 10, pp. 957–1020, 1932.
28. D. A. McGee: West Edmond Oil Field, *Petroleum Engr.*, pp. 227–250, October, 1944.

29. H. E. Minor and M. A. Hanna: East Texas Oil Field, Texas, "Stratigraphic Type Oil Fields," pp. 600–640.
30. W. A. Ver Wiebe: Unconformity at Top of Trenton in Lima, Indiana, *Bull. Am. Assoc. Petroleum Geol.*, vol. 13, no. 6, p. 688, 1929.
31. G. C. Gester and H. J. Hawley: Geology of the Yates Pool, "Structure of Typical American Oil Fields," vol. II, pp. 480–499, 1929.
32. R. W. Pack: The Sunset–Midway Oil Field, California, *USGS Prof. Paper* 116, 1920.
33. Geology of Salt Dome Oil Fields, American Association of Petroleum Geologists, 1926.
34. R. D. Reed and J. S. Hollister: *Structural Evolution of Southern California*, vol. 20, no. 12, p. 1603, 1936.
35. D. P. Carlton: West Columbia Salt Dome and Oil Field, Brazoria Co., Texas, "Structure of Typical American Oil Fields," vol. II, pp. 451–469, 1929.
36. J. B. Stevens: McKittrick Area of the McKittrick Oil Field, Kern County, California, Economic Development of the Oil and Gas Fields of California, part III, *Bull.* 118, pp. 510–511, Division of Mines, Department of Natural Resources, California, March, 1943.
37. R. K. DeFord: Surface Structure, Florence Oil Field, Fremont County, Colorado, "Structure of Typical American Oil Fields," vol. II, pp. 75–92, 1929.
38. R. R. Templeton and C. R. McCollom: Santa Fe Springs Field, *Bull. Am. Asso . Petroleum Geol.*, vol. 8, pp. 178–194, 1924.
39. C. L. Kaiser: Wheeler Ridge Field, *California Oil Fields*, vol. 9, no. 12, pp. 25–29, 1924.
40. E. L. Estabrook: Production Problems in the Grass Creek Oil Field, *Mining and Metallurgy*, no. 182, pp. 65–66, 1922.
41. V. C. Scott: Apache Oil Pool, Caddo Co., Oklahoma, *Bull. Am. Assoc. Petroleum Geol.*, vol. 29, no. 1, pp. 100–105, 1945.
42. C. S. Ross: Bald Hill Dome, Eastern Osage Co., Oklahoma, *USGS Bull.* 686-N, 1922.
43. T. and I. B. Wasson: Cabin Creek Field, West Virginia, "Structure of Typical American Oil Fields," vol. I, pp. 462–475, 1929.
44. R. E. Davis and E. A. Stephenson: Synclinal Oil Fields in Southern West Virginia, "Structure of Typical American Oil Fields," vol. II, pp. 571–576, 1929.
45. A. E. Fath: Geology of the Eldorado Oil and Gas Field, Butler Co., Kansas, *State Geological Survey of Kansas Bull.* 7, 1921.
46. F. Buttram: The Cushing Oil and Gas Field, Oklahoma, *Oklahoma Geological Survey Bull.* 18, pp. 1–60, 1914.
47. S. Powers: The Healdton Oil Field, Oklahoma, *Economic Geology*, vol. 12, pp. 594–606, 1917.
48. S. K. Clark: Thomas Oil Field, Kay County, Oklahoma, *Bull. Am. Assoc. Petroleum Geol.*, vol. 10, pp. 643–655, 1926.
49. J. R. Reeves: El Dorado Oil Field, Butler County, Kansas, "Structure of Typical American Oil Fields," vol. II, pp. 160–167, 1929.
50. F. E. Kendrick and H. C. McLaughlin: Relation of Petroleum Accumulation to Structure, Petroleum Field, Clay County, Texas, "Structure of Typical American Oil Fields," vol. II, pp. 542–555, 1929.
51. E. H. Sellards and L. T. Patton: The Subsurface Geology of the Big Lake Oil Field, *Bull. Am. Assoc. Petroleum Geol.*, vol. 10, pp. 365–381, 1926.
52. G. C. Clark and F. L. Aurin: The Tonkawa Field, Oklahoma, *Bull. Am. Assoc. Petroleum Geol.*, vol. 8, pp. 269–283, 1924.
53. Gulf Coast Oil Fields, American Association of Petroleum Geologists' Symposium, 1936.
54. E. DeGolyer: *Trans. AIME*, vol. III, p. 269, 1915.
55. C. S. Ross: Structure of the Delaware Anticlinal Terrace, *USGS Bull.* 686, 1922.
56. W. W. Rubey: *USGS Bull.* 751-B, 1923.
57. D. D. Condit: Structure of the Berea Oil Sand in the Woodsfield Quadrangle, Belmont, Monroe, Noble and Guernsey Counties, Ohio, *USGS Bull.* 621, pp. 233–249, 1916.
58. F. H. Lahee: Oil and Gas Fields of the Mexia and Tehuancana Fault Zones, Texas, "Structure of Typical American Oil Fields," vol. I, pp. 304–388, 1929.

59. P. de Chambrier: Les Mines de pétrole de Pechelbronn, Société Industrielle, Strasbourg, 1920.
60. W. A. J. M. Van Waterschoot van der Gracht: Eindverslag over de Onderzoekingen en Uitkomsten van den Dienst der Rijkopsporing van Delfstoffen in Nederland, 1903–1916, The Hague, Netherlands, 1918, 664 pp.
61. X. Stainier: Sur les recherches du sel en Campine, *Ann. mines Belg.*, pp. 117–169, 1911.

SELECTED REFERENCES ON OIL-FIELD CLASSIFICATION

1929

Clapp, F. G.: Role of Geologic Structure in the Accumulation of Petroleum, "Structure of Typical American Oil Fields," vol. 2, American Association of Petroleum Geologists, pp. 667ff.

1934

Wilson, W. B.: Proposed Classification of Oil and Gas Reservoirs, "Problems of Petroleum Geology," American Association of Petroleum Geologists' Symposium, pp. 433ff.

1941

Ducloux, A. H.: Classification of Stratigraphic Traps, *Mines Mag.*, Petroleum number.

1945

Brod, I. O.: Geological Terminology in Classification of Oil and Gas Accumulation, *Bull. Am. Assoc. Petroleum Geol.*, vol. 29, no. 12, pp. 1738ff.
Pirson, S. J.: Genetic and Morphologic Classification of Reservoirs, *Oil Weekly*, June 18, pp. 54ff.
Wilhelm, O.: Classification of Petroleum Reservoirs, *Bull. Am. Assoc. Petroleum Geol.*, vol. 29, no. 11, pp. 1537ff.

SELECTED REFERENCES ON OIL AND GAS MIGRATION AND ACCUMULATION IN GEOLOGIC TRAPS

1861

Andrews, E. B.: Rock Oil, Its Relations and Distribution, *Am. J. Sci.*, vol. 32, pp. 85ff.
Hunt, J. S.: Notes on the Geology of Petroleum and Rock Oil, *Can. Naturalist*, vol. 6, pp. 241ff.

1865

Winchell, A.: On the Oil Formation in Michigan and Elsewhere, *Am. J. Sci.*, vol. 39, pp. 252ff.

1873

Newberry, J. S.: Devonian System, *Ohio Geol. Sur.*, vol. 1, pp. 160ff.

1885

White, I. C.: The Geology of Natural Gas, *Science*, vol. 6, June 26.

1889

Orton, E.: The Trenton Limestone as a Source of Petroleum and Inflammable Gas in Ohio and Indiana, *USGS 8th Ann. Rept.*, part 2, pp. 475ff.

1904

White, I. C.: Petroleum and Natural Gas, *West V. Geol. Survey*, vol. A, pp. 48ff

1917

McCoy, A. W.: Some Effects of Capillarity on Oil Accumulation, *Bull. Am. Assoc. Petroleum Geol.*, vol. 1, pp. 140ff.

1920

Mills, R. van A.: Experimental Studies of Subsurface Relationships in Oil and Gas Fields, *Econ. Geol.*, vol. 15, pp. 398ff.

1923

Cook, C. W.: Study of Capillary Relationships of Oil and Water, *Econ. Geol.*, vol. 18, pp. 167ff.

1926

American Association of Petroleum Geologists' Symposium: "Geology of Salt Dome Oil Fields."

McCoy, A. W.: A Brief Outline of Some Oil Accumulation Problems, *Bull. Am. Assoc. Petroleum Geol.*, vol. 10, pp. 1015ff.

1928

Stamp, L. D.: The Connection between Commercial Oil Deposits and Major Structural Features (with Special Reference to Asiatic Fields), *J. Inst. Petroleum Technol.*, vol. 14, pp. 28ff.

1929

Taylor, E. M.: The Replaceable Bases in the Shales and Clays Overlying Petroliferous Strata, *J. Inst. Petroleum Technol.*, vol. 15, pp. 207ff.

1930

Athy, L. F.: Compaction and Oil Migration, *Bull. Am. Assoc. Petroleum Geol.*, vol. 14, pp. 25ff.

1933

Lockwood, R. P.: Role of Cap Rock in Oil Accumulation, *Bull. Am. Assoc. Petroleum Geol.*, vol. 17, pp. 713ff.

1934

Dake, C. L., and L. F. Dake: Role of Cap Rock in Oil Accumulation, *Bull. Am. Assoc. Petroleum Geol.*, vol. 18, pp. 1086ff.

Levorsen, A. I.: Relation of Oil and Gas Pools to Unconformities in the Mid-Continent Region, "Problems of Petroleum Geology," American Association of Petroleum Geologists' Symposium, pp. 761ff.

McCoy, A. W., and W. R. Keyte: Present Interpretations of Structural Theory for Oil and Gas Migration and Accumulation, "Problems of Petroleum Geology," American Association of Petroleum Geologists' Symposium, pp. 253ff. and 581ff.

1936

American Association of Petroleum Geologists' Symposium: "Gulf Coast Oil Fields."

1941

American Association of Petroleum Geologists' Symposium: "Stratigraphic Type Oil Fields."

1943

Levorsen, A. I.: Discovery Thinking, *Bull. Am. Assoc. Petroleum Geol.*, vol. 27, pp. 887ff.

Sanders, C. W.: Stratigraphic Type Oil Fields and Proposed Classification of Reservoir Traps, *Bull. Am. Assoc. Petroleum Geol.*, vol. 27, no. 4, pp. 540ff.

1949

Stewart, W. A.: Meaning and Importance of Unconformities in Stratigraphic Rocks, *Mines Mag.*, April, pp. 19ff.

1950

Alexander, C. I.: Graphic Representation of Reservoir History, *Bull. Am. Assoc. Petroleum Geol.*, vol. 34, no. 3, pp. 454.
Carsey, J. B.: Geology of Gulf Coastal Area and Continental Shelf, *Bull. Am. Assoc. Petroleum Geol.*, vol. 34, no. 3, pp. 361ff.
Link, T. A.: Theory of Transgressive and Regressive Reef (Bioherm) Development and Origin of Oil, *Bull. Am. Assoc. Petroleum Geol.*, vol. 34, no. 2, pp. 263ff.

1951

Landes, K. K.: Oil and Gas Traps, *Oil Gas J.*, Feb. 8, pp. 83ff.
McCoy, A. L., III, et al.: Types of Oil and Gas Traps in Rocky Mountain Region, *Bull. Am. Assoc. Petroleum Geol.*, vol. 35, no. 5, pp. 1000ff.
Selk, E. L.: Types of Oil and Gas Traps in Southern Oklahoma, *Bull. Am. Assoc. Petroleum Geol.*, vol. 35, no. 3, pp. 582ff.

1952

Marshall, J W.: Spraberry Reservoir of West Texas, *Bull. Am. Assoc. Petroleum Geol.*, vol. 36, no. 11, pp. 2189ff.
Shepard, F. P.: Revised Nomenclature for Depositional Coastal Features, *Bull. Am. Assoc. Petroleum Geol.*, vol. 36, no. 10, pp. 1902ff.
Weeks, L. G.: Factors of Sedimentary Basin Development That Control Oil Occurrence, *Bull. Am. Assoc. Petroleum Geol.*, vol. 36, no. 11, pp. 2071ff.

1953

Adams, J. E.: Non Reef Limestone Reservoir, *Bull. Am. Assoc. Petroleum Geol.*, vol. 37, no. 11, pp. 2566ff.
Anderson, K. C.: Wellman Field, Terry County, Texas, *Bull. Am. Assoc. Petroleum Geol.*, vol. 37, no. 3, pp. 509ff.
Bates, C. C.: Rational Theory of Delta Formation, *Bull. Am. Assoc. Petroleum Geol.*, vol. 37, no. 9, pp. 2119ff.
Johnson, J. H.: Reefs and the Petroleum Geologist, part 1, Definitions and Types, *Mines Mag.*, September, pp. 21ff.
Sernton, P. C.: Deposition of Evaporites, *Bull. Am. Assoc. Petroleum Geol.*, vol. 37, no. 11, pp. 2498ff.
Shepard, F. P.: Sedimentation Rates in Texas Estuaries and Lagoons, *Bull. Am. Assoc. Petroleum Geol.*, vol. 37, no. 8, pp. 1919ff.

1954

Bush, D. A.: Deltas Significant in Subsurface Exploration, *World Oil*, December, pp. 95ff.
Halbouty, M. T., and G. C. Hardin, Jr.: Salt Dome Geology May Enter New Phase, *Oil Gas J.*, Nov. 1, pp. 93ff.
Johnson, J. H.: Reefs and the Petroleum Geologist, part 2, Reef Building Animals, *Mines Mag.*, January, pp. 15ff.

1955

Bush, D. A.: Deltas Significant in Subsurface Exploration, *World Oil*, January, pp. 82ff.
Halbouty, M. T., and G. C. Hardin, Jr.: Factors Affecting Quantity of Oil Accumulation around Some Texas Gulf Coast Piercement Type Salt Domes, *Bull. Am. Assoc. Petroleum Geol.*, vol. 39, no. 5, pp. 697ff.
Irwin, J. S., et al.: Differential Entrapment of Oil and Gas, *Bull. Am. Assoc. Petroleum Geol.*, vol. 39, no. 2, pp. 260ff.

Russell, W. L.: "Structural Geology for Petroleum Geologists," McGraw-Hill Book Company, Inc., New York.

Shepard, F. P., and D. G. Moore: Central Texas Coast Sedimentation: Characteristics of Sedimentary Environment, Recent History and Diagenesis, *Bull. Am. Assoc. Petroleum Geol.*, vol. 39, no. 8, pp. 1463ff.

Sloss, L. L.: Facies Studies—an Important Tool in Oil Finding, *Oil Gas J.*, Sept. 12, pp. 111ff.

1956

Halbouty, M. T., and G. C. Hardin, Jr.: Genesis of Salt Domes of Gulf Coastal Plain, *Bull. Am. Assoc. Petroleum Geol.*, vol. 40, no. 4, pp. 737ff.

Hunt, J. M., and G. W. Jamieson: Oil and Organic Matter in Source Rocks of Petroleum, *Bull. Am. Assoc. Petroleum Geol.*, vol. 40, no. 3, pp. 477ff.

Johnson, J. W.: Nearshore Sediment Movement, *Bull. Am. Assoc. Petroleum Geol.*, vol. 40, September, pp. 2211ff.

Krumbein, W. C.: Regional and Local Components in Facies Maps, *Bull. Am. Assoc. Petroleum Geol.*, vol. 40, no. 9, pp. 2163ff.

Stevens, N. P., et al.: Hydrocarbons in Sediments of Gulf of Mexico, *Bull. Am. Assoc. Petroleum Geol.*, vol. 40 ,no. 5, pp. 975ff.

CHAPTER 2

PHYSICAL PROPERTIES OF RESERVOIR ROCKS

Considered on a hand-specimen scale, rocks susceptible of containing oil and gas in commercially producible quantities have definite ranges of physical properties which are of paramount interest to the reservoir engineer. It is not the purpose of this chapter to make a complete study of core analysis and testing but rather to review the significance of the terminology, of the measuring techniques, and of the results in terms of expected reservoir behavior. The three engineering characteristics of a reservoir rock are *porosity;* oil, gas, and water *saturation;* and *permeability,* specific, effective, and relative. Each characteristic will be reviewed in the above order.

POROSITY (ϕ)

Porosity (ϕ) is the best-known physical characteristic of an oil reservoir. It determines the volume of oil or gas present, and all recovery computations must be based on a knowledge of its value.

One of the earliest reports on the porosity of an oil sand was made by J. F. Carll in a publication of the Second Pennsylvania Survey in 1877. Carll carried out experiments, which would appear crude by modern standards, on a number of samples of the "third sandstone," taken from oil wells at Tidioute, Pennsylvania. His conclusion was that the third sandstone was capable of holding 7 to 10 per cent of its own volume of oil. Carll's experiments were made on specimens of rock whose pores were more or less clogged with residuum from oil that had been held inside, and without saturation of the specimen under pressure. However, Carll's experiments and conclusions dispelled the popular idea of underground lakes and streams of oil.

Porosity of a material is defined as that fraction of the bulk volume of this material that is not occupied by the solid framework of the material. In oil reservoirs, the porosity represents the percentage of the total space that is available for occupancy by either liquids or gases. It determines the *storage capacity of the sand* and is generally expressed on a percentage basis or as a fraction or a decimal.

Regardless of the method employed, the necessary equipment for the determination of porosity is relatively simple. The actual preparation, testing, and calculation of porosity is routine work and can be learned quickly by an inexperienced operator. However, the application of the data and the interpretation of results demand the skilled services of a technician who is well versed in reservoir performance.

One may distinguish two types of porosity, namely, *absolute* and *effective*. Absolute porosity is the percentage of total void space with respect to the bulk volume regardless of the interconnection of the pore voids. A rock may have considerable absolute porosity and yet have no conductivity to fluid for lack of pore interconnection. This is the case for lava and other igneous rocks with vesicular porosity.

Effective porosity is the percentage of *interconnected* void space with respect to the bulk volume. It is an *indication* of conductivity to fluid but not necessarily a measure of it.

Effective porosity is a function of a great many lithological factors. Some of the most important of these are heterogeneity of grain size, packing, cementation, weathering and leaching, clay content, clay types, and clay hydration status.

Experimental porosity-determination procedures may be divided into two classes, namely, those designed to measure *effective porosity* and those which measure *absolute porosity.*

Effective-porosity Measurements. *Grain-volume Methods.* In these methods the consolidated sample is solvent extracted and dried; the *bulk volume* is determined either by the displacement of a liquid which does not penetrate the sample or by saturating the sample and volumetrically displacing a suitable liquid with the saturated sample. The *grain volume*, or volume of the solid framework of the sample, may be measured by the volumetric displacement of a gas or a liquid, while the *pore volume* may be measured by determining the amount of liquid necessary to saturate the sample. An alternate method of obtaining the grain volume, which may be used for approximate work, is to divide the dry weight of the sample by the average grain density of 2.65, since the average density of most reservoir rock minerals seldom deviates by more than 3 to 5 per cent from this figure. The results are, however, a measure of absolute porosity rather than of effective porosity.

It is obvious that the percentage of porosity may be calculated from such data by use of either of the two following relationships:

$$\text{Per cent porosity} = 100\left(\frac{\text{bulk volume} - \text{grain volume}}{\text{bulk volume}}\right)$$

or

$$\text{Per cent porosity} = 100\,\frac{\text{pore volume}}{\text{bulk volume}}$$

In preparation of samples for porosity testing, they are selected to be preferably 10 to 20 cc in bulk volume and are obtained from the center of the core. Their surfaces are cleaned to remove traces of drilling mud. The samples are extracted in a soxhlet, or equivalent apparatus, using oil solvents such as benzene, toluene, or a light hydrocarbon fraction.

Chloroform or carbon tetrachloride, although excellent oil solvents which possess the advantage of noninflammability, are not recommended because of the possibility of hydrolysis which results in the formation of acids and the possibility of porosity and permeability changes by reaction with the mineral rock framework.

During the extraction, the samples should be kept in an unglazed porcelain or paper thimble, covered with plugs of cotton or glass wool, in order to avoid erosion of loosely cemented grains. After extraction, the samples are dried in an oven at 100 to 105°C and cooled in a desiccator. This operation removes the solvent and moisture from the samples.

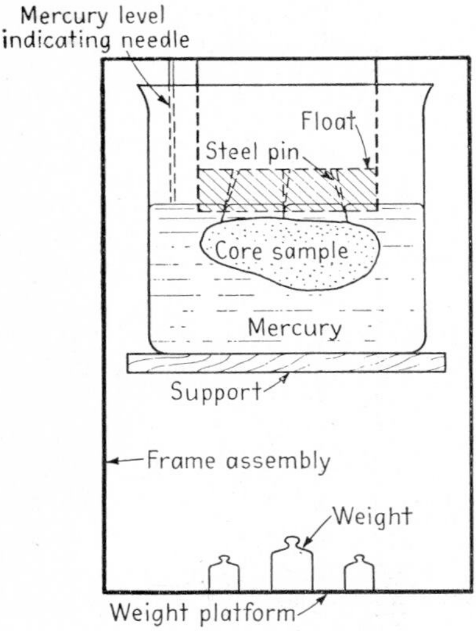

FIG. 2-1. Apparatus for the determination of bulk-volume by mercury displacement (Westman balance).

The time required for extraction may be decreased appreciably if the samples are presaturated with the extracting solvent. This presaturation may be accomplished by placing the samples in a suitable vessel, evacuating the air from the vessel with a vacuum pump or water jet, admitting the solvent over the samples while evacuated, then bringing the vessel to atmospheric pressure. For very tight samples, it may be necessary to apply pressure over the solvent in order to achieve complete saturation.

For cleaning large cores, a succession of pressuring and depressuring with a carbon dioxide–toluene mixture at elevated temperatures has proved very successful (1952, Stewart and Spurlock).

Bulk-volume Determination. The bulk volume of the extracted and dried samples may be determined by volumetric displacement of mercury. The following bulk-volume determination procedures have proved satisfactory.

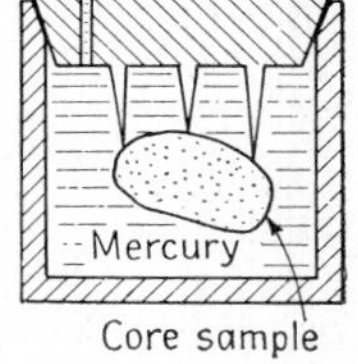

FIG. 2-2. Steel pycnometer.

1. Determine the dry weight of the sample and the weight necessary to submerge it in mercury. The sample should be submerged while held by pointed steel rods, and the weight required to submerge the rods to a reference depth is determined (Fig. 2-1). The bulk volume is calculated by dividing by the density of mercury (at the operating-room temperature) the sum of the weights of the dry rock and the weight required to submerge the sample, less the weight required to submerge the blank apparatus (minus sample) to the same reference mark [Westman balance (1926)].

2. A steel or glass pycnometer, with a cap which rests on a ground taper joint and with a small hole drilled through the cap, is filled with mercury, the cap is pressed into its seat, and the excess mercury which overflows

through a hole in the cap is collected and removed. The pycnometer is opened, and the sample is placed on the surface of the mercury and submerged by a set of pointed rods which project from the lower side of the cap (Fig. 2-2). The cap is again pressed into its seat, which causes a certain amount of mercury equivalent to the bulk volume of the sample to overflow. The rods which submerge the sample should be adjusted so that the sample does not touch the sides of the pycnometer; this avoids trapping air bubbles. Either the volume of mercury which overflows or the loss of weight of the mercury in the pycnometer may be measured and the core's bulk volume calculated.

3. The sample's bulk volume may be measured by submerging the sample in mercury which is contained in an apparatus designed for determining the rise of the mercury level caused by the introduction of the sample. The rise in mercury level causes the movement of a less dense liquid in an inclined glass tube and results in a magnified fluid level displacement. This apparatus may be calibrated with steel balls or glass plugs of known volume.

The determination of the bulk volume by mercury displacement is rapid and dependable under most conditions. The method cannot be applied to loosely cemented samples which have a tendency to disintegrate when immersed in mercury. A serious source of error is the trapping of gas bubbles at the surface of the sample. The depth to which the sample is submerged should be kept small (less than 5 cm) in order to avoid the penetration of mercury into the pore spaces.

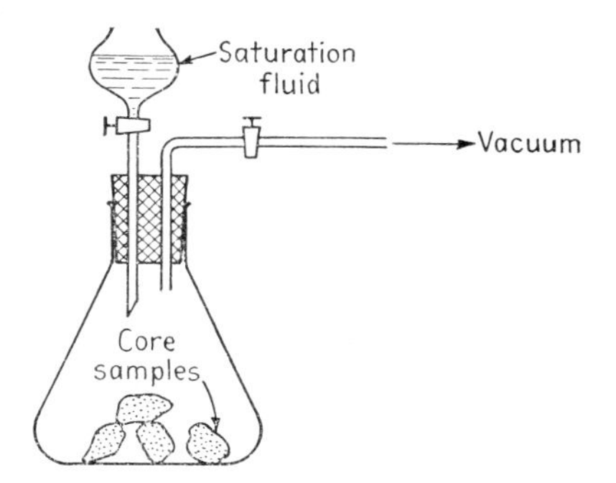

FIG. 2-3. Saturation apparatus for core samples.

In general, where a large number of routine analyses must be made per day and where the samples to be tested are well cemented and can be shaped by smooth, hard surfaces, the use of a mercury-displacement method is a practical way of measuring bulk volume.

Bulk volume may also be determined by submergence of a saturated sample. The sample is saturated with a suitable liquid, and the volumetric displacement of the same liquid caused by submerging the saturated sample in a suitable container is determined. The liquid used should have a low viscosity and surface tension; it should wet and penetrate the sample freely. Liquids, such as chloroform and tetrachloroethane, have been used for this purpose; kerosene, however, is equally satisfactory. In addition, kerosene is readily available and less expensive. The first step requires saturation of the sample. To this end, the extracted and dried sample is placed in a widemouthed bottle, which is closed with a rubber stopper fitted with a two-way stopcock (Fig. 2-3). One side of the stopcock is connected to a vacuum pump and the other to a funnel containing kerosene. The sample is evacuated, and the stopcock is then turned to admit enough kerosene into the evacuated bottle to cover the sample. Air is then admitted to bring the pressure to atmospheric. Several samples may be saturated simultaneously by using a sufficiently large size bottle. With very tight samples, it is necessary to apply pressure in order to approach full saturation. After saturation, the sample is removed with forceps; the excess liquid which drips to the bottom of the sample is removed by touching the sample to a piece of filter paper or a paper towel. The volume of kerosene displaced by the saturated sample is then determined in a widemouthed pycnometer, as described above. Another instrument used for this purpose, which operates on a similar principle, is the Russell volumeter, pictured in Fig. 2-4.

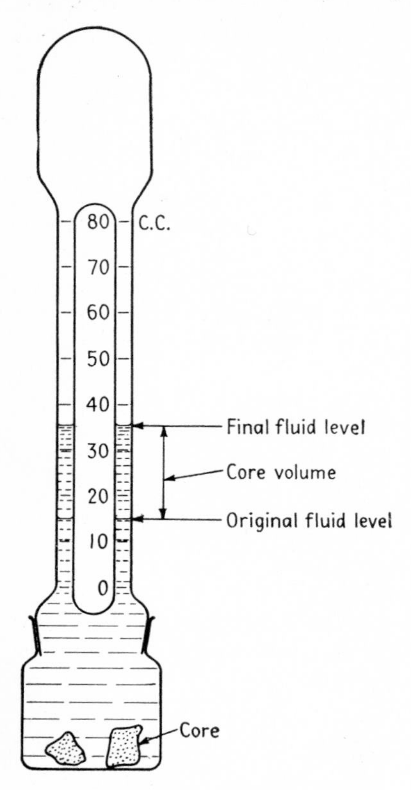

FIG. 2-4. Russell volumeter.

The procedure just described for measuring bulk volume, although somewhat more time-consuming than the mercury-displacement method, has the advantage of applicability to loosely cemented samples and to samples with irregular surfaces. Since the liquid displaced is transparent, trapped air bubbles may be seen and steps taken to remove them. The proper removal of the excess liquid after saturation, although requiring some care and experience, may be achieved dependably to a few milligrams of kerosene. The method is practical also for the determination of porosity on small core fragments or drill cuttings. With granular reservoir samples, reasonably accurate results have been obtained with core chips as small as 0.05 cc in volume. However, the saturation method may not be used with cavernous and vuggy cores because the fluid escapes during transfer under the influence of gravity.

Boyle's Law Porosimeter. The measurement of grain volume, or of the solid framework of the core samples, may be made by gas displacement (Fig. 2-5). The extracted and dried sample is placed in a steel cup, filled with gas (usually air) at a known pressure of 4 to 5 atm. The gas in the cup is then expanded into a calibrated volume of comparatively large size with respect to the cup, and the resulting pressure in the system is measured. By comparison of the gas pressure obtained by expansion from the cup when the sample is present to that obtained in a duplicate determination without the sample, the bulk volume of the solid framework of the sample may be calculated from Boyle's law. The above test is repeated, using nonporous dummy cores of approximately the same size as the core samples.

Let P_d be the pressure read on the manometer when the dummy core is in the holder, P_b be the pressure for the blank test without core, and P_c

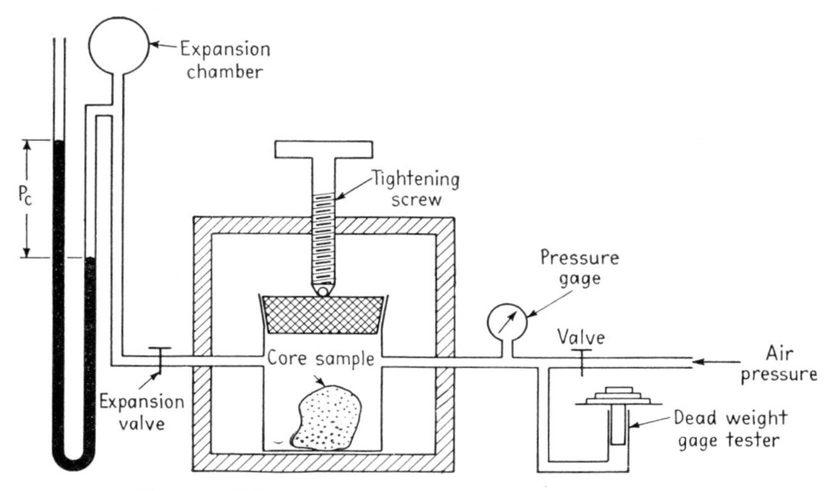

FIG. 2-5. Schematic diagram of Boyle's law porosimeter.

the pressure when the core is present. Assuming that the holder had been pressured in each test to the same reading on the gauge, manometer, or dead-weight gauge tester, the porosity ϕ is obtained by

$$\phi = 100 \frac{P_c - P_d}{P_b - P_d}$$

in per cent of bulk volume.

Another porosimeter which works on a similar principle is the Ruska porosimeter, a schematic diagram of which is given in Fig. 2-6. In this case, if a knowledge of the bulk volume of the sample is necessary, it may be obtained by using the instrument's cup as a pycnometer. A micrometer piston is used to pressure the sample cup so that the mercury reaches a given reference on the manometer. Let the reading be R_H in the absence of a core sample in the cup. When a core floats on the mercury within the cup, the displacement of the micrometer piston gives a reading of R_c to reach the same reference mark. The porosity of the sample is then calculated by

$$\phi = 100 \left(1 - \frac{R_c}{R_H}\right)$$

in per cent of bulk volume.

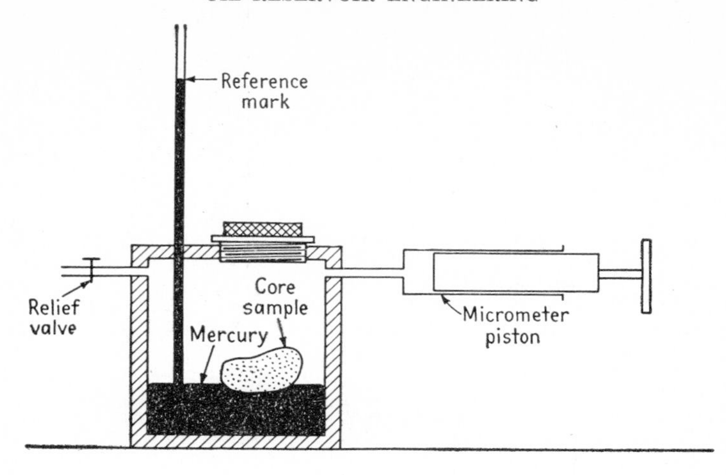

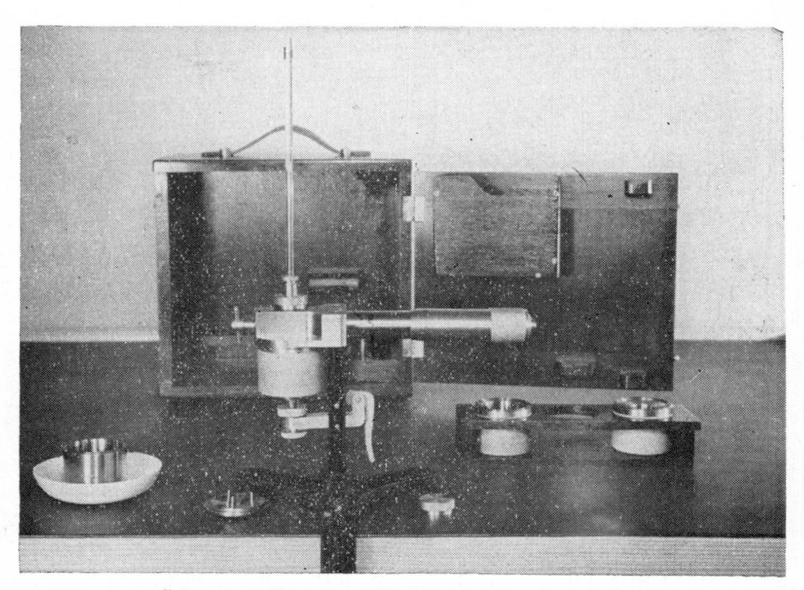

FIG. 2-6. Schematic diagram and photograph of Ruska porosimeter.

Pore-gas Expansion Method. The measurement of porosity may also be made by the pore-gas expansion method, or so-called Washburn-Bunting method (1922). This method makes use of a modified Toepler pump so much in use in high-vacuum techniques in order to produce the barometric vacuum and remove air from a dried core. The bulk volume of the core must be known from other tests.

The procedure applies best to well-consolidated cores. They are placed in the cup receptacle as shown in Fig. 2-7. The upper assembly is replaced; the ground-glass joint is rendered gastight by means of a good grade of vacuum stopcock grease. The procedure requires the following steps:

1. Make a blank determination with a piece of glass of approximately the same shape and size as the core sample to be tested. This gives a zero reading which corresponds to absorbed air on the surface of the test piece.
2. Place the core sample above the mercury, and replace the graduated column; fasten with rubber bands, and leave the upper stopcock open.
3. Raise the leveling bulb until the mercury reaches above the stopcock; this must be done slowly and carefully in order to avoid the jetting of mercury through the upper stopcock.
4. Close the stopcock.
5. Lower the leveling bulb until the core floats in the barometric vacuum on top of the mercury. Let the core stand in this position for a few minutes in order to allow the complete escape of air from the core.
6. Lift the leveling bulb slowly until the two levels in the two branches are at the same height. This ensures the restoration of atmospheric pressure on the air which escaped from the core. Since the apparatus as well as the core is presumably at room temperature, the air volume in the graduated capillary represents the true effective pore volume of the core. The effective porosity in per cent is given by

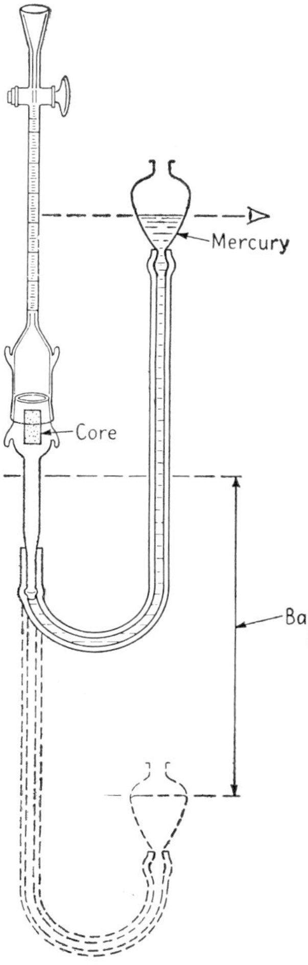

FIG. 2-7. Washburn-Bunting porosimeter.

$$\phi = 100 \frac{\text{volume from step 6} - \text{zero reading}}{\text{bulk volume}}$$

This method when applied to friable and highly permeable cores gives rise to some troublesome mercury penetration into the cores, rendering them completely useless for further core tests.

Mercury-injection Method. When a rock has a very small fraction of void space, it is difficult to measure it by methods previously discussed. One may then resort to forcing a noncompressible liquid into the sample under very high pressure. The original idea appears to have been that of Horner (1944). Apparatus of this type are commercially available, one of which is the Ruska high-pressure porosimeter shown in Fig. 2-8.

The porosity of a sample is obtained by measuring its bulk volume under atmospheric pressure with a suitable displacement fluid (mercury) in a pycnometer and then forcing this fluid under pressure into the pore space of the sample and measuring the volume of the fluid entering the space. This method makes the instrument valuable for cores of low permeability where accurate results cannot be obtained with other porosity equipment.

FIG. 2-8. Ruska high-pressure porosimeter.

A high-pressure stainless-steel pycnometer, large enough to accommodate samples up to approximately 30 cc, is closed by a lid with a needle valve. To this pycnometer is attached a measuring cylinder with a metering plunger. A scale and dial arrangement permits the reading of the movement of the metering plunger. The scales are graduated to read in cubic centimeters, and the dial is graduated to read 0.01 cc. A 1,000 psi pressure gauge is attached to the cylinder for reading the pressure under which the measuring fluid is forced into the pores.

The high-pressure porosimeter is equipped with two sliding scales. The volume scale is arranged in such a way that the volume of a body placed in the pycnometer may be read in cubic centimeters without calculations. The pore-space scale has a friction engagement with the plunger of the pump and moves with the plunger unless it is locked to its slide bar. It is graduated for the porosity to be read in cubic centimeters. The index is arranged in such a way that the use of a correction factor in the calculation is eliminated. This pore-space scale is locked when the needle valve on the pycnometer lid is closed. (The correction factor is the volume displacement required to increase the gauge reading from zero to the reference pressure. This factor corrects for any air trapped in the system and for elastic changes in the pump when applying pressure.)

To determine the porosity of a core, the sample is first extracted and dried. The bulk volume of the core is determined by mercury displacement in the pycnometer, the volume scale giving direct readings of the bulk volume in cubic centimeters to 0.01 cc. The reading is taken by placing the core in the pycnometer, closing the lid, and observing the appearance of the first drop of mercury in the pycnometer valve. After the bulk volume is obtained, this valve is closed, the pore-space scale locked, and the pressure in the system is brought to the desired reference pressure, usually 750 psi. The cubic centimeters of mercury necessary to raise the pressure from 0 to 750 psi indicates the pore space in the sample and is read directly on the pore-space scale.

Loss-of-weight Method. The measurement of the grain volume of a core sample may also be determined by the loss in weight of a saturated sample plunged in a liquid. The extracted and dried sample is weighed, saturated with a liquid such as kerosene, tetrachloroethane, or other suitable liquid, and the apparent weight of the saturated sample while immersed in this liquid is determined. The saturation may be carried out as described above, and the apparent weight while immersed is determined by suspending the sample from a balance arm by a fine wire and weighing when the sample is completely submerged in the liquid. The grain volume is equal to the difference between the weight dry and the weight when saturated and submerged, divided by the density of the liquid used.

This method is capable of high precision and is as rapid as the gas-expansion method described above. It is especially suitable to the analysis of large numbers of samples.

Liquid-saturation Method. Measurement of pore volume may also be achieved by liquid saturation. This procedure may be employed suitably in connection with the measurement of bulk volume. It is necessary to weigh the dry sample before saturation with kerosene or another suitable liquid, as well as after saturation. The saturated sample is weighed after the excess kerosene has been removed. Bulk and pore volumes may both be determined on the same sample. It is not necessary to know the density of the kerosene because the weight of the kerosene in the saturated sample, divided by the weight of the kerosene displaced by the saturated sample and multiplied by 100, is equal to the percentage of porosity.

Porosity of Large Core Samples. A technique is advocated by Locke and Bliss (1950) for the measurement of porosity in large cores, i.e., cores as recovered from drilling operations without further reduction in size by sampling of small plugs. The technique is of further interest because it permits the evaluation of the types of porosity present in the sample and of the extent to which each is present—whether intercrystalline, vuggy, channel, fissures, and even fractures (provided the sample does not fall apart). Before the sample is tested, large vugs and openings on the surface of the core are covered with adhesive tape. The sample is placed in a container of sufficient size, filled with water containing a wetting agent.

The container is then closed, but the injection of water is continued and volumetrically measured in increments. A pressure reading is made at each increment. When the cumulative volume of water injected is plotted vs. pressure, which ultimately reaches 1,000 psi, a curve is obtained which discloses definite changes in slope. It is presumed that these changes occur when pore openings of a definite type and size range have been filled with water. At the pressure of 1,000 psi it is also presumed that all the pores have been completely filled. When the bulk volume of the core is known, its total effective porosity is calculated as the ratio of the total water injected to bulk volume. The porosity of vugs and large channels is represented by the fraction of water injected to the first change in slope on the pressure curve because such vugs and channels constitute the pore space filled up under low injection pressures. The intergranular-pore-space volume is that obtained at the higher injection pressures.

Absolute-porosity Measurement. In the determination of absolute porosity, it is required that all nonconnecting as well as interconnecting pores be accounted for. The procedure requires that the sample be crushed. The extraction and drying steps, which are necessary for the determination of the effective porosity, can be dispensed with in absolute-porosity measurements. The method is as follows: Break off a suitable sample, preferably 10 to 15 cc in volume, from the well core; clean the surface of the sample to remove the drilling mud; measure the bulk volume by any of the procedures described above; crush the sample to its constituent grains; wash the grains with suitable solvents (to remove oil and water) such as acetone; and determine the volume of the grains. It is, of course, necessary to dry the rock grains before their volume is determined. The volume of the dry grains may be determined in a pycnometer, or with a Russell volumeter, containing a suitable liquid such as kerosene or tetrachloroethane.

Geologic Factors Affecting Porosity. Porosity is a rock property of paramount importance in an oil and gas reservoir, for it provides the fluid *storage capacity* when it is present to a sufficient degree over adequate thickness of rock and when it is sufficiently continuous laterally.

Porosity in sediments is both created and destroyed by natural geologic processes. Geologic conditions are responsible for both primary and secondary porosity.

Primary porosity results from voids which are left between mineral fragments and grains after their accumulation as sediments.

Secondary porosity results from geologic agents such as leaching, fracturing, and fissuring which occur after lithification of sediments.

Sandstones, of all the sediments, are the most commonly porous and permeable rocks. Although carbonates presumably contain most of the world's known reserves, there are many oil provinces in which limestones and dolomites are absent.

Sandstone Porosity. Sandstone porosity is of two types, *intergranular* and *fracture*.

Intergranular porosity is the net void space that remains after the initial porosity has been decreased by geologic agents such as compaction, cementation, recrystallization, granulation, crushing, etc.

The primary porosity of a sandstone or other clastic rock depends initially upon the degree of sorting of the grains according to size.

Well-sorted, moderately rounded sand grains settle in water giving a packing of 30 to 40 per cent porosity. In poorly sorted sediments, the smaller grains fit into the spaces between the larger ones, and porosity is considerably decreased.

Some apparently tight sandstones and siltstones owe part of their porosity to *fractures*. A typical example of this is the Spraberry formation of West Texas in which fractures in place are estimated to account for only 10 per cent of the porosity. However, fractures provide most of the reservoir permeability. Because fractured rocks may not often be recovered undisturbed in a core, core-analysis methods are generally inadequate to evaluate fractures.

Compaction is the geologic factor which reduces porosity due to overburden pressure of the overlying sediments or due to orogenic pressure. Sandstones, however, exhibit very little compressibility (3×10^{-7} per psi), whereas shales may be reduced to a small fraction of their original sedimentation volume.

Cementation is the agent which has the greatest effect on the original porosity and which affects the size, shape, and continuity of pore channels through possible deposition of secondary quartz, calcite, and dolomite singly or in combination. In addition, clay may often act as cementing material.

Silica cement may be present to various degrees in a rock. In its initial state and in a well-sorted unconsolidated sand, the actual pore shape approximates the theoretical shape.

In the early stage of secondary silica cementation, the original pore shape is not altered greatly but the total pore space is reduced and some of the connections are cut off. With greater degree of cementation, the secondary quartz overgrowth invades mostly the larger openings of the pore space and numerous reentrant angles are developed. In the final stage of secondary silica cementation, the adjacent individual quartz grain overgrowths coalesce and a quartzite rock is formed from which pore space is virtually eliminated.

Carbonate cement in sandstone may be formed at the same time as the sand or may be deposited in the pore space shortly after sedimentation. Secondary cementation by calcite or dolomite deposited from circulating waters is possible but is less important than secondary silica cementation. In most cases dolomite cement forms well-defined crystal structures, whereas calcite cement is irregular in shape. Calcite cement may become dolomitized with additional increase in porosity.

Clay cement is not properly a process that causes induration of sands, as all that is provided by the clay particles is a loose binding action which leaves the rocks very friable.

Clay cement is deposited at the same time as sand grains and generally it adheres to them so that after deposition considerable porosity still exists and the over-all porosity of a sandstone may not be lowered greatly by a small amount of clay.

Recrystallization is not an important factor in the porosity of sandstone.

Granulation and *crushing* of sand grains and their effect on porosity at great depth under overburden pressure are of interest. With increasing overburden pressure, quartz grains in a sandstone show a progressive change from random packing to a closer packing. Some crushing and plastic deformation of the sand grains occur. With deeper drilling, the persistence of porosity at great depth in deep sedimentary basins is of concern to the oil industry. Bell (1943) has suggested this limit to be about 21,000 ft, based on laboratory crushing-strength tests of dried cores. However, when rocks are fluid-saturated and confined from all directions, it is expected that porosity may still exist to greater depths.

Limestone Porosity. Porosity development in carbonate reservoirs is different in many respects from that in sandstones. While in sandstones a high degree of horizontal continuity may be expected, porosity development in carbonate rocks is very localized both laterally and vertically. Sheet porosity development is very rare in limestones; one instance, however, is that in the Lansing–Kansas City lime where pay zones are less than a few feet in thickness.

Although individual pore openings in carbonate rocks may be very large, the average porosity over a section is generally smaller than in sandstones. It is because of their greater bed thickness that limestones form such prolific reservoirs.

As in sandstones, porosity in carbonate rocks may be both primary and secondary.

Primary pore space in carbonate rocks may result from:

1. Interstitial voids between clastic grains of a detrital carbonate rock such as in conglomerates, breccia, coquina, oölites, chalk, etc.

2. Intercrystalline voids in crystalline limestones along cleavage planes and because of difference in crystal size

3. Skeleton voids produced by the removal of organic matter from corals and calcareous algae

Primary porosity in limestones accounts only for relatively unimportant oil and gas reservoirs except in oölitic and chalky facies.

But primary porosity provides the avenues for the development of secondary porosity by permitting circulation of ground waters.

Secondary pore space in carbonate rocks may result from:

1. *Jointing* caused by consolidation contraction, tectonic stresses, or mineralogic changes.

Jointing consists of a series of fractures that follow a consistent pattern with groups of fractures running parallel to each other and other groups intersecting these at a fixed angle. Some of these intersecting fractures are larger than others and they constitute a major set of joints.

Joints are most often vertical. Because of the brittleness of carbonates it takes only small tension forces to produce jointing. They are found most often on the crest of anticlines.

Therefore, solution porosity develops mostly on structural highs where meteoric waters find easy access.

2. *Leaching action of ground water.* This process develops solution porosity and is related to the topography of old erosion surfaces. It requires a period of erosion of sufficiently long duration and a sufficient surface relief above the ground-water table to permit the leaching action of percolating waters. A very large fraction of limestone reservoirs are associated with this type of porosity development.

3. *Dolomitization.* The mechanism of porosity development by dolomitization is open to question but it is believed to be the result of molecular replacement of calcium by magnesium in limestones, a process which gives rise to 12 per cent pore space.

Dolomitization may be a very localized process, and it is not unusual to find limestones grading laterally into dolomites and to observe that porosity is altogether confined to the dolomite.

In the main it may be said that limestones are characterized by having more than one system of porosity, i.e., *intercrystalline, channels,* and *vugs.*

Some limestones may also have a combination of intergranular-fracture type of porosity.

This multiple-pore system in limestones is responsible for a set of channels through which fluids predominantly flow, whereas in small and dead-end pores of the intergranular type oil flows to the main conducting channels only under the influence of expanding solution gas. This is the reason why primary production by solution gas drive may be more efficient in limestones than by secondary stimulation (by gas injection or by water drive) because these external displacing agents preferentially follow the line of least resistance and may bypass large volumes of reservoir oil.

Archie (1951) has classified carbonate porosity in a manner which is useful for engineering purposes. The three classes are compact-crystalline, chalky, and granular-saccharoidal.

Compact-crystalline limestones are recognized by their shiny, resinous appearance on fresh fractures. In cutting examination, they have sharp edges. The individual crystals are tightly interlocked, and where no secondary porosity has developed, there is no visible pore space between the crystals. The diameters of the pores are less than 0.01 mm and overall pore volume is less than 5 per cent of bulk volume. Permeability is less than 0.1 millidarcy (md). This type of rock may become a commercial oil and gas producer when secondary porosity development attains a total porosity of 7 to 10 per cent. Then pore space becomes visible under hand lens magnification. With further leaching, vugs and solution channels may develop.

Chalky limestones have a dull, earthy appearance and individual crystals are seldom recognized because of their imbricated packing; i.e., the crystal faces join at various angles. This type of limestone requires larger porosity in order to produce oil commercially. Ten per cent porosity yields a permeability of 0.1 md and 15 per cent becomes commercially productive of oil and gas.

Granular-saccharoidal limestones are recognized by their coarse granular or sugary appearance. This includes oölitic limestones. The porosity-permeability relationship of granular limestones is similar to compact-crystalline, and a porosity of 7 to 10 per cent is required to establish pay.

Knowledge of lithology as recognized from drill cuttings or cores is of paramount importance in determining pay and nonpay in carbonate reservoirs.

SELECTED REFERENCES ON POROSITY OF ROCKS

1877

Carll, J. F.: "Oil Well Records and Levels," Pennsylvania Geologic Survey, Second Report.

1921

Melcher, A. F.: Determination of Pore Space of Oil and Gas Sands, *Trans. AIME*, vol. 65, pp. 469ff.

1922

Washburn, E. W., and E. N. Bunting: Determination of Porosity by the Method of Gas Expansion, *J. Am. Cerm. Soc.*, vol. 5, pp. 48ff and 112ff.

1923

Meinzer, O. E.: The Occurrence of Ground Water in the U.S.A. with a Discussion of Principles, *USGS Water Supply Paper* 489, 321 pp.

1924

Melcher, A. F.: Texture of Oil Sands with Relation to Production of Oil, *Bull. Am. Assoc. Petroleum Geol.*, vol. 8, pp. 716ff.

1926

Lang, W. B.: A Soxhlet Extractor for Porosity Determination, *Bull. Am. Assoc. Petroleum Geol.*, vol. 10, pp. 998ff.

MacGee, A. E.: Several Gas Expansion Porosimeters, *J. Am. Cerm. Soc.*, vol. 9, pp. 814ff.

Russell, W. L.: A Quick Method of Determining Porosity, *Bull. Am. Assoc. Petroleum Geol.*, vol. 10, pp. 931ff.

Westman, A. E. R.: The Mercury Balance. An Apparatus for Measuring the Bulk Volume of Brick, *J. Am. Cerm. Soc.*, vol. 9, pp. 311ff.

1927

Haines, W. B.: Studies in the Physical Properties of Soils, *J. Agri. Sci.*, vol. 17, pp. 264ff.

Howe, W. L., and C. J. Hudson: Studies in Porosity and Permeabilities Characteristics of Porous Bodies, *J. Am. Cerm. Soc.*, vol. 10, pp. 443ff.

1928

Sutton, C. E.: Use of the Acetylene Tetrachloride Method of Porosity Determination in the Petroleum Engineering Field Studies, *U.S. Bur. Mines Rept. Invest.* 2876.

1929

Gealy, W. B.: Use of Mercury for Determination of Volume of Rock Specimens in Russell Porosity Apparatus, *Bull. Am. Assoc. Petroleum Geol.*, vol. 13, no. 6, pp. 677ff.

Melcher, A. F.: Profile Showing Porosity of Bradford Sand in Bradford Field, Pa. and N.Y., "Structure of Typical American Oil Fields," American Association of Petroleum Geologists' Symposium, vol. 2, pp. 430ff.

1930

Athy, L. F.: Density, Porosity and Compaction of Sedimentary Rocks, *Bull. Am. Assoc. Petroleum Geol.*, vol. 14, no. 1, pp. 1ff.

Barnes, K. B.: A Method of Determining the Effective Porosity of a Reservoir Rock, *Penn. State Coll. Mineral Ind. Exp. Sta. Bull.* 10.

Haines, W. B.: Studies in the Physical Properties of Soils, *J. Agri. Sci.*, vol. 20, pp. 97ff.

Honess, A. P.: A Study of the Microscopic Characteristics of Pennsylvania Oil Sands with Special Reference to Porosity Determinations, *Penn. State Coll. Mineral Ind. Exp. Sta. Bull.* 9.

Sullivan, J. D., et al.: Methods for Measuring Voids in Porous Materials, *U.S. Bur. Mines Rept. Invest.* 3047.

Westman, A. E. R., and H. R. Hughill: The Packing of Particles, *J. Am. Cerm. Soc.*, vol. 13, pp. 767ff.

1932

Brankstone, H., et al.: Improved Technique for Determination of Densities and Porosities, *Bull. Am. Assoc. Petroleum Geol.*, vol. 16, no. 9, pp. 915ff.

Honess, A. P.: Further Observations on the Temperature–Porosity Relations in Oil Sands, *Penn. State Coll. Mineral Ind. Exp. Sta. Bull.* 11.

1933

Coberly, C. J., and A. B. Stevens: Development of Hydrogen Porosimeter, *Trans. AIME Petroleum Development and Technol.*, pp. 261ff.

Tickell, F. G.: Some Studies on the Porosity and Permeability of Rocks, *Trans. AIME Petroleum Development and Technol.*, pp. 250ff.

1934

Jaugey, J.: Contribution théorique à l'étude d'un problème de granulométrie, *Génie civil* 8.

1935

Fraser, H. J.: Experimental Study of the Porosity and Permeability of Clastic Sediments, *J. Geol.*, vol. 43, no. 8, pp. 910ff.

Graton, L. C., and H. J. Fraser: Systematic Packing of Spheres with Particular Relation to Porosity and Permeability, *J. Geol.*, vol. 43, no. 8, pp. 785ff.

Gross, P. L. K., and R. E. Echis: Porosity and Sorting of Southern California Fanglomerates, *Calif. Div. Water Resources Bull.* 45.

Thomas, W. H., et al.: Two Methods for the Estimation of the Porosity of Limestones, *J. Inst. Petroleum Technol.*, vol. 21, no. 8, pp. 725ff.

1936

Buwalda, J. P.: Apparatus for Determination of Apparent Volume and of the Volume of Voids, *J. Inst. Petroleum Technol.*, vol. 22, no. 149, pp. 177ff.

Clough, K. H.: The Evaluation of Oil Bearing Cores, *Oil Weekly*, June 15, pp. 31ff.

Horner, W. L.: Core Analysis, *Oil Weekly*, June 1, pp. 31ff.

1937

Krause, L., and G. N. Powell: Core Analyses Valuable in Water Flooding Work, *Oil Weekly*, Feb. 1, pp. 36ff.

Taliaferro, D. B., et al.: A Method of Determining Porosity—A List of Porosities of Oil Sands, *U.S. Bur. Mines Rept. Invest.* 3352.

Yuster, S. T.: Determining Porosity of Oil Sands, *Producers Monthly*, October, pp. 21ff.

1938

Barnes, K. B., and H. L. Karsch: Boyle's Law Type Porosimeter, *API Prod. Bull.* 223, pp. 97ff.

Coomber, S. E.: The Porosity of Reservoir Rocks, "Science of Petroleum," vol. 1, pp. 220ff.

Ryder, H. M., and D. T. May: Accurate Sand Measurements Aid in Establishing Method of Recovery, *Oil Gas J.*, Apr. 21, pp. 36ff.

1939

Pyle, H., and J. E. Sherborne: Core Analysis, *AIME Tech. Pub.* 1024.

Stevens, A. B.: A New Device for Determining Porosity by the Gas-expansion Method, *AIME Tech. Pub.* 1061.

1940

Leamer, R. W., and J. F. Lutz: Determination of Pore-size Distribution in Soils, *Soil Sci.*, vol. 49, pp. 347ff.

1943

Bell, H. W.: Porosity Limit with Depth, *Oil Gas J.*, July 8, pp. 66ff.

1944

Horner, W. L.: "Method of Determining Porosity," U.S. Patent 2,345,535.

Law, Jan: A Statistical Approach to the Interstitial Heterogeneity of Sand Reservoirs, *AIME Tech. Pub.* 1732.

1945

Westbrook, M. A., and J. F. Redmond: A New Technique for Determining Porosity of Drill Cuttings, *AIME Tech. Pub.* 1943.

1946

Bulnes, A. C.: An Application of Statistical Methods to Core Analysis Data of Dolomitic Limestone, *AIME Tech. Pub.* 2025.

1947

Nuss, W. F., and R. L. Whitting: Technique for Reproducing Rock Pore Space, *Bull. Am. Assoc. Petroleum Geol.*, vol. 31, no. 11, pp. 2044ff.

1948

Goldstein, A., Jr.: Cementation of the Dakota Sandstones of the Colorado Front Range, *J. Sediment. Petrol.*, December, pp. 108ff.

1949

Griffiths, J. C.: Petrographic Evaluation of Porosity Measurements, *Producers Monthly*, April, pp. 38ff.

Kaye, E., and M. L. Freeman, Jr.: A New Type of Porosimeter, *World Oil*, March, pp. 94ff.

Rall, C. G., and D. B. Taliaferro: Improved Method of Measuring Porosity in Oil Field Cores, *Producers Monthly*, September, pp. 34ff.

Rosenfeld, M. A.: Some Aspects of Porosity and Cementation, *Producers Monthly*, May, pp. 39ff.

1950

Locke, L. C., and J. E. Bliss: Core Analysis Technique for Limestone and Dolomite, *World Oil*, September, pp. 204ff.

Kelton, F. C.: Analysis of Fractured Limestone Cores, *AIME Tech. Pub.* 2913, pp. 225ff.

Taylor, J. M.: Pore Space Reduction in Sandstone, *Bull. Am. Assoc. Petroleum Geol.*, vol. 34, no. 4, pp. 701ff.

1951

Rosenfeld, M. A., and J. C. Griffiths: A New Approach to the Problem of Porosity Measurement, *Producers Monthly*, vol. 15, pp. 23ff., July, pp. 31ff., August.

1952

Archie, G. E.: Classification of Carbonate Rocks and Petrophysical Considerations, *Bull. Am. Assoc. Petroleum Geol.*, vol. 36, no. 2, pp. 299ff.

Pollard, T. A., and P. P. Reichertz: Core Analysis Practice—Basic Methods and New Developments, *Bull. Am. Assoc. Petroleum Geol.*, vol. 36, no. 2, pp. 230ff.

Stewart, C. R., and J. W. Spurlock: How to Analyze Large Core Samples, *Oil Gas J.*, Sept. 15, pp. 89ff.

1954

Davis, D. H.: Estimating Porosity of Sedimentary Rocks from Bulk Density, *J. Geol.*, vol. 62, no. 1, pp. 102ff.

FLUID SATURATION (σ)

Methods for the determination of reservoir fluid saturations in place consist in analyzing reservoir core samples for water and oil, the saturation in gas being obtained by difference since the sum of the saturations in the three fluids is equal to unity.

As a general practice a simple procedure is to determine the water saturation of a sample by a suitable technique and then to measure the total loss of weight of the sample on extraction and drying. The quantity of oil present is then calculated by subtracting the weight of water found from the total loss in weight. The methods which may be recommended for this determination will be discussed briefly.

In the calculation of connate or interstitial water saturation, the amount of water determined from the analysis should be corrected to formation conditions, because the reservoir temperature and the salts in solution are responsible for an increase in the volume of the water above that measured in the laboratory, owing to thermal and solubility expansion. However, the volumetric reduction due to compression under the hydrostatic head compensates almost quantitatively for the above expansion.

Distillation Method. Water saturation may be determined by distillation methods such as the ASTM method and the Dean and Stark method. To this end, samples ranging in volume from 50 to 60 cc are broken from the central part of the larger cores, transferred to an extraction thimble, and weighed. The thimble is then placed in a flask or retort containing a liquid solvent such as xylene, toluene, or a gasoline fraction boiling at about 150°C. A reflux condenser is fitted to the flask, the function of which is to return the condensate to a calibrated glass trap from which it overflows back to the flask or retort (Figs. 2-9*a* and *b*). The liquid hydrocarbon is boiled and the water present in the sample vaporized, carried into the reflux condenser, and caught in the trap. When the volume of water in the trap remains constant under continued extraction, the volume of water collected is read and the thimble containing the samples is then transferred to a soxhlet apparatus (Fig. 2-9*c*) for final extraction. Then thimbles and samples are dried and weighed. The total fluid saturation is obtained by weight difference and includes both oil and water. By weight difference again, the weight of oil is obtained, and, by use of an appropriate oil density, its volume is calculated. The saturations on a percentage of pore-volume basis are readily calculated for both water and oil.

If desired, the extraction thimble may be supported above the boiling extraction liquid and the complete extraction is carried out in one apparatus without transferring to a soxhlet extractor (Yuster, 1944, and Rall and Taliaferro, 1947).

If sufficiently large core samples are available so as to contain 5 to 10 cc of water, the method is dependable to about 2 per cent, an accuracy considered satisfactory in view of the uncertainties unavoidably introduced

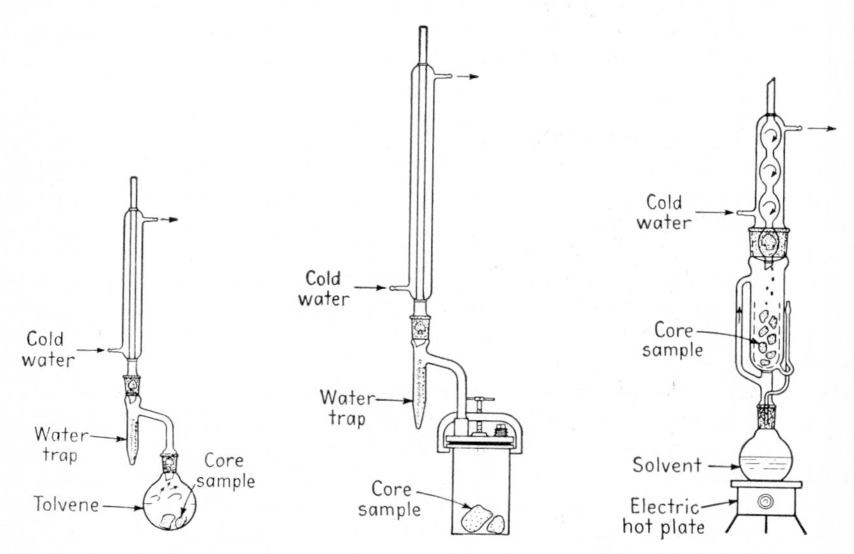

FIG. 2-9*a*. Solvent extraction-type water-determination apparatus.

FIG. 2-9*b*. Retort-type water-determination apparatus.

FIG. 2-9*c*. Soxhlet extractor for cleaning core samples.

during coring the reservoir formations. When smaller samples are used, the dependability of the results is correspondingly lower. The method is well suited to mass analysis of a large number of samples per day provided that a sufficiently large bank of extractors is available. An individual distillation requires about 2 hr with an additional 6 to 24 hr for the soxhlet extraction.

Critical Solution Temperature Method. A fluid saturation method which makes use of the critical solution temperature has been described by Taylor (1938). The water present in the sample is extracted with ethyl or isopropyl alcohol; then the temperature at which a mixture of equal volumes of the alcohol solution used for extraction and kerosene becomes clear when heated (or turbid when cooled) is measured. This is the critical temperature of the solution. Because this temperature is somewhat affected by the presence of salts in the water and the oil extracted, it is necessary to calibrate the method for the particular field brine and crude oil of interest. The extraction step is most conveniently carried out by crushing the sample under alcohol and decanting a portion of the alcohol solution for analysis. If about 50 cc of a mixture of 98 per cent ethyl alcohol or of 96 per cent isopropyl alcohol is used for each 1 or 2 cc of water in the sample tested, the critical solution temperature falls in a convenient range (between 25 and 60°C). When these quantities are used, the critical solution temperature obtained varies about 20°C per cc of water present. The method is capable of high accuracy even when only small core samples are available. It is rapid, and a complete saturation and porosity determination may be made for a given sample in 1 hr. However, the method is not well suited for handling large numbers of core samples per day; the distillation method previously reviewed is better adapted for mass routine tests.

The oil content is determined by difference by weighing the sample before extraction with alcohol and weighing the rock grains after drying. The difference between the weight of the total fluid extracted and the weight of water found by the critical solution temperature test gives the weight of oil present. A density reduction gives the volume of oil, and oil saturation may readily be computed.

Titration Method. Another procedure for saturation determination makes use of the titration method. The water content is obtained by extracting the sample with anhydrous alcohol (methyl, ethyl, or isopropyl) and titrating the alcohol solution to determine its water content. The total water content of core samples may also be obtained by distilling the water from the samples heated under vacuum, condensing the water vapor in a trap cooled with dry ice, and titrating the contents of the trap. The titration in either case is carried out with Fischer's reagent (sulfur dioxide, iodine, and pyridine dissolved in anhydrous methyl alcohol). As long as water is present in the titration vessel, iodine is reduced by sulfur dioxide; when all the water extracted has been used, the brown color of iodine indicates the end point of the reaction. The reagent is somewhat unstable and should be protected from light and water vapor. It must be standardized against known quantities of water.

The oil content is again determined by difference by weighing before extraction and after extraction, drying, and then subtracting the weight of the water determined.

The method gives reproducible results and may be applied when small samples only are available. Individual samples can be analyzed in an hour's time when operating on a crushed specimen, which speeds greatly extraction and drying.

Retort Method. The procedures discussed above are nearly all combinations or modifications of methods previously described in the available literature which have been found satisfactory in handling a great variety of core samples with various requirements of rapidity and accuracy. Other methods have been tested and found to be less desirable, such as the retort method (Yuster and Levine, 1938). The main objection to the retort method, still in common use, is the cracking of the oil with the resulting production of gases and the possibility of driving out water of crystallization. The calibration of the retort loss as a function of oil distilled is of dubious value as the intensity of cracking may be a function of the mineral composition and porosity of the cores.

Pentane Extraction Method. Other special techniques such as the extraction of oil with pentane, followed by recovery of the oil by evaporation of the pentane, have proved dependable. Without an accelerating procedure, however, pentane extraction methods are somewhat slow for routine work.

The Ryder-Scott Company has developed a practical pentane solvent extraction method which will be described briefly. It is applicable to large cores as well as to small fragments or chips obtained by rotary or cable-tool drilling.

A close pentane cut, free of unsaturates, is used. Pentane extraction makes it possible to leave very little solvent in the final oil sample, as pentane is driven off readily by distillation. Extreme care is essential in collecting cores or reservoir formation samples and in placing them under solvent with the least possible disturbance to their oil and water content. In the Ryder-Scott practice, the sample is placed under solvent on the derrick floor within a closed container and delivered to the laboratory in this condition. Extraction of the oil starts on the derrick floor within a very short time after the rock sample is recovered from the bailer. In the laboratory, extraction is accelerated by placing the sample under pentane in a bomb, where it is held at a temperature of about 300°F for nearly 1½ hr. A pressure of about 170 psi is developed during this time. Before opening, the bomb is chilled, thereby creating a vacuum. This is for the purpose of safety as well as to avoid fluid losses which would inevitably occur if the bomb were opened when still at high pressure. During this process, connate water is also extracted from the samples, and it collects in the form of a globule under the solvent. It is removed and directly measured with a micropipette. The sand, solvent, and oil are then placed in a soxhlet apparatus where final extraction is accomplished within an hour or two. The end point of the extraction is determined when the solvent in the upper part of the soxhlet fails to fluoresce under an ultraviolet light. The oil solution is next concentrated to a total volume of about 25 cc. It is then transferred, through a filter, to a small side-tube distillation flask. This flask in turn is placed in an oil bath held at about 210°F for final removal of the solvent. After cooling, the weight of the oil is determined. Following this, the density of the oil is measured by weighing exactly 0.2 cc of the oil in a special pipette at a known temperature. From these values, a density reduction on the weight of oil collected is made, and the volume of the oil is determined.

At this point, a correction is introduced to determine the volume of the oil under field conditions of temperature and density. For this purpose, an evaporation curve is used. This curve is obtained by the evaporation of a crude sample taken preferably from the well being tested. If such is not available, a sample is obtained from the nearest producing well in the the same reservoir.

The extracted sand, in the meantime, has been dried and weighed and its bulk and pore volumes determined. The oil saturation, or fraction of the pore space occupied by oil, is the ratio of the corrected volume of oil to that of the pore volume of the sand from which it was extracted.

The water saturation is similarly determined by measuring the water volume extracted simultaneously with the oil but separated at an earlier stage and measured in a micropipette.

Chloride Method. A rapid and convenient method of formation water determination makes use of the relative constancy of connate water salinity within a given reservoir and even within a given geologic formation in a restricted region. The salinity may be determined from the connate water extracted from a relatively tight or low-permeability core sample, because such a rock sample is not likely to have been contaminated by drilling fluid. Samples of brine obtained from wells producing from a particular reservoir or formation may also be tested. The salinity is expressed in parts per million of sodium chloride, although other salts may be and often are present. Chlorides may be determined readily by chemical titration, but a more rapid method consists in using a conductivity dip cell.

Chloride calibration of the connate water may be performed by silver-nitrate titration of about 50 cc of a diluted sample, neutralized if necessary, using potassium chromate as an indicator. The determination of connate water from a core sample consists in determining the amount of chloride ions that can be leached from the sample. To this end, the sample is crushed. About 10 grams of the crushed sample is weighed and digested at boiling temperature in 100 cc of distilled water and 5 cc of saturated potassium nitrate, which serves to flocculate the clay particles of the sand. The mixture is then cooled before filtration. The filtrate is neutralized, if necessary, then titrated with a standardized silver-nitrate solution, using potassium chromate as an indicator. Knowing the salinity of the connate water, a quantitative reduction is readily made for the calculation of saturation in interstitial water in the core sample.

The chloride method may be criticized because it is based on the determination of a single ion, whereas a large number of different ions are actually present in a core's connate water. A method which gives a measure of the total ions present in a core is based on the measurement of the electrical conductivity of the water extracted from a crushed core. The method uses a standard electrolytic dip cell with an a-c bridge. This method is particularly sensitive to small variations in electrolyte content when dilute solutions are tested. In practice, a core sample weighing about 50 grams is crushed, then mixed thoroughly in 250 cc of distilled water, and stirred occasionally thereafter. The sample is allowed to settle at room temperature, and the electric conductivity of the supernatant fluid is measured. This reading is converted to connate water saturation of the core sample. The procedure requires calibration of the dip cell with known volumes of the representative connate water of the reservoir. In addition, it is advisable to perform the experiments under temperature-controlled conditions and, if not, to make corrections for temperature variations because of the high-temperature coefficient of electrolytic solutions' conductivity.

A major difficulty encountered in the accurate determination of fluid saturations is the contamination of core samples by drilling fluid. Contamination is particularly troublesome in the case of a water-base drilling fluid inasmuch as most reservoir rocks are water-wet. Hence formation water is either diluted or partially flushed out by drilling water. Tracer techniques have been tried, and some are used as a regular part of all coring operations. Horner (1935) and Pyle and Jones (1936) suggested the use of such tracers as acetone, arsenic, propanol, dextrose treated with octanol to prevent fermentation, and others. While these techniques permit the measurement of the contamination of the cores by invasion of the aqueous phase of the drilling fluid, they cannot reveal the degree to which the connate water and oil might have been displaced and swept out. This difficulty is particularly serious in highly permeable reservoir formations. The dilution of formation water by the aqueous phase of the drilling fluid precludes the direct measurement of connate water. An indirect measurement may be obtained by making a correction for the chloride content of the drilling fluid. Schilthuis (1938) has proposed the use of oil-base drilling fluid in order to avoid the above difficulty. He observed that the connate water is undisturbed by this type of drilling fluid, except in very highly permeable formations where some water is displaced by oil infiltration from the mud.

The dextrose tracer technique for the determination of the degree of contamination of cores by water-base mud has been rendered practical by Clark (1947), especially in its application to the measurement of connate water saturation for water-flooding projects from cores obtained by cable-tool methods. In this case, it is to be noted that there is no appreciable gas pressure left in the field, and drilling is done under a relatively low head of water. Contamination of the dextrose drilling fluid may occur by water produced from the reservoir. Hence one must have a knowledge of the dextrose content of the drilling fluid at all times. This is done by analyzing a sample of drilling water from the Baker core barrel.

The tracer solution, which is also the drilling water, contains about 0.5 per cent of dextrose to which is added 0.05 per cent, by weight, of octyl alcohol to prevent fermentation.

The concentrations of tracer are determined by means of the Benedict's solution in which the dextrose reduces the cupric ions to the cuprous state. Thereafter the cuprous ions are dissolved in hydrochloric acid and titrated by a standard iodine solution in the presence of starch as an indicator of the end point.

The determination of residual connate water is made through chloride analysis by conductivity titration on the basis of a standard interstitial water salinity.

In view of the inherent uncertainties involved in the determination of reservoir sample saturation, and more particularly of connate water, it seems advisable to resort to oil-base mud coring. Russell et al. (1946) have stressed the lack of mobility of connate water during clean oil production and infer that there is little likelihood of formation water displacement by oil invasion when coring with oil. However, in depleted formations and for secondary recovery projects, coring with oil still leaves uncertain the value of the oil saturation, unless a suitable tracer be added to the drilling fluid.

A further difficulty in the path of obtaining a representative core sample for fluid-saturation determination resides in the expansion of solution gases from the oil once the core is depressured when brought to the surface of the earth. Hence the saturation tests performed do not represent the actual fluid content in place. Experiments carried out by Botset and Muskat (1939) indicate that the depressuring process is responsible for a production of oil equivalent to about 25 per cent of pore space, with little or no loss of water unless the sands have abnormally high connate water content. This oil production is representative of the expected recovery by internal gas drive inasmuch as the depressuring process is nothing more than permitting a small sample of the reservoir to go through its complete production history by gas depletion.

A further uncertainty in the determination of fluid saturations comes from evaporation of the fluids from the cores in the interval between coring and the analyses. This may be minimized by coating the cores with paraffin immediately after their recovery or, better yet, by quick freezing them with dry ice as proposed by Wisenbaker (1947). However, when connate water saturation is high, quick freezing may fracture the cores.

Capillary-pressure Method. In view of the difficulties involved in fluid-saturation determinations from cores, Thornton and Marshall (1947) have proposed the use of capillary-pressure curves (capillary suction vs. brine saturation) as a substitute for the direct measurements of connate water. The procedure involves the determination of air-water capillary-pressure curves on selected core samples, the determination of the distance above the water-oil contact at which the samples were secured, and the application of a correction in order to reduce the air-water capillary-pressure curve to an oil-water capillary pressure. This correction is necessitated by the difference in interfacial tension between air and water and oil and water, which may be allowed for, generally, by the use of a reduction factor of about $\frac{3}{8}$, or the ratio of the surface tensions of water and oil under reservoir conditions. This correction assumes the angles of contact with solids and the radii of curvature of the fluid globules to be the same at a given saturation state. The capillary pressure P_c being equal to the suction pressure on the wetting fluid (water) and being further a function of the fluid saturation for a given height h above the 100 per cent water-saturation level, the corresponding water saturation may be read immediately from the capillary-pressure curve at the level P_c, calculated from $P_c = gh\,\Delta\vartheta$, where g is the acceleration of gravity and $\Delta\vartheta$ is the density contrast between water and oil. In practical units $P_c = \dfrac{h}{2.31}\,\Delta\vartheta$, where P_c is in psi and h is in feet. Using this procedure, Thornton and Marshall (1947) report comparative measurements among the retort, the salinity, and the capillary-pressure methods of connate water measurements. Retort results are somewhat higher than the last two, probably owing to the release of water of crystallization from the minerals of the samples, and more particularly from the clays. All cores were cut by oil-base mud, and the connate water saturations measured by salinity and capillary-pressure methods check within acceptable limits of precision.

A discouraging feature of the ingenious capillary-pressure method of measuring water saturation is the lengthy procedure required for the capillary-pressure tests. With low-permeability cores, high pressures need be applied, and difficulties are encountered because of the friability of the high bubble-point filters through which the brines are squeezed out of the cores. Good core samples, sufficiently consolidated to stand shaping, are required for the capillary-pressure tests; this places another limitation upon the use of the method. However, the capillary-pressure measurements by injection of mercury, proposed by Purcell (1948) (see Chap. 7), may dispel the above objections.

Summarizing, fluid-saturation determinations are probably the least reliable of the measurements performed on reservoir-rock samples. Perhaps the best approach to a true solution of the problem is by correlation of quantitative information from various independent measuring means, two of which have been reviewed before, namely, by direct measurements on core samples and by indirect measurements through the use of capillary-pressure curves. Other approaches will be reviewed later, namely, by interpretation of electric and radioactivity well logs.

SELECTED REFERENCES ON FLUID-SATURATION DETERMINATIONS

Fischer, K.: *Angew. Chem.*, vol. 48, pp. 394ff.

1929

Lindtrop, N. T., and V. M. Nikolaeff: Oil and Water Content of Oil Sands, *Bull. Am. Assoc. Petroleum Geol.*, vol. 13, pp. 811ff.

1935

Hill, E. S.: Determination of Water in Core Samples by the Distillation Method, *Penn. State Coll. Mineral Ind. Exp. Sta. Bull.* 19.

Horner, W. L.: Determination of Oil Content of Sands for Water Flooding, *Petroleum Eng.*, April, pp. 33ff.

Horner, W. L.: Contamination of Cores by Drilling Fluid Can Be Estimated by Dissolving Simple Chemicals in the Mud, *Oil Weekly*, July 1, pp. 29ff.

1936

Barnes, K. B.: Porosity and Saturation Methods, *API Drill. and Prod. Pract.*, pp. 191ff.

Lewis, J. A., and W. L. Horner: Interstitial Water Saturation in the Pore Spaces of Reservoirs, *Oil Weekly*, Oct. 19, pp. 36ff.

Pyle, H. C., and P. H. Jones: Quantitative Determination of the Connate Water Content of Oil Sands, *API Drill. and Prod. Pract.*, pp. 171ff.

1938

Botset, H. G.: A Method of Determining the Water Content of Sands, *AIME Tech. Pub.* 972.

Schilthuis, R. J.: Connate Water in Oil and Gas Sands, *Trans. AIME Petroleum Development and Technol.*, pp. 199ff.

Taylor, M. D.: Determining Water Content of Cores by the Application of a Critical Solution Temperature Method, *Oil Gas J.*, June 16, pp. 59ff.

Yuster, S. T., and J. S. Levine: Determination of Oil and Water Saturation by the Retort Method, *Oil Weekly*, May 23, pp. 22ff.

1939

Botset, H. G., and M. Muskat: Effect of Pressure Reduction upon Core Saturation, *Trans. AIME Petroleum Development and Technol.*, pp. 172ff.

Pyle, H. C., and J. E. Sherborne: Core Analysis, *AIME Tech. Pub.* 1024.

Sage, J. F., and D. M. Armstrong: Estimation of Connate Water from the Salt Content of the Core, *API Prod. Bull.* 223, pp. 90ff.

Smith, D. M., and W. H. D. Bryant: *J. Am. Chem. Soc.*, vol. 61, pp. 2407ff.

Yuster, S. T.: Blank Determinations in the Retort Method of Saturation, *API Prod. Bull.* 223, pp. 87ff.

1940

Barnes, K. B.: An Improved Design of Retort Equipment for Saturation Tests, *API Prod. Bull.* 226, pp. 133ff.

Taliaferro, D. B., and G. B. Spencer: A Method for Determining the Water Content of Oil Sands, *U.S. Bur. Mines Rept. Invest.* 3535.

1941

Taylor, M. D.: Critical Review of Methods for the Determination of Permeability and Saturation of Core Samples, *Oil Gas J.*, Nov. 20, pp. 40ff.

1943

Differentiation of Water in Oil Field Cores, *Producers Monthly*, June, pp. 45ff.

1944

Yuster, S. T.: Determining Saturations by an Extraction-distillation Method, *Oil Weekly*, Mar. 20, pp. 20ff.

1946

Beeson, C. M., and N. Johnston: Core Analysis Based on Vacuum Distillation, *AIME Tech. Pub.* 2017.

Brunner, E., and E. S. Mardock: A Neutron Method for Measuring Saturations in Laboratory Flow Experiments, *AIME Tech. Pub.* 1986.

Russell, R. G., et al.: Some Experiments on the Mobility of Interstitial Waters, *AIME Tech. Pub.* 2054.

1947

Boyer, R. L., et al.: A New Method for Measurements of Oil Saturation in Cores, *AIME Tech. Pub.* 2124.

Bruce, W. A., and H. S. Welge: The Restored State Method of Determination of Oil in Place and Connate Water, *API Drill. and Prod. Practice*, pp. 166ff.

Clark, A. P.: A Method for Determining Connate and Drilling Water Saturation for Cable Tool Cores, *Producers Monthly*, July, pp. 11ff.

Rall, C. G., and D. B. Taliaferro: A Method for Determining Simultaneously the Oil and Water Saturations of Oil Sands, *U.S. Bur. Mines Rept. Invest.* 4004.

Thornton, O. F., and D. L. Marshall: Estimating Interstitial Water by the Capillary Method, *AIME Tech. Pub.* 2126.

Wisenbaker, J. D.: Quick Freezing of Cores Preserves Fluids, *Oil Weekly*, Jan. 20, pp. 36ff.

1949

Edinger, W. M.: Interpretation of Core Analysis Results on Cores Taken with Oil or Oil Base Muds, *API Drill. and Prod. Practice*, pp. 229ff.

1950

Ruehl, W.: The Connate Water Content of Oil Reservoir Rocks, *Producers Monthly*, August, pp. 10ff.

1951

Brown, H. W.: Capillary Pressure Investigations, *AIME Tech. Pub.* 3025, pp. 67ff.

Messer, E. S.: Interstitial Water Determination by an Evaporation Method, *AIME Tech. Pub.* 3076, pp. 269ff.

1952

Dodd, C. G.: An Analysis of the Evaporation Method for Determining Interstitial Water, AIME Fall Meeting Presentation (unpublished).

Meyer, H. I.: Critique of Present Methods Used in Determining Interstitial Water Saturation, *Oil Gas J.*, Jan. 14, pp. 113ff.

PERMEABILITY TO FLUIDS (K)

The permeability of a reservoir rock may be defined as its *fluid conductivity*, or ability to let fluid flow within its *interconnected pore network*. If the pores of the medium were not interconnected, there would be no permeability; hence it is natural to expect a relation between permeability of a medium and *effective porosity* but not necessarily with *absolute porosity*. All factors which influence effective porosity also influence permeability, namely, grain size, grain packing, grain angularity, grain size distribution, and degree of lithification (cementation and consolidation). The amount and the kind of *clay*, as well as its distribution throughout the reservoir rock, has an important bearing on liquid permeability, particularly on whether or not the flowing fluid reacts with the clays. The passage of gas is not expected to react with clays except for the possible removal of some of their adsorbed water. However, the physicochemical properties of the water flowing through a porous medium control the physical state of clays. In fresh water, certain clays swell and partially or even fully plug some of the pore openings. This is particularly the case for montmorillonite clays, which deflocculate and swell in the presence of fresh water. Salt water of salinity equivalent to the connate water within the reservoir rock has no effect when flowing past reservoir clays.

The hydrogen-ion concentration or pH of the flowing water is the cause of wide variations in the flocculation properties of clays. Acid waters of low pH flocculate most clays, and fluid conductivity to water of low pH is much higher than to alkaline waters. The wetting properties of reservoir rock with respect to reservoir fluids are responsible for the *relative-permeability* relationships (to be discussed later), because of their control on the distribution of the reservoir fluids within the pore spaces. The capillary size distribution is also a factor which controls the shape of the relative-permeability curves.

Darcy's Empirical Law. Fluid permeability characteristic of a medium is the result of an empirical discovery of the French hydrologist Darcy (1856) to the effect that it proportionately relates flow rate Q of the flowing fluid to the hydrostatic head $gh\vartheta$ of the fluid augmented by the pressure P exerted over the free liquid surface $(P + gh\vartheta) = H$, causing the flow over a path of length L. H is the fluid flow potential. Darcy's law in its elementary form is

$$Q = -AK\frac{\Delta(P + gh\vartheta)}{L} = -AK\frac{\Delta H}{L} \tag{2-1}$$

where A is the cross-sectional area perpendicular to the fluid flow path, g is acceleration of gravity, ϑ is the density of the flowing fluid, and h is the height above a constant datum level. Darcy was working with one fluid only, namely, water, which is of unit viscosity. Therefore this fluid property does not appear in the original work of Darcy. In order to render Darcy's observations of general applicability to all fluids, the observations must be generalized by introducing in the relationship the fluid viscosity. It is intuitively evident that for a fluid of viscosity (μ) different from that of water, its rate of flow compared to that of water in the same medium is inversely proportional to the said viscosity. The generalized Darcy law for a homogeneous fluid is therefore

$$Q = -A\frac{K}{\mu}\frac{\Delta(P + g\,\vartheta h)}{L} \tag{2-2}$$

If L is measured in an up-dip direction making an angle α with the horizontal direction, $h = L \sin \alpha$ and Darcy's law becomes

$$Q = -A\frac{K}{\mu}\left(\frac{\Delta P}{L} + g\vartheta \sin \alpha\right) \tag{2-3}$$

$\Delta P/L$ is the pressure gradient in the direction of flow; α is considered positive for up-dip flow and negative for down-dip flow. Contrary to a prevalent belief the pressure gradient is not always negative in the direction of flow; i.e., flow direction is not always in the direction in which pressure decreases. Consider the case of downward vertical flow when $\alpha = -90°$ and when no external pressure is exerted. The pressure at any point within the fluid is solely the result of density and is $g\vartheta$ per unit length downward. Since $\sin \alpha = -1$ and considering a vertical hypothetical line of flow, it is seen that $\Delta P/L - g\vartheta = 0$ when the fluid is in static equilibrium. If a slow downward rate of flow is now permitted under the influence of gravity by opening a valve at the bottom of the porous medium, the value of $\Delta P/L$ measured in the downward direction becomes less positive and the net value of $\Delta P/L - g\vartheta < 0$. Should the outlet end of the porous medium be completely uncovered, the maximum rate of flow by gravity is attained and $\Delta P/L = 0$; i.e., the flow takes place without any pressure drop whatever between inlet and outlet.

This observation should be further stressed by stating that one way of observing if pure gravity drainage takes place is by ascertaining that complete pressure equilibrium exists at all levels within the reservoir. Hubbert (1940) seems to have been the first to point out these interesting relationships.

The proportionality constant K, or *absolute permeability* (at 100 per cent saturation in the flowing fluid), is a *specific property* which characterizes the porous medium. It was found empirically to be independent of the dimensions of the medium, of the pressure differential exerted on the flowing fluid (at least for liquids), and of the fluid viscosity. The permeability constant should, therefore, be expressible in terms of other physically measurable properties of the porous medium, and considerable thought and research effort have been given by numerous investigators to the search for such a relationship ever since the days of Darcy's formulation. The first to introduce grain size into the relationship seems to have been Seelheim (1880), who found that the rate of fluid flow is proportional to the square of the grain diameter. Hence the finer the sand, the smaller the permeability. Hazen (1892) introduced thereafter the effective grain size to a power of two. Slichter (1899) made a theoretical analysis of fluid flow through ideal homogeneous media composed of spheres of uniform size and was the first to introduce the effect of packing as a factor which influences permeability. In modern terminology Slichter's formulation of the permeability relationship would read

$$K_{\text{darcy}} = \frac{10.2d^2}{K_s} \tag{2-4}$$

where d = diameter of spheres, cm
K_s = packing constant depending on porosity

Table 2-1 gives the value of the packing coefficient (K_s) as a function of porosity (ϕ) for spheres of equal diameter.

TABLE 2-1. VALUES OF PACKING COEFFICIENT AS A FUNCTION OF POROSITY

	ϕ	K_s
Hexagonal packing..........	26.0	84.4
	30.0	52.5
	35.0	31.6
	40.0	20.3
Cubic packing..............	45.0	13.7

King (1899) reversed the calculation process and applied Slichter's theory to the determination of the average-particle diameter for sands of irregular shape. According to Mavis and Wilsey (1936), the value of K_s may be obtained from

$$K_s = 20\left(\frac{40}{\phi}\right)^{3.3} \tag{2-5}$$

Further contributors to the relationship of the absolute-permeability constant (K) to rock texture and porosity are Terzaghi and Uren.

Terzaghi (1925) proposed the following relation:

$$K = Cd^2 \left[\frac{\phi - 0.13}{(1 - \phi)^{1/3}} \right]^2 \tag{2-6}$$

whereas Uren (1925) proposed the following:

$$K = Cd^2 \phi^{3.31} \tag{2-7}$$

In each case, C is an experimental coefficient to be determined.

Kozeny (1927) is responsible for one of the most fundamental and remarkable relationships of the type discussed above. In its original form, which was derived from theoretical and basic physical concepts, the relationship for an unconsolidated packing is as follows:

$$K = \frac{\phi^3}{5.0 S_v^2 (1 - \phi)^2} \tag{2-8}$$

in which S_v represents the total grain surface per unit volume of reservoir rock exclusive of pore space. For spherical grains, the specific surface per unit volume increases as the inverse of the grain diameter. Hence Kozeny's equation may be rewritten as follows:

$$K = Cd^2 \frac{\phi^3}{(1 - \phi)^2} \tag{2-9}$$

in which C is a conversion constant for the units used.

Fair and Hatch (1933) arrived, apparently without knowledge of Kozeny's previous work, at an identical relationship.

Kozeny's equation gives the permeability directly in square centimeters, 1 sq cm being equal to 1.013×10^8 darcys. An example of application will illustrate the conversion method. Let us assume an unconsolidated sand of porosity $\phi = 0.36$, made of uniform grains, for which the specific surface is 215 sq cm per cc of reservoir rock. The permeability is, therefore, equal to

$$K_{\text{darcy}} = 1.013 \times 10^8 \times \frac{(0.36)^3}{5(215)^2(1 - 0.36)^2} = 48.6 \text{ darcys}$$

In the preceding equations, the effects of *porosity* and of *grain size* are recognized. However, the *shape*, the uniformity or *grading* of the particles, their *size distribution*, their *orientation*, *packing*, *layering*, etc., are all physical characteristics which characterize a porous medium made of unconsolidated grains. An attempt to include some of these factors in a permeability relationship was made by Krumbein and Monk (1942), who derived the following experimental relation:

$$K = Cd^2 e^{-1.31t} \tag{2-10}$$

where t = standard deviation of a sand of geometric mean diameter d, mm
C = a constant of value 760

Of all the above equations, the most valuable is undoubtedly that of Kozeny, as it makes no assumptions concerning the consolidation status of the reservoir rock and is presumably valid for consolidated rocks. Measurement of the specific surface of rocks may be achieved by other methods, such as by the use of dye adsorption, and, therefore, a new and independent approach is available for the evaluation of permeability, which does not necessitate the flow of fluid through a test sample.

If the permeability K and porosity ϕ of a grain aggregate are known, the specific surface S_v may be calculated with a precision which experiments have shown to be of the order of ± 5 per cent, even for heterogeneous substances such as fibers and kieselguhr. Kozeny's equation is a remarkable relationship which gives us an inside view of the dependence of permeability upon *effective porosity;* for it is effective porosity which enters the equation, inasmuch as an aggregate of loose grains is unable to produce nonconnected void spaces. To a first approximation it indicates that permeability varies directly as the first power of porosity and inversely as the second power of the specific surface. Both quantities are a function of lithification factors: cementation and consolidation. The cement which enters into the consolidation of a granular aggregate localizes itself initially at the contact points between grains from which it gradually fills the pores as the proportion of cement increases. The specific surface decreases; hence the permeability increases as the degree of cementation increases. However, the porosity also decreases as cementation increases. Therefore, cementation influences two compensating factors. This explains why two consolidated cores with identical porosity may show a wide difference in permeability. The main factor which influences grain specific surface is grain size, and permeability is inversely proportional to the square of the grain size. This explains why fine-grain rocks have low permeability, even though their porosity may be high. A case in point is chalk.

Although rock permeability to a fluid is presumably independent of the differential pressure, it is not altogether independent of the mean pressure of the flowing fluid, especially if that fluid is compressible; for at high average pressure, the mean free path of the gas molecules is no longer large compared with the size of the capillaries. Consequently, the contribution brought about by gas diffusion owing to the kinetic energy of each individual molecule is now reduced to a low value. This relationship has been established by Klinkenberg (1941).

It is well to mention at this point the modified concept of gas and liquid permeability as developed by Klinkenberg.

Klinkenberg states that "*the permeability to a gas is a function of the mean free path of the gas molecules* and thus depends on factors which influence the mean free path, such as temperature, pressure and the nature of the gas." Therefore, when the molecules' mean free paths are small, i.e., at high pressure, the permeability K should be expected to approach that for liquids:

$$K_a = K_\infty \left(1 + \frac{b}{P_m}\right) \tag{2-11}$$

where K_a = air permeability at mean pressure P_m

K_∞ = newly defined permeability which is the extrapolated value of K_a to infinite pressure

b = a constant which depends on the size of the pore openings and is approximately inversely proportional to radius of capillaries

As stated, b is a function of the average capillary size distribution within the sand, becoming greater as permeability decreases and conversely. However, the laws of variation of b with reservoir-rock characteristics are not known. The Klinkenberg permeability K_∞, or permeability at infinite pressure, is obtained by

$$K_\infty = \frac{K_a}{1 + b/P_m} \tag{2-12}$$

This quantity may be considered as the *equivalent liquid permeability* of the reservoir medium.

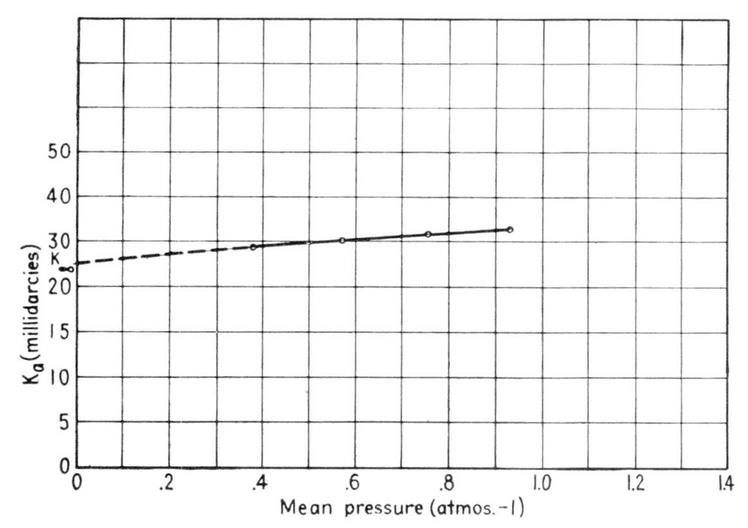

FIG. 2-10. Method of determining equivalent liquid permeability (Klinkenberg method) by extrapolating to infinite-pressure air permeabilities measured at various mean pressures.

b/P_m may be looked upon as a correction factor which may be neglected if high mean pressures prevail. If several measurements are made at different mean pressures and the air permeability K_a and the reciprocal mean pressure $1/P_m$ are plotted (Fig. 2-10), a straight line results. The intercept of this line with the K_a axis determines the value of K_∞. The value of b is determined by computing the slope of the curve K_a vs. $1/P_m$.

In tight reservoir rocks (below 1.0 md) the air permeability K_a, as measured in routine laboratory tests, may be 50 to 100 per cent higher than the equivalent liquid K_∞ permeability, as defined by Klinkenberg.

Permeability Measurements. The experimental laboratory determinations of permeabilities require some precautions which it is well to point out at this time:

The permeabilities ordinarily reported in core analysis refer to the permeability to dry air at atmospheric pressure. The test-sample data required are the length and cross-sectional area of the sample. Fluid flow is established through the test sample by the application of a known differential pressure across the core length. The viscosity of air or other fluids used must be known at the laboratory temperature. The test

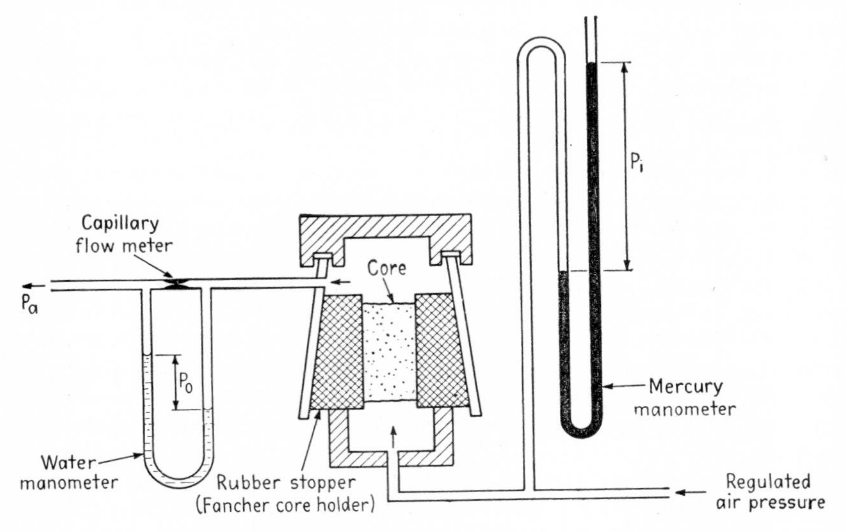

Fig. 2-11. Schematic diagram of permeability-measuring apparatus.

samples are usually cut with a diamond drill from the well cores in a direction parallel to the bedding plane of the formations to be tested. Common practice is to obtain cylindrical specimens about 2 cm in diameter and 2 to 3 cm long. Samples are extracted and dried as described above. Individual samples are mounted in such a way that the sides of the samples are sealed, and a fluid pressure differential can be applied across their full length. For cylindrical samples this mounting may be accomplished quickly and conveniently by the use of a Fancher core holder (1933), in which the core sample is inserted into a tapered, soft rubber stopper provided with a smooth-centered drilled hole of a diameter somewhat smaller than that of the specimen under test. The stopper is forced into a tapered metal holder which compresses the rubber around the sample and prevents fluid from bypassing the test sample (Fig. 2-11). Another convenient holder is the Hassler core holder (1936), which is a rubber tube into which the sample is slipped. Pressure is applied to the outside of the tube in order to press it tightly against the core plug and seal the sides.

Owing to the high cost of coring the reservoir rock, it is advisable to develop methods of core testing which make use of very small samples such as rotary-drill and cable-tool cuttings. The Ryder-Scott Company has developed a procedure whereby permeability of formations may be determined from small chips obtained during cable-tool drilling operations. Chips as small as ½ in. in size are shaped into a standard volume cylinder by means of a grinding wheel and subsequently tested, using a Fancher core holder.

In sampling cores for permeability tests, at least three to four samples per foot of clean sand should be secured in order to obtain representative values. For determinations from cable-tool chipping operations, one sample per screw seems sufficient. The length of the chip screws should be regulated in order to represent a foot of formation.

There are no limitations or requirements on test samples; however, it is expected that samples with a cross section of 1.5 to 2.0 sq cm and approximately 1.50 cm in length give more representative values than smaller samples.

Test specimens may be drilled out with a diamond-drill bit or steel tubing in the shape of a cylindrical plug or ground to rectangular and even cylindrical shape with a coarse grinding wheel. Great care should be taken so that there is no filling of the sand openings during grinding.

As stated previously, the permeability test samples must be dry and free from fluid other than the test fluid. There are many suitable solvents for the extraction of the crude oil, and any one of the following common solvents may be used for removing the oil from the sand: carbon tetrachloride, butanol, pentane, naphtha, etc. The extraction is performed in large soxhlets (Fig. 2-9*c*), heated over electric hot plates or open bunsen burners. The extraction, in general, requires a period of 10 to 12 hr for tight sands, whereas it may require only a few hours for more permeable sands. The time of extraction of tight sands could be reduced materially by passing a preheated solvent under pressure through the sample. After the oil-extraction period, the samples are placed in a drying oven at a temperature not to exceed 210 to 215°F, for an excessive temperature might break down the sand-grain structure and possibly dehydrate some of the minerals. Drying removes water as well as the solvent from the test samples. When the samples have been completely dried, they are ready for permeability testing by mounting in sealing wax or in a core holder (Fancher or Hassler type). The wax used for mounting must not be too brittle so as to break or crack by internal stress during the test. Samples which are sealed in wax must be inspected for leaks or cracks. Care should be exercised in detecting cracks and in noting that there is no bypassing of air along the sides of the sample. The air throughput may be computed directly by the use of a flowmeter or by measuring the volume of air collected during a measured length of time in a graduate or water-filled tube inverted over a water container. For very low permeability samples, a convenient flowmeter consists of a traveling soap bubble in a calibrated titration burette.

Water permeability is reasonably comparable with dry-air permeability reduced to infinite pressure provided that care is given to the quality of the testing water and the test specimen is completely water saturated beforehand. By definition, the permeability of a porous medium is a specific constant determined only by the textural make-up of the medium itself and independent of the type of homogeneous fluid passing through it. However, under many circumstances, liquid permeability is lower than air permeability owing to the following reasons:

Plugging by the swelling of clays and cementing material or by particles in suspension in the liquid.

Air trapping, as a result of incomplete liquid saturation previous to the test. The permeability reduction may be interpreted as the plugging of pore openings by bubbles of nonwetting fluid (insular saturation stage) of diameter smaller than the capillary constrictions. Before the bubbles are allowed to pass a constriction, it is necessary that the bubbles contract; this may be achieved by an increase of the average fluid pressure within the core.

The following pieces of apparatus represent the complete equipment needed for testing permeabilities:

1. Sample holder (Fancher or Hassler type, or wax-core mounting)
2. Manometers for measuring the inlet and outlet pressure
3. Adequate valves and regulators for rate of fluid-flow control
4. Equipment for measuring the volume of fluid effluent by positive displacement or by flowmeters: capillary flowmeter, rotameter, wet-test meter, traveling soap bubble, etc.
5. Thermometer for measuring the temperature of the fluid during test
6. Drying agent to remove moisture from the flowing gas
7. Stop watch, calipers for measuring of the core samples, barometer, and an adequate supply of gas: compressed air, bottled nitrogen, etc.

For a cylindrical sample of cross section other than a circle, it is necessary to mount the specimen by coating the sides with sealing wax (deKhotinsky cement, picein cement, or brewer's wax may be used) and to mount it into a suitable metal tube. After mounting the specimen, a pressure differential is applied across its core length with dry air and the rate of flow of air through the sample is measured. The rate of flow may conveniently be measured by the use of a calibrated capillary flowmeter in which the pressure drop is measured when the gas flows through a glass capillary tube. If the rate of flow of air is measured at the exit end of the sample and the inlet and outlet pressures are, respectively, represented by P_i and P_o, the average rate of flow of air in the sample is calculated from the formula

$$Q_a = Q_o \frac{2P_o}{P_i + P_o} \tag{2-13}$$

where Q_o = observed rate of flow at outlet pressure P_o
Q_a = average rate of flow

The viscosity of air at the temperature of the experiment T (in degrees centigrade) may be calculated from the relationship

$$\mu = 0.01808 + 4.9 \times 10^{-5}(T - 20) \tag{2-14}$$

where μ is the viscosity in centipoises. This relationship is valid for temperatures between 10 and 50°C. Figure 2-12 gives the variation of viscosity for air as well as other test gases, as a function of temperature.

The absolute permeability K of the sample, when using gas flow, may be calculated from the relationship

$$K = \frac{Q_a \mu L}{(P_i - P_o)A} \tag{2-15}$$

where L = length of test sample
A = its cross-sectional area

If Q_a is measured in cubic centimeters per second, μ in centipoises, the length of the sample L in centimeters, the cross-sectional area A in square centimeters, and the pressure differential $P_i - P_o$ in atmospheres, the

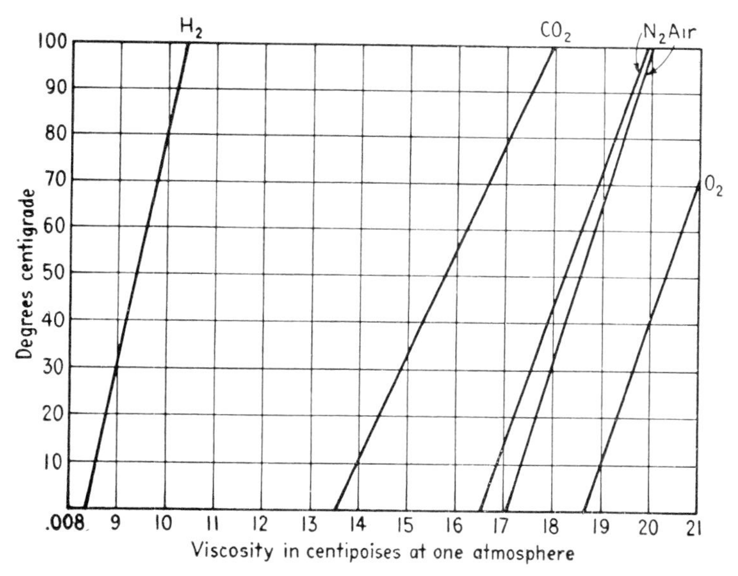

FIG. 2-12. Viscosities of various gases vs. temperature. (*Ruska Instrument Corp.*)

computed permeability K will be obtained in darcys. If μ is measured in poises (1.0 poise = 100 centipoises) and $P_i - P_o$ in dynes per square centimeter (1 atm = 1.013×10^6 dynes per sq cm) and the rest of the quantities are in the same units as above, the permeability will be obtained in square centimeters. Thus 1 sq cm of cross-sectional pore space is equivalent to 1.013×10^8 darcys, or 1.013×10^{11} md. This sets forth the relation between permeability and the fractional cross-sectional area of the reservoir rock available for fluid flow.

In measuring the permeability, the rate of fluid flow during the test must be sufficiently low to avoid turbulence within the pore space which may easily set in under high-pressure gradients in high-permeability test samples.

As pointed out, the permeabilities ordinarily determined are made with dry air at about atmospheric pressure. These values are, however, somewhat higher than those obtained with gas at higher average pressures or with liquids. For specimens which do not contain minerals susceptible of swelling in contact with certain liquids, the permeabilities obtained by making a series of measurements with gas at various mean pressures and by extrapolating to infinite pressure (Klinkenberg permeability) are practically identical with those obtained with the same liquids.

The permeability values generally reported in core-analysis data are air permeabilities in a direction parallel to the bedding plane from measurements performed on dry-core samples. In some cases it is necessary and desirable to test for permeability at right angles to the bedding plane, such as for water and gas coning studies and in gravity-drainage studies. Experience has shown that the permeability measured normal to bedding is usually less than permeability measured parallel to bedding. In addition, variations of the order of 100 per cent have been observed between permeabilities at the same level but in different directions in the bedding plane. Permeability is therefore a highly directional property in most reservoir rocks (Johnson and Hughes, 1948).

Cylindrical cores provided with a central hole, as frequently used for laboratory flooding tests, may be tested for radial permeability by flowing air through the dry sample. Computation of radial permeability is then obtained from the following equation:

$$K = \frac{Q_a \mu \ln (r_e/r_w)}{2\pi h(P_i - P_o)} \tag{2-16}$$

where K = permeability, darcys
Q_a = volume rate of flow, cc per sec, at mean pressure $(P_i + P_o)/2$
μ = viscosity of fluid, centipoises
r_e = outer radius of medium
r_w = inside radius of hole
h = axial thickness of core, cm
P_i = inlet pressure, atm
P_o = outlet pressure, atm

Thus far, the permeability parameter discussed assumed complete saturation in one single fluid before and during flow tests. The parameter so measured is the *specific permeability*, but it is well to qualify the numerical value reported according to the mode of testing, either by air or gas, water or other liquid, gas at infinite pressure, etc. The latter test gives the Klinkenberg permeability, which is often interpreted as *equivalent liquid permeability*, though it may not necessarily be representative of the actual formation water permeability. In all probability it is not equivalent to fresh-water permeability because fresh water is likely to give rise to surface reactions with the active minerals of the reservoir rock, mainly with clays which have a tendency to hydrate and swell when in contact with fresh waters. Permeability to a liquid should be tested with a liquid of the same composition, especially in salinity and pH, as the one for which engineering predictions are desired.

Permeability of a porous medium should be an invariant physical property of the medium. However, in practice various investigators have found that conditions of laboratory measurements are responsible for significant differences in the results, but there is considerable variation in the claims made. Grunberg and Nissan (1943) reported that the permeability of porous solids to gases and liquids varies with each liquid, and with each liquid with temperature. Their temperature effect was of 0.8 md per °C. They also found effects due to viscosity, density, surface tension, brine salinity, mean capillary radius, and adsorptive power of the solids for the flowing fluids. This last effect was also confirmed by Wentworth (1944), who flowed water through a fissured lava and observed a thousandfold decrease of the flow rate with time. However, Klinkenberg (1941) and Calhoun and Yuster (1947) deny the importance of surface tension and adsorption in reducing the flow of fluids through porous media as a result of their investigation of many substances, liquids and wetting agents. On the other hand, Hodgins et al. (1946) reported a falling off in the value of permeability when flowing condensable vapors at a pressure below their saturation pressures; the cause was attributed to surface adsorption within the pores.

Another factor which may affect the results of laboratory permeability measurements is the generation by the fluid flow of an electric effect called "streaming potential," the result of which is to oppose the flow. Grunberg and Nissan (1943) also found a 10 per cent increase in permeability when the brine salinity was increased, whereas Calhoun and Yuster (1947) found only a small effect in synthetic unreactive cores, but they reported the effect of pH to be high with an observed minimum permeability at the neutral point. When measuring permeability to brine of natural rocks, it is well known that the value declines as flow proceeds until a stabilized value is reached. If a less saline brine is used, another and lower stabilized permeability is again reached. This effect is attributed to clay swelling and other surface reaction with water.

Geologic Factors Which Affect Specific Permeability. The presence of porosity is not necessarily an indication that permeability exists, for the ability of a porous rock to conduct fluid is also dependent on the continuity of the pores and of their degree of interconnection. Permeability is also a function of the size and shape of the pore spaces. Since these in turn are dependent upon the geometric properties of the mineral grains and of their arrangement, the value of permeability is also a function of the grain packing and fabric as well as of cementation.

For a given size of unconsolidated grains of spherical shape, permeability depends only on their packing since it affects porosity. This is readily deduced from the Kozeny equation when specific surface is maintained constant and porosity is varied. Packing of grains may also be viewed as their spacing or their density pattern in space.

The fabric of a rock is the property concerned with the orientation in space of the component particles of the rock. According to origin there are two types of fabric: apposition and deformation. An apposition fabric is generally primary in origin, as it results from the orientation of the grains at the time of deposition. Sedimentation observations show that grains tend to fall with their greatest cross section in the horizontal plane and to orient themselves with their longest axis parallel to water currents. As a result of these tendencies, permeability is a directional property with the smallest value perpendicular to bedding. In the bedding plane itself, the largest permeability is found parallel to the dominant direction of old depositional shore lines. This radial anisotropy of permeability has been observed by Johnson and Hughes (1948) and has been further studied by Griffiths (1950, 1953).

A geologic factor of great importance in controlling the value of specific permeability to a certain fluid is the presence and nature of clays. Permeability measured with dry air (even when reduced for the Klinkenberg effect) or to oil is seldom the same as to water. As mentioned previously, permeability to water depends on the water salinity as well as on the number of pore volumes throughput. The reason for these differences is attributed to clay swelling in water, especially when fresh waters are used in the tests. Clay particles hydrate in the presence of water and restrain water from moving under the application of a pressure gradient. Shaly sands have a high irreducible water saturation and may produce clean oil with as much as 70 per cent water present.

Effective- and Relative-permeability Relationships. Should the test core be saturated partially with a fluid other than the test fluid and should the saturation in both fluids be maintained constant throughout the flow, the permeability to each test fluid will now be different from the specific permeability and, except at one saturation, will be different from one another. It is called the *effective permeability* to each fluid. Effective permeability may be determined in two- and three-phase flow inasmuch as two or three phases may flow simultaneously.

Effective permeability to a given fluid is the fluid conductivity of the porous medium at a given saturation state. Obviously, the presence of several fluid phases within a porous medium reduces the ability of the test fluid to flow; hence effective permeabilities are always lower than the specific permeabilities. They are expressed in darcys. *Relative permeability* is the ratio of effective permeability to absolute permeability and is a fraction which varies between 0 and 1. There are *effective* and *relative* permeabilities to all three reservoir fluids: oil, gas, and water, and they will be represented, respectively, by capital K_o, K_g, and K_w and lower case k_o, k_g, and k_w.

The shapes of the relative-permeability curves, as expected, are a function of the *fluid distribution* within the porous medium under test. The segregation of the fluids in the porous network of a reservoir rock is a function of the saturation as well as of the *wetting characteristics* of the respective fluids. From the wetting standpoint, a reservoir rock may be either *oil-wet* or *water-wet.* Oil-wet means that oil preferentially adheres to the reservoir rock surfaces, thus expelling water. Truly oil-wet reservoirs are relatively uncommon; the Oklahoma City Wilcox sand is generally considered to be so, whereas other reservoirs are known to be partially oil-wet, such as the Bradford third sand, the Springer sand, and the Tensleep sand.

Water-wet reservoirs are in great majority; their connate water preferentially adheres to the rock surface. Most reservoir rocks having been water-laid, this relationship is not unexpected as wetting is often dependent upon which fluid comes in contact with the reservoir surfaces first. However, prolonged contact with oil, particularly if the latter contains easily adsorbable polar compounds, may partially and locally change the wetting properties of a reservoir and give rise to wettability gradients.

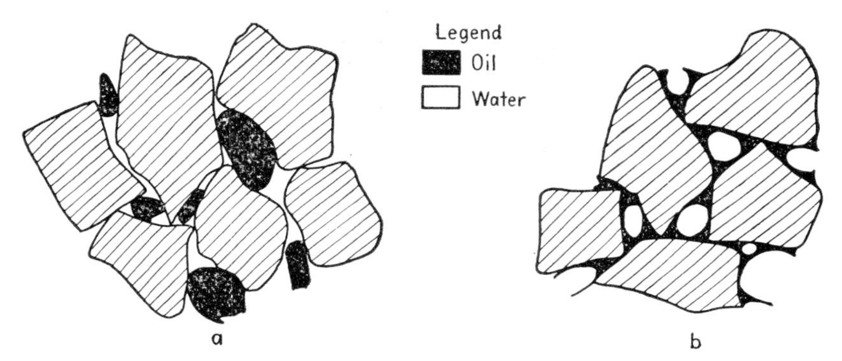

FIG. 2-13. Fluid distribution in the pore spaces as a function of fluid wettability. Water and oil saturations in (*a*) a water-wet sand and (*b*) an oil-wet sand.

Figure 2-13 represents graphically two possible states of oil and water saturations for water-wet and oil-wet sands. The sand grains are the hachured angular-shaped figures; water is left blank, and oil is shaded black. Although the round globules of either oil or water, as the case may be, appear isolated in the figure because of the plane representation, they must be construed as making a continuous mesh, or network, through which pressure is transmitted and fluid flows.

The recognition of the wetting characteristics of a reservoir is a debatable question. An empirical rule may be offered. *A water-wet sand is likely to have a high connate water saturation, whereas an oil-wet sand has a low connate water saturation.* The demarcation between the two is probably in the range of 10 to 20 per cent connate water. The Oklahoma City Wilcox sand, which is known to be truly oil-wet, has less than 10 per cent connate water.

One of the recent advances in the understanding of reservoir behavior is the recognition of the relative independence of the flow of nonmiscible fluids within a permeable medium. Hence the effective permeability to a given phase is a function of the *mobility* of that phase at its prevailing saturation distribution. The mobility is a function of the *wetting properties* of the reservoir and of the average cross-sectional area of the fluid channels, i.e., of *saturation.* It is expected, therefore, that the wetting fluid at low saturation has little mobility owing to its adhesion to the reservoir surfaces, whereas the nonwetting fluid which occupies the balance of the pore openings has more mobility. This expected relationship is fully verified by relative-permeability measurements. See, by way of example, the early results reported by Botset (1936) in Fig. 2-14. The unconsolidated sand requires an oil saturation of 63 per cent to equal the permeability to gas at 37 per cent. The gas is more mobile, because it occupies the center part of the pore openings. The relationship is intensified in the case of the consolidated sand in which 74 per cent oil saturation is required to equal gas permeability at 26 per cent gas saturation.

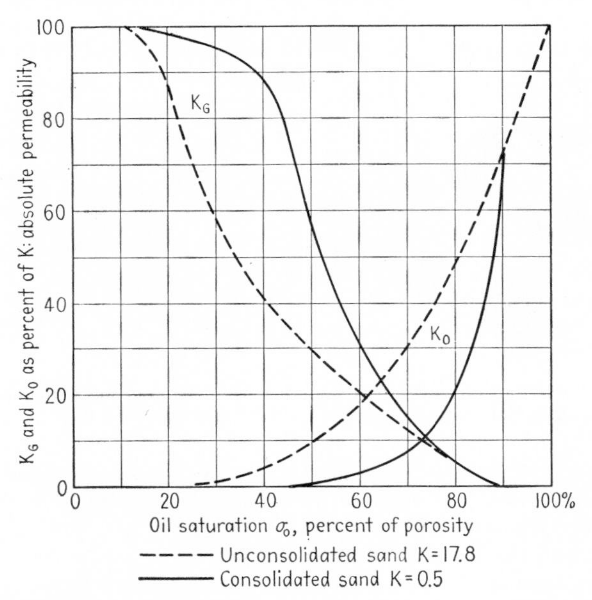

FIG. 2-14. Relative permeabilities to gas k_g and to oil k_o vs. oil saturation σ_o. (*After Botset, courtesy AIME.*)

The shape of the relative-permeability curves is intimately related to the liquid saturation status and to its critical points in even a more direct way. Leverett (1940) has shown that one may distinguish three types of fluid saturation between the limits of 0 and 100 per cent. These saturation states are again dependent upon the fluid wetting characteristics of the reservoir rock. These are represented in Fig. 2-15. Consider a water-wet sand; the water adheres to the solid surfaces of the grains. For very low saturations in water (upper diagram), water forms rings around the grain contact points; they are called *pendular rings* and have a doughnut shape, so to speak. If saturation is very low, these rings do not touch one another nor do they communicate with each other, except perhaps through a very thin film of water of nearly molecular thickness. Neither pressure differentials nor electrical-potential differences can be transmitted from one pendular ring to another. Hence the pendular rings are immobile, although they may be reduced in size by evaporation as would be the case in dry-gas cycling. As the wetting-phase saturation increases, the

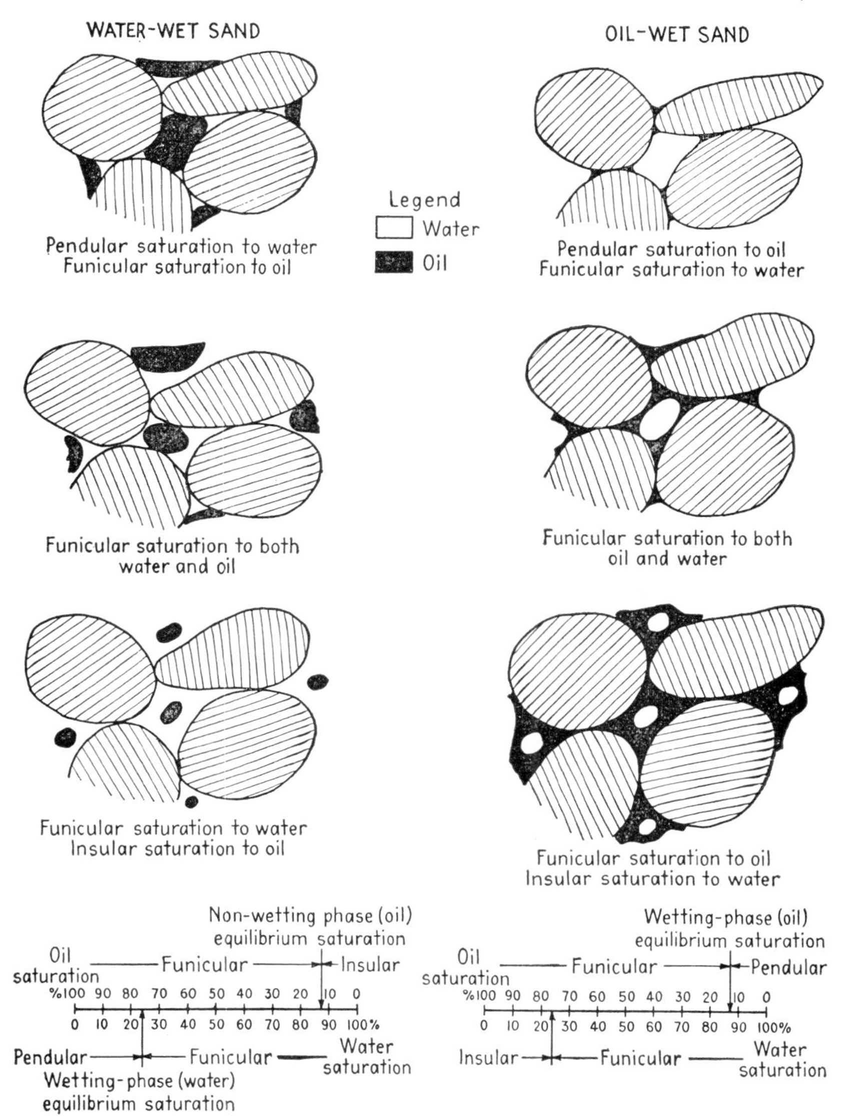

FIG. 2-15. Possible fluid-saturation states as a function of wettability.

size of the pendular rings increases and finally, with a sufficiently high fluid saturation, they come in physical contact and form a continuous mesh; the saturation at which this transition takes place is termed the *equilibrium saturation to the wetting phase.* Above this critical saturation, the wetting phase (water) offers a continuous but tortuous path to its movement under the application of a pressure differential. This saturation status is called *funicular* perhaps by analogy with a funicular railway typical of mountainous terrain. Pressure differentials will cause wetting fluid to flow, the rate of flow being controlled by the fluid's average cross-sectional area and the tortuosity of the path. The fluid saturation controls the cross-sectional area available to the flow; it increases with saturation. Hence permeability to the wetting fluid increases as its saturation increases. Yet at a given percentage of saturation in the wetting and nonwetting fluids, respectively, the permeability to the wetting phase is less than to the nonwetting phase. This is because of the retardation induced by adhesion of the wetting phase to solid surfaces as well as the greater tortuosity of the path. It is indeed easier for the nonwetting fluid to keep in the middle of the channels and slip on a wetting-fluid film. As the saturation in wetting fluid increases further, a situation develops when the nonwetting fluid no longer exists as a continuous phase, and it breaks into individual droplets seeking large pore openings in which to lodge themselves. The transition saturation point is called the *equilibrium saturation to the nonwetting phase*. The nonwetting phase is now dispersed and is said to be in a state of *insular saturation* by analogy with the inhabitants of an island remote from a continent. An insular globule of nonwetting fluid moves only by virtue of the differential pressure applied across it within a moving wetting fluid. In order for the globule to be displaced, the pressure differential across it must be sufficient to squeeze it through capillary restrictions; but such squeezing offers a large resistance, the so-called *Jamin effect*, which has been studied in detail by Gardescu (1930). This investigator showed the resistance (ΔP) offered to fluid displacement by a bubble of nonwetting fluid when squeezed from its original radius r_1 to the capillary radius r_2 to be

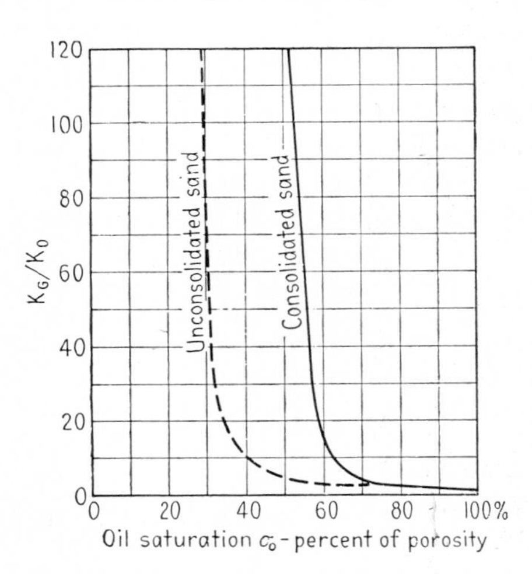

FIG. 2-16. Relative-permeability ratio k_g/k_o vs. oil saturation σ_o for consolidated and unconsolidated sands. (*After Botset, courtesy AIME.*)

$$\Delta P = \gamma \left(\frac{1}{r_2} + \frac{1}{r_1} \right) \tag{2-17}$$

where γ is the interfacial tension between the wetting and the nonwetting fluids. However, in a porous medium it appears impossible to apply sufficiently large pressure gradients in the wetting phase in order to displace an insular bubble in view of the interconnected nature of the capillary network. The saturation terminology used above was introduced by Versluys (1917).

To summarize, it may be stated that the shape of relative-permeability curves is controlled by *wettability* and by the *equilibrium saturation points* to the wetting and nonwetting phases. It is of interest to understand the lithological factors involved in their control. An inspection of Figs. 2-14 and 2-16, which summarize the investigations of Botset (1940), indicates that the lithification process of a reservoir rock (cementation and consolidation) is the property which influences most the transition point between the pendular and funicular saturation to the wetting phase, whereas lithification seems to have but a negligible effect upon the equilibrium saturation to the nonwetting phase. Cementation is a process which preferentially takes place at the contact points between the clastic grains of a sand, which contact points would normally be occupied initially by the wetting fluid in an unconsolidated sand.

Flow of gas at equilibrium saturation seems to be unaffected by the degree of consolidation of a reservoir rock, the transition occurring in the neighborhood of 10 per cent saturation in the nonwetting phase. The flow of the wetting phase is, however, unsteady in the zone of insular saturation to the nonwetting phase, which condition renders unreliable the measurement of relative permeability in this region.

At equilibrium saturation to the wetting fluid, it is noted also that the effective permeability to the wetting phase is nearly nil, whereas that to the nonwetting phase is nearly equal to the absolute permeability. Hence the presence of wetting fluid, at this status of saturation and for lower values, has no effect on the mobility to the nonwetting phase. The equilibrium saturation to the wetting phase may also be considered as the *irreducible saturation* below which it is impossible to reach by indefinitely flowing a nonwetting phase through the porous medium (provided that no evaporation takes place from the wetting into the nonwetting phase, as may be the case if dry gases were injected or if retrograde vaporization were taking place). The irreducible saturation is the ultimate saturation which may be reached in production practice where the problem consists in removing a valuable wetting fluid by injecting a less valuable nonwetting fluid. This is illustrated by the problem of removing oil from an oil-wet sand by water flooding.

Conversely, the equilibrium saturation to the nonwetting phase may be considered as the irreducible saturation below which it is impossible to reach by indefinitely injecting a wetting phase through the porous medium. It is again the ultimate saturation which can be reached by a driving wetting fluid to remove a nonwetting fluid. This is the general case of water flooding of oil in a water-wet sand. Should the nonwetting phase be compressible by or soluble in the driving fluid, an increase in average pressure helps the recovery by reducing the size of the bubbles in the insular saturation region.

In many reservoir calculations, the ratio of the permeability to gas to that of oil enters the calculations. Such is the case in gas-oil ratio computations, fractional-flow studies, etc. It is then convenient to read this ratio from a curve already drawn, as shown in Fig. 2-16, for consolidated and unconsolidated sands, but preferably drawn on semilogarithmic coordinates.

The above results and comments apply to two-phase flow such as oil and gas in the absence of connate water or to water and oil in the absence of gas. The known relative-permeability curves are the results of experimental determinations carried out on packed sand columns or on long cores of consolidated sands. The relative-permeability determinations of Leverett (1939) on oil-water mixtures for unconsolidated sands are shown in Fig. 2-17. Those used by Muskat for gas and oil in unconsolidated-sands flow studies are given in Fig. 2-18.

In Figs. 2-17 and 2-18 the departure from unity of the transmissivity curve ($K_o + K_w$ and $K_g + K_o$, respectively) is a measure of the interference which one fluid exerts on the other within the pore space.

Techniques for the measurement of relative permeability to two-phase flow are fairly well developed as a routine procedure to be applied to ordinary small rock samples drilled parallel to the bedding plane from cores obtained in regular coring operations of the reservoir rock. While the methods employed by Botset (1936) and Leverett (1939) in their fundamental investigations could undoubtedly be used and even improved for routine laboratory testing, this has not been done because the general technique involved is too cumbersome and expensive.

Effective- and Relative-permeability Measurements. There are many laboratory techniques which are used for the routine measurement of effective and relative permeability of porous media. They may be divided into three classes:

1. Those methods where *capillary equilibrium* exists between the various fluid phases at all times, including the time when they enter the core.
2. Those methods where the various test fluids are introduced in the sample core at the *same pressure* and possibly seek a capillary and saturation equilibrium at a point away from the inlet. This last group is also called "dynamic methods."
3. Those methods making use of *solution gas drive* where the oil is expulsed from the test sample by the internal expansion of solution gas.

The first group of methods was introduced by the work of Hassler (1944). He proposed a solution of the relative-permeability-measurement problem for two- as well as for three-phase flow through the use of "semipermeable membranes." Under fixed conditions of surface wetting and fluid saturation it is known that certain porous media offer considerable flow resistance to the nonwetting phase throughout a considerable saturation range, namely, within the zone of insular saturation to the nonwetting fluid. A water-wet sand is nonpermeable to gas and oil for the water saturations from about 85 to 100 per cent. Conversely, a compressed pyrite disk is nonpermeable to gas and water within approximately the same range. Therefore a semipermeable membrane firmly applied against the core permits the measurement of the pressure to one phase of the sample under test. Although there is a discontinuity in the wetting-phase saturation at the contact between the sample under study and the semipermeable disk,

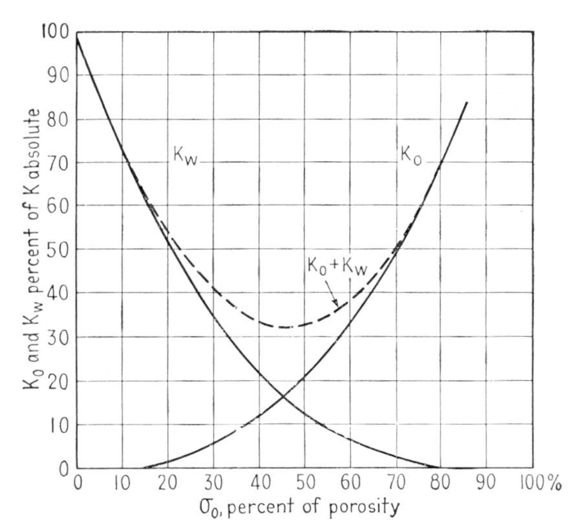

FIG. 2-17. Average relative permeability to oil k_o and water k_w vs. oil saturation σ_o for unconsolidated sands in the permeability range from 1.04 to 6.8 darcys. (*After Leverett, courtesy AIME.*)

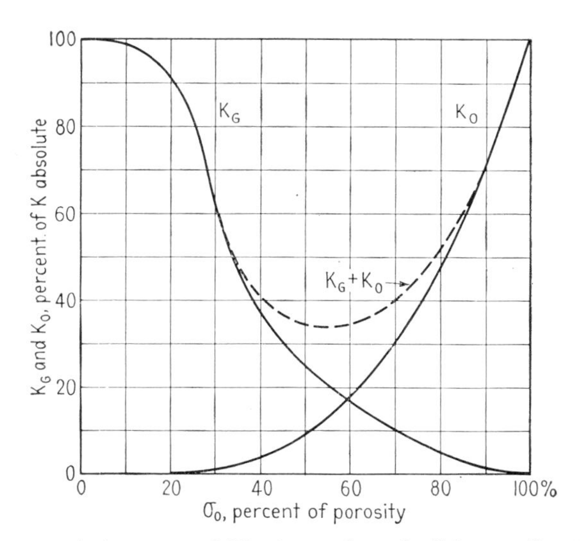

FIG. 2-18. Average relative permeability to gas k_g and oil k_o vs. oil saturation σ_o for unconsolidated sands in the permeability range from 11 to 260 darcys. (*After Muskat, courtesy AIME.*)

there is continuity of pressure within the wetting phase across the boundary; thus this device permits making pressure contact to a single-fluid phase. By this procedure, Hassler is able to measure the pressure drop within each individual phase flowing within a sample under study, either oil, gas, or water. His apparatus for two-phase flow is shown in Fig. 2-19. In this apparatus the fluid phases flow simultaneously through the core sample with the pressure differential between the phases maintained con-

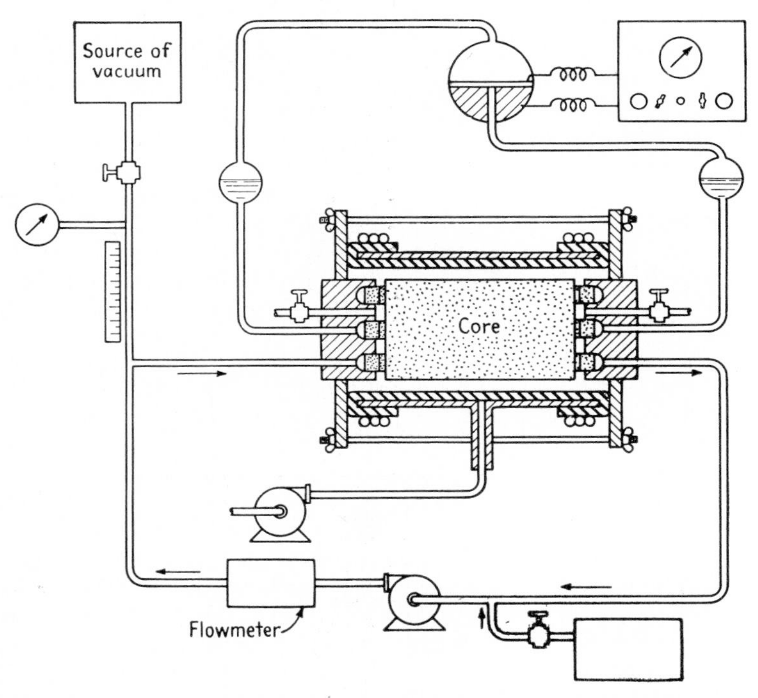

FIG. 2-19. Apparatus for measuring the relative permeability of simultaneous flow of two fluids. (*After Hassler.*)

stant at all points in the core. This ensures uniform fluid saturation and prevents "end effect" or accumulation of wetting fluid at the outlet end. The desaturation of the core in wetting fluid is carried out by increasing the pressure on the nonwetting fluid. The wetting fluid passes through the semipermeable membranes which it wets and which are in capillary contact at each end of the core.

Similarly, the nonwetting fluid passes through the semipermeable membranes which it wets.

The two phases are kept in completely separate flow systems, joining only in the core sample. This permits the measurements of the rate of flow of each phase. The saturation values to each liquid within the test core may also be determined by the material-balance method. The flowing pressure gradient in each phase and a uniform pressure differential may be maintained between the phases.

The measurement of the pressures exerted by each phase at the two ends of the test core must be measured with gauges that register sufficiently accurately with small fluid-volume displacement in order that errors in sample saturation values may not be introduced.

Brownscombe et al. (1950) have given a detailed description and operation of a Hassler-type apparatus in which many of the original difficulties have been eliminated.

This technique permits counterflow of the fluid phases and three-phase flow studies. The disadvantages of this technique are possible plugging of the core and geometric distortion of the flow paths near the ends. The Hassler technique may perhaps be considered as the *standard of relative-permeability measurements* because when properly used it duplicates in every respect the conditions of fluid flow in the reservoir. Unfortunately it is extremely slow in its operation, often requiring laboratory time of a week to a month to obtain complete relative-permeability curves over a full range of fluid saturations. Several methods for simplifying and speeding the measurements without impairing their accuracy have been proposed and will be discussed briefly.

It has been suggested by Hafford (1952) that the semipermeable barriers be placed at one end of the core only. The wetting-phase outlet pressure is atmospheric and the nonwetting-phase pressure is the displacement pressure of the core. The flowing phases are again introduced into the core from separate fluid systems. This method has not been received with much favor since the results are possibly influenced by presence of end effects when operating at low pressure differentials.

Leas et al. (1950) make relative-permeability measurements to gas only, while maintaining the liquid-phase saturation stationary within the test core. The various constant liquid saturations are obtained by desaturating the core over a high displacement pressure porous plate such as in capillary-pressure tests. This procedure had already been suggested by Hassler et al. (1936). A capillary-pressure curve is obtained simultaneously with the tests; the relative permeability to the wetting phase may be calculated from this curve. Since the wetting phase is not moving, there is no capillary-pressure gradient and the phases are in capillary equilibrium. Leas et al. have shown that a nonmoving wetting phase has no substantial effect on the flow of gas. This is thought to be correct only when the flowing pressure gradients are an order of magnitude lower than the capillary pressure and when the flow originates from conditions of stable capillary equilibrium. The fluid distribution then remains stable during the flow tests. Leas et al. enclose their test core in a Hassler core holder. However, a method proposed by Branson (1951) dispenses with any outside holder for the core. This is possible as long as the pressure in the nonwetting phase is kept below that corresponding to the threshold value.

Rapoport and Leas (1951) proposed a similar procedure for the measurement of relative permeability to water or oil (with connate water present) in the presence of a stationary gas phase. In their experiments the gas phase is established and controlled by maintaining a capillary pressure between gas and liquid by pressure applied to the gas phase through semi-permeable barriers. Capillary barriers cemented to both ends of the core and permeable only to liquid permit the flow tests.

The methods of Leas et al. and Rapoport and Leas are relatively rapid and the complete test of one core is possible in one laboratory day's work. They have the advantage of maintaining capillary equilibrium between the phases and of eliminating end effects. They also eliminate the flow-

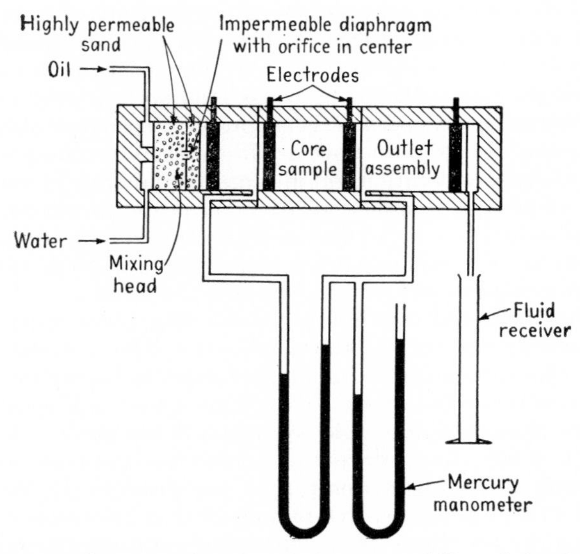

FIG. 2-20. Apparatus for measuring the relative permeability of simultaneous flow of two fluids. (*After Morse et al.*)

pattern distortion originally present in the Hassler technique. Flow may take place under low pressure gradients, and the fluid distributions during test are static. There is, however, an element of uncertainty concerning the reliability of the tests because only one phase is moving.

The second group or "dynamic method" of measuring relative permeability was introduced by Morse (1947) and coworkers. They proposed a method which may be applied to ordinary core sizes. The procedure suggested involves the simultaneous flow of a highly dispersed mixture of two fluids into a sample core mounted and sealed in a plastic sleeve (Fig. 2-20). The core is cut into three parts. Saturations are measured in the central section from a relative electrical-conductivity curve, and pressure differentials are measured in the nonwetting phase (air) between the ends of the central section by mercury and water manometers, as the case may be. A more dependable way of measuring saturation is by weight measurements of the test core, inasmuch as electric conduction is a function of the water-saturation distribution. The relative-permeability testing method of Morse has been investigated further by Henderson (1947 and 1948), and several laboratories are using it extensively.

To achieve the various fluid saturations at which it is desired to measure relative permeability, the fluid-injection ratios into the mixing head are changed until a steady-state equilibrium is established. The fluid saturations within the core adjust themselves in response to the pressure difference between the various fluid phases resulting from the imposed flow ratios.

At equilibrium the saturation distributions become fixed. Flow must be continued to maintain this steady-state condition and measurements may then be made. They consist of measuring the pressure differential across the test core or center section, the rates of flow of each fluid individually, and the saturation in the various fluids within the test core.

The measurements must be made under high pressure differentials in order to compress the end effect, or wetting-phase accumulation, into the outlet or third core section. It is not known to what extent the fluid-phase distribution in a porous medium is different when established by capillary displacement or by dynamic displacement.

Comparative tests of relative permeability by the Hassler and dynamic techniques on a single rock sample made by Osoba et al. (1951) indicate the relative permeability values for the wetting phase (oil) to be very different, whereas they were substantially the same for the nonwetting phase (gas). The wetting-phase curve obtained at high flow rate by the dynamic method is located above that obtained by the Hassler technique, whereas at low rates they are again substantially the same.

A difficulty of the three-core dynamic method is to achieve capillary contact between them. The use of thin tissue paper at these contacts has been found useful. However, a good deal of precision machining is still required. A technique called the "single-core dynamic" eliminates most of these difficulties. Fluids are again injected simultaneously upstream into the core and under a sufficiently high pressure differential to compress the end effect fluid accumulation into a negligible length of the core. This requires high rates of flow. It was determined that the results obtained were rate sensitive at low injection rates but not at high rates (Osoba et al., 1951).

Another dynamic method is called the "gas-drive technique." This procedure uses a single core initially 100 per cent liquid saturated. Gas pressure is admitted at the upstream end. To minimize boundary effects, high rates of gas flow are used. This method differs from the stationary liquid method of Leas et al. (1950) in that both phases are flowing simultaneously. It differs from the single-core dynamic method in that only gas is admitted to the core. The flow of both phases results from the displacement of part of the liquid phase by the injected gas. This procedure is also called "external gas-drive" technique. In practice an oil of high viscosity is used as the liquid phase to be driven out. A connate water phase may also be present. The reason for an oil of high viscosity is that it will be driven out at a relatively slow rate, which will thus permit higher accuracy in the measurements. The results are again rate sensitive at low rates of flow. At high rates the boundary effect is again compressed to such a small distance that it is believed negligible. Both the rates of flow of oil and gas are measured. The liquid saturations are obtained by material balance.

A modified external gas-drive technique is known as the Welge method (1952). Actually, the laboratory technique is the same as for the external gas drive; the difference is mostly in the interpretation of the results. However, it is also applicable to external water drive of a test core. The procedure is good only for the determination of k_g/k_o or k_w/k_o, depending on whether gas or water is used as the driving fluid. In a linear system with negligible end effect and driven by an incompressible fluid (gas at high pressure or water) nonmiscible with the driven fluid (oil), an equation relates the cumulative displacing fluid injection expressed in pore volume Q_i and measured at mean core pressure to the fractional flow of driven fluid f_o in the total outlet stream, the average displacing fluid saturation $\sigma_{D,\text{av}}$, and the outlet saturation σ_{De}:

$$\sigma_{D,\text{av}} = \sigma_{De} + Q_i f_o \tag{2-18}$$

The value of f_o may be obtained graphically from a cartesian plot of $\sigma_{D,\text{av}}$ vs. Q_i.

The justification for the above statement is given in Chap. 11.

Instantaneous gas-oil ratio (GOR) measurements are made during the tests and are related as follows:

$$\text{GOR} = \frac{1 - f_o}{f_o} = S + \frac{\beta}{\alpha}\frac{k_g}{k_o}\frac{\mu_o}{\mu_g} \tag{2-19}$$

from which relation k_g/k_o is computed and plotted vs. σ_{De}, as computed by Eq. (2-18).

The gas-oil ratio value must be expressed at the pressure when σ_{De} prevails. This pressure is approximately equal to the outlet pressure plus the displacement pressure of the core. However, with high pressure differentials across the core this correction is negligible.

The third group of methods for measuring relative permeability is by *solution gas drive.* It consists in allowing gas to evolve from solution by reducing the pressure on the core containing live oil possibly with connate water present at its irreducible saturation. There are two procedures which may be used:

1. Stage depletion and flushing by dead oil (Caudle et al., 1951)
2. Continuous depletion drive (Stewart et al., 1953)

In the first procedure when the evolution of gas has created the desired gas saturation, dead oil is injected into the core at very low rate. This rate is measured and from it the relative permeability to oil k_o is determined. The pressure drop across the core permits the calculation of the effective permeability to oil at the prevailing gas saturation. After the measurements are completed, the dead oil is flushed by live oil and the measurements are repeated at a lower pressure. In practice only two points on the curve are obtained, one at the equilibrium gas saturation and the other when gas has expanded to atmospheric pressure.

The continuous gas depletion-drive procedure of Stewart was specifically devised to test the relative-permeability characteristics of large cores, more specifically those from carbonate reservoir rocks. In this procedure the cores are saturated with a live oil of 200 psi bubble point. The pressure is lowered at the downstream end of the core until production of oil and gas begins. The pressure drop across the core is then adjusted until a 20 psi differential pressure exists across the core. This differential is maintained at all times until the outlet pressure is atmospheric. This rather high pressure differential serves to suppress the end effect.

In this type of experiment by solution gas drive it is noted that at all but the latest stages of depletion, less gas is released from solution than would have been predicted from equilibrium *PVT* relationships of the oil mixture used. More gas remained in solution in the oil left in the core than would remain at equilibrium conditions. This is called supersaturation. Relative permeability ratios k_g/k_o obtained from the laboratory solution gas drive must be corrected for this excess solution gas in the oil. The flowing gas-oil ratio is determined by a gas material balance as follows:

1. The total gas remaining in the core at any stage of depletion is equal to the dissolved gas initially in place less the cumulative gas production. The gas in the core exists partly in solution in the oil and partly as free gas in the space vacated by liquid production.

2. If the space vacated by liquid production and the mean pressure are known, the calculation of the amount of free gas is straightforward. The difference between the total gas remaining in the core and the free gas is the solution gas in the oil.

3. When the volume of oil remaining in the core by difference between initial and produced oil is known, the mean solution gas-oil ratio is calculated. This solution gas-oil ratio is subtracted from the produced gas-oil ratio to obtain the flowing gas-oil ratio, and thereby the relative-permeability ratio.

The mean bubble-point pressure within the core at any time is determined from a graph where the solution gas-oil ratio is plotted vs. equilibrium pressure for the particular gas-oil mixture used.

A surprising observation made by various laboratories is the dependence of relative-permeability characteristics upon the direction in which the liquid saturations are varied, whether by increasing or by decreasing the nonwetting-phase saturation. Figure 2-21 shows this relationship. Consider first the case when the pores of a rock are completely saturated with brine. The representative point is the 100 per cent point on the saturation scale at which the permeability to water is 100 per cent of specific to water. Let a nonwetting fluid, oil, be forced into the core. Its behavior is similar to what happens when gas is forced into the rock from the outside. This direction of flow and saturation change is called "drainage." In this desaturation direction, the water is selectively displaced from the larger toward the successively smaller capillaries, and "channellike" distribution of the two fluids, oil and gas, exists in the pore space. They are in contact only through small surfaces located in the capillaries transverse to the general flow direction. Hence the two fluids do not react upon one another, and the flow should be independent of the fluid viscosities, interfacial tension, and rates of flow. By contrast, when the water-saturation changes

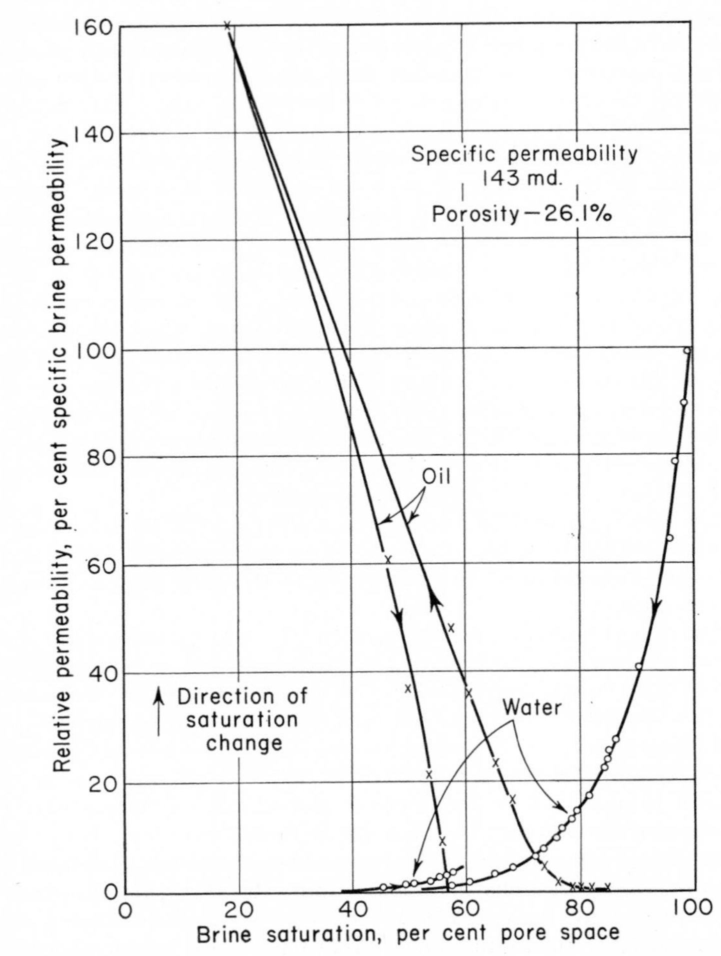

Fig. 2-21. Oil-water flow characteristics in the Nellie Bly sandstone. (*After Terwilliger, courtesy AIME.*)

are toward larger saturation values or in the "imbibition" direction (which is also the direction of displacement of oil by water, or water flooding), the brine is initially located as a film over the pore walls, in the reentrant angles of the pore constrictions, as well as filling completely some of the minute pores. Oil fills the remaining pore space. Each capillary opening, by virtue of its size and saturation, tends to imbibe the available water and to displace some of the oil it contains. The oil saturation is reduced by virtue of the changes in the oil-water interface curvature in the continuous oil phase. As the curvature becomes less, some pore constrictions, because of their size, contain filaments of oil that are confined near the axis of the pores, and "coaxial flow" of oil and water takes place simultaneously in each pore. This lasts for a certain range of water-saturation increments. Owing to the large interface between oil and water, the two fluids now react upon one another, and the respective flow rates as well

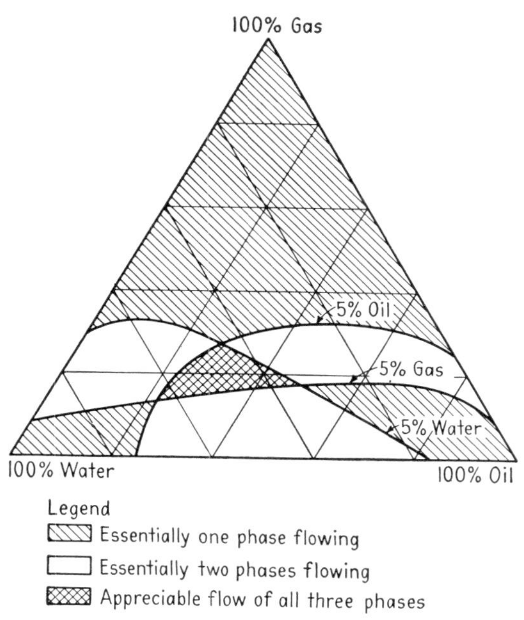

FIG. 2-22. Composition of a three-phase fluid-flow stream in a permeable medium as a function of fluid saturations. (*After Leverett, courtesy AIME.*)

as the relative permeability characteristics should be sensitive to viscosity ratio, interfacial tension, and pressure gradient, although this effect should be of second-order magnitude. When the oil filaments are constricted further by increasing the water saturation to the point where they acquire a "link sausage" appearance, the filaments break off at the thinnest constrictions and the bubbles of oil so formed seek rest positions in the large pore openings as a trapped phase or residual oil saturation. It is the ultimate nonwetting-phase saturation at which the relative permeability to oil vanishes.

While some of the methods reviewed above are applicable to the measurement of three-phase relative permeabilities, the results obtained by Leverett (1939) are still considered classic. Figure 2-22 indicates the composition of the three-phase fluid-flow stream where all phases are flowing simultaneously. The coordinates of any point within the triangle represent

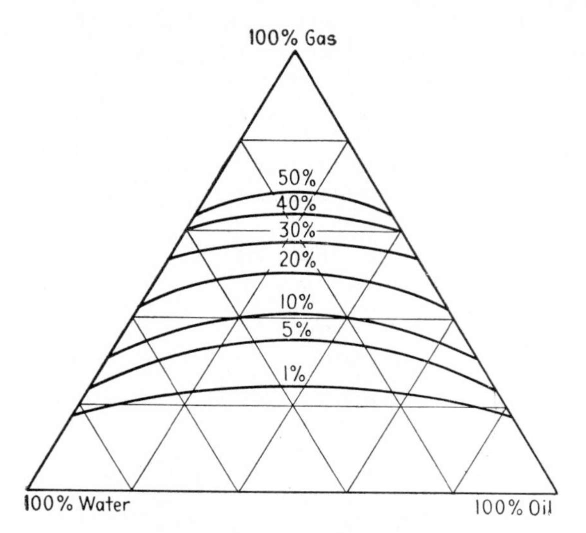

FIG. 2-23. Relative permeability to gas in three-phase flow as a function of water and oil saturations. (*After Leverett, courtesy AIME.*)

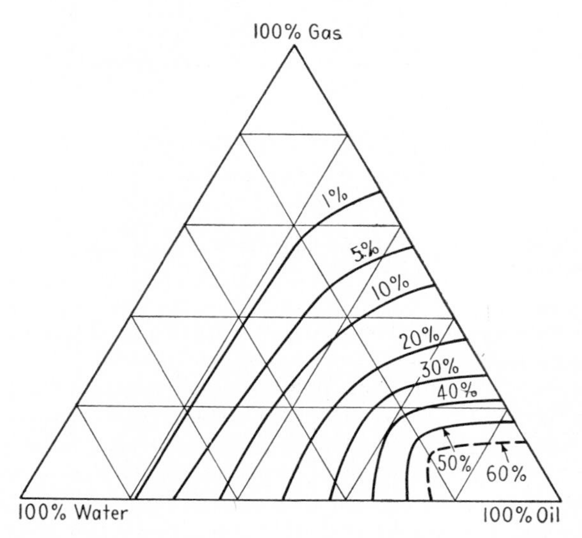

FIG. 2-24. Relative permeability to oil in three-phase flow as a function of gas and water saturations. (*After Leverett, courtesy AIME.*)

the different saturations in all three phases. It may be observed that the necessary conditions permitting the simultaneous flow of all three phases delineate an extremely restricted range. It has been shown also that the total fluid transmissivity in this range is considerably reduced over the minimum attained when two phases only are flowing. In his experiments, Leverett used an unconsolidated sand which was presumably water-wet. For an oil-wet sand, the positions of oil and water phases are interchanged

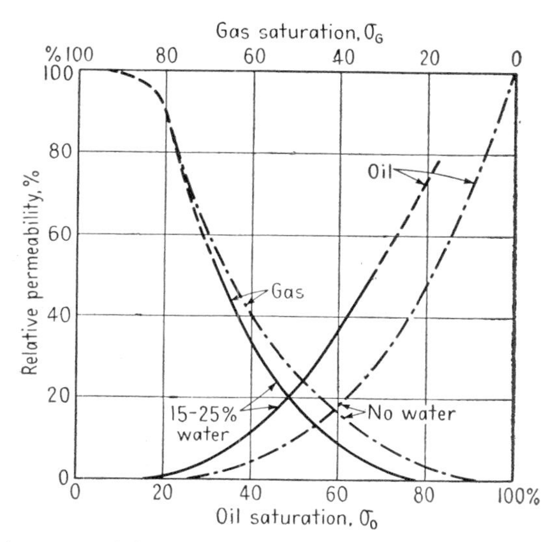

FIG. 2-25. Relative permeability to gas and oil as a function of connate water saturation. (*After Leverett, courtesy AIME.*)

and so are the relative-permeability characteristics. Considering the effective permeability to gas (Fig. 2-23) one may observe an almost symmetrical distribution of k_g from the vertical axis of the triangle, indicating a smaller permeability to gas when oil and water are distributed in substantially equal saturations. Permeability to gas is dependent only on the total liquid saturation.

On the other hand, the diagram representing the relative permeability to oil, k_o (Fig. 2-24), is not symmetrical with respect to any axis of the triangle. The symmetry is destroyed toward the high percentage in gas saturation which indicates a lowering of the mobility of oil by the presence of gas. This is to be expected inasmuch as both oil and gas are nonwetting phases in Leverett's experiments.

Cross plotting of the data from the triangular diagrams brings out some other interesting relationships.

Figure 2-25 indicates a shift of relative permeability to oil and gas, owing to the presence of connate water, the mobility of oil being increased and that of gas decreased. These relationships are further indicated in Figs. 2-26*a* and *b*, where the ratios k_g/k_o and k_w/k_o are plotted in much more usable form as a function of connate water saturation. The k_g/k_o curves indicate a considerable reduction in the mobility of gas (or an increase in the mobility of oil) as the saturation in connate water increases and at a given oil saturation.

The k_w/k_o curves indicate a rapid decrease in the mobility of water (or an increase in the mobility of oil) as connate water saturation decreases and at a given oil saturation.

The experiments of Leverett (1939) have shown relative permeabilities to be substantially independent of liquid viscosity, of density, of inter-

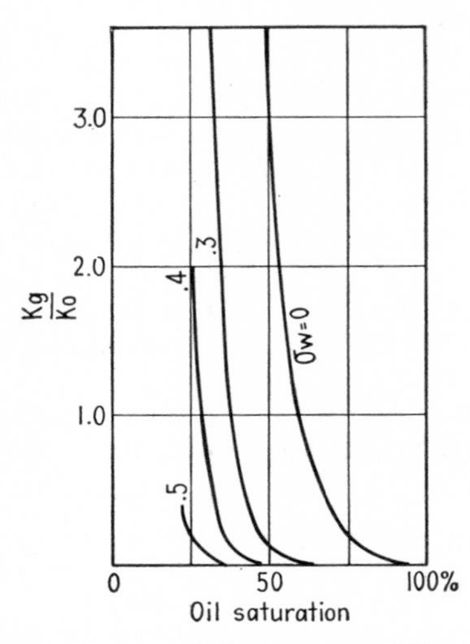

FIG. 2-26a. Relative-permeability ratio to gas and oil vs. oil saturation as a function of a fixed and nonmovable connate water saturation.

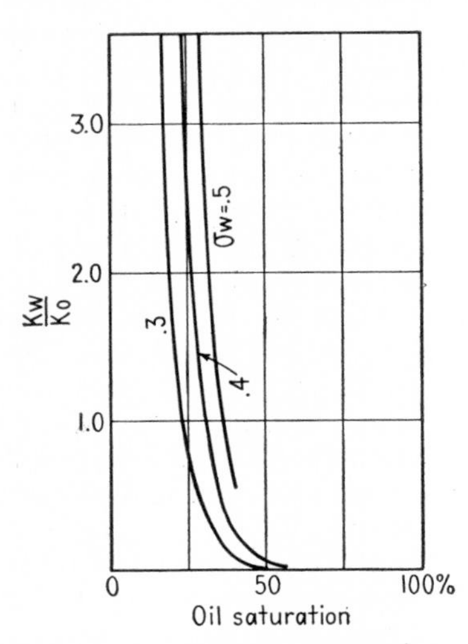

FIG. 2-26b. Relative-permeability ratio to water and oil k_w/k_o vs. oil saturation as a function of a fixed connate water saturation.

facial tension, of pressure gradient, and of the effective porosity of the medium. Leverett significantly remarked, however, that there was a small but definite effect of surface tension. However, there is a definite relation to pore-size distribution and to the wetting characteristics of the reservoir surfaces. The latter controls the fluid distribution within the pore-space network and the former, the transition points between the different saturation states, as previously discussed. In a water-wet reservoir rock, water is believed to flow through the channels that are not occupied by oil and is a continuous film around each sand grain or porous channel. Leverett attributed to Jamin action the fact that the over-all transmissivity to all fluids in motion within a permeable substance is not equal to the permeability to a homogeneous fluid phase or specific permeability. According to this effect, the nonwetting phase (oil in a water-wet sand) finds its way into certain pores and does not flow. This results in restricting the freedom of movement of the wetting phase (water in a water-wet sand).

While viscosity has no substantial effect on relative permeability characteristics, the ratio of the viscosities of the fluid phases flowing simultaneously has a considerable bearing upon the composition of the effluent mixtures.

RELATIONS BETWEEN ROCK PROPERTIES AND RESERVOIR BEHAVIOR

The main geologic characteristic of all the physical rock properties that have a bearing on reservoir behavior when producing oil and gas is the extreme variability in such properties within the reservoir itself, both laterally and vertically, and within short distances. An important consideration for all reservoir engineers to bear in mind is that there are no homogeneous reservoirs, only varying degrees of heterogeneity. All formulas derived for the purpose of reservoir engineering calculations are always presumed to apply to fictitiously uniform reservoir properties, and the engineer should be forewarned of the dangers which this assumed and false uniformity may lead to.

It is of interest therefore to discuss at this point some of the statistical approaches which inform the engineer of the degree of variation he is dealing with.

Statistical treatment may be applied to physical properties measured in a single well or to physical properties measured between wells.

Properties measured in a single well may be statistically treated so as to obtain their:

1. Weighted average
2. Degree of homogeneity
3. Variance

Properties measured in several wells may be statistically treated so as to obtain their:

1. Degree of stratification or of correlation
2. Degree of lenticularity or of lensing
3. Degree of thickening or thinning

The *weighted average* $\bar{x}$ of a property x of the reservoir which varies over a total pay thickness h may be calculated by

$$\bar{x} = \frac{\Sigma h_i x_i}{h} \tag{2-20}$$

where h_i is the interval thickness where the property has value x_i. Also, the relation $h = \Sigma h_i$ exists. The properties of interest are porosity ϕ, fluid saturations σ_w, σ_o, and σ_g, and specific permeability K.

Weighted-average relative permeabilities k_r to a particular fluid should include saturation considerations to that fluid and may be obtained by

$$\bar{k}_r = \frac{\Sigma h_i \sigma_i k_{ri}}{\Sigma h_i \sigma_i} \tag{2-21}$$

The *degree of homogeneity* of a reservoir property is a number which characterizes the departure from uniformity or constancy of that particular measured property through the thickness of reservoir. A formation is said to have a uniformity coefficient of unity in a specified property when that property is constant throughout the formation thickness. A completely heterogeneous formation has a uniformity coefficient of zero. Between the two extremes, formations have uniformity coefficients comprised between zero and one. Intermediate values may be ascertained by means of cartesian graphic plots wherein the abscissa is cumulative dimensionless thickness $\Sigma h_i/h$ and the ordinate is cumulative dimensionless property $\Sigma h_i x_i/h\bar{x}$, according to Fig. 2-27.

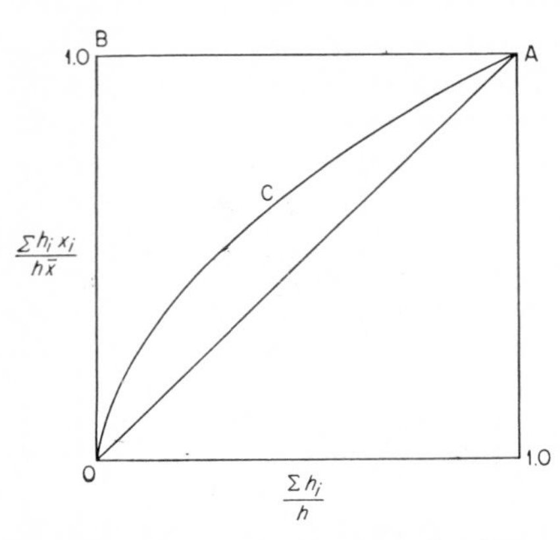

FIG. 2-27. Cartesian plot for the determination of the coefficient of uniformity of a physical property of reservoir rock measured at intervals over a total pay thickness **h**.

For the purpose of this graph the property values were previously arranged in tabulation form in the order of constantly decreasing values vs. the corresponding interval thickness. The diagonal line OA is that of complete uniformity. The line OBA is that of complete heterogeneity. A curved line such as OCA is that of partial uniformity. The coefficient of heterogeneity or *Lorenz coefficient* is the ratio of the area $OCAO$ to the area $OBAO$. Recoveries of oil by water drive (natural encroachment or artificial flooding) have been related to the Lorenz coefficient by Rahme and Schmalz (1951), and their correlation is shown in Fig. 9-10.

The *variance*, a statistical measure of nonuniformity of data, has been suggested by Parsons and Dykstra (1950) for the representation of well properties. It is generally applied to the property of permeability but any other rock physical property could be so treated. The procedure for computing the variance of a property is as follows:

1. Tabulate the property measurements in decreasing order of their magnitude. This property should be read at equal intervals, such as every foot.

2. Compute the percentage of the property magnitudes exceeding each tabulated entry in a column entitled "Cumulated Per Cent Greater than."

3. The property values under (1) are plotted on the log scale and the cumulative values under (2) are plotted on the probability scale of a log-probability graph paper such as that shown in Fig. 2-28.

4. The best straight line is drawn through the points so obtained.

5. The property value at 84.1 cumulative per cent is read from the straight line.

6. The *median* property value is then determined. The median is the value at the middle item when the items are arranged according to magnitude as stipulated under (1). The median is an average of position in the series, and not a magnitude average.

7. The variance of the property magnitudes is the difference between that obtained under (5) and the median divided by the median value.

Dykstra and Parsons have related the recovery of oil by water drive to the variance of permeability in a reservoir and to the mobility ratio of the fluids involved. Their results are given in Figs. 9-11 and 9-12.

Physical rock properties which are measured in several wells may be studied statistically. The most common method of doing so is by in-

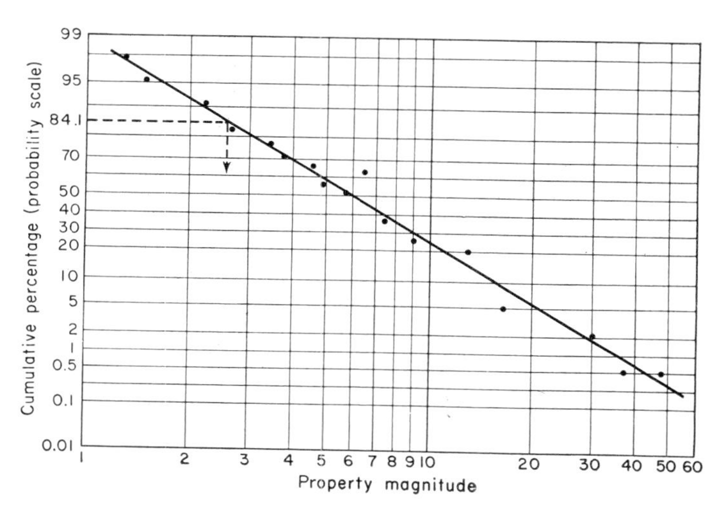

FIG. 2-28. Method for calculation of the variance of a well property.

spection and correlation of the obvious features of coregraphs or logs. Well-defined reservoirs, in which formational sequences and thickness are the same, do not offer any difficulties in finding the corresponding depth and thickness of the various features; this situation is not generally faced by reservoir engineers. In special cases of heterogeneous sediments where considerable lithologic variations are common, as in deltaic and continental deposits, the matching of the coregraph and logs is no longer obvious and it becomes increasingly difficult to interpret the continuity of the matched units. The interpreter is then faced with the problem of finding the most probable correlation and its degree of reliability. Statistical methods permit him to do so. The method involves computing a correlation function and a significance function, the latter indicating the degree of confidence which one may have in the most probable correlation. The procedure which is called the "moment method" is as follows:

1. Designate a passive and an active log and line them up at a reference

depth in such a way that the following sequences will be obtained:

Reference depth	*Attribute of:* *Passive log*	*Active log*
1	a_1	b_1
2	a_2	b_2
3	a_3	b_3
4	a_4	b_4
.	.	.
.	.	.
.	.	.
i	a_i	b_i
.	.	.
.	.	.
.	.	.
n	a_n	b_n

2. Multiply the correlating attributes at each level by one another, make the sum of the pair products, and determine the mean pair product by dividing the sum by the number of pairs.

3. Move the active log one reference depth unit, and repeat procedure 2.

The most probable correlation is obtained for the active log position which yields the maximum value for the mean pair product.

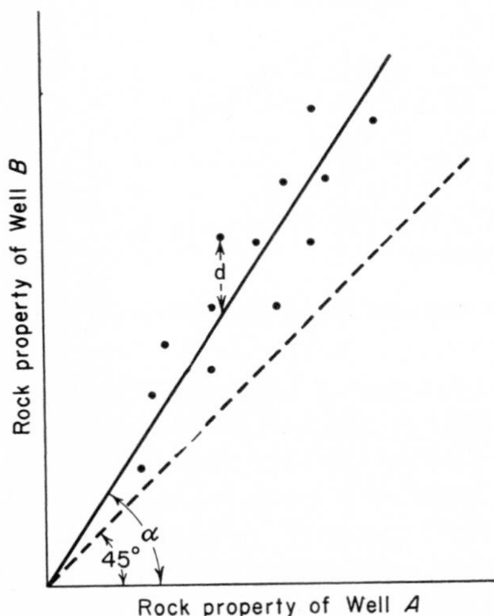

FIG. 2-29. Example of scattergram for the correlation between two wells of a specific rock property.

The reliability of the correlation may be evaluated by means of the chi-square test, but this is not necessary in engineering practice.

The various logs having been correlated either by inspection or by the moment method, a correlation or *stratification coefficient* may be determined. It is the degree to which a particular property of the rock is continuous from one well to another. This coefficient may be obtained conveniently by plotting on cartesian paper the property of one well vs. the same property in the other well (Fig. 2-29). Draw the best straight line through the points so obtained. Measure for each point the distance d, and tabulate the results according to Table 2-2.

The coefficient of correlation or stratification s is obtained from

$$s = \sqrt{1 - \frac{{d_m}^2}{{x_m}^2}}$$

Its value is comprised between zero and one. $s = 1$ means that perfect correlation exists for the property from well to well. $s = 0$ means that there is no correlation; i.e., there is no continuity in the measured property from well to well. The coefficient of correlation is not an additive property from well to well.

TABLE 2-2. CORRELATION OF A ROCK PROPERTY BETWEEN TWO WELLS

Rock property, well 1	Rock property, well 2	Deviation from a_m	x^2	Deviation from line of regression	d^2
a_1	b_1	x_1	x_1^2	d_1	d_1^2
a_2	b_2	x_2	x_2^2	d_2	d_2^2
a_3	b_3	x_3	x_3^2	d_3	d_3^2
a_4	b_4	x_4	x_4^2	d_4	d_4^2
.	.	.	.	.	.
.	.	.	.	.	.
.	.	.	.	.	.
a_i	b_i	x_i	x_i^2	d_i	d_i^2
.	.	.	.	.	.
.	.	.	.	.	.
.	.	.	.	.	.
a_n	b_n	x_n	x_n^2	d_n	d_n^2
$a_m = \frac{\Sigma a_i}{n}$			$x_m^2 = \frac{\Sigma x_i^2}{n}$		$d_m^2 = \frac{\Sigma d^2}{n}$

The *degree of lensing* or *lenticularity* of a rock property is the tendency of that property to converge or diverge in the direction joining two wells. This is a vectorial property which is additive with its sign between wells. Lensing may exist between wells with or without total bed thickness change. If there are bed thickness changes between two series of well data to be correlated, they should be reduced to equal thickness by proportional reduction unless truncation by an unconformity is in evidence. Should the line passing through the scatter of points in Fig. 2-29 make an angle of 45 deg with the coordinates, there is no lenticularity. For other slopes the lenticularity coefficient λ is given by

$$\lambda = \frac{\alpha}{45°} - 1$$

If $\lambda > 0$, there is divergence of the rock property from well a to well b. If $\lambda < 0$, there is convergence from well a to well b.

The coefficient of thinning or thickening (t) between two wells is the ratio of the gross pay thickness between the two wells: $t > 1$ for thickening; $t < 1$ for thinning. In general $t < 1$ will be associated with a negative lensing coefficient and conversely.

The value of the coefficient of correlation in planning the primary or secondary operation of a reservoir or in evaluating its reserves is obvious. In depletion drive, a well-stratified rock with a high correlation coefficient and a low uniformity coefficient should yield low recoveries because of differential depletion between the various strata. An external drive by either water or gas should also yield low recovery because of differential bypassing in the various strata. Conversely, a heterogeneous reservoir with high lensing and low correlation coefficient should provide higher recoveries by depletion and gas drive, and if water-wet by water drive also.

SELECTED REFERENCES ON FLUID PERMEABILITIES OF ROCKS

1839

Hagen, G.: Über die Bewegung des Wassers in engen cylindrischen Röhren, *Poggendorf Ann.*, vol. 46, pp. 423ff.

1846

Poiseuille, J.: Recherches expérimentales sur le mouvement des liquides dans les tubes de très petits diamètres, *Mém. savants étrangers*, vol. 9, pp. 543ff.

1856

Darcy, H.: "Les Fontaines publiques de la ville de Dijon," Victor Dalmont, Paris.

1860

Jamin, J. C.: Mémoire sur d'équilibre et le mouvement des liquides dans les corps poreux, *Compt. rend.*, vol. 50.

1892

Hazen, A.: Some Physical Properties of Sands and Gravels, *Mass. State Board of Health, 24th Ann. Rept.*, pp. 541ff.

1899

King, F. H.: Principles and Conditions of Movement of Ground Water, *USGS 19th Ann. Rept.*, part 2, pp. 59ff.

Slichter, S. C.: Theoretical Investigation of the Motion of Ground Water, *USGS 19th Ann. Rept.*, part 2, pp. 295ff.

1909

Wologdine, S.: Conductivity, Porosity, and Gas Permeability of Refractory Materials, *Electrochem. Met. Ind.*, vol. 7, pp. 435ff.

1917

Versluys, J.: Die Kappillaritat der Boden, *Inst. Mitt. Bodenk.*, vol. 7, pp. 117ff.

1923

Meinzer, O. E.: Outline of Ground Water Hydrology with Definitions, *USGS Water Supply Paper* 494, 71 pp.

1925

Melcher, A. F.: Apparatus for Determining Absorption and Permeability of Oil and Gas Sands for Certain Liquids and Gases under Pressure, *Bull. Am. Assoc. Petroleum Geol.*, vol. 9, pp. 442ff.

Terzaghi, K.: Principles of Soil Mechanics, *Eng. News-Record*, vol. 95, pp. 193ff.
Uren, L. C.: The Elements of the Oil-well Spacing Problem, *Bull. Am. Assoc. Petroleum Geol.*, vol. 9, pp. 193ff.

1927

Kozeny, J.: Über Kapilläre Leitung des Wassers im Boden, *Sitzber. Akad. Wiss. Wien, Math-naturw. kl.*, vol. 136–2*A*, pp. 271ff.
Nutting, P. G.: The Movements of Fluids in Porous Soils, *J. Franklin Inst.*, pp. 314ff.
Stearns, N. D.: Laboratory Tests on Physical Properties of Water Bearing Materials, *USGS Water Supply Paper* 596*F*, pp. 148ff.

1929

Tickell, F. G.: Capillary Phenomena as Related to Oil Production, *Trans. AIME Petroleum Development and Technol.*, pp. 343ff.

1930

Barb, C. F.: Porosity-permeability Relations in Appalachian Oil Sands, *Penn. State Coll. Mineral Ind. Exp. Sta. Bull.* 12.
Gardescu, I. I.: Behavior of Gas Bubbles in Capillary Spaces, *AIME Tech. Pub.* 306.
Nutting, P. G.: Physical Analysis of Oil Sands, *Bull. Am. Assoc. Petroleum Geol.*, vol. 14, no. 10, pp. 1337ff.
Schriever, W.: Law of Flow of the Passage of a Gas-free Liquid through a Spherical Grain Sand, *Trans. AIME Petroleum Development and Technol.*, pp. 329ff.

1931

Richards, L. A.: Capillary Conduction of Liquids through Porous Mediums, *Physics*, vol. 1, pp. 318ff.

1933

Fair, G. M., and L. P. Hatch: Fundamental Factors Governing the Stream Line Flow of Water through Sand, *J. Am. Water Works Assoc.*, vol. 25, pp. 1551ff.
Fancher, G. H., et al.: Some Physical Characteristics of Oil Sands, *Penn. State Coll. Mineral Ind. Exp. Sta. Bull.* 12.

1934

Plummer, F. B., et al.: A New Multiple Permeability Apparatus, *AIME Tech. Pub.* 578.
Wyckoff, R. D., et al.: Measurement of Permeability of Porous Media, *Bull. Am. Assoc. Petroleum Geol.*, vol. 18, no. 2, pp. 161ff.

1936

Clough, K. H.: A Study of Permeability Measurements and Their Application to the Oil Industry, *Oil Weekly*, Sept. 28; Oct. 5, 12, 19, 26; Nov. 2.
Hassler, G. L., et al.: Investigations on the Recovery of Oil from Sandstones by Gas Drive, *Trans. AIME Petroleum Development and Technol.*, pp. 116ff.
Krutter, H. M.: Nomographs for the Calculation of Permeability, *Oil Gas J.*, July 16, pp. 40ff.
Traxler, R. N., and L. A. H. Baum: Permeability of Compacted Powders—Determination of Average Pore Size, *Physics*, vol. 7, pp. 9ff.
Wenzel, L. K.: The Thiem Method of Determining Permeability, *USGS Water Supply Paper* 679*A*.
Wyckoff, R. D., and H. G. Botset: The Flow of Gas-Liquid Mixtures through Unconsolidated Sands, *Physics*, vol. 1, no. 9, pp. 325ff.

1937

Arnquist, W. N.: Note on the Filtering Action of Porous Media, *J. Appl. Phys.*, vol. 8, pp. 363ff.
Bakhmeteff, F., and N. V. Feodoroff: Flow through Granular Media, *J. Appl. Mechanics*, vol. 4, no. 3, pp. A97ff.

Carman, P. C.: Fluid Flow through Granular Beds, *Trans. Inst. Chem. Engrs.* (*London*), vol. 15, pp. 150ff.

Lewis, M. R.: Rate of Flow of Capillary Moisture, *U.S. Dept. Agr. Tech. Bull.* 579.

Muskat, M.: "The Flow of Homogeneous Fluids through Porous Media," McGraw-Hill Book Company, Inc., New York.

Plummer, F. B., and J. S. Woodward: Experiments on the Flow of Fluids through Sands, *Trans. AIME Petroleum Development and Technol.*, pp. 120ff.

Plummer, F. B., et al.: Flow of Mixtures of Oil and Water through Sand, *Oil Gas J.*, Apr. 8, pp. 42ff.

1938

Dunlap, E. N.: Influence of Connate Water on Permeability of Sands to Oil, *AIME Tech. Pub.* 874.

Johnson, T. W., and D. B. Taliaferro: Flow of Air and Natural Gas through Porous Media, *U.S. Bur. Mines Tech. Paper* 592.

Reid, L. S., and R. L. Huntington: Flow of Oil-Gas Mixtures through Unconsolidated Sands, *AIME Tech. Pub.* 874.

1939

Illing, V. C.: Some Factors in Oil Accumulation, *J. Inst. Petroleum*, vol. 25, pp. 201ff.

Leverett, M. C.: Flow of Oil-Water Mixtures through Unconsolidated Sands, *Trans. AIME Petroleum Development and Technol.*, pp. 149ff.

Schoene, H. J.: New Apparatus for the Measurement of Specific Permeability, *Oel u. Kohle*, vol. 15, pp. 67ff.

1940

Botset, H. G.: Flow of Gas-Liquid Mixtures through Consolidated Sand, *AIME Tech. Pub.* 1111.

Hubbert, M. King: The Theory of Ground Water Motion, *J. Geol.*, vol. 48, pp. 785ff.

Leverett, M. C.: Capillary Behavior in Porous Solids, *AIME Tech. Pub.* 1223.

Leverett, M. C., and W. B. Lewis: Steady Flow of Gas-Oil-Water Mixtures through Unconsolidated Sands, *AIME Tech Pub.* 1206.

Richards, L. A.: Concerning Permeability Units for Soils, *Proc. Soil Sci. Soc. Am.*, vol. 5, pp. 49ff.

1941

API Code 27: "Determination of Permeability," 1st ed., 1935; 2d ed., 1941, Dallas, Tex.

Cloud, W. F.: Effect of Grain-size Distribution upon Porosity and Permeability, *Oil Weekly*, Oct. 27, pp. 26ff.

Klinkenberg, L. J.: The Permeability of Porous Media to Liquids and Gases, *API Drill. and Prod. Practice*, pp. 200ff.

Krutter, H., and R. J. Day: Modifications of Permeability Measurements, *Oil Weekly*, Dec. 29, pp. 24ff.

1942

Krumbein, W. C., and G. D. Monk: Permeability as a Function of the Size Parameters of Unconsolidated Sands, *AIME Tech. Pub.* 1492.

Sullivan, R. R., and K. L. Hertel: The Permeability Method for Determining Specific Surface, *Advances in Colloid Sci.*, vol. 1, pp. 36ff.

1943

Grunberg, L., and A. H. Nissan: The Permeability of Porous Solids to Gases and Liquids, *J. Inst. Petroleum*, vol. 29, pp. 236ff.

1944

Hassler, G. L.: "Method and Apparatus for Permeability Measurements," U.S. Patent 2,345,935.

1945

Cardwell, W. T., Jr., and R. L. Parsons: Average Permeabilities of Heterogeneous Oil Sands, *AIME Tech. Pub.* 1852.

Johnston, N., and C. M. Beeson: Water Permeabilities of Reservoir Sands, *AIME Tech. Pub.* 1871.

1946

Jacob, C. E.: Notes on Darcy's Law and Permeability, *Trans. Am. Geophys. Union*, vol. 27, pp. 265ff.

Martinelli, R. C., et al.: Two-phase, Two Component Flow in the Viscous Region, *Trans. Am. Inst. Chem. Engrs.*, vol. 42, pp. 681ff.

Miller, K. T., et al.: Some Permeability Experiments on Cores from the Stevens Sand, Paloma Field, Calif., *Producers Monthly*, November, pp. 31ff.

1947

Brownell, L. E., and D. L. Katz: Flow of Fluids through Porous Media, *Chem. Eng. Progr.*, vol. 43, pp. 601ff.

Calhoun, J. C., and S. T. Yuster: A Study of the Flow of Homogeneous Fluids through Ideal Porous Media, *Producers Monthly*, May, July, August, September.

Henderson, J. H., and S. T. Yuster: Relative Permeability Studies, *Producers Monthly*, vol. 12, pp. 13ff.

Morse, R. A., et al.: Relative Permeability Measurements on Small Core Samples, *Producers Monthly*, August, pp. 19ff.

1948

Henderson, J. H.: Progress Report on Multiplephase Flow Studies, *12th Ann. Tech. Meeting, Penn. State Coll.*

Johnson, W. E., and R. V. Hughes: Directional Permeability Measurements and Their Significance, *12th Ann. Tech. Meeting, Penn. State Coll.*

Rose, W.: Permeability and Gas Slippage Phenomena, *API Drill. and Prod. Practice*, pp. 209ff.

1949

Purcell, W. R.: Capillary Pressures—Their Measurements Using Mercury and the Calculation of Permeability Therefrom, *AIME Tech. Pub.* 2544.

Rose, W.: Theoretical Generalizations Leading to the Evaluation of Relative Permeability, *AIME Tech. Pub.* 2563.

1950

Brownscombe, E. R., et al.: Laboratory Determination of Relative Permeability, *Oil Gas J.*, Feb. 9, pp. 66ff.; Feb. 16, pp. 98ff.

Dykstra, H., and R. L. Parsons: The Prediction of Oil Recovery by Water Flood, *API Secondary Recovery of Oil in the United States*, pp. 160ff.

Griffiths, J. C., and M. A. Rosenfeld: Progress in Measurement of Grain Orientation in Bradford Sand, *Producers Monthly*, vol. 15, pp. 24ff.

Leas, W. J., et al.: Relative Permeability to Gas, *AIME Tech. Pub.* 2810, pp. 65ff.

1951

Branson, U. S., Jr.: Measurement and Use of Permeability Data, *World Oil*, July, pp. 184ff.

Caudle, B. H., et al.: Further Developments in the Laboratory Determination of Relative Permeability, *AIME Tech. Pub.* 3056, pp. 145ff.

Fatt, I., and H. Dykstra: Relative Permeability Studies, *AIME Tech. Pub.* 3078, pp. 249ff.

Fulton, P. F.: The Effect of Gas Slippage on Relative Permeability Measurements, *Producers Monthly*, October, pp. 14ff.

Geffen, T. M., et al.: Experimental Investigation of Factors Affecting Laboratory Relative Permeability Measurements, *AIME Tech. Pub.* 3053, pp. 99ff.

Rapoport, L. A., and W. J. Leas: Relative Permeability to Liquid in Liquid-gas Systems, *AIME Tech. Pub.* 3021, pp. 83ff.

Yuster, S. T.: Theoretical Considerations of Multiple Flow in Idealized Capillary Systems, *Proc. Third World Petroleum Congr.*, Sec. II, pp. 437ff.

1952

Chatenever, A.: An Introduction to Flow of Oil and Water in Porous Media, *Oil Gas J.*, May 26, pp. 174ff.

Josendal, V. A., et al.: Improved Multiphase Flow Studies Employing Radioactive Tracers, *AIME Tech. Pub.* 3284, pp. 65ff.

Richardson, J. G., et al.: Laboratory Determination of Relative Permeability, *AIME Tech. Pub.* 3375, pp. 187ff.

Slobod, R. L., and H. A. Blum: Method for Determining Wettability of Reservoir Rocks, *AIME Tech. Pub.* 3245, pp. 1ff.

1953

Burdine, N. T.: Relative Permeability Calculations from Pore Size Distribution Data, *Trans. AIME*, vol. 198, pp. 71ff.

Fatt, I.: The Effect of Overburden Pressure on Relative Permeability Data, *J. Petroleum Technol.*, vol. 10, October.

Griffiths, J. C.: A Review of Dimensional Orientation of Quartz Grains in Sediments, *Producers Monthly*, January, pp. 14ff.

Hall, H. N.: Compressibility of Reservoir Rocks, *AIME Tech. Note* 149, pp. 17ff.

Osoba, J. S.: Practical Field Application of Relative Permeability Data, *Petroleum Engr., Ref. Annual*, sec. B, pp. 117ff.

Stewart, C. R., et al.: Determination of Limestone Performance Characteristics by Model Flow Tests, *AIME Tech. Pub.* 3517, pp. 93ff.

Wadsworth, A. H., Jr.: Percentage of Thinning Chart—New Technique in Subsurface Geology, *Bull. Am. Assoc. Petroleum Geol.*, vol. 37, no. 1, pp. 158ff.

Wilson, D. A., et al.: A Visual Examination of Fluid Saturations in a Porous Medium, *Oil Gas J.*, May 26, pp. 175ff.

1954

Aronofsky, J. S.: Effect of Gas Slip on Unsteady State Flow of Gas through Porous Media, *J. Appl. Phys.*, vol. 25, no. 1, pp. 48–53.

Corey, A. T.: The Interrelation between Gas and Oil Relative Permeabilities, *Producers Monthly*, Nov. 19, pp. 38ff.

Plaim, G. J., and H. L. Morrison: Critical Reynolds Number and Flow Permeability, *Am. J. Phys.*, vol. 22, no. 3, pp. 143–146.

Rose, W.: Conflicting Ideas on Problem of Relative Permeability, *Petroleum Engr.*, vol. 26, no. 4, pp. B58ff.

Wallick, G. C., and J. S. Aronofsky: Effect of Gas Slip on Unsteady Flow of Gas through Porous Media, Experimental Verification, *AIME Tech. Note* 239.

CHAPTER 3

PETROPHYSICS

Petrophysics is the study of the relationships that exist between physical and textural rock properties. Although the reservoir engineer is mostly interested in porosity, permeability, and fluid saturation of reservoir rocks, there are certain physical properties, such as the formation resistivity factor, the resistivity index, and the hydraulic formation factor (relative permeability), which provide a link between reservoir engineering and well logging and from which derivations may be made leading to the possible determination of relative permeabilities from electric logs. This is of special interest when the reservoir rocks are shaly, for it is then possible to obtain oil and gas production devoid of water even when formation water exists in the pore space to the extent of as much as 60 to 70 per cent.

While electric-log interpretation is mainly concerned with the determination of the presence or absence of oil and gas in the reservoir, ascertaining expected hydrocarbon productivity and reserves from a well or field requires determining certain physical properties of the reservoir rock such as porosity, permeability, and relative permeability to the reservoir fluids. To understand how such properties can be obtained from logs, it is necessary to investigate the theoretical interrelationships of the quantities measured in logging to these basic reservoir properties. This chapter shows how the properties of rocks most commonly used in fluid-flow mechanics and electric-log interpretation are interrelated. It is possible to divide the subject matter of this study into four parts:

1. Petrophysics of clean rocks (water-wet)
2. Petrophysics of clean rocks (oil-wet)
3. Petrophysics of multiple-porosity systems
4. Petrophysics of shaly rocks

PETROPHYSICS OF CLEAN ROCKS (WATER-WET)

Clean rocks, for the purpose of this study, will be considered as devoid of adsorptive reactions with the aqueous fluids they contain or might be receiving through the process of infiltration from drilling fluids or of fluid injection designed to stimulate oil production. The reactions involved (which are presumed absent in this discussion) are mainly between the clay minerals (which may line the pores of rocks) and the waters of varying chemical composition.

Poiseuille's Law

Poiseuille (1846) derived an equation which relates the rate of efflux Q of an incompressible liquid of known viscosity μ through a horizontal straight capillary of length L and radius r under the influence of a pressure differential ΔP.

The starting point of the derivation is the experimental law of viscosity. This law states that the tangential force F expressed in dynes required to maintain a constant difference between the velocities of two parallel layers of a liquid moving in the same direction varies directly with the difference in velocity dv and the area A of the surface of contact of the two layers, and inversely with the distance dx between the layers. The liquid is said to have a viscosity of 1 poise when a force of 1 dyne is required to maintain a velocity difference of 1 cm per sec between two parallel areas of the fluid each 1 sq cm in surface and separated by a distance of 1 cm. This experimental law may be written

$$F_y = -\mu A \frac{dv}{dx} \tag{3-1}$$

where F_y is the component of the force that causes the shearing of the fluid and is measured perpendicular to x. Applying this relation to the flow of fluid in a capillary tube of radius r, length L, and under a pressure differential ΔP:

Shearing force on the fluid tube of radius $x = \Delta P\,(\pi x^2) = -\mu(2\pi x)L\,\dfrac{dv}{dx}$

Separating the variables x and v and integrating between the limits $v = 0$ at r and $v = v$ at x

$$\frac{\Delta P}{2\mu L}\int_r^x x\,dx = -\int_0^v dv$$

or

$$v = \frac{\Delta P}{2\mu L}\,\frac{r^2 - x^2}{2}$$

An infinitesimal rate of flow dQ between radii x and $x + dx$ is given by

$$dQ = v(2\pi x)\,dx$$

Integrating now to obtain the total rate of flow Q,

$$Q = \frac{\pi\Delta P}{2\mu L}\int_0^r (r^2 - x^2)x\,dx = \frac{\pi}{8}\frac{r^4}{\mu}\frac{\Delta P}{L} \tag{3-2}$$

where Q = cc per sec
r = cm
μ = poise
L = cm
ΔP = dynes per sq cm

If we consider a linear porous medium of physical length L and cross-sectional area A as made up of a bundle of n capillaries of average radius $\bar{r}$ and of average length tL where t is a tortuosity coefficient, Poiseuille's law is written

$$Q = \frac{n\pi}{8}\frac{\bar{r}^4}{\mu}\frac{\Delta P}{tL} \tag{3-3}$$

The tortuosity coefficient t is a conceptual dimensionless number representing the departure of a porous system from being made up by a bundle of straight-bore capillaries. It is also in effect a measure of the tortuous path length which a particle of fluid must travel, expressed in terms of the shortest distance between two points on that path.

It is of interest to compare Poiseuille's law with Darcy's law expressed in the same consistent system of units:

$$Q = 1.013A\frac{K}{\mu}\frac{\Delta P}{L} \times 10^{-8} \tag{3-4}$$

where ΔP is expressed in dynes per sq cm, μ in poises, and K in darcys.

Equating (3-3) and (3-4), an expression is found for the permeability K:

$$K = \frac{n\pi\bar{r}^4}{8At} \times \frac{10^8}{1.013} \tag{3-5}$$

Porosity

Volume porosity ϕ_v is the pore-space volume expressed on a bulk-rock-volume basis and for the idealized tortuous system previously discussed. It is given by

$$\phi_v = \frac{n\pi r^2 Lt}{AL} = \frac{n\pi r^2}{A}t \tag{3-6}$$

Surface porosity ϕ_s can be considered as the cross-sectional area of all the pores that are intersected by a plane surface and expressed as a fraction of the total cross-sectional area A of the rock.

In evaluating surface porosity it is necessary to consider the angle at which the surface cuts the axis of the capillaries and to compute the average effect of this section for a random distribution of tortuous capillaries. It has been shown statistically that for a random distribution of capillary sinuosities, surface porosity is equal to volume porosity. Many laboratory experimenters have also shown that the linear rate of advance of fluid, in a core fully saturated by that fluid, is inversely proportional to *volume* porosity, whereas the expectancy is inversely proportional to the *surface* porosity. Therefore, surface porosity is considered equal to volume porosity, and the subscripts to ϕ will be dropped.

Relation between Porosity, Permeability, Tortuosity, and Mean Capillary Radius. By elimination of common symbols between Eqs. (3-2), (3-3), and (3-6), a relation for permeability expressed in darcys is obtained:

$$K = \frac{1}{8}\frac{\phi \bar{r}^2}{t^2} \times 10^8 \tag{3-7}$$

or by solving for the mean pore radius $\bar{r}$

$$\bar{r}_{cm} = \sqrt{\frac{8Kt^2}{\phi}} \times 10^{-4} \tag{3-8}$$

In Eqs. (3-7) and (3-8), the factor 1.033 has been considered equal to unity; this simplification is made throughout.

Specific Surface. The specific surface of a porous material is the total area exposed within the pore space per unit volume. The unit volume may be the solid-mineral framework, in which case the specific surface is represented by S_v. The unit volume may also be pore space, in which case the specific surface is represented by S_ϕ. The two are related by the following expression:

$$S_v = S_\phi \frac{\phi}{1 - \phi} \tag{3-9}$$

For a packing of capillary tubes, on a unit-rock-volume basis

$$S_v = \frac{n(2\pi\bar{r})Lt}{AL(1 - \phi)} = \frac{n(2\pi\bar{r})t}{A(1 - \phi)}$$

where n is the number of capillary tubes; substituting

$$\frac{n\pi\bar{r}}{A} = \frac{\phi}{\bar{r}t}$$

we obtain

$$S_v = \frac{2}{\bar{r}}\frac{\phi}{1 - \phi} \tag{3-10}$$

On a unit-pore-volume basis

$$S_\phi = \frac{n(2\pi\bar{r})Lt}{n(\pi\bar{r}^2)Lt} = \frac{2}{\bar{r}} \tag{3-11}$$

For a packing of spheres, on a unit-rock-volume basis

$$S_v = \frac{n(4\pi\bar{r}^2)}{n(\frac{4}{3}\pi\bar{r}^3)} = \frac{3}{\bar{r}} \tag{3-12}$$

where n is the number of spheres.

On a unit-pore-volume basis

$$S_\phi = \frac{n(4\pi\bar{r}^2)}{n(\frac{4}{3}\pi\bar{r}^3)\phi/(1 - \phi)} = \frac{3}{\bar{r}}\frac{1 - \phi}{\phi} \tag{3-13}$$

Kozeny Equation

A useful expression can be derived by combining Eq. (3-8) with the specific surface relationships derived previously.

1. For capillary tubes or consolidated rocks:
   a. Unit-rock-volume basis:
   Equating values of $\bar{r}$ obtained from (3-8) and (3-10),

$$\bar{r} = \frac{2}{S_v}\frac{\phi}{1-\phi} = \sqrt{\frac{8Kt^2}{\phi}} \times 10^{-4}$$

$$K = \frac{\phi^3}{2t^2S_v{}^2(1-\phi)^2} \times 10^8 \tag{3-14}$$

   b. Unit-pore-volume basis:
   Equating values of $\bar{r}$ obtained from (3-3) and (3-11),

$$\bar{r} = \frac{2}{S_\phi} = \sqrt{\frac{8Kt^2}{\phi}} \times 10^{-4}$$

$$K = \frac{\phi}{2t^2S_\phi{}^2} \times 10^8 \tag{3-15}$$

The above derivations assume that the capillaries of mean radii $\bar{r}$ have no roughness. However, capillary tubes in a porous medium do not have constant cross section, and a shape factor representing the increase in surface caused by successive constrictions should perhaps be introduced into the specific surface expressions. However, it will be assumed that the roughness factor is included in the tortuosity because the simplest method of measuring t, namely, by resistivity formation-factor determination, is inclusive of the shape factor. The coefficient $2t^2$ by analogy could be called the Kozeny constant for consolidated rocks.

2. For packings of spheres or unconsolidated rocks:

It is impossible to derive Kozeny's equation for a packing of spheres as simply as for capillary tubes, because in the case of a packing of spheres the mean hydraulic radius of the capillaries is unknown. Therefore, a derivation of a general nature borrowed from Carman (1939) will be offered. From hydraulic studies, it is known that the internal velocity inside a circular pipe is given by

$$v_i = \frac{\bar{r}^2}{s\mu}\frac{\Delta P}{L} \tag{3-16}$$

where $\bar{r}$ is the mean hydraulic radius and s is a shape factor for the internal roughness of the pipe, the average value of which is 2.5.

Applying (3-16) to a porous medium

$$v_i = \frac{\text{velocity in free space}}{\phi} t$$

Solving for the velocity in free space and expressing it both by Poiseuille's law and Darcy's law

$$\text{Velocity in free space} = \frac{\phi}{t} v_i = \frac{\phi}{t} \frac{\bar{r}^2}{2.5\mu} \frac{\Delta P}{L} = \frac{K}{\mu} \frac{\Delta P}{L} \times 10^{-8}$$

from which

$$K = \frac{\phi}{2.5t} \bar{r}^2 \times 10^8 \tag{3-17}$$

But, by definition, the mean hydraulic radius of a porous body is also the ratio of the pore volume per unit-bulk volume divided by the wetted surface per unit-bulk volume. The latter is $S_v(1 - \phi)$ or $S_\phi \times \phi$. Therefore,

$$\bar{r} = \frac{\phi}{S_v(1 - \phi)} = \frac{1}{S_\phi} \tag{3-18}$$

Substituting (3-18) in (3-17)

$$K = \frac{\phi^3}{2.5tS_v^2(1 - \phi)^2} \times 10^8 = \frac{\phi}{2.5tS_\phi^2} \times 10^8 \tag{3-19}$$

The value $2.5t$ is also called the Kozeny constant for unconsolidated packings and is equal to $2t^2$ previously defined for consolidated rocks. The value of tortuosity t may therefore be readily calculated for unconsolidated sand packing and is 1.25. This figure agrees very closely with experimental determinations for packing of spherical grains. When the grains are nonspherical, a shape factor t_s must be introduced, which has been determined experimentally by Fair and Hatch (1933). The values of these coefficients are given in Table 3-1.

TABLE 3-1. SHAPE FACTORS FOR PACKING OF NONSPHERICAL GRAINS

Grain shape	t_s
Spherical	1.00
Well-rounded	1.02
Worn	1.07
Sharp (subrounded)	1.17
Angular	1.27

Introducing the shape factor into Kozeny's equation, we obtain for unconsolidated granular material

$$K = \frac{\phi^3 \times 10^8}{2.5tt_sS_v^2(1 - \phi)^2} = \frac{\phi \times 10^8}{2.5tt_sS_\phi^2} \tag{3-20}$$

where S_v and S_ϕ are, respectively, the specific surface of the packing on a rock-volume and pore-volume basis.

Flow of Electric Current through Clean Reservoir Rocks

The rocks considered here are sedimentary in origin. The solid framework of such rocks (grains, matrix, and cement) is made up of minerals for the most part nonconductive of electricity, such as quartz, silicates, oxides, carbonates, etc. Sedimentary rocks are conductive of electricity because they are porous and because their interconnected void spaces contain electrically conductive fluids, namely, formation waters: connate water, interstitial water, ground water, and the like.

There are, however, minerals found in sediments which are conductive of electricity, but they are relatively rare; when found they occur in a dispersed and noncontinuous form such as pyrite, magnetite, etc., and have little effect on rock resistivity. An exception exists, however, in the case of glauconite, which is conductive of electricity per se.

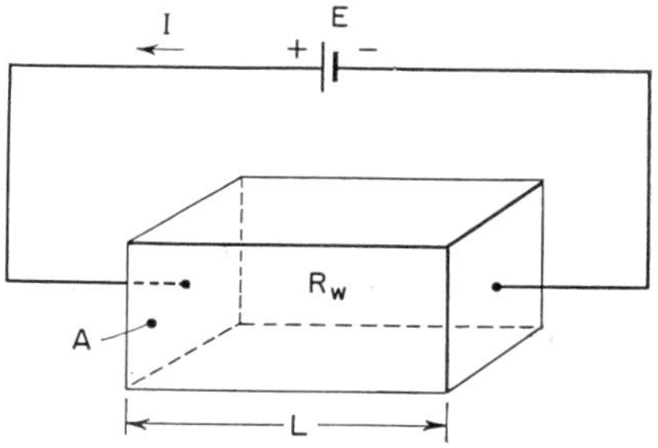

FIG. 3-1. Resistance of a parallelepiped completely filled with salt water.

Formation Resistivity Factor Measurements

Resistivity of Rocks 100 Per Cent Saturated with Formation Waters. Let a boxlike container be completely filled with salty water of resistivity R_w in ohm-meters (Fig. 3-1).

Let the length of the box be L meters and its cross-sectional area be A meters^2. The resistance of the box to the flow of current will be in ohms:

$$R = R_w \frac{L}{A} \tag{3-21}$$

and when a voltage E (in volts) is applied between the sides A, a current I (in amperes) will flow as obtained by Ohm's law:

$$E = RI = R_w \frac{L}{A} I$$

or

$$I = A \frac{1}{R_w} \frac{E}{L} \tag{3-22}$$

This last expression is analogous to Darcy's law for the horizontal flow of fluids.

Now let the box be completely filled with clean sand and salt water of the same resistivity as before (Fig. 3-2). The resistance of the box will be considerably increased, in fact, by a factor called the "resistivity formation factor" F, which always is larger than 1. A new and smaller current I' will now flow such that

$$E = FRI' = FR_w \frac{L}{A} I' \tag{3-23}$$

If we consider as before the resistivity of a unit volume of the box $1m^3$ and call it R_o, Eq. (3-23) may also be written

$$E = R_o \frac{L}{A} I' \tag{3-24}$$

from which

$$R_o = FR_w \tag{3-25}$$

This relation is an important one in electric-log interpretation because if we know R_w in a formation of interest and if its formation factor F is also known, it is possible to calculate the resistivity R_o which it has when fully saturated with formation water. Such a condition, of course, precludes any possibility of oil production.

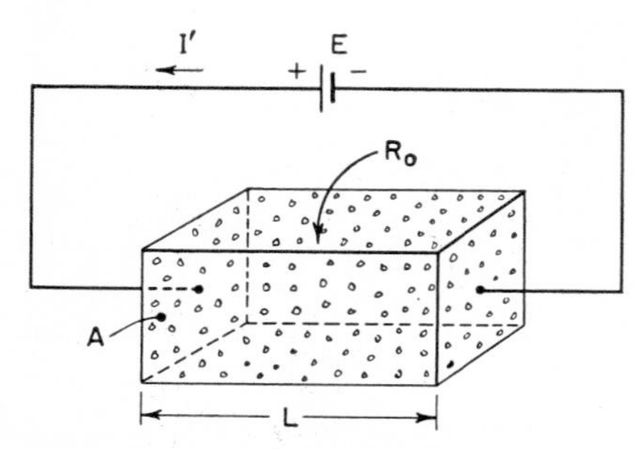

FIG. 3-2. Resistance of a parallelepiped completely filled with clean sand and salt water to 100 per cent saturation of the pore space.

Laboratory Determination of Formation Factors. These determinations are made on small rock-sample plugs used for permeability testing in routine core analysis as well as on full-size cores. The procedure involves two steps:

1. Saturate the core 100 per cent with a synthetic brine of known resistivity R_w at the operating room temperature.

2. Measure the core plug's electric resistance when so saturated. Various saturation methods are possible:

a. Saturation after air evacuation. The water may contain a wetting agent (aerosol) in order to facilitate penetration of the core. Pressure on the water may also be applied later.

b. Salt water may be flowed through the core for some time (10 to 100 pore volumes). However, if the brine is not in chemical equilibrium with the rock minerals, the latter may be dissolved and the porosity increased.

The salinity of the saturating water is of some concern especially in rocks containing clays and other hydratable minerals. Dependable measurements applicable to prevailing formation conditions are likely to be obtained with a brine of the approximate composition of connate water.

Several methods for making the measurements are possible.

1. Clamp the saturated core between two jaws faced with water-saturated porous disks (leather, chamois skin, felt) and pass an a-c current of known intensity i through the core (Fig. 3-3). Apply two prongs of known spacing a in the center of the body of the core and measure the potential drop e between the prongs by means of a vacuum-tube voltmeter which draws a negligible current from the core. The resistivity R_o of the saturated core is obtained from

$$V = \frac{a}{A} R_o i$$

in which A is the cross-sectional area of the core.

The potential drop V could also be measured between the end porous disks, in which case the length of the core L would be substituted for a. F is thereafter obtained from $R_o = R_w F$.

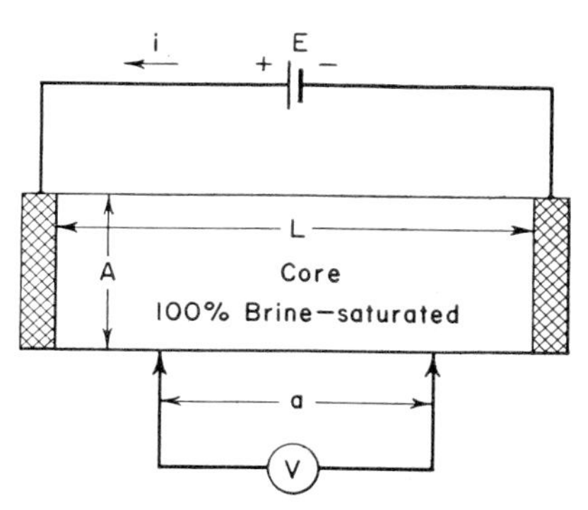

FIG. 3-3. Four-electrode method of measuring formation resistivity factors.

2. Another procedure for measuring formation factors is to saturate the core as above using a special procedure developed in capillary-pressure measurements to maintain the proper degree of wetting on the outside core surface previous to testing. This procedure consists in leaving the cores to rest on a porous capillary diaphragm under which a constant degree of suction prevails (= 10 cm of water). When the proper degree of surface glistening prevails over the core, it is placed in a special core holder of the Hassler design. Mercury contact is made both at the bottom and top of the core. Electric potential-drop measurements are made between the mercury contacts.

3. Formation factors may also be obtained from the electric log itself when a true resistivity value can be obtained in a formation which is known to be 100 per cent saturated in formation or in mud-filtrate water of a known resistivity. Such methods will be discussed later.

Lithologic Factors That Affect the Value of Formation Factors. As was observed before, the formation-resistivity factor is a dimensionless quantity by which the resistivity of formation water is to be multiplied in order to obtain the resistivity of the rock when 100 per cent saturated in formation water.

The mineral framework of most rocks, including sedimentary rocks and especially in clean rocks, is nonconductive of electricity. Therefore, the saturated rock conducts electricity by virtue of the salty waters it contains in its pores. It is natural that the total volume of such pores per unit-bulk-volume of rock (i.e., porosity ϕ) should be a main factor in controlling the passage of current. Whereas porosity controls the volume of fluid through which electricity may flow, the rock induration (or cementation) and the grain-size distribution control the size of the interconnected pores and of their tortuosity. Various formulas have been proposed to relate the formation factor F to the lithological factors of porosity ϕ and cementation. Only two, both of which are empirical, have survived the test of usefulness:

Archie's formula: $$F = \phi^{-m} \quad (3\text{-}26)$$

Humble's formula: $$F = 0.62\phi^{-2.15} \quad (3\text{-}27)$$

In Archie's formula, the exponent m, called the "cementation factor," varies with the degree of consolidation of the rocks, as indicated in Table 3-2. It permits the selection of the proper value of m from a lithologic

TABLE 3-2. CEMENTATION FACTOR (m) AND LITHOLOGY

Rock description	*m values*
Unconsolidated rocks (loose sands, oölitic limestones)	1.3
Very slightly cemented (Gulf Coast type of sand, except Wilcox)	1.4–1.5
Slightly cemented (most sands with 20% porosity or more)	1.6–1.7
Moderately cemented (highly consolidated sands of 15% porosity or less)	1.8–1.9
Highly cemented (low-porosity sands, quartzite, limestone, dolomite of intergranular porosity, chalk)	2.0–2.2

description of the rock of interest. Figure 3-4 permits the direct reading of the formation factor.

The Humble formula for the evaluation of the formation factor has the advantage of not requiring the selection of a value of m and includes the empirical observation that rocks of high porosity have low values of m and those of low porosity have high values of m. For comparison the Humble formula is drawn on Fig. 3-4.

Resistivity of Rocks Partially Saturated with Formation Waters. When oil and gas, which are nonconductors of electricity, are present within a porous rock together with a certain amount of salty formation water, its resistivity is larger than R_o since there is less available volume for the flow of electric current. The available volume of water to current flow is designated as its saturation in the pore space. It is represented by σ_{wc}.

Resistivity of a partially water-saturated rock depends not only on the value of σ_{wc} but also on its distribution within the pore space. The fluid-phase distribution within the rocks depends on the wetting properties of the rock, on the direction in which it was established (drainage or imbibition), and on the type of porosity (whether intergranular, vuggy, or both). Figure 3-5 gives an idea of how the ratio R_t/R_o varies as a function of saturation. Curves 1 and 2 are for sands the slope of which is 2 for the first and 1.8 for the second. These slopes are called "saturation exponent" or n. Curve 3 is for oil-wet sand, in which case the value of n is variable with saturation and the degree of wetting.

The generally accepted formula which relates connate water saturations

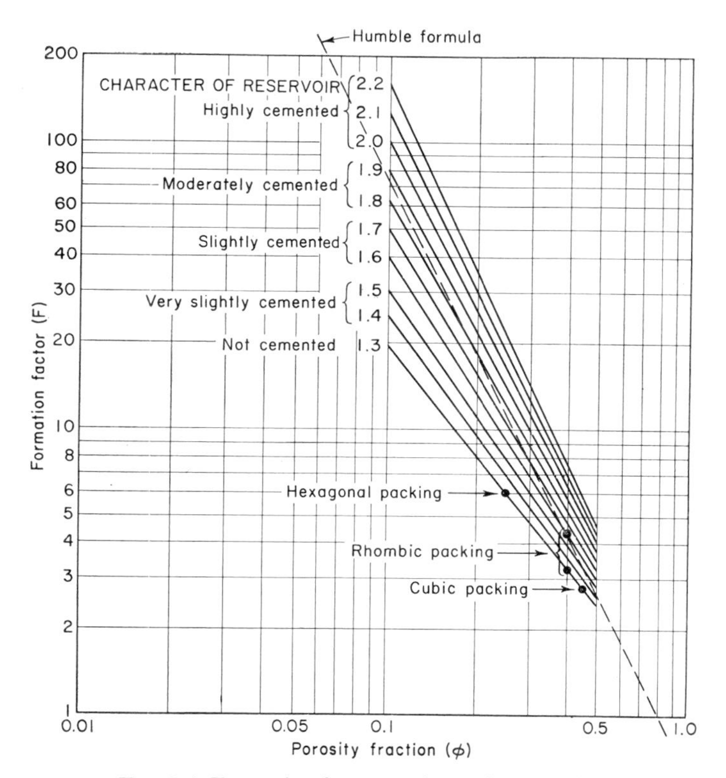

FIG. 3-4. Formation factor vs. formation porosity.

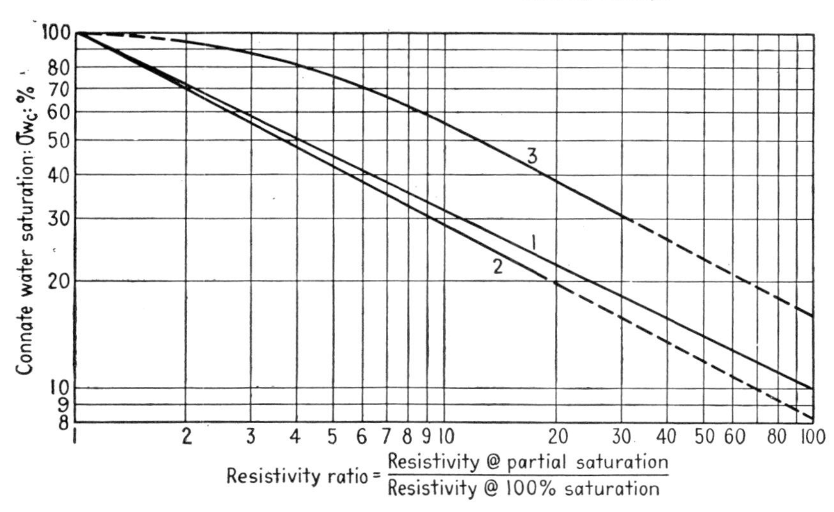

FIG. 3-5. Connate water saturation vs. resistivity ratios. Curve 1 is a composite of data from Wyckoff, Leverett, Jakosky, and Martin; curve 2 is for brine-air displacement results of Morse et al. on artificially consolidated sands; curve 3 is for brine-oil displacement results.

σ_{wc} and true resistivity R_t is that of Archie (1942–1947), which may be written in the following different forms:

$$\sigma_{wc} = \sqrt[n]{\frac{R_o}{R_t}} = \sqrt[n]{\frac{R_{wc}F}{R_t}} = \sqrt[n]{\frac{R_{wc}\phi^{-m}}{R_t}} \qquad (3\text{-}28)$$

n is the saturation exponent, the value of which is most generally assumed to be 2.0.

Saturation-exponent (n) Measurements. Laboratory methods for determining saturation exponents require measurement of electrical con-

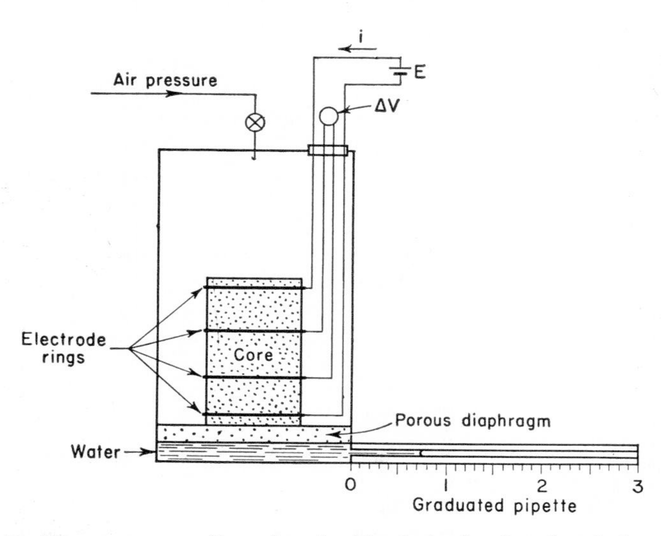

FIG. 3-6. Capillary-pressure cell equipped with electrodes for electrical-conductivity measurements and saturation-exponent determination.

ductivity of a rock at partial saturation, this saturation corresponding to the same fluid distribution as *in situ*.

The Atlantic Refining Company laboratory (Dunlap, 1949) makes the measurements at various stages of water desaturation in a capillary-pressure cell (Fig. 3-6). A core of known bulk volume and porosity is initially saturated with brine and placed in capillary contact with the porous diaphragm of a capillary-pressure cell. Increments of air pressure desaturate the core, the volumes of displaced water being measured in a graduated pipette. The core is provided with four electrode rings substantially equally spaced and between any two of which the potential drop can be measured. In this way saturation anomalies or end effect can be ascertained. Average water saturations are calculated at each stage of desaturation. A plot such as that in Fig. 3-5 is made, from which n is computed. The results reported by Atlantic show wide discordance, and it is known that difficulties are encountered which result from a lack of electrical contact between the electrode rings and the fluid network in the core pore space.

Another method uses the same apparatus and technique as devised for the two-electrode method of formation-factor measurements already described. Before testing, the samples are desaturated in a capillary-pressure cell to various saturation stages and weighed before and after electrical measurements so that possible loss in saturation during measurements can be ascertained.

Birks (1954) has suggested a novel method of determining the resistivity-water-saturation characteristics of cores. This method makes use of the water evaporation from a core originally fully saturated with a water containing saturated calcium sulfate in solution (i.e., ready to precipitate its salts at the temperature of the measurements). The water solubility of $CaSO_4$ at room temperature is about 0.2 per cent by weight. Previous to saturation the core plugs must be extracted with distilled water to remove all traces of salt. If the cores should contain anhydrite, they should be extracted with water containing $CaCO_3$ to prevent the removal of anhydrite. After bulk-volume and porosity determination, the saturated cores are placed in a stream of dry air so that their interstitial water will be evaporated. In one-half hour a 10 per cent water-saturation reduction can be achieved. Solid $CaSO_4$ will precipitate inside the porous network but, because of the minute volume of precipitation, the pore volume is considered unchanged. The water resistivity also remains unchanged since the solution remains saturated. It is believed that capillary equilibrium is obtained at all times. A reliable relation between water saturation and resistivity is expected. Measurement of resistivity can be made at the various desaturation stages by means of the two- or four-electrode method. Measurements over a complete saturation range can be obtained in a 12-hr period.

Tortuosity Determination. There are three methods by which tortuosity of rock capillaries can be determined.

1. The simplest method is by computation from the values of formation factor and porosity.

For consolidated rocks, where the porosity may be represented by tortuous capillaries of length tL and ending in number n in a cross-sectional area A, a theoretical expression for the formation factor F can be derived as follows:

$$R = R_o \frac{L}{A} = R_w \frac{tL}{n(\pi \bar{r}^2)} = R_w \frac{t^2 L}{A\phi} \qquad (3\text{-}29)$$

where R is the resistance of a cylindrical core sample of length L and cross-sectional area A and R_o is resistivity of the rock at 100 per cent water saturation of resistivity R_w.

Thus $$R_o = R_w \frac{t^2}{\phi} = FR_w$$

and $$t^2 = F\phi \qquad (3\text{-}30)$$

Formula (3-30) provides a ready laboratory means of determining t^2 since both porosity and formation-factor measurements are easily made with good accuracy.

2. Winsauer et al. (1952) have proposed a measurement of tortuosity by ionic transit-time studies. Core samples are saturated first with sodium nitrate solution and placed in contact at one end with a sodium chloride solution. The chloride ion is forced to migrate from one end of the core to the other under the application of a constant potential difference. The appearance of the chloride ion at the end of the core is easily detected by means of a chloride-sensitive electrode. The tortuosity factor is determined by comparison with similar transit-time measurements in straight capillary channels formed by glass rods embedded in a plastic cylinder of the same size as the core samples. Many results are given in the original paper which verify that the equation $t^2 = F\phi$ gives the right order of magnitude for tortuosity. The same technique was used by Perkins et al. (1956) and substantially proved the validity of Eq. (3-35) to be derived.

A similar method had been proposed by Garrels et al. (1949) which makes use of ionic diffusion through intergranular spaces in water-saturated rocks. It is shown in this study that the rate of advance of a given concentration front is independent of permeability or porosity. However, the amount of material transferred depends on the porosity in the direction of diffusion. Therefore, the ionic movement through rock pores takes place independently of the size of the pores, provided they are in size at least two to three times the ionic diameter. Garrels introduced the concept of an *effective directional porosity*, which in effect is porosity divided by tortuosity. The apparatus consists of a cell composed of two compartments separated by a slice of the rock a few millimeters thick. A similar cell had been previously suggested by Gordon (1945). Klinkenberg (1951) suggested that diffusional and electrical tortuosities in rock are identical from a theoretical standpoint, since the two processes of ionic flow are governed by identical equations. In addition, Klinkenberg suggested a gaseous-diffusion method for measuring tortuosity which may be applicable to measurement of the effective tortuosity at partial liquid saturation.

3. A third method suggests making use of the streaming potential for the determination of tortuosity. The derivation of the theory that justifies this approach is based on Perrin's (1904) streaming-potential equation as applied to a porous rock by making use of the tortuous-capillary model. The Perrin equation is as follows:

$$E_s = \frac{D\zeta R_w \, \Delta P}{4\pi\mu} \times 10^{-7} \tag{3-31}$$

where E_s = streaming potential, volts
D = dielectric constant of the flowing liquid
R_w = its resistivity, ohm-cm
ΔP = pressure differential, dynes per sq cm
μ = fluid viscosity, poise
ζ = zeta potential of the substance of the core with respect to the flowing liquid

The Perrin equation indicates that the streaming potential E_s created by the application of pressure differential ΔP is independent of the distance between the points of application of ΔP and of the porosity and permeability of the medium. The potential is, however, dependent upon the fluid properties: dielectric constant, resistivity, and viscosity. The zeta potential is a function of the surface properties of the medium.

Combining the Perrin equation with a modified expression of flow rate Q which can readily be derived by electrochemical considerations:

$$Q = \frac{A\phi E_s \zeta D}{4\pi\mu t^2 L}$$

By eliminating the zeta potential and solving for the tortuosity coefficient

$$t^2 = \frac{\phi A}{L} \frac{E_s^2}{QR_w \, \Delta P} \times 10^7 \tag{3-32}$$

Equation (3-32) permits the evaluation of tortuosity since all quantities in the second term of the equation are measurable on test samples.

By combining with Eq. (3-30) and eliminating tortuosity

$$F = \frac{A}{L} \frac{E_s^2}{QR_w \, \Delta P} \times 10^7 \tag{3-33}$$

an expression for the formation factor is found which permits evaluation of the order of magnitude of streaming potential E_s in wells, F being the formation factor of the mud cake, Q/A the filter loss rate, L the mud-cake thickness, R_w the mud-filtrate resistivity, and ΔP the differential pressure between well and formation.

Effective Tortuosity. In a completely brine-saturated rock, the passage of electric current is not expected to take place effectively through the full volume of brine. This is analogous to fluid flow in porous media at 100 per cent saturation where all the fluid is not movable. The nonmovable brine is the irreducible water saturation σ_{wi}. Passage of fluid and electric current through pore space is presumably taking place through identical paths, and the irreducible water saturation, which occupies cross capillaries through which there is neither pressure differential nor potential drop, looks to either phenomenon like nonconductive mineral framework. Tortuosity at irreducible water saturation can then be written

$$t^2 = F\phi(1 - \sigma_{wi}) \tag{3-34}$$

The concept of effective tortuosity t_e takes in another aspect when partial brine saturation σ_{wc} prevails in a water-wet rock, for in this situation the nonwetting phase is nonconductive of electricity. An effective formation factor F_e can then be written

$$t_e^2 = F_e\phi(\sigma_{wc} - \sigma_{wi}) \tag{3-35}$$

Since the ratio F/F_e is also the ratio $R_o/R_t = 1/I$ where I is the resistivity index at a particular brine saturation, the following relationship can be written:

$$\frac{F}{F_e} = \frac{R_o}{R_t} = \frac{t_e^2}{t^2} \frac{1 - \sigma_{wi}}{\sigma_{wc} - \sigma_{wi}} \tag{3-36}$$

This relationship can be compared to the empirical relation of Archie (3-28) previously discussed.

For consistency, the capillary-radius formula (3-8) must be changed to

$$\bar{r} = \sqrt{\frac{8Kt^2}{\phi(1 - \sigma_{wi})}} \times 10^{-4} \tag{3-37}$$

Similar adjustment should be made in the Kozeny equations.

Figure 3-7 permits the determination of σ_{wi} once porosity and permeability are known.

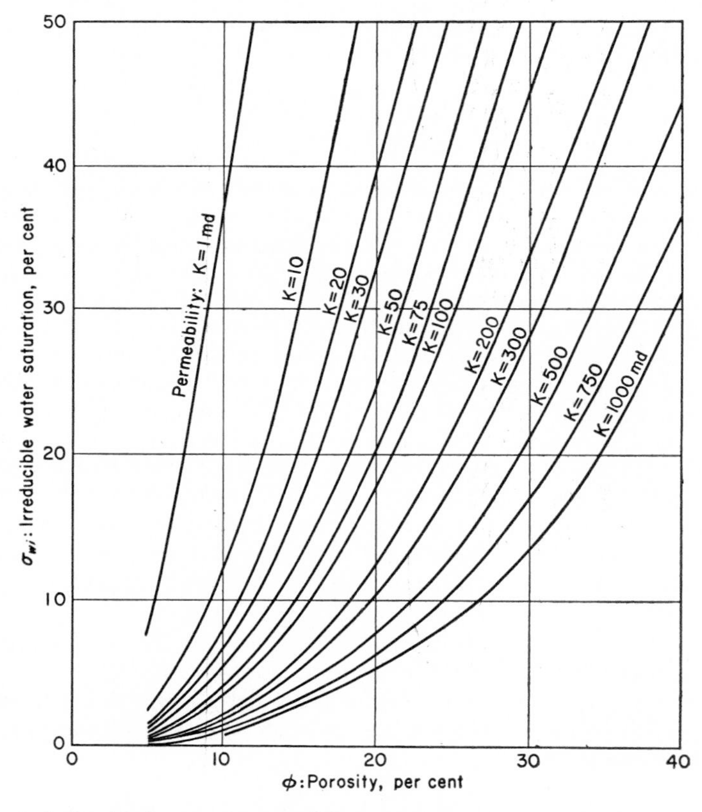

FIG. 3-7. Relationship between permeability-porosity and irreducible water saturation for clean sands.

Hydraulic Formation Factor and Index

By analogy with the formation-resistivity factor, the hydraulic formation factor F_h may be written

$$F_h = \frac{\text{Darcy flow rate}}{\text{Poiseuille flow rate through } \pi R^2} = \frac{(\pi R^2)\dfrac{K}{\mu}\dfrac{\Delta P}{L} \times 10^{-8}}{\dfrac{\pi R^4}{8\mu}\dfrac{\Delta P}{L}}$$

$$= \frac{8K}{R^2} \times 10^{-8} \tag{3-38}$$

where R is the radius of a test core. But

$$\frac{\pi R^2 \phi(1 - \sigma_{wi})}{\pi \bar{r}^2} = nt = \frac{R^2\phi(1 - \sigma_{wi})}{8Kt^2/[\phi(1 - \sigma_{wi})]} \times 10^8 = \frac{R^2\phi^2(1 - \sigma_{wi})^2}{8t^2K} \times 10^8$$

from which

$$F_h = \frac{\phi^2(1 - \sigma_{wi})^2}{nt^3} \tag{3-39}$$

n is the total number of capillaries, all of them being occupied by the wetting fluid.

At partial saturation in the wetting fluid σ_{wc}, an effective hydraulic formation factor F_{he} may be conceived to exist, and by analogy to Eq. (3-39), an expression for it is

$$F_{he} = \frac{\phi^2(\sigma_{wc} - \sigma_{wi})^2}{n_e t_e^{\,3}} \tag{3-40}$$

where n_e is the number of capillaries occupied by the wetting phase and t_e is their tortuosity. Similarly for the nonwetting phase, one may write by analogy

$$F_{hnw} = \frac{\phi^2(1 - \sigma_{wc})^2}{n_{nw} t_{nw}^{\,3}} \tag{3-41}$$

where n_{nw} is the number of capillaries occupied by the nonwetting phase and t_{nw} is their tortuosity.

The effective hydraulic index I_{eh} for the wetting phase is by analogy the ratio of (3-40) to (3-39), which is also by definition the *relative permeability k_w to the wetting phase*, or

$$I_{eh} = k_w = \frac{F_{he}}{F_h} = \frac{n}{n_e}\left(\frac{t}{t_e}\right)^3 \left(\frac{\sigma_{wc} - \sigma_{wi}}{1 - \sigma_{wi}}\right)^2 \tag{3-42}$$

Similarly, the *relative permeability to the nonwetting phase* k_{nw} is obtained by dividing (3-41) by (3-39):

$$k_{nw} = \frac{n}{n_{nw}} \left(\frac{t}{t_{nw}}\right)^3 \left(\frac{1 - \sigma_{wc}}{1 - \sigma_{wi}}\right)^2 \tag{3-43}$$

The ratio $(\sigma_{wc} - \sigma_{wi})/(1 - \sigma_{wi})$ is called the *free-wetting-phase* saturation σ_{wf} and when substituted in (3-42) and (3-43), we have

$$\begin{aligned} k_w &= \frac{n}{n_e} \left(\frac{t}{t_e}\right)^3 \sigma_{wf}^2 \\ k_{nw} &= \frac{n}{n_{nw}} \left(\frac{t}{t_{nw}}\right)^3 (1 - \sigma_{wf})^2 \end{aligned} \tag{3-44}$$

The formulas (3-44) are fully general and are valid whether the saturation changes are by *imbibition* or by *drainage*. However, they are not useful as such and it is necessary to eliminate from them the number of capillaries involved and the tortuosity coefficients in order to obtain practical relative-permeability formulas.

Relative Permeability to the Wetting Phase k_w. *Imbibition Direction.* When the wetting phase is increased from a low saturation value (i.e., from the irreducible saturation σ_{wi}) all the capillaries acquire simultaneously a movable wetting-phase saturation. Hence we have $n = n_e = n_{nw}$ and

$$k_w = \left(\frac{t}{t_e}\right)^3 \sigma_{wf}^2$$

Substituting the value of t/t_e from (3-36)

$$\underset{\text{(imbibition)}}{k_w} = \sigma_{wf}^{1/2} \left(\frac{R_o}{R_t}\right)^{3/2} \tag{3-45}$$

Drainage Direction. When the wetting-phase saturation is decreased because of the injection of a nonwetting phase starting with 100 per cent wetting-phase saturation, the largest capillaries are originally occupied by nonwetting fluid, then the next largest, and so on. At any intermediate saturation, the distribution of fluids may be visualized as being in two bundles of capillaries, one occupied by nonwetting and the other by wetting fluid. Hence we have the relation $n = n_e + n_{nw}$.

It is no longer possible to eliminate the number of capillaries involved from Eq. (3-44), and after substitution of t/t_e from (3-36)

$$\underset{\text{(drainage)}}{k_w} = \frac{n}{n_e} \sigma_{wf}^{1/2} \left(\frac{R_o}{R_t}\right)^{3/2} \tag{3-46}$$

Equations (3-45) and (3-46) differ only by the ratio of the number of capillaries n/n_e. From laboratory investigations it has been shown that k_w (drainage) and k_w (imbibition) show very little deviation from one another and that such deviation as there is may be considered to be due to errors of measurements. Hence in the drainage direction $n \cong n_e$, and a single relative-permeability formula (3-45) may be used for the wetting phase.

Relative Permeability to the Nonwetting Phase k_{nw}. *Imbibition Direction.* In the imbibition direction, the wetting-phase saturation accretion occurs simultaneously in all the capillaries because the small capillaries are already saturated at the start of imbibition in the wetting phase (i.e., the irreducible wetting-phase saturation σ_{wi}). Because of the large degree of interconnection between the capillaries of all sizes, the wetting-phase saturation increases simultaneously in all of them and the nonwetting phase becomes constricted in all the pores simultaneously, giving rise to coaxial flow of both phases within a certain range of saturation changes. The nonwetting-fluid saturation distribution must not be considered to be made up of filaments of constant cross section, but rather the nonwetting phase is a succession of inflations and constrictions connected along the capillaries' axes. As the wetting-phase saturation increases farther in the imbibition direction, the constrictions become very narrow and eventually break down, leaving an insular nonwetting bubble in each pore enlargement. When all the filaments are broken in their continuity, permeability to the nonwetting phase ceases, although a large residual saturation to the nonwetting phase may be present. It will be represented by σ_{nwt} and is called the *trapped nonwetting-phase saturation.*

According to the above physical concept of the nonwetting-phase distribution in a porous medium during imbibition, $n = n_{nw}$ in Eq. (3-44). In addition the tortuosity of the nonwetting filaments, which have the same axes as that of the capillaries themselves, is equal to the tortuosity at 100 per cent saturation: $t_{nw} = t$. Therefore

$$\underset{\text{(imbibition)}}{k_{nw}} = (1 - \sigma_{wf})^2$$

The expression $1 - \sigma_{wf}$ represents the free nonwetting-phase saturation. In the limit when $k_{nw} = 0$ at the trapped nonwetting-phase saturation, the formula must yet be valid; hence the formula for k_{nw} should have the form

$$\underset{\text{(imbibition)}}{k_{nw}} = \left(1 - \frac{\sigma_{wc} - \sigma_{wi}}{1 - \sigma_{wi} - \sigma_{nwt}}\right)^2 \tag{3-47}$$

An approach has been suggested by Albert and Butault (1952) whereby σ_{nwt} can be evaluated from a knowledge of the capillary size distribution, as can be obtained by means of a capillary-pressure curve run with either a wetting fluid or with a nonwetting fluid such as mercury (Purcell method). In effect the method states the residual nonwetting-phase saturation σ_{nwt}, after the passage of a displacing wetting phase, is two-thirds of the net pore-space volume made up of capillaries of smaller radii than the most common capillary size. The most common capillary size is that corresponding to a maximum on the derivative of the capillary-pressure curve. It may also be recognized as corresponding to the plateau of a capillary-pressure curve. The net pore-space volume is then the volume or saturation comprised between the P_c plateau and the irreducible water saturation σ_{wi}. The value of two-thirds has a theoretical significance, as when imbibition takes place in capillaries of different sizes, the volume noninvaded at any one time is two-thirds of the total volume invaded measured by the maximum linear advances in the largest capillary. This is by virtue of Poiseuille's law, since the imbibition rate is proportional to r^4 and the fluid velocity in the capillary is inversely proportional to r^2. When the rates of advance are lined up in order of increasing capillary radius, the locus of these advances is a parabola representing the volume invaded, which is half as large as the noninvaded volume.

According to the simplified reasoning of Albert, the occluded nonwetting-phase saturation could never be any larger than about 60 per cent of pore space, which figure is borne out by experience.

Another approach to the determination of the irreducible, trapped, or occluded nonwetting-phase saturation is simply to calculate it by the method of displacement-efficiency determination established for frontal drives using the relative-permeability curve established in the drainage direction. This saturation would then appear to be a function of the fluid-viscosity ratio, dip, and rate. This question is not yet solved.

Another way of determining the trapped nonwetting-phase saturation *in situ* is by means of microresistivity logging devices, which respond to fluid conditions as they exist in the flushed zone around a well bore. These methods will be studied in Chap. 5 but the formula of interest will nevertheless be given here:

$$\sigma_{nwt} = 1 - \frac{1}{\phi}\left(\frac{R_{mf}}{R_{xo}}\right)^{1/2} \tag{3-48}$$

where ϕ is the porosity of the reservoir rock and R_{mf}/R_{wc} is a value related to the SP-curve deflection (and is the ratio of the mud-filtrate resistivity R_{mf} to flushed zone resistivity R_{xo}).

It is possible that the trapped nonwetting-phase saturation is a function of the fluid properties of the trapped phase such as viscosity, surface tension, etc., as it is known that in a water-wet rock the trapped saturation is different for oil and gas.

Drainage Direction. In the drainage direction the desaturation in the wetting phase occurs gradually from individually larger capillaries toward smaller ones. At any one condition of liquid saturation, the nonwetting phase is found in the largest capillaries and the wetting phase in the smaller capillaries.

Let S_{nw} represent the specific surface of the nonwetting phase on a pore-space basis. The volume of the pores having a surface S_{nw} is the reciprocal of S_{nw}. Let S_w represent the specific surface of the wetting phase on a pore-space basis. The volume of the pores having a surface S_w is the reciprocal of S_w. Let S_{wi} represent the specific surface of the porous medium with irreducible wetting phase present. The total pore-space volume not occupied by irreducible water is the reciprocal of S_{wi} and is the sum of the two preceding volumes:

$$\frac{1}{S_{wi}} = \frac{1}{S_{wc}} + \frac{1}{S_{nw}} \tag{3-49}$$

But

$$\frac{2}{S_{wi}} = \bar{r}_{wi} \qquad \frac{2}{S_{wc}} = \bar{r}_w \qquad \frac{2}{S_{nw}} = \bar{r}_{nw} \tag{3-50}$$

Hence Eq. (3-49) becomes after substitution

$$\bar{r}_{wi} = \bar{r}_w + \bar{r}_{nw} \tag{3-51}$$

From Eq. (3-35) it is possible to write equations analogous to Eq. (3-37) for the mean capillary radii of the wetting and nonwetting phases:

$$\bar{r}_w = \sqrt{\frac{8K_w t_e^2}{\phi(\sigma_{wc} - \sigma_{wi})}} \times 10^{-4} \quad \text{and} \quad \bar{r}_{nw} = \sqrt{\frac{8K_{nw} t_{nw}^2}{\phi(1 - \sigma_{wc})}} \times 10^{-4} \tag{3-52}$$

Combining Eqs. (3-37) and (3-52) we have

$$\frac{\bar{r}_w}{\bar{r}_{wi}} = \frac{t_e}{t}\sqrt{\frac{k_w}{\sigma_{wf}}} \quad \text{and} \quad \frac{\bar{r}_{nw}}{\bar{r}_{wi}} = \frac{t_{nw}}{t}\sqrt{\frac{k_{nw}}{1 - \sigma_{wf}}} \tag{3-53}$$

Substituting (3-53) into (3-51) we have

$$\frac{t_{nw}}{t}\sqrt{\frac{k_{nw}}{1 - \sigma_{wf}}} + \frac{t_e}{t}\sqrt{\frac{k_w}{\sigma_{wf}}} = 1 \tag{3-54}$$

From (3-36) we have

$$\frac{t_e}{t} = \sigma_{wf}^{1/2}\left(\frac{R_o}{R_t}\right)^{1/2}$$

which when substituted in (3-54) and after solving for the nonwetting-phase relative permeability, yields

$$\underset{\text{(drainage)}}{k_{nw}} = (1 - \sigma_{wf})\left(\frac{t}{t_{nw}}\right)^2\left[1 - \sigma_{wf}^{1/4}\left(\frac{R_o}{R_t}\right)^{1/4}\right]^2 \tag{3-55}$$

It does not appear that t/t_{nw} can be evaluated independently but it is reasonable to postulate that t and t_{nw} should be substantially the same, as the tortuosity of the bundle of largest capillary sizes controls to a large extent the value of the tortuosity at full saturation. This is because the capillary tubes act as conducting circuits in parallel. When adding, in parallel, circuits of low conductance (small capillaries) to highly conductive circuits (large capillaries), the former change the over-all conductance relatively little. Hence, the formula for the relative permeability to the nonwetting phase in the *drainage direction* is

$$\underset{\text{(drainage)}}{k_{nw}} = (1 - \sigma_{wf}) \left[1 - \sigma_{wf}^{1/4} \left(\frac{R_o}{R_t} \right)^{1/4} \right]^2 \tag{3-56}$$

It appears that there are three fundamental equations useful in predicting relative-permeability characteristics from electrical measurements on clean rocks at full and partial saturation in an electrically conductive fluid, namely, Eq. (3-45) for the wetting phase, valid regardless of the direction of saturation changes; Eq. (3-47) for the nonwetting phase in the imbibition direction; and Eq. (3-56) for the nonwetting phase in the drainage direction. The formulas were derived, however, for the case when the wetting phase is electrically conductive (i.e., water in a water-wet rock). More general formulas for relative permeability in *clean water-wet rock* can be written as follows, after substitution of Archie's relationship:

$$k_w = \sigma_{wf}^{1/2} \sigma_{wc}^{3}$$

$$\underset{\text{(imbibition)}}{k_{nw}} = \left(1 - \frac{\sigma_{wc} - \sigma_{wi}}{1 - \sigma_{wi} - \sigma_{nwt}} \right)^2 \tag{3-57}$$

$$\underset{\text{(drainage)}}{k_{nw}} = (1 - \sigma_{wf})(1 - \sigma_{wf}^{1/4} \sigma_{wc}^{1/2})^2$$

Capillary-pressure Relationships

Capillary pressure, P_c, is the differential pressure that exists between two fluid phases at their interface when they are distributed under static equilibrium within a porous material. Considering oil and water as the two fluids, the following relationship exists between the measurable physical properties of rocks and fluids:

$$P_c = \gamma \left(\frac{2}{r} \right) \cos \theta = gh(\vartheta_w - \vartheta_o) \tag{3-58}$$

where γ = interfacial tension, dynes per cm
r = capillary radius, cm
θ = angle of contact of the wetting phase measured through the liquid
g = acceleration of gravity, cm per sq sec
h = height above free water surface, cm
ϑ_w = density of water, g-mass per cu cm
ϑ_o = density of oil g-mass per cu cm
P_c = capillary pressure, dynes per sq cm

In addition to the above relationships, P_c is known to be a function of fluid saturation and of the direction of change of fluid saturation, whether by *drainage* or *imbibition*. In drainage, the fluid distribution is of the channel type; in imbibition, of the coaxial type.

Wettability Determinations. Relationship with the drainage curve will be considered.

While formula (3-58) is written for a particular value of P_c and a corresponding radius r of the capillary swept out by the application of that pressure, let us consider the mean capillary-pressure value $\bar{P}_c$ and the mean capillary radius $\bar{r}$ to which relation (3-58) applies.

By substitution of the values of $\bar{r}$ and t^2, an expression useful for the evaluation of the angle of contact θ is obtained:

$$\cos\theta = \frac{\bar{P}_c}{\gamma}\sqrt{2KF(1-\sigma_{wi})} \times 10^{-4} \tag{3-59}$$

The angle and degree of wetting of a fluid inside a core may therefore be evaluated from simple physical laboratory measurements of $\bar{P}_c$, γ, K, and F. By way of example, let $\bar{P}_c = 2$ psi, $\gamma = 34.5$ dynes per cm, $K = 0.1$ darcy, $F = 20$, $\sigma_{wi} = 0.2$, $\cos\theta = 0.7$, and θ calculates to be 45°. The angle θ may be considered as a measure of rock wettability, for when $\theta = 0$, the rock is fully wet by the liquid phase closest to the rock surface. When $\theta = 90°$, the wetting by either phase present is indifferent.

Interfacial Area and Relative Permeability. By definition, interfacial tension is the change in free energy per unit surface: $dF = \gamma\, dS$. In a unit-rock volume of porosity ϕ and saturation σ_w, let us say that the area of the interface is S. Let a change in water saturation $d\sigma_w$ take place corresponding to the change in interfacial area dS. The change in volume energy which is also the change in free energy is $dF = -\phi(P_w - P_o)\, d\sigma_w$, where P_o is the pressure in the oil and P_w the pressure in the water. $P_c = P_w - P_o$. Hence

$$dF = -\phi P_c\, d\sigma_w = \gamma\, dS \tag{3-60}$$

or

$$dS = -\frac{\phi}{\gamma} P_c\, d\sigma_w \tag{3-61}$$

The interfacial area between oil and water at any specific saturation σ_{wc} per unit volume of pore space is therefore obtained by

$$S_{wc} = -\frac{1}{\gamma}\int_{\sigma_w=100}^{\sigma_w} P_c\, d\sigma_w \tag{3-62}$$

The specific surface (unit-pore-volume basis) for texturally nonuniform rock at the irreducible water saturation σ_{wi} is

$$S_{wi} = -\frac{1}{\gamma}\int_{\sigma_w=100}^{\sigma_{wi}} P_c\, d\sigma_w \tag{3-63}$$

These formulas are valid whether the saturation changes are obtained by drainage or by imbibition. The specific surface to the nonwetting phase

S_{nw} in each case can be deducted from the pertinent form of the additive properties of specific surfaces.

For the drainage direction

$$\frac{1}{S_{wi}} = \frac{1}{S_{wc}} + \frac{1}{S_{nw}} \tag{3-64}$$

For the imbibition direction

$$\frac{1}{S_{wi}} = \frac{1}{S_{wc}} + \frac{1}{S_{wc} + S_{nw}} \tag{3-65}$$

The relative-permeability curves can thus be obtained from the capillary-pressure curves by direct substitution of the values of S_{wi}, S_{wc}, S_{nw} into formulas (3-64) and (3-65) at each desired saturation.

In the main, there is no advantage to following the capillary-pressure approach to determine relative permeability since a lengthy measurement of capillary pressure is substituted for one of shorter duration.

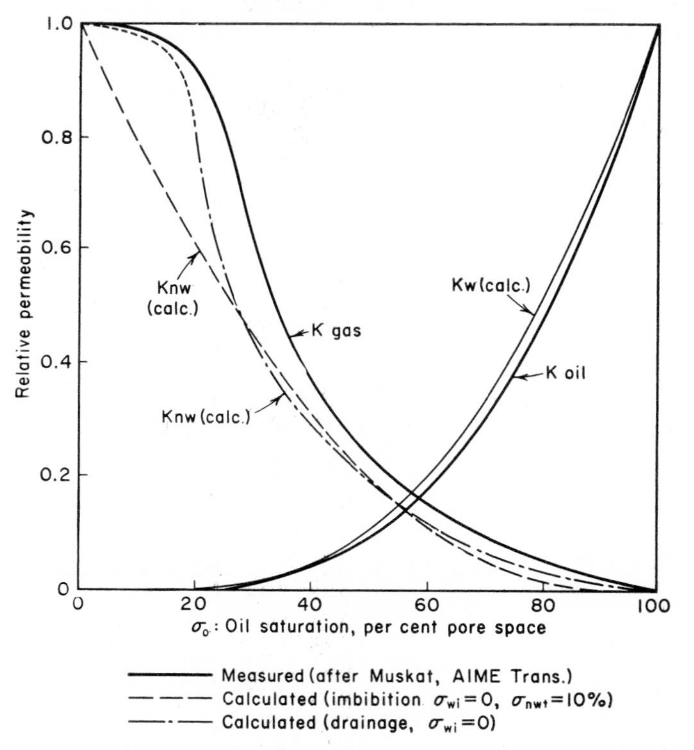

FIG. 3-8. Comparison of measured and calculated relative permeability for unconsolidated sand.

Test of Validity of Relative-permeability Expressions

Relative-permeability formulas (3-45), (3-47), and (3-56) were derived on the assumption of the absence of conductive material in the rock other than the capillary network of water filaments distributed in the pore space. The water is considered as the wetting phase. In particular, the derivation of the nonwetting-phase permeability is based on the simplification of assumptions which may place certain limitations on its applicability range.

For the purpose of ascertaining these limitations, the results obtained by formulas (3-45), (3-47), and (3-56) were compared to the relative-permeability curves published by Leverett (1939), Muskat and Botset (1936), and Terwilliger et al. (1950).

In the belief that introducing Archie's saturation relationship in the equations would unnecessarily cause errors of empirical fit, the water-saturation values were not replaced as a function of the resistivity index I. The values of $R_t/R_o = I$ used as calibration curves for fluid-saturation determination by the various authors cited above were found to be in surprisingly good agreement. Therefore, only one set of such values was

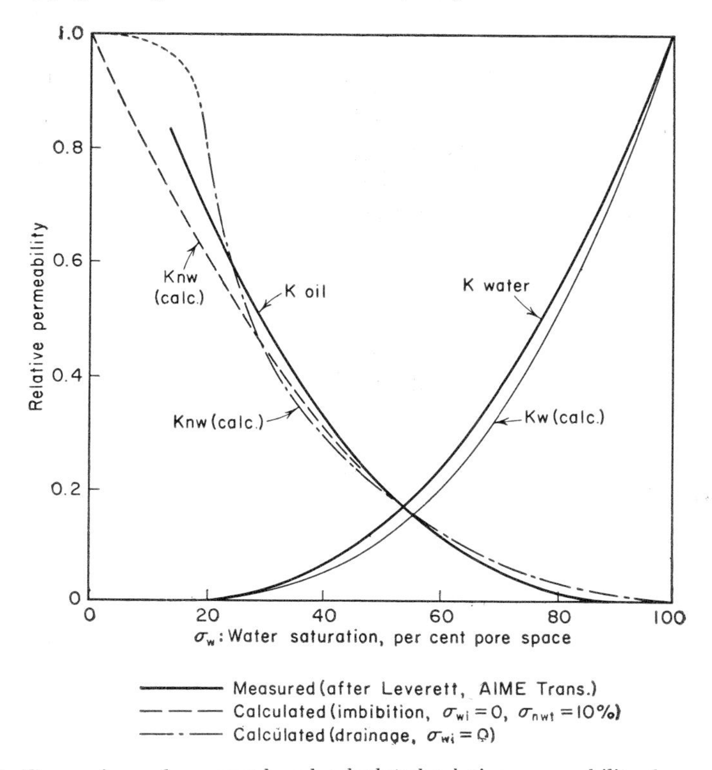

FIG. 3-9. Comparison of measured and calculated relative permeability for unconsolidated sand.

TABLE 3-3. RELATIVE-PERMEABILITY CALCULATIONS FOR UNCONSOLIDATED SAND (DRAINAGE DIRECTION)

σ_{wi} assumed to be zero

Water saturation, σ_{wc}	$\frac{1}{I} = \frac{R_o}{R_t}$	$\sigma_{wc}^{1/2}$	$\left(\frac{R_o}{R_t}\right)^{3/2}$	$k_w = \sigma_{wc}^{1/2}\left(\frac{R_o}{R_t}\right)^{3/2}$	$\sigma_{wc}^{1/4}$	$\left(\frac{R_o}{R_t}\right)^{1/4}$	$k_{nw} = (1 - \sigma_{wc})\left[1 - (\sigma_{wc})^{1/4}\left(\frac{R_o}{R_t}\right)^{1/4}\right]^2$
20	0.000	0.447	0.000	0.000	0.668	0.000	0.800
30	0.075	0.548	0.0205	0.01125	0.740	0.525	0.428
40	0.165	0.633	0.067	0.0425	0.795	0.637	0.296
50	0.275	0.707	0.144	0.102	0.840	0.724	0.196
60	0.400	0.775	0.252	0.195	0.880	0.795	0.120
70	0.535	0.836	0.391	0.327	0.915	0.856	0.064
80	0.685	0.886	0.567	0.502	0.940	0.910	0.029
90	0.840	0.950	0.770	0.730	0.972	0.949	0.008

TABLE 3-4. RELATIVE-PERMEABILITY CALCULATIONS FOR UNCONSOLIDATED SANDS (DRAINAGE DIRECTION)

$\sigma_{wi} = 0.2$ assumed

Water saturation, σ_{wc}	Free water saturation, σ_{wf}	$\frac{R_o}{R_t}$	$\sigma_{wf}^{1/2}$	$\left(\frac{R_o}{R_t}\right)^{3/2}$	$k_w = \sigma_{wf}^{1/2}\left(\frac{R_o}{R_t}\right)^{3/2}$	$\sigma_{wf}^{1/4}$	$\left(\frac{R_o}{R_t}\right)^{1/4}$	$k_{nw} = (1 - \sigma_{wf})\left[1 - \sigma_{wf}^{1/4}\left(\frac{R_o}{R_t}\right)^{1/4}\right]^2$
0.20	0.00	0.000	0.000	0.000	0.000	0.000	0.000	1.000
0.30	0.125	0.075	0.354	0.0205	0.0072	0.595	0.525	0.417
0.40	0.25	0.165	0.500	0.067	0.0335	0.707	0.637	0.226
0.50	0.375	0.275	0.612	0.144	0.088	0.782	0.724	0.119
0.60	0.50	0.400	0.707	0.252	0.178	0.840	0.795	0.056
0.70	0.625	0.535	0.790	0.391	0.309	0.890	0.856	0.021
0.80	0.75	0.685	0.866	0.567	0.491	0.930	0.910	0.006
0.90	0.875	0.840	0.935	0.770	0.720	0.966	0.949	0.001

used. It is also well known that only a small, trapped nonwetting-phase saturation exists for unconsolidated sands. Hence, it is expected that drainage calculations only should be significant.

The results of the relative-permeability computations appear in Tables 3-3 to 3-5.

The results of Table 3-3 have been plotted for comparison on Figs. 3-8, 3-9, and 3-10. It may be noted that the fit for the wetting-phase relative

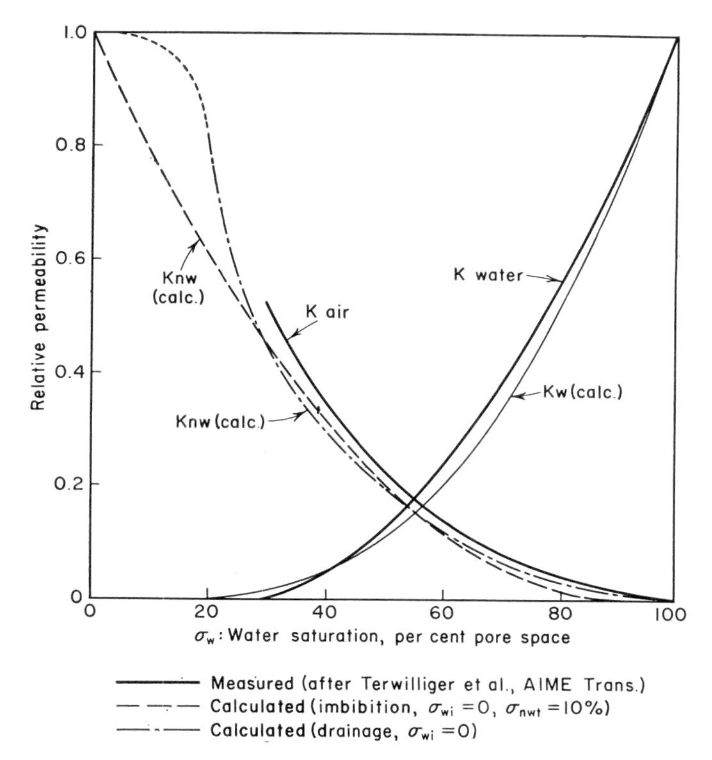

Fig. 3-10. Comparison of measured and calculated relative permeability for unconsolidated sand.

permeability is almost perfect whereas in the case of the nonwetting-phase permeability, the fit depends on the assumed value for the irreducible water saturation. It is observed also that only the drainage calculations give a fit to the experimental curves and that this occurs when σ_{wi} is assumed to be about 20 per cent, which is in agreement with the irreducible water saturation obtained by drainage in experiments by Terwilliger et al.

Calculations of relative permeabilities, with an irreducible water saturation of 0.20, have been made and are reported in Table 3-4.

Although relative-permeability curves for *clean unconsolidated* sand as reported in the literature seem to be independent of direction of saturation changes, it is of interest to compute them for the imbibition direction for comparison purposes. This is done in Table 3-5.

TABLE 3-5. RELATIVE-PERMEABILITY CALCULATIONS TO THE NONWETTING PHASE FOR CLEAN UNCONSOLIDATED SANDS (IMBIBITION DIRECTION)

Water saturation, σ_{wc}	Free water saturation, σ_{wf}	$1 - \sigma_{wf} - \sigma_{nwt}$	$k_{nw} = \left(1 - \frac{\sigma_{wc} - \sigma_{wi}}{1 - \sigma_{wi} - \sigma_{nwt}}\right)^2$
$\sigma_{wi} = 0;\ \sigma_{nwt} = 10\%$			
10	10	0.80	0.790
20	20	0.70	0.605
30	30	0.60	0.445
40	40	0.50	0.308
50	50	0.40	0.198
60	60	0.30	0.111
70	70	0.20	0.049
80	80	0.10	0.012
90	90	0.00	0.000
$\sigma_{wi} = 20\%;\ \sigma_{nwt} = 10\%$			
20	0.000	0.900	1.000
30	0.125	0.775	0.750
40	0.250	0.675	0.510
50	0.375	0.525	0.325
60	0.500	0.400	0.184
70	0.625	0.275	0.082
80	0.750	0.150	0.020
90	0.875	0.025	0.000

PETROPHYSICS OF CLEAN ROCKS (OIL-WET)

The existence of partially oil-wet reservoir rocks is unquestionable, although at this writing no totally oil-wet reservoir rock has been reported. The Athabaska tar sand of Canada, which is made up of sand grains totally coated with tar, may, however, come close to being fully oil-wet. A totally oil-wet sand should be recognizable on an electric log; when its resistivity is corrected for bore-hole effects and invasion it should be infinite, provided the connate water has attained the irreducible insular saturation. Partially oil-wet sands are the Wilcox at Oklahoma City, the Springer sand at Sholem Alechem, Oklahoma, the Tensleep at Little Buffalo Basin, Wyoming, and many Permian Basin limestones and dolomites.

For an oil-wet rock and oil-water flow, Eq. (3-57) becomes

$$k_o = \sigma_{of}^{1/2}\sigma_o^3$$

$$\underset{\text{(imbibition)}}{k_w} = \left(1 - \frac{\sigma_o - \sigma_{oi}}{1 - \sigma_{oi} - \sigma_{wt}}\right)^2 \tag{3-66}$$

$$\underset{\text{(drainage)}}{k_w} = (1 - \sigma_{of})(1 - \sigma_{of}^{1/4}\sigma_o^{1/2})^2$$

where σ_o = total oil saturation obtained by difference from $1 - \sigma_{wc}$
σ_{of} = free-oil saturation = $(\sigma_o - \sigma_{oi})/(1 - \sigma_{oi})$
σ_{oi} = irreducible oil saturation and is the equivalent of σ_{wi} for a clean water-wet rock
σ_{wt} = trapped-water saturation, which is determinable by Albert and Butault's method

The connate water saturation σ_{wc} in an oil-wet sand is obtained by Archie's formula when the appropriate value of n as saturation exponent is used, a value that depends on the degree of oil-wettability of the rock. The irreducible oil saturation σ_{oi} in an oil-wet rock is obtainable from the same correlation for irreducible wetting-phase saturation vs. porosity and permeability established for water in clean rocks (Fig. 3-7).

The value of the saturation exponent n to be used in the Archie formula is greatly in doubt. Keller (1953) has shown that under an increasing degree of wettability of the reservoir rock, the value of n required should be slightly larger than 2.0 for slightly oil-wet sands and may be as high as 10 for totally oil-wet sands. Tentatively, experience has shown that the Springer sands seem to require an exponent $n = 3.0$ and the Tensleep $n = 4.0$.

Technique for recognition of oil-wettability and the degree thereof are in their infancy. From electric logs, except for totally oil-wet rock in capillary equilibrium, means of recognizing oil-wettability are of a circumstantial nature; when the various approaches whereby porosity and water saturation are obtained do not satisfactorily check one another, oil-wettability may often be suspected, and the value of n to be used is that one which gives such a check. This approach will be discussed further in Chap. 5.

From formation samples and cores, simple imbibition tests for water and oil are satisfactory to ascertain wettability, provided the samples of rock, water, and oil have not been exposed to air. A nuclear resonance test was recently advocated (Brown and Fatt, 1956) whereby the degree of oil-wettability can be determined from formation samples, provided the intermediate degree of wettability can be ascribed to a mixture of totally oil-wet and totally water-wet grains.

PETROPHYSICS OF MULTIPLE-POROSITY SYSTEMS

Rocks with multiple-porosity systems are those which do not have a uniform pore structure but which exhibit various systems of porosity in parallel, the pore or opening size of which is widely different in magnitude. Such is the case for:

1. Fractured rocks—these may be limestones (such as the Ellenburger, Arbuckle, Hunton, etc.), sandstones (such as in the Spraberry field, Texas), shales (Florence field, Colorado, and Roosevelt field, Utah), or basement schist (California).

2. Vuggy rocks—as generally encountered in dolomites, weathered limestones, etc.

3. Oölitic rocks—where porosity exists inside the oölites, such as the Grayburg lime of the Permian Basin.

The complexity of such systems may perhaps be simplified by considering that there are only two porosity systems in parallel and that the respective proportions of each may be evaluated by such procedure as large-core analysis, and especially by porosity testing by the Locke and Bliss (1950) method. Let v represent the fraction of total porosity made up of vugs, fractures, and the like. v represents, in effect, the fraction of total porosity through which a path of least resistance exists to any flowing fluids, especially by injection.

In the undisturbed state, *in situ,* various fluid-saturation conditions can be postulated.

1. Reservoir rock at 100 per cent formation-water saturation. If the resistivity R_{fo} of such a rock is measured, the following relation exists:

$$\frac{1}{R_{fo}} = \frac{v\phi}{R_{wc}} + \frac{1-v}{R_o} \tag{3-67}$$

by the application of the formula for conductivity systems in parallel. R_o is the resistivity of the blocks of intergranular porosity, the value of which is given by the usual formula $R_o = FR_{wc}$.

The formation factor of the blocks F can be obtained in the laboratory from homogeneous formation samples or in the well bore from micrologging tools.

2. Reservoir rock at partial formation-water saturation in the blocks but 100 per cent formation-water saturation in the vugs and fractures. If the resistivity R_{ft} of such a rock is measured, the following relation obtains:

$$\frac{1}{R_{ft}} = \frac{v\phi}{R_{wc}} + \frac{1-v}{R_t} \tag{3-68}$$

where R_t is the resistivity of the blocks and can be expressed by Archie's formula:

$$R_t = FR_{wc}(\sigma_{wc})^{-2}$$

The true resistivity of the blocks can be ascertained indirectly, and the possible productivity from the blocks can thus be determined. This case represents the fluid-saturation conditions that would prevail in a fractured oil-wet rock, for the nonwetting phase (water) tends to occupy the largest openings.

3. Reservoir rock at partial formation-water saturation both in the fractures and in the blocks.

If the resistivity R_{ft} of such a rock is measured, the following relation obtains:

$$\frac{1}{R_{ft}} = \frac{v\phi\sigma_{fw}}{R_{wc}} + \frac{1-v}{R_t} \tag{3-69}$$

where σ_{fw} is the formation-water saturation in the fractures and vugs. In such a system, it is expected that the electric conductivity will be directly proportional to saturation in conductive fluid. σ_{fw} is, of course, a difficult quantity to evaluate, and judicious guessing may be the only approach at this writing.

4. Reservoir blocks at 100 per cent connate water saturation and fracture-vug system at partial water saturation. The resistivity of the blocks is $R_o = FR_{wc}$. The resistivity of the whole system is

$$\frac{1}{R_{ft}} = \frac{v\phi\sigma_{fw}}{R_{wc}} + \frac{1-v}{R_o}$$

$$= \frac{1}{R_{wc}}\left(v\phi\sigma_{fw} + \frac{1-v}{F}\right) \tag{3-70}$$

This represents the conditions that would likely prevail in a water-wet rock, for the nonwetting phase (oil or gas) tends to occupy in it the largest pore spaces (vugs and fractures), whereas water would occupy the fine capillaries in the blocks.

The relative permeabilities that would prevail during production from such a reservoir are *directly proportional* to fluid saturation in the vug-and-fracture system because production of water from the block system is not likely to occur.

During drilling operation, fractured and vuggy rocks are subjected to infiltration by mud filtrate of resistivity R_{mf}. The latter preferentially finds its way in the fractures and vugs, and little, if any, fluid is displaced from the blocks unless it be by capillary imbibition.

In a water-bearing fractured rock, the following relation holds in the invaded zone for its resistivity R_i:

$$\frac{1}{R_i} = \frac{v\phi}{R_{mf}} + \frac{1-v}{R_o} \tag{3-71}$$

In an oil-bearing fractured rock, the following will hold for the invaded zone:

$$\frac{1}{R_i} = \frac{v\phi}{R_{mf}} + \frac{1-v}{R_t} \tag{3-72}$$

It is expected that complete displacement of formation water from the fracture-vug system takes place regardless of the original saturation.

By solving the invaded-zone equations, it can be ascertained whether or not the blocks contain oil or gas. The equations for the noninvaded section provide a verification of the interpretation. The expected productivity from fractured reservoir rocks can be ascertained by the application of the relative-permeability formulas (3-45), (3-47), and (3-57), previously derived as applied to the block system. However, the water-oil ratio will be controlled mostly by the saturation conditions existing in the fracture system and the proximity to the water-oil contact.

In a fractured or vuggy system, the effective permeability to each phase is directly proportional to the saturation in that phase such that:

$$\begin{aligned} K_{fo} &= K\sigma_{fo} \\ K_{fw} &= K\sigma_{fw} \\ K_{fg} &= K\sigma_{fg} \end{aligned} \tag{3-73}$$

where the subscript f refers to the fracture system.

PETROPHYSICS OF SHALY ROCKS

Shaly rocks for the purpose of this study will be considered as those which exhibit adsorptive reactions with the fluids they contain or might be receiving through the process of infiltration from drilling fluids or of fluid injection designed to stimulate oil production. The reactions involved are mainly between the clay minerals and interstitial waters of varying composition.

The previous simple relationships between resistivity of rocks, fluid saturation, and relative permeability were established for rocks devoid of electrolytically (clay) and of electronically (metallic) conductive minerals. Besides the recognition of such rocks by mineralogic examination, the measurement of formation factors on sample cores containing fluids of varying salinities reveals the electrical departure from a clean-rock (nonreactive mineral) behavior. In clean rocks, the formation factor F value is independent of water salinity; it is an invariant lithologic property which characterizes its porosity and degree of consolidation. However, should the rock contain hydratable "clays" such as from the montmorillonite, illite, kaolinite, bauxite, and limonite groups, the formation-factor value becomes a function of the saturating water salinity. In particular, at low water salinities, shaly-rock formation factors have low values. This has been explained by calling the clays "conductive solids," a misnomer, as the crystal lattice of the minerals is not conductive of electricity. However, in dilute water solution, clay minerals are desorbed of their positive ions, which form a layer of hydration (or solvation layer) of high electrical conductivity. Therefore, the clay minerals acquire "surface conductance." The resistivity of the hydration layer can be represented by R_h and the pore space occupied by it by ϕ_h. Inside the pore space there are thus two systems of different resistivity (R_h and R_w) which occupy, respectively, volume ϕ_h and $1 - \phi_h$ and which are connected in parallel. By the equation of parallel circuits, the resistivity of the combined water R_{wc} is

$$\frac{1}{R_{wc}} = \frac{1 - \phi_h}{R_w} + \frac{\phi_h}{R_h} \tag{3-74}$$

For concentrated brines R_w is low and the effect of hydration is negligible. For fresh solution R_w is high and the hydration layer causes R_{wc} to be much smaller than R_w.

The difficulty of the interpretation of electric logs in shaly sands comes in part from the existence of two formation-factor values; one is the invaded zone and one is the noninvaded zone. Shaly sands may be recognized from the logs by SP reduction and low resistivities even when oil-saturated. Typical examples of shaly sands are the Gulf Coast Frio, Tuscaloosa, Mesa Verde, Muddy, and Aux Vases.

Rocks containing electronically conductive minerals are relatively rare. The main disturbing minerals are glauconite, pyrite, and magnetite. In testing the formation factors of rocks containing such minerals, they may be recognized by their low F values but be independent of brine salinity if free of clays. On electric logs they may be recognized by their lack of SP reduction and by their very low resistivity even when saturated to a high degree in oil and gas. Typical examples of glauconitic sands are the Bromide sands: Tulip Creek, Oil Creek, and McLish, in southern Oklahoma.

The mechanism of clay swelling, water retention, and electric conductivity is still a matter for conjecture. Certain facts are known, however, especially with respect to sodium montmorillonite. This mineral has a layer structure similar to mica but does differ from it in that the interlayer distance is variable and dependent on water content (i.e., it gives rise to one-dimensional swelling). The exchangeable cations situated between the silicate sheets are largely responsible for the swelling. Initially, swelling is a result of hydration of the cations, and the interlayer expansion is stepwise. Until the interlayer spacing reaches 22 angstroms (Å), it proceeds in steps of 3 Å, or slightly larger than the thickness of one molecule of water: 2.8 Å. Beyond this value there is a sudden jump to 35–40 Å, and thereafter the lattice expansion is continuous and independent of the nature of the monovalent cations. In this region of swelling, montmorillonite develops a diffuse double layer and behaves as a colloid. The swelling is essentially osmotic and is therefore expected to be independent of the nature of the cation for ions of the same valence. With calcium-montmorillonite, the interlayer swelling does not proceed beyond 20 Å.

Methods for Determination of the Hydration or Bound-water-filled Pore Space ϕ_h in Shaly Sands. Shaly sands exhibit two well-known bulk properties:

1. A reduced specific permeability to brine over the specific permeability to air measured on the dry core and reduced to infinite pressures (Klinkenberg permeability: K_∞). The brine permeability will be represented by K_b and should be the stabilized value obtained after passing a sufficient

number of pore volumes of brine through the test core. The value of K_b varies with the water salinity.

2. A reduced formation-factor value at low brine salinity compared with its value at high salinity. The implication here is that cations are dissociated from the clays and form a double layer of resistivity R_h within the hydration layer of pore volume ϕ_h.

The permeabilities K_∞ and K_b can be obtained by writing modified Kozeny equations:

$$K_\infty = \frac{10^8}{2F_t S_{\phi a}{}^2} \tag{3-75}$$

$$K_b = \frac{(1 - \phi_h)10^8}{2F_t S_{\phi w}{}^2} \tag{3-76}$$

where $S_{\phi a}$ and $S_{\phi w}$ are the specific surfaces on a pore-volume basis in dry air and under hydration conditions, respectively.

By virtue of Eq. (3-11) we can write

$$S_{\phi a} = \frac{2}{\bar{r}} \qquad \text{and} \qquad S_{\phi w} = \frac{2}{\bar{r}(1 - \phi_h)}$$

After substituting in (3-75) and (3-76), and making their ratio, we obtain

$$\frac{K_b}{K_\infty} = (1 - \phi_h)^3 \tag{3-77}$$

The latter equation is readily solved, for the pore volume of the bound water ϕ_h or the equilibrium brine permeability may be calculated from K_∞ and ϕ_h. The hydration water volume is tightly held by electrostatic attraction and will not flow under the application of a moderate pressure gradient; hence it constitutes a form of *irreducible water saturation* and it is considered as part of σ_{wi}.

The approach just discussed to determine ϕ_h is practical in the laboratory, but in the field, where cores are not available but only electric logs, it would be of advantage to determine ϕ_h from them. This may be done by measuring formation factors at two salinities. These are provided when an invaded water sand is encountered.

Let F_t be the true formation factor as would be obtained when measured with very saline water, the resistivity of which approaches zero; then we have

$$R_o = F_t R_{wc} \tag{3-78}$$

Let this shaly rock sample originally saturated 100 per cent in water of resistivity R_{wc} be invaded by water of resistivity R_{mf} and let R_i be the resistivity measured:

$$R_i = F_t R_{wi} \tag{3-79}$$

where R_{wi} is the resistivity of the combined water inside the porous system, such that

$$\frac{1}{R_{wi}} = \frac{1 - \phi_h}{R_{mf}} + \frac{\phi_h}{R_{wc}} \tag{3-80}$$

assuming that the hydration layer of volume ϕ_h will have the same resistivity R_{wc} as originally. By substitution we find

$$F_t = \frac{R_i}{R_{mf}} \left(1 - \phi_h + \phi_h \frac{R_{mf}}{R_{wc}}\right) \tag{3-81}$$

Call $R_i/R_{mf} = F_a$ the apparent formation factor of the invaded rock, and by substitution in (3-81)

$$F_t = F_a \left(1 - \phi_h + \phi_h \frac{R_{mf}}{R_{wc}}\right) \tag{3-82}$$

This formula permits calculation of ϕ_h when F_t is obtained from a salt-water horizon, F_a from the invaded zone, and when R_{mf} and R_{wc} are known.

Determination of Free Water Saturation σ_{wf} in Shaly Sands. A true resistivity index $I_t = (R_o/R_t)_t^{-1}$ can be obtained from

$$I_t^{-1} = 1 - \frac{1}{1 - \phi_h} (1 - I_a^{-1}) \tag{3-83}$$

where I_a is the apparent resistivity index $\left(\frac{R_o}{R_t}\right)_a^{-1}$

For various values of ϕ_h, Fig. 3-11 indicates the shape of the various curves of apparent resistivity ratios.

The true resistivity index may be considered as being that from which the true water saturation can be calculated by Archie's formula modified or

$$\sigma_{wc} = \sqrt[n]{I_t^{-1}} = \sqrt[n]{1 - \frac{1}{1 - \phi_h} (1 - I_a^{-1})} \tag{3-84}$$

In this formula n can always be selected as equal to 2.0 because shaly sands that behave as such on the electric log are always water-wet.

If the apparent resistivity index curve I_a vs. saturation is known from laboratory measurements, as is often the case in relative-permeability or capillary-pressure tests, the value of the bound-water saturation ϕ_h can also be determined by matching the curve with the curves of Fig. 3-11.

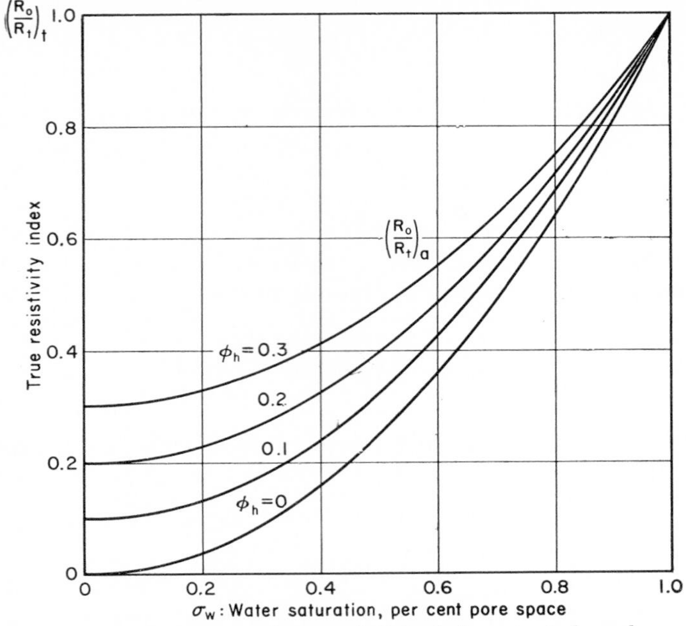

FIG. 3-11. Apparent and true resistivity indexes in shaly rocks.

Another approach for the determination of free water saturation is derived from the following considerations:

$$\frac{1}{(R_t)_a} = \frac{\phi_h}{R_{wc}} + \frac{1 - \phi_h}{R_t} \tag{3-85}$$

but

$$\frac{1}{R_t} = \frac{\sigma_{wf}^2}{R_o} = \frac{\sigma_{wf}^2}{F_t R_{wc}} \tag{3-86}$$

by substitution

$$\frac{1}{(R_t)_a} = \frac{\phi_h}{R_{wc}} + \frac{(1 - \phi_h)\sigma_{wf}^2}{F_t R_{wc}} \tag{3-87}$$

from which

$$\sigma_{wf} = \sqrt{\frac{F_t(R_{wc}/R_{ta} - \phi_h)}{1 - \phi_h}} \tag{3-88}$$

A simpler and equivalent method of determining the free water saturation is to consider that the total and true water saturation is given by

$$\sigma_{wc} = \sigma_{wi} + \sigma_{wm}$$

where σ_{wi} contains the water of hydration ϕ_h and σ_{wm} is the mobile water.

The true water saturation is obtained by

$$\sigma_{wc} = \sqrt{\frac{F_t R_{wc}}{R_t}} \tag{3-89}$$

F_t in (3-89) is obtained from (3-82). The free water saturation is then

$$\sigma_{wf} = \frac{\sigma_{wc} - \sigma_{wi}}{1 - \sigma_{wi}}$$

Determination of Relative Permeability in Shaly Sands. The relative-permeability formulas (3-45), (3-47), and (3-57) derived for clean, water-wet rocks can readily be modified for application to shaly sands.

1. Wetting-phase relative permeability (to water):

$$k_w = \sigma_{wf}^{1/2}\left[1 - \frac{1}{1 - \phi_h}(1 - I_a^{-1})\right]^{3/2} \tag{3-90}$$

2. Nonwetting-phase relative permeability (to oil or gas):
   a. Drainage direction:

$$k_{nw} = (1 - \sigma_{wf})\{1 - \sigma_{wf}^{1/4}[1 - (1 - I_a^{-1})]^{1/4}\}^2 \tag{3-91}$$

   b. Imbibition direction:

$$k_{nw} = \left(1 - \frac{\sigma_{wc} - \sigma_{wi}}{1 - \sigma_{wi} - \sigma_{nwt}}\right)^2 \tag{3-92}$$

where σ_{wi} includes both the irreducible water saturation for a clean sand of equivalent porosity and permeability and the water of hydration. σ_{nwt} is the trapped nonwetting-phase saturation which is determinable by the method of Albert and Butault in the laboratory or from the microresistivity logging tools in a well.

Attempts to verify formulas (3-90), (3-91), and (3-92) from laboratory tests of relative permeability in shaly sands were unsuccessful because no such test could be found in which the water of hydration was not removed by flow of the nonwetting phase resulting from the use of high-pressure gradients during the experiments. However, it is felt that they are of sufficient accuracy for the purpose of electric-log interpretation and the prediction of well productivity thereof, as they were successfully used in predicting water-oil ratios and water-gas ratios in wells producing from shaly sands.

SELECTED REFERENCES ON PETROPHYSICS

1846

Poiseuille, J.: Recherches expérimentales sur le mouvement des liquides dans les tubes de très petits diamètres, *Mém. savants étrangers*, vol. 9, pp. 543ff.

1904

Perrin, J.: Mechanism of Contact Electrification and Colloidal Solutions, *J. chim. phys.*, vol. 2, pp. 601ff.

1927

Kozeny, J.: Über Kapilläre Leitung des Wassers im Boden, *Sitzber Akad. Wiss. Wien, Math-naturw. Kl.*, vol. 136-2A, pp. 271ff.

1933

Fair, G. M., and L. P. Hatch: Fundamental Factors Governing the Stream Line Flow of Water through Sand, *J. Am. Water Works Assoc.*, vol. 25, pp. 1551ff.

1936

Wyckoff, R. D., and H. G. Botset: The Flow of Gas-liquid Mixtures through Unconsolidated Sands, *Physics*, vol. 1, no. 9, pp. 325ff.

1937

Jakosky, J. J., and R. H. Hopper: The Effect of Moisture on the Direct Current Resistivities of Oil Sands and Rocks, *Geophysics*, vol. 2, no. 1, pp. 33ff.

1939

Carman, P. C.: Permeability of Saturated Sands, Soils and Clays, *J. Agr. Sci.*, vol. 29, pp. 262ff.

1942

Archie, G. E.: The Electrical Resistivity Log as an Aid in Determining Some Reservoir Characteristics, *AIME Tech. Pub.* 1422.

1944

Guyod, H.: Electrical Well Logging, *Oil Weekly*, series of 16 articles, August to December.

1945

Gordon, A. R.: The Diaphragm Cell Method of Determining Diffusion, *Ann. N.Y. Acad. Sci.*, vol. 46, pp. 285ff.

Guyod, H.: Electric Log Interpretation, *Oil Weekly*, series of 4 articles, December.

1947

Archie, G. E.: Electrical Resistivity—An Aid in Core Analysis Interpretation, *Bull. Am. Assoc. Petroleum Geol.*, vol. 31, no. 2, pp. 350ff.

Morse, R. A., et al.: Relative Permeability Measurements on Small Core Samples, *Oil Gas J.*, Aug. 23, pp. 109ff.

1949

Chalkley, H. W., et al.: A Method of Estimating Volume-Surface Ratios, *Science*, vol. 110, pp. 295ff., Sept. 23.

Dunlap, H. F., et al.: The Relation between Electrical Resistivity and Brine Saturation in Reservoir Rocks, *Trans. AIME*, vol. 186, pp. 259ff.

Garrels, R. M., et al.: Diffusion of Ions through Intergranular Spaces in Water Saturated Rocks, *Bull. Geol. Soc. Amer.*, vol. 60, pp. 1809ff.

Miles, F. V.: Resistance Measurements on Small Cores, M.Sc. thesis, Univ. of Oklahoma.

Reh, F. J.: Theoretical Investigations of the Resistivity-Saturation Relationship in Porous Material, M.Sc. thesis, Univ. of Oklahoma.

1950

Archie, G. E.: Introduction to Petrophysics of Reservoir Rocks, *Bull. Am. Assoc. Petroleum Geol.*, vol. 34, no. 5, pp. 943ff.

Banks, J. E.: Particle-type Well Logging, *Bull. Am. Assoc. Petroleum Geol.*, vol. 34, no. 8, pp. 1729ff.

De Witte, L.: Relations between Resistivities and Fluid Content of Porous Rocks, *Oil Gas J.*, Aug. 24, pp. 120ff.

De Witte, L.: Resistivity and Saturation Distribution in Infiltrated Zones of Porous Formations around Drill Holes, *Oil Gas J.*, July 27, pp. 246ff.

Locke, L. C., and J. E. Bliss: Core Analysis Techniques for Limestone and Dolomite, *World Oil*, September, pp. 204ff.

Patnode, H. W., and M. R. J. Wyllie: The Presence of Conductive Solids in Reservoir Rocks as a Factor in Electric Log Interpretations, *Trans. AIME*, vol. 189, pp. 47ff.

Rose, W. D., and M. R. J. Wyllie: Specific Surface Areas and Porosities from Photomicrographs, *Bull. Am. Assoc. Petroleum Geol.*, vol. 34, no. 8, pp. 1748ff.

Wyllie, M. R. J., and W. D. Rose: Application of Kozeny-Carman Equation to Consolidated Porous Media, *Nature*, vol. 165, pp. 972ff.

Young, J. W., and R. Pot: Resistivity Measurements on Limestone Cores, *Petroleum Engr.*, January, pp. B50ff.

1951

Chin, W. S., and W. Rose: Examination of Components of Limestone Porosity by Chalkley Method, *Bull. Am. Assoc. Petroleum Geol.*, vol. 35, no. 3, pp. 615ff.

Klinkenberg, L. J.: Analogy between Diffusion and Electrical Conductivity in Porous Rocks, *Bull. Geol. Soc. Amer.*, vol. 62, pp. 559ff.

Terwilliger, P. L., et al.: An Experimental and Theoretical Investigation of Gravity Drainage Performance, *AIME Tech. Pub.* 3199.

1952

Albert, P., and L. Butault: Étude des caractéristiques capillaires du reservoir du Cap Bon par la Méthode Purcell, *Rev. inst. franç. pétrole et Ann. combustibles liquides*, vol. 7, no. 8, pp. 250–266, August.

Archie, G. E.: Classification of Carbonate Reservoir Rocks and Petrophysical Considerations, *Bull. Am. Assoc. Petroleum Geol.*, vol. 36, no. 2, pp. 278ff.

Winsauer, W. O., et al.: Resistivity of Brine Saturated Sands in Relation to Pore Geometry, *Bull. Am. Assoc. Petroleum Geol.*, vol. 36, no. 2, pp. 253ff.

Wyllie, M. R. J., and M. B. Spangler: Application of Electrical Resistivity Measurements to Problem of Fluid Flow in Porous Media, *Bull. Am. Assoc. Petroleum Geol.*, vol. 36, no. 2, pp. 359ff.

1953

Keller, G. V.: Effect of Wettability on the Electrical Resistivity of Sand, *Oil Gas J.*, Jan. 5, pp. 65ff.

Scheidegger, A. E.: Flow Through Cavities in Porous Media, *Petroleum Engr.*, May, pp. B121ff.

1954

Birks, J.: An Evaporation Method for Measuring the Resistivity-water Saturation Characteristics of Cores, *J. Inst. Petroleum*, January, pp. 14ff.

Calhoun, J. C., Jr.: Basic Parameters for Describing Porous Systems, *Producers Monthly*, vol. 18, no. 11, pp. 35ff., September.

Holmes, C. R.: Some Factors Related to the Measurement of the Electrical Properties of Porous Sandstones, *Producers Monthly*, vol. 19, no. 1, pp. 21ff.

Norrish, K.: Manner of Swelling of Montmorillonite, *Nature*, vol. 73, pp. 256ff, Feb. 6.

Norrish, K., and J. P. Quirk: Crystalline Swelling of Montmorillonite, *Nature*, vol. 173, pp. 255ff., Feb. 6.

1955

Harmsen, G. J.: The Concept "Hydraulic Radius" in Porous Media, *J. Petroleum Technol.*, vol. 7, no. 12, pp. 53ff.

Wyllie, M. R. J.: Verification of Tortuosity Equations, *Bull. Am. Assoc. Petroleum Geol.*, vol. 40, no. 2, pp. 266ff.

1956

Brown, R. J. S., and I. Fatt: Measurements of Fractional Wettability of Oil Fields' Rocks by the Nuclear Magnetic Relaxation Method, *J. Petroleum Technol.*, vol. 8, no. 11, pp. 262ff.

Bucker, H. P., Jr., et al.: A Simplified Pore Size Distribution Apparatus, *J. Petroleum Technol.*, vol. 8, no. 4, pp. 65ff.

Carman, P. C.: "Flow of Gases Through Porous Media," Academic Press, Inc., New York.

Perkins, F. M., et al.: Resistivity of Sandstones as Related to the Geometry of Their Interstitial Water, *Geophysics*, vol. 21, no. 4, p. 1071.

CHAPTER 4

ELECTRIC AND RADIATION LOGGING OF WELLS

The purpose of well logging is to obtain a graphic record as a function of depth of one or more physical and/or chemical properties of the geologic formations encountered by the drill. Many such properties may be measured but from the point of view of the reservoir engineer only electric and radioactivity well logs supply him with measurements that he may use with dependability and reliability in his daily work. This chapter is altogether concerned with the types of logs obtained by electrical and radioactivity measurements made in well bores and with their *qualitative* significance. Qualitative interpretation of well logs is based mostly on curve appearance and shape and requires a widespread experience with prevailing geologic conditions. Understanding of the basic principles involved in the measurements is nevertheless invaluable in the empirical analysis of well logs.

EFFECT OF DRILLING OPERATIONS ON FORMATION CONDITIONS NEAR THE WELL BORE

The manner in which a well is drilled affects the logging conditions and, more particularly, with respect to the resistivity of the fluid in the well bore, the diameter of the well, and the mud-filtrate invasion in the immediate neighborhood of the well. Wells may be drilled with rotary or cable tools. However, very few wells which are logged are presently drilled with cable tools. The majority of commercial oil-drilling operations are done with rotary tools.

Rotary Drilling

In rotary drilling the bore hole is made by circulating a mud through a drill pipe which brings the cuttings back to the surface in the annular space between the drill pipe and the well bore. The formations are therefore subjected to the hydrostatic pressure of a column of mud fluid, and they respond to mud-filtrate invasion in different ways, depending on the type of mud, the type of formation, and other conditions. In this study we are mainly interested in the reaction of porous and permeable formations to the effect of rotary drilling fluids.

Hole Size. In sandy formations, hole size is generally the bit size or smaller. The reason why hole size may be smaller than bit size is because after the removal of the bit, a certain amount of mud filtration still takes place and a filter cake is still formed in a manner which reduces the hole size below bit size. This is very often observed in caliper logging.

In limestone and dolomite, hole size is generally bit size. In limestone and dolomite containing anhydrite and gypsum, the hole size is generally larger than bit size because of the solution activity of the mud on the anhydrite and gypsum.

Mud-filtrate Invasion. The response of porous and permeable formations to invasion by drilling-mud filtrate depends on various factors which are, on one hand, a function of the quality and the type of mud used and, on the other hand, a function of the properties of the formations drilled.

Filtrate Characteristics of Mud. It has been shown by laboratory studies that the cumulative infiltration of mud fluid through a filter cake is proportional to the square root of the time of exposure to the filtration action. However, for long exposures there exists a certain amount of deviation from this simple law. Since the filter cake is the result of the precipitation of solid matter contained in the mud, the mud-cake thickness e_{mc} is also directly proportional to the square root at the time of exposure. The permeability and porosity of the mud cake were found to be a function of the pressure differential existing between the well bore and the formation as well as of the salt content of the drilling fluid. With an increasing pressure differential, at first, there is a very rapid decrease in the permeability and porosity of the mud cake. But for pressure differentials of about 50 atm, the permeability and porosity of the filter cake reach asymptotically stable values. The electrolyte or salt content of the drilling fluid also affects the permeability and porosity of the mud cake. Laboratory experiments have shown that the permeability of the mud cake increases in a constant manner with an increase in sodium chloride added to the drilling mud. Salt mud will therefore have a larger filter loss to the formation than fresh mud. The porosity of the filter cake shows a variable relationship to the electrolyte content of the drilling mud. At first, the porosity may decrease very rapidly with an increase in sodium chloride, and later with further addition of salt, the porosity increases rather rapidly. The increase in permeability and porosity of the mud cake with the salinity of the mud is attributed to the aggregation of the solid particles contained in the mud which reduces their specific surface.

Type of Formation. Other conditions being equal, that is, given a certain drilling fluid, the response of a porous and permeable formation to invasion will be a function of the porosity and permeability of this formation. In low-porosity and low-permeability formations, a deep invasion is generally observed. This is the case, for instance, in limestones, dolomites, highly cemented sands, etc. In high-porosity and high-permeability formations, a shallow invasion is generally observed. This is the case, for instance, in Gulf Coast formations. These relationships appear contrary to expectation, but on examination they are quite reasonable. Since we have assumed the use of the same drilling mud in the different formations for comparison purposes, the rate of filtrate loss from the mud is conditioned by the mud only and the filtrate loss is constant in all cases since it is controlled by the filter-cake conditions and the differential pressure. In the high-porosity formations, there is more space to fill in the invaded zone and therefore the front of the invasion zone will advance more slowly. After a certain time, the rate of the advance of the invasion front may be so slow as to be smaller than the rate of back diffusion of the ions in solution in the formation water. In highly porous formations, the invasion front may recede toward the well bore on account of the ionic diffusion. In low porosity formations, this back diffusion may not take place. A further reason for the low invasion in high-porosity and high-permeability formations is the gravity segregation which will take place between the fresh mud filtrate of low density and the heavier salt water contained in the formations. In such case, the fresh mud filtrate forms an inverted cone around the well bore.

Residual Oil and Gas. In considering the residual oil and gas saturation in the invaded zone, we must distinguish two zones, namely, the *flushed zone* and the *invaded zone proper*. The flushed zone is that which immediately surrounds the well bore and perhaps does not extend more than 3 to 6 in. away from it. The invaded zone proper is that beyond the flushed zone. For the purpose of calculations and interpretation of electric logs, it is generally assumed that the amount of residual oil or gas will be the same in the two zones. Residual oil and gas figures are postulated for lack of better information, but they are assumed, using the physical characteristics of the rock as a guide. For this purpose, the rocks are divided into two classes: those of low porosity and those of high porosity. In low-porosity formations (less than 15 per cent), if the permeability is less than a few millidarcys, there may not be any invasion at all. If the permeability is comprised between 5 and 100 millidarcys (md), the residual oil and gas will be a function of the filtrate loss. If the filtrate loss recorded on the heading of the log is less than 10 cc per 30 min, a moderate invasion may be expected with the residual saturation of 30 per cent for heavy oils and 20 per cent for light oils. If the filtrate loss is larger than 10 cc per 30 min, a large invasion may be expected with residual of 20 per cent for heavy oils and 10 per cent for light oils.

In high-porosity formations (larger than 15 per cent) and for permeabilities less than 100 md, a moderate invasion is observed with residual oil of about 20 per cent. If the permeability is larger than 100 md, a low invasion results with residual oil of the order of 30 per cent.

Flushing and Mixing of Mud Filtrate with Formation Waters. The effectiveness of flushing and mixing of formation waters with mud filtrate is a function of the distance traveled away from the well bore. Near the well bore, that is, in the flushed zone, the formation water is completely displaced by the mud filtrate in clean rocks. However, in shaly rocks, because of the formation of a hydration layer around shale particles, the reaction is more complex and is beyond the scope of the present treatment. In clean rocks, it may be expected that logging measurements which do not probe beyond the flushed zone measure the true formation factor of such rocks; whereas in shaly rocks only an apparent formation factor is obtained. Further away from the well bore than the flushed zone, the *invaded zone proper* is encountered. This is a zone of mixing between the mud filtrate and the formation waters. The mixing factor, represented by z, is the fraction of pore space filled with connate water which mixes with mud filtrate. The value of z for clean rocks may be selected from the following:

$$z = 5 \quad \text{when } 10 < \phi < 18 \text{ per cent}$$
$$= 7.5 \quad \text{when } 18 < \phi < 25 \text{ per cent}$$
$$= 10 \quad \text{when } 25 < \phi$$

To facilitate the computations of the resistivity of the combined water in the invaded zone as a function of the mud-filtrate resistivity R_{mf}, the connate water resistivity R_{wc}, and the mixing factor z, a chart was prepared by Tixier (Fig. 4-1).

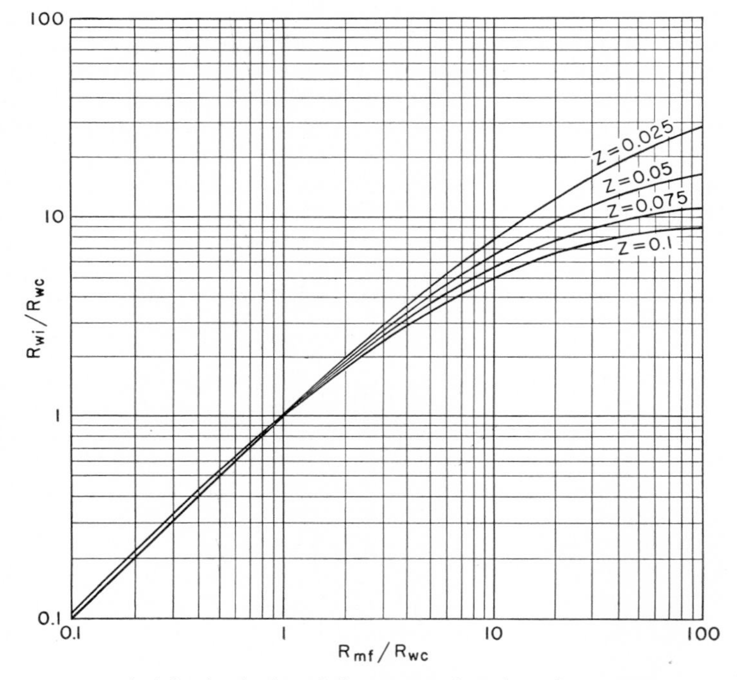

Fig. 4-1. Water resistivity in the invaded zone as a function of connate water and mud resistivities. (*After Tixier.*)

An example illustrates the use of this chart:

Let $R_{mf} = 1.0$

$R_{wc} = 0.1$

Formation porosity is 20 per cent; therefore $z = 7.5$ per cent

We compute $R_{mf}/R_{wc} = 1.0/0.1 = 10$; thus $R_{wi}/R_{wc} = 5.8$ and $R_{wi} = 0.58$

In shaly rocks the invasion relationship becomes more complicated because of incomplete flushing of the formation water, of the formation of a hydration layer around the clay particles, and of the existence of free water.

The reactions of mud filtrate with the porous and permeable rocks subjected to invasion are responsible for formation of permeability blocking which prevents free flow of oil and gas to wells should those be contained in a reservoir subjected to drill-stem tests. The proper understanding of the well-bore conditions involved in shaly reservoirs permits the rediscovery of many oil fields that may have been passed up by not realizing the possible presence of permeability blocks which could have been relieved by such special well-completion treatments as formation fracturing, mud-acid treatments, etc.

Mud-cake and Filtrate Characteristics. As was stated above, the thickness of the mud cake is directly proportional to the square root of time of exposure to filtration during laboratory experiments. But in a well bore where drill pipes rotate, the filter cake is subjected to a plastering action which results in compaction and the mud cake is much reduced in thickness, changes which invalidate the simple relationship expressed above. The mud-cake thickness may be obtained in a positive manner by means of caliper logging, when recorded on an amplified scale, and especially by the microcaliper logging technique. It may also be obtained indirectly from microlog computations. The resistivity R_{mc} of the mud cake and the resistivity R_{mf} of the mud filtrate are characteristics which have great

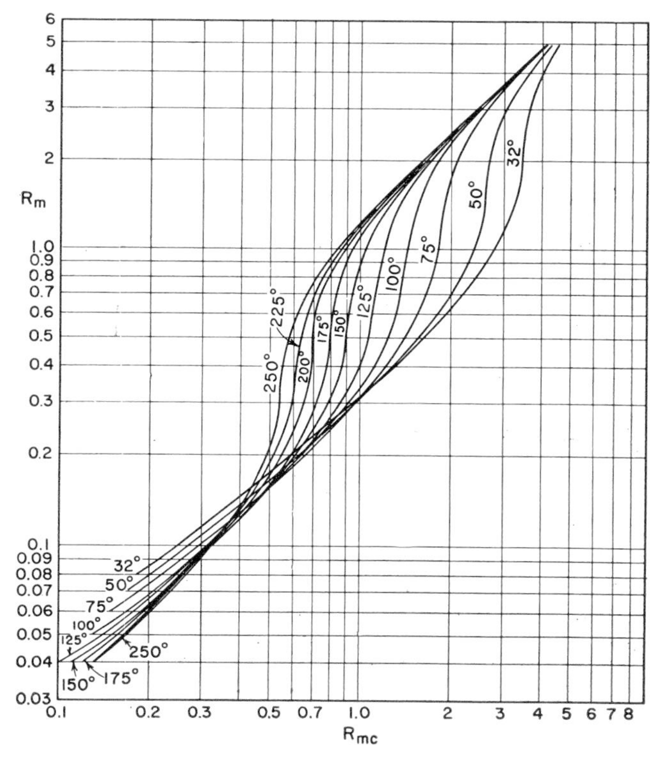

FIG. 4-2*a*. Mud-cake resistivity vs. mud resistivity. (*Continental Oil Co.*)

importance in the interpretation of electric logs. The former is difficult to measure directly in a mud cell but by collecting a mud-filtrate sample, it is possible to obtain a direct measurement of its resistivity. Field practice has been introduced whereby measurements of mud-filtrate resistivity are made on the derrick floor by the logging companies, provided an adequate sample is supplied by the operators. In the absence of such

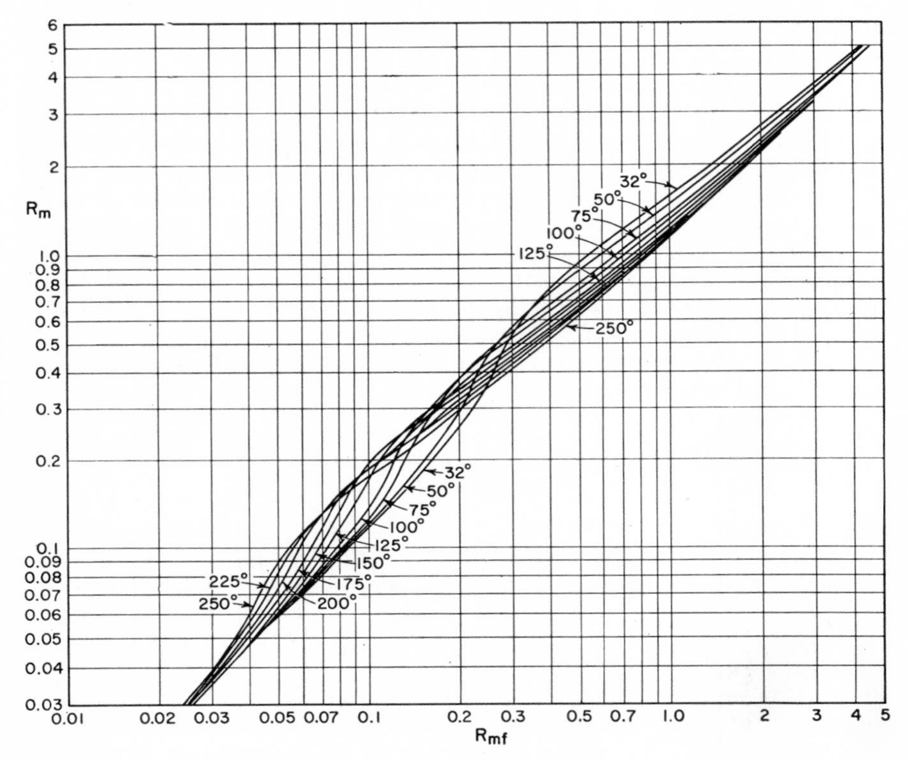

FIG. 4-2*b*. Mud-filtrate resistivity vs. mud resistivity. (*Continental Oil Co.*)

measurements, statistical information collected in the past may be used to obtain a fair approximation of the value of the resistivity of the mud cake and mud filtrate. Such information has been collected in a chart given in Figs. 4-2*a* and *b*.

An example illustrates its application. Let a mud have a resistivity of 0.35 ohm-meter at a bottom-hole temperature of 175°F. The mud-cake resistivity is 0.76 and the mud-filtrate resistivity is 0.22.

Rotary Drilling in Shales

Shales are not of commercial importance and therefore very little attention has been given to the reaction of shales on the electric log. There are two observations which are well known. One is the hole-size enlargement which is generally present in shales unless an unreactive mud is used in drilling, and the other is the base-exchange reaction which takes place between ordinary mud and shale. This reaction may cause some shale resistivity change in the immediate neighborhood of the well bore, and it may extend a short distance, that is, 1 or 2 in. This reaction is best observed on the microlog, and at times it may be misinterpreted as that of a porous and permeable formation. Base exchange is also very likely the reason for sloughing of shale which results in hole-size enlargement.

Cable Tool and Gas Drilling

In cable-tool drilling, there is an insignificant mud-filtrate invasion because only a small amount of drilling fluid is maintained at all times on the bit. Therefore, most of the logging problems encountered in rotary drilling because of invasion are nonexistent. However, very few electric logs are run in cable-tool wells unless they be of the induction type. Radioactivity logs are probably more commonly used in cable-tool wells than electric logs. In wells drilled with gas or air, there is absolutely no invasion by mud filtrate and again most of the electric logs which are run in such wells are of the induction type or of the radioactivity type. Again the problems of log interpretation encountered in rotary drilling because of mud invasion are nonexistent.

STATEMENT OF THE LOG-INTERPRETATION PROBLEM IN TERMS OF BORE-HOLE CONDITIONS

Depending on whether or not a sand is oil- or water-bearing, the well bore and invasion conditions show variable reactions on the electric log because of variations in the resistivity profile characteristics across the well bore.

The case of a water sand is pictured in Fig. 4-3. The undisturbed water sand has a low resistivity ($R_o = FR_{wc}$), perhaps less than 1 ohm-meter; this will depend, however, on the value of the formation factor F and the resistivity of the formation water R_{wc}. This sand is invaded by mud filtrate of resistivity R_{mf}. In the flushed zone, mud filtrate has completely replaced the connate water. This is probably true, provided the rock is devoid of clays and shale particles. The resistivity of the flushed zone R_{xo} may then be obtained by making the product of the formation factor F by the mud-filtrate resistivity R_{mf}: $R_{xo} = FR_{mf}$. If fresh mud is used, as is generally the case, R_{mf} is larger than R_{wc} and the resistivity of the flushed zone is larger than the resistivity of the water sand R_o. The two values of R_{xo} and R_o plotted vertically in Fig. 4-3*b* are connected by a resistivity variation curve of a decreasing trend through the invaded zone proper. It is impossible to characterize the resistivity of the invaded zone by a definite value, and to say that it is R_i is a gross approximation, though of considerable usefulness. It is best to look at R_i as being a mean resistivity value of the invaded zone which includes both the geometric effect of the radial fluid distribution and of the decreased flushing of the connate water away from the well bore. These effects are empirically included in the R_z considerations, i.e., the resistivity of the combined water of the invaded zone (Fig. 4-1). Therefore, we have $R_i = FR_z$ which expressed the resistivity of the invaded zone as the product of the formation factor F by the combined water resistivity R_z.

Under most conditions, there are three unknowns to the problem of electric-log interpretation, namely, connate water resistivity R_{wc}, formation factor F, and true formation resistivity R_t. The diameter or extent

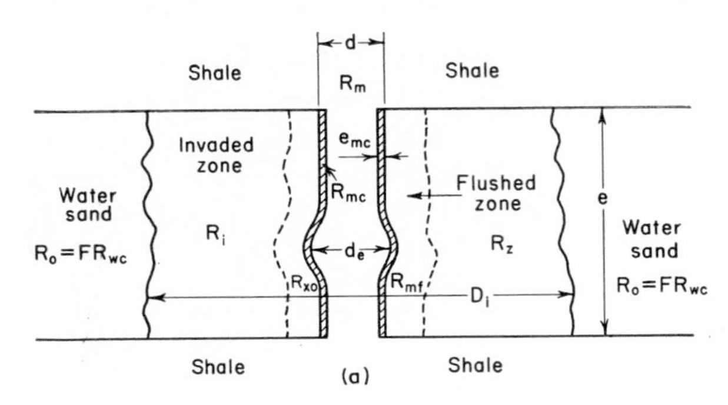

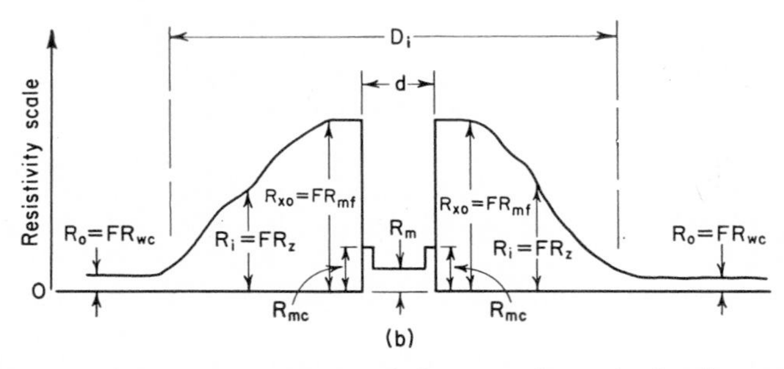

FIG. 4-3. Well-bore and invasion characteristics around a water-bearing sand. (*a*) Invasion characteristics viewed in cross section and (*b*) resistivity profile across the well bore through the sand.

of invasion D_i is also an unknown of interest in ascertaining the probing distance of the various logging tools. The value of R_{wc} should preferably be obtained from a representative formation water sample, or by geographic and geologic interpolation, but most generally it will have to be *estimated* from the SP curve, by methods to be studied later. The formation factor may be evaluated from the flushed zone by means of a very short investigation tool such as the microlog, or microlaterolog, and the like, or from a short investigation tool which probes mostly in the invaded zone such as a short-normal curve (AM = 8, 10, 16, or 18 in.), or a limestone curve (AO = 32 or 37 in.). In a water sand no assumption as to residual oil in such zones need be made since there is none. The third unknown R_t may be obtained from a long investigation tool, or one which effectively measures beyond the invaded zone without being affected too much by such a zone. Such a tool is the lateral curve (AO = 15 ft 8 in., to 24 ft) or the curves obtained by a long normal (AM = 64 in.) in low resistivity, slightly invaded formations, or the focused current logs: laterolog, guard log, or induction log. The diameter of invasion D_i may only be ascertained when combinations of logs are available which progressively probe to greater and greater distances away from the well bore, such as by the use

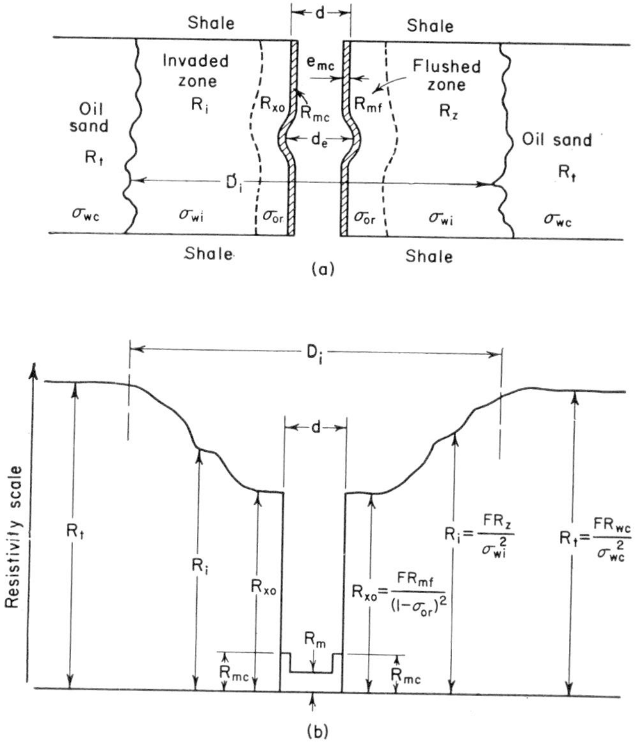

FIG. 4-4. Well-bore and invasion characteristics around an oil-bearing sand. (*a*) Invasion characteristics viewed in cross section and (*b*) resistivity profile across the well bore through the sand.

of a combination of short normals (two or more) and lateral (one or more) curves and by a judicious use of departure curves.

The case of an invaded oil sand is pictured in Fig. 4-4. Here, the undisturbed oil-sand resistivity has a high value R_t, the magnitude of which depends on the connate water saturation in place σ_{wc} and also on the formation factor F, according to Archie's relationship. The sand is invaded by mud filtrate of resistivity R_{mf}. In the flushed zone, this filtrate has completely replaced the connate water, but only part of the oil, a residual saturation σ_{or}, is present, the value of which may be estimated by considerations previously made. The resistivity of the flushed zone

R_{xo} may now be obtained by application of Archie's relation such that $R_{xo} = FR_{mf}(1 - \sigma_{or})^{-2}$. It is noted that this value of R_{xo} is larger than in the case of a water sand of the same formation factor and drilled with the same mud. This is because of the presence of residual oil σ_{or}. In the diagram it is assumed that R_{xo} is less than R_t. This is not necessarily so, as they may be equal or R_{xo} may be larger than R_t. In any case the two

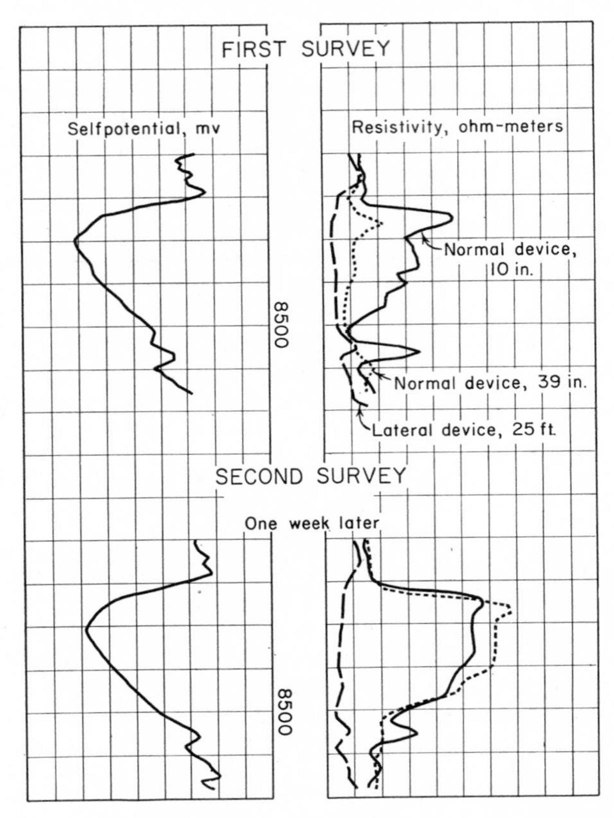

FIG. 4-5. Logs showing an increasing invasion effect with time.

zones are again connected by the invasion zone proper of resistivity R_i intermediate in value. It is generally assumed that a residual oil σ_{or} identical in value to that in the flushed zone will prevail in the invasion zone. Again the mud filtrate and the formation water mix and give a combined resistivity R_z. By application of Archie's law we have $R_i = FR_z\sigma_{wi}^{-2}$, where σ_{wi} is the saturation in combined water in the invaded zone ($\sigma_{wi} = 1 - \sigma_{or}$). The third unknown R_t is again obtained by means of a long investigation tool, as previously discussed.

The above considerations concerning the extent of invasion in a water sand apply as well to an oil and gas sand and are perhaps of greater importance because it becomes more difficult to recognize the invaded from the noninvaded zone in an oil sand drilled with fresh mud. In fact the invaded and the noninvaded zones could have the same resistivity and the problem would become indeterminate. Even a departure-curve study is of no avail in resolving this indetermination.

An example of variation of the mud-filtrate invasion with time is given in Fig. 4-5. The two logs were obtained one week apart and considerable difference exists in the two normal curves. However, the lateral curve was long enough to be unaffected.

The use of departure curves is beyond the scope of this elementary treatment. If the user suspects that the long investigation resistivity-measuring tools on which he relies to obtain R_t are affected by invasion, he should refer his questions to someone skilled in the art of using departure curves, for in this chapter it will always be presumed that the long investigation tool is not affected by invasion and may be read directly. This assumption must be made for the sake of simplification. Advance logging interpretation would be devoted almost altogether to the use of departure curves. The interpretations derived from the use of this simplified study are therefore fraught with the danger of insufficiency and if important decisions are at stake on the basis of simplified interpretations, specialists versed in the subject matter not fully discussed here should be consulted.

THE SPONTANEOUS POLARIZATION POTENTIAL OR SELF-POTENTIAL (SP) CURVE

To understand the SP curve we must review the fundamental physical principles involved in the relatively simple measurement of the electric potential existing between an electrode at the surface of the ground and an electrode within a well filled with drilling fluid. Essentially the well may be likened to a large test tube extending through the geologic formations containing primarily salty connate waters. Normally the test tube itself is filled with relatively fresh water, the aqueous phase of a water-base mud. The formations are mostly shales (clay), sands (quartz), or limestones and dolomites (carbonates) having more or less connate water saturation in the pore volume.

There are two classes of reactions which occur when the relatively fresh water of the well contacts the rock formations, one with the solid framework of the rocks, the other with their fluid content, both of which give rise to electrical potentials.

Diffusion Potential or Concentration Cell Effect

The salinity contrast between well water and formation or connate water gives rise to a concentration cell at the well boundary of a water-bearing porous formation. Owing to the differential mobility of the ions in solution in both fluids, a diffusion potential takes place in such a manner that the dilute solution acquires the electric charge of the fastest moving ion. The diffusion potential in a well may be explained on the basis of sodium chloride as the sole electrolyte for which the absolute mobilities are as follows:

$$Na^+ = 0.000456 \text{ cm per sec}$$
$$Cl^- = 0.000676 \text{ cm per sec}$$

at a temperature of 18°C. The mobilities given above are the absolute velocities of the ions at 18°C under a potential gradient of 1 volt per cm. Ionic diffusion is from the concentrated solution to the dilute solution and the well fluid facing a saline water-bearing horizon acquires negative charges with respect to geologic formations as a result of the higher mobility of the Cl^- ions. The magnitude of the diffusion potential E_d, in *volts*, may be evaluated by

$$E_d = \frac{v - u}{u + v} \frac{RT}{nF} \log \frac{C_2}{C_1} \tag{4-1}$$

for a single salt, where C_1 and C_2 are the salt concentrations in the two solutions (activities should be used for concentrated solutions) and v and u are, respectively, the mobilities of the cation and anion; $RT/F = 0.0575$ at 18°C. For sodium chloride the diffusion-potential equation may be written as follows, after substitution of u and v by their values taken from Table 4-1 and of $n = 1$ for the valency:

$$E_d = -11.2 \log \frac{C_2}{C_1} \tag{4-2}$$

from which E_d is directly obtained in *millivolts* at 18°C. At 25°C, or 78°F, the coefficient of Eq. (4-2) is 11.6. It may readily be seen that for a hundredfold concentration contrast, the diffusion potential for sodium chloride is only 23.2 mv. For a thousandfold salinity contrast, the reading will be only 34.8 mv. It may be of interest to speculate upon the magnitude of the part played by the diffusion potential in an SP log. Although sodium

TABLE 4-1. MOBILITIES OF IONS AT 18°C

Cation	Mobility, cm per sec × 10^5 (v)	Anion	Mobility, cm per sec × 10^5 (u)
H^+	324.2	OH^-	180.2
K^+	66.5	$\frac{1}{2}SO_4^{=}$	70.4
$\frac{1}{2}Ba^{++}$	56.9	Br^-	69.7
$\frac{1}{2}Ca^{++}$	53.4	I^-	68.5
Na^+	45.6	Cl^-	67.6
Li^+	34.4	HCO_3^-	39.4
$\frac{1}{2}Mg^{++}$	46.6	$\frac{1}{2}S^{=}$	119.0
		$\frac{1}{2}CO_3^{=}$	76.8

chloride is generally the most common salt in solution in both connate waters and well fluid, there may be a considerable number of other ions in more or less greater concentrations. In Table 4-1 are listed the ions which may be found in either connate water or well fluid together with their respective mobilities.

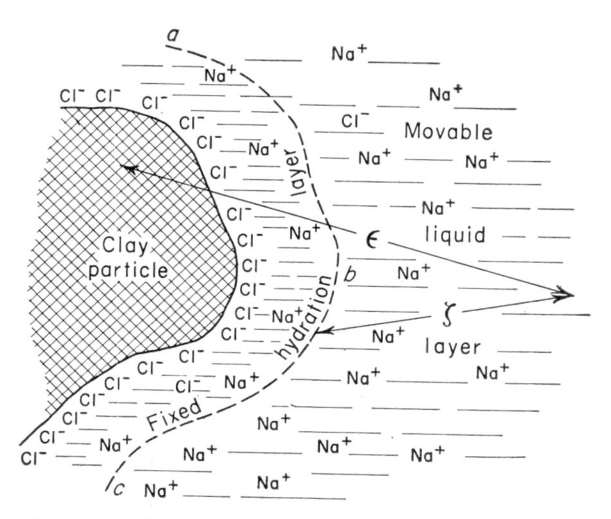

FIG. 4-6. Ionized clay micelle. The system represented is electrically balanced, there being as many Cl^- ions as there are Na^+ ions, yet there are electrical potential differences between the clay particle and the liquid.

Reactions of Fresh Water with the Solid Framework of Rocks (Double-layer Potential, Mounce Potential, Shale Potential)

As relatively fresh water comes in contact with rocks, we may have preferential adsorption of some of the salt ions in solution in the well water and ionization or passage into a movable state of some of the adsorbed ions on the rock particles. We have the formation of a Helmholtz double electric layer between the solid framework of rocks and the well fluid. What happens may be more readily understood from a consideration of Fig. 4-6, where the rock framework is a particle of clay. Originally most of the sodium chloride (NaCl) ions present in the system were adsorbed by the clay. At the introduction of fresh water to the right of the clay particle, as when in contact with drilling mud, the negatively charged chlorine ions (Cl^-) remain preferentially adsorbed by the clay and the positively charged sodium ions (Na^+) enter into solution. However, some of the Na^+ ions are electrostatically attracted by the negatively charged clay particle and remain in the vicinity of the clay (forming a fixed layer), whereas others wander at near liberty away from the clay particle (forming a movable layer). Hence, if one measures the potential difference that exists between the clay particle and a point farther and farther away within the water solution, one measures an increasingly greater potential difference with respect to the clay. The greatest possible potential difference is called the thermodynamic potential $\mathcal{E}$ of the substance and is given in volts by the Nernst formula:

$$\mathcal{E} = -\frac{RT}{nF}\ln\frac{a_1}{a_2} \tag{4-3}$$

where a_1 and a_2 = the activities of the sodium chloride solutions in the movable and fixed layers, respectively
R = gas constant = 8.314 joules
T = absolute temperature, °K
n = valency of the ions ($n = 1$ in the case of NaCl)
F = the faraday = 96,500 coulombs
ln = natural logarithm (base e) = 2.303 ($\log_{10}$)

For a temperature of 25°C the above expression simplifies to

$$\mathcal{E}\text{ volts} = -\frac{0.0591}{n}\log\frac{a_1}{a_2}$$

For a temperature of 18°C, the constant of the above expression is 0.0575.

The activities a of the solutions in contact, namely, in the fixed and movable layers, may be replaced, as a first approximation, by the electrical conductivities of the two solutions. Conductivity is the reciprocal of resistivity R. Equation (4-3) becomes

$$\mathcal{E}\text{ volts} = -\frac{0.0591}{n}\log\frac{R_2}{R_1} \tag{4-4}$$

The resistivities R_1 and R_2 are essentially the resistivities of the connate (or formation) water R_{wc} and of the mud filtrate R_{mf} in the hole. Hence, the Nernst equation applied to a water-base mud gives the potential due to the reaction of rock surface as follows:

$$\mathcal{E}\text{ volts} = -\frac{0.0591}{n}\log\frac{R_{wc}}{R_{mf}} \tag{4-5}$$

A further observation is made relative to the clay particle shown in Fig. 4-6. Owing to electrostatic attraction between the negatively charged clay and some of the Na^+ ions, the water solution to the left of line *abc* is fixed and immobile with respect to the clay particle. The water to the right of line *abc* is free to move with respect to clay. The largest possible potential difference within the movable water is known as the zeta potential (ζ). The fixed water layer is also termed *water of hydration* or *solvation water*.

The phenomena which have been described here with respect to clay are also present with respect to sands, limestones, and dolomites, but possibly to a smaller degree, and possibly with a reverse sign.

It must also be remarked that the phenomena described are surface ones;

hence, a sand covered with a thin veneer of clay should behave as a shale made principally of the same clay. This is the reason that shaly sands exhibit reduced SP deflections.

An explanation of the shale potential may be obtained by considering Eq. (4-3) as a particular case of the diffusion-potential equation (4-1) when one of the ions has lost its mobility. In the case of shale and clays, the negative ions (Cl^-, $CO_3^=$, HCO_3^-, . . .) lose their mobility ($u = 0$) as a result of strong adsorption and Eq. (4-1) becomes Eq. (4-3). For the case of clean sands, completely devoid of preferential adsorption for one or the other ion, the diffusion equation (4-1) would be entirely valid. It is believed that certain carbonate rocks adsorb preferentially positive ions (cations) such as Na^+, K^+, Ca^{++}, etc. Should the cationic adsorption be complete ($v = 0$), their mobility would be reduced to zero and again Eq. (4-1) would reduce to Eq. (4-3) but with reverse sign. In either case, the mobility reduction of the anions or cations may be incomplete and the potential obtained may vary with the mineralogy of the rock causing the adsorption. Variability in ionic adsorption seems to be particularly noticeable in carbonate rocks, depending on whether they are limestones or dolomites.

The seat of the SP potential is located in three types of rocks: (1) *shales*, in which the potential for complete anion adsorption is given by $\frac{0.0591}{n} \times \log \frac{R_{mf}}{R_{wc}}$; (2) *sands*, in which the diffusion potential only exists in view of the rock being completely inert, and is given by $\frac{0.0591}{n} \frac{u - v}{u + v} \log \frac{R_{mf}}{R_{wc}}$; (3) *carbonates*, in which the potential for complete cation adsorption is given by $-\frac{0.0591}{n} \log \frac{R_{mf}}{R_{wc}}$. Should they be porous, an additional diffusion potential would be superposed.

For the ideal case represented in Fig. 4-7, one may recognize *three base lines:* the left base line or carbonate base line is for complete cation adsorption by carbonate, the center line is the inert base line for clean sands, and the right base line or shale base line is for complete anion adsorption by shales. A resistivity contrast R_{mf}/R_{wc} of 10 is assumed in Fig. 4-7, the connate water being more saline than the mud.

The above theory explains why massive limestones in a shale section appear as oil- or gas-bearing porous sands by their high self-potential and high resistivity deflections, even though they have no porosity or permeability. This is especially the case in the Kincaid limestone of Illinois and in many of the Pennsylvanian limestones of Oklahoma and North Texas. Hollowcast oölitic limestones which are devoid of permeability have also given the appearance of oil-bearing sands.

The practice generally resorted to in order to eliminate the possibility of misinterpreting limestones for porous sands is to correlate with sample and stratigraphic logs. Other means of ascertaining whether or not one is dealing with a massive limestone are through the use of the micro-log and by computing the true resistivity of the formation from the various resistivity curves. If they all correct to the same value of R_t, there is no invasion, and one is dealing with a massive limestone.

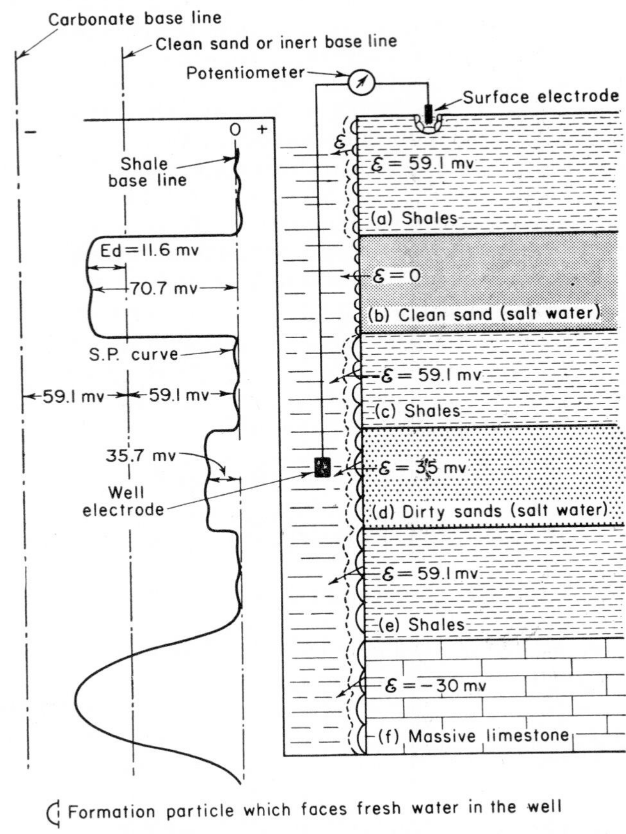

FIG. 4-7. Hypothetical self-potential log based solely on the existence of differential electrochemical potentials.

A better insight into the working of the SP log may be gained by considering the hypothetical geological section of Fig. 4-7 in which it is assumed that electrofiltration effects are absent. The SP log shown to the left of the figure is based upon the existence of differential Nernst potentials at the contact of the well mud with the geologic formations and of diffusion potentials in porous layers. The assumed values of the Nernst potential are indicated in millivolts at each level and it is further assumed that the well fluid is rendered positive in each case with respect to the rock framework, although the previous discussion indicates the possibility of a reversal in sign. Inasmuch as the well fluid is less conductive than the formations, it is normal to assume that they are all at the same potential and that the differential potential gradient is altogether located within the well fluid. The well-fluid facing sand *b* is at the same potential as the surface electrode. When the well electrode passes from shales *a* to sand *b*, a 70.7-mv differential is observed with the well electrode potential swinging negative. The SP deflection 70.7 mv from the shale base line is the sum of the shale potential 59.1 mv and the diffusion potential 11.6 mv. In shaly sand *d*, the total SP deflection is 24.1 + 11.6 = 35.7 mv from shale base line. In massive limestone *f*, a large SP deflection is registered but it falls short of the carbonate base line because of the high resistivity associated with a nonporous limestone.

The Streaming Potential, Electrokinetic Potential or Electrofiltration Potential

It was explained previously that when an electrolyte (a salt solution or brine) is in contact with a dielectric (sand, clay, etc.), a segregation of electrically charged particles takes place. Depending on the type of salt, the pH, the concentrations, etc., various situations may prevail. The zeta potential (ζ) may be either positive, negative, or zero.

If a fluid flow occurs in a porous medium, mechanical shear takes place within the liquid between the fixed hydration layer and the movable layer, electric charges are transported downstream, and a potential, the so-called streaming potential, is observed between upstream and downstream electrodes.

A relation has been established by Perrin (1904) to express the streaming potential as a function of its factors, namely, the differential pressure between mud column and formation, filtrate viscosity and resistivity, and other properties of lesser interest.

It is of interest to ascertain the importance which the streaming potential may play in the SP deflections recorded in wells.

For this purpose, the Perrin equation was modified and rewritten after substitution of quantities difficult to measure in the field and in terms of measurable properties of the filter cake, such as thickness e_{mc} and formation factor F. It is assumed that the filter cake is responsible for most, if not all, of the streaming potential. This is a reasonable assumption since to a large measure the pressure difference ΔP between mud and formation takes place across the filter cake. The following equation was obtained:

$$E_s^2 = Fe_{mc}\left(\frac{Q}{A}\right) R_{mf}\,(\Delta P) \times 10^{-7} \qquad (4\text{-}6)$$

The following assumptions are made for the purpose of illustration:

F = mud-cake formation factor = 2.0
e_{mc} = mud-cake thickness = ⅛ in., or 0.3 cm
Q = measured filter loss = 10 cc per 30 min through standard press 9 cm in diameter and under 100-psi pressure drop

This filter loss should be that obtained after the filter cake has been formed in place and subjected to the plastering action of drill pipe. The filter loss recorded on the log heading is accordingly an upper limit and filter loss to be used is arbitrarily taken to be 100 times smaller than the measured value reported on the log heading.

ΔP = pressure differential between mud column and formation = 500 psi

$\frac{Q}{A}$ = actual filter loss per sq cm per sec = $\frac{10}{\pi/4 \times 9^2} \times \frac{1}{30 \times 60} \times \frac{500}{100} = 4.39 \times 10^{-6}$ cc per sq cm per sec

R_{mf} = mud-filtrate resistivity assumed to be 1 ohm-meter = 100 ohm-cm

P = 500 psi = $\frac{500}{14.7} \times 10^6$ dynes per sq cm = 34×10^6 dynes per sq cm

Substituting in (4-6),

$$E_s^2 = 2 \times 0.3 \times 4.39 \times 10^{-6} \times 100 \times 34 \times 10^6 \times 10^{-7} = 792 \times 10^{-6} \text{ volts}^2$$

Therefore, the streaming potential in millivolts is

$$E_s = 28.2 \text{ mv}$$

In view of the pessimistic considerations made in regard to the mud quality and the actual filter loss which is the cause of the streaming potential while the SP log is run, it appears that the streaming potential may be neglected in most instances. A chart for the rapid evaluation of streaming potential is given in Fig. 4-8.

Self-potential Lithologic Factors (K)

In view of the fact that the SP log measures relative to the shale base line the sum of the diffusion and shale potentials placed in series, the total SP deflection observed in the case of sodium chloride mud would essentially be obtained by adding the values given by Eqs. (4-2) and (4-5), written for a temperature of 25°C and for NaCl ($n = 1$). Hence

$$\text{SP}_{\text{mv}} = -(59.1 + 11.6) \log \frac{C_1}{C_2} \tag{4-7}$$

or when substituting the reciprocal of resistivity for concentration,

$$\text{SP}_{\text{mv}} = -70.7 \log \frac{R_{mf}}{R_{wc}}$$

The coefficient 70.7 is the SP lithologic factor, at 25°C for a geologic sequence of clean sands and shales. It depends on temperature since the above coefficient includes a temperature of 25°C.

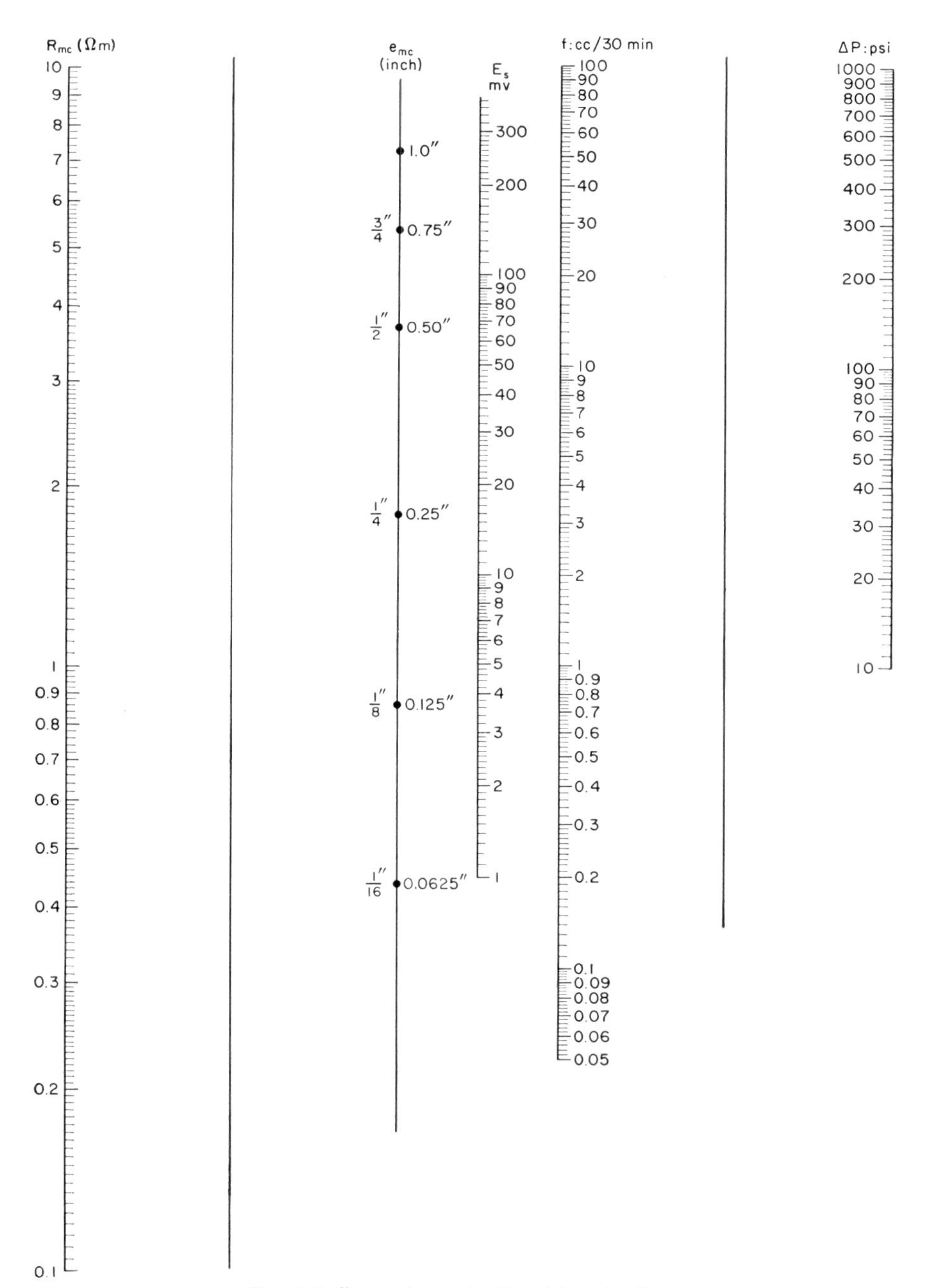

FIG. 4-8. Streaming-potential determination.

The general equation for the SP deflection, which is also called the static SP (SSP), is

$$SSP = -70.7 \frac{T_f}{298} \log \frac{R_{mf}}{R_{wc}} \tag{4-8}$$

where T_f is absolute formation temperature in °C. A chart for the rapid evaluation of the SP is reproduced in Fig. 4-9 in which the variations of

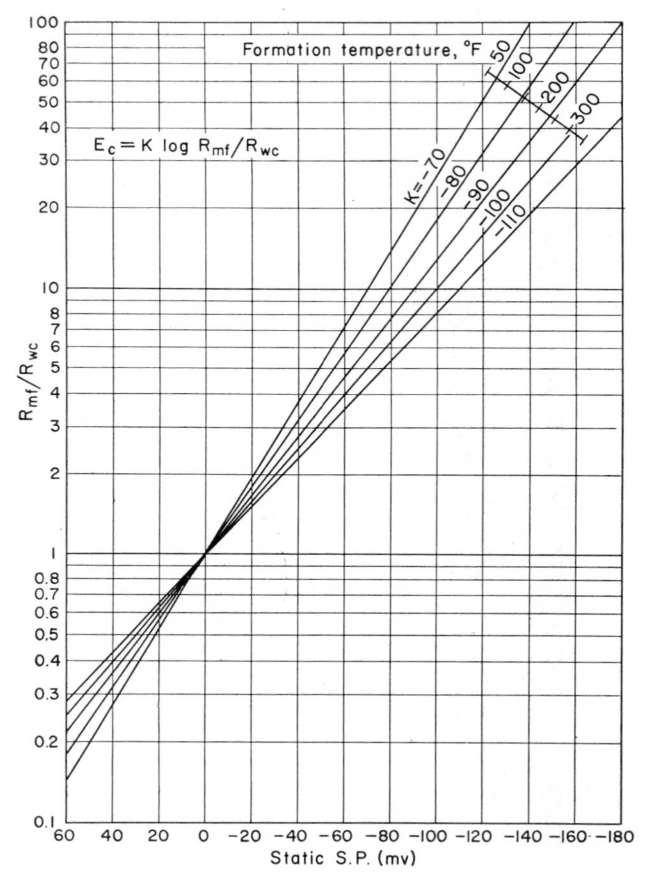

FIG. 4-9. Determination of R_{mf}/R_{wc} from the SP curve. (*Schlumberger Well Surveying Corp.*)

bottom-hole temperature, mud filtrate, and connate water resistivities are taken into account. In using the chart for the determination of formation-water resistivity, it is assumed that the formation temperature is available. This is provided on the heading of the well log.

The value of R_{mf} may be derived from empirical chart Fig. 4-2*b* from a knowledge of mud resistivity R_m at the formation temperature. However, the practice of measuring R_{mf} from an actual mud sample is rapidly developing. Carbonate-bearing formations may require higher values of the SP lithologic factors, as high as 110, because of the carbonate potential, but adjustments made for this effect are purely empirical and depend on experience.

Modifying Factors of the Self-potential Curve

Thus far the discussion of the SP curve has been concerned with the deflections which would be observed in the absence of disturbing factors, or when the so-called "static" SP is measured. This is the value which would be measured in the absence of a current supplied by the emf source, or as if insulating plugs were introduced above and below the horizon of interest and the measuring electrode were located between the two plugs (Fig. 4-10).

The presence of the plugs does not affect the emf generated at the various boundaries. Since the plugs prevent current flow, the potential within each single medium, enclosed by the boundaries or plugs, remains constant. However, the potential varies from medium to medium and if SP measurements were made using insulating plugs through a section of the well, a sharp SP diagram would be obtained which is the SSP diagram, as indicated on Fig. 4-10*a*. In the absence of insulating plugs, electric current is taken out of the SP cell and it circulates in the formations and borehole as shown in Fig. 4-10*b*. Because of the ohmic loss or *ir* drop, what will now be measured is a much less sharp diagram, or "dynamic" SP log.

The following discussion of the dynamic SP is adapted from Doll (1949).

Along its path, the SP current has to force its way through a series of resistances, both in the ground and in the mud. In so doing, it produces potential differences according to Ohm's law. Along a given line of flow, the potential falls down continuously in the direction of the current, as indicated by arrows, but at each boundary where an electromotive force occurs, the potential is raised by an amount corresponding to the value of the electromotive force. Along a closed line of current flow, the total drop of potential is necessarily equal to the sum of the electromotive forces encountered.

Also, the intensity of the current being constant along its path, the potential drop varies according to the resistance of the section through which it flows. This means that the total potential drop (which is equal to the sum of the electromotive forces) is divided between the different formations and the mud in proportion to the resistances, respectively, encountered by the current in each medium. Accordingly, the potential drop in the mud of the drill hole measures only part of the total emf, unless the electrical resistance offered by the mud is very large compared to that in the formations.

The SP log records the potential drop occurring in the mud. It follows that the amplitude of the peak of the SP log approaches the amplitude of the static SP, which is the sum of the partial emf's, only in favorable cases. When the resistance of the mud to the flow of SP current is not large compared to the resistance in the formations, then the SP log will show a peak of lesser amplitude than the static SP diagram.

It may also be seen on Fig. 4-10*b* that the current circulates in the mud, not only opposite the permeable formation (salt-water sand), but also part way beyond its boundaries. As a result, though the static SP diagram indicates a sharp break corresponding to the boundaries of the permeable bed, the SP log exhibits a more progressive change in potential, extending along the drill hole beyond the boundaries of that bed.

In the case illustrated by Fig. 4-10*b*, the permeable bed is thin; so the resistance in that bed is appreciable compared to the total resistance in the SP current path. This is why, in that case, the deflection of the SP log, which measures the potential

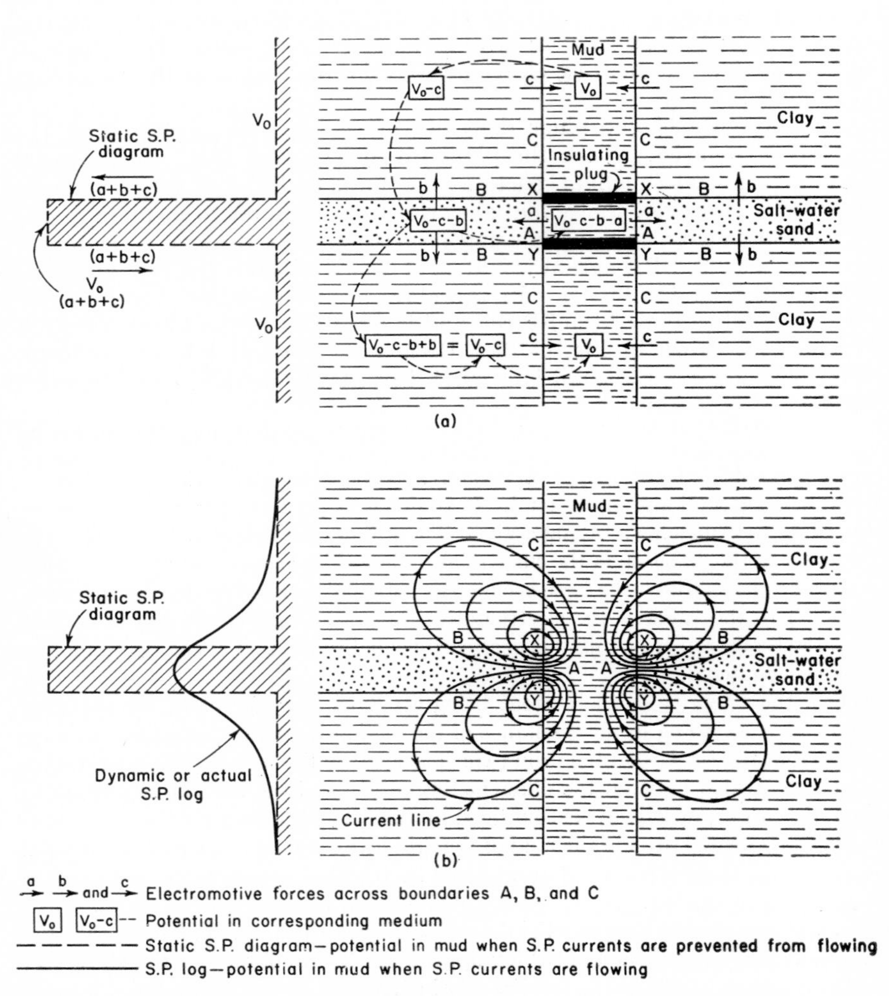

FIG. 4-10. Schematic representation of potential and current distribution in and around a permeable bed. Static and dynamic SP. (*After Doll, Schlumberger Well Surveying Corp.*)

drop in the mud, is only a fraction of the total emf. To make that point clearer, the SP log has been represented in solid line, together with the static SP diagram whose deflection characterizes the total emf involved.

As shown by Fig. 4-10*b*, the deflection of the SP log is not only smaller than the one of the static SP diagram, but it is also much more progressive. It is interesting to remark that the slope of the SP log measures the potential drop per unit length in the hole, which is proportional to the intensity of the SP current in the mud at the corresponding level. Starting from the top part of the log and going down, the slope increases progressively because the current in the hole increases progressively, until the level X (contact clay-sand) is reached. At that level, the intensity of the current in the hole is maximum, and this corresponds on the SP log to a maximum slope, or in other words, to an *inflection point*. Below that level, the current progressively decreases until it becomes nil in the middle of the sand; this corresponds to the point of maximum deflection. Farther down, the current flows in the opposite direction, so that the slope of the SP log is reversed. That slope increases progressively, until a new maximum is reached at the level Y (lower sand-clay contact), which corresponds to *another inflection point* on the SP log; and still farther down, the slope progressively decreases again because the current itself decreases.

The above remark about the inflection points of the SP log is important for their interpretation. There was a tendency in the past to place the boundary between a permeable and an impervious bed at the point which corresponds to half the total deflection on the SP log. This may be substantially in error in certain cases. The contact level should be taken as corresponding to the inflection point on the SP log.

As a result of the SP current through the formations, the static SP curve is modified as to the magnitude of its deflection and as to its shape. The following factors are of importance:

1. SP current distribution
2. Bed thickness
3. Well diameter and fluid invasion
4. True resistivity of formation
5. Bed shalyness
6. Carbonate rocks and waters

Self-potential Current Distribution. The geometric distribution of the SP current generated by the SP cells (hydration and diffusion cells) depends upon the distribution of bed resistance through which current circulates. Electric current avoids formations of high resistivity and favors flowing through formations of low resistivity. Examples of SP current distribution are shown in Fig. 4-11.

Figure 4-11*a*, of a low-resistivity shale (R_s = 1 ohm-meter) in contact with a low-resistivity sand (1 ohm-meter), shows that the current is concentrated in the immediate vicinity of the formation contact. As a result, the SP curve shows sharp breaks at this formation contact. Because of the equality between the formation resistivity, the contact is indicated by the inflection point of the SP curve located at half the total SP deflection. The SP deflection reaches a steady value in front of the sand (characterized by a flat top) and this is the *static SP*.

Figure 4-11*b* shows a high-resistivity shale (R_s = 500 ohm-meters such as might be the case for the Woodford shale) in contact with a high-resistivity sand (R_s = 500 ohm-meters), as might be the case for an oil

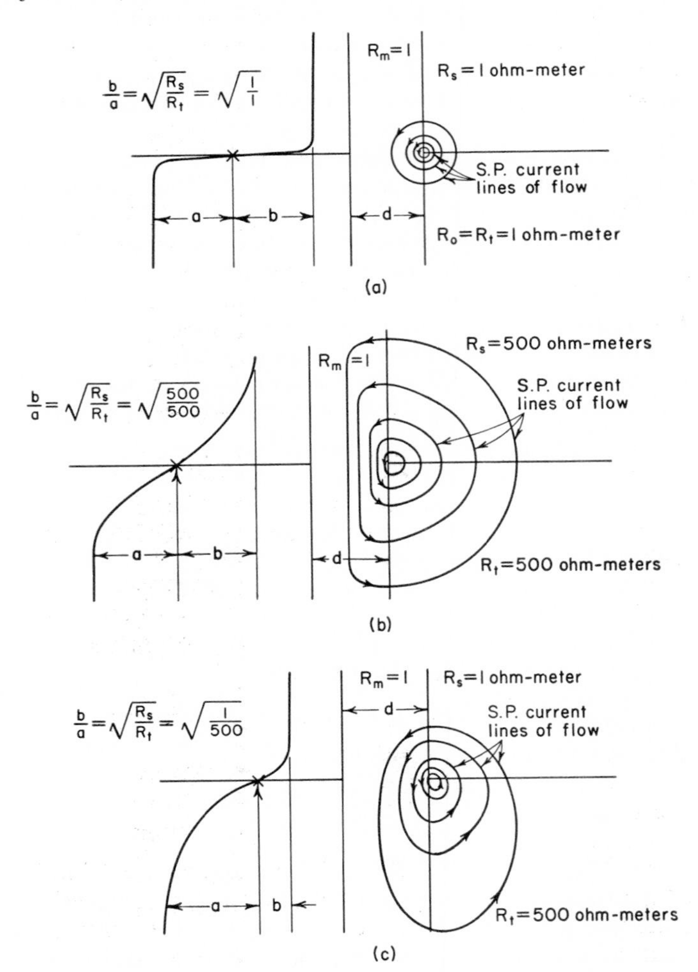

FIG. 4-11. Self-potential curve as modified by current distribution. (*a*) Low-resistivity shale R_s in contact with low-resistivity sand R_t; (*b*) high-resistivity shale in contact with high-resistivity sand; (*c*) low-resistivity shale in contact with high-resistivity sand.

sand or a low-porosity limestone (Hunton limestone). Because of the high resistivity of the formation and of the greater difficulties encountered by the SP current in penetrating the formation, the lines of current spread farther apart and encompass a larger formation volume than in Fig. 4-11*a*. As the probing electrode of the SP measuring device scans the well bore in the vicinity of the stratigraphic contact, it is seen that the boundary is no longer indicated by a sharp and abrupt change in the potential curve but rather by a smooth curve. Because of the resistivity symmetry in the system, the inflection point of the curve which marks the boundary is still located halfway between the shale base line and the point of maximum deflection. Because the lower and porous medium is presumably of infinite thickness, the actual SP curve again reaches a flat top or static SP, which is the battery potential of the diffusion and shale cells placed in series.

Figure 4-11*c* records the situation that obtains when a low-resistivity shale ($R_s = 1$ ohm-meter) is in contact with a high-resistivity porous bed ($R_t = 500$ ohm-meters). In this case the resistivity symmetry is destroyed; the current density (number of lines of current per unit area) is greater in the shale than in the high-resistivity porous bed. The latter could be a water-bearing limestone of low porosity (high formation factor) or a highly porous and oil-bearing sandstone containing low formation-water saturation. Because of the spreading of the current lines in the high-resistivity formation and their concentration in the shale, the SP curve takes on a symmetrical aspect with the location of the inflection point still at the stratigraphic contact, but its value (b) read from the shale base line is given by

$$\frac{b}{a} = \sqrt{\frac{R_s}{R_t}} \tag{4-9}$$

where $a + b =$ static SP, or total deflection.

Bed-thickness Effect on the Self-potential. The previous considerations were made for beds of infinite thickness in which case the maximum deflection is always the static SP. Should there be two boundaries limiting a porous bed, as indicated in Fig. 4-10*b*, then the maximum SP deflection is less than the static value. This is especially true if the porous formation is very thin or very resistive. Of special interest is the case of interbedded thin sand and shale forming sandwichlike layers.

The following discussion on the SP curve of thin interbedded sands and shales is adapted from Doll (1948).

The strata under consideration have thus far been bounded usually by comparatively thick beds. It is desirable, however, to examine the effect of interbedded layers of permeable and impervious strata. When there are thin layers of sand in shale, or thin layers of shale in sand, their combination constitutes what has been called a "sandwich," which can be considered as more or less shaly sand.

The effect of sandwiches is illustrated by Figs. 4-12 to 4-15, which are believed to be self-explanatory. These figures show the following points, with respect to the SP log:

1. On thick sandwiches the average deflection is approximately proportional to the percentage of permeable beds.

2. The average contour corresponding to a sandwich of finite thickness is the same for a homogeneous permeable bed of the same thickness and resistivity but for which the total emf involved would apparently be smaller.

3. The amplitude of the ripples around the average curve decreases very quickly with decreasing thickness of the individual beds, so that the ripples are hardly noticeable when the individual thickness of both the impervious and permeable beds is less than one-half the diameter of the hole.

The following properties, which are not illustrated by the figures, must also be mentioned:

1. The amplitude of the ripples decreases when the permeable beds are invaded by the mud filtrate.

2. The average amplitude of the peaks decreases when the resistivity of the permeable beds increases with respect to that of the impervious beds.

This latter phenomenon is of particular interest when a certain section of a shaly sand is oil-bearing, while another section is water-bearing.

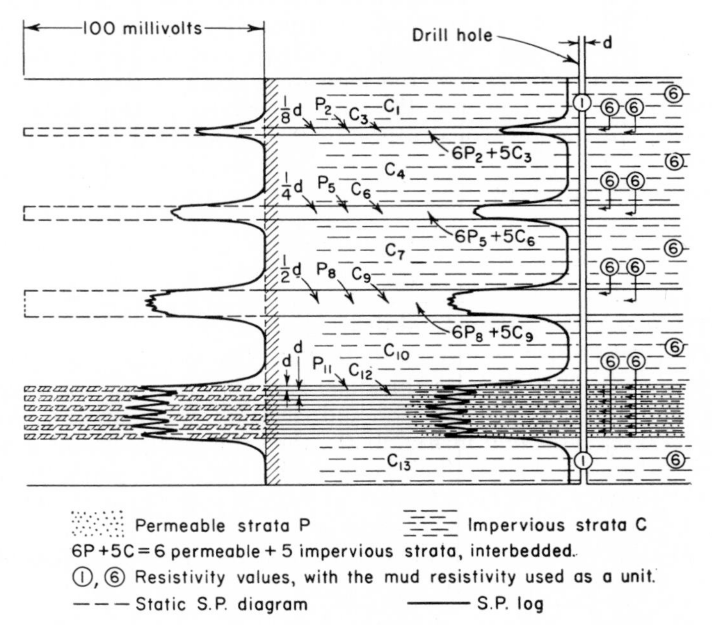

FIG. 4-12. SP logs for different thicknesses of interbedded strata ($R_t = 6R_m$). (*After Doll, courtesy AIME.*)

Well Diameter and Fluid Invasion. Consider that a sand layer is embedded between two shales and that for some reason the hole is considerably enlarged at the sand level. This is equivalent to adding resistance into the circuit traversed by the SP current. However, part of this circuit is no longer within reach of the measuring electrode and a permanent *ri* voltage drop is lost. Accordingly, smaller SP voltages will be read in enlarged hole sections.

The existence of invasion has a similar effect in reducing the SP deflection because, in effect, invasion merely makes the position of the diffusion cell move away from the well bore. Because of the high resistivity of

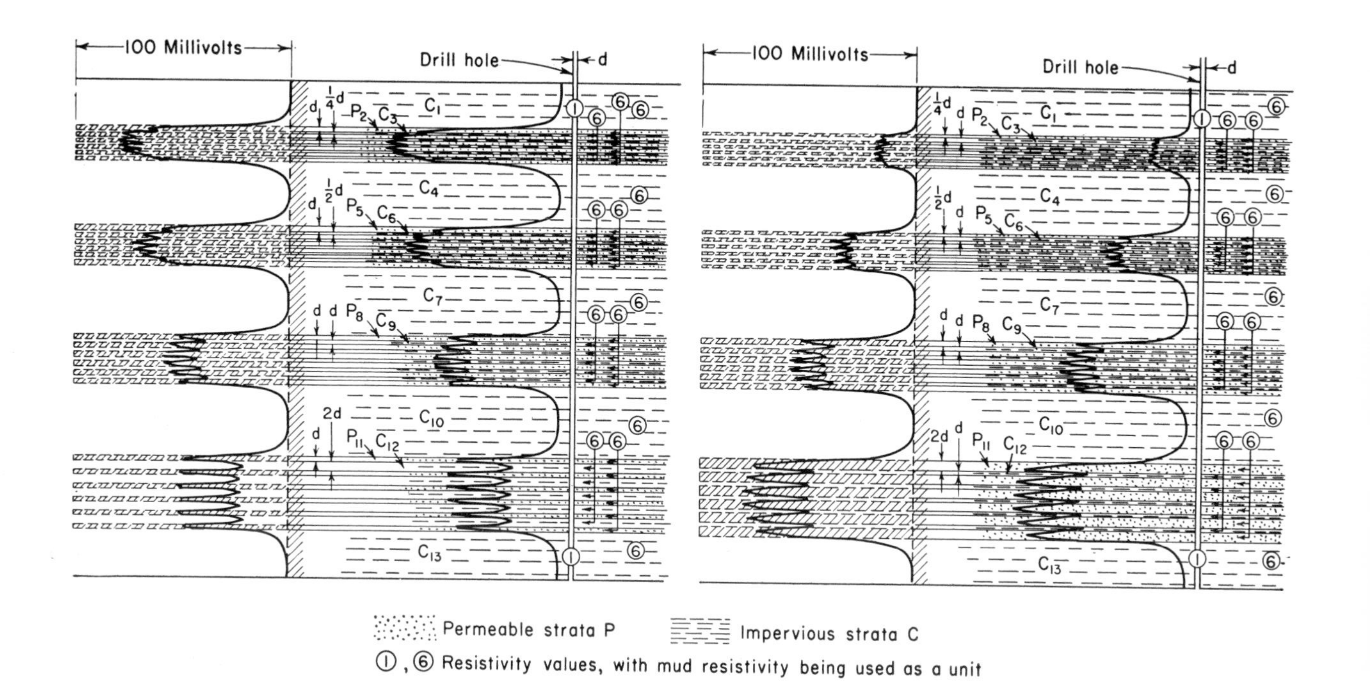

FIG. 4-13. SP logs for various combinations of interbedded thin permeable and impervious strata ($R_t = 6R_m$). (*After Doll, courtesy AIME.*)

the invaded zone, a permanent *ri* voltage drop is lost from the measuring circuit and smaller SP voltages are read.

When the enlarged well-bore diameter d is known (as determined from caliper surveys) or the diameter of invasion D_i is known (as determined from resistivity departure curves), dependable corrections may be made in order to correct the *actual or dynamic SP* deflections to *static* values.

True Formation Resistivity R_t. It must be emphasized that what is measured in the well bore as an SP curve is the ohmic potential drop along

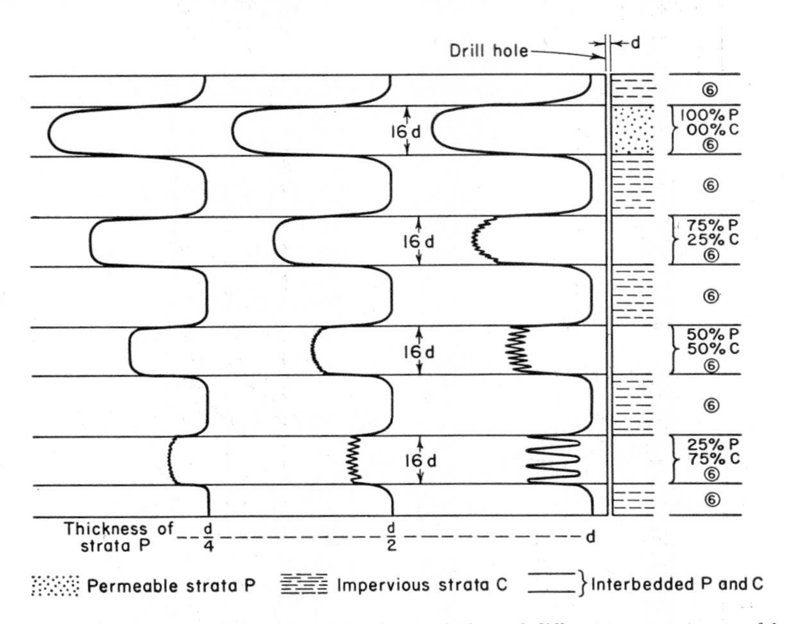

FIG. 4-14. SP logs for uniformly thick beds consisting of different percentages of interbedded permeable and impervious strata varying in thickness ($R_t = 6R_m$). (*After Doll, courtesy AIME.*)

a mud column of presumably constant cross section $\pi d^2/4$ and resistivity R_m as it is traversed by the SP current. The latter enters the porous formations and if they are of high resistivity R_t, the current intensity is reduced. Hence, the potential drop along the mud column is also reduced. As a result high-resistivity porous formations show reduced SP deflections, less than the static SP; this is the case in formations containing oil and it is not unusual to observe an SP gradient in thick sands containing a transition zone, i.e., where the oil column grades from 100 per cent water saturation at the bottom of the reservoir to irreducible water saturation at the top.

The many reasons why the measured SP is less than the static SP have been shown to be that oftentimes permeable beds are too thin, too resistive, too invaded, etc. Figure 4-16 is a correction chart according to Doll (1948), from which the SP deflections as percentage of static SP can

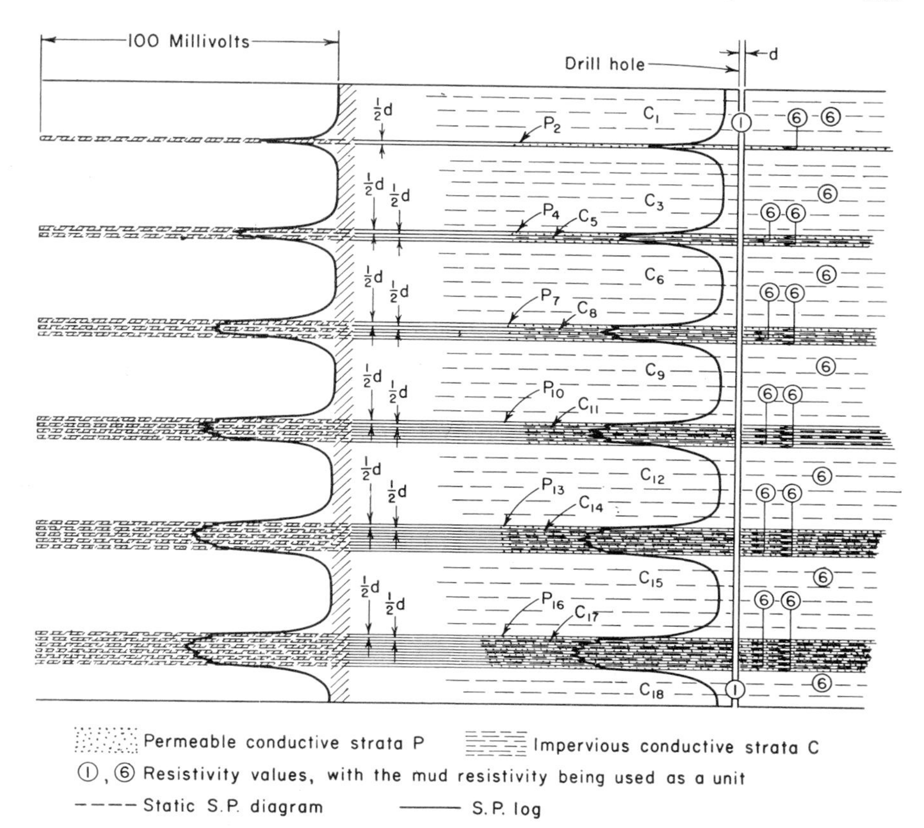

FIG. 4-15. SP logs for increasing layers of thin interbedded permeable and impervious strata ($R_t = 6R_m$). (*After Doll, courtesy AIME.*)

be read on the ordinate scale as a function of bed thickness expressed as multiple of hole diameter d and of

$$\frac{R_t}{R_m} = \frac{\text{true resistivity of object bed}}{\text{mud resistivity}}$$

Correction chart Fig. 4-16 may also be used to compute approximately the reduction in SP caused by the presence of an invaded zone around the well bore, provided the diameter D_i of the invaded zone may be ascertained. In this eventuality it may be considered that the well acts as a bore hole of diameter D_i and where the well fluid is of resistivity R_i, the invaded zone resistivity. Actually, a combination of R_i and R_m should be used for the equivalent resistivity of the material of diameter D_i. Hence, Fig. 4-16 may be used for the evaluation of the effect of invasion on the SP curve by reading R_t/R_m in abscissa and $(x)D_i$ as the thickness of permeable strata $(x)d$, where x is the coefficient of d in Fig. 4-16. As a rule of thumb D_i is generally taken to be five times bit size.

Shalyness of Formations. While the case of interbedded clean sands was considered above as a problem in thin beds, the present discussion is concerned with disseminated shale and clay particles within a porous and permeable section. When the shaly particles are contained in the bulk of the shaly and permeable rock, the reactive particles are entirely surrounded by mud filtrate in the invaded zone or by the original connate water in the noninvaded zone and they generate no SP current. However, when

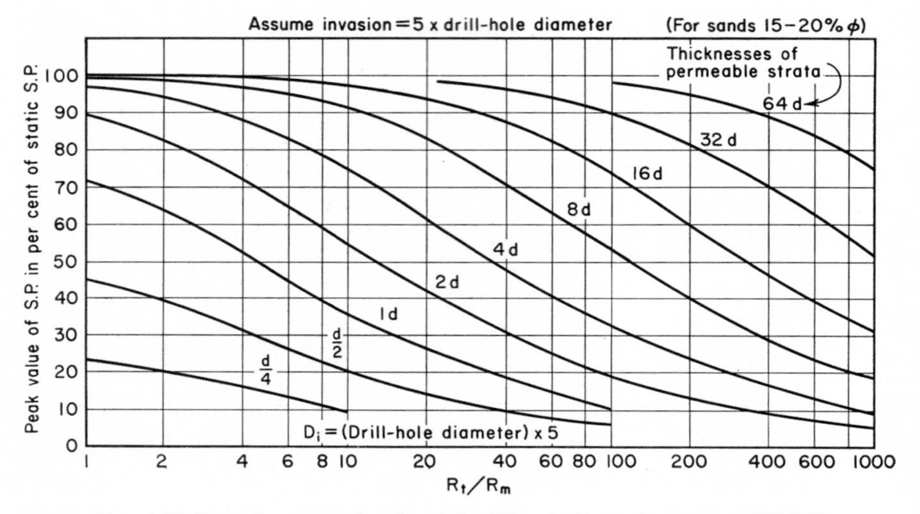

FIG. 4-16. Invasion correction for static SP. (*After Doll, courtesy AIME.*)

the shale particle is in contact on one side with the mud filtrate and on the other side with connate water, the conditions are identical to those which give rise to the shale potential, and SP currents are generated around each shaly particle. This effect is added with its sign to the total usual SP source. Since the voltage contribution by each shale particle is opposite to the normal SP, the latter is reduced in value.

Pseudostatic Self-potential for Shaly Sands. The SP log for a shaly water-bearing sand, in which the average proportion of shaly material is the same at all levels, may be considered to be that of a clean water sand containing water of lower salinity. It may be represented by a uniformly reduced static SP. This lower emf will be called the "pseudostatic SP." In fact it is the SP that would be measured in front of the shaly water-bearing sand if insulating plugs were set at its upper and lower boundaries, as in Fig. 4-10a to interrupt the mud continuity at these levels. The pseudostatic SP represents the maximum possible average deflection for such shaly sand, and it is reached only if the shaly sand is thick enough. Water-bearing thin shaly sands do not produce a full pseudostatic SP deflection; it is necessary to correct the actual SP deflection for bed thickness, invasion, and true resistivity in order to obtain it.

Shaly Sands Containing Oil. The presence of oil in a shaly sand increases its resistance over the value recorded when water-bearing. It can be shown that this increase will lower further the actual SP recorded. Accordingly, the amplitude of the deflections on the SP log can be expected to be smaller opposite an oil-bearing section than opposite a water-bearing section. Such a change in the deflections of the log is only found for shaly sands or for thin, clean sands; it does not occur in thick, clean sands.

Since many sands are shaly, it is not surprising that reductions in the SP deflection are found when passing above the oil-water contact in a sand. It is to be noted, however, that the reduction in SP deflection is not sufficiently diagnostic for the detection of oil, since the same effect would be obtained if the salinity of the interstitial water were reduced, or if the percentage of shale were increased. If there are good reasons to believe that the salinity of the water remains substantially constant in the interval under study and that the shale content within the sand remains the same throughout, then the level at which the SP deflection is reduced is a good indication of the presence of oil. Such a possibility is at least to be considered if concurrently the resistivity is higher, indicating that an increase in shale percentage is not the probable explanation for the lower SP deflection.

The presence of gas in shaly sands may affect the SP log in the same manner as the presence of oil. It seems, however, that there is a tendency for such shaly sands to show even less SP, and that there is a slightly higher resistivity when they contain gas than when they contain oil. This may be due to lower formation-water saturation in gas reservoirs.

The Self-potential Log in Limestone Fields. The case of limestone fields, and more generally of permeable beds in compact and highly resistive formations, deserves special considerations. This discussion is adapted from Doll (1948).

The permeable zones, whether oil-bearing or water-bearing, are somewhat conductive because of the capillary water (generally high in salinity) present in the pores. Conductive beds of low resistivity like shales, for example, are not permeable. When the permeable and impervious beds are thick and sufficiently conductive, the SP deflections approach the "static" values.

However, when the conductive beds are not very thick, and are separated by thick, hard formations of high resistivity, the SP log has a shape which is difficult to understand at first glance. This comes from the fact that the very resistive formations tend to prevent the SP currents from leaving or entering the hole opposite their level. The SP currents thus have to flow into the hole almost entirely by way of the permeable beds and of the nearest conductive impervious beds. In so doing, the SP currents produce linear potential gradient by ohmic effect in the mud in front of the hard resistive formation. The result is that the peaks corresponding to the permeable zones spread above and below these zones in an apparently abnormal manner.

The shape of the SP log is easily understood if the circulation of the SP currents is studied. This circulation is represented, in a schematical way, in Fig. 4-17*c*. The SP currents, which issue from the different sources of emf, flow into the sands. They cannot traverse the adjacent hard formations through sections located close to the drill hole, because these sections

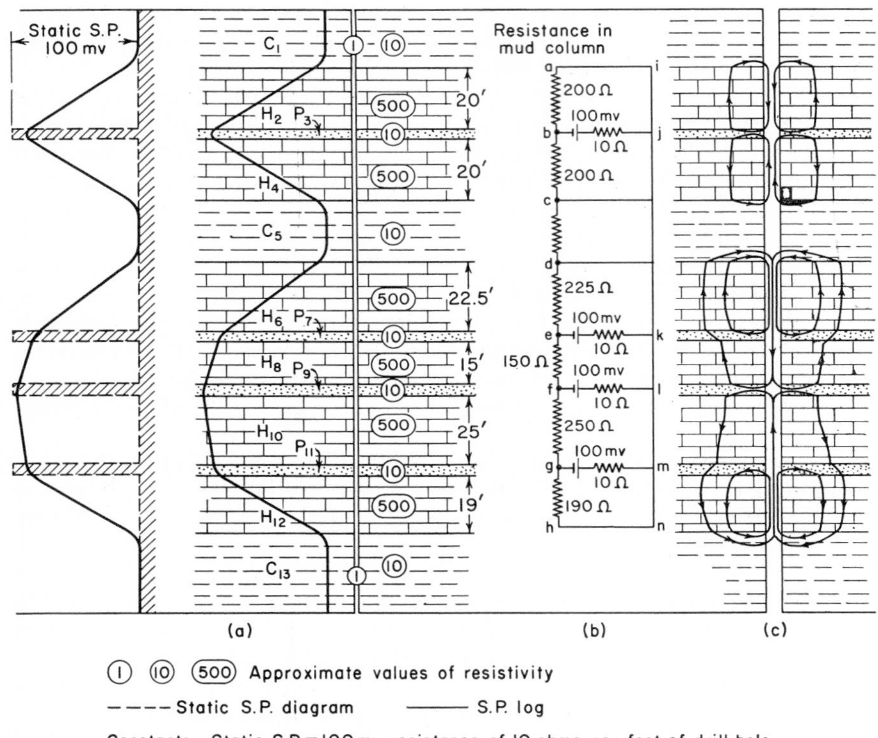

FIG. 4-17. A schematic representation of self-potential phenomena in highly resistive formations (limestones and dolomites). (*a*) Schematic representation of formations and self-potential log; (*b*) equivalent electrical network; (*c*) schematic distribution of self-potential currents. (*After Doll, courtesy AIME.*)

are too small in area and, therefore, introduce into the circuit large resistances which would practically prevent the current flow. On the contrary, the SP current penetrates deeper than usual in the permeable beds and, consequently, enters the hard formations through larger cross sections. From there on, it is easier for the SP currents to continue their path into the hard formations. The SP currents flow therefore toward conductive beds in the hole, then through the hard formation and the shale, and then through the mud, back to the permeable beds, to close their circuits. They cannot come back to the mud through other permeable beds, because they would encounter emfs which would oppose the flow of current in that direction. When the first conductive beds they encounter are of the permeable type, they simply cross them until they reach conductive and impervious beds. This is the case for the SP currents which penetrate the permeable bed P_9; they have to cross the permeable bed P_7 in order to reach the impervious bed C_5, or have to cross the permeable bed P_{11} in order to reach the impervious bed C_{13}.

All along a drill hole opposite a given hard formation, the current in the mud column remains substantially the same, and so does the drop of potential per unit length of hole, thus giving a constant slope to the SP log.

At the level of each conductive bed, some SP current generally penetrates or leaves the hole, and therefore the slope of the SP log is modified at such levels. In Fig. 4-17*a*, for example, the SP log changes its slope at the level of the permeable bed P_7, because part of the current leaves the hole and flows into that bed. In the particular case of bed P_7, the SP current in the drill hole flows in the same direction above and below it, and the slope is simply changed but not reversed. The situation is different in the case of the permeable beds P_3 and P_9; at their levels, the direction of the current in the hole is reversed, and so is the slope of the SP log.

When there is only one permeable bed like P_3 between two successive shale beds like C_1 and C_5, that permeable bed is easy to detect on the SP log, even when hard formations like H_2 and H_4 are present, because a very definite slope reversal occurs opposite the permeable bed. In the case of such an isolated permeable bed, a remaining difficulty is to determine its boundaries exactly.

The interpretation is less evident when there is a succession of permeable beds separated by hard formations, as in the case of beds P_7, P_9, and P_{11}.

Summary of Self-potential Characteristics. In conclusion, the characteristics of the SP curve may be summarized by the following observations:

1. The boundary between a permeable bed and an impervious bed is characterized by an inflection point on the SP log. This inflection point does not correspond to mid-deflection when the resistivities of the two beds in contact are different, or when one of the beds is thin. For the boundary of two thick beds the SP curve inflection point is nearer to the SP plateau corresponding to the more conductive of the two beds.

2. When permeable beds are bounded by highly resistive formations, as in limestone sections, the corresponding peaks spread appreciably beyond the boundaries (triangular effect). The boundaries can no longer be determined with good accuracy without the help of the resistivity log and especially of the micrologs. Permeable beds, however, are characterized on the SP log by slope changes, or curvatures, with the convexity toward the negative. Conversely, shale beds of low resistivity are characterized by slope changes, or curvatures, with the convexity toward the positive. Highly resistive formations correspond to substantially straight parts of the SP log.

3. When the permeable beds are reasonably clean, are of sufficient thickness, and contain the same interstitial water, they furnish a base line which

is just as good as the shale line. This condition is met when the static SP is measured.

4. The static SP is obtained from the amplitude recorded on thick sands that are known to be substantially clean and to contain the same type of interstitial water.

5. Sands containing colloidal clay and shaly material, or sandwiches of thin strata of sand and shale, behave as if the emf involved were a function of the percentage of shale or colloidal material. Other conditions being the same, the apparent emf decreases when the oil saturation in these sands increases, even though their colloidal content is only a few per cent. Accordingly, in the case of thick beds, the amplitude may be used to indicate approximately the percentage of shaly material and to assist in the discrimination between oil-bearing and water-bearing sections of a shaly sand.

The behavior of shale itself is not always uniform. While the "shale base line" of the SP log is considered as a reference line, it is by no means constant. In many wells there is drift of this reference line; this is generally attributed to formation-temperature variation with depth. However, the degree of compaction of a shale seems to have an effect on the shale base-line behavior. The more dense and compact a shale is, the more will the SP be positive in fresh mud. An example of this is the Woodford shale (Oklahoma), the compaction and induration of which are indicated by its unusually high resistivity. The Woodford shale always shows a positive deviation from the shale base line recorded in less resistive shales.

6. The SP curve is often considered to be a diagnostic lithologic curve. This is true to a certain extent, but it is well to bear in mind that it distinguishes only the geologic formation contacts between rocks that are reactive and nonreactive with the well fluid. In the most general case the reactive rocks are shales and the nonreactive rocks are sands. Because nonreactive rocks contain little pore-space-filling reactive minerals, they are often porous and permeable.

This is all that the SP curve tells us.

A reactive-nonreactive rock contact may well be of another nature than sand and shale. A well-known case is that of coal beds: lignite is nonreactive, whereas hard coal (anthracite) is reactive.

Another less well-known case is that of contacts between igneous rocks of various kinds: diabase is reactive, whereas rhyolite is not. A contact between those two rocks gives a most normal type of SP curve.

The mineralogy of the rocks is not inscribed on the SP curve; the only information recorded is whether or not the rocks are *reactive* and *nonreactive* with respect to the *mud* in the hole. This points out the necessity of supplementing the logs with lithological observation of cuttings and cores.

Uses of the Self-potential Curves

1. The most obvious use of the SP curve is in determining the absence of reactive minerals in rocks, which absence is generally related to the existence of porosity whether it be in sand, limestone, dolomite, lignite,

or rhyolite. The SP curve used to be called the "porosity curve"; this terminology is now discarded for good reasons because contrary to a still prevalent belief in the geological profession a well-defined SP kick is not a measure of the magnitude of porosity, although it is an *indication of the existence* of porosity because of the absence of reactive minerals. In addition because of the existence of porosity, a diffusion-potential cell exists at the level of a good SP kick which favors the entrance of SP current at that level.

The SP curve and its kicks are therefore geological indicators of lithologic changes. The exact *top* and *thickness* of the changes can be picked very accurately by the inflection point in the SP curve. These characteristics are of use in geological correlation.

2. From the shape of the SP curve, the order of magnitude of the true resistivity may often be derived. A well-rounded SP curve, with the inflection point close to the shale base line indicates high resistivity even though the resistivity curves cannot be used to find R_t because of invasion, thin beds, shielding, decay, reflections, etc.

3. In quantitative analysis of electric logs the SP curve is used mostly, notwithstanding its pitfalls and inaccuracies, for the evaluation of formation-water resistivities and salinities. The SP equation (4-8) is used to this end. It is to be noted that the static SP is the value that enters the equation, i.e., the actual observed SP deflection from the shale base line with its sign, corrected for bed thickness, hole enlargement, invasion, true resistivity, and streaming potential. If a shaly sand, it should be corrected for the presence of oil, but this is most unsatisfactory.

In determining formation-water resistivities from the static SP deflections, adjustments for the SP lithologic factor are made only for formation temperatures in clean sand-shale sections. In carbonate rock, upward empirical adjustments of the lithologic factor are often necessary.

Formation-water Resistivities. A dependable knowledge of formation-water resistivities is basic to the interpretation of electric logs. While the SP curve provides a means for their determination, it is advisable to ascertain their values from representative samples. Formation waters are conductive of electricity by virtue of the ionized salts which they contain in solution. Under the application of an electric potential gradient to an electrolyte, ions migrate toward the electrode of opposite polarity to their respective charges. Cations (positive ions) move to the cathode (the negative electrode), and conversely. Monovalent cations when reaching the cathode are neutralized by accepting an electron; conversely, monovalent anions when reaching the anode are neutralized by giving up an electron. Since each monovalent ion is responsible for carrying a unit charge of electricity and may carry no more, the ability of an electrolyte to conduct electricity depends on the number of ions per unit volume (concentration) and on the velocity of the ion (mobility) under the application of a unit potential gradient. Besides monovalent ions, such as Na^+, K^+, Cl^-, HCO_3^-, there may be polyvalent ions in solution in the formation waters. Each such ion may carry more than one unit electric charge such as Ca^{++}, Mg^{++}, $CO_3^=$, $S^=$, $SO_4^=$. Another factor which affects the ability of formation waters to conduct electricity is their temperature, because it influences the mobility of the ions.

Determination of Formation-water Resistivities. There are various means by which formation-water resistivities may be obtained:

1. Direct measurement on a representative sample
2. Chemical analysis and computation
3. Consultation of water-sample catalogues and interpolation from isocon maps of specific geologic formations

Direct Measurement. The basis for reliable formation-water resistivities is a representative sample of the waters. Methods of sampling are listed in the order of decreasing degree of reliability:

1. Sample from pumping well flow lines when producing with high water-oil ratio.
2. Sample from flowing well obtained from separator when producing with high water-oil ratio.
3. Sample from drill-stem tests obtained from bottom of stand pipe. Several samples should be obtained along the pipes to ascertain degree of dilution of formation water by water cushion.

Water samples obtained from the following types of wells are not to be relied upon:

1. Flowing wells with a high gas-oil ratio
2. Distillate wells and gas wells
3. Wells with leaky casing

Water samples from tank bottoms, gas-well drips, etc., are considered unreliable.

Measurement of formation-water resistivity is made directly in the laboratory at a standard temperature (68°F) by means of a conductivity dip cell and the results reported directly in ohm-meters.

Temperature Reduction. A common problem is the reduction of water resistivity from one temperature to another. This may be done by the following approximation formula:

$$(R_w)t_f = (R_w)t_a \frac{t_a}{t_f} \qquad (4\text{-}10)$$

where $(R_w)t_f$ = water resistivity at formation temperature t_f
$(R_w)t_a$ = water resistivity at atmospheric temperature t_a

A somewhat more accurate procedure for this reduction is by means of the salinity chart of Fig. 4-18, especially at high salt concentrations. Although the well temperature is or should be recorded on the heading of all logs, it is at times necessary to estimate earth temperature at certain depth from the geothermal gradient. The latter may be interpolated from Fig. 4-19 for the southwestern United States.

Computation of Formation-water Resistivity from Water Analysis. When direct resistivity measurements are no longer possible on a sample but where chemical water analyses from representative formation samples have been made in the past, a reliable value for the resistivity may be computed.

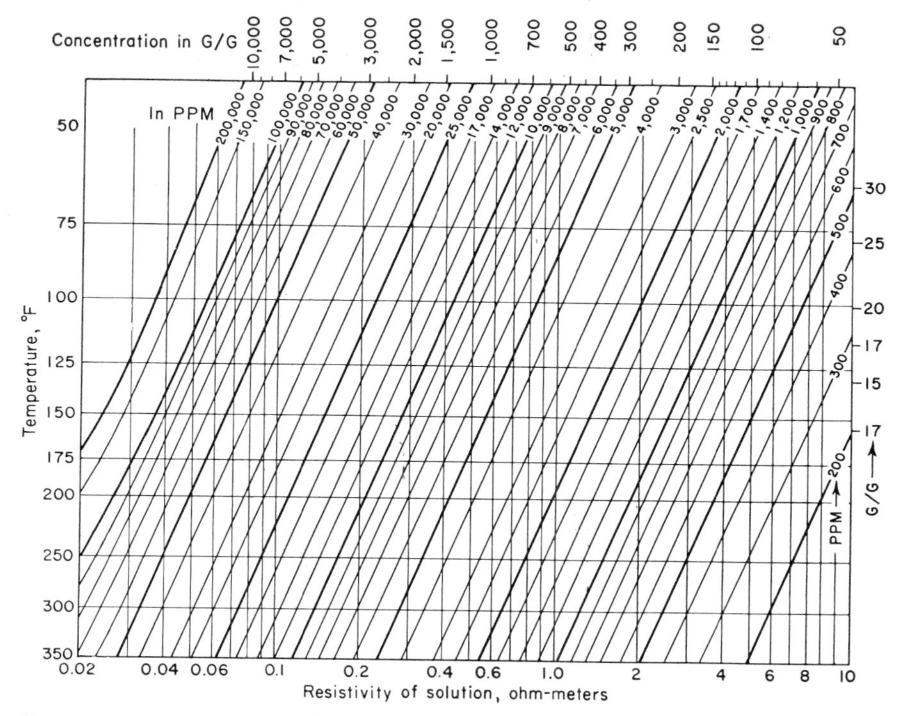

FIG. 4-18. Resistivity graph for salinity and temperature of NaCl solution. (*Schlumberger Well Surveying Corp.*)

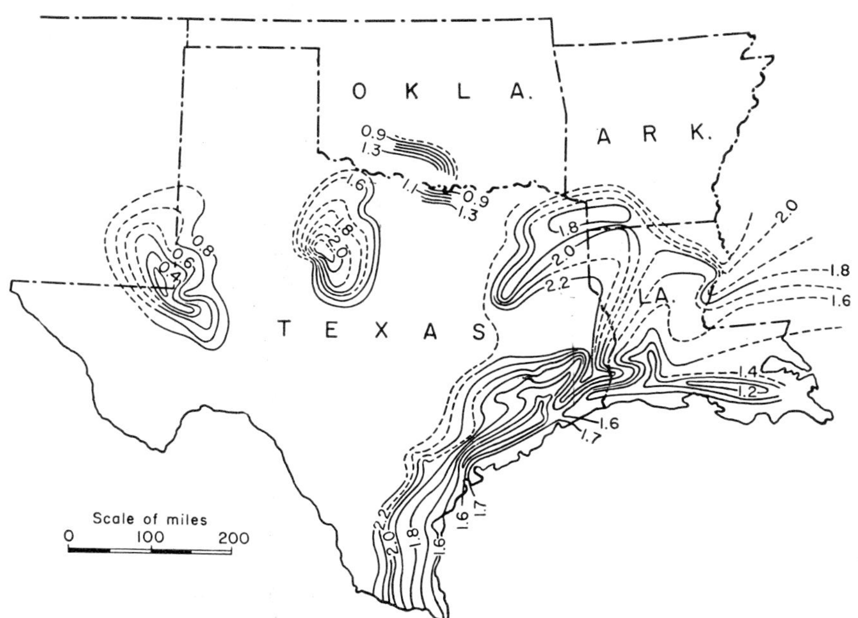

FIG. 4-19. Geothermal gradient map of the Southwestern states. (*After Nichols, courtesy AIME.*)

If most of the salinity of the water consists of NaCl, a good approximation of the resistivity in ohm-meters can be read from the salinity chart of Fig. 4-18.

The resistivity values obtained by means of the salinity chart may, however, be considerably in error when connate waters are rich in salts of ions with mobilities greatly different from Na^+ and Cl^-, and especially if they contain bicarbonate, carbonate, sulfate, and magnesium ions. In this eventuality it is necessary to reduce the chemical composition to an equivalent NaCl composition. A method worked out by the Atlantic Refining Co. Laboratories has proved very dependable for this purpose. The parts per million (ppm) of each ion are reduced to equivalent NaCl salinity by means of conversion factors, a list of which appears in Table 4-2.

TABLE 4-2. TABLE OF CONVERSION FACTORS TO NaCl WHEN SALINITY IS GIVEN IN IONIC PPM
(According to Atlantic)

Ions	*Factor*
Na	1.00
K	1.00
Ca	0.95
Mg	2.00
SO_4	0.50
Cl	1.00
HCO_3	0.27
CO_3	1.26

In order to obtain the total equivalent salinity, the parts per million of each ion are multiplied by the conversion factor and the products so obtained are added together.

The water resistivity is obtained directly from the salinity chart (Fig. 4-18) when read at the desired bottom-hole temperature.

Should the water analysis be available only as a function of the Palmer method of representation, the equivalent NaCl salinity may also be obtained by a similar method through the use of the conversion factors given in Table 4-3.

TABLE 4-3. TABLE OF CONVERSION FACTORS TO NaCl WHEN THE SALINITY IS GIVEN IN PPM PALMER SALTS
(According to Schlumberger)

Palmer salts, ppm	*Factor*
Primary salinity: (NaCl), (KCl)	1.00
Primary salinity: (Na_2SO_4)	0.40
Secondary salinity: ($CaSO_4$), ($MgSO_4$), ($CaCl_2$), ($MgCl_2$)	0.37
Primary alkalinity: (Na_2CO_3), ($NaHCO_3$)	0.50
Secondary alkalinity: ($Ca(HCO_3)_2$), ($Mg(HCO_3)_2$)	0.27

Water Salinity by Geographic and Geologic Interpolation. Where no sample or chemical analysis of formation water is available from the wells under study, an approximation of the water salinity may be obtained by interpolation between analyses of water from the same formation or geologically neighboring formations. Several compilations of such basic information have been made; by way of example, a map is reproduced in Fig. 4-20 pertaining to the Mid-Continent area. Some observations of general significance may be made relative to isocon maps:

1. The salinity of formation waters expressed in ppm solids generally increases with depth. In regions of relatively weak structural deforma-

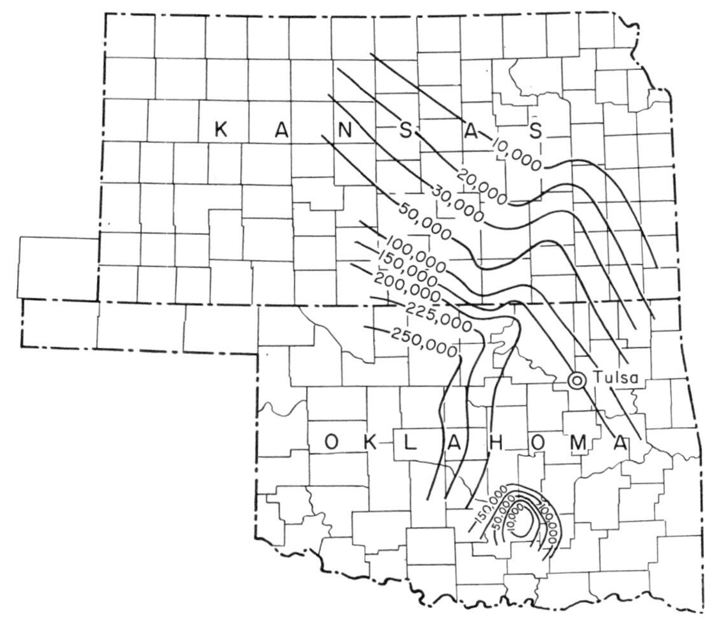

FIG. 4-20. Isocon map of Ordovician waters. *(After Case, courtesy AAPG.)*

tions, at shallow depths there is a zone of fresh to brackish water until waters that are definitely salty are encountered. The depth where the transition occurs rather abruptly varies with all provinces but is generally of the order of 1,000 ft or more below the surface. In regions of high structural deformations, fresh waters may be found at great depth because of the infiltration of meteoric waters at the outcrops. This is particularly the case in the Rocky Mountain area.

2. In structural sedimentary basins, meteoric waters infiltrate on the edge of the basins and a gradual increase in salinity toward the deepest part of the basin is observed. A good illustration of this rule is the Arbuckle water of Oklahoma and Kansas illustrated in Fig. 4-20 where the highest salinity is observed in the deepest part of the Anadarko Basin. Allowing for temperature variations, the resistivity of the Arbuckle formation water varies from 0.6 ohm-meter in northeastern Kansas to 0.015 ohm-meter in the central part of Oklahoma, a fortyfold variation.

The importance of accurate information on connate water salinity and resistivity cannot be overstressed in logging interpretation. The fact that an approximation to these values may be obtained from the SP curve (however unreliable it may be) has deterred many from making the necessary effort to acquire these basic data when the opportunity presents itself during well-testing and producing operations.

MEASUREMENT OF FORMATION RESISTIVITY IN WELLS

By definition, the specific resistivity of a medium is the resistance of a unit cube of this medium. Since the resistance to current flow in an electric conductor is proportional to its resistivity times its length and is inversely proportional to the cross-sectional area available to current flow, the unit of specific resistivity is expressed in ohms times the linear unit chosen. When the linear unit is measured in meters, the resistivity is expressed in ohm-meters. When in feet, the resistivity is expressed in ohm-feet. When in centimeters, the resistivity is expressed in ohm-centimeters. There exists the following relation between the various resistivity units:

$$1 \text{ ohm-cm} = \frac{1}{30.5} \text{ ohm-ft} = \frac{1}{100} \text{ ohm-meter}$$

The resistivity so defined is the true resistivity of a medium. When measuring the resistivity in a well of a formation of finite thickness with electrode spacings of comparable dimensions (and owing to bore-hole effect), a resistivity is measured which is apparent only but which is related to the true resistivity. To obtain the true resistivity from the apparent value measured, complex corrections must be made which will be briefly studied. To show how rock resistivity is measured in a well, it is necessary to consider the electric potential created at a point by the application of an electric-current source at another point within a homogeneous medium of uniform resistivity.

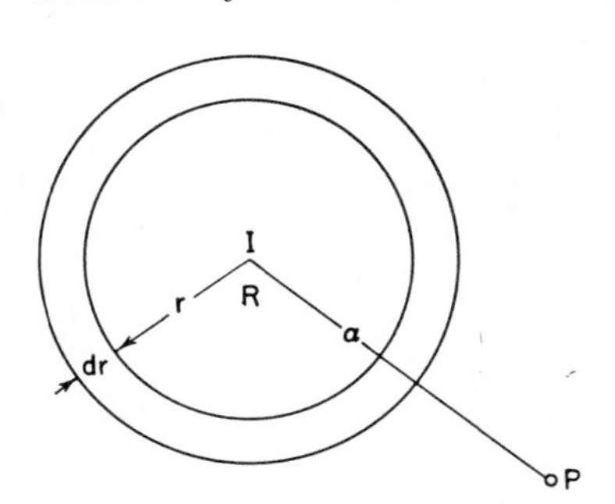

FIG. 4-21. The potential at a point P caused by a current I in a medium infinite in all directions is $RI/4\pi a$.

Conventional Logging Devices

Potential at a Distance from a Point Source of Current. When an electrode supplying a current is embedded in an infinite medium (Fig. 4-21), consider the resulting potential drop dV between two spherical shells of radii r and $r + dr$. We have, by Ohm's law,

$$dV = -\frac{Ri}{4\pi r^2} dr$$

(the minus sign is chosen because as we proceed along increasing values of $dr > 0$, the potential V decreases).

Integrating between infinity and a, we obtain

$$V_p = -\frac{Ri}{4\pi}\int_\infty^a \frac{dr}{r^2} = \frac{Ri}{4\pi a} \tag{4-11}$$

where R is the resistivity of the medium. Equation (4-11) is fundamental to the understanding of all resistivity measurements by means of multiple-electrode systems.

Earth Resistivity from Different Well-electrode Systems. Resistivity measurements in wells are always made through the use of commutated d-c (pulsated) or a-c in order to avoid electrode polarization.

Three-electrode Systems. A common electrode setup in electric logging is indicated in Fig. 4-22; this is generally called the *lateral system,* wherein a current (i) is applied at electrode A within the well and withdrawn at electrode B at the surface of the earth after passing throughout the formations. The potential difference ΔV is measured between electrodes M and N located below the energizing electrodes A and B.

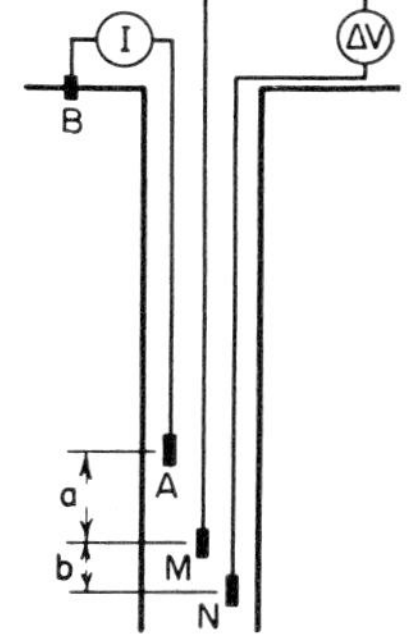

FIG. 4-22. Lateral logging system.

By application of the potential at a point formula (4-11) and by noting that potential from various sources are additive at a point, we have

$$V_M = \frac{Ri}{4\pi}\left(\frac{1}{AM} - \frac{1}{BM}\right) = \frac{Ri}{4\pi a} \tag{4-12}$$

since BM may be considered infinite with respect to $AM = a$.

Similarly,

$$V_N = \frac{Ri}{4\pi}\left(\frac{1}{AN} - \frac{1}{BN}\right) = \frac{Ri}{4\pi}\frac{1}{a+b} \tag{4-13}$$

Hence

$$\Delta V = V_M - V_N = \frac{Ri}{4\pi}\left(\frac{1}{a} - \frac{1}{a+b}\right) = \frac{Ri}{4\pi}\frac{b}{a(a+b)} \tag{4-14}$$

from which equation the true resistivity R_t could be computed in the case of a perfectly homogeneous earth where the mud fluid has the same resistivity as the earth. However, these conditions are never fulfilled in oil field practice and the resistivity solution from the formula (4-14) yields only an apparent resistivity R_a:

$$R_a = 4\pi\frac{\Delta V}{i}\frac{a(a+b)}{b} \tag{4-15}$$

Equation (4-15) is essentially the calibration equation for the lateral device.

ΔV is normally obtained by potentiometric measurements or from the deflections of a high-sensitivity galvanometer; $4\pi[a(a + b)]/b$ is an instrumental constant which depends on the geometry of the electrode assembly and which has been called the K coefficient of the logging device.

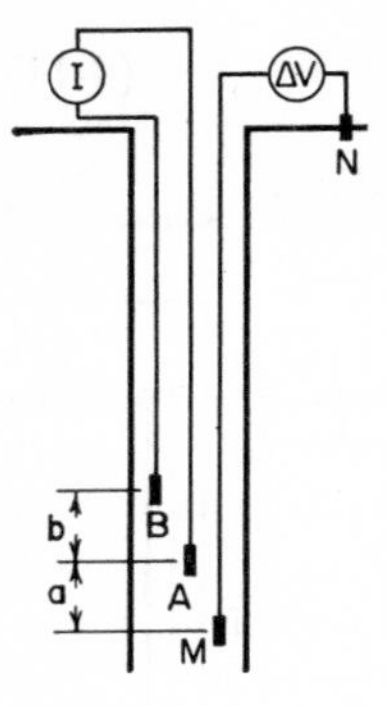

FIG. 4-23. Normal logging system.

The lateral device has the potential pickup electrodes (M and N) below the current electrode A. This has the advantage of probing to the very bottom of the well. The lateral device is characterized by the distance AO where O is the center of MN and varies in length from 6 to 24 ft, depending upon conditions. A standard length is 18 ft, 8 in. In practice the return electrode B is also located in the well at a distance far above A; this procedure eliminates induction effects on the pickup circuit.

Another commonly used electrode configuration is pictured in Fig. 4-23, and is designated as the *normal system*. In this setup the current is applied between electrodes A and B within the well; the potential difference is measured between a surface electrode N and a well electrode M. We have in a homogeneous earth

$$V_{AM} = \frac{Ri}{4\pi a}$$

The potential at the surface electrode N caused by A and B as well as the effect of B on M may be assumed to be zero, owing to the large distance from the current electrodes compared to the distance AM. Hence, the apparent resistivity is obtained by

$$R_a = 4\pi a \frac{V_{MN}}{i} \tag{4-16}$$

In practice both electrodes B and N are also in the hole but sufficiently distant from A and M so that the simplifications made are still valid. This is especially the case in low-resistivity formations. The Schlumberger resistivity departure curves are based on this assumption. However, in high-resistivity formations an appreciable error may be introduced through this simplification. Modified departure curves are then required.

In the early days of electric logging, other electrode combinations were in use, in particular the monoelectrode and the four-electrode curves. They are, however, no longer used and will not be discussed.

The Investigation Radius Concept. The terminology of "radius of investigation" or "distance of penetration" of a logging device is often misleading as there is no definite distance beyond which no signal is obtained. Theoretically, all the elementary formation volumes subjected to the flow of current have an effect on the potential-measuring electrode, as shown by the derivation of Eq. (4-11). The investigation radius of a logging device for convenience is defined, for a homogeneous earth, as the radius of a sphere which delineates a volume of formation such that it has an equal effect on the potential electrode as the volume of formation outside that sphere and extending to infinity.

For the homogeneous earth conditions postulated, without bore hole, the radius of investigation of the normal system is approximately twice the spacing ($RI = 2.0AM$), and the radius of investigation of the lateral system is approximately one electrode spacing ($RI = 1.0AO$). It is observed that a normal device has an investigation radius twice that of a lateral device of the same nominal spacing.

In a nonhomogeneous earth, the current flow lines are distorted from their spherical shape. More specifically, for the case of a resistive ground traversed by a bore hole containing conductive mud, the current flow lines tend to form an ellipsoid the axis of which is along the well, and the radius of investigation is thereby considerably reduced. This condition is the case in limestone formations which are normally of high resistivity. Because of the highly distorted current flow paths produced by these formations, they offer real problems of interpretation which have not as yet been fully elucidated. The solution to the problem resides in the introduction of new logging devices making use of directionally controlled current flow such as in the laterolog and guard electrode logs to be discussed later.

Conventional Electrode Configurations Used in Commercial Logging. *Schlumberger Sonde for Chronological Recording.* The electrode configuration represented in Fig. 4-24 is the system used by the Schlumberger Well Surveying Corporation and is the system by which all the curves can be obtained in one trip down the hole. The sonde is composed of five electrodes, numbered from 1 to 5, spaced on an insulated mandrel, and of two cable electrodes. Electrode 2 is the reference electrode to which all depth measurements are referred; it is the point of the sonde which represents the average earth property during the measurements.

The electrodes are used in the curves as follows:

SP curve. For the SP measurement, electrode 2 is in use.

AM curve. For the short-normal measurements ($AM = 16$ in.), electrodes 1, 2, and 5 are in use, 1 being the current source A, 2 the potential electrode M, and 5 the N electrode. Cable armor 7 is the B electrode.

AM' curve. For the long-normal measurements, electrodes 1 and 4 are in use on the sonde mandrel and 6 and 7 on the cable. Effectively, 1 and 7 are the current electrodes A and B and 4 and 6 are the pickup electrodes M' and N'. However, by virtue of the reciprocity theorem, the measurement results are as if electrode 4 were the source and electrode 1 the pickup electrode. The measurement is therefore 16 in. below the reference level and must be moved up optically on the photographic record to the reference level.

The three measurements above are all made simultaneously through a six-conductor cable. The self-potential, being a d-c measurement, is separated out at the surface by means of filters from the signals, received as short- and long-normal measurements, which are made by pulsating current interrupted 15 times per second.

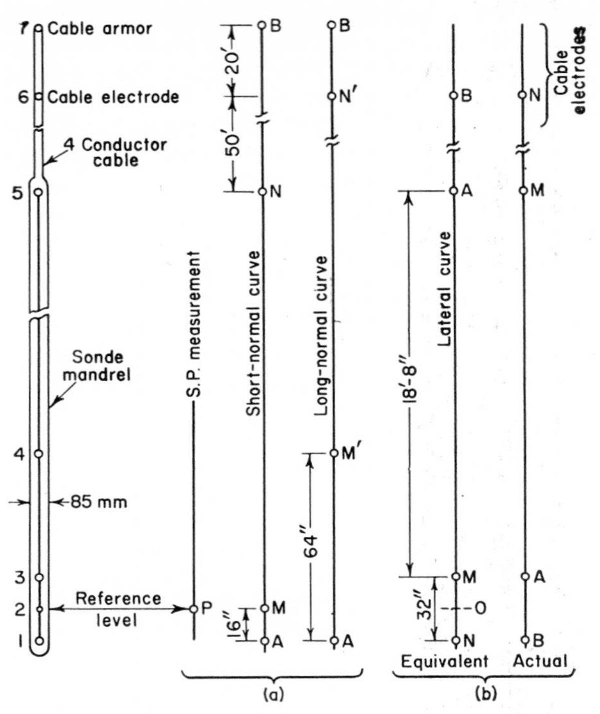

FIG. 4-24. Schlumberger electrode configuration for chronological recording. The configurations in (*a*) are used during a fraction of a second and those in (*b*) during another fraction; both groups are used successively several times per second.

OA curve. For the lateral measurements, electrodes 1, 3, 5, and 6 are in use, 5 and 6 are actually the pickup electrodes *M* and *N*, and 1 and 3 are the current electrode *A* and *B*. By virtue of the reciprocity theorem, the actual system is equivalent to the one shown on the left after inverting current and pickup electrodes. The lateral measurements cannot be made simultaneously with the first three measurements. Chronological recording consists of recording the first three curves during a fraction of a second and the lateral curve during the other fraction by means of a sufficiently damped galvanometer which will not follow the oscillations which result from chopping the time scale.

Halliburton Logging System. All Halliburton logging devices are designed around the primary requirement of a single conductor cable to be used for all well operations and they use the frequency modulation (F.M.) principle to transmit the multiple-measured signals along the single conductor cable. The electrode configuration for the F.M. logging system is represented in Fig. 4-25. The SP curve is obtained from electrode 2 at the reference level of the system. The short investigation curve is a two-electrode curve (2*Z* 18 in.) obtained by supplying a current to electrode 1 (as *A*), electrode 2 (as *M*) being the pickup electrode. The 2*Z* 18 in. curve is recorded as a solid line. Electrodes 1 and 3 are used as current electrodes for both the lateral curves $3iZ$ 6 ft and $3iZ$ 16 ft. The signals are picked up at electrodes 4 and 5, respectively. The symbol i stands for inverted.

In all the resistivity curves the measured signal modifies the frequency of an electronic oscillator located in the logging device. The components of the device's electric circuit have been properly compensated to avoid

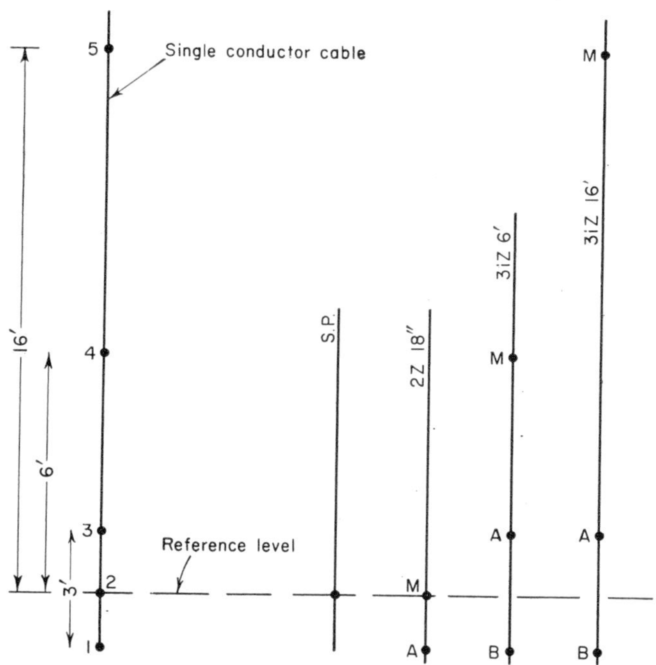

FIG. 4-25. Electrode configuration for Halliburton frequency modulation logging system.

the drift inherent to all electronic circuits subjected to large temperature variations.

The $3iZ$ . . . curves are the equivalent of lateral measurements with the electrode pickups at the reference level by virtue of the reciprocity theorem. Accordingly, the measurements may be treated quantitatively by means of departure curves for the lateral device.

Perforating Guns Atlas Corp. (PGAC) Logging System. The Perforating Guns Atlas Corp. (PGAC) provided an electric logging service comparable to the Schlumberger system but which includes an extra resistivity curve, namely, a 38-in. normal. Besides the SP curve the complete PGAC log includes:

A short-normal curve = AM = 16 in.
An amplified short-normal curve = AM = 16 in.
A long lateral curve = AO = 18 ft
A long-normal curve = AM'' = 64 in.
A medium-normal curve = AM' = 38 in.

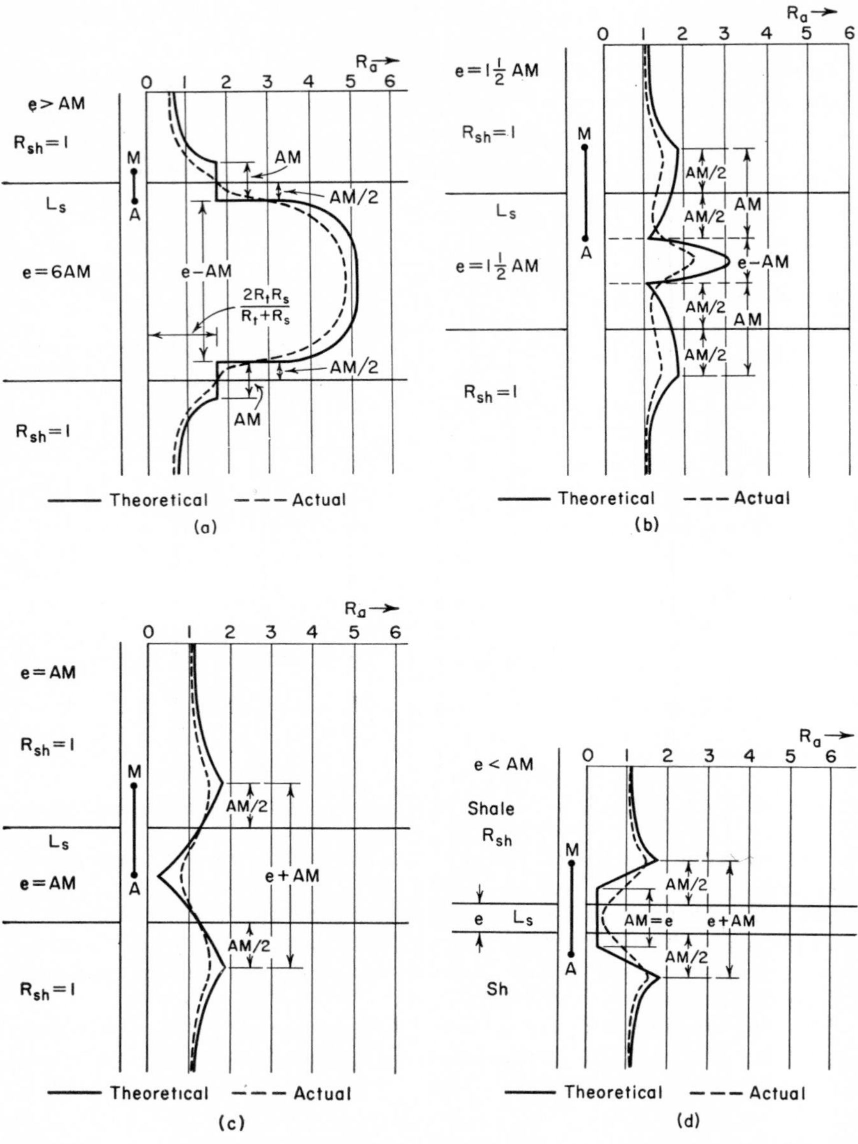

FIG. 4-26. Normal curve shape (theoretical and actual) for beds of varying thicknesses and resistivities. Resistive beds. (*Schlumberger Well Surveying Corp.*)

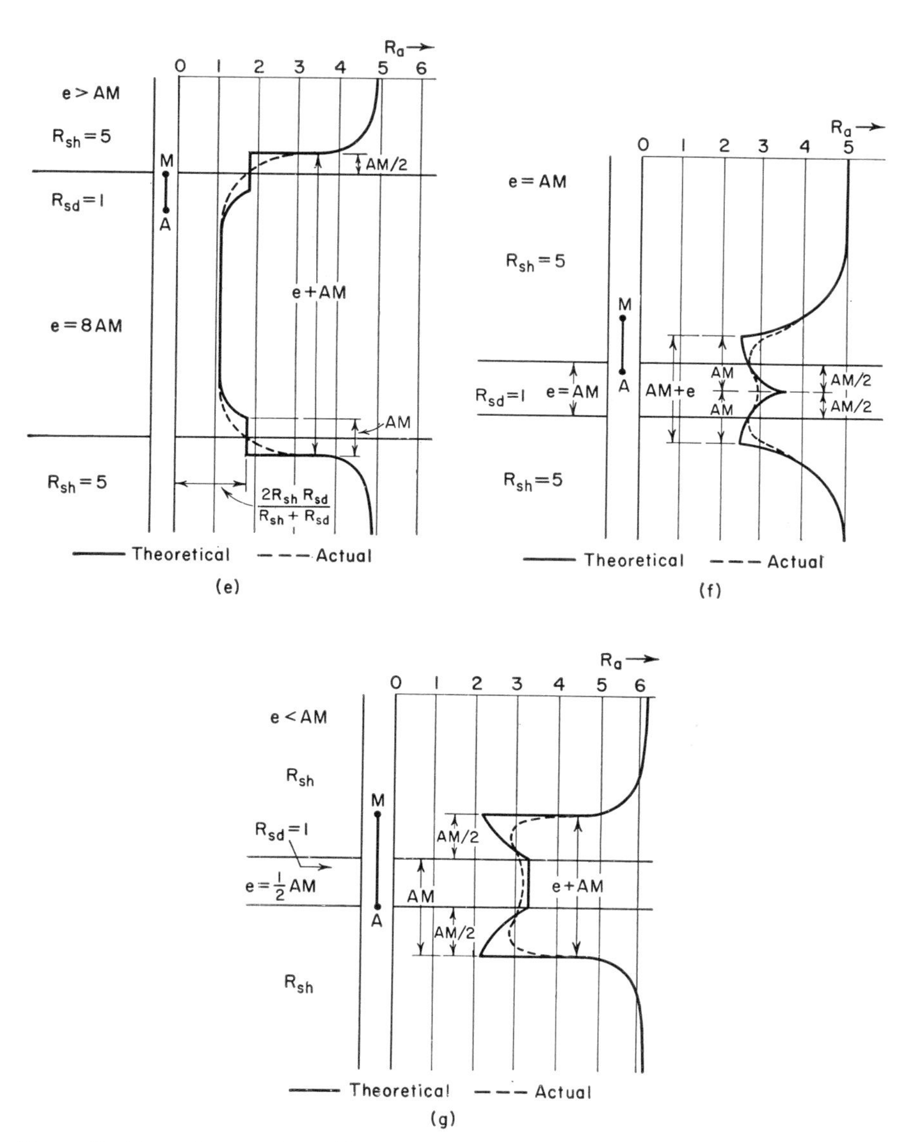

FIG. 4-26. Normal curve shape (theoretical and actual) for beds of varying thicknesses and resistivities. Conductive beds. *(Schlumberger Well Surveying Corp.)*

One of the claims made by PGAC is the use of a sensitive galvanometer for recording the SP curve, thereby achieving fine details especially when recording in a sequence of thin alternations of sands and shales.

Factors Which Affect Apparent Formation Resistivities Measured by Conventional Logging Tools

Boundary Effect. For the proper interpretation of electric logs it is necessary to study the factors which influence the departure of apparent resistivity R_a curves as recorded in a well from true formation resistivity R_t, which is the actual resistivity profile in the well. These factors include the presence of a well fluid of resistivity R_m in a bore hole of diameter d, the presence of a possible mud-filtrate invaded zone of resistivity R_i and of diameter D_i, the electrode configurations AM or AO, $2Z$ or $3iZ$, and the formation thickness e.

Let us first study the effect of the relative electrode spacing to formation thickness. From the start, it may be stated that a complete mathematical solution of the problem is extremely complicated and is beyond the scope of this study. Nevertheless, it is of interest to know how the shape of a resistivity curve depends on the relative values of electrode spacings and formation thicknesses.

It is considered that the true resistivity is read from an electric log with most electrode systems when the formation thickness is four to five times larger than the spacing, is not invaded, and is in a well of negligible diameter. For formation thicknesses below the above figures, the effects of the lower and upper boundaries start to interfere, and for very small formation thicknesses with respect to electrode spacing a large aberration exists. Theoretically, the mathematical derivations of apparent resistivity curves for any assumed number of boundaries are possible but they become too complicated to be of practical use. It is then necessary to resort to some simplifying assumptions in order to derive the true resistivity from the apparent resistivity curves.

Figures 4-26, 4-27, and 4-28 are typical of the type of boundary distortions which are encountered with conventional logging tools. In each figure two curves are given. The theoretical curve would be recorded in the absence of a bore hole or with a well of infinitely small diameter but still permitting the measurements to be made. Since this is virtually impossible and since a hole of finite size containing conductive mud must be present during logging, the sharp angles of the theoretical curves are smoothed out in the actual curves.

In the making of quantitative evaluations from resistivity curves, a question arises as to how to pick significant values from the curves in view of their highly distorted nature; this will be discussed fully under interpretation techniques.

When resistivity readings have been made, even in a thick formation, they still need to be corrected for bore-hole effect, i.e., hole size d and mud resistivity R_m and in the case of thin beds, for bed thickness.

The bore-hole correction is made by computing the ratios R_a/R_m and AO/d and plotting the values, respectively, in ordinate and abscissa in

Figs. 4-29 and 4-30. A point is thus determined by these coordinates which indicates by interpolation a value of R_t/R_m, from which R_t is readily computed.

Good electric-log interpretation is often dependent on the qualitative evaluation of electrode distortion effects which result from sequences of thin beds of high-resistivity contrast.

The first task in interpreting resistivity curves is to evaluate and eliminate all electrode distortion effects. This may be done by representing to scale the electrode configuration on a small strip of paper and by imagining the current distribution as it emanates from the current electrode and the effect of this distribution on the potential pickup electrodes while the electrode assembly is moved in the hole.

If the current which emanates from electrode A (Fig. 4-31) flowed equally in all directions, there would be no distortion on the curve. This is very nearly the case in a thick bed of shale. However, when the current electrode is in the vicinity of a resistive bed the current flow is distorted. The flow of current is deflected away from the resistive bed. The current flowing past the measuring electrodes may be increased or decreased, depending on the position of the electrode assembly with respect to the resistive bed.

If the current flowing past the measuring electrodes is increased, then an abnormally high voltage, and consequently a higher resistivity, is recorded as indicated by Eq. (4-11). Conversely, if the current flowing past the measuring electrodes is decreased, an abnormally low voltage is measured.

The following examples illustrate the effect on the lateral curve of resistive beds of various thicknesses depending on the location of the electrode assembly.

Fig. 4-31*a*. Current concentrates downward. The voltage measured at MN is increased. Most of the distortion is caused when all current from A is deflected in a downward direction. Voltage measured at MN then approaches twice its true value. The curve shows a bulge known as the "reflection."

Fig. 4-31*b*. Current concentrates in an upward direction. The voltage measured at MN is decreased. Maximum distortion is caused when all current from A emanates upward. Voltage measured at MN then approaches zero. (This effect is known as "shielding.")

Fig. 4-31*c*. As soon as the M electrode enters the resistive bed an increased voltage is measured across MN. This lasts until the N electrode leaves the resistive bed. Very thin formations therefore log on the lateral curve with a thickness of approximately 32 in. greater than the actual thickness of the formation, 16 in. below and 16 in. above the bed.

Figures 4-26 and 4-27, in addition to the distortion introduced by the formation boundaries and electrode configuration, indicate the smoothing-out effect of the mud column. In this series of figures, the continuous lines indicate the theoretical resistivity response of the electrode configuration without mud column and the dashed lines are the actual measured resistivity profiles with the mud column present.

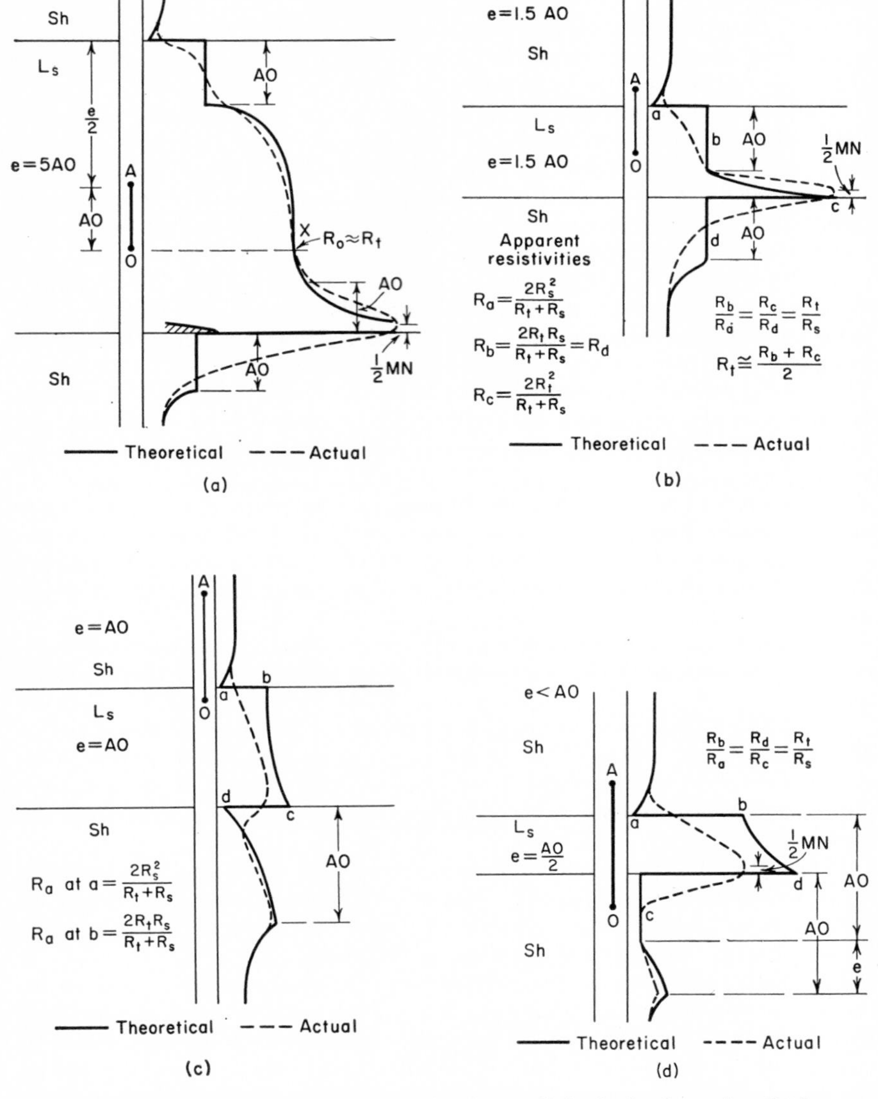

Fig. 4-27. Lateral curve shape (theoretical and actual) for beds of varying thicknesses and resistivities. Resistive beds. (*Schlumberger Well Surveying Corp.*)

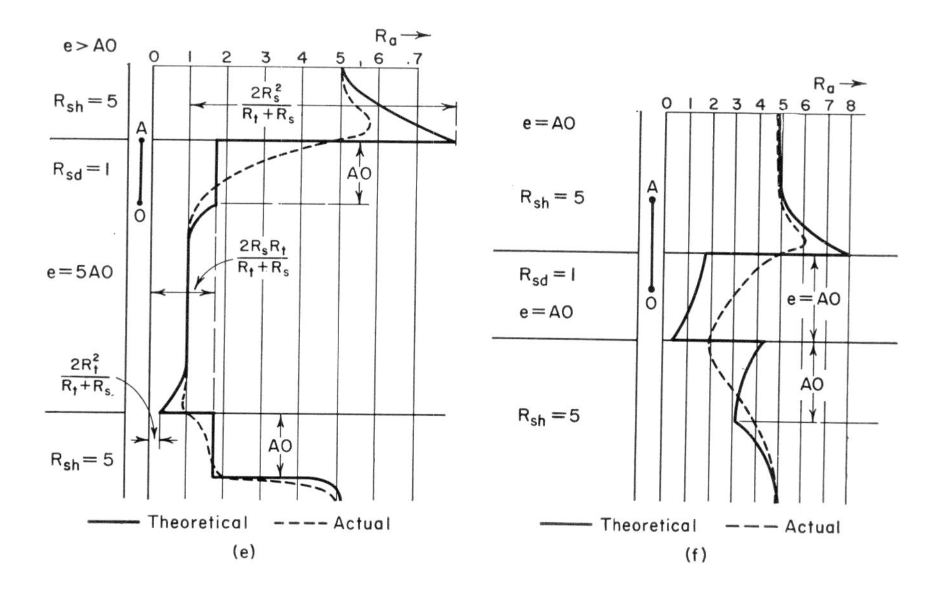

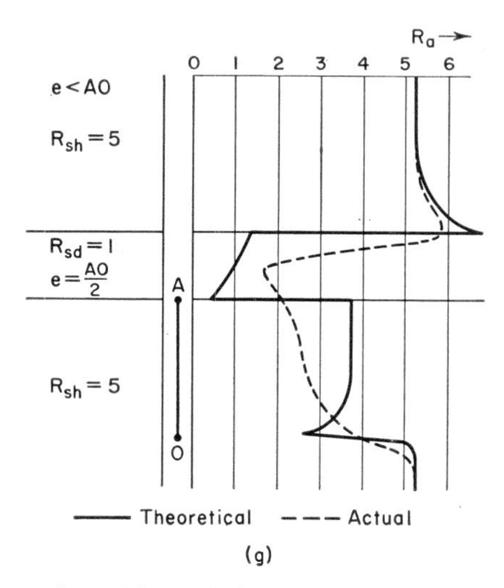

FIG. 4-27. Lateral curve shape (theoretical and actual) for beds of varying thicknesses and resistivities. Conductive beds. *(Schlumberger Well Surveying Corp.)*

Figure 4-26 shows the normal device. In this series of figures it is to be noted that the reference point of the log is the center point O of the spacing AM; this results in symmetrical curves. Note also the "crater" obtained for a thin resistive bed of thickness less than electrode spacing AM.

Figure 4-27 is for the lateral device. A feature worthy of note is the "shielded" zone. This zone exists when the current electrode A is on the

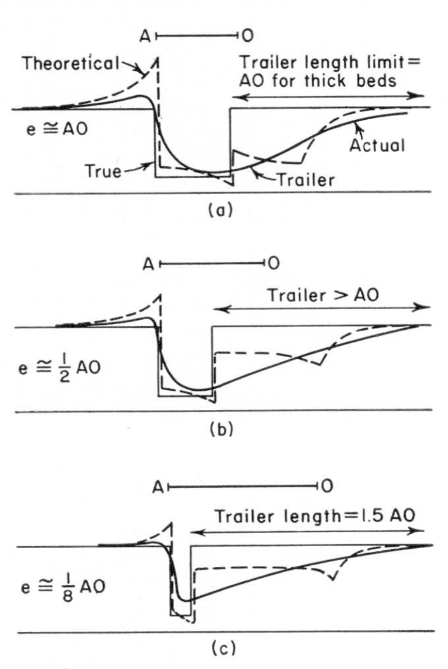

FIG. 4-28. Lateral curve shape (theoretical and actual curves) for conductive beds of various thicknesses showing "water trailer" on lateral curve.

opposite side of an insulating or high-resistivity layer from the pickup electrodes M and N. The dead zone length is $AO - e$. Note also the "shadow peak" or reflection below high-resistivity thin formations. Below low-resistivity formations (salt-water sands) a decay zone is observed. The bore-hole effect smooths this zone into a "trailer" effect, the length of which varies with the bed thickness. This is an important feature in recognizing thin water sands and is illustrated more fully in Fig. 4-28.

Logging Devices for Limestone (High-resistivity) Formations. In regions of high formation resistivity, as is the case in limestone and dolomite reservoirs, the main problem of log interpretation consists in the determination of the existence of porous zones and of the effective pay thickness. Two devices are helpful in this respect, the limestone sonde (LS 32 in.) and the microlog. For the determination of fluid content focused current tools were introduced, the laterolog, the guard log, and the induction log. However, they have also found wide acceptance in low-resistivity formations.

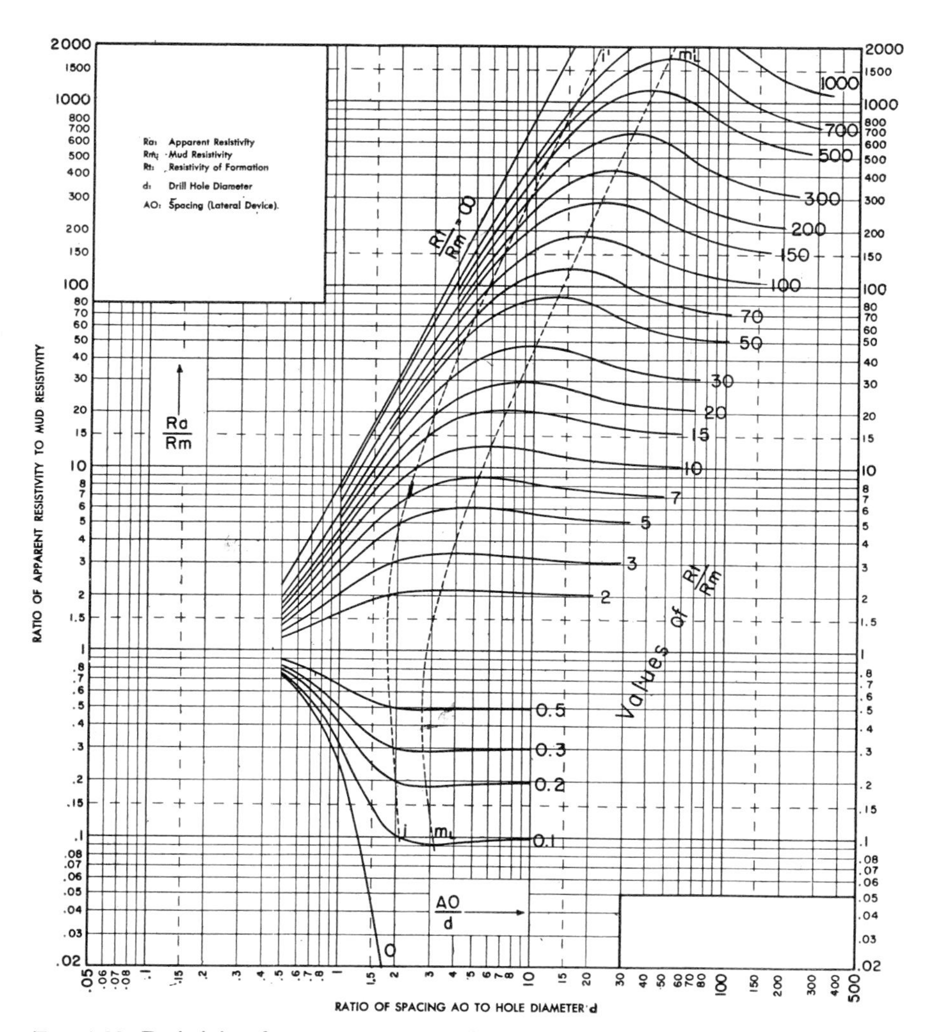

FIG. 4-29. Resistivity departure curves for lateral curve; no invasion; beds of infinite thickness. (*Schlumberger Well Surveying Corp.*)

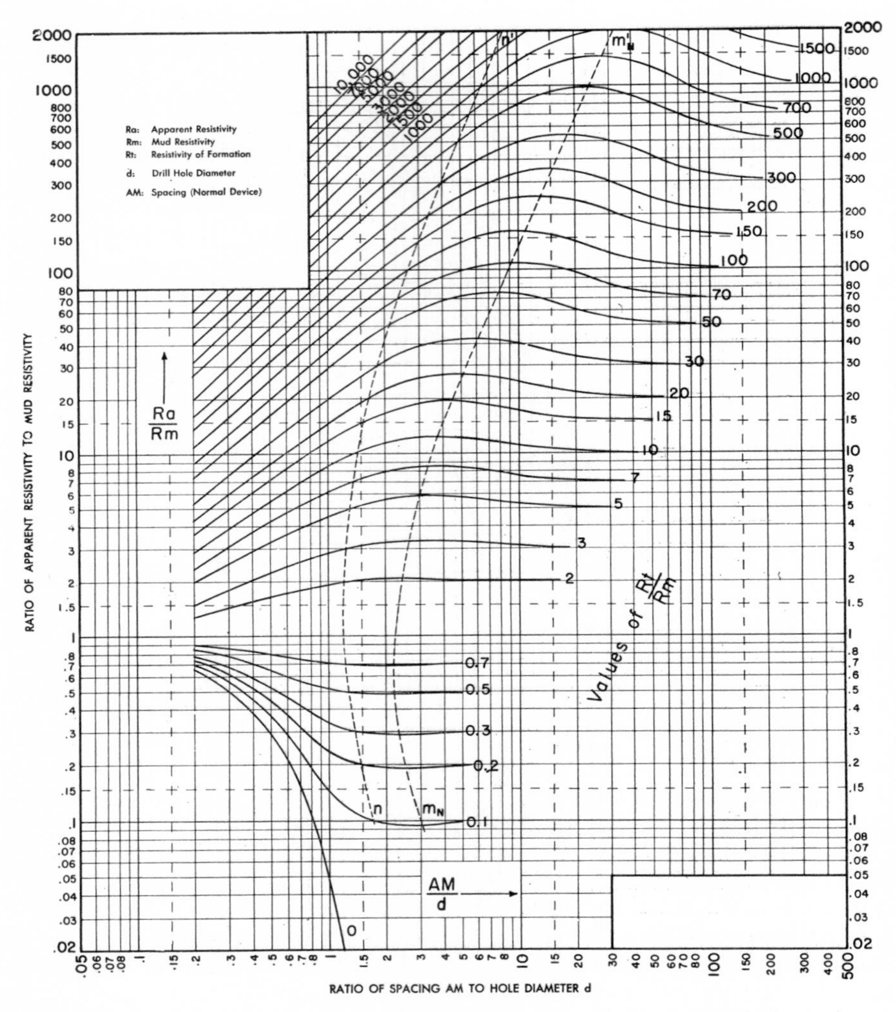

FIG. 4-30. Resistivity departure curves for normal curve; no invasion; beds of infinite thickness. (*Schlumberger Well Surveying Corp.*)

Limestone Sonde. The purpose of this device is to locate permeable zones of low resistivity in highly resistive limestones. The low resistivity is often the result of infiltration of salty mud filtrate into the porous zones. This is especially true in the Permian Basin where drilling is conducted through thick sections of salt-bearing formations before reaching the oil-bearing zones. The limestone sonde is a symmetrical arrangement of electrodes which combines two short-circuited lateral devices, as shown on Fig. 4-32. Its effective radius of investigation is about 10 in. Hence, it is not likely to probe much beyond the zone of invasion and the information obtained cannot be used for quantitative evaluation of connate water saturation.

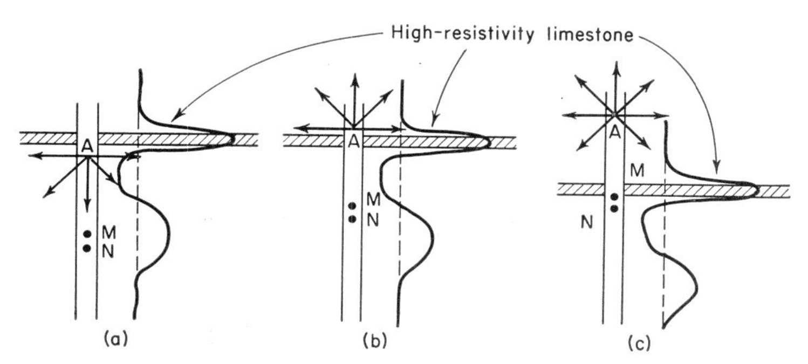

FIG. 4-31. Method of studying electrode distortion as applied to the lateral curve for a thin bed.

Because of its very short radius of investigation the limestone curve probes mostly in the invaded zone and responds mostly to its formation factor. Its main quantitative use is therefore the determination of porosity.

Wall-resistivity Devices: Microlog, Contact Log, Microresistivity. The microlog devices were introduced originally for the exact location and thickness determination of porous and permeable zones in limestone rocks. Since then they have found widespread use in sand-shale sections.

They are actually a combination of a normal and a lateral curve of very short spacing (1½ and 2 in.), Fig. 4-33. The electrodes are supported by and recessed in a flexible rubber pad strongly held against the well bore by a spring which applies a constant pressure against the walls of the well for diameters comprised between 4½ and 16 in. The log is made on the up-hole trip and the electrodes are applied firmly against the walls and slide against it or against the mud cake if present.

The investigation radii of the wall-resistivity log curves are very small, being of the same order of magnitude as the electrode spacing. Hence, the penetration shown by the 1½-in. lateral (microinverse) curve is not much more than the mud cake and nearly measures the mud-cake resistivity. The mud cake is almost a perfect arrangement of unconsolidated particles which approach cubic packing (porosity = 46 per cent) and for which the formation factor F is of the order of 2:3. Hence, for a thick mud cake the resistivity indicated by the 1½-in. spacing is two to three times the mud resistivity. The 2-in. normal (micronormal) spacing probes a certain distance beyond the mud cake and nearly measures the formation resistivity beyond the mud cake, but is affected somewhat by the presence of the mud cake. The microlog is essentially a mud-cake detector. The

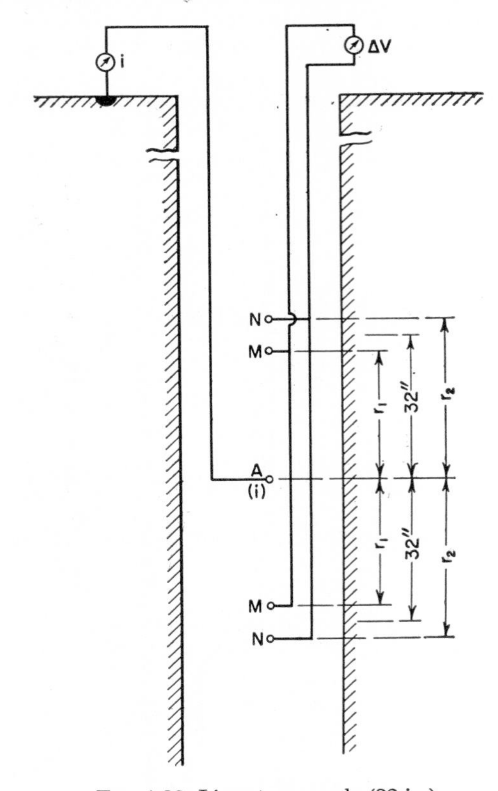

FIG. 4-32. Limestone sonde (32 in.).

characteristics of the microlog are derived immediately from the above observations:

1. In a shale section, because of the lack of formation permeability, no infiltration from the fluid column takes place and no mud cake is built up. Accordingly, the 1½- and 2-in. curves are superposed.

2. In hard, massive, and nonpermeable rock sections such as massive limestone, dolomite, and anhydrite no mud cake is built up. Hence, both the 1½- and 2-in. curves show high resistivity. Owing to the rugosity of the well walls, however, the curve is very jagged and irregular because of current leakage around the pad and imperfect fit of the electrodes against the well bore.

3. In a porous and permeable section in which infiltration took place during drilling, the 1½-in. curve approximately records the filter-cake resistivity, which should be two to three times the mud resistivity at that

depth. The 2-in. curve probes beyond the mud cake and responds mostly to the resistivity of the flushed zone R_{xo}. As the mud-filtrate resistivity is approximately the same as that of the mud, the response is nearly equal to mud resistivity times formation factor ($R_{xo} = R_mF$). Generally, the values recorded by the 2-in. curve are larger than the corresponding values for the 1½-in. curve because the formation factor F is larger than the

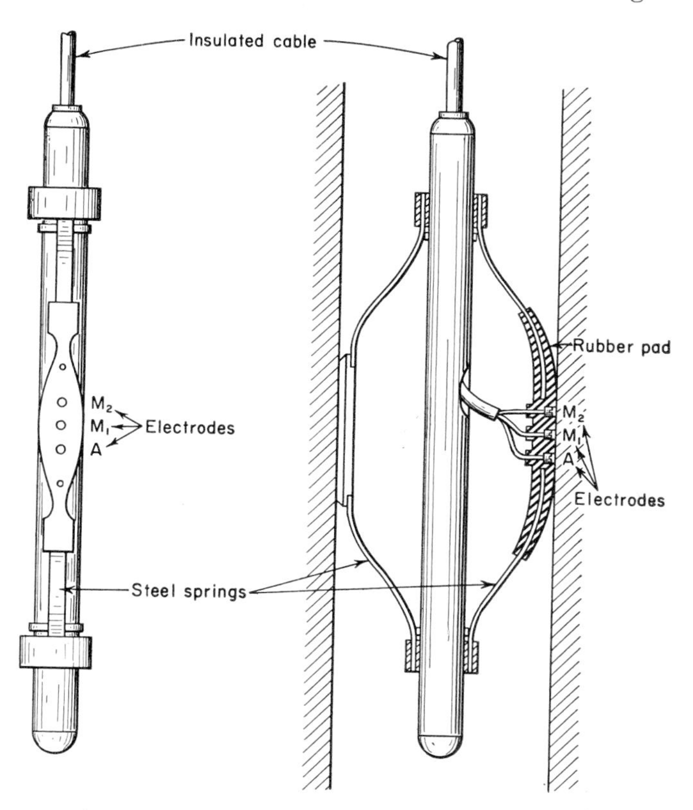

FIG. 4-33. Micrologging apparatus showing distribution of electrodes. (*Schlumberger Well Surveying Corp.*)

mud-cake formation factor. However, under certain conditions of connate water saturation gradient with depth, in a thick reservoir, there may be a complete reversal of this relationship. The upper permeable zone may contain a small connate water saturation, whereas in the lower permeable section, the connate water saturation is so high that the resistivity of the mixture (connate + filtrate water) near the mud cake is lowered and more than compensates for the larger formation factor; as a result, the 2-in. curve records lesser deflections than the 1½-in. curve. In the middle permeable zone the two effects may exactly compensate and the 1½- and 2-in. curves may be superposed. In such a case the middle permeable zone may be mistaken for a shale section. The ambiguity must be resolved by the interpretation of the SP and conventional resistivity curves.

4. The microlog offers the possibility of determining the presence and location of fissures, fractures, and vugs. The latter fill up with unfiltered

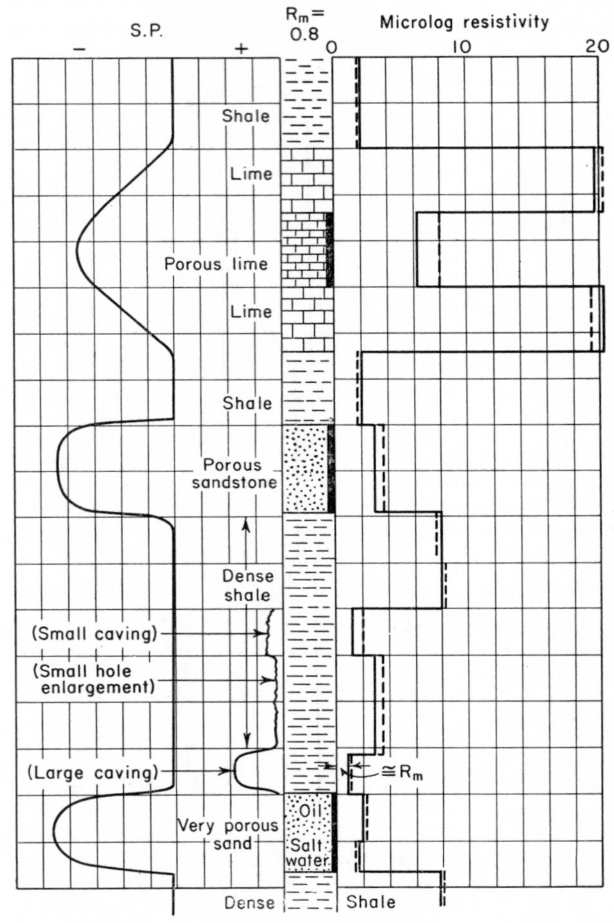

FIG. 4-34. Simplified microlog-interpretation chart. *(Schlumberger Well Surveying Corp.)*

mud and the resistivity measured should be approximately that of the mud, which is lower than that of the mud cake. The presence of fractures in massive rocks is revealed by the microlog through its sharply hachured character.

Similarly, the presence of prominent well enlargement can be ascertained by the same means, provided the caves are large enough so that the tool cannot follow the contour of the caves, i.e., $d > 16$ in. In such a case the microlog again reads mud resistivity.

Difficulties are at times experienced with the microlog when the tool does not make a perfect seal against the well walls and electrical leakage to the mud column takes place. Mechanical difficulties such as wedging of mud cake under the pad and oscillation of position are eliminated by upper and lower guides.

In order to facilitate qualitative microlog interpretation, a chart is given in Fig. 4-34. All high microlog deflections correspond to impermeable and nonporous rocks.

Small deflections with large negative departure indicate nonporous and nonpermeable formations. For small microlog deflections and positive or negative departure, the SP trend must be considered, as it differentiates between shales (positive SP trend) and porous and permeable (or pay) sections (negative SP trend), provided the mud in the hole is less saline than formation water.

The microlog is primarily a qualitative tool which permits determining if a filter cake is present or absent, and hence whether or not the formations are permeable and allow the passage of mud filtrate. However, the microlog does not permit direct evaluation of the degree of permeability.

The microlog is quantitative in its evaluation of the effective pay thickness of a reservoir. Serious attempts are made to derive quantitatively the magnitude of porosity from the microlog inasmuch as the 2-in. normal responds mainly to the flushed zone resistivity in a porous and permeable section. This will be discussed in Chap. 5.

The main uses for the microlog are:

1. To determine formation boundaries accurately and to permit a fine evaluation of net pay thickness by outlining thin interbedded horizons which may not be recognized on conventional logs.

2. To determine the mud-cake thickness facing permeable zones. This information is especially useful for interpreting microlaterologs when such surveys are made.

3. To measure the mud resistivity in the well. For this purpose the measurements are recorded during the down-hole trip with the sonde collapsed. Dependable readings of R_m are made especially in the enlarged portions of the wells.

4. To determine the presence and degree of continuity of permeability barriers within reservoir-rock sections. This ability of the microlog is of special usefulness in applied reservoir-engineering technology where fluid injection is planned as a means of increasing oil recovery. The presence of continuous horizontal impermeable barriers, as observed from micrologs, was instrumental in selecting a center-to-edge water flood rather than a bottom-water drive in the reef reservoirs of the Salt Creek, Kent County, and Kelly-Snyder, Scurry County, Texas. Bottom-water flood would have been doomed to failure in these fields, because of the presence of horizontal, impermeable, and continuous barriers.

Additional pointers on the qualitative evaluation of the microlog are:

1. A large positive (separation) departure, with the 2-in. curve larger than the 1½-in. curve, means the presence of a thick mud cake, as a rule. However, conditions of improper pad fitting and of logging current leakage

around the pad may give the same effect. When such conditions exist, meaningless departure may be ruled out by correlation with other features on the log.

2. An average mud-cake thickness is ¼ to ½ in.; for such conditions the microlog departure is good, definite, and unmistakable. It is a sure indicator that a porous zone exists. It is for this condition that empirical porosity vs. microlog-deflection charts may be constructed and used with success.

3. Negative or zero departure means that there is no mud cake or that it is thin ($e_{mc} < 1/16$ in.). It also occurs in impermeable formations (shales or limestones) and when salt muds are used, because salt muds are known to give thin mud cakes. Negative separation is often present in salt-water sands of high porosity and permeability because such sands have little or no invasion; thus the 2-in. curve responds mostly to R_o and the 1½-in. curve to the mud-cake resistivity, which is often larger than R_o. In the oil zone of such a sand, however, positive departure is observed because of residual oil in the flushed zone. In highly permeable sands, the change in separation of the microlog curves from negative to positive may be used to pick oil-water contact.

4. The existence of fracture porosity may often be suspected from a careful examination of the microlog in conjunction with ascertaining the existence of SP deflections and a low-resistivity level on the short-normal curve. When fracture porosity exists, it gives a very jagged and hachured appearance to the microlog.

Focused Current Electric Logs

In the conventional type of electric log, the energizing current spreads from the power electrodes in an uncontrolled manner and the current flow lines seek the paths of least resistance; i.e., the current flows preferentially into the formations of low resistivity. The formations of high resistivity, such as limestone, dolomite, and anhydrite, are energized very little and it is difficult to investigate them by conventional logging devices. In order to do so it is necessary to force the current laterally into such formations by focusing means.

Focused current logs are divided into two classes:

1. Conductive measuring devices:
   a. Schlumberger type:
      Laterolog 3
      Laterolog 7
      Laterolog 9 (pseudolaterolog)
      Microlaterolog
   b. Halliburton type:
      Guard log
2. Inductive measuring device:
   Schlumberger induction log

Conductive Measuring Devices. The need for improved logging devices more suitable for logging high-resistivity carbonate formations is quite apparent in view of the geometric distortion of conventional logs. The limestone curve and microlog are only partially successful in solving this problem because of their small investigation radii. At best they are able to evaluate effective pay thickness but are unable to give information concerning the true nature of fluid saturations. Other conventional logging devices are also lacking in this respect because of the highly distorted nature of the resistivity curves. This is because, in limestone fields, pay sections are low-resistivity sections encased in high-resistivity sections. Departure curves have not as yet been worked out for these cases.

Further complication in limestone reservoirs comes about from the high salinity of the mud and from the thinness of the pay sections generally encountered.

New devices called laterolog and guard log are especially designed to overcome the above limitations, as they read essentially true formation resistivity in many cases, work best in salty muds, and need only thickness corrections for extremely thin beds.

Laterolog. The laterolog system is an electric-log method which makes use of a sheet of current of constant intensity and of calibrated thickness, focused by means of an automatic control. This system can be used with point electrodes, which, among other advantages, make possible the simultaneous recording of the SP curve, or other electric logs.

With the laterolog device, the effect of the mud column may generally be neglected, and the effect of the adjacent formations is practically eliminated in all beds whose thickness is greater than that of the focused sheet of current, i.e., from a few inches to a few feet, depending on the electrode combination used.

Were it not for the invaded zone, a laterolog would show directly the true resistivity of all beds whose thickness is greater than the limit mentioned above. In practice, the resistivity recorded is close to the true value when the diameter of the zone invaded by the mud filtrate does not exceed about two to three times the diameter of the hole, and provided that the resistivity of the invaded zone is not greater than the true resistivity of the bed under investigation. This condition is frequently satisfied for oil-bearing formations, especially when the salinity of the mud is of the same order of magnitude as that of connate water.

Because of the comparatively small thickness of the focused sheet of current, the laterolog gives a very detailed curve, and puts clearly in evidence the sharp contrasts between successive beds, however conductive the mud may be.

The most commonly used laterolog device is the laterolog 7. The laterolog 7 device (Fig. 4-35) comprises one electrode A_0 and three pairs of electrodes M_1M_2, $M'_1M'_2$, A_1A_2, positioned symmetrically with respect to A_0, with the pairs being, respectively, short-circuited. A current of constant and calibrated intensity is fed through electrode A_0. Additional currents of the same polarity as the current flowing through A_0 are fed into the auxiliary power electrodes A_1 and A_2. The intensity of these currents is automatically and continuously adjusted in such a way that the difference of potential between M_1M_2 and $M'_1M'_2$ is maintained substantially equal to zero. The potential prevailing at any of these latter four electrodes is recorded. The apparent resistivity measured with the device is proportional to the value of this potential and to a certain geometrical factor which depends on the distances between the various electrodes.

According to this system, the current emitted from A_0 is prevented from flowing upward and downward past the measuring electrodes M_1M_1' and

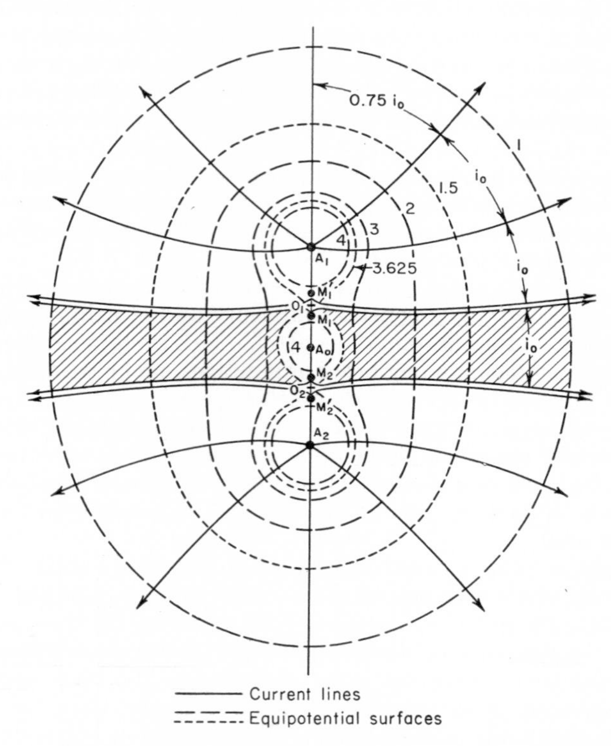

FIG. 4-35. Laterolog: equipotential lines and lines of current flow in homogeneous medium. To obtain the potentials in millivolts, multiply the figures by $\frac{R_{io}}{4\pi a}$ (with a in meters, R in ohm-meters, and i_o in milliamperes). (*After Doll, courtesy AIME.*)

M_2M_2', as if insulated plugs were placed in the hole at the level of these electrodes. Hence, the mud column, which handicaps seriously the conventional logs when the formations are much more resistive than the mud, has very little influence on the measurements made with the laterolog. Moreover, the electrical conditions created by the controlling system are such that the current emitted by A_0 behaves as if the insulated plugs were extended horizontally some distance away from the bore hole. The current is therefore forced to flow within an approximately horizontal slice of space, whose thickness is about equal to the distance separating the middle points O_1 and O_2, of M_1M_1' and M_2M_2'.

Figure 4-35 shows the distribution of the current lines and the equipotential surfaces for a laterolog device placed in a homogeneous medium. The sheet of current issued from A_0, represented by a shaded area, is bounded by two surfaces, which up to a considerable radial distance from the drill hole are close to the two horizontal planes passing through O_1 and O_2. The potential of any of the electrodes $M_1M'_1M_2M'_2$ represents the drop of potential produced by ohmic effect in the sheet of current, from its origin in the bore hole to a large distance from the hole, and is therefore proportional to the resistivity of the medium. The volume of ground where the resistivity is measured is essentially a horizontal slice, having the same thickness and the same position as the sheet of current.

To explain the operation of the system in the case of thin beds, it is convenient to consider that it is placed in front of a homogeneous bed having the same thickness as the current sheet and is bounded above and below by thick homogeneous formations. It is also convenient to neglect the effect of the mud column.

If the resistivities of the upper and lower formations are equal to that of the bed, the situation is substantially that of an infinite homogeneous medium, and the distribution of current and potential is as represented in Fig. 4-35. If it is now assumed that the upper and lower formations are, for example, ten times more conductive than the bed, the auxiliary currents flowing through A_1 and A_2 are automatically increased to about ten times what their value would be in a homogeneous medium—otherwise the potential differences at $M_1M'_1$ and $M_2M'_2$ would not be nil—so that the distribution of potential above and below the bed is automatically brought back to what it would have been in the homogeneous medium. There is, therefore, no tendency for the current of the sheet to be attracted by the upper and lower conductive beds. The sheet of current keeps nearly its normal shape, and produces in the bed a drop of potential which is practically the same as if the bed had been considerably thicker. The apparent resistivity observed opposite the center of the bed is therefore very little different from the true resistivity of the bed, provided there is no invasion or the invaded zone is of low resistivity.

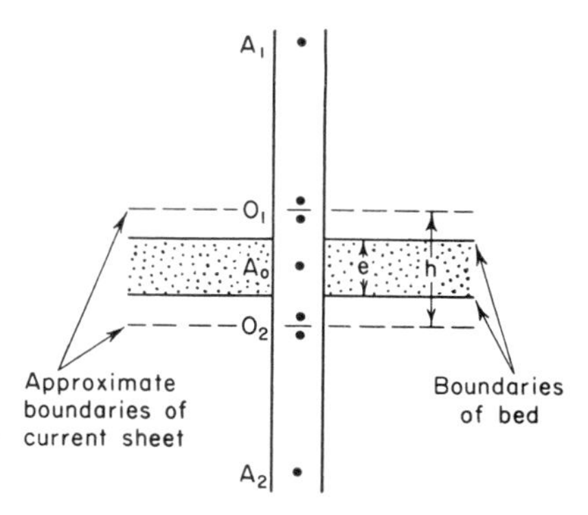

FIG. 4-36. Laterolog device opposite a bed thinner than the thickness of the sheet of current. (*After Doll, courtesy AIME.*)

When the upper and lower formations are more resistive than the bed, the auxiliary currents are automatically decreased, and an equivalent result is obtained.

The result is practically the same when the sheet of current penetrates a homogeneous bed that is thicker than the current sheet, and the apparent resistivity is again substantially equal to the true resistivity of the bed.

In the converse case of a bed whose thickness is smaller than that of a sheet of current (Fig. 4-36) the constant current from A_0 divides itself, according to conductivities and respective thicknesses of the bed and that part of the surrounding formations which is within the lower and upper limits of the sheet of current. The apparent resistivity, as recorded, is in that case a sort of average between the resistivity of the bed and that of the surrounding formations, and depends, of course, on the thickness of the bed. Furthermore, the presence of the more conductive formation within the sheet has a predominant effect on the apparent resistivity.

The laterolog measures nearly true resistivity of the formations regardless of mud resistivities unless they be invaded or be too thin. Generally there will be no thickness correction for beds thicker than 2 to 3 ft.

For invaded formations, the diameter of invasion being D_i and the resistivity of the invaded zone being R_i, the following relationship has been shown to be approximately correct:

$$R_a \cong \frac{n}{10} R_i + \left(1 - \frac{n}{10}\right) R_t \tag{4-17}$$

where $$n = \frac{D_i}{d}$$

d being the diameter of the well bore. By way of example, if $D_i/d = 3$,

$$R_a \cong 0.3R_i + 0.7R_t$$

indicating that the laterolog reads 30 per cent too low for a high value of the true formation resistivity.

More accurate corrections may be made for the bore-hole and invasion effects by means of special departure curves (Schlumberger's *Document* No. 6), provided information is available on the resistivity and diameter of the invaded zone.

Figure 4-37*a* shows schematically the circuit generally used for recording the *laterolog* 7 curve. An a-c of constant intensity is fed through electrode A_0 by means of a generator located at the surface. Electrodes M_1M_2 and $M_1'M_2'$ on the one hand and electrodes A_1A_2 and surface electrode B_1 on the other hand are connected to the input and putput terminals, respectively, of an automatic-control apparatus (1). By means of this apparatus, a current is fed through A_1 and A_2 which acts continuously to maintain the difference of potential between M_1M_2 and $M_1'M_2'$ substantially equal to zero. The common potential of electrodes $M_1M_2M_1'M_2'$ is recorded by means of a meter (2), with reference to an electrode N placed in the bore hole at a great distance from the measuring device.

Laterolog 3. The automatic-control system used to keep the potential difference between M_1M_2 and $M_1'M_2'$ equal to zero can be applied equally well to another electrode arrangement, as shown in Fig. 4-37*b* (laterolog 3). In this case, instead of the point electrodes of the standard laterolog, elongated electrodes are used, namely, one central electrode A_0' and two symmetrical and short-circuited electrodes $A_1'A_2'$. The technique of measurement is essentially the same as that just described; a current of constant intensity is fed to electrode A'_0 and the difference of potential between A'_0 and $A'_1A'_2$ is maintained substantially nil by means of the same automatic-control apparatus (1′). The common potential of $A'_0A'_1A'_2$ is recorded by means of a meter 2′.

It appears that with laterolog 3, the current is made to flow within a substantially horizontal sheet of space, whose thickness is about equal to

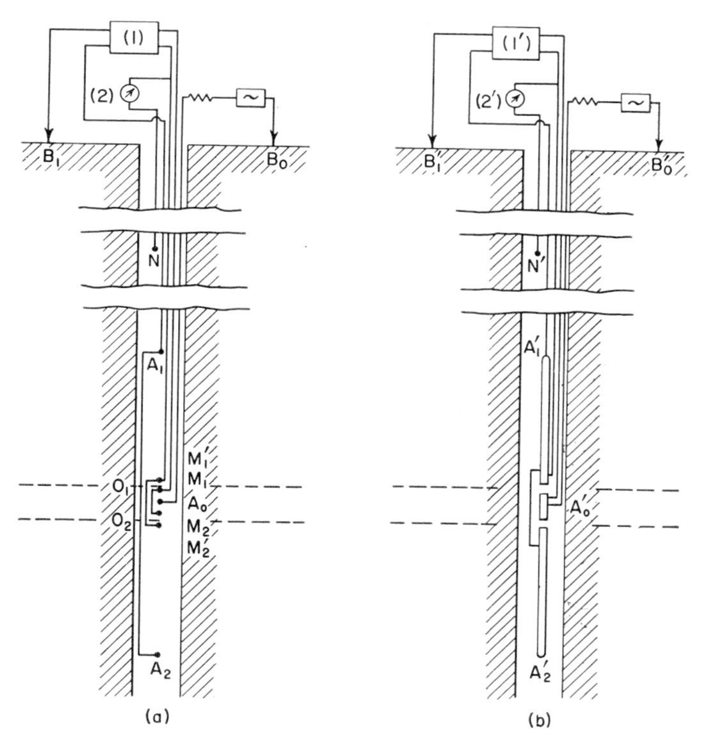

Fig. 4-37. Schematic circuits of (*a*) laterolog 7 and (*b*) laterolog 3. (*After Doll, courtesy AIME.*)

the length of electrode A'_0. If the length of electrode A'_0 in laterolog 3 is taken equal to the distance O_1O_2 in laterolog 7, the thickness of the sheets of current in both cases will be the same, and both devices will have similar abilities for the detection of details. It may be observed that laterolog 3 is essentially a "guard electrode" system. Figure 4-38 gives a comparison of standard logs with the two laterologs discussed.

Guard Log. The Halliburton guard log uses essentially the same electrode arrangement as the Schlumberger laterolog 3 system; however, the measuring technique employed by Halliburton is altogether different. Whereas the laterolog devices use a monitored current of controlled intensity, the guard log lets the current intensity of the device seek its own level and measures the ratio E/i of the potential E between the center surveying-ring electrode and the guard electrode and the surveying current i that issues from the central electrode. This ratio has the dimension of a resistance and it is related through calibration and instrument geometry to the resistivity of the formation directly facing the surveying-ring electrode.

The principles of the guard-electrode log device are illustrated in Fig. 4-39. All surfaces of the electrode assembly are kept at substantially the same potential. The guard-electrode assembly is made up of an upper

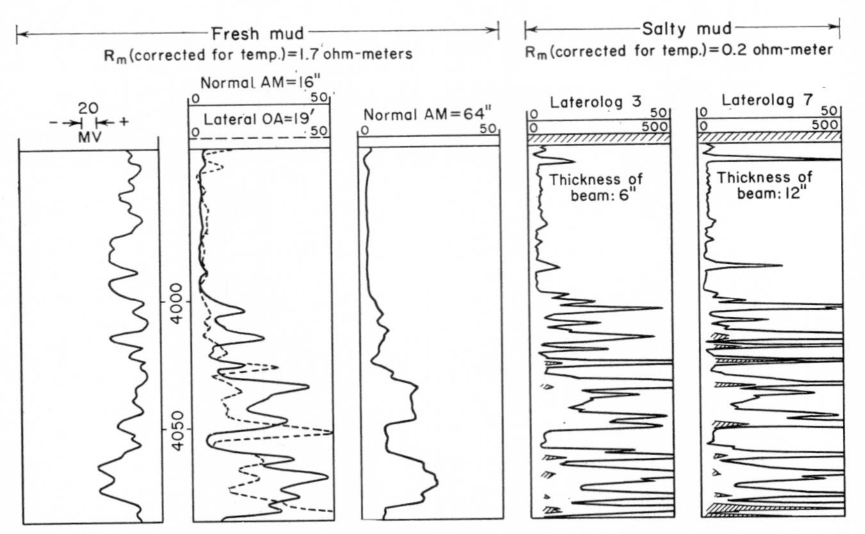

FIG. 4-38. Comparative example of laterolog 3, laterolog 7, and conventional logs in hard formations (Kansas). (*Schlumberger Well Surveying Corp.*)

guard electrode, a measuring electrode, and a lower guard electrode. An alternating current is passed between the bottom electrode assembly and the current-return electrode. The path the current takes in going from the guard-electrode assembly to the current-return electrode through the earth is indicated by the dotted lines. The important feature of this system is that the current from the measuring electrode flows outwardly in essentially a horizontal direction for a considerable distance, and hence is confined to a disk-shaped space having a thickness approximately the same as the length of the measuring electrode. Variations in earth resistivity within this disk-shaped region control the amount of current flowing from the measuring electrode.

The electrical measurements needed from this system to provide the desired readings of resistivity and conductivity consist of (1) a measurement of the current emitted by the measuring electrode and (2) a measurement of the voltage between this electrode and a point remote from any area of current concentration. A resistivity value is obtained by recording the ratio of the voltage between the measuring electrode and this distant point to the current passing into the earth from the measuring electrode. A conductivity value is obtained by recording the ratio of the current from the measuring electrode to the voltage between it and the distant point. Because the measured voltage is from the measuring electrode to a remote point which does not change in potential, the resistivity and conductivity

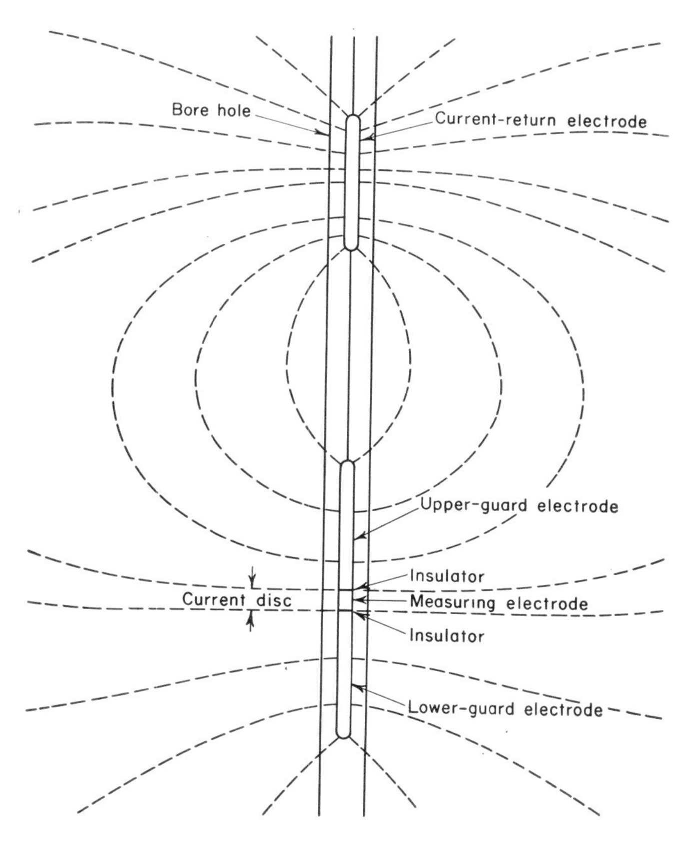

FIG. 4-39. Current-flow pattern in the guard-electrode system. (*Halliburton.*)

values which are determined are not influenced by resistivity changes near the current-return electrode in the hole. The reference depth is the depth of the measuring electrode.

The claim made for the Halliburton guard log is its extreme penetration of the formations by the surveying current, without distortion. It is claimed that in a homogeneous and isotropic medium the thickness of the current beam is only 6 in. at a distance of 17.3 ft from the axis of the electrode. As a result of this extreme penetration, resistivity gradients as they exist in the transition zone between oil and water in certain reservoirs are

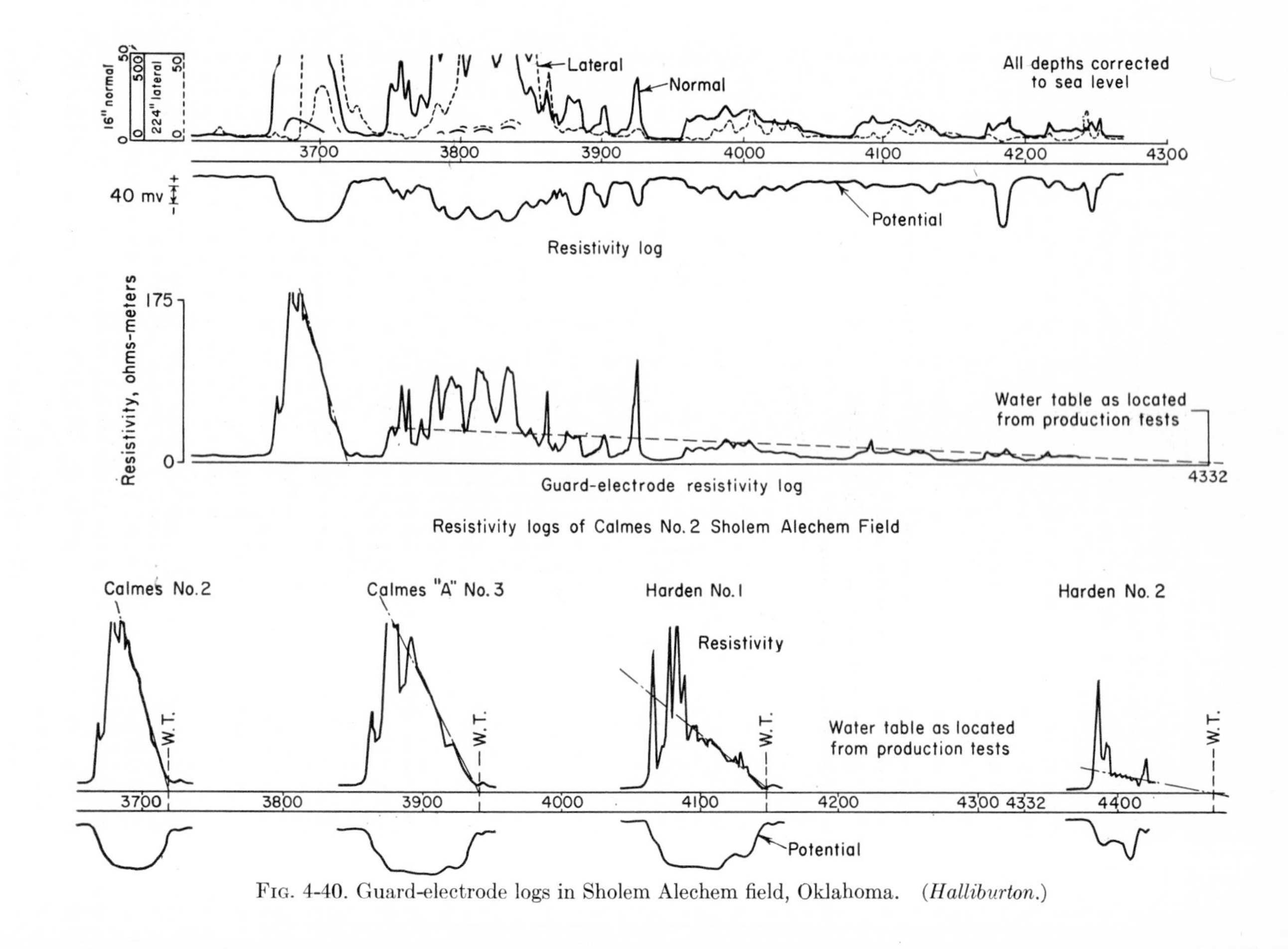

FIG. 4-40. Guard-electrode logs in Sholem Alechem field, Oklahoma. (*Halliburton.*)

much more in evidence. Examples of such condition in the Sholem Alechem field of Oklahoma are given in Fig. 4-40.

The focused logging systems by themselves are deficient in providing a sufficient number of equations (or curves) for solving completely the electric-log problems, for there is no way by which the resistivity of the invaded zone R_i may be had, nor its diameter D_i. Certain supplementary logs must therefore be provided, such as the microlog, the microlaterolog, and the laterolog 9 (experimental).

However, none of these extra logs, even when available, provide an answer to the diameter in invasion. Conventional logs need also be run for a complete solution, but in view of the salty nature of the mud when the devices under discussion are used, conventional logs are of poor quality.

Simplifying assumptions are therefore made when laterologs and guard logs are interpreted. The simplest of all is that they read R_t directly This is close to the truth when salt muds are used, for then the bore hole and invasion zone effects are negligible. The hole effect with salt mud is certainly always negligible, but it is not so for the invaded zone, especially when the formation has a high formation factor (low porosity). The laterolog may then read only the invaded-zone resistivity. In fresh muds, the laterolog is always reading mostly the invaded-zone resistivity.

It is prudent to allow in an empirical manner for the invaded zone, as suggested above, by formula (4-17). In using this formula to calculate R_t from the recorded laterolog or guard log readings R_a, judicious values are assumed for the diameter of invasion D_i, considering well depth, mud and formation pressure, filtrate loss, porosity, etc. R_i may be computed or measured by short investigation tools: microlog, microlaterolog, etc.

Microlaterolog. The microlaterolog device of Schlumberger's comprises one center electrode A_0 of very small size and three circular (ring) electrodes M_1, M_2, and A_1, each concentric with A_0 and spaced with short gaps (about ½ to 1 in.) between successive rings (Fig. 4-41a). These electrodes are embedded in an insulating support, commonly designated as a pad, which is applied against the wall of the bore hole by means of an appropriate spring system.

A current of constant and known intensity is sent through the center electrode A_0; another current of the same polarity is fed through the outer ring electrode A_1. The intensity of the latter current is automatically and continuously adjusted in such a way that the difference of potential between rings M_1 and M_2 is maintained substantially equal to zero. The potential prevailing at either M_1 or M_2 is recorded. The apparent resistivity measured with the device is proportional to the value of this potential and to a factor which depends on the geometrical characteristics of the system. This factor is determined experimentally.

According to this system, the current issued from the center electrode A_0 is prevented by the current emitted by the ring electrode A_1 from diverging freely in all directions, and is confined to a beam which penetrates the formations horizontally. This beam is approximately limited by a surface of revolution around an axis crossing electrode A_0 and perpendicular to the wall of the hole.

Figure 4-41*b* is a cross section of the bore hole, of the pad, and of the formations in the vertical plane containing the axis of the hole and the center of the pad. It is admitted that the plane of the figure is also a plane of symmetry for the pad, which it crosses along the line XX'. This condition is substantially realized in practice. It is further supposed in Fig. 4-41*b* that the formation is impervious (noninvaded) and homogeneous.

The figure shows schematically the distribution of the current lines. The surface enclosing the current beam issued from electrode A_0 (shaded area

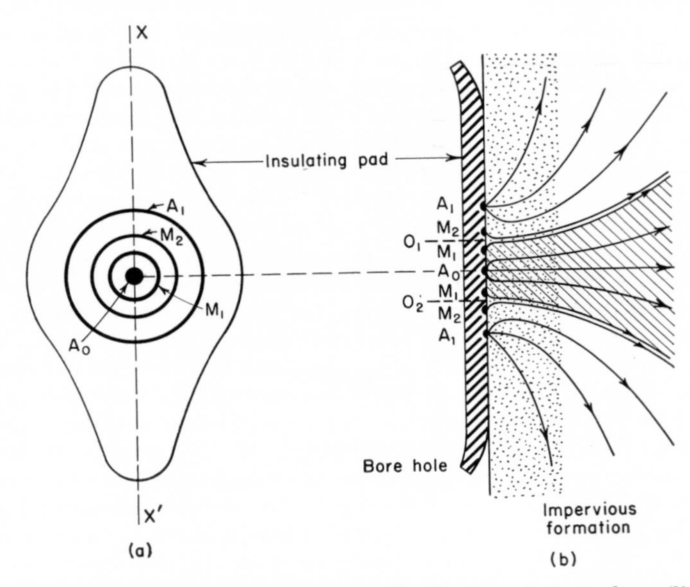

Fig. 4-41 (*a*). Microlaterolog device showing distribution of electrodes. (*b*). Vertical cross section showing the current lines issuing from the microlaterolog. (*Both after Doll, courtesy AIME.*)

on the drawing) is substantially perpendicular to the pad, and its diameter close to the pad is approximately the arithmetic average of the diameters of the ring electrodes M_1 and M_2, which amounts in practice to about 2 in. The diameter of the beam increases, first slowly and then more and more rapidly, with the distance from the wall. (The current beam somewhat recalls the shape of a "trumpet"; hence the colloquial term often used to designate the microlaterolog.) The exact shape of the current beam has been determined by means of laboratory models.

In the case of a porous and permeable formation, the electrode system is separated from the formation by the mud cake. This, nevertheless, does not change appreciably the general shape of the current beam. Inasmuch as the current crosses the mud cake in a substantially horizontal direction, the distance the current has to travel across the mud cake is very small in comparison with the distance it has to travel across the formation; furthermore, the resistivity of the mud cake is usually less than the resistivity of the formations. As a result of these two causes, the ohmic drop of potential through the mud cake is a very small part of the total ohmic drop. The influence of the mud cake on the measurement is, therefore, much reduced, and even negligible for all practical purposes, if the mud cake thickness is not too great. If the mud cake thickness is less than ½ in., the readings are not influenced by the mud cake. This device thus works best in muds that produce thin mud cakes, and in salt mud in particular. Examples of focused logs are given in Fig. 4-42.

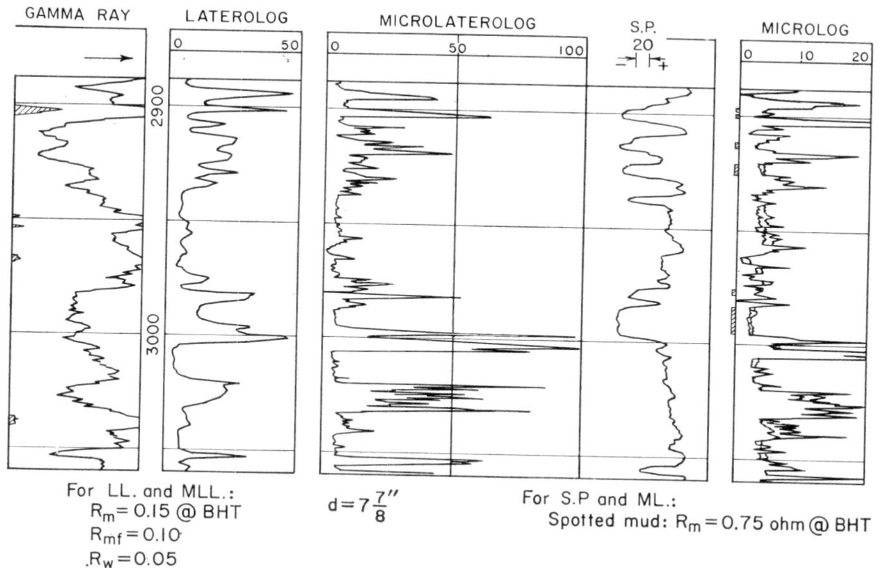

FIG. 4-42. Laterolog and microlaterolog in Kansas City–Lansing formation. (*Schlumberger Well Surveying Corp.*)

Inductive Measuring Device. *Schlumberger Induction Logging System.* All logging systems previously discussed depend upon the presence of an electrically conductive fluid in the bore hole in order to transmit the electrical energy to the formations and study the laws of its dissipation therein, which in turn give information on the nature of the formations. In most rotary wells, the drilling fluid is a water-base mud which is conductive of electricity.

However, a certain percentage of the wells drilled contain nonconductive fluids such as oil-base muds, crude oil, fresh water, or even air or gas in cable-tool wells and in the technique of gas drilling with rotary tools. Under such conditions it is impossible to obtain a satisfactory electric log through the usual procedure. Contact electrodes in the form of porous nonpolarizable electrodes containing a saturated copper sulfate solution or in the form of spring metal slider such as Weatherford scratchers and knives have been tried with limited success and have not found much favor owing to the jagged nature of the recorded curves resulting from highly variable contact resistances with the formations.

Induction logging does not depend on physical contact with the walls of the well bore in order to energize the formations, the electrical energy being transmitted through induction in a manner not unlike that in a transformer. The simplest type of induction log is composed of a transmitter coil (Fig. 4-43), the primary circuit of the transformer, which is energized with a 20,000-cycle current and induces a secondary current into the rocks which flows around the well bore in ringlike fashion. The intensity of the secondary currents is proportional to the electrical conductivity (1/resistivity) of the geologic formation and to the cross-sectional area of the "doughnutlike" formation element under consideration and is inversely proportional to its length. The higher the conductivity of the formation (or the lower its resistivity), the larger the formation current. This latter current in turn induces a signal into a receiver coil, the intensity of which is proportional to the formation current and conductivity. This picked-up signal is amplified, rectified, and recorded at the surface on the resistivity side of the log. The deflections are therefore proportional to formation conductivity. Since a resistivity scale is desired to conform to the usual procedure, this scale appears as a logarithmic (or hyperbolic) succession of numbers.

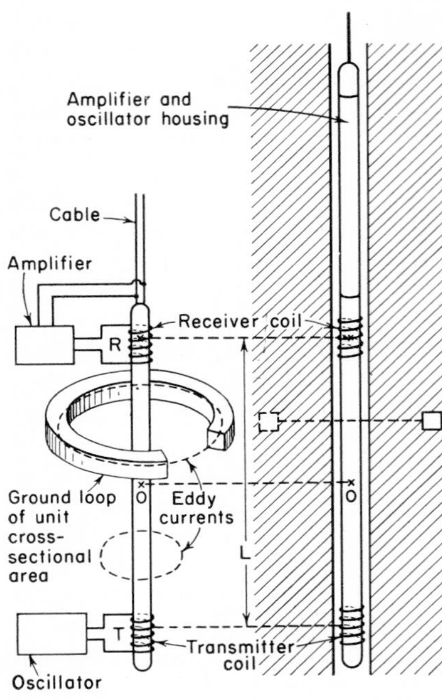

FIG. 4-43. Schematic diagram of induction logging system. (*After Doll, courtesy AIME.*)

A difficulty in locating the scale on the log is encountered because a logarithmic scale has no zero. In ordinary logging, the zero is obtained by short-circuiting the electrodes. If a similar test were made with an induction-log instrument, the deflection would be to minus infinity. The induction-log resistivity heading includes plus infinity which corresponds to a nonconductive medium for which a weak signal or none is obtained. This infinity point is placed arbitrarily at the maximum value (to the right) recorded on the log. Another standardized reading is made by a test signal produced within the instrument (i.e., 40 ohm-meters). Actually the only deflection well calibrated on the log is that of the test signal. The resistivity scale, however, cannot be located with high precision on the log. Hence, for quantitative evaluations made from the induction log, the absolute values of the resistivity figures read on the curves are much in doubt, possibly by as much as 10 to 20 per cent on the high-resistivity side of the scale. Errors due to scale uncertainties are, however, insignificant on the low-resistivity side of the scale if reasonable care was exercised in placing it. On modern induction logs, another resistivity curve is replotted by hand or by means of a reciprocator on a linear scale in order to facilitate readings and to deemphasize the relative deflections, especially on the low-resistivity side of the scale.

The induction-log system has many advantages which render its use advisable under certain conditions. The induction log has some special advantages over conventional logs. In the conventional logging methods using point electrodes for the determination of the resistivity, the flow of current is spherical and it is not possible to study separately the influence of the different regions of ground surrounding the electrode system. This is because the lines of current flow cross the boundaries between the different media, for example, the boundary between two adjacent beds or the boundary between the mud and the bed. If the resistivity of a given medium is changed, this affects the lines of current flow in their path through the other media. This is why the mathematical computation of departure curves for conventional logs is rather complicated and leads only to a fair approximation when the beds are not very thick and homogeneous.

In induction logging, the situation is completely different. If the hole is vertical, the lines of current flow may be represented as concentric circles in a horizontal plane the centers of which are on the axis of the hole. Since there is generally a symmetry of revolution of the ground around the axis of the drill hole, each line of current flow remains in the same medium all along its path and never crosses a boundary between media of different conductivities. On the other hand, provided that the frequency of the energizing current is not too high, the reaction of the different circular currents on each other may be neglected. Therefore the action of the different regions of ground, which individually have a symmetry of revolution around the hole, may be considered separately, and the measured signal is simply the sum of the individual signals given by the different regions. Therefore the theoretical computation of charts or of typical logs, corresponding to any distribution of earth conductivities, is always possible, provided, of course, that there be a symmetry of revolution about the well bore.

Most generally it is possible to use the direct readings of the induction logs as true resistivity. It is only when dealing with very large-diameter wells, very thin formations, or highly invaded formations that corrections are needed. Such corrections are made by applying the principle of additive effects of the various sections of the earth on the instrument. For this purpose it is assumed that the induction-log sonde is centered in the hole and that the formations are horizontal and symmetrical about the axis of the well. In addition the formations around the well bore may be divided into a series of sections which are homogeneous in character: the mud in the hole R_m, the invaded zone R_i, the undisturbed object formation R_t, and the surrounding beds R_s.

Various typical computation cases are represented in Fig. 4-44. In Fig.

4-44*a*, an infinitely thick bed traversed by a bore hole is considered. The effect on the instrument centered in the hole is the sum of the individual effects of the bed and of the hole and their effects are weighted by means

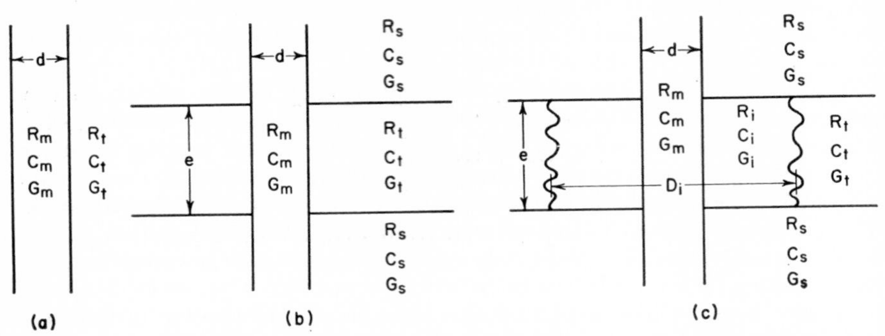

FIG. 4-44. Representation of electrical conductivity and geometric-factor distribution around a well bore. Beds of (*a*) infinite thickness, (*b*) finite thickness (uninvaded), and (*c*) finite thickness (invaded).

of geometric factors which are a function of the spacial distribution of each. We have

$$\frac{1}{R_a} = G_m \frac{1}{R_m} + G_t \frac{1}{R_t}$$
$$1 = G_m + G_t \tag{4-18}$$

where G_m = geometric factor of the mud in the well of resistivity R_m
G_t = geometric factor of the object bed of resistivity R_t
R_a = apparent resistivity measured by the induction log

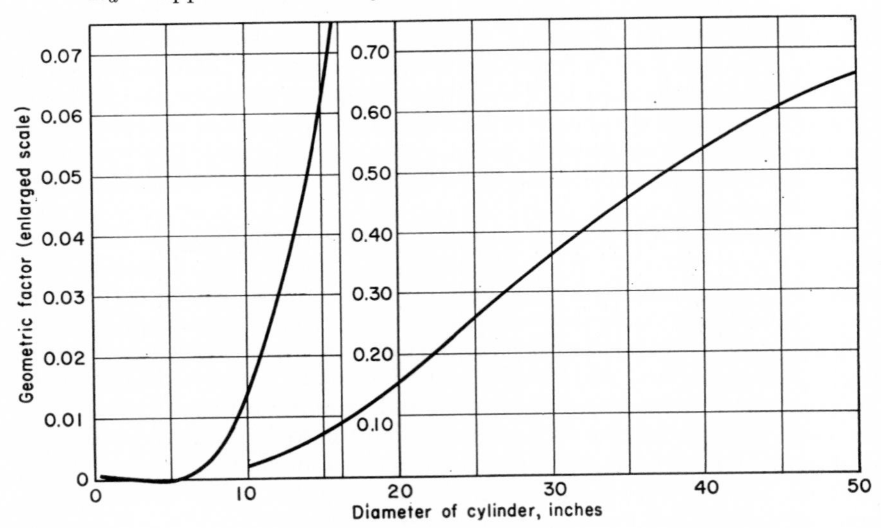

FIG. 4-45. Chart for geometric-factor determination of well bore. (*After Poupon.*)

The values of G_m may be read directly from Fig. 4-45 as a function of the hole size.

In Fig. 4-44*b*, a bed of finite thickness, noninvaded, is considered. The equations required for solving the true resistivity are the following:

$$\frac{1}{R_a} = G_m \frac{1}{R_m} + G_t \frac{1}{R_t} + G_s \frac{1}{R_s}$$
$$1 = G_m + G_t + G_s \tag{4-19}$$

where G_s is the geometric factor of the surrounding beds of resistivity R_s. The geometric factor G_t may be read from Fig. 4-46 as a function of bed thickness and hole size. G_m is obtained as before and G_s is obtained by difference.

In Fig. 4-44*c*, a bed of finite thickness which is invaded to a diameter D_i and resistivity R_i is considered.

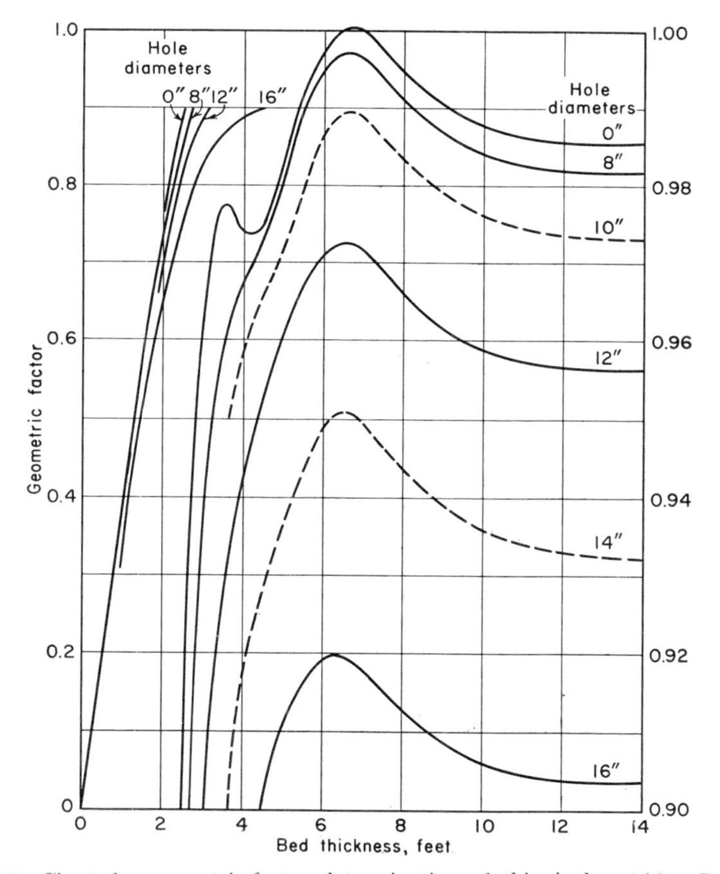

FIG. 4-46. Chart for geometric-factor determination of thin beds. (*After Poupon.*)

The required equations for the solution of R_t are

$$\frac{1}{R_a} = G_m \frac{1}{R_m} + G_t \frac{1}{R_t} + G_i \frac{1}{R_i} + G_s \frac{1}{R_s}$$
$$1 = G_m + G_t + G_i + G_s \qquad (4\text{-}20)$$

If the diameter of invasion is not too large G_i may be obtained by difference from Fig. 4-46 by reading the geometric factor for a finite thickness bed when the hole diameter is d and D_i, respectively. G_s is again obtained by difference.

RADIOACTIVITY WELL LOGGING

One of the main limitations of electric logging for subsurface geologic and engineering studies is its inability to investigate the formations in a cased bore hole. Many old wells now cased have been or were improperly logged either geologically or electrically. In order to fill the gaps in a reservoir structure, or stratigraphic map, and plan perforating and reconditioning an old well, it is often advisable to secure information on the depth and thickness of certain prospective producing formations traversed by the cased bore hole. This may be obtained by means of gamma-ray and neutron logging for which the presence of a casing in the bore hole is no hindrance. Radioactivity logs prove very useful also in wells containing salty muds too conductive to permit good electric-log definition, but with advent of the laterolog, this advantage over electric logging is disappearing, although the gamma-ray curve remains a fundamental element of the salt-mud survey.

Gamma-ray Logging. Gamma-ray logging of bore holes is dependent upon the radioactivity or spontaneous disintegration of unstable chemical elements contained in the geologic formations. Most of the radioactive elements belong to three different series, namely, the uranium, the thorium, and the actinium series (Fig. 4-47). The radioactive elements uranium, actinium (actino-uranium), and thorium are the parent elements of three radioactive series containing more than 40 distinctive naturally occurring members. Each radioactive element disintegrates to form the next lower member of the series, i.e., one of lower atomic weight. Nonradioactive lead is the stable end product of all three series. The elements potassium, rubidium, samarium, and lutecium (cassiopeium) are known to be feebly radioactive. Potassium is widely distributed in comparatively large quantities and presumably contributes a part of the total radioactivity in many sedimentary rocks.

During their spontaneous disintegration, radioactive elements give off three types of rays. The alpha rays (positively charged particles which are helium nuclei) are expelled at relatively moderate velocities (several thousand miles per second) and yet are of insufficient energy to penetrate the casing of wells because of the material nature of the radiation constituted of electrically charged particles.

The beta rays or high-speed electrons (negatively charged particles) are expelled from the radioactive elements of rocks at higher velocities than alpha particles, but they are yet of too small penetrating power to register on the measuring devices used in radioactivity logging.

The gamma rays, which are electromagnetic waves like those of light or radio, are often produced simultaneously with beta-ray generation. While the visible light is a wave of length averaging 1/50,000 in., the gamma rays have a wavelength of 10^{-10} in. Gamma rays are similar in nature to X rays but of shorter wavelength and of greater power of penetration.

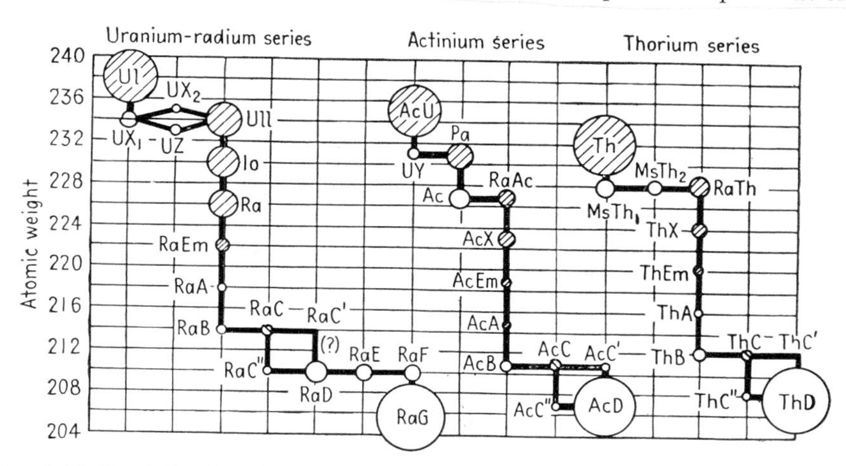

FIG. 4-47. Chart showing three radioactivity families. The size of the circle is an index of the life of the element. Uranium, actinium, and thorium are extremely long-lived, their half-life being about one thousand million years. Radium is a member of the uranium series and its half-life is 1,590 years. (*From J. B. Hoag, "Electron and Nuclear Physics," D. Van Nostrand Company, Inc., Princeton, N.J.*, 1948.)

This renders radioactivity logging of cased wells possible since the gamma radiations emitted at some distance from behind the walls of the wells can still penetrate the casing.

It has been ascertained that all rocks contain some radioactive material, although, in some cases, it may be present only in extremely minute amounts. Of the igneous rocks, the light-colored or acidic types like granite, syenite, monzonite, etc., contain larger amounts of radioactive material than the dark-colored or basic types like gabbro, diorite, peridotite, etc. Since the sedimentary rocks were formed at the expense of igneous-rock weathering, sediments are also radioactive, but the radioactive materials are very unequally distributed among the different types of sedimentary rocks. Pure limestones and sandstones show very low radioactivity. Ordinary shale exhibits high radioactivity. A large number of intermediate possibilities may be obtained according to the proportion of shales and clays mixed with either limestone or dolomite. Certain dark bituminous shales, e.g., the Chattanooga, the Heebner, etc., show unusually high radioactivity; argillaceous sandstones and limestones show a radioac-

Lithologic type	No. of samples	Avg-radioactivity in radium equivalents per gram, $\times 10^{-12}$
Black and grayish-black shale	40	26.1
Dark to black shales, neither calcareous nor sandy	74	22.4
Shales including sandy shales	164	16.2
Marls and limy shales, grayish-black and black	3	16.5
Sand and shale	9	13.5
Dark to black shales, not calcareous, but sandy	16	13.2
Medium to light gray shales, neither sandy nor calcareous	17	11.3
Siltstone	11	10.3
Medium to light gray shales, not calcareous, but sandy	18	9.0
Marls and limy shales, dark	10	8.8
Sandstones, silty but not shaly	26	7.3
Shaly sandstones	40	7.0
Marls and limy shales of light shades	16	6.8
All sandstones, including shaly sandstones	131	5.3
All sandstones, excluding shaly sandstones, but including silty types	105	4.0
Sandstones free from silt and shale	76	4.1
Shale-free limestones and dolomites	64	4.1
Microcrystalline to earthy limestones and dolomites of medium to light shade	28	4.0
Medium to light shade, shale-free limestone	33	3.8
Finely to coarsely crystalline limestones and dolomites of medium to light shade	24	3.1
Medium to light shade, shale-free dolomite	21	3.1
Effect of shale in shale-free limestone and dolomite:		
Light gray to white	30	3.1
Medium shade	22	4.1
Dark to black	10	6.1
Estimated original permeability of sandstone before cementation:		
Very high	35	2.9
High	37	5.1
Low	40	6.6
Very low	24	7.5

FIG. 4-48. Radioactivity of various sediments. (*After Russell, Lane-Wells Company.*)

tivity intermediate between that of pure sandstones and limestones and the ordinary shales. Coals are weakly radioactive. Certain volcanic ashes have a high radioactivity, about equal to that of ordinary shales. Salt and anhydrite are low, whereas other evaporite rocks rich in potassium are high in radioactivity. Figure 4-48 gives a better idea of the radioactivity of some lithologic types commonly encountered in logging. Figure 4-49 summarizes in a graphic manner the radioactivity scale of sedimentary rocks. Numerous exceptions are encountered to these empirical relationships; the following are a few of the well-known ones: the Tubbs sand

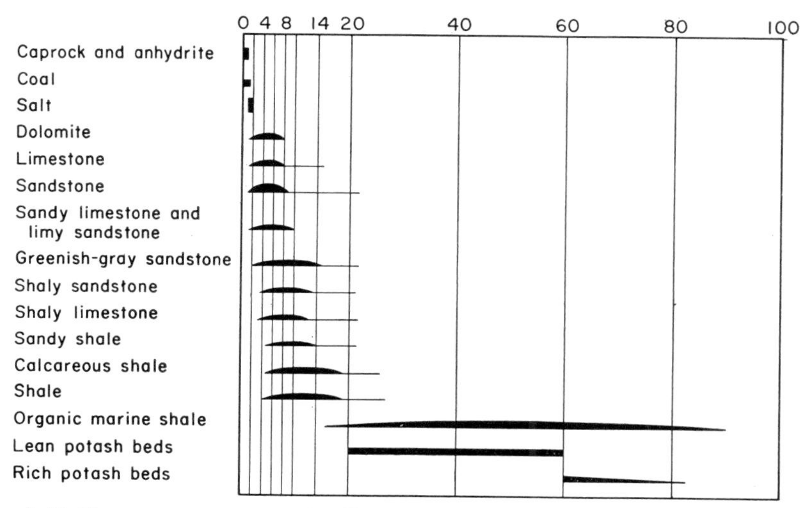

FIG. 4-49. Gamma-ray response of sedimentary rocks. (*After Russell, courtesy AAPG.*)

(North Texas) is highly radioactive, a layer of unusual radioactivity is encountered in the Embar-Phosphoria (Wyoming), several streaks in Gulf Coast sediments, etc.

There are three different types of gamma-radiation detectors which are suitable for radioactivity measurements in wells; they will be reviewed briefly. They are the ionization chamber, the Geiger-Müller (GM) counter, and the scintillometer.

The ionization chamber, in the form of a proportional counter, was the first instrument introduced in the radiation logging technique by Well Surveys, Inc., in 1940, and commercially used first by Lane-Wells and other licensees: Welex, Western Company. The logging ionization chamber is a cylinder 3 ft in length and 3⅝ in. in diameter. It contains argon under pressure (600 to 1,200 psi). An electrically insulated rod occupies the axis of the chamber and a potential of 180 volts is applied between center rod and housing. When a gamma radiation strikes the chamber, the argon gas is ionized and causes an avalanche of secondary ionization which is proportional to the number of primary ion pairs formed. Because of the gas multiplication of the incident radiation, the electrical pulses issuing from the chamber are of different magnitudes and of weak intensity. Before recording of the pulses at the surface becomes possible, their amplification at the bottom of the well is required, which implies electronic circuits and perhaps batteries in the well. When batteries are used, there is possibility of temperature drift in the recorded curves and this effect must be eliminated.

The efficiency of the ionization chamber in detecting gamma rays is about 10 per cent; i.e., 10 per cent of the incident photons emitted by the formation are recorded. These pulses are superposed over a background count which is generally of one count per minute per square centimeter of surface of the chamber. Gamma-ray pulses are not recorded individually, but the circuit is so arranged as to read the rate of arrival of the pulses by charging a condenser which is allowed to discharge in a high resistance. The condenser leakage current is recorded at the earth surface.

The Geiger-Müller counter is used in logging by Schlumberger, Perforating Guns Atlas Corp., and others. The Geiger detector is similar in design and construction to the ionization chamber and may have the same dimensions (36 in. long) but the contained gas is under low pressure (below atmospheric) and the applied voltage between central rod and housing is much higher (900 to 1,200 volts). The low-pressure gas in the chamber is often argon under 10 cm mercury pressure. Under the passage of a gamma ray this gas ionizes and produces a discharge which would continue indefinitely under the application of high voltage if it were not for the introduction into the argon of a quenching polyatomic vapor such as ether, alcohol, acetone, etc., to the extent of about 10 per cent. The efficiency of an ordinary Geiger counter is relatively low (1 per cent) but with special construction material for the chamber housing and other grid and guard devices the efficiency may be raised to 12 to 15 per cent. Other advantages of the GM tube are the higher amplitude of the pulses (2 to 3 volts) requiring no amplification for their transmission to the surface. Shorter length GM tubes grouped in a bundle of a larger number of individual tubes are also in use. They permit finer logging resolution of thin beds.

The scintillometer or scintillation counter makes use of the luminescence induced in certain substances when bombarded by radioactive substances. This phenomenon was used by early workers in radioactivity, especially Lord Rutherford, who discovered that pitchblende caused crystals of sphalerite to scintillate. It was not until the light intensity so produced could be electronically amplified and more efficient phosphors were found that practical instrumentation for measuring radiation intensity could be built. At about 1947, stable photomultiplier tubes became available to replace visual observation and counting of light flashes. Scintillating phosphors are of various types, solids and liquids. They must be extremely clear to permit transmission of light through the window of the photomultiplier tube so that it may produce free electrons from the light-sensitive cathode of the photomultiplier tube. The production of light by gamma rays in the scintillator may be by the photoelectric effect, by Compton recoil, or by the ion pair production. This produces ionization of atoms in the phosphor and breaks many chemical bonds. The recovery of the excited atoms is almost instantaneous and electrons return to atoms with the attendant emission of light.

Scintillators are crystalline or liquid substances which may be either organic or inorganic. Several are listed here by way of examples and a coefficient of sensitivity with reference to anthracene is also given for some:

Type	Substance	Coefficient of sensitivity
Organic crystals	Anthracene	1.0
	Naphthalene	0.25
	Phenanthrene	
	Polystyrene	
Inorganic crystals	Sodium and Potassium Iodide (thallium activated)	2.0
	Calcium tungstate	1.0
	Cadmium tungstate	2.0
Solutions	Terphenyl in xylene } Anthracene in toluene }	0.5

The counting efficiency for gamma rays by phosphors is very high by comparison to the ionization chamber and the Geiger tube. It increases with the density of the substance and theoretically should be 100 per cent for infinitely dense matter. However, for the substances available, the maximum efficiency is about 40 to 60 per cent. This is because matter is mostly empty space as far as radiations of short wavelength are concerned.

The scintillation counter is used in logging by the McCullough Tool Co. and a crystal reportedly 3 in. long is used as detector. Schlumberger's is reported also to use such a counter. The short length of the counter gives unusually high definition in thin beds. The higher efficiency of the counter permits much higher logging speeds.

One disadvantage of scintillators as gamma-ray detectors is the high level thermal noise associated with the photomultiplier tube. This produces a background count of the order of thousands per minute. To reduce it to an acceptable level, the tube must be kept at low constant temperature while logging.

The gamma-ray log measures radiation intensity and in view of the variable efficiency of the different devices used by the logging companies a great deal of confusion exists when it is desired to compare logs calibrated in the various units. The quantitative unit of radioactive matter is the *curie*. It is an amount of radioactive matter containing 1 g of radium in equilibrium with its daughter products.

Gamma-ray logs available commercially are calibrated in various manners:

1. *Inches of deflections* for a standard known radiation intensity. This is Well Surveys' practice, the standard being No. 274. This unit is used by Lane-Wells, Welex, and Western.

2. *Microroentgen per hour.* The microroentgen (μr) is the unit used by the Perforating Guns Atlas Corp. and the McCullough Tool Co. The roentgen is the unit of cumulative ionization. An ionization effect of 0.84 roentgen is received from a point source of 1 curie at a distance of 1 meter.

3. *Microgram radium equivalent per ton.* This is the Schlumberger unit. It corresponds to about four to five counts per minute. The radium content of the rock is assumed to be in equilibrium with its parent elements and the unit is then equivalent to 2.8 g (0.0062 lb) of uranium per ton or to 5.7 g (0.0125 lb) of thorium per ton.

The equivalence of radioactivity log scales among the various radiation logging services is approximately as follows:

One standard unit of Well Surveys, Inc., type of logs, which is the deflection measured in inches produced by the radioactive standard 274, is equivalent to 13.1 μg radium equivalent per ton or 21 μr per hr.

Many factors affect the readings recorded by the gamma-ray curves, and when it is desired to obtain a true natural radioactivity reading, correction must be applied to the curve deflections for eccentricity of detector in the well, for radial thickness of mud in the well, for mud density, for casing

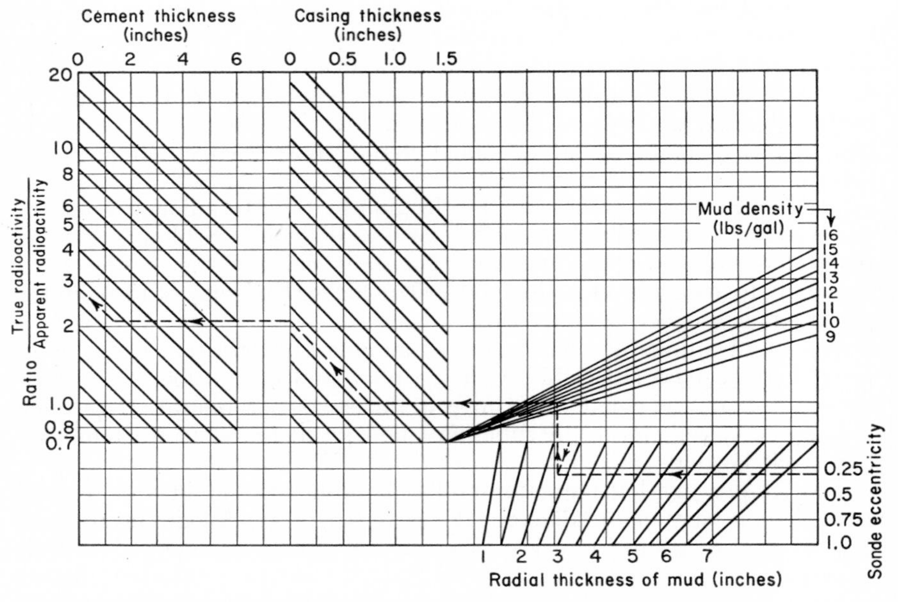

FIG. 4-50. Gamma-ray departure curves taking into account five well-bore parameters. (*After Dewan and Allaud, courtesy The Petroleum Engineer.*)

thickness, and for cement thickness. Such corrections are facilitated by means of the gamma-ray departure curves of Fig. 4-50 due to Blanchard and Dewan (1953). The chart indicates how to proceed to obtain the true over apparent radioactivity ratio for the case of 0.3 eccentricity, 2.25-in. mud thickness, 11-lb mud weight, ⅜-in. casing thickness, and 1.3-in. cement thickness. Sonde eccentricity is computed from $(dc - ds)/(d - ds)$, where dc is the inside-casing diameter, d is the bore-hole diameter, and ds is the diameter of the sonde. It is zero for a centered sonde and unity for a sonde against the wall. Average mud thickness is $\frac{1}{2}(dc - 2 \times e_c - ds)$, where e_c is the casing thickness. Average cement thickness is $\frac{1}{2}(d - dc)$.

Other important factors in correcting apparent radioactivity to a true value are the speed of logging, bed thickness, and instrumental time constant. This last correction may be made as a function of the "drag" of the gamma-ray curve which is defined as the speed of logging in feet per second times the time constant in second. The correction factor to obtain the true radioactivity is obtained from the relationship

$$\frac{R_t}{R_a} = \left(1 - \exp\left[\frac{-e}{D}\right]\right)^{-1}$$

where e = bed thickness, ft

D = drag, ft, as defined above

This relation is due to Edwards and Simpson (1955). Figure 4-51 permits the value of R_t/R_a to be obtained readily as a function of e/D.

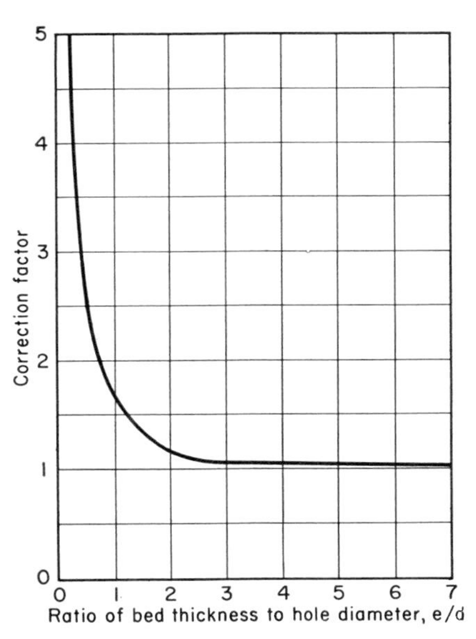

FIG. 4-51. Bed-thickness correction for radioactivity. (*McCullough Tool Company.*)

Corrections are especially important when converting the gamma-ray readings in terms of radioactive mineralization. It is seen that corrections are needed only for very thin beds.

The following conversion factors may be of interest. The standard units of deflection on a Well Surveys' type of gamma-ray log are equivalent to about 0.01 per cent uranium content in the formation, when such uranium is in equilibrium with its daughter products, i.e., for sufficiently old formations (older than 10 million years). For logs calibrated in microroentgens per hour, the uranium content in per cent is about equal to 0.0004 times the true radioactivity. For logs calibrated in microgram radium equivalent per ton, the uranium content in per cent is equal to 0.00033 per cent U_3O_8 per unit.

The gamma-ray log corresponds essentially to the self-potential curve in electrical logging which measures also, in the main, lithologic parameters.

By analogy again to electric logging, the gamma-ray log is of ambiguous interpretation unless some idea of fluid content in porous formations is obtainable. This is provided by neutron logging.

Neutron Logging. The neutron ($_0n^1$) (a fundamental particle of matter together with protons and electrons) is one of the main building blocks of nature, as it is a constituent part of the nucleus of all chemical elements except common hydrogen. The name implies that the particle is free of

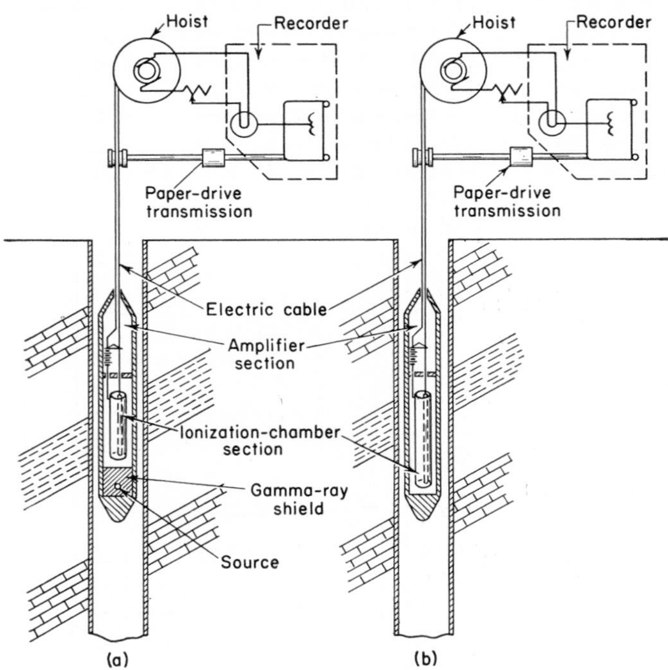

FIG. 4-52. Radioactivity logging equipment. Components of (*a*) neutron and (*b*) gamma-ray logging equipment. (*Lane-Wells Company.*)

electric charges and is electrically neutral. Hence, it is able to penetrate matter (made up of electrically charged particles, positive protons ($_1H^1$) and negative electrons ($_{-1}e^0$) without much interference from electrical repulsions or attractions. In particular, it can be caused to penetrate several thicknesses of casing without much loss in energy. When neutron radiations strike chemical elements within the geologic formations, certain nuclear reactions take place, namely, neutron scattering and the production of artificial or induced radioactivity by neutron capture. Both phenomena are used in neutron logging and are the basis of two entirely different neutron logging systems: the systems of the Perforating Guns Atlas Corp. and of Well Surveys, Inc. Figure 4-52*a* shows a schematic diagram of a neutron logging tool.

The Perforating Guns Atlas Corp. (PGAC) system makes use of the scattered neutrons altogether, called Brons neutrons. This necessitates the use of a slow-neutron detector. While the manufacturing details of the detector are not available, in principle it can be made by coating the walls of an ionization chamber with a boron compound or by filling it with boron trifluoride under pressure. When struck by a slow neutron, the boron nucleus gives off two alpha particles which ionize the gas in the chamber and actuate the detector. The neutron-detecting device is completely insensitive to gamma rays and no shielding from the neutron source, which also emits gamma rays, is required. This neutron log was introduced in 1950.

The Well Surveys' system makes use altogether of the induced gamma radioactivity or of the gamma rays of capture which results from irradiation of the formations by a beam of fast neutrons. The neutron source is a mixture of radium and beryllium of uniform composition and density and highly compressed. Because of the alpha particles emitted by radium, the following nuclear reaction takes place in the source and gives rise to fast neutrons:

$$_2He^4 + {}_4Be^9 = {}_6C^{12} + {}_0n^1$$

As a result of successive collisions with atoms in the neighborhood of the source, the fast neutrons are transformed into slow neutrons or neutrons with thermal energy, i.e., 0.025 ev. Thermal neutrons have a tendency to diffuse mostly into the bore hole, and to a lesser extent into the formation where they are captured by atoms. Hydrogen-rich substances may be the predominant slow-neutron capturing nuclei; in so doing the hydrogen nucleus is transformed into heavy hydrogen (deuterium) and emits a gamma ray of 2.3 Mev energy.

$$_0n^1 + {}_1H^1 = {}_1H^2 + 2.3 \text{ Mev}$$

Next in line in ability to capture slow neutrons is chlorine giving off gamma rays of capture of 4 and 7 Mev. Capture by other nuclei is small when H and Cl are present as may be inferred from the following table for the capture cross section of various substances and minerals:

Substance	*Capture cross section*
H_2O	0.0207
NaCl (sat. brine)	0.1230
SiO_2	0.0039
Al_2O_3	0.0054
$CaCO_3$	0.0070
$(CaMg)(CO_3)_2$	0.0087

However, the energy of the gamma ray of capture given off by such elements is high, 9 Mev for silicon, 6 Mev for calcium.

The Well Surveys' neutron logging device is so constructed that the detecting ionization chamber is very insensitive to the natural gamma-ray radiation emanating from the strata, and it responds mostly to the induced radiations caused by the neutron bombardment. The sensitivity of the neutron-log detecting device is one-sixteenth that of the gamma-ray log device. Owing to the high intensity of the gamma rays of capture and the short length of the detecting chamber (9 in.), the neutron curve provides good definition of the thinner geologic strata traversed, as well as the location of the possible porous zones within the strata. The neutron curve is also highly sensitive to change in bore-hole diameter and to the shielding effects of casing and bore-hole fluids, whether oil, gas, water, or oil-base or water-base mud. Careful consideration of bore-hole conditions must, therefore, enter into the interpretation of neutron logs.

Owing to the neutron distribution around the source and the detector location (Fig. 4-53) when the neutron source faces a porous zone containing

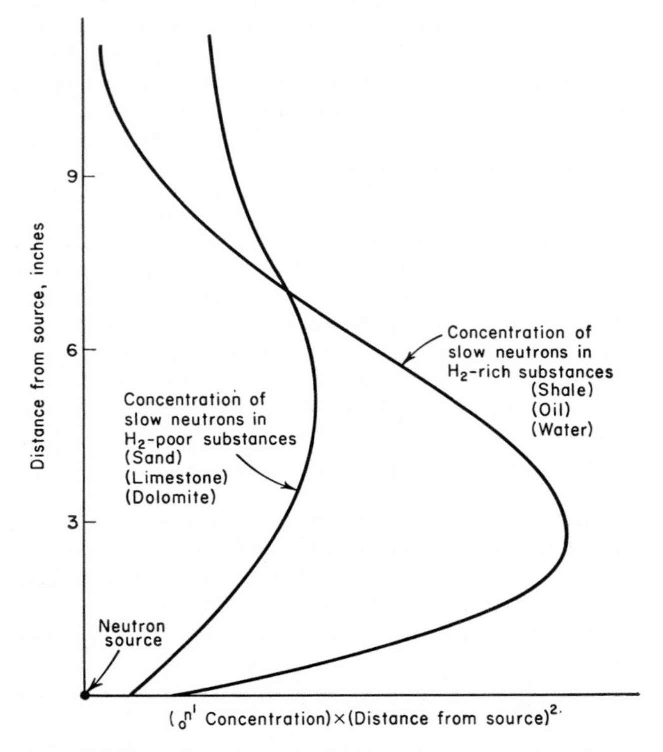

Fig. 4-53. Schematic thermal-neutron distribution or "neutron cloud" around a source.

oil, gas, and/or water, readings are low on the radiation detector located about 10 in. above, but shielded from, the neutron source, which emits also gamma rays together with the neutrons. A high activity indicates the absence of hydrogen-containing substances; a low activity, their presence. Hence, the presence of porous and permeable formations which are always saturated, below certain depths, by hydrogen-containing substances, either water or oil and gas, is characterized by low neutron activity. The explanation for the gamma reaction is as follows: When a formation is rich in hydrogen, the neutron is slowed down and captured near the source, the emitted gamma ray has a considerable distance to travel to reach the detector, and its intensity is reduced, giving rise to a small deflection. When the formation is poor in hydrogen, in low-porosity rocks, the neutron is slowed down only after it has traveled a considerable distance and is captured near the gamma-ray detector which reads high intensity. Therefore the spacing between source and detectors is a critical distance in the response obtained from a neutron curve.

It appears that the neutron log is a fluid-composition log (in much the same manner as the electric-resistivity log) and, more specifically, a hydrogen-composition log. It matters not in what form the hydrogen occurs, whether oil, water, gas, or shales; the neutron curves show deviations to the left on the log, i.e., conventionally a decrease in induced gamma-ray activity.

The total gamma radiation reaching the ionization chamber of the Well Surveys' type of neutron logging instrument is made up of three components as follows:

$$I \text{ (total gamma radiation)} = I_1 + I_2 + I_3$$

where I_1 = intensity of gamma rays induced by actions of neutrons upon formation; this is the quantity which it is desired to record

I_2 = intensity of scattered radiation, i.e., gamma radiation which was originally emitted by the source capsule and which has been scattered by the formation or bore hole

I_3 = intensity of natural gamma radiation emitted by formation rocks

It is desirable to reduce to a minimum the effect of I_2 and I_3. This is done by providing a shield between source and neutron detector. Only in highly radioactive formations or in an enlarged hole is it necessary to pay attention to components I_2 and I_3.

While the neutron curve always has a component consisting of the gamma radiation emitted by the rock through natural disintegration processes, it will usually be too small to merit consideration in most reservoir rocks.

However, important exceptions to this rule have been noted. Certain bentonitic sands of South Texas, partially silty sands, radioactive limestone, and other types of formations mentioned above, exhibit sufficient natural gamma-ray activity so that the neutron curve is seriously affected.

It is important to note that the neutron curve may be corrected for this natural activity by means of the gamma-ray curve. This is done by taking into account the relative sensitivities of the two ionization chambers for gamma rays. For any given sensitivity scale in the Well Surveys' type of logs the gamma-ray instrument is sixteen times more sensitive than the neutron instrument. For example, opposite a bentonitic sand let the gamma-ray curve indicate a high intensity of natural gamma radiation making an 8-in. swing to the right of the normal value for sands. If the sensitivity scales were 6 and 10 in., respectively, for the gamma-ray and neutron curves, the correction to be applied to the neutron curve is

$$\frac{8}{16} \times \frac{10}{6} = 0.833 \text{ in.}$$

This is the deflection to subtract from the neutron curve in order to correct it for the natural gamma radiation.

The predominating component of the neutron curve is I_1 or induced radiation. For most cases, where the bore-hole diameter is small and does not change appreciably, the I_2 or scattered component is very small and exhibits no large variations. The I_3 or natural radiation component is usually small enough to be neglected when the log is used in stratigraphic correlation work; but where a quantitative application is to be attempted, it is sometimes found necessary to perform the correction previously outlined on the neutron curve.

A third possibility for a neutron log is to record fast neutrons; the McCullough Tool Co. claims to be recording such a curve by means of a fast-neutron scintillator.

Qualitative Interpretation of Radioactivity Logs. *Gamma-ray Logs.* Gamma-ray logs are continuous curves of the intensity of natural radioactivity vs. depth. The curve shows the relative intensity of the gamma rays and not the absolute amount of radioactive material in the formations. The intensity varies with the composition of the sediments; therefore, the log indicates the lithology of the formations penetrated. Most radioactivity logs closely resemble the spontaneous potential curves of electric logs; where the bore hole traverses sandstones and shales, the two curves are almost identical.

Increased radioactivity is indicated by the curve shifting to the right; decreased radioactivity by the curve shifting to the left (Fig. 4-54). The pure sandstones and limestones are represented on the log by the minima, to the left, and the shales by the maxima, to the right. Argillaceous sandstones and limestones are represented on the average or central portion of the log. Certain dark shales (such as the Chattanooga) are represented by especially prominent peaks to the right. Shale breaks in thick sandstones or limestones are represented by secondary peaks to the right, and vice versa, thin sandstones or limestones in shales are represented by secondary peaks to the left. The distinction between sandstone and limestone cannot always be made from the radioactivity log alone. In certain cases, it may be advisable to correlate the radioactivity log with some sample log in the field, although an interpreter familiar with the stratigraphic sequence can easily recognize the formations.

The homogeneous salt normally found in the central part of salt domes has a low radioactivity and is represented by a monotonous curve to the left of the arbitrary median; in wells where the salt overhang has been penetrated, it is easily distinguishable from the detrital sediments. Anhydrite in the cap rock of salt domes is normally less radioactive than salt, and is marked by the curve shifting to the left at the salt-anhydrite contact. The character of the curve at the top of the anhydrite is dependent upon the kind of sediments overlying the cap rock. In relogging producing wells, an increase in natural radioactivity is often observed at the producing level which is attributed to incrustation by radioactive salts of liner, perforation, slots, tubing, or other metallic parts present at that level (Campbell, 1951).

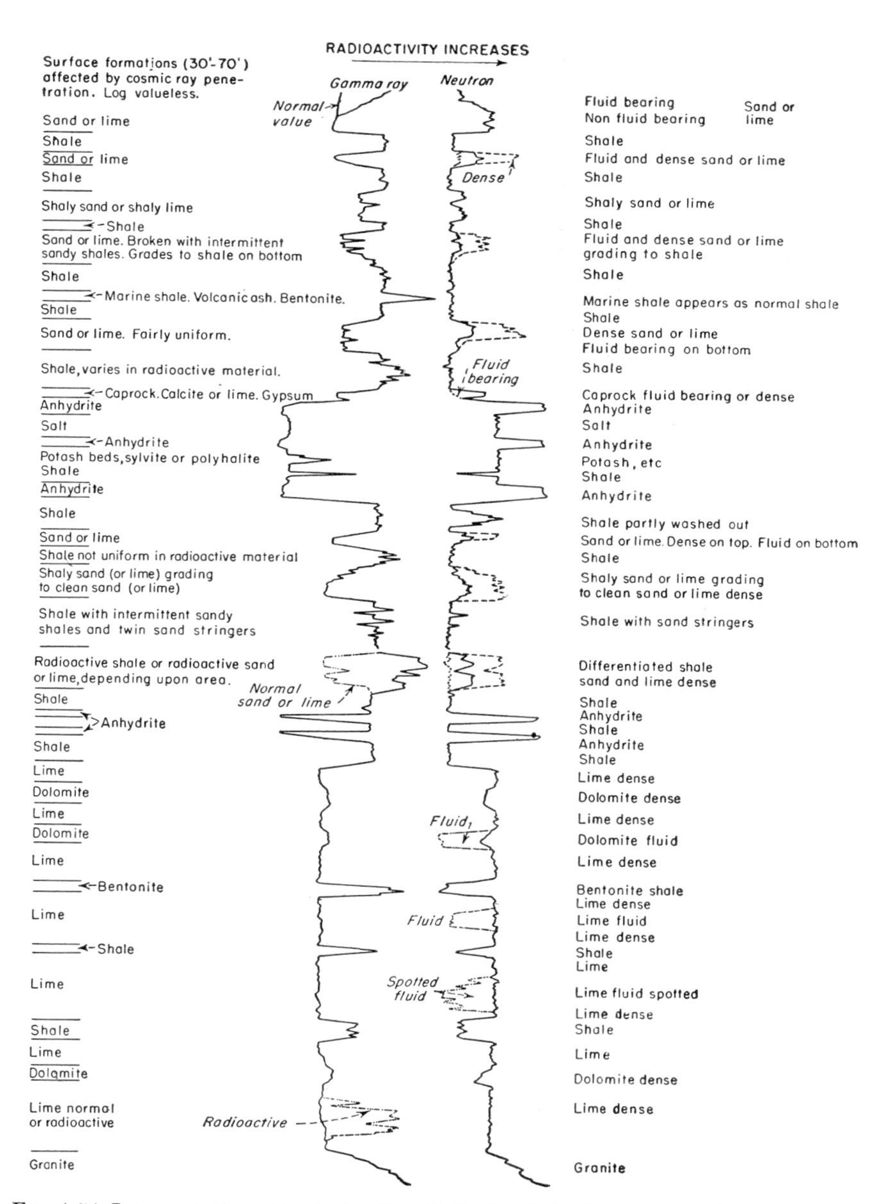

FIG. 4-54. Interpretation of typical radioactivity-log deflections. (*Lane-Wells Company.*)

Formational contacts, especially if marked by abrupt changes in lithology, are indicated by rapid and nearly horizontal shifts of the curve. The middle point of the nearly horizontal shift is usually interpreted as marking the contact, rather than the point at the beginning or end of the shift. Gradual shifts in the intensity curve usually indicate gradational contacts.

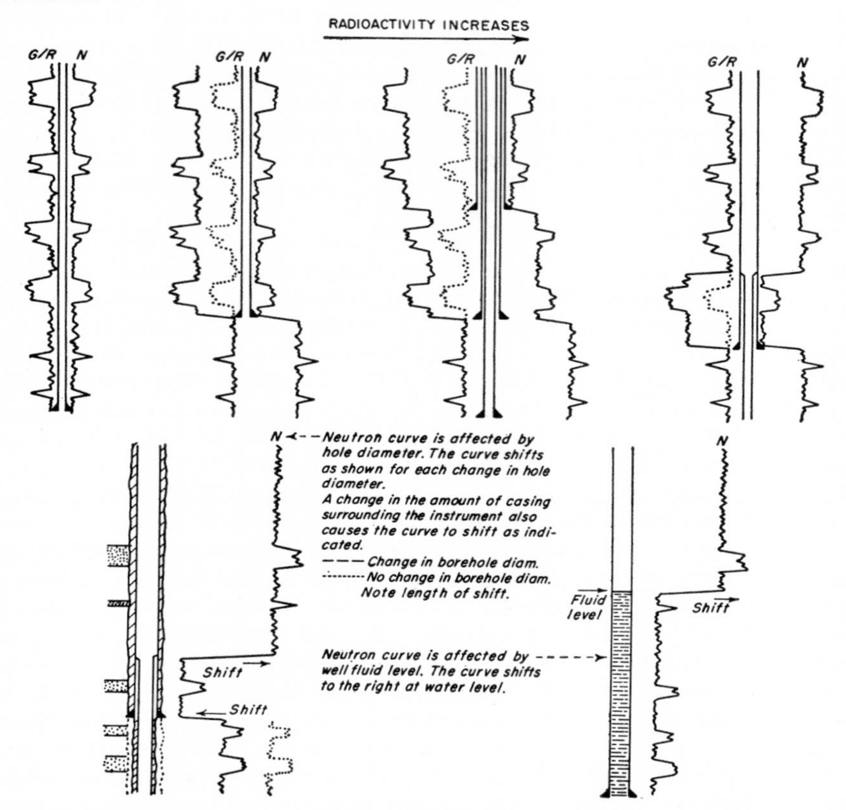

FIG. 4-55. Effect of physical bore-hole conditions on gamma-ray and neutron curves. (*Lane-Wells Company.*)

In wells with a considerable thickness of cement behind the casing, the bottom of the cement is usually marked by a shift of the curve to the left; the top of the cement may be marked by a gradual shift of the curve to the right (Fig. 4-55). A somewhat similar shift may result from the varying amount of casing in the well (overlap and parted casing) and from other physical conditions under which a survey is made. However, such variations in intensity are seldom confused with those resulting from the radioactivity of the surrounding formations. The shifts observed in the gamma-ray curve due to physical conditions are also of lesser magnitude than on the neutron curve.

Neutron Logs. The qualitative interpretation of a neutron curve is not too unlike that of the resistivity curve. Since neutron logs are responsive to formation fluids, the intensity of the recorded curve in saturated porous formations is considerably less than if they were dense and devoid of fluids. Hence, the neutron log helps to resolve the ambiguity of the gamma-ray curve interpretation. For instance, a minimum value on the gamma-ray curve may be interpreted as either sandstone or limestone. However, if the neutron curve indicates a maximum at the same level, a dense limestone devoid of fluids (water or oil) and porosity is definitely the interpretation. Deflections of the neutron curve below a well-established shale base line are indicative of lignite streaks (Campbell, 1951).

The responsiveness of the neutron curve to the presence of formation fluids renders possible the identification of zones of porosity in limestone and chalk sections.

Although the neutron curve is responsive to well fluids, it cannot readily distinguish between them in the present state of instrumental and interpretative development. However, future refinements may permit differentiations between oil, gas, and water. The differentiation possibilities of the neutron curve rest upon the hydrogen abundance ratios of the various fluids. For water (H_2O), the ratio is 2:16, whereas for most saturated oils ($C_nH_{2n} + 2$) it is $(2n + 2)/(14n + 2)$. As most oils contain a large number of atoms, n is large and the hydrogen abundance ratio for oils approaches 2:14. Natural gas is mostly methane (CH_4) for which the hydrogen abundance ratio is 4:16. Hence, it appears that the differentiation between oil and water in the reservoir is a difficult matter, but that at equal density, a gas cap should show about twice as much neutron absorption as either a water or oil zone. However, the contrast in hydrogen abundance between the gas zone and the oil zone on a mass basis is such as to reverse this expectation. At 2,000 psia pressure, for an oil density of 0.8, the gas density (methane basis) is of the order of 0.1. The neutron-stopping power of oil compared to gas should then be in the ratio of 4:1. The neutron log should therefore show a significant deviation toward high radioactivity when the detector passes from the oil to the gas zone. Campbell and Winter (1947) have reported some significant results in this respect. In particular, dry gas sands record consistently a high neutron activity on the log and in one case it was possible to determine the contact level between dry gas and water. There seems to be considerable difficulty in delineating a gas cap from the oil zone below, and this difficulty is aggravated when water infiltration from the drilling fluid invades the formations in the neighborhood of the well. A longer-spacing neutron curve introduced by Lane-Wells (multiple-spaced neutron curve) holds promise of better differentiation of the oil-water contact because of its greater penetration.

Figure 4-54 is a graphic interpretation chart covering the common types of formations and showing both the typical radioactivity response normally experienced and the range through which the response may vary as a result of certain factors. These factors concern principally the amount of contamination of the formations with such materials as silt, bentonite, volcanic ash, shale partings, etc. These substances are of the more radioactive type and, accordingly, serve to vary the normal response of the formations. Careful study and investigation of the effects of these contaminating substances have permitted definite response patterns to be established.

Simple rules of qualitative interpretation may be indicated graphically as follows, the directions of the arrows indicating radioactivity deflection changes:

Gamma Ray	Neutron	
←	→	Tight, nonporous formation
→	←	Shale
←	←	Hydrogen-filled porosity in clean formation
→	→	Radioactive formation

Example of Qualitative Interpretation Procedure for Combination Gamma-ray–Neutron Logs. The interpretation procedure for radioactivity logs will be better illustrated by using the actual example related by Mercier (1946) which is quoted below. Figure 4-56 is a log from a well in northwestern Kansas. In this figure, the space separating the neutron from the gamma-ray curve is divided into four columns, numbered 1 to 4, for purposes of explanation.

Taking a straightedge in hand, we can begin by a basic interpretation of the gamma-ray curve. Since it is known that an increase in radioactivity is indicative of an increase in silt or shale, and that is represented by a displacement to the right on the curve, it becomes a simple matter to go through the log marking what is believed to be shale. This is shown in column 1. The tops and bottoms are picked at the inflection points.

Now that the shales have been indicated, we need to name the formations of low radioactivity on the log. It has been stated previously that a knowledge of the local lithology is imperative for interpretation. At this point we call upon this knowledge. In this case, the well is in Ellis County, Kansas, and recognizing the black Heebner shale by the very extreme throw to the right, it is a simple matter to progress down Column 2 from the Heebner shale through the Toronto limestone, Douglas shale, Lansing–Kansas City limestone, Marmaton shales, and the Arbuckle dolomite. This example is naturally a local one, but the same procedure can be followed anywhere. It serves to illustrate the need for local lithologic knowledge to correctly identify the formations traversed.

We have by this time completed the geologic interpretation possible with the gamma ray curve. Now, projecting our straightedge across the log to include the neutron curve, we assay the log once more to confirm or correct our tops. It will be remembered that due to the high intensity of neutron bombardment, the large secondary ray response, and the shorter ionization chamber length, the neutron curve gives us a more definite "break" on tops of strata. Also, since hydrogen is contained in shale, both as connate water and as chemically combined water, shales should respond on the neutron curve as a near mirror image to the response of the gamma ray curve. There are several excellent examples of this in Fig. 4-56, the Heebner shale just above minus 1200 being one of the best. The corrected and final lithologic column is shown as Column 3.

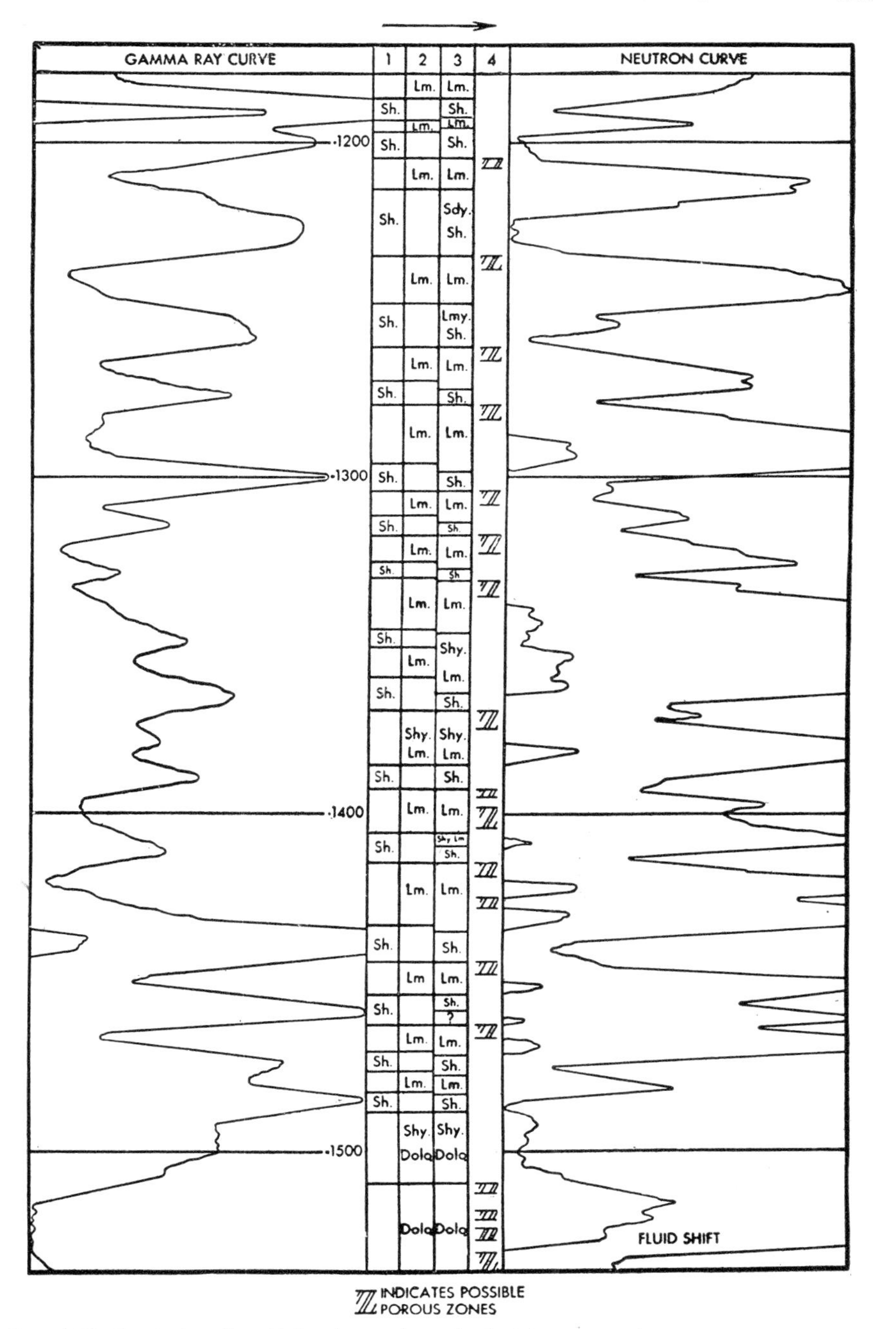

FIG. 4-56. Typical radioactivity log and method of interpretation. (*Lane-Wells Company.*)

Satisfied that our geologic determinations are as nearly correct as possible, the procedure now is to interpret the remaining portions of the neutron curve. When both curves are showing low response, that is, to the left on their respective graphs, the log is interpreted as a possible porous section in a possible producing strata, and such zones are indicated by the diagonally cross-hatched symbol in Column 4. Since hydrogen has an absorbing effect on the neutrons emanating from the source chamber, secondary ray recovery is very small opposite fluid-bearing strata and this condition is reflected on the log as a low response curve. By the same token, when no hydrogen is present in the strata, neutron response is very high and these portions are considered as being devoid of porosity.

Reservoir-engineering Uses of Radioactivity Logs. *Locating Zones of Porosity.* Since zones of porosity in limestones and sandstones usually contain fluid, any system of logging that will accurately locate the porous zones has a wide application, particularly in limestone sections. A combination of the gamma-ray and neutron curves is necessary to develop this information. The gamma-ray curve defines the stratigraphic breaks in the section with limes and sands recorded as minimum radioactivity values.

The response of the neutron curve is proportional to the amount of hydrogen within the neutron field. The greater the amount of hydrogen within the formation, the lower the value recorded on the curve. Therefore, dense, barren horizons are recorded as comparatively high neutron values. Shales, because of their connate water and of crystallization water within their constituent minerals, contain more hydrogen than saturated porous limes or sands. As a result, they usually are recorded as minimum values. Porous limes and sands containing fluids are usually recorded with proportional intermediate values somewhere between the values for shale and the value for a dense formation.

Figure 4-57 is a reproduction of a section of a log made in a well in Kansas to locate zones of porosity in the Mississippian limestone. Note that the gamma-ray curve on the left clearly outlines the limits of the limestone body with a shale layer above and below. The minimum values of the neutron curve very clearly indicate the porous zones labeled A, B, C, and D within the otherwise dense limestone.

Radioactivity Tracer Studies. In those instances where selective completion of wells is desired for the injection of gas or water in secondary recovery operations, or other operations where the location and permeability profile of several exposed zones is to be determined, the gamma-ray and neutron curves can be used with a radioactive tracer to obtain information not readily available by other means.

For permeability-profile studies, a combination radioactivity log consisting of both gamma-ray and neutron curves is first run through the section to be studied. The gamma-ray curve provides a log of the natural formation radioactivity, indicating stratigraphy, while the neutron curve indicates porous and fluid-bearing zones. Following this, a quantity of fluid, oil or water, containing a radioactive tracer in suspension is spotted over the section and pressure is applied to force the tracer into the permeable zones. A second gamma-ray curve is run over the section. A comparison of the two gamma-ray curves indicates the permeable zones, because these

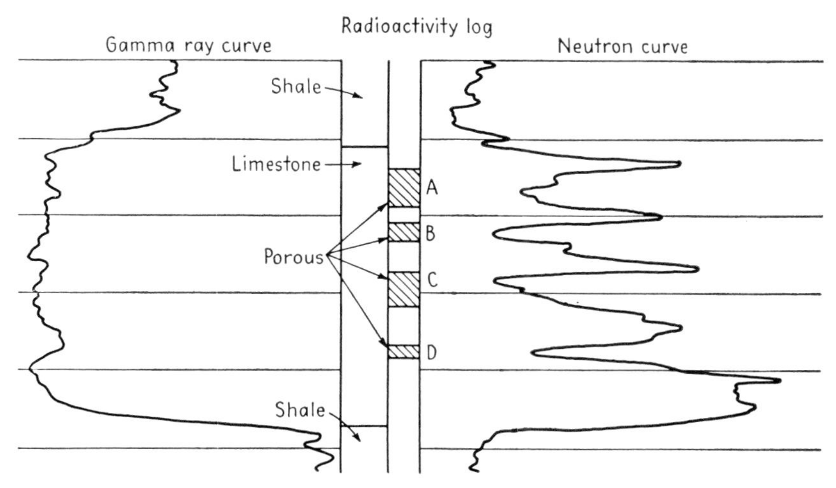

FIG. 4-57. Gamma-ray neutron log of a well in Kansas showing ability of neutron curve to indicate porous zones. (*Lane-Wells Company.*)

zones have changed from their natural radioactivity values to the much higher ones resulting from the presence of the tracer. The effective permeabilities of the various zones can be estimated from the progressive evidence of invasion by the tracer under increasing pressures.

A wide variety of tracers are used, depending on the purpose of the study. In the past, most tracer studies in wells were carried out with a waste product from the radium industry (casing compound 60), but this product was objectionable because of its long half-life. In most studies it is desirable that the radioactivity of the tracer should disappear after a certain time.

The following table gives tracers commonly used:

Elements	*Half-life*
Radon	4 days
Iodine 131	8 days
Barium 140	13 days
Antimony	60 days
Iridium 192	75 days
Caesium	2.3 years
Cobalt 60	5.3 years

The tracers may be used in the following forms:

1. Crystalline powders finely divided, of grain size to suit the purpose
2. Water-wet suspension
3. Oil-wet suspension
4. Solution
5. Coating on exchange resins
6. Adsorbed on charcoal
7. Coating on sand grains

For permeability-profile logging it is desirable to run a base line at low sensitivity. This is readily accomplished using the neutron-ionization detector (without neutron source) which is 1/16 as sensitive as the gamma-ray detector. Tracers used should be relatively short-lived such as radioactive iodine or antimony and supported by a finely powdered material such as charcoal, resins, etc. Grain size of 50 to 60 mesh is used for sandstone and 200 mesh for limestone. During injection the radioactive material forms a filter cake plating on the permeable sections of the well bore, the amount of plating and its radioactivity being proportional to the rate of fluid intake at each level. A gamma-ray log of the plated material is made soon after the slug arrives at well bottom and compared with the base log. The area between the two curves is proportional to the total intake rate of the well's net permeable section; individual intake may be related to the total by planimetering the areas between the curves at selected levels.

Injection is often continued for a while and further logging is done at successive intervals in order to determine the washing out of the radioactive material with time. Iodine 131 may also be used as an oil-soluble tracer or in a gas phase. This washing-out effect is also a function of the rate of intake at various levels and is a further check on the initial determination of the permeability profile.

Another reservoir engineering use of tracer studies in a well is to ascertain the effectiveness of formation fracturing and the location and orientation of such fractures. For this purpose the radioactive tracer is plated on part of the propping sand and is used as the last batch injected with the fracturing fluid. The logging procedure is the same as for permeability-profiling determination: conventional log, base log, first run after completion of injection, and continued logging at intervals to ascertain wash out of plating material. Vertical fractures are determined by a relatively uniform distribution of radioactivity along the length of the treated well section, whereas horizontal fractures are indicated by concentration of radioactivity at discrete levels.

Other reservoir and well-completion uses of radioactive tracers are for studying the effectiveness of plastic and cement squeeze and of acidizing, locating points of loss circulation and casing leaks, etc.

Of more interest are field-wide and well-to-well tracer studies. Since time is important, tracers used for this purpose are gaseous and are injected dispersed in natural-gas injection wells. The tracer most commonly used is tritium (heavy hydrogen, H_3) which is readily determined in minute concentration. Helium has also been used, but may not be detected by radiation instruments.

SELECTED REFERENCES ON ELECTRIC LOGGING

1926

Hunkel, H.: Modern Undersuchung von Langensuflussen mit Hilfe elektrischer Verfahren, *Kali*, vol. 1, no. 1.

1929

Hummel, J. N.: Der Scheinbare spezifische Widerstand bei vier planparallelen Schichten, *Z. Geophyzik*, vol. B5, pp. 228ff.

Schlumberger, C., and M. Schlumberger: Communication sur le carrotage électrique, Deuxième Congrès International des Forages, Paris.

1934

Pirson, S. J.: Interpretation of Three Layer Resistivity Curves, *Trans. AIME*, pp. 148ff.

1935

Peters, O. S.: Resistance to Earth of Ground Connections, Natl. Bur. Standards Tech. Pub. 108, pp. 219ff.

Schlumberger, C., M. Schlumberger, and E. G. Leonardon: A New Contribution to Subsurface Studies by Means of Electrical Measurements, *Trans. AIME*, pp. 273ff.

Schlumberger, C., M. Schlumberger, and E. G. Leonardon: Electrical Coring, a Method of Determining Bottom-hole Data by Electrical Methods, *Trans. AIME*, pp. 237ff.

1938

Gillingham, W. J., and W. B. Stewart: Application of Electric Logging Methods to West Texas Problems, *Petroleum Engr.*, vol. 9, no. 7, pp. 52ff.; no. 8, pp. 84ff.

Schlumberger, C.: "Electrical Coring—The Science of Petroleum," vol. 1, pp. 351ff., Oxford University Press, London.

1939

Houston Geological Society Study Group: Electrical Well Logging, *Bull. Am. Assoc. Petroleum Geol.*, vol. 23, no. 9, pp. 1287ff.

1940

Byck, H. T.: Effect of Formation Plastering—Behavior of Mud, *Oil Weekly*, June 3, pp. 19ff.

1942

Bowsky, M. C.: The Effect of Mud Resistivities on the Intensities of Electrical Logs, *Geophysics*, no. 1, pp. 82ff.

Dickey, P. A.: Electrical Well Logging in the Eastern States, *Penn. Top. Geol. Survey, Progr. Rept.* 129.

Zinszer, R. H.: The Use of Electrode Spacing in Well Logging, *AIME Tech. Pub.* 1590.

1943

Dawson, L. R., Jr.: Amplified Curves Widen Value of Electric Logs, *Oil Weekly*, March 1, pp. 26ff.

Dickey, P. A.: Natural Potentials in Sedimentary Rocks, *AIME Tech. Pub.* 1625.

Mounce, W. D., and W. M. Rust, Jr.: Natural Potentials in Well Logging, *AIME Tech. Pub.* 1626.

1944

Guyod, H.: Electrical Well Logging, *Oil Weekly*, series of 16 articles, August to December.

1945

Guyod, H.: Electric Log Interpretation, *Oil Weekly*, series of four articles, December

1946

White, C. C.: Electrical Well Logging—A Study of the Self Potential Curve, *Oil Gas J.*, Dec. 14, pp. 88ff.

1947

Doll, H. G., et al.: "True Resistivity Determination from the Electric Log—Its Application to Log Analysis," API Pacific Coast District Meeting, May 15.

Guyod, H.: Electrical Logging Developments in the USSR, *World Oil*, December, 1947, to August, 1948.

Schlumberger Well Surveying Corp.: "Resistivity Departure Curves," Houston, Texas.

Stick, J. C., et al.: New Electric Logging Techniques in California, *Oil Gas J.*, May 17, pp. 82ff.

1948

Doll, H. G.: The S.P. Log: Theoretical Analysis and Principles of Interpretation, *AIME Tech. Pub.* 2463.

1949

Bacon, L. O.: Formation Clay Minerals and Electric Logging, *Producers Monthly*, January, pp. 18ff.

Doll, H. G.: Introduction to Induction Logging and Application to Logging of Wells Drilled with Oil-base Mud, *AIME Tech. Pub.* 2641.

Doll, H. G.: Selective S.P. Logging, *AIME Tech. Pub.* 2850.

Keller, G. V.: An Improved Electrode System for Use in Electric Logging, *Producers Monthly*, August.

Kozary, M. T.: Streaming Potentials in Electric Well Logging, *Producers Monthly*, February, pp. 14ff.

Wyllie, M. R. J.: A Quantitative Analysis of the Electrochemical Component of the S.P. Curve, *AIME Tech. Pub.* 2511.

1950

Barber, R. C.: Porosity Permeability Check by Electric Log, *World Oil*, August, pp. 165ff.

Claudet, A. P.: New Method of Correlation by Resistivity Values of Electrical Logs, *Bull. Am. Assoc. Petroleum Geol.*, vol. 34, no. 10, pp. 2027ff.

Doh, C. A.: Practical Application of Micrologging in the Northeastern United States, *Oil Gas J.*, Dec. 14, pp. 80ff.

Doll, H. G.: The Microlog—A New Electrical Logging Method for the Detailed Determination of Permeable Beds, *Trans. AIME*, pp. 155ff.

Keller, G. V.: Modified Monoelectrodes for Improved Resistivity Logging, *Producers Monthly*, July, pp. 13ff.

Martin, M.: Application of Micrologging, *Drilling Contractors*, October, November.

Morazzani, A., and W. J. Lytle, Jr.: Micrologging in West Texas and New Mexico, *World Oil*, September, pp. 127ff.

Tapper, W., and W. J. Greer: A New System of Electric Logging, *World Oil*, October, pp. 119ff.

Walstrom, J. E.: Optimum Use of Coring, Electric Logging, and Other Testing Methods in Exploratory Wells, *Oil Gas J.*, Nov. 16, pp. 298ff.

Wyllie, M. R. J.: An Investigation of the Electrokinetic Component of the Self Potential Curve, *AIME Tech. Pub.* 2940.

1951

Doll, H. G.: The Laterolog—A New Resistivity Logging Method with Electrodes Using an Automatic Focussing System, *AIME Tech. Pub.* 3198.

——— and M. Martin: Electric Logging in Limestone Fields, Third World Petroleum Congress.

Guyod, H.: Principles of Microlog Interpretation, *Oil Gas J.*, Dec. 6, pp. 102ff.

———: The Shielded Electrode Method, *World Oil*, December, pp. 134ff.

Jones, Park J.: Electric Log—Invasion of Filtrate in Water, Oil and Gas Sandstone Beds, *World Oil*, Apr. 1, pp. 204ff.

Owen, J. E., and W. J. Greer: The Guard Electrode Logging System, *AIME Tech. Pub.* 3222.

1952

Ayers, M. L., et al.: Resistivities of Waters from Subsurface Formations, *Petroleum Engr.*, December, pp. B36ff.

Decker, G. J., and M. Martin: The Laterolog and Salt Mud Logging in Kansas, *Oil Gas J.*, Feb. 18, pp. 119ff.

De Witte, L.: Simplified Departure Curves, *Oil Gas J.*, Feb. 11, pp. 117ff.

Guyod, H.: Resistivity Departure Charts, *Oil Gas J.*, Mar. 24, pp. 195ff.

Hamilton, R. G.: Common Fallacies in Electric Log Interpretation, *World Oil*, April, pp. 141ff.

Puzin, L. A.: Connate Water Resistivity in Oklahoma: Its Application to Electric Log Interpretation, *Petroleum Engr.*, August, pp. B67ff.

1953

Elliott, W. C., Jr.: Characteristics of Waters from the Canyon, Strawn, and Wolfcamp Formations in Scurry, Kent, Borden, and Howard Counties, Texas, *Petroleum Engr.*, June, pp. B77ff.

Howell, B. F., Jr.: Electrical Conduction of Fluid Saturated Rocks, *World Oil*, February, pp. 113ff.; March, pp. 142ff.

Keller, G. V.: Effect of Wettability on the Electrical Resistivity of Sand, *Oil Gas J.*, Jan. 5, pp. 62ff.

Whiting, R. L., E. T. Guerrero, and R. M. Young: Electrical Properties of Limestone Cores, *Oil Gas J.*, July 17, pp. 309ff.

1954

Birks, J.: An Evaporation Method for Measuring the Resistivity–Water Saturation Characteristics of Cores, *J. Inst. Petroleum*, January, pp. 14ff.

Buckner, G. O.: Subsurface Electrical Measurements about Two Plane Interfaces, *Soc. Expl. Geophys.*, vol. 19, no. 2, pp. 297ff.

Doll, H. G.: Filtrate Invasion in Highly Permeable Sands, *Petroleum Engr.*, January, pp. B53ff.

——— and M. Martin: How to Use Electrical Log Data to Determine Maximum Producible Oil Index, *Oil Gas J.*, July 5, pp. 120ff.

McConnell, E. B., Jr.: Self Potentials of Reservoir Sands, *Producers Monthly*, June, pp. 19ff.

Poupon, A., M. E. Loy, and M. P. Tixier: A Contribution to Electrical Log Interpretation in Shaly Sands, *Trans. AIME Petroleum Div.*, June, pp. 27ff.

Puzin, L. A.: New Well Logging Developments, *World Oil*, December, 1953, and January, 1954.

Ruddick, C. K.: How to Select the Correct Logging Method, *World Oil*, April.

Smith, H. D., and H. A. Blum: Microlaterolog versus Microlog for Formation Factor Calculations, *Geophysics*, vol. 19, no. 2, pp. 310ff.

Von Engelhardt, W., and P. A. Witherspoon: Filter Cake Formation and Water Losses in Deep Drilling Muds, *Illinois State Geol. Survey Circ.* 191, 24 pp.

1955

Edwards, J. M., and A. L. Simpson: A Method of Neutron Derived Porosity Determination for Thin Beds, *AIME Tech. Pub.* 4101.

Guyod, H.: Electric Analogue of Resistivity Logging, *Geophysics*, vol. 20, no. 3, pp. 615ff.

Martin, M.: With the MicroLog . . . You Can Be Sure, *Oil Gas J.*, Oct. 24, pp. 106ff.

1956

Campbell, J. L. P., and J. M. Myer: Double Neutron Logging, *Tomorrow's Tools Today*, vol. 22, no. 2, pp. 14ff.

Dewan, J. T.: Neutron Log Correction Charts for Borehole Conditions and Bed Thickness, *J. Petroleum Technol.*, vol. 8, no. 2, pp. 50ff., February.

Gondouin, M., et al.: An Experimental Study on the Influence of the Chemical Composition of Electrolytes on the S.P. Curve, *AIME Paper* 657G.

SELECTED REFERENCES ON RADIOACTIVITY WELL LOGGING

1938

Bramley, A., and A. K. Brewer: Radioactivity of Potassium, *Phys. Rev.*, vol. 53, pp. 502ff.

1939

Howell, L. G., and A. Frosch: Gamma Ray Well Logging, *Geophysics*, vol. 4, no. 2, pp. 106ff.

——— and ———: Detection of Radioactive Cement in Cased Wells, *AIME Tech. Pub.* 113.

Landsberg, H., and M. R. Klepper: Radioactivity Tests of Rock Samples for the Correlation of Sedimentary Horizons, *AIME Tech. Pub.* 1103.

1940

Bell, K. G., et al.: Radioactivity of Sedimentary Rocks and Associated Petroleum, *Bull. Am. Assoc. Petroleum Geol.*, vol. 24, no. 9, pp. 1529ff.

Green, W. G., and R. E. Fearon: Well Logging by Radioactivity, *Geophysics*, vol. 5, no. 3, pp. 272ff.

Russell, W. L.: Well Logging by Radioactivity, *Oil Weekly*, Nov. 11, pp. 16ff.

Westby, G. H., and S. A. Scherbatskoy: Well Logging by Radioactivity, *Oil Gas J.*, Feb. 22, pp. 62ff.

1941

Beers, L. C.: Radioactivity Logging through Casing, *Petroleum World*, November, pp. 95ff.

Evans, R. D., and C. Goodman: Radioactivity of Rocks, *Bull. Geol. Soc. Amer.*, vol. 52, part 1, pp. 459ff.

Pontecorvo, B.: Neutron Well Logging, *Oil Gas J.*, Sept. 11, pp. 32ff.

Russell, W. L.: Well Logging by Radioactivity, *Bull. Am. Assoc. Petroleum Geol.*, vol. 25, no. 9, pp. 1768ff.

1942

Pontecorvo, B.: Radioactivity Analysis of Oil Well Samples, *Geophysics*, vol. 7, no. 1, pp. 90ff.

Russell, W. L., and R. B. Downing: Neutron Logs Find Porous Zones in West Kansas Lime, *Oil Gas J.*, Aug. 6, pp. 66ff.

1943

Sawdon, W. A.: Locating Cased Off Production by Radioactivity Logging, *Petroleum Engr.*, May, pp. 43ff.

Uren, L. C.: Radioactivity and Geochemical Well Logging, *Petroleum Engr.*, January, pp. 50ff.

1944

Campbell, J. L.: Gamma Ray Logging in East Texas, *Petroleum Engr.*, January, pp. 156ff.

Howell, L. G.: Gamma Ray Measurements in Oil Wells, *Electronics*, March, pp. 130ff.

Russell, W. L.: The Radioactivity of Sedimentary Rocks, *Geophysics*, vol. 9, no. 2, pp. 180ff.

1945

Barcklow, J. C.: Better Interpretation of Neutron Curves, *Oil Weekly*, June 11, pp. 53ff.

Barnes, K. B.: Six Different Engineering Methods Compared in Study of Pay Formations, *Oil Gas J.*, Apr. 7, pp. 70ff.

Beers, R. F.: Radioactivity and Organic Content of Some Paleozoic Shales, *Bull. Am. Assoc. Petroleum Geol.*, vol. 29, no. 1, pp. 1ff.

Fearon, R. E.: Radioactivity Well Logging, Gamma Ray Measurements, *Oil Weekly*, June 4, pp. 33ff., and June 11, pp. 38ff.

Fearon, R. E.: Oil Uses for the Atom, *Oil Weekly*, Sept. 10, pp. 51ff.

Jackson, W. L., and J. L. P. Campbell: Some Practical Aspects of Radioactivity Well Logging, *AIME Tech. Pub.* 1923.

Mercier, V. J.: Radioactivity Well Logging, *Oil Gas J.*, May 5, pp. 90ff.

Russell, W. L.: Relation of Radioactivity, Organic Content, and Sedimentation, *Bull. Am. Assoc. Petroleum Geol.*, vol. 29, no. 10, pp. 1470ff.

1946

Fearon, R. E.: Influence of Atomic Science on Petroleum, *Oil Weekly*, Oct. 14, pp. 47ff.

Mercier, V. J.: Radioactivity Well Logs—Interpretation and Application, *Oil Weekly*, Oct. 14 and Oct. 21, part 1, pp. 56ff.; part 2, pp. 41ff.

1947

Campbell, J. L. P., and A. B. Winter: Dry Gas Sand Location by Neutron Logs, *Tomorrow's Tools Today*, vol. 13, no. 1, pp. 22ff.

1949

Fearon, R. E.: Gamma Ray Well Logging, *Nucleonics*, vol. 4, no. 4, pp. 67ff.

Fearon, R. E.: Neutron-well Logging, *Nucleonics*, vol. 4, no. 6, pp. 30ff.

1950

McGaha, S. W.: Radioactivity Well Logging in Canada, *World Oil*, September, pp. 266ff.

1951

Campbell, J. L. P.: Radioactivity Well Logging Anomalies, *Petroleum Engr.*, June, pp. B7ff.

Faul, H., and C. W. Tittle: Logging of Drill Holes by the Neutron, Gamma Method, and Gamma Ray Scattering, *Geophysics*, vol. 16, no. 2, pp. 260ff.

Kokesh, F. P.: Gamma Ray Logging, *Oil Gas J.*, July 26.

Tittle, C. W., et al.: Neutron Logging of Drill Holes: The Neutron-Neutron Method, *Geophysics*, vol. 16, no. 4, pp. 626ff.

1952

Anonymous: New Method Advanced for Determining Radioactivity, *Petroleum Engr.*, January, pp. B76ff.

Toelke, L. W.: Scintillometer Used in Radiation Logging, *World Oil*, August, p. 143.

1953

Blanchard, A., and J. T. Dewan: The Calibration of Gamma Ray Logs, *Petroleum Engr.*, August, pp. B76ff.

1954

Meyers, J.: Interpretation of Radioactivity Tracer Surveys, *Tomorrow's Tools Today*, pp. 27ff., Midyear.

CHAPTER 5

QUANTITATIVE INTERPRETATION OF WELL LOGS

In reservoir engineering, quantitative interpretation of well logs entails determining effective pay thickness, porosity, fluid saturation, permeability—effective and relative—well productivity, and expected ultimate oil and gas recovery. The discussion of the techniques involved in such determinations is the objective of this chapter.

However, quantitative information derived from logs is also useful to production engineers and geologists. In production engineering, well logs are useful in designing well completion involving location of water-oil contact, drill-stem tests, packer setting, coring section, and well work-over. In exploration for oil and gas, well logs are used as subsurface geological tools for well correlation, isopach mapping, convergence mapping, and structural studies. In drilling wells or in wells already abandoned they are also used to discover commercial production originally unrecognized at the time of drilling by other methods such as drill-cutting examination, mud logging, drill stem testing, and even core analysis.

The large space devoted to well-log interpretation in this volume may seem unwarranted to the casual reader. However, the practical reservoir engineer knows that well logs provide him with the one permanent record which is always available for future reference as well as a daily working tool which may be reevaluated at any time and as often as desired; well logs are indeed one of his constant working tools.

The ultimate aim of log interpretation is to obtain reservoir engineering data of equal if not of greater validity than those secured by core testing and analysis; yet both techniques are looked upon as being complementary to one another.

Petrophysical theories have shown that all reservoir-rock characteristics are reflected in the electric log's various curves but for some it is presumptuous to expect high accuracy unless well and rock conditions are unusually favorable.

A complete solution of the electric log in terms of useful and usable reservoir parameters and characteristics involves securing the following data:

1. Lithology of the formation
2. Effective reservoir-porosity (ϕ)
3. Reservoir-fluid-saturation

   σ_o = oil saturation

   σ_{wc} = connate water saturation

σ_{wi} = invaded-zone water saturation
σ_{xo} = flushed-zone water saturation
σ_{wf} = free water saturation

4. Reservoir-permeability
   Specific = K
   Effective $\begin{cases} K_o = \text{permeability to oil} \\ K_w = \text{permeability to water} \\ K_g = \text{permeability to gas} \end{cases}$
5. Effective-pay thickness, h_e
6. Fluid productivity and recovery
   Water-oil ratio
   Ultimate oil recovery

LITHOLOGY OF THE FORMATIONS

The determination of the lithology entails the location and identification of the formations traversed by the bore hole and more particularly of porous zones. This and the determination of the thicknesses of the formations are made in a satisfactory manner, though the methods used are somewhat empirical in nature. Lithological interpretation of electric logs is always empirical.

Empirical Interpretation of the SP Curve. The self-potential (SP) data are measured relative to a so-called "shale base line" to which the galvanometer is arbitrarily adjusted by means of a bucking potential. The shale base line is not necessarily constant in a well. As a matter of fact, a shift or drift in its position is often observed when passing from salty formation waters to predominantly fresh formation waters, as well as when crossing a geologic unconformity.

The polarity of the SP data with respect to the shale base line is primarily a function of the salinity contrast between well fluid R_m and formation water R_{wc} resistivities. For a normal fresh-water drilling mud, SP deflections in fresh-water horizons are positive, whereas they are negative for salt-water horizons.

The existence of SP kicks is primarily predicated upon the existence of salinity contrasts; thus there is no deflection from the shale base line in the absence of a salinity contrast between mud-filtrate and formation-water salinity. In order to obtain a salinity contrast, porous formations containing connate or fresh waters must be present. An SP kick is then an indication (but not a measure) of porosity within the formation. This conclusion is partially invalidated in the case of carbonate rocks and more particularly for dolomite, as was indicated in the theory of the SP curve where it is postulated that limestones preferentially adsorb cations and release negative ions when in contact with the mud fluid. This is a tentative explanation of why carbonate rocks give rise to anomalously high SP deflections even when they are of low porosity.

The magnitude of the SP deflections depends on many factors, discussed in Chap. 4. However, in a well in which conditions are stabilized the following factors are influential: the total emf generated within formations, the relative thicknesses of the beds, and the resistivities of the well fluid and of the rocks in the immediate vicinity of the point of observation. The presence of oil or gas in a porous bed appears to have no appreciable effect on the magnitude of the emf generated except when the reservoir rock is shaly. However, the presence of these nonconducting fluids within a rock reduces its conductivity. Should the conductivity drop to zero owing to the absence of connate water, there would be no SP kick observed. This might be the case for a 100 per cent saturation in oil and gas. As oil and gas saturation decreases, reservoir-rock resistivity decreases and an SP deflection of increasing magnitude is observed. In thick reservoir rocks of uniform porosity, a gravity segregation of gas, oil, and water is often observed from top to bottom of the pay. Hence, a general increase in the magnitude of the SP deflection in such a reservoir is the rule as one moves from top to bottom of a pay horizon as a result of the change in resistivity of the enclosing formations. In a sand the magnitude of this SP gradient can be no more than $11.6 \times T_f/T_a \log (R_{mf}/R_{wc})$ in millivolts.

A massive hard nonporous streak interbedded in an otherwise good oil and gas reservoir is indicated by a small SP deflection toward the positive.

Self-potential deflections are primarily measurements of mud-filtrate reactivity with the rocks, and the deflections observed in a rhyolite-diabase sequence in igneous rocks may accordingly be mistaken for a sand-shale sequence of sedimentary rocks.

For correlation purposes from well to well, it is necessary to make a correction for the SP amplitude when the well-fluid resistivities are not comparable during the SP run. A quantitative correction may be made if desired through the SP equation.

The diameter of the bore hole and of the invaded zone may have appreciable effect on the magnitude of the SP kicks, and corrections may be made by means of the Doll chart (Fig. 4-16).

Empirical Interpretation of Resistivity Curves. The following general rules may be used for the lithologic interpretation of the resistivity curves:

1. A low resistivity facing a well-defined SP kick indicates a porous formation containing a conductive fluid, generally connate water. This may be a porous sand or limestone and dolomite. The resistivity of porous formations varies a great deal with the degree of saturation in nonconductive fluids (oil and gas) and this requires special attention from a quantitative standpoint. This will be taken up in greater detail from this point of view.

Though they appear compact, shales have relatively high porosity, oftentimes as high as 40 per cent. In place, they are fully saturated with connate water and contain water of hydration in addition. The pore sizes of shale are extremely small. The shale particles (which are predominantly clays of one sort or another) carry adsorbed ions in equilibrium through base exchange with connate water. The presence of different mineralogical species of clays within reservoir rocks is responsible for some unexpected behaviors: it is known that some highly illitic and glauconitic sands always exhibit low resistivities regardless of oil and gas saturation, probably as a result of the mobility of the ions within their hydration layer.

2. A high resistivity indicates either a porous or a nonporous formation. Solid rocks, devoid of porosity and hence of formation water, are poor conductors. Examples are rock salt, anhydrite, massive limestone, quartzite with high degree of cementation, etc. Porous formations may be of two types: permeable and nonpermeable. Permeable porous formations exhibit high resistivity when they are fully or nearly saturated with a nonconducting fluid: oil, gas, or fresh water. This point will be discussed in detail later. Nonpermeable porous formations always exhibit high resistivity regardless of the saturation (shales excepted). Such formations may occur as lava flows interbedded with sediments.

DETERMINATION OF POROSITY AND FORMATION FACTOR

There are various situations in which a determination of the average porosity of a reservoir is possible from electric logs.

In certain reservoirs, the porosity ϕ may be assumed uniform throughout; this is often the case in quartzose sediments. The porosity may be highly variable within a given pay especially in graywacke sediments, as is often the case in the Appalachian fields, the Mid-Continent Pennsylvanian sediments, the Gulf Coast and California fields, and others.

There are two main approaches by which the formation porosity may be determined from conventional electric logs, namely, from the *invaded zone* and from the *flushed zone*. From radioactivity logs, porosity is obtained from some empirical correlations of neutron deflections with core analysis.

Invaded-zone Methods of Porosity Determination. These methods make use of resistivity investigation tools which probe mainly in the invaded zone and may be distinguished as:

1. Short-normal methods
2. Combination short-normal 10-in.–limestone 32-in. method
3. Tixier (RM) method

All 3 methods are based on the same principle, namely, the application of Archie's saturation formula to the invaded zone with appropriate allowance for mixing of mud filtrate with formation water and for residual oil or gas in the invaded zone.

The equation to be solved is as follows:

$$\sigma_{wi}^2 = \frac{FR_{wi}}{R_i} = \frac{\phi^{-m}R_{wi}}{R_i} \tag{5-1}$$

where σ_{wi} = combined water saturation in invaded zone and is 1 minus residual oil or gas saturation (1 − ROS)

R_{wi} = resistivity of combined water and depends on mixing factor z

R_i = true resistivity of invaded zone obtained by a short investigation device such as a short-normal or limestone curve

In using either curve, the readings must be corrected for bore-hole effect.

Short-normal Methods. For rapid calculation of *porosity from the short-normal* the chart of Fig. 5-1 has been devised. It is especially applicable to carbonate rocks where $m = 2$. Other simplifying assumptions have been made, namely, $R_{mf} = 0.8R_m$ and $z = 0.075$. These are reasonable assumptions in most cases. However, to postulate that $m = 2$ is too general and, depending on formation lithology, another value should be selected. The procedure is then to determine F and to solve for ϕ using the appropriate value of m. An example will illustrate the use of the chart.

Let the short normal (16 in.) read 40 ohm-meters in a 9-in. hole. The mud resistivity is 0.5. R_{AM}/R_m is 80 and $AM/d = 1.8$. Let the SP deflection be -90 mv. The lines drawn on Fig. 5-1 indicate the computing procedure. In a limestone the porosity is 6.5 per cent if water-bearing (no residual oil) or 9 per cent if oil-bearing with 30 per cent residual oil. In the water-bearing case, the formation factor is 240; in the oil-bearing case it is 124. Other values for residual oil might be selected with variable answers for porosity. The assumed values of 0 and 30 per cent for residual oil bracket the answer; in an actual log interpretation, one or the other hypothesis would be eliminated by the results of fluid-saturation calculations.

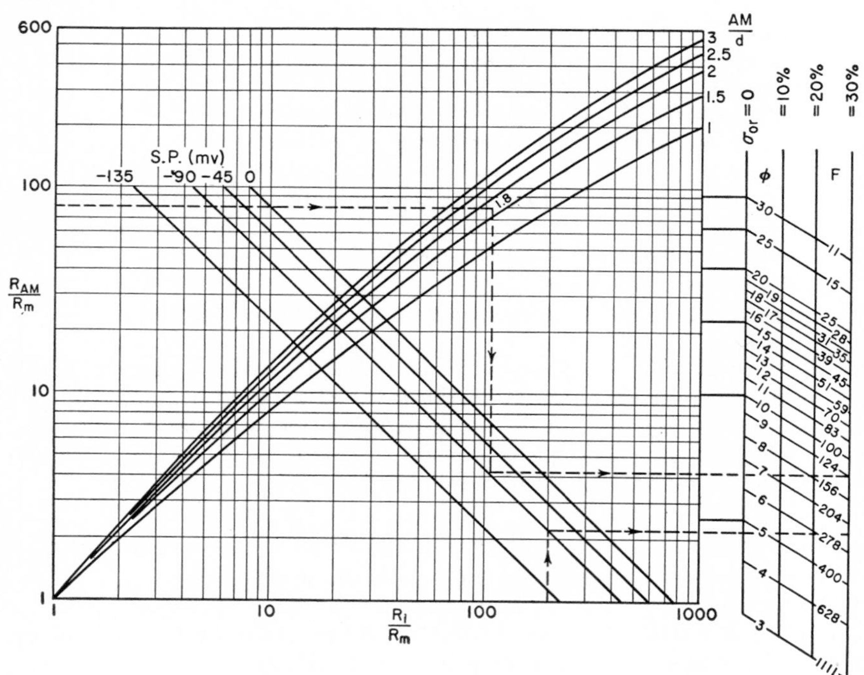

FIG. 5-1. Chart for the determination of porosity and formation factor from short-resistivity investigation tools (short-normal limestone curve). $R_{mf} = 0.8R_m$; $z = 0.075$; $m = 2.0$; $F = \phi^{-2}$.

Short-normal–Limestone Method. The *limestone curve* is run in conjunction with a short-normal curve ($AM = 10$ in. or $2Z = 10$ in.). The two curves have completely different departure-curve characteristics to the well-bore diameter and to the ratio of the resistivity of the invaded zone to that of the mud (R_i/R_m). Therefore, by cross-plotting the departure

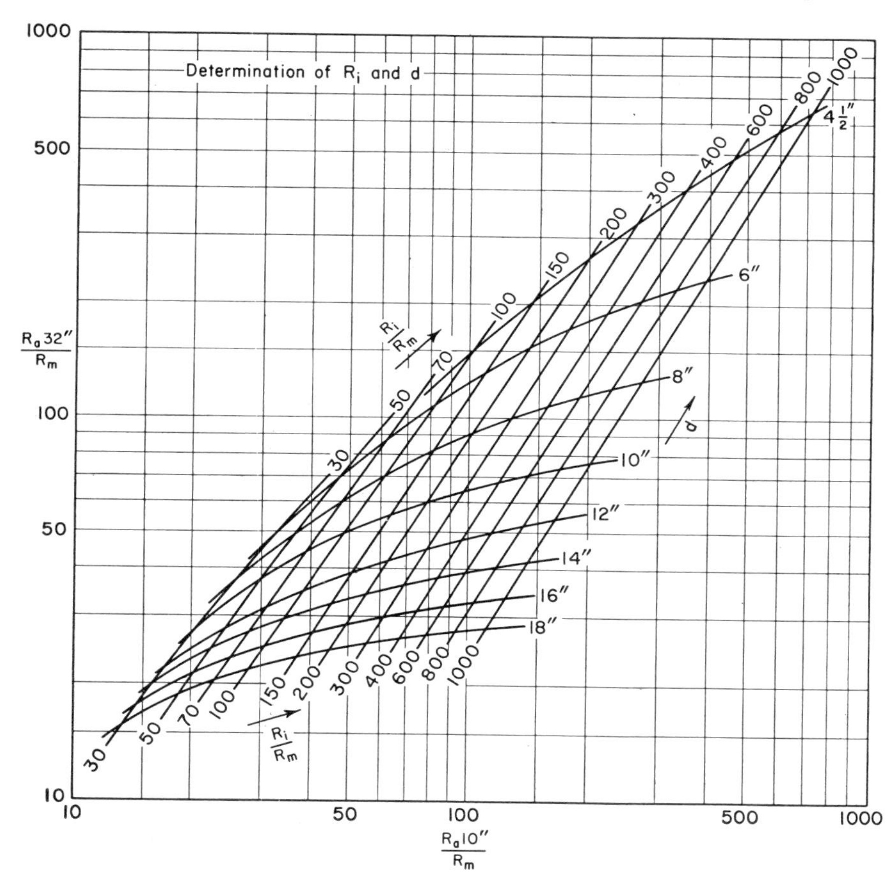

Fig. 5-2. Departure curves for 10-in. normal and 32-in. limestone logs for use in determining hole enlargement and invaded-zone resistivity.

curves for both (Fig. 5-2), a chart is obtained which may serve both as a caliper and as a determinator of the invaded-zone resistivity.

Before using this chart various requirements must be ascertained:

1. Mud resistivity R_m must be known at formation level with good accuracy, especially if the log is to be used as a caliper.

2. It is not advisable to use this method in thin beds ($e < 5$ ft).

3. This method should not be used in a small-size hole ($d < 6$ in.) unless $R_i/R_m > 100$.

4. If the objective of the interpretation is to determine invaded-zone resistivity and formation porosity, there must be sufficient invasion ($D_i > 2d$). This is, however, difficult to ascertain and experience must be a guide. For this purpose R_i/R_m should at least be 20.

5. The chart is useless to determine the size of enlarged holes in shale sections because of their inherent low resistivity.

Let $R_m = 0.5$
R 10 in. = 40 ohm-meters
R 32 in. = 30 ohm-meters

We have

$$\frac{R \text{ 10 in.}}{R_m} = 80 \qquad \frac{R \text{ 32 in.}}{R_m} = 60$$

giving, from Fig. 5-2,

$$\frac{R_i}{R_m} = 200 \qquad \text{and} \qquad d = 10 \text{ in.}$$

If in addition the SP value is -90 mv, the plot of $R_i/R_m = 200$ vs. SP = -90 in Fig. 5-1 gives a porosity of 4.6 per cent if the formation is water-bearing and 6.3 per cent if there is 30 per cent residual oil.

Porosity Evaluation by the Tixier (RM) Method. The Tixier (RM) procedure preassumes the availability of the same information as for the determination of connate water by the Rocky Mountain method, namely, the existence of invasion and of suitable electrode spacings for the measurement of the invaded and noninvaded zones' resistivity. The nomograph of Fig. 5-3 provides a rapid solution to the problem of porosity determination at any level from the Archie equation:

$$S_{wc}^2 = \frac{R_{wc}\phi^{-m}}{R_t} \tag{5-2}$$

if the connate water saturation is known and the value of R_{wc} is obtained from the SP curve. The connate water saturation should be determined by one of the methods to be discussed later on, but preferably by the Tixier (RM) method.

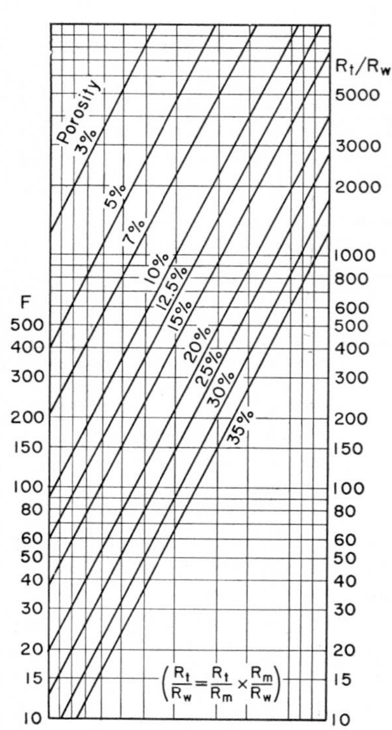

FIG. 5-3. Nomogram for the determination of porosity. (*After Tixier, Schlumberger Well Surveying Corp.*)

It is noted that a saturation exponent $n = 2$ is postulated. Hence, this nomograph should not be used in formations in which a wide departure from this value is known to exist, as is the case in highly colloidal sands. The special shaly-sand technique should then be resorted to.

In the design of Fig. 5-3 a gradual change in the value of the cementation exponent m was included as its value approaches 1.3 to 1.5 for unconsolidated sands of high porosity and it becomes as high as 2.0 to 2.2 for highly cemented clean rocks.

In use, the values of the ordinate R_t/R_w are computed from the product R_t/R_m by R_m/R_w, and when the water saturation is known, the porosity is obtained by interpolation.

Flushed-zone Methods of Porosity Determination. These methods make use of wall-resistivity measuring devices: the microlog (Schlumberger), the contact log (Halliburton), or the microresistivity (PGAC). Because of the different geometry of the tools used by the various service companies the techniques of interpretation must follow the recommendations and calibrations of the companies.

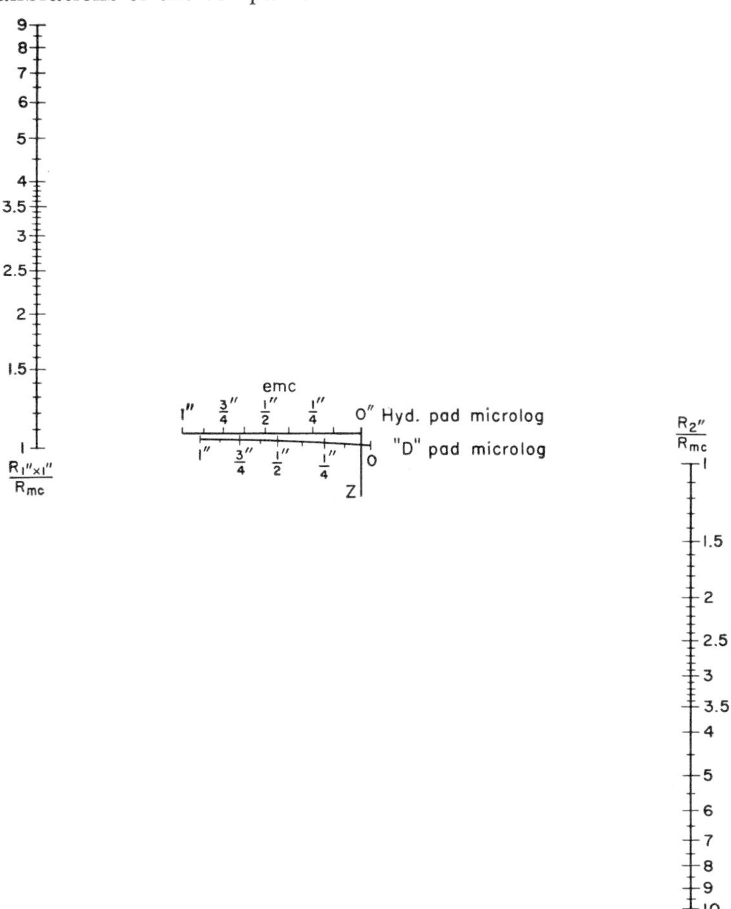

FIG. 5-4. Mud-cake thickness determination from microlog. (*Schlumberger Well Surveying Corp.*)

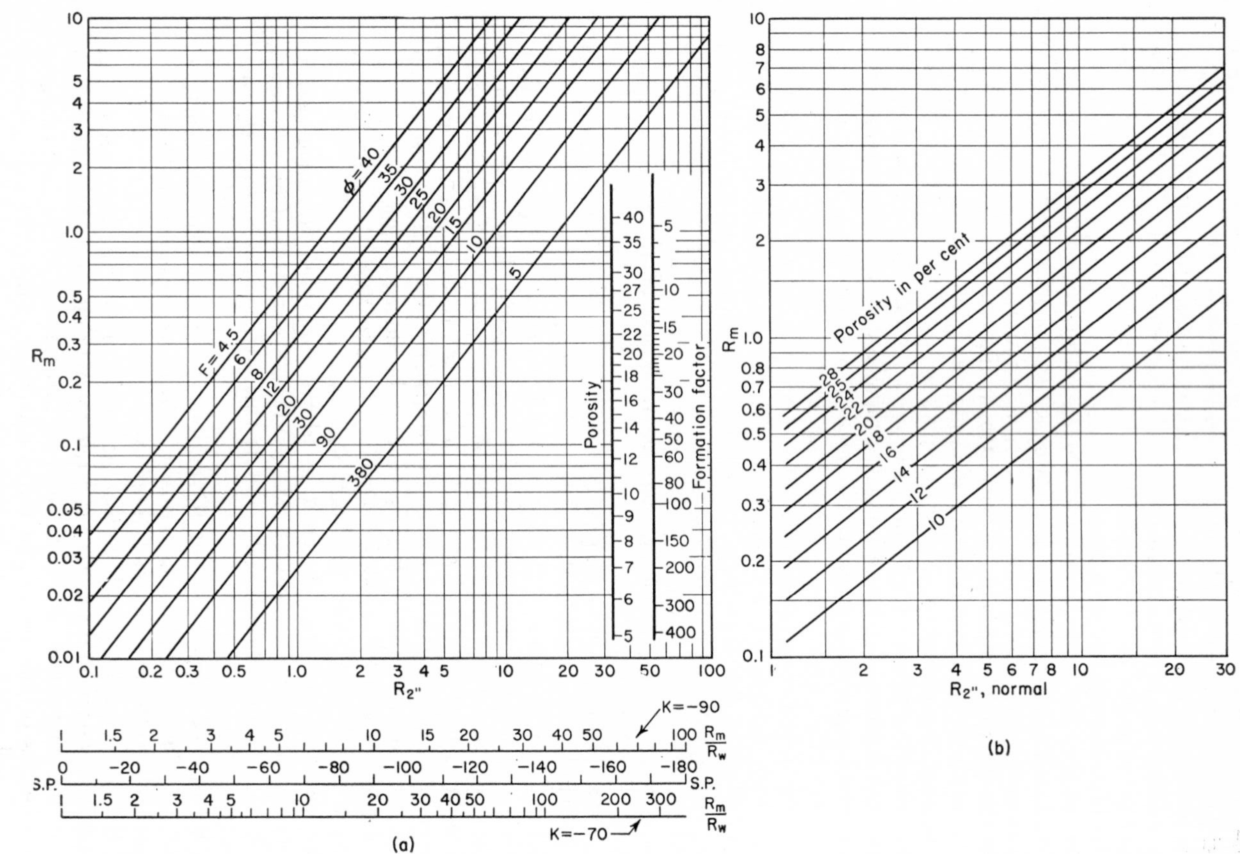

FIG. 5-5(*a*). Empirical correlation of microlog vs. porosity. (*After Tixier, Schlumberger Well Surveying Corp.*) (*b*). Empirical hydraulic microlog porosity chart. (*After Puzin.*)

For the microlog, there have been various tool designs, the oldest (WRSD) having been superseded by the 60° hydraulic microlog pad. Since it is often required to interpret older micrologs of the D pad type, their interpretation will be discussed as well as that of the hydraulic pad (H pad).

The first step in interpretation is to determine mud-cake thickness by means of Fig. 5-4. To this end the values of $R1 \times 1/R_{mc}$ and $R2/R_{mc}$ are read on their respective axis and joined by a straight line. The intersection in the center of the chart with the appropriate axis (H or D pad) gives the mud-cake thickness (e_{mc}). When the latter exceeds $\frac{1}{8}$ in. for the D pad and $\frac{3}{8}$ in. for the H pad, empirical charts are used for the determination of porosity.

The empirical chart (Fig. 5-5*a*) devised by Tixier has found wide use for the rapid determination of porosity from D-pad micrologs. The latter is obtained by merely plotting the value of R_m vs. the value read from the 2-in. curve (R_2), both values being read at the same depth level. This chart is designed for average mud-cake thickness ($\frac{1}{4}$ in. $< e_{mc} <$ $\frac{1}{2}$ in.) and average residual oil of 15 per cent. The chart should not be used for thin mud cakes (no departure, or negative departure) or for thick mud cakes: $e_{mc} > 1$ in. (wide departure).

The empirical chart (Fig. 5-5*b*) devised by Puzin is to be used in the same manner for the hydraulic pad when mud-cake thickness is larger than $\frac{3}{8}$ in. or less than 1 in.

Quantitative evaluation of porosity may be made from micrologs (D and H pads) with considerable degree of reliability when the mud-cake thickness is not too large: $e_{mc} < \frac{1}{8}$ in. for D pad; $e_{mc} < \frac{3}{8}$ in. for H pad.

Figure 5-6 is to be used for the microlog D pad. The value of ratios $R1 \times 1/R_{mc}$ and R_2/R_{mc} are located on their respective axes and joined by a straight line until the "R_{xo}/R_{mc}" axis is intercepted. The numerical value read on this axis is translated horizontally to the right to the proper hole size where the value of R_{xo}/R_{mc} is read by interpolation.

A similar procedure is carried out for the microlog hydraulic pad by means of Fig. 5-7, in order to obtain R_{xo}/R_{mc}.

The value of R_{xo}/R_{mc} obtained as above for either microlog pad is transferred to the corresponding axis of Fig. 5-8 and, joined by a straight line to R_{mc}, R_{xo} is obtained. By joining this latter value to R_{mf}, R_{xo}/R_{mf} is obtained.

In the case of a water-bearing formation, R_{xo}/R_{mf} is also the formation factor F. The corresponding porosity is read by translating this value horizontally to the axis marked "porosity."

In the case of a hydrocarbon-bearing formation (oil or gas), calculation of formation factor and porosity is made by making a reasonable assumption on the magnitude of the residual-oil saturation (ROS), according to the properties of the rocks and fluids involved. From the axis selected for ROS, a slanting line parallel to those shown is interpolated and the corresponding values for F and ϕ are read. A larger porosity is always obtained when a saturation in residual oil is presumed to exist.

As discussed before, the unlikely assumption made (whether hydrocar-

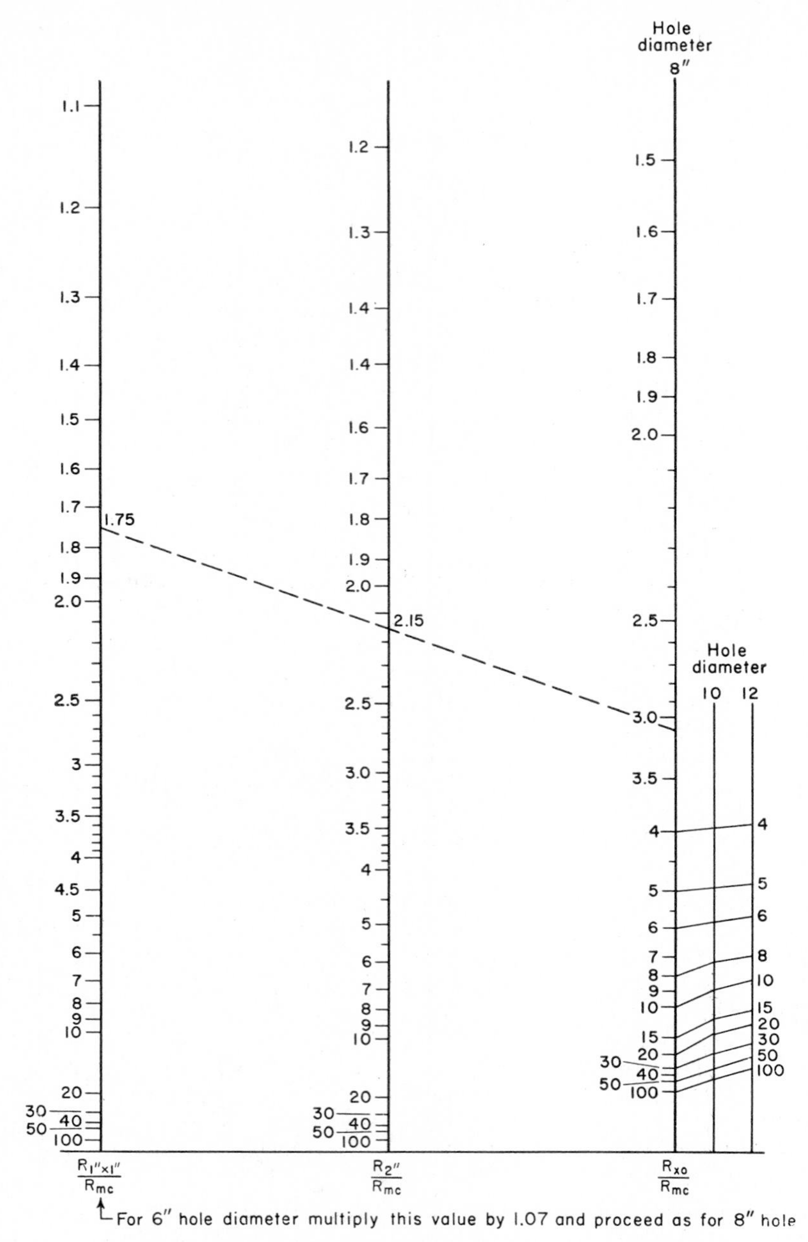

FIG. 5-6. Nomographic microlog chart (D pad). (*Schlumberger Well Surveying Corp.*)

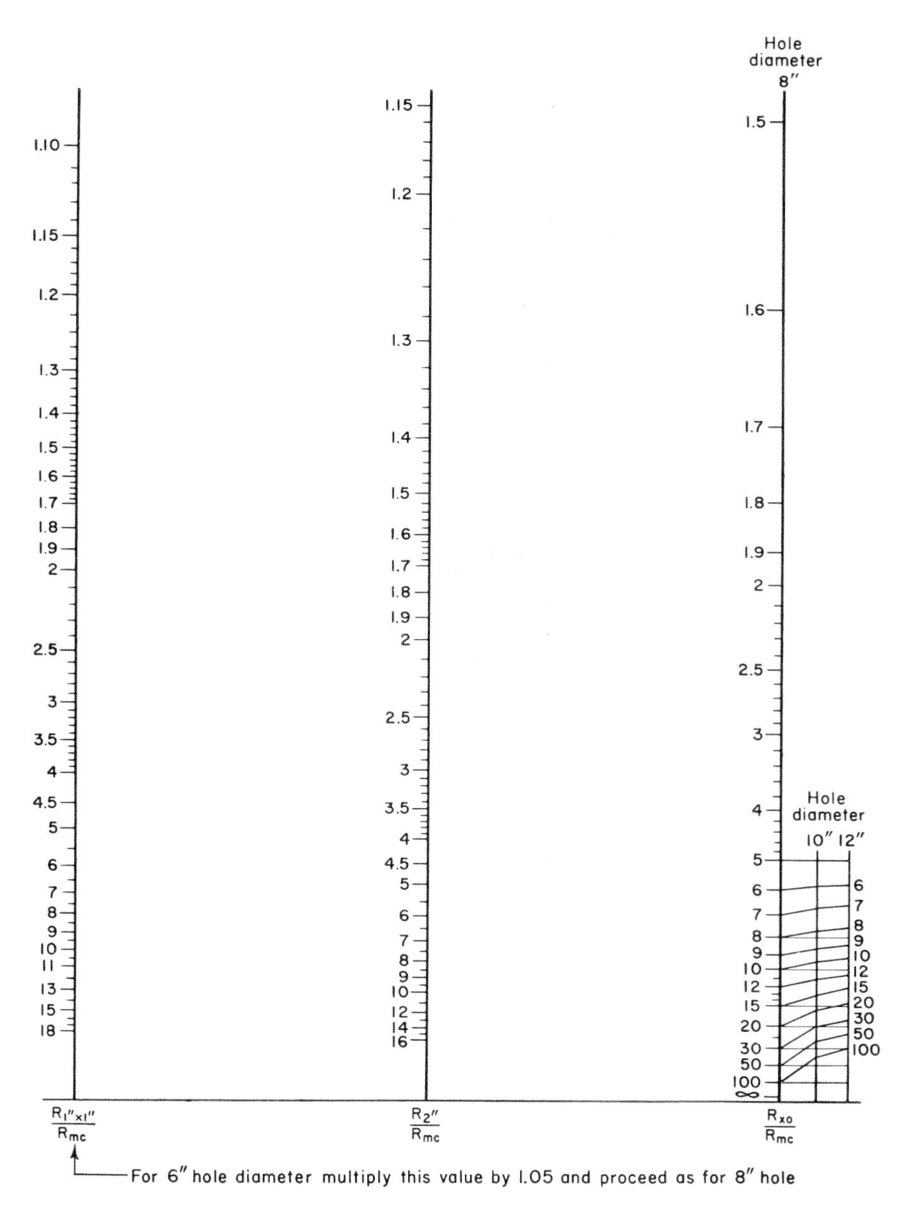

FIG. 5-7. Nomographic microlog chart (H pad). *(Schlumberger Well Surveying Corp.)*

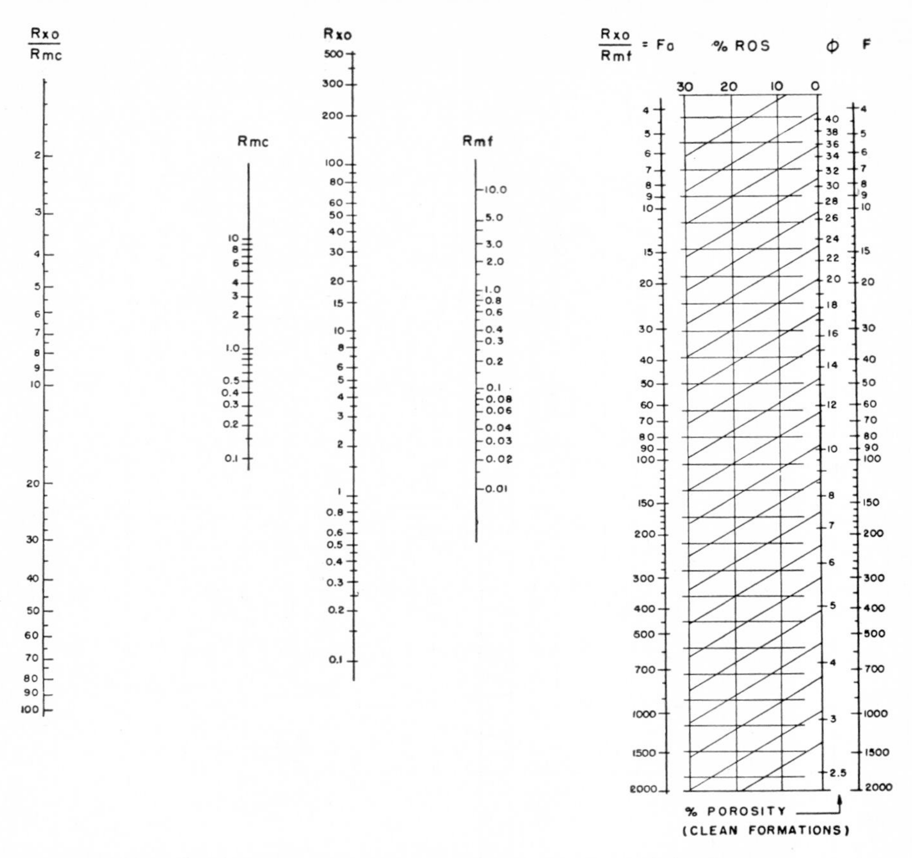

FIG. 5-8. Chart for determining porosity from micrologs. (*Schlumberger Well Surveying Corp.*)

bon- or water-bearing) will be eliminated by computing the prevailing connate water saturation.

The procedure for determining porosity and formation factors from Halliburton contact logs is not unlike the procedure used for the Schlumberger logs, but because of differences in tool characteristics, the calibration charts provided in Halliburton's "Charts for Log Interpretation" (July, 1954) should be used.

Halliburton has two "contact log" types, Type I and Type II, and the appropriate charts should be used for the log under study.

It is presumed that interpretation of the microresistivity logs of the Perforating Guns Atlas Corp. may be made from either Schlumberger's or Halliburton's charts, using the appropriate spacing; but the advisability of doing so has not been ascertained.

Neutron-curve Methods of Porosity Determination. *Neutron-gamma Log.* It is known that the neutron curve indicates the absence or presence of hydrogen-containing material in rocks surrounding the well bore. Therefore, one may expect the neutron absorption to be a quantitative indication of the porosity of the formations. An approach to such an evaluation has

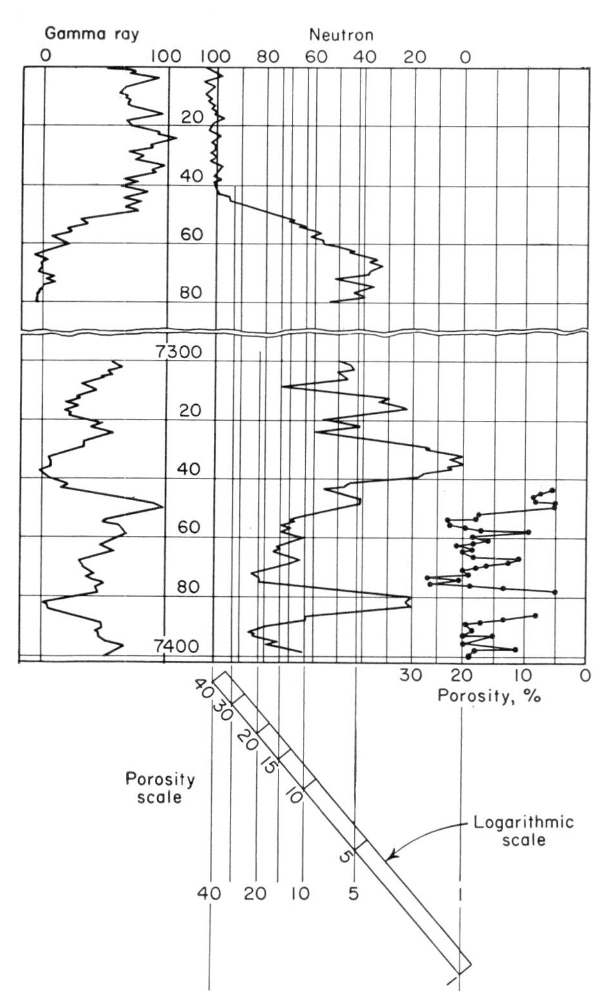

FIG. 5-9 Method or placing logarithmic porosity scale on a neutron-gamma log.

been made by Bush and Mardock (1949). It consists in determining a relative reference line for the neutron curve and, by correlation with known core-analysis data, establishing an empirical quantitative relationship specific to a selected formation of interest. This relationship, when established from a sufficient number of cored wells in the reservoir rock of interest, can be extended to uncored wells in the not too distant vicinity of the known wells.

The method proposed by Bush and Mardock applies only to liquid-filled (no free gas) porosities and preassumes that the neutron reactions of oil and water are substantially identical. Therefore, the method is not offered as a means of distinguishing between oil and water saturations.

To determine the relationship between the deflections of a particular neutron curve and porosity, it is necessary that sufficient core data be available in order that a wide range of porosity values be at hand. When these porosity values are compared with the neutron curve, it must be kept in mind that there may be slight discrepancies in depth between the core log and the radioactivity log and the comparison must be made with the core-porosity log properly correlated as to depth with the radioactivity log. This matching of core log with radioactivity log is the first and one of the important steps in making the interpretation.

The second important step is to establish the proper reference line for the neutron curve for the older type logs which have no absolute zero line or surface radiation zero line.

There are three possible choices for reference lines. First, there is the combination of a shale line and a dense limestone or anhydrite line; second, there is the shale line alone; and third, there is the dense limestone or anhydrite line alone.

In the making of many calibrations of the neutron–gamma-curve deflections vs. porosity, it has been observed that the correlation is logarithmic. This makes the interpretation very simple because it suffices to divide logarithmically the distance between the maximum deflection and a known reference. The latter may be the line of *zero neutron radiation* or *instrument zero* which might be considered as corresponding to a zone of 100 per cent porosity. The point of maximum deflection in a hard zone may be considered as being a nominal porosity such as 1 per cent. To obtain a porosity scale, it suffices to lay a double-cycle logarithmic scale with 100 per cent at the zero radiation line and 1 per cent at the dense zone. If a good shale reference line is available and if the porosity of it is known (such as 40 per cent), then a similar procedure may be followed between it and the dense zone. It is illustrated in Fig. 5-9.

Practice in various regions has indicated that best results are obtained for the following reference values:

Region	Shale porosity, %	Dense-zone porosity, %
Oklahoma		
North	40	3 (Oswego lime)
South	35	7 (dense lime)
Kansas	40	3 (in lime)
Big Horn Basin	35 (Chugwater shale)	1 (gypsum or dense lime)
Williston Basin	40 (Pierre shale)	1 (anhydrite)
Permian Basin	40	1 (dense lime)
North Louisiana	40	4 (dense lime)

Neutron–Slow Neutron Log (Perforating Guns Atlas Corp.). In the neutron–slow neutron log the chemical response to the mineral elements in the formation is greatly reduced since the gamma rays of capture do not affect the slow-neutron detector. However, the log response is still a function of the neutron capture cross section of the chemical elements. The probability of capture of the neutron depends to a great extent on the abundance of hydrogen and chlorine, i.e., of the presence of water, hydrocarbons, and brine in the formations as well as in the bore hole. In order to obtain a neutron–slow neutron log that will respond mostly to

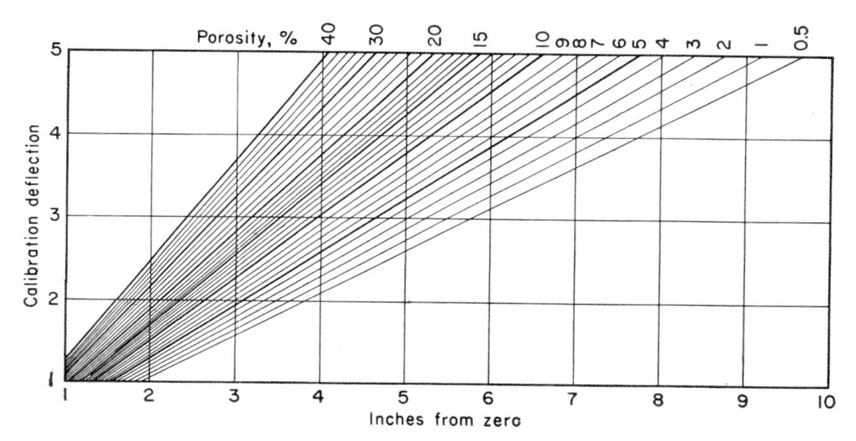

FIG. 5-10. Porosity scale for a neutron–slow neutron log. (*Perforating Guns Atlas Corp.*)

hydrogen abundance it is necessary to eliminate as much as possible the effect of chlorine. This is done by the Perforating Guns Atlas Corp. by taking a sample of the mud and placing it around the detector in a special container so that it will have the same effect as mud in the hole. The sensitivity of the instrument is then adjusted to give the desired galvanometer deflection for the standard hydrogen-containing absorber which serves as calibrator. The practice of Perforating Guns Atlas Corp. is to adjust deflections during calibration to a standard 4 in., regardless of mud conditions and bore-hole size. In this manner all logs have the same sensitivity and the same porosity scale is used. This porosity scale for carbonate rocks is reproduced in Fig. 5-10. It departs from the logarithmic scale used for the neutron-gamma log. The response of the latter reaches a plateau at about 25 per cent, whereas the slow neutron curve still shows sensitivity to porosity changes in the 40 per cent range.

In determining porosity, the scale of Fig. 5-10 at the 4-in. deflection level is transferred to the log so that its zero corresponds to the line of zero radiation and porosity values are read directly from the curve.

The adjustment of the recorder sensitivity, before logging, for halides in the mud and hole size makes it possible to run the log with a predetermined porosity scale.

Neutron–Fast Neutron Log. In a fast neutron log where neutrons of energy larger than 60,000 ev are detected, a true hydrogen abundance curve should be obtained because at high energies, the capture cross section of the elements for neutrons is very small. Such a log should be practically independent of lithology. There is too little known presently on the fast neutron log to give an evaluation of its possibilities and special characteristics.

Radiation–Guard-log Combination (Halliburton). The combination of a gamma-ray neutron log with a guard log has been advocated for the solution of logging interpretation in limestone reservoirs in which the

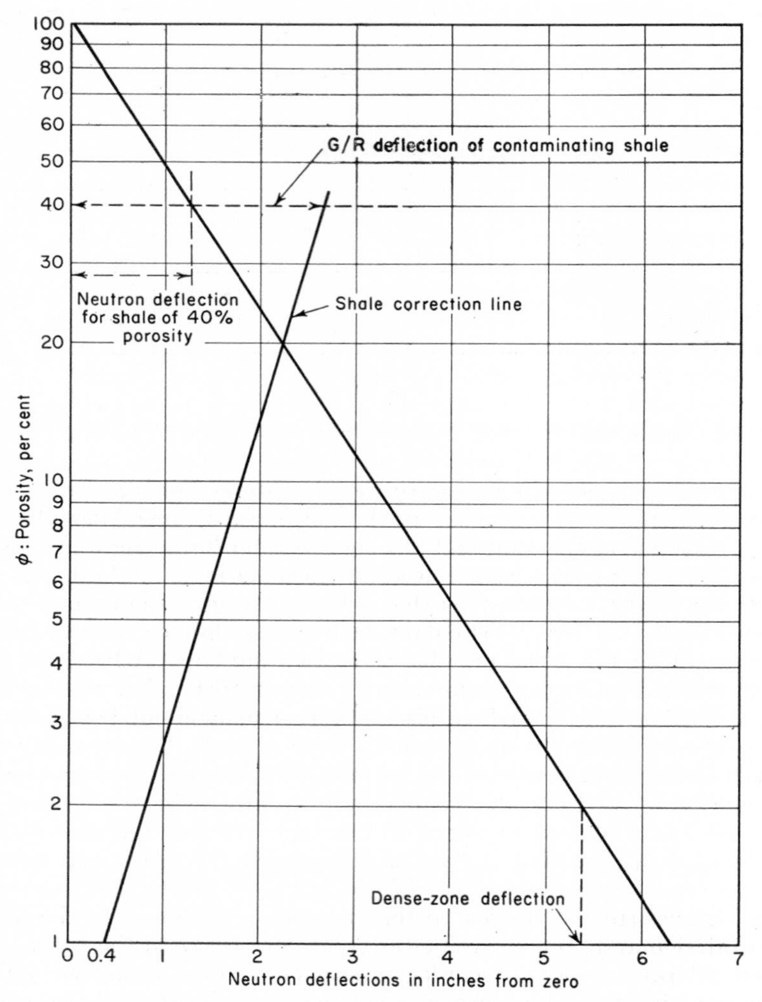

FIG. 5-11. Porosity determination in sands from a neutron curve with subtractive correction for shale contamination. (*After Bishop, Lane-Wells Company.*)

pay sections are normally very thin. The neutron curve provides a means of determining porosity, whereas the guard log is presumed to read true resistivity and provides means for solving for fluid saturation. The technique is formalized in a booklet available from the company selling the service.

The quantitative determination of porosity from the neutron curve is especially applicable to limestone and dolomite in which contamination by shale (with attendant porosity reduction) is generally inconsequential. However, in order to extend the interpretation technique to sands and sandstones, correction for porosity reduction due to shalyness is a prerequisite. A rapid method to achieve this end was suggested by Bishop (1955) for radioactivity logs of the Well Surveys' types. The natural radioactivity of a perfectly clean sand would be 0.4 in. from the line of zero radiation. The porosity shale correction depends on the type of contaminating shale in the sand and it is necessary to ascertain by mineralogical investigations by which type of shales (the one above or below the sand) the reservoir rock is contaminated. When this study has been made, the linear neutron deflection (in inches) of this sand is plotted on a neutron calibration curve previously drawn, using the appropriate porosity for the contaminating shale. The point so obtained is joined by a straight line to the 0.4-in. point and this gives the shale correction curve. The sand gamma-ray deflection at any particular level is read on this correction curve and the subtractive porosity is obtained directly. This type of diagram is illustrated on Fig. 5-11.

Porosity determination from the neutron curve becomes direct when it is obtained with a very short spacing of source to detector and when it is obtained from a tool making close contact with the well bore. This is a development of the Schlumberger organization whereby the detecting devices are embedded in a microlog-type pad which slides against the walls of the well (microneutron). Porosity calibration is given directly on a scale of the log and interpretative elements are completely unnecessary.

Another device of a direct-porosity-reading nature is provided by the continuous velocity logger originally introduced for seismic velocity determination in bore holes (Summers and Broding, 1952). This instrument measures the sound velocity between an acoustic sender and a receiver closely spaced from one another. Direct measurement of interval seismic velocity is thereby obtained. Because there is a relationship to porosity, sound velocity being smaller in highly porous rocks, a porosity calibration is given directly on a scale of the log and interpretative elements appear unnecessary.

DETERMINATION OF FORMATION-WATER SATURATION

The knowledge of connate water saturation is the most important quantitative information to be derived from the electric log, for this information determines whether or not a formation of interest has oil and gas productive ability. To be sure, it is not the only factor in the decision of whether or not to test a formation, but it is often the deciding factor.

Formation-water saturation determines also where to complete wells and what porous sections to include as pay in an overall porous zone.

Before an attempt is made to determine quantitatively the connate water saturation (σ_{wc}) it is advisable to derive a qualitative view on the productivity and water saturation of the horizon. This is readily done by means of the chart of Fig. 5-12. It indicates schematically the SP deflections on the left and the relative positions of the resistivity curves (short-normal and lateral) under various assumptions of mud–connate water resistivity contrasts which are reflected in the value of the SP curve and for various degrees of water saturation. Two limits are indicated: for sands and sandstones in general, water saturation less than 40 per cent will produce oil or gas; for carbonate rocks the limit is 20 per cent. The lower limit for limestones results from the vuggy nature of their porosity in most instances.

These two limiting values should be taken as guides only as there is nothing intrinsic about them. More refined calculations of the relative-permeability characteristics of both sandstone and limestone are required before final decision can be made. Caution must be exercised in using the chart of Fig. 5-12 in high-resistivity formations such as limestones when it becomes necessary to correct both the lateral and normal readings for the effect of mud conductivity and hole size. In thin beds, thickness correction should also be made.

An example will illustrate the use of this chart. A log shows an SP deflection of -90 mv and a ratio of readings of the short-normal curve to the lateral is 1.6. These conditions interpolate between the -100-mv and -75-mv cases and the water saturation should be approximately 30 per cent. In a sand, oil production should be expected, whereas it might be doubtful in a limestone reservoir.

Archie's Method of Water-saturation Determination. In interpreting logs, two situations may be encountered: (1) the resistivity R_o of a porous zone 100 per cent saturated in connate water can be ascertained on the log and the lithology of this zone may be considered substantially the same as that of the prospective producing zone to be evaluated. This is the case of many sands on the Gulf Coast where it is fairly safe to take as R_o the lowest value of resistivities observed on the log.

When the conditions stipulated are satisfied, the connate water saturation is directly obtained from Archie's relation

$$\sigma_{wc} = \sqrt[n]{\frac{R_o}{R_t}} \tag{5-3}$$

This approach has the advantage of eliminating any errors due to uncertainties concerning the values of R_{wc} and formation factors. In practice, the value of n is always 2.0; in the past the value of n was often varied to suit the lithological description of the reservoir rock but this practice is disappearing with the introduction of the shaly-sand technique. For oil-wet sands the value of n could be chosen higher than 2. In vuggy

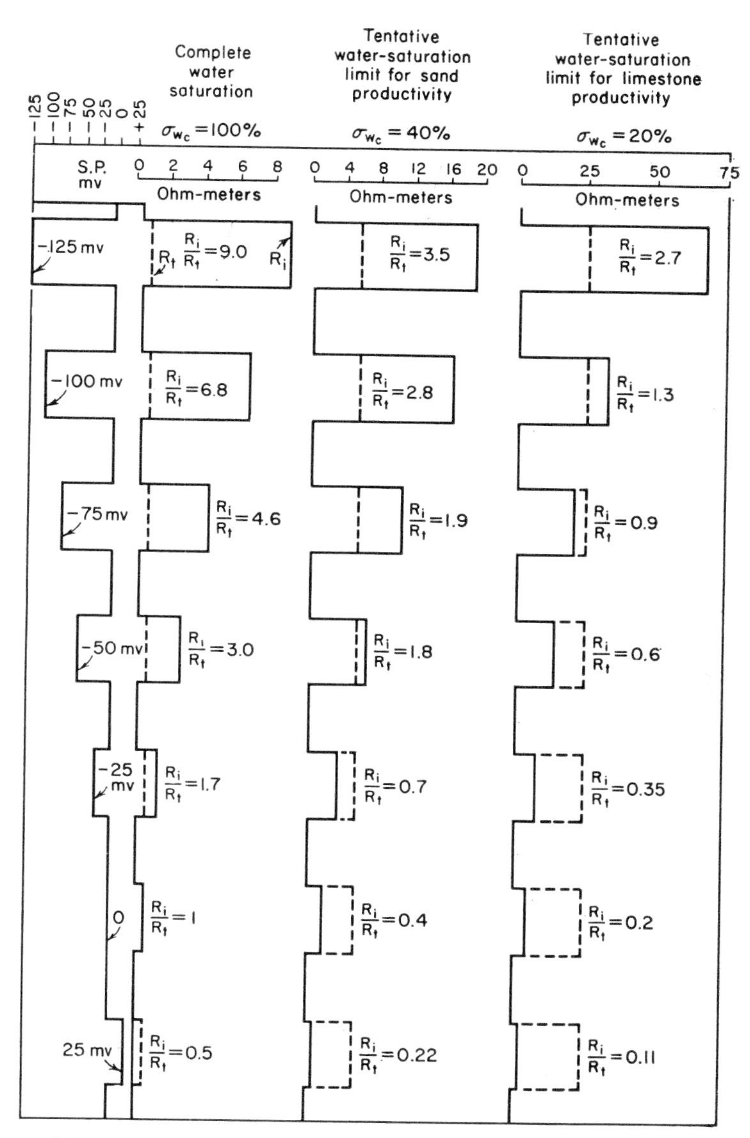

FIG. 5-12. Schematic representation of the relative position of the various electric-log curves for various SP values and water saturations. (*After Tixier.*)

limestones it may be advisable to select a value of n less than 2.0. (2) The resistivity R_o may not be read from the log. In this eventuality R_o must be computed from

$$R_o = R_{wc}\phi^{-m} \tag{5-4}$$

by making judicious evaluations of the connate water resistivity from a sample of water, its chemical analysis, or by interpolation of the information collected in a salinity atlas. An estimate of the porosity ϕ must be made from core or cutting samples or from log interpretation methods previously reviewed. The appropriate cementation factor m must be selected from a lithological description of the reservoir rock. The connate water saturation may then be evaluated from Archie's formula

$$\sigma_{wc} = \sqrt[n]{\frac{R_{wc}\phi^{-m}}{R_t}} \tag{5-5}$$

A common practice is to use the Humble formula for the formation factor; this avoids the problem of selecting a value of m according to lithological conditions.

Should formation factors have been determined in the laboratory on representative samples from the subject formations, or from a short investigation logging tool such as short-normal, micrologs, limestone curve, etc., then uncertainties of porosity and cementation factors are eliminated and the solution may more readily be obtained from

$$\sigma_{wc} = \sqrt[n]{\frac{R_{wc}F}{R_t}} \tag{5-6}$$

Tixier's Method of Water-saturation Determination. In order to avoid the limitations of the Archie approach of water-saturation determination, Tixier (1949) developed a method for which the only requirements are the following:

1. Reservoir formations must be porous and invaded with a mud filtrate or resistivity R_{mf} preferably considerably different from the formation water R_{wc}. If the resistivities are nearly the same, indetermination may result.

2. Resistivity curves of the proper electrode spacings must be available from which the resistivity of the invaded zone R_i and the true resistivity of the noninvaded zone R_t may be secured.

With the above requirements satisfied, the Tixier method permits water-saturation determinations at any level without knowing formation factor F and formation-water resistivity R_{wc}. It needs only the logging measurements made at a single level for its calculations; hence, interpretations may be made even when the reservoir is not fully penetrated by the drill.

The method is based on some empirical observations deduced from electric-log analyses to the effect that the total water saturation in an invaded zone σ_{wi} is a function of the original connate water saturation S_{wc} as follows:

$$\sigma_{wi} \cong \sqrt[2]{\sigma_{wc}} \tag{5-7}$$

The trend indicated by this relation is substantially as expected from a fluid-displacement mechanistic standpoint as it is known that less and less oil is displaced from a porous medium as the initial water saturation increases until a critical saturation is reached at which no further oil displacement takes place.

By Archie's law, the following two relations may be written at any depth on the log:

$$\sigma_{wc} = \sqrt[2]{\frac{R_{wc}F}{R_t}} \tag{5-8}$$

$$\sigma_{wi} = \sqrt{\frac{R_{wi}F}{R_i}} \tag{5-9}$$

where R_t is the true resistivity of the uninvaded zone, which can generally be obtained from the lateral curve in high-resistivity formations or from the long-normal curve in low-resistivity formations. R_{wi} is the resistivity of the combination of water of invasion and connate water.

It has been shown experimentally that about 7.5 per cent of the original connate water will not be replaced by the mud filtrate. Call z the ratio of the volume of the formation water to the total volume of all the water in the invaded zone; then the conductivity $1/R_{wi}$ of the mixture may be computed as the combined conductivity of two networks in parallel:

$$\frac{1}{R_{wi}} = \frac{1 - z}{R_{mf}} + \frac{z}{R_{wc}}$$

from which the ratio R_{wi}/R_{wc} is obtained:

$$\frac{R_{wi}}{R_{wc}} = \frac{R_{mf}/R_{wc}}{(1 - z) + zR_{mf}/R_{wc}} \tag{5-10}$$

Combining Eqs. (5-7) to (5-10), we obtain successively

$$\sigma_{wc} = \frac{R_i/R_t}{R_{wi}/R_{wc}}$$

$$\sigma_{wc} = \frac{R_i/R_t}{R_{mf}/R_{wc}}[(1 - z) + zR_{mf}/R_{wc}] \tag{5-11}$$

According to Eq. (5-11), the connate water saturation σ_{wc} can be obtained from a knowledge of the three quantities z, R_{mf}/R_{wc}, and R_i/R_t.

As mentioned, the average value of z is taken as 7.5 per cent but there may be some deviations from this value in certain formations. z is a measure of the mixing of the mud filtrate and connate water in the invaded zone.

The value of R_{mf}/R_{wc} may be obtained from the static self-potential formula:

$$SP = -70.7 \frac{T_f}{T_a} \log \frac{R_{mf}}{R_{wc}} \tag{5-12}$$

The value of R_i/R_t may be obtained from resistivity readings made on two curves. One curve must essentially give the resistivity R_i of the

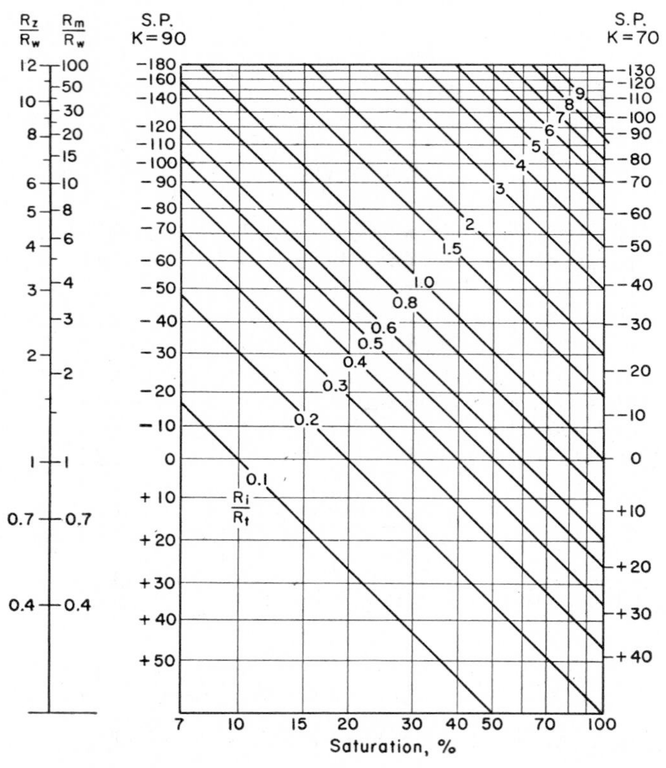

FIG. 5-13. Water-saturation determination from a conventional log. (*After Tixier, Schlumberger Well Surveying Corp.*)

invaded formation. In most instances this will be obtained from the short-normal curve, corrected for hole size, mud resistivity, and bed thickness by means of the departure curves.

The other curve must give R_t, the true resistivity of the noninvaded formations. Rules for reading R_t under various conditions will be reviewed in a later section.

To facilitate the computations, Tixier has combined Eqs. (5-10) and (5-11) into a nomograph (Fig. 5-13) which is valid only when the SP coefficient $70.7 \frac{T_f}{T_a}$ is 90, i. e., when T_f is 100°F. For other formation temperatures, a fictitious SP value should be computed from SP $(100 + 460)/T_f$ before entering the chart of Fig. 5-13.

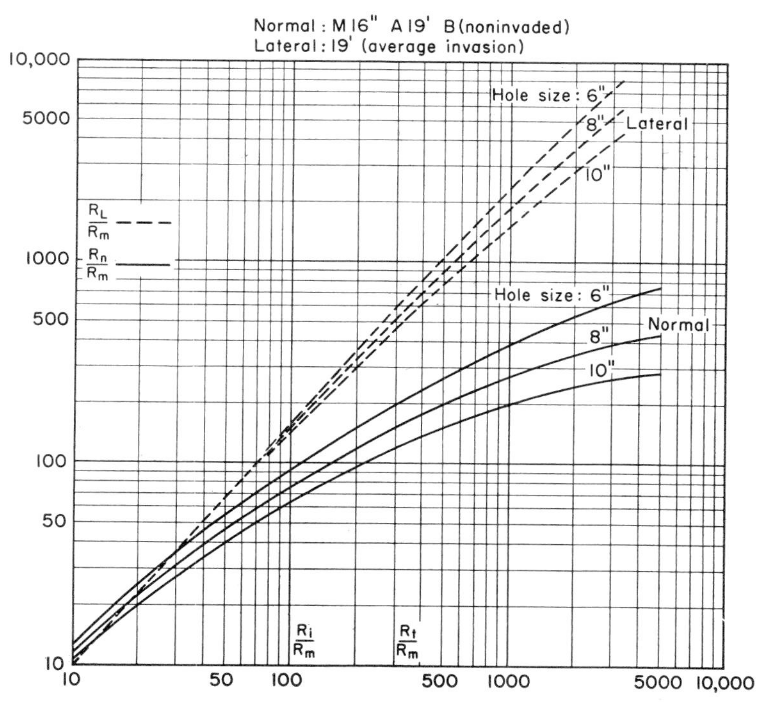

FIG. 5-14. Simplified departure curves for normal and lateral devices. (*Schlumberger Well Surveying Corp.*)

Hole-size correction may be made very rapidly by means of the chart of Fig. 5-14, which is especially designed to be used for this method for the more commonly used electrode spacings: $AM = 16$ in. and $AO = 18$ ft, 8 in. In addition this chart includes the effect of the current electrode B located at a finite distance from M in the normal configuration of electrodes.

Remarks on and Limitations of the Tixier Method of Water-saturation Determination. *Self-potential Curve.* A great deal of reliance is placed on the SP curve. Hence, it is necessary to read the SP values and to make the necessary corrections for bed thickness, invasion, hole size, and R_t with a great deal of care. For thin formations in low-resistivity ground (soft-rock country), the thickness correction chart of Fig. 4-16 may be used. For instance, for a 5-ft bed when $R_t/R_m = 20$, only 50 per cent of the static self-potential is measured; in a 30-ft bed under the same conditions 95 per cent of the self-potential is read. If $R_t/R_m = 200$, 80 per cent of the self-potential is measured on a 60-ft bed and only 55 per cent on a 10-ft bed.

The Tixier nomograph is designed for an SP lithological factor $K = 90$. There are two ways of modifying the procedure such that Fig. 5-13 may still be used when it is ascertained that $K = 90$ does not apply:

1. If R_m and R_{wc} are known in a dependable manner for the case under study, a fictitious self-potential corresponding to $K = 90$ can be calculated by the SP equation and the corresponding SP value is then used on the nomograph.

2. If the K value for the case at hand is known, the fictitious SP value (SP_f) is calculated from

$$SP_f = SP \times \frac{90}{K}$$

where SP is the actual value read on the curve.

Invaded-zone Resistivity (R_i). The invaded-zone resistivity must be obtained from an appropriate electrode configuration. Generally, this will be the short-normal (AM = 10 to 16 in.). This spacing is appropriate in the hard-rock country as it probes just within the invaded zone. In the soft-rock country, however, the 16-in. normal may reach beyond the invasion and the readings may be too distorted to allow valid corrections to obtain R_i. In low-resistivity formations, a shorter normal spacing (AM = 10 in.) may be more suitable for the application of the method.

True Formation Resistivity (R_t). This value is normally obtained from the lateral curve which probes presumably beyond the invaded zone. However, in thin formations a correction should be applied for thickness.

The invaded zone constitutes a "shield" through which R_t must be measured by supplying electrical energy to the formations. If R_i is small, the invaded zone does not provide much shielding and R_t is dependably obtained from the lateral curve by simply making hole-size and mud corrections. In low-resistivity formations (soft-rock country), the long-normal often measures R_t. It may even be advisable to use the long-normal in this case if the beds are thin, but of greater thickness than AM'.

If R_i is large, it is difficult to energize the noninvaded formations behind the invaded zone, unless a very long spacing is used. In this case the lateral curve must be used. Then corrections for thin beds become unreliable.

The Tixier method is still applicable (and for that matter Archie's method as well) when there is no self-potential. (This condition may occur if the mud and formation water resistivities are equal.) In fact, this is when the Tixier method may be used with the greatest degree of certainty since the value of the SP lithological factor K is then immaterial.

Indetermination occurs when $R_i/R_t = 1$, in which case it is necessary to establish if permeability exists. This point may be ascertained by observing if the self-potential exists. The existence of SP deflection indicates that we are dealing with a permeable formation except in the case of a formation where $R_{mf}/R_{wc} = 1$. In such a situation the availability of a microlog is invaluable since it is almost infallible in outlining permeable sections.

R_i Method of Water-saturation Determination. This method may be used as a last resort for the study of water saturation in clean formations when R_t cannot be obtained. It is advisable that $R_{16\text{ in.}}/R_m > 10$. In the Tixier Rocky Mountain method the formation factor F is eliminated from the saturation equation. If F is known with some accuracy from the microtools or from core measurements, the Tixier method may be revised so that R_t is not required. Then we may write

$$\sqrt{\sigma_{wc}} = \sigma_{wi} = \sqrt{\frac{FR_z}{R_i}} \qquad \text{where} \qquad \frac{1}{R_z} = \frac{z}{R_{wc}} + \frac{1-z}{R_{mf}} \tag{5-13}$$

After substitution and cancellation we have

$$\frac{1}{\sigma_{wc}} = \frac{R_i}{FR_{mf}}\left(z\frac{R_{mf}}{R_{wc}} + 1 - z\right)$$

or

$$\sigma_{wc} = \frac{F}{aR_i/R_{mf}} = \frac{R_{xo}}{aR_i} \tag{5-14}$$

where

$$a = z\left(\frac{R_{mf}}{R_{wc}}\right) + 1 - z$$

If we select $z = 0.1$ and $z = 0.2$, we have the following table of values for a:

R_{mf}/R_{wc}	51	41	31	21	11	9	8	7	6	5	4	3	2	1
$a\ (z = 0.1)$	6	5	4	3	2	1.8	1.7	1.6	1.5	1.4	1.3	1.2	1.1	1
$a\ (z = 0.2)$	11	9	7	5	3	2.6	2.4	2.2	2	1.8	1.6	1.4	1.2	1

The values of R_{xo} and F may be obtained from microtools or short investigation tools. R_i is preferably obtained from a short-normal or limestone curve after correction for hole size and mud. R_{mf} is determined from the mud resistivity at T_f or better yet from a sample of mud filtrate. In limestones and other low-porosity formations it is believed that very deep invasion occurs, such that the laterolog reading is closer to R_i than to R_t. In salt muds the resistivity of the hole fluid is close to R_{wc}, and the factor a becomes unity. Then, when R_{mf} is placed in the numerator of (5-14), we get

$$\sigma_{wc} = \frac{FR_{mf}}{R_i} \qquad \text{or} \qquad \sigma_{wc} \approx \frac{R_{xo}}{R_i} \approx \frac{R_{MLL}}{R_{LL}}$$

The R_i method of water-saturation evaluation is not as accurate as other methods using R_t. In particular, errors on the formation-factor value greatly affect the computed saturation. We must have the formation factor F and the ratio R_{mf}/R_{wc} before the method can be used. However, in thin beds the value of R_i/R_m can often be determined with good accuracy.

A reliable value of R_t is always the best tool to use for the determination of water saturation but sometimes mud invasion seriously affects the lateral readings, at which time the R_i method should be tried.

Interpretation steps for the R_i method are as follows:

1. Determine F from the microlog by $F = R_{xo}/R_{mf}$.
2. Correct the self-potential from the log to static self-potential.
3. Obtain R_{mf}/R_{wc} from the SP equation with appropriate K factor. Also determine R_{wc} and compute $R_o = FR_{wc}$.
4. Assume $z = 0.1$ in low-permeability and 0.2 in high-permeability rocks and read value of a from the tabulation above.
5. Obtain R_i from the short-normal ($R_{16\text{ in.}}$), making bore-hole correction for d and R_m, or from $R_{10\text{ in.}}$ or from LS 32 in.
6. If $R_i < 2R_o$, we have a water-bearing horizon.
7. If $R_i > 2R_o$, calculate σ_{wc} from formula (5-14).

A chart is provided in Fig. 5-15 for facilitating the computations by the R_i method.

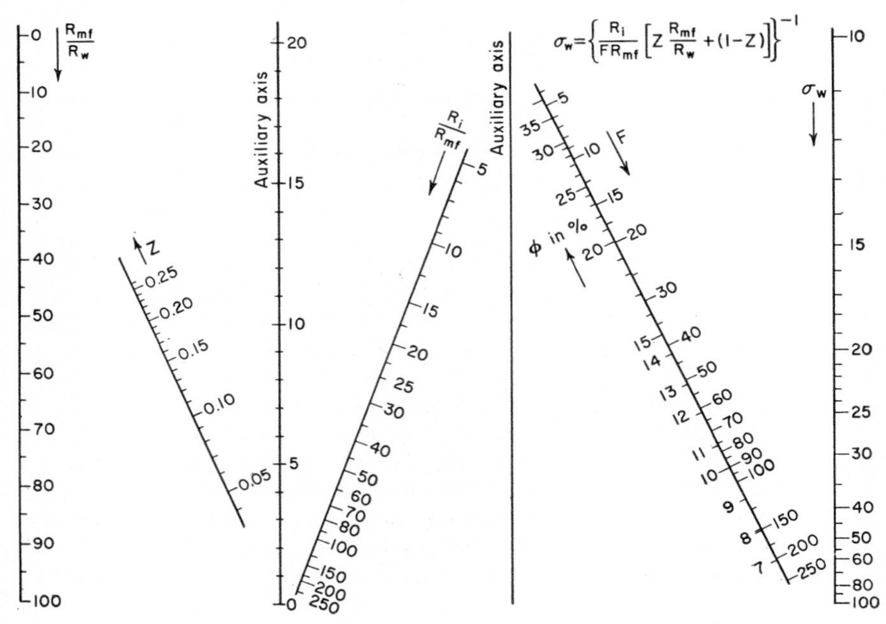

FIG. 5-15. Water-saturation determination by the R_i method. (*Schlumberger Well Surveying Corp.*)

Special Interpretation Technique in Shaly Sands. A shaly sand is one in which the pore spaces between the sand grains are partially filled with clay. Such a sand still gives rise to negative SP deflections in fresh muds, but the magnitudes of the SP values are smaller than those obtained in a clean sand; this SP reduction is a measure of the amount of pore space filling by clays. An SP reduction is therefore one of the main characteristics of shaly sand. A further reduction in the SP value may be due to the presence of oil and gas and because of the attendant increase in resistivity.

One may distinguish the following types of shaly sands:

1. *Laminated (sandwich) type.* This is an alternation of shale and clean sand partings. A typical example is the Mesaverde formation (Wyoming). On the logs they are characterized by an SP reduction in accordance with the percentage of shale in the gross section. Close examination of the self-potential and short investigation resistivity devices show small ripples in the curve at each of the partings.

2. *Dispersed or interstitial clayey sands (colloidal shaly sands).* Examples are most of the Cherokee sands of the Mid-Continent: Red Fork, Bartlesville, Prue, etc., and most of the Gulf Coast Frio sands. These sands are characterized by SP reduction, but without ripples on the SP curve or on the short-normal curve. They lead very readily to clay blocking of the formation by mud filtrate because of hydration of the reactive clay which they contain. The minerals responsible for the SP reduction are presumably illite and montmorillonite.

3. *Combined colloidal-laminated shaly sands* where interbedding of dirty sands is present in shale laminations. The electric-log characteristics are the same as above. Examples may be found in the Mesaverde formation in Wyoming, the Fruitland section in San Juan Basin, etc.

4. *Nonreactive ashy sands.* These are characterized by no SP reduction but very low resistivity even when oil productive. Typical examples are the Tuscaloosa and Eutaw sands (Louisiana, Mississippi, and Alabama). It is believed that these sands have an unusually high specific surface because of the fine, silty, ashy, but electrochemically inert minerals which they hold. The inert nature of the fine-grain minerals is the reason for the lack of SP reduction. They retain a large amount of bound water by adsorption because of their large specific surface, and clean oil may yet be produced from such reservoirs when formation-water saturation is as high as 65 and 70 per cent pore space. Interpretation of such sands requires a knowledge of local conditions, but quantitative evaluation of productivity may be made through evaluation of bound-water-filled porosity.

5. *Sand containing electronically conductive minerals* such as sulfides, oxides, and more specifically glauconite. Green sands containing glauconite exhibit very low resistivity even when producing clean oil because of the electric path provided by the conductive minerals. This occurs whether or not oil is present. Such formations do not give rise to an SP reduction and are characterized by very low formation factors. Typical examples are the McLish, Oil Creek, Tulip Creek sands of Simpson Age (Oklahoma), the Olmos sand (South Texas), the Aux Vases sand (Illinois), the Big Creek field sand (Louisiana), etc. Interpretation of these sands

is by the conventional procedure but high-sensitivity logging scales are required in order to be able to read resistivity values with the required precision.

Only the shaly sands giving rise to an SP reduction effect lead to special interpretation problems, for the others may be solved by standard techniques carefully applied. A method has been proposed by Poupon, Loy, and Tixier (1954) for the interpretation of shaly sands with SP reduction.

In a *clean* water-bearing sand the static self-potential (SSP) is given by

$$\text{SSP} = -K \log \frac{R_{mf}}{R_{wc}} \tag{5-15}$$

where K in a sand-shale section varies with temperature only: $K = 70.7\, T_f/538$, T_f being the absolute formation temperature in °R.

Archie's formula for clean rocks, water-wet and of intergranular type porosity, may be written as follows:

$$\sigma_{wc}^2 = \frac{R_o}{R_t} = \frac{FR_{wc}}{R_t} \tag{5-16}$$

In the flushed zone around a well bore, this formula becomes

$$\sigma_{xo}^2 = \frac{FR_{mf}}{R_{xo}} \tag{5-17}$$

Since the rocks considered are clean and devoid of reactive clays and shales (or other minerals reactive with the mud filtrate), the formation factor F is an invariant, and substituting the value of F obtained from (5-16) into (5-15),

$$\sigma_{wc}^2 = \sigma_{xo}^2 \frac{R_{xo}}{R_t} \frac{R_w}{R_{mf}} \tag{5-18}$$

Substituting (5-17) into (5-14) and transforming,

$$\text{SSP} = -K \left[\log \frac{R_{xo}}{R_t} + 2 \log \frac{\sigma_{xo}}{\sigma_{wc}} \right] \tag{5-19}$$

Equation (5-19) is the derived Archie formula and should be considered fully valid for clean rocks since no assumption has been made besides those already implied by the original Archie formula.

In a water-bearing formation, $\sigma_{wc} = 1.0$ and $\sigma_{xo} = 1.0$; hence (5-19) becomes

$$\text{SSP} = -K \log \frac{R_{xo}}{R_o} \tag{5-20}$$

Now, should the water sand be *shaly* (laminated or interstitial type), formula (5-20) still applies but R_{xo} is a smaller value than for clean sand.

What is then obtained is the pseudostatic self-potential (PSP):

$$\text{PSP} = -K \log \frac{R_{xo}}{R_o} \tag{5-21}$$

The ratio PSP/SSP $= \alpha$ is the SP reduction factor of the shaly sand:

$$\alpha = 1 \text{ for clean sand}$$

$$\alpha = 0 \text{ for pure shale}$$

By simple mathematical manipulations it is shown that

$$\text{PSP} = -K \log \frac{R_{xo}}{R_t} - 2\alpha K \log \frac{\sigma_{xo}}{\sigma_{wc}} \tag{5-22}$$

which relates the pseudostatic self-potential to the resistivity of the flushed zone R_{xo}, the true formation resistivity R_t, and the water saturation in the flushed zone σ_{xo} and in the sand σ_{wc}.

The unknown of the problem is σ_{wc}, but various reasonable assumptions must be made on the value of the residual oil in the flushed zone ($\sigma_{xo} = 1 -$ ROS), the value of σ_{xo}, and the value of K. α may be computed if a neighboring clean-water sand is present or it may be computed if R_{wc} is known. R_{xo} may be obtained from a microlog or microlaterolog; R_t may be obtained from a conventional log. Figure 5-16 provides a chart for a rapid solution of the problem. An example will illustrate the technique:

Let a shaly sand show $R_t = 5.0$ ohm-meters
PSP $= -45$ mv
SSP $= -75$ mv (in a clean-water sand)
$R_{xo} = 12.5$ ohm-meters
$R_{mf} = 1.25$ ohm-meters

We have
$$\frac{R_{xo}}{R_t} = 2.5$$

With the coordinates PSP $= -45$ mv and $K = 70$, point A is determined on the graph (Fig. 5-16), which indicates a total water saturation of 70 per cent. However, in a colloidal sand, part of that water is bound and not movable. To find to what extent this is so, the static self-potential value is plotted and a straight line drawn from 0 through A, which determines point B and 55 per cent free water saturation. Fifteen per cent of pore space is therefore occupied by water of hydration which is not movable mechanically.

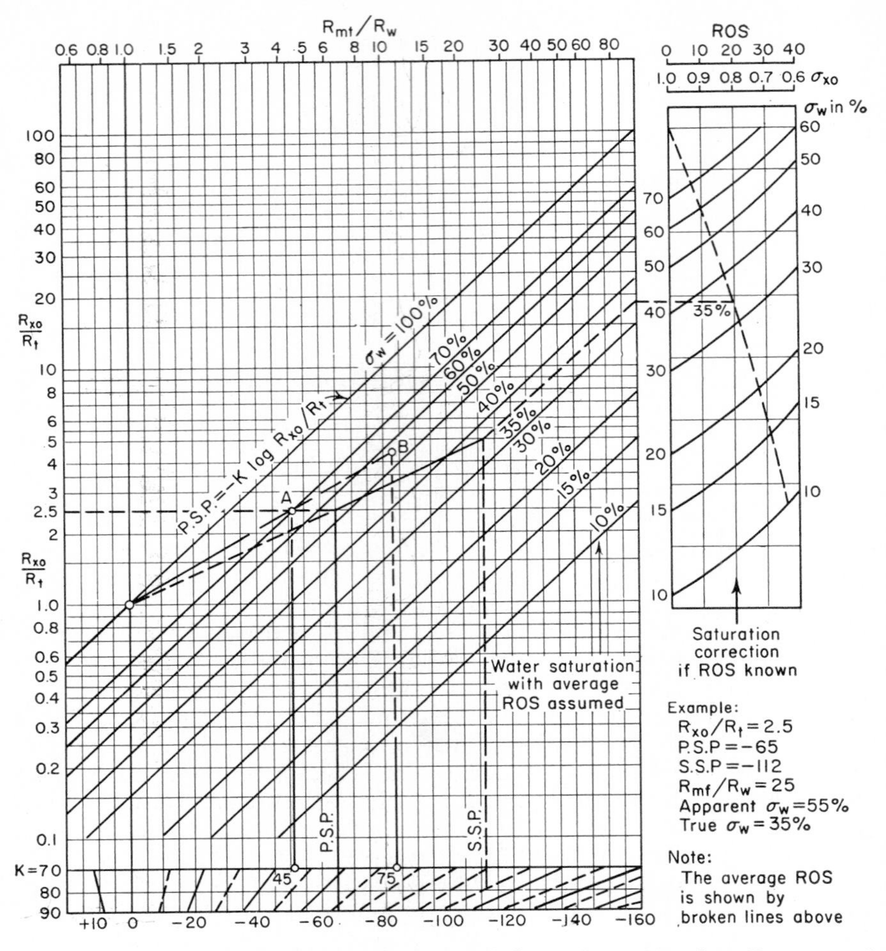

FIG. 5-16. Water-saturation determination in shaly sands. (*After Loy, Poupon, and Tixier, Schlumberger Well Surveying Corp.*)

For the determination of porosity, the chart of Fig. 5-17 is used. We have

$$\alpha = \frac{\text{PSP}}{\text{SSP}} = \frac{-45}{-75} = 0.6$$

$$F_a = \frac{R_{xo}}{R_{mf}} = \frac{12.5}{1.25} = 10$$

$$\frac{R_{xo}}{R_t} = \frac{12.5}{5} = 2.5$$

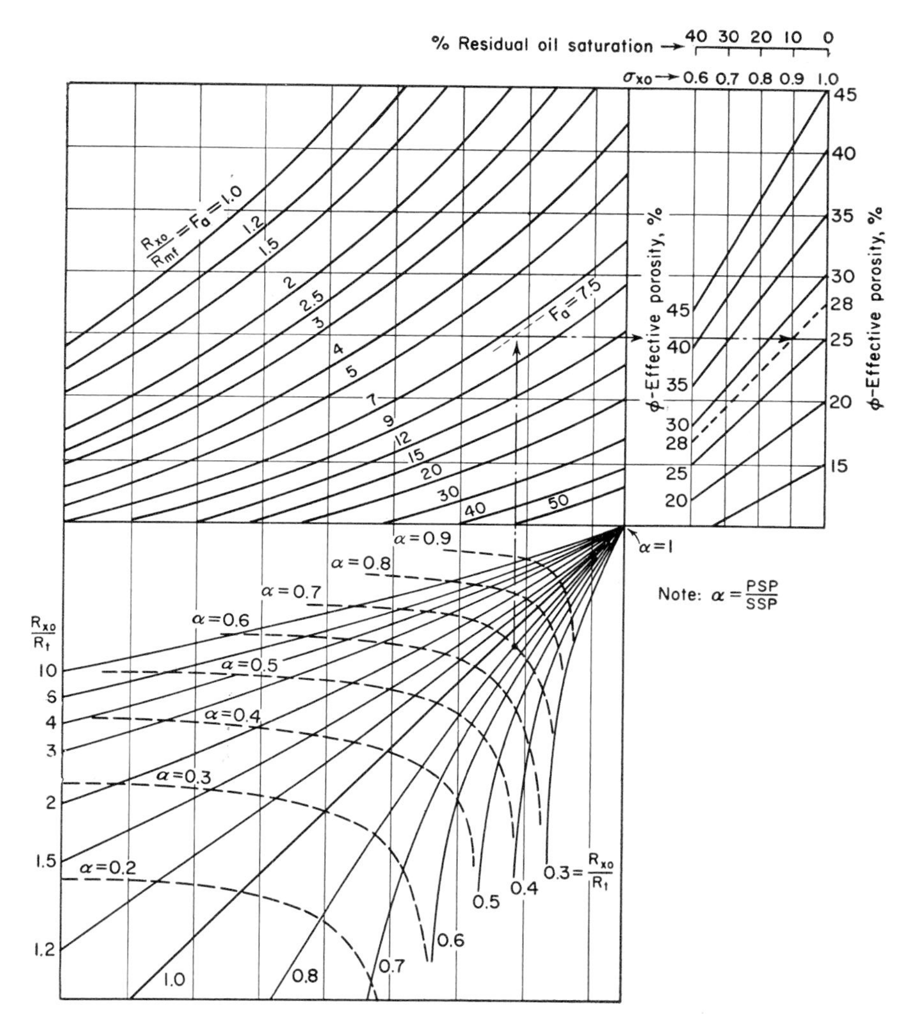

FIG. 5-17. Porosity determination in shaly sands. (*After Loy, Poupon, and Tixier, Schlumberger Well Surveying Corp.*)

The values of 0.6 and 2.5 locate point *A* in the lower left of Fig. 5-17 and $R_{xo}/R_{mf} = 10$ locates point *B* in the upper left of the diagram. Translating point *B* horizontally to the right, we find 18 per cent effective porosity for a water sand or 23 per cent if 20 per cent residual oil is present in the case of an oil sand. Residual-oil saturation observed in cores may be used as a guide to the values of ROS to be chosen.

Other Techniques for Shaly-sand Interpretation. The shortcomings of the methods previously discussed for water-saturation determination are their empirical nature or the empirical way in which formation productivity is inferred from the results. A more positive answer and breakdown into bound and movable water is desirable.

The following postulates are made and have been experimentally verified:

$$F_t R_{wc} = F_a R_{wa} \tag{5-23}$$

$$F_t = F_a \left(1 - \phi_h + \phi_h \frac{R_{mf}}{R_w}\right) \tag{5-24}$$

where F_t = true formation factor at R_{wc}

F_a = apparent formation factor at R_{mf} and obtained from $\frac{R_{xo}}{R_{mf}}(1 - \text{ROS})^2$

R_{wa} = apparent water resistivity as derived from PSP by the SP equation

ϕ_h = portion of pore space occupied by bound water of hydration in the form of an adsorbed double layer (solvation water)

The following derivation is then made:

$$\text{PSP} = -K \log \frac{R_{mf}}{R_{wa}} = -K \log \frac{R_{mf}}{F_t R_{wc}/F_a} = -K \log \frac{R_{mf}}{R_{wc}} \frac{F_a}{F_t}$$

$$= -K \log \frac{R_{mf}}{R_{wc}} - K \log \frac{F_a}{F_t} = \text{SSP} - K \log \frac{F_a}{F_t} \tag{5-25}$$

$$\text{SSP}\,(1 - \alpha) = K \log \frac{F_a}{F_t} = -(1 - \alpha) K \log \frac{R_{mf}}{R_{wc}}$$

or

$$\frac{F_a}{F_t} = \left(\frac{R_{wc}}{R_{mf}}\right)^{1-\alpha} \tag{5-26}$$

From (5-26) and knowing R_{wc}, R_{mf}, and α, F_a/F_t is calculated. Solving (5-24), the fraction of pore space ϕ_h occupied by bound water is obtained.

The total water saturation σ_{wc} is obtained by solving the usual Archie equation using a saturation exponent of 2.0.

$$\sigma_{wc} = \sqrt{\frac{F_t R_w}{R_t}} \tag{5-27}$$

The mobile water saturation σ_{wm} is computed by difference:

$$\sigma_{wm} = \sigma_{wc} - \phi_h \tag{5-28}$$

Relative-permeability relationships developed from petrophysical studies may now be used with σ_{wm} as basis to calculate well productivity (Chap. 3).

The limitation of this method resides in the usual inadequate information on the basic data needed.

Special Interpretation Techniques in Salt-mud Surveys. When the mud in the well is very salty, special logging techniques are used because conventional logs lose their character and definition. Focused current logs are then used. Schlumberger advocates the microlaterolog-laterolog combination, whereas Halliburton advocates the radiation–guard log combination.

Schlumberger Salt-mud Survey. While standard interpretation techniques may be used for the combination microlaterolog-laterolog, because of the special properties of these tools, a simplified interpretation technique is possible. At a given level within a well let the respective readings of each be represented by R_{MLL} and R_{LL}. When SP deflections are very small, no large error is made by assuming that mud filtrate and formation water have the same resistivity. Mud-cake thickness is also assumed negligible (this is often verified in salt mud so that $R_{MLL} = R_{xo}$). Mud-filtrate loss to the formation is assumed moderate so that invasion diameter is small and $R_{LL} = R_t$. This last statement is incorrect when mud-filtrate loss is very high and when formations are very thin.

In the invaded zone it is assumed that the Tixier relation $\sigma_{wi} = \sqrt{\sigma_{wc}}$ holds. Other valid relations are

$$\sigma_{wc} = \sqrt{\frac{R_o}{R_t}}$$

$$\sigma_{wi} = \sqrt{\frac{R_o}{R_{xo}}}$$

Combining the three relations, we find

$$\sigma_{wc} = \sigma_{wi}^2 = \frac{R_o}{R_{xo}} = \sqrt{\frac{R_o}{R_t}}$$

or

$$\sigma_{wc} = \frac{R_o}{R_{xo}} = \frac{R_{xo}}{R_t} = \frac{R_{MLL}}{R_{LL}} \qquad (5\text{-}29)$$

Hence, connate water saturation may be obtained directly by making the ratio of the microlaterolog reading (R_{MLL}) to that of the laterolog (R_{LL}), provided the assumptions made in the above derivation are substantially verified.

Halliburton Salt-mud Survey (Radiation–Guard log). In the Halliburton combination of a guard log and a gamma-ray–neutron log, the latter may be substituted for the determination of porosity, from which the formation factor and R_o are calculated. The true resistivity is read from the guard log. The technique advocated is somewhat empirical and requires a certain degree of calibration in each geological province. Details may be obtained from the Halliburton Logging Services.

DETERMINATION OF SPECIFIC PERMEABILITY

Specific permeability of porous rocks may be determined from electric logs by petrophysical correlations with porosity or from logs exhibiting well-defined resistivity gradients.

Empirical Correlation. Data obtained from various sources have brought out the correlation shown in Fig. 5-18, which is the representation of the equation

$$F\phi = 5.55 \times K^{-.108} \tag{5-30}$$

where F = formation factor
ϕ = fractional porosity
K = permeability, md

The product of $F\phi$ is equal to the square of the rock's tortuosity.

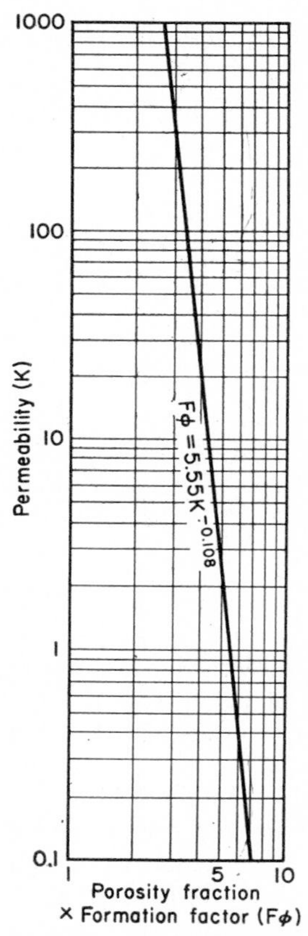

FIG. 5-18. Relation between the product ($F\phi$) and permeability.

To use this relation, F may be known from measurements on core samples, from porosity measurements and lithological description, or from direct evaluation on the log from a 100 per cent brine-saturated zone, provided the brine salinity is known. ϕ may be known from cores or drill cuttings, or from the electric log by one of the various methods studied previously. Then from the product $F\phi$, the permeability may be evaluated from the graph of Fig. 5-18.

It goes without saying that this correlation gives only an approximate evaluation of permeability, especially in view of the fact that the permeability curve vs. $F\phi$ is very steep and a small variation in the $F\phi$ value results in an appreciable variation in K. At best it can only be hoped that the relation gives an idea of the order of magnitude of permeability.

Petrophysical Correlation. Another approach to permeability determination from electric logs may be had from observing that above the transition zone (i.e., in the irreducible water-saturation zone), the prevailing water saturation σ_{wir} is a function of both porosity and permeability through the empirical relation

$$K^{1/2} = 250 \frac{\phi^3}{\sigma_{wir}} \tag{5-31}$$

where K is permeability in millidarcys and ϕ is porosity as a fraction. To facilitate computations, the above relation is plotted on Fig. 5-19 as an alignment chart. Porosity and water saturation may be known from cores or log interpretation. Should the water saturation so obtained be different from the irreducible value, the determined permeability by the above expression would naturally be erroneous; generally it will be too small.

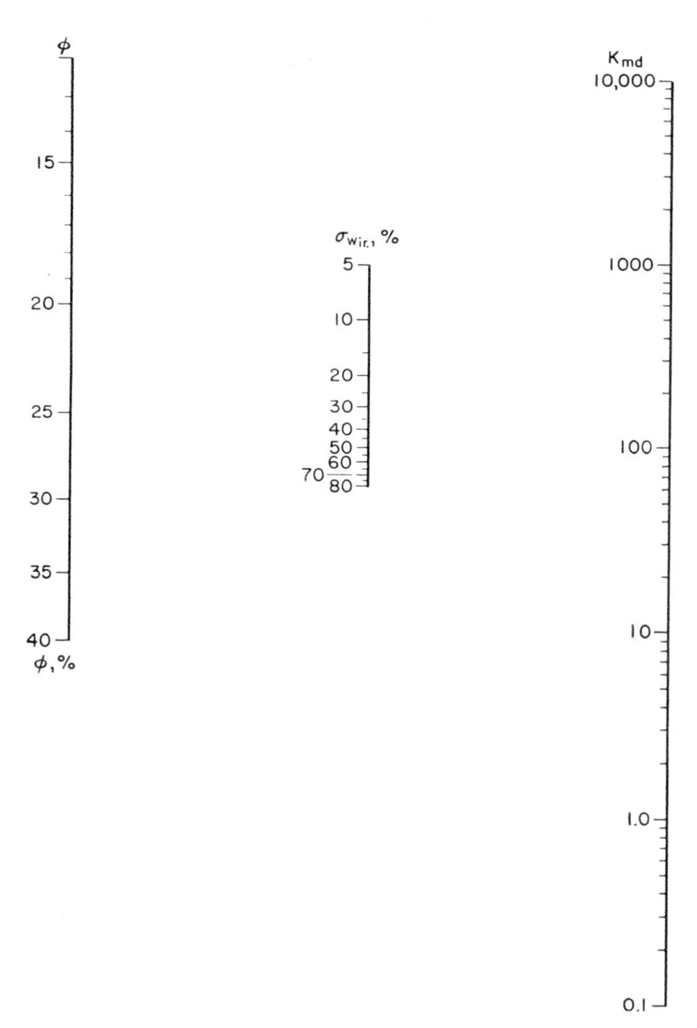

FIG. 5-19. Permeability determination from correlation to porosity and irreducible water saturation.

It will be observed that the irreducible water saturation may also be the so-called "critical water saturation," for it is the saturation above which permeability to water exists, i.e., above which on production test, a water cut will be obtained in the effluent of the well. If the permeability is known by core measurements or other means, the chart may be used to determine the critical water saturation. Then the water saturation determined from the log, if larger than the critical water saturation, will indicate that a water cut will be obtained on production test.

Tixier Method of Permeability Determination. There are three conditions which must be fulfilled before the Tixier method of permeability evaluation may be applied:

1. The reservoir formation must be of reasonable uniformity throughout the pay section; i.e., the porosity must be fairly uniform.
2. The resistivity curves which probe behind the invasion front (namely, the lateral curve, and also the long-normal in certain cases) must exhibit a relatively linear gradient with depth. This is an indication that the formation is not uniformly saturated with connate water, and that the latter is held by capillarity against the force of gravity, which is effective by virtue of the difference of density between oil and connate water. Therefore, the resistivity gradient is positive evidence of the existence of oil or gas saturation in a formation of uniform lithology.
3. The resistivity of the 100 per cent water-saturated zone must be known from either direct logging measurements or by evaluation from formation-factor considerations. Therefore, the method is still applicable whether or not the well penetrates the water zone. However, in this last instance it is necessary that the depth of the water table be known. If several individual sands are holding their connate water by capillarity above a common water table, the method may still be applied even though all the zones' permeabilities are not of the same order of magnitude.

In a thick section containing bottom water, the resistivity gradient is particularly in evidence within the transition zone. Should equilibrium water saturation be reached at the top of the zone, the resistivity gradient flattens out in it, indicating a negligible change in water saturation with height.

Let h be the height in feet above the water table, at which level the resistivity measured on the lateral curve is R_L, and is R_t when corrected to true resistivity.

Let R_o be the true resistivity (after correction) for the water-bearing zone.

The resistivity gradient may be evaluated from the difference in true resistivity ΔR_t read between two levels separated by a distance Δh. It is obtained by $\Delta R_t/\Delta h$.

Hence, we have at any level h

$$R_t = R_o + \frac{\Delta R_t}{\Delta h} h \tag{5-32}$$

By Archie's empirical law, we have

$$\sigma_{wc} = \sqrt{\frac{R_o}{R_t}}$$

Substituting R_t by its value in the above,

$$\sigma_{wc} = \sqrt{\frac{R_o}{R_o + h\dfrac{\Delta R_t}{\Delta h}}} = \sqrt{\frac{1}{1 + h\dfrac{1}{R_o}\dfrac{\Delta R_t}{\Delta h}}} = \sqrt{\frac{1}{1 + ha}} \tag{5-33}$$

where $a = \dfrac{1}{R_o}\dfrac{\Delta R_t}{\Delta h}$ and is called the basic resistivity gradient.

At the level h, we have the following capillary-pressure relationship:

$$h = 2.3\frac{P_c}{\vartheta_w - \vartheta_o} \tag{5-34}$$

where P_c is the capillary pressure of the reservoir rock in pounds per square inch.

ϑ_w and ϑ_o are, respectively, the specific gravity of water and oil.

From empirical data, the following relation is known:

$$\sigma_{wc} = \sqrt{\frac{1}{1 + F_kP_c}} \tag{5-35}$$

where F_k is a lithological factor which varies with the nature of the reservoir.

Equating (5-33) and (5-35), and after substitution of h by its value (5-34), we obtain

$$\sqrt{\frac{1}{1 + F_kP_c}} = \sqrt{\frac{1}{1 + a[2.3P_c/(\vartheta_w - \vartheta_o)]}}$$

or, after simplifying,

$$F_k = 2.3\frac{a}{\vartheta_w - \vartheta_o} \tag{5-36}$$

From empirical study of capillary data from Hassler et al., it was shown by Tixier that

$$F_k = \sqrt{\frac{K}{C}} \tag{5-37}$$

where K is permeability in millidarcys and C has an average value of 20.

Hence

$$\sqrt{\frac{K}{C}} = 2.3\frac{a}{\vartheta_w - \vartheta_o}$$

or

$$K = (2.3)^2\frac{a^2}{(\vartheta_w - \vartheta_o)^2} \tag{5-38}$$

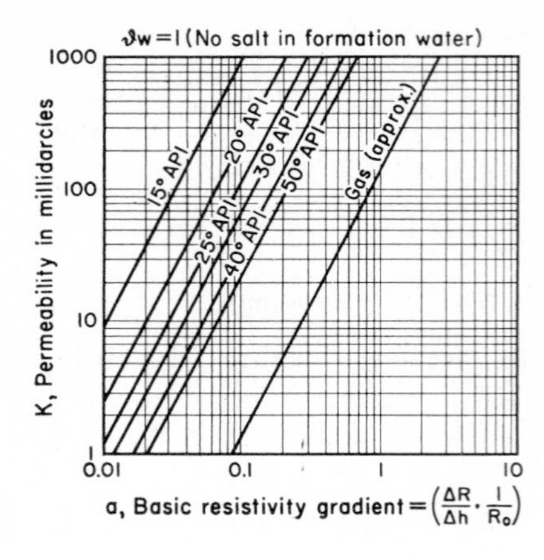

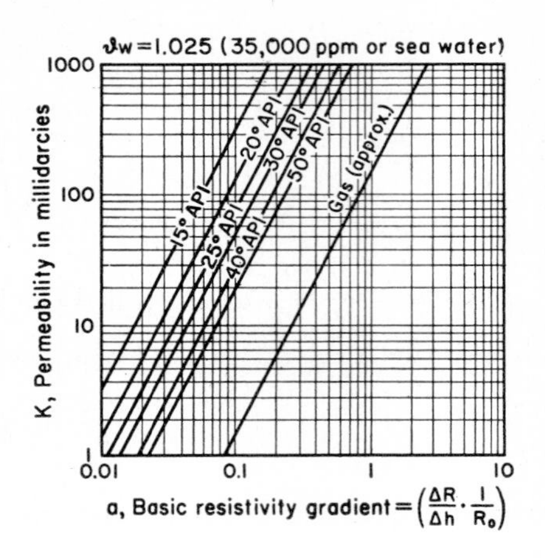

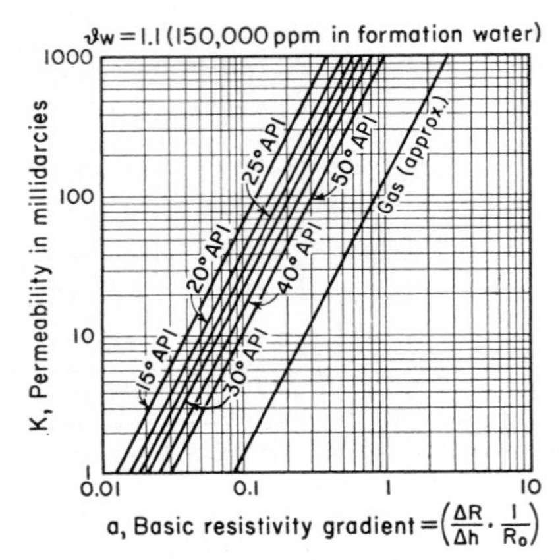

FIG. 5-20. Nomogram for evaluation of permeability from the true resistivity gradient. (*After Tixier, Schlumberger Well Surveying Corp.*)

from which the permeability K may be calculated if we know the basic resistivity gradient a and the differential density of the fluids involved under reservoir conditions $\vartheta_w - \vartheta_o$. This differential varies with the API gravity of the oil and with the water salinity.

Computations are greatly simplified by means of nomographs shown in Fig. 5-20a to c. However, it may be necessary to interpolate between the three charts in the case of intermediate water salinities. This may be done through proportionality fractions by calculating the permeabilities K_1 and K_2 corresponding to two different water salinities (e.g., sea water and 150,000 ppm) and using the following interpolation formula:

$$K = K_1 + (K_1 - K_2)\,\frac{1.1 - 1.025}{\vartheta_w - 1.025} \tag{5-39}$$

Example of Application of Permeability Determination by the Tixier Method. The Layton sand, Kay County, Oklahoma (Fig. 5-21), shows a well-defined resistivity gradient through the reservoir rock which is an indication of capillary water distribution through the sand.

Log characteristics are as follows:

R_m = 1.5 ohm-meters at BHT = 120°F
d = 7 in.
Salinity = 200,000 ppm
Oil gravity = 40° API or $\vartheta_w - \vartheta_o = 0.2$
Lateral spacing AO = 15 ft
Average porosity = 20 per cent
Sand fairly well cemented

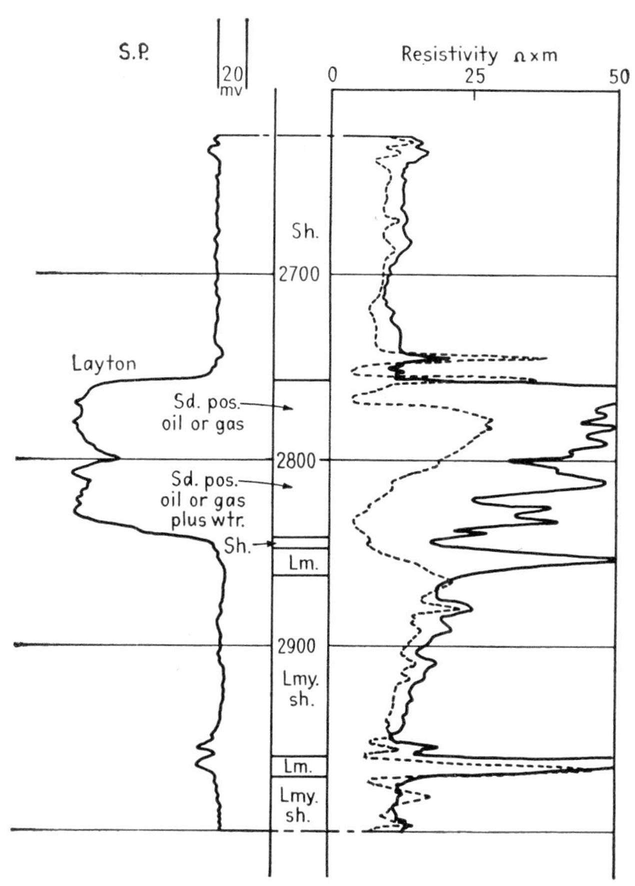

FIG. 5-21. Electric log from Layton sand (oil-bearing), Oklahoma. (*Schlumberger Well Surveying Corp.*)

R_o may be read directly from the log at 2,833 ft as 3.5 ohm-meters; when corrected $R_o = 3.0$. At 2,785 ft $R_L = 28$ ohm-meters and needs no correction. $\Delta h = 48$ ft. $\Delta R = 28 - 3 = 25$. Hence, the basic resistivity gradient $a = 25/48 \times 1/3 = 0.172$. Reading the permeability on the 150,000-ppm chart, we find $K = 34$ md, whereas the average permeability from core analysis of this well is 27 md.

DETERMINATION OF WELL PRODUCTIVITY AND RECOVERY

Determining well productivity and recovery requires solving the following problems:

1. Water-oil or water-gas ratios
2. Daily rate of production of oil or gas
3. Oil and gas in place
4. Ultimate recovery

Fluid-flow Ratios. In a water-wet rock the desirable information from the log is whether or not the well will produce a certain amount of water and how much water it will yield. A prohibitive amount may render the well uneconomical.

First, it is desirable to know whether or not the well will make any water at all. This may be ascertained if the critical or irreducible water saturation σ_{wir} is known. A technique for ascertaining the value of σ_{wir} was discussed above. It requires a knowledge of porosity and permeability only (Fig. 5-19).

Another approach to determine this value is through the Kozeny equation, for it is reasonable to expect that the irreducible water saturation in clean as well as shaly sands is a direct function of the specific surface S_v of the rock. We have, therefore,

$$\sigma_{wir} \cong S_v \cong \frac{1}{\sqrt{FK}} \frac{\phi^2}{(1 - \phi)^2} \tag{5-40}$$

This formula introduces formation factor F as a factor of σ_{wir} in addition to porosity and permeability. The coefficient of proportionality has been experimentally determined to be unity.

To facilitate the calculations of the irreducible water saturation, the alignment chart of Fig. 5-22 is provided: first, join the values of K and F, note the intersection with the unmarked vertical line, and join this intersection with the ϕ axis. The value of σ_{wir} is obtained at the intersection of its marked axis.

In an oil-wet sand, the previous deductions are no longer valid. In fact, the water-saturation determination should be made from Archie's formula using a saturation exponent n whose value may range well above 2, as suggested by Keller (1953). For equal resistivity index R_o/R_t in a water-wet and oil-wet rock, water saturation is considerably larger in the oil-wet rock. In addition, because of the relative permeability characteristics of oil-wet rocks where k_w at a given saturation is generally larger than in the corresponding water-wet case, the ability to produce

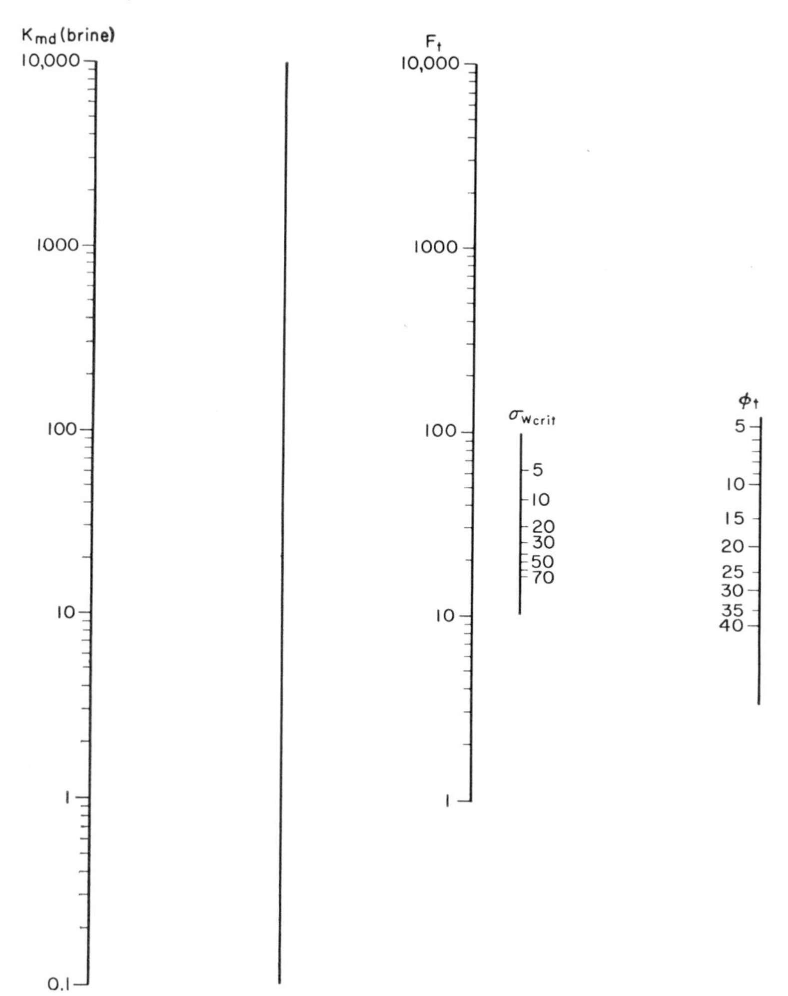

FIG. 5-22. Determination of irreducible water saturation from correlation with permeability and porosity.

water is much enhanced. This is the main reason why oil-wet reservoir rocks require much larger true resistivity values in order to become oil producers; typical examples are the Springer sands of southern Oklahoma. This is expressed by saying that the critical water saturations of such sands, even though considered as shaly, are very low, of the order of 15 to 20 per cent.

Once the critical water saturation is known, the next step is to determine the water cut in the effluent fluid stream from the reservoir rock. This entails the determination of relative permeabilities to the wetting and non-wetting phases. Of course, if it is found that the water saturation is just equal to the critical value, this step is unnecessary as no water whatsoever should be produced from a properly completed well. However, if this is not the case it is desirable to determine the water-oil (WOR) and gas-water (GWR) ratios:

$$\underset{\text{bbl/bbl}}{\text{WOR}} = \frac{\beta}{1}\frac{k_w}{k_o}\frac{\mu_o}{\mu_w} \tag{5-41}$$

$$\underset{\text{cu ft/bbl}}{\text{GWR}} = \frac{5.61}{\alpha}\frac{k_g}{k_w}\frac{\mu_w}{\mu_g} \tag{5-42}$$

where α = gas-reservoir-volume factor or volume of one unit of gas at reservoir conditions
β = oil-reservoir-volume factor or volume of one unit of oil with its gas in solution at reservoir conditions
k_w = relative permeability to water (wetting phase)
k_o = relative permeability to oil (nonwetting)
k_g = relative permeability to gas (nonwetting)
μ_w, μ_o, μ_g = viscosity of water, oil, and gas, respectively

k_w and k_{nw} may be determined from petrophysical relationships previously established in Chap. 3:

$$k_w = \sigma_{wf}{}^{1/2}\left(\frac{R_o}{R_t}\right)^{3/2} \tag{5-43}$$

$$k_{nw} = (1 - \sigma_{wf})\left[1 - \left(\sigma_{wf}\frac{R_o}{R_t}\right)^{1/4}\right] \tag{5-44}$$

where k_w stands for wetting-phase permeability and k_{nw} for nonwetting-phase permeability.

To facilitate computation of relative permeabilities, the chart of Fig. 5-23 has been devised. It is to be noted that σ_{wf} is the free water saturation; i.e., in a shaly sand it is the total water saturation minus the bound water.

An example will illustrate the use of the chart.

Let $\sigma_{wf} = 30\%$
$R_o = 2$ ohm-meters
$R_t = 20$ ohm-meters or $R_o/R_t = 0.1$

we find

$$k_w = 0.019$$

$$1 - B = 0.38$$

$$B = 0.62$$

$$k_{nw} = 0.26$$

The next step is to ascertain the values of α, β, μ_w, μ_o, μ_g, which are fluid properties of the reservoir fluids. This can only be done when fluid samples

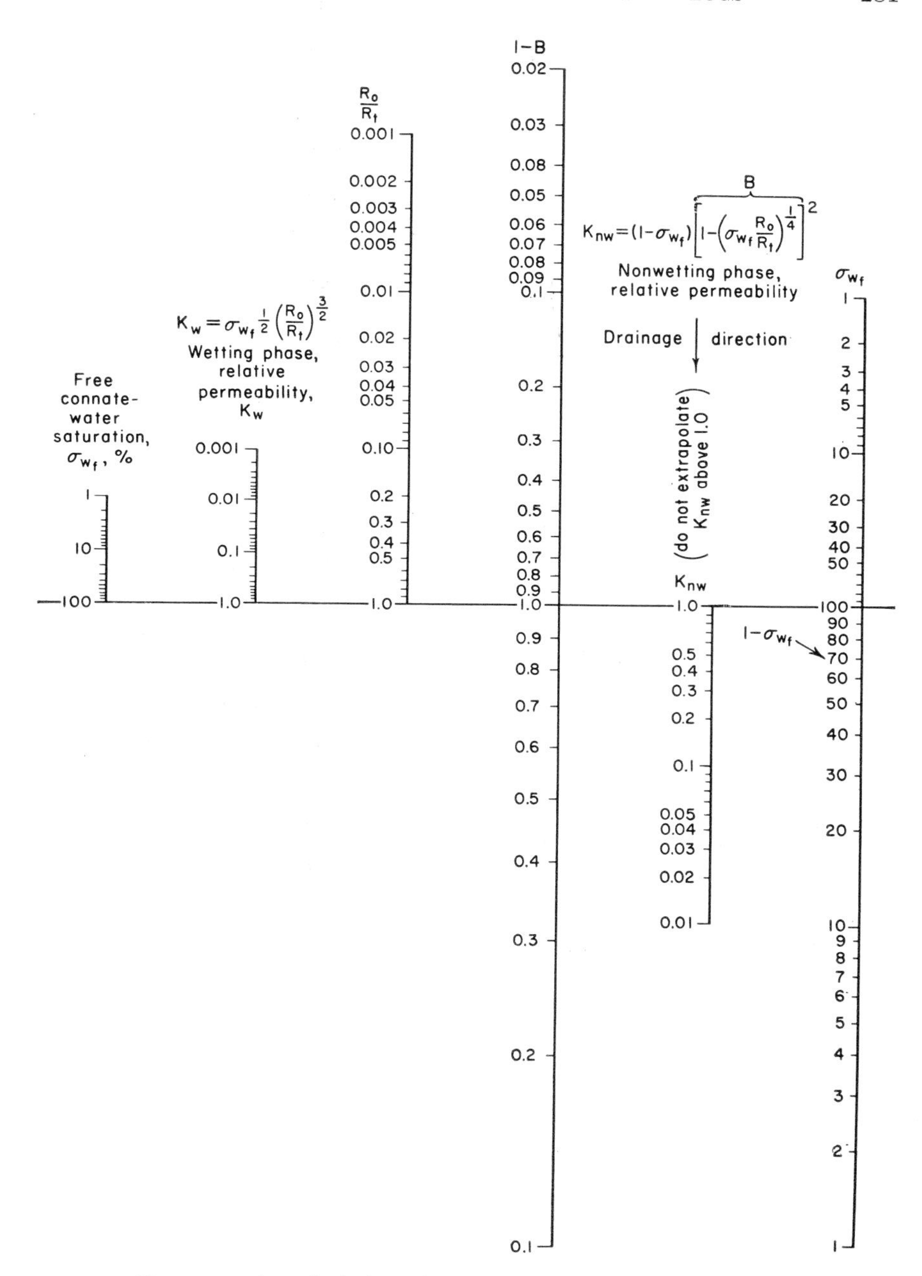

FIG. 5-23. Nomogram for calculating relative permeabilities from electric logs (drainage direction) in intergranular porosity. (Intergranular porosity only.)

from the producing formations are available; otherwise judicious guesses must be made. By way of example, let

$$\alpha = 0.010$$

$$\beta = 1.25$$

$$\mu_w = 0.3 \text{ cps}$$

$$\mu_o = 3 \text{ cps}$$

$$\mu_g = 0.02 \text{ cps}$$

and, using the relative permeabilities determined above,

$$\text{WOR} = \frac{1.25}{1} \times \frac{0.019}{0.26} \times \frac{3}{0.3} = 0.915 \text{ bbl water/bbl oil}$$

$$\text{GWR} = \frac{5.61}{0.01} \times \frac{0.26}{0.019} \times \frac{0.3}{0.02} = 1.15 \times 10^6 \text{ cu ft gas/bbl water}$$

Daily Rate of Production of Oil or Gas. Other desirable information to which log interpretation contributes is the expected daily rate of production, especially through the determination of effective pay thickness h_e and specific permeability K. In addition, related information must be known:

Pressure differential to well bore = ΔP, psi
Drainage radius = r_e
Well-bore radius = r_w

Daily production rates are given by

For oil

$$Q_o \text{ bbl STO/day} = 3.07 \frac{h_e K k_o}{\beta \mu_o} \frac{\Delta P}{\log (r_e/r_w)} \tag{5-45}$$

For gas

$$Q_g \text{ cu ft/day} = 17.5 \frac{h_e K k_g}{\alpha_m \mu_g} \frac{\Delta P}{\log (r_e/r_w)} \tag{5-46}$$

in which α_m is the reservoir volume factor for gas at mean reservoir pressure.

Oil and Gas in Place. It is convenient to express the oil and gas in place on the basis of a unit-reservoir-rock volume, namely, the acre-foot (acre-ft) which is equivalent to 7,758 bbl or 43,560 cu ft. We have

$$\text{STO bbl/acre-ft} = 7{,}758 \times \frac{h_e \phi}{\beta} (1 - \sigma_{wc}) \tag{5-47}$$

$$\underset{\left(\substack{\text{at standard}\\\text{conditions}}\right)}{\text{Cu ft gas/acre-ft}} = 43{,}560 \times \frac{h_e \phi}{\alpha} (1 - \sigma_{wc}) \tag{5-48}$$

Ultimate Oil and Gas Recovery. Properly speaking, electric-log interpretation does not solve the problem of predicting the ultimate oil and gas recovery (except in the case of a water-drive field), but it does provide basic information which leads to a better early evaluation of the reserves.

Basically, recoveries may be expressed by

$$\text{Recoverable STO/acre-ft} = \text{ST oil in place } (1 - \sigma_{or}) \qquad (5\text{-}49)$$

$$\text{Recoverable gas/acre-ft} = \text{cu ft in place} \left(1 - \frac{\alpha_o}{\alpha_a}\right) \qquad (5\text{-}50)$$

where σ_{or} is the residual-oil saturation and α_a is the gas-reservoir-volume factor at abandonment pressure in a gas field, α_o being the original value.

In an oil field, the residual-oil saturation σ_{or} depends a great deal on the recovery mechanism involved, singly or in combination, and the extent to which one predominates over the others.

For a simple water drive, σ_{or} may perhaps be evaluated from the flushed zone as was suggested by Doll (1954):

$$\text{Recoverable STO/acre-ft} = \frac{7{,}758}{\beta_o}\left[\left(\frac{R_{mf}}{R_{xo}}\right)^{1/2} - \left(\frac{R_{wc}}{R_t}\right)^{1/2}\right] \qquad (5\text{-}51)$$

where the symbols have their usual meaning.

For any other production recovery mechanism than water drive, the Doll formula has no usefulness. It is indeed the purpose of this volume to establish techniques which permit the predetermination of the value of residual-oil saturation under the application of various recovery mechanisms operating singly or in combination and thereby arrive at a prediction of ultimate oil recovery from a specific reservoir under postulated operating conditions.

INTERPRETATION TECHNIQUES AND TYPICAL EXAMPLES

One of the first tasks in analyzing a log is to pick values of SP deflections and resistivities which may be used in the computations with assurance that the values chosen are the best that may be selected.

Self-potential deflections are read between the shale base line and maximum deflection to the left if fresh muds, to the right if salt muds. The selection of the shale base line is at times a problem. With respect to a certain bed of interest, it should be the nearest shale. There are, however, possibilities that large positive shalelike deflections may be present, though meaningless as is the case for lignite, coal, diabase, and other formations deposited in an oxidizing environment. These should be discarded in drawing the shale base line. Knowledge of local lithology is necessary for this purpose. Once a satisfactory shale base line is selected, peak SP deflections are measured in the interval of interest. These peak deflections may need corrections for bed thickness, resistivity, and mud invasion. It is of interest to observe that if a flat top is present on the SP kick, corrections are seldom needed and static SP is read. Of interest also is that static SP is seldom read in salty mud unless the formations are very thick; this is because R_t/R_m is very large.

In picking resistivity values, especially of true resistivity, the aim of the practical interpreter is to select values that will need a minimum of correction and especially to avoid the use of departure curves as much as possible. Depending upon the type of formation dealt with, a set of rules listed in Table 5-1 may be used as a guide. It should be stressed that the following set of rules is *highly empirical* and more *particularly for thin beds.* If more accuracy is desired, especially for borderline cases, departure-curve fitting techniques must be used.

For the purpose of interpretation, Tixier proposes to divide formations into three classes according to a certain measure of their formation factor, namely, $R_{16\text{ in.}}/R_m$ (Table 5-1).

Low-resistivity Formations ($R_{16\text{ in.}} < 10R_m$). This condition is most generally encountered in young formations such as Gulf Coast Miocene beds or other highly porous and permeable sands.

Medium-resistivity Formations ($10R_m < R_{16\text{ in.}} < 50R_m$). Such formations are generally consolidated sands such as the Gulf Coast Eocene Wilcox, the Mid-Continent Cherokee sands, the Springer sand, etc.

High-resistivity Formations ($R_{16\text{ in.}} > 50R_m$). These will be found mostly in limestones and dolomites, but also in quartzites such as the Tensleep (Wyoming).

Each class of formation requires somewhat special treatment.

Interpretation of Low-resistivity Formations. Such formations are generally not highly invaded because of their high porosity and permeability. Therefore short investigation tools may read R_t. Rules for reading R_t are given in Table 5-1 A and B. It is observed that the short-normal curve may even give a good value of R_t in such rocks, especially in thin beds when no other curve gives any information of value.

Difficulties are often encountered in picking R_t values in complex layer situations, especially under lignite beds from the lateral curve where resistivity values are shielded in sands below hard streaks. One way of solving this problem is by using a shorter lateral such as 6 to 9 ft, the induction log in fresh mud, or an inverted lateral.

In analyzing a log for oil possibilities at any level, one must bear in mind that R_o is made up of two factors, F and R_w, and control must be had on each. The only way to have control on the possible lithologic variations which are reflected in the values of F is by means of microtools; they are essential to good logging interpretations for this very reason. One may exert control on the possible variations of R_{wc} from the SP curve, water samples, or water salinity and resistivity catalogues. Most of the errors of interpretation come from wrong assumptions in regard to the values of F and R_{wc} when no control is available on them.

An important point to decide in this group is whether or not beds are conductive (or resistive), especially in thin beds (5 ft $< e <$ 15 ft). If the thin bed is resistive, the lateral curve will exhibit the well-defined characteristic of shielding and a reflection peak below the bed. If the bed is conductive, the lateral will again show it and generally will read less

TABLE 5-1. RULES FOR DETERMINING TRUE RESISTIVITY FROM LOGS WITHOUT DEPARTURE CURVES *

A. Low-resistivity formations $\frac{R_{16\text{in.}}}{R_m} < 10$; **oil sands**; fresh mud

Type curves	Thick beds			Thin beds		
	$e > 20$ ft	20 ft	15 ft	10 ft	6 ft	3-to-6 ft
$AM' = 64$ in.	$R_a = R_t$	$R_a = R_t$	$R_a = \frac{2}{3}R_t$	$R_a = \frac{1}{2}R_t$		
$AM = 16$ in.† (Assume $R_i = R_t$)				$R_a = R_t$	$R_a = R_t$	$R_a = R_t$
Induction log	$R_a = R_t$	$R_a = R_t$	$R_a = R_t$	$R_a = R_t$	$R_a = R_t$	$R_a = R_t$ ($e \geq 4$ ft)
$AO = 19$ ft	Ordinarily not used					

B. Low-resistivity formations $\frac{R_{16\text{in.}}}{R_m} < 10$; **water sands**; fresh mud

Use $AO = 19$ ft. This curve not affected by bed thickness in conductive formations

C. Medium-resistivity formations $10 < \frac{R_{16\text{in.}}}{R_m} < 50$; **oil sands**; fresh mud

Type curves	Thick beds			Thin beds		
	>20 ft	20 ft	15 ft	10 ft	6 ft	3-to-6 ft
$AM' = 64$ in. If $\frac{R_{16\text{in.}}}{R_m} < 25$	$R_a = R_t$	$R_a = R_t$	$R_a = \frac{2}{3}R_t$	$R_a = \frac{1}{2}R_t$		
$AM' = 64$ in. If $25 < \frac{R_{16\text{in.}}}{R_m} < 50$	Use as above but confirm with lateral					
$AM = 16$ in. If $\frac{R_{16\text{in.}}}{R_m} < 25$				$R_a = R_t$	$R_a = R_t$	$R_a = R_t$
$AO = 19$ ft	1. Center rule $e > 38$ ft 2. ⅔ rule $e = 28$-to-38 ft 3. Peak rule $e = 25$ ft	Critical spacing (no reading possible)	$R_t = \frac{R_{lat\ max}}{R_{lat\ min}} R_{sh}$ ← $4\text{ ft} < e < 13\text{ ft}$ →			
Induction log	Good resolution down to $e = 4$ ft. Not necessarily reading R_t but may be corrected					

TABLE 5-1. RULES FOR DETERMINING TRUE RESISTIVITY FROM LOGS WITHOUT DEPARTURE CURVES * (*Continued*)

D. Medium-resistivity formations $10 < \frac{R_{16in.}}{R_m} < 50$; **water sands**; fresh mud

Use lateral—not affected by bed thickness in conductive zones

E. High-resistivity formations $\frac{R_{16in.}}{R_m} > 50$; **oil sands**; fresh mud

Type curves	Thick beds				Thin beds
	Bed thickness				Bed thickness
	>38 ft	28-to-38 ft	25 ft	20 ft	4-to-13 ft
$AO = 19$ ft	Center rule ‡	⅔ rule ‡	Peak rule ‡	Critical (no reading possible)	$R_t = \frac{R_{lat\ max}}{R_{lat\ min}} R_{sh}$

F. High-resistivity formation $\frac{R_{16in.}}{R_m} > 100$; salty mud

Use current focusing devices

* After Tixier, courtesy of Schlumberger Well Surveying Corp.
† Lateral resistivity must be higher than shale resistivity to use $AM = 16$ in. as R_t.
‡ Correct R_{lat} for hole size and mud.

than shale resistivity. The characteristic lateral trailer should also be observed.

To determine whether or not a thin highly resistive streak is porous, a microlog is required.

The Archie method of interpretation, namely, $\sigma_{wc} = \sqrt{R_o/R_t}$, is safe to use only when it may be ascertained that no lithologic change takes place between the level of 100 per cent water saturation where R_o is read and the level of interest where R_t is read. Again the microlog provides the means to ascertain this.

If lithologic variations are minor in an area, a good interpretation technique is to draw the R_o line on the log. Oil will be indicated in Miocene Gulf Coast sands if $R_t > 3R_o$ and in the Eocene Wilcox if $R_t > 4R_o$.

The Tixier (RM) method must not be used in this group of formations.

Interpretation of Medium-resistivity Formations. A typical formation of this type is the Eocene Wilcox sand which is hard and cemented by contrast with other Gulf Coast sands. Most mid-continent sands (in North Texas and Oklahoma) also fall in this classification. These rocks are generally highly invaded, especially when drilled with fresh muds, and the probing distance of the long-normal or of a medium-lateral curve is insufficient as a general rule to give a good value of R_t. The long-lateral curve must be used in most cases. Rules for finding R_t in such rocks are given in Table 5-1 C and D. Under certain conditions given in the tabulation, the long-normal, and even the short-normal, curves give R_t, but the answer must be verified by the lateral. The short-normal curve could, however, be used as a last resort. In fresh muds, readings of R_t are difficult to make because of the large diameter of invasion and because the high resistivity of the invaded zone reduces the radius of investigation by preventing the current flow into the R_t zone. Everything being equal, low-resistivity formations provide larger radius of investigation for logging tools than high-resistivity formations.

Although the hole size and mud corrections applied to the resistivity values read by the lateral curve are generally small for this class of rocks, it is advisable to check this point and to make a correction, if required, by means of the simplified departure curves (Fig. 5-14).

A logging practice which has been advocated, and which finds many supporters, for these formations is to log in brackish mud such that R_m at bottom-hole temperature (BHT) = four to five times R_{wc}. In this manner the SP still exists and is not reversed; by amplifying the SP deflections to 5 mv per division, a normal-looking SP curve is obtained, although the corners are rounded. This drilling practice leads to thinner mud cake and less invasion. When the microlog is used, it shows sharp boundaries and good lithological control is provided.

Because of the much lower R_i value, long-normal curves provide R_t after some hole and mud correction, and at times without. But the normal curves in salt mud often lack in definition, and focused current logs are helpful in picking out small detailed resistivity variations.

The use of brackish mud has another logging advantage in providing porosity information from microtools relatively unaffected by sand shalyness.

Interpretation of High-resistivity Formations. Typical formations of this type are limestones, dolomites, and highly cemented quartzitic sandstones.

The class of high-resistivity formations is conveniently divided into two groups: thick and thin beds.

1. In order to obtain R_t from the lateral curve in thick beds of high resistivity, it is *absolutely* necessary to make a correction for hole size and mud. The correction is no longer optional as for the first class and at times for the second class of formations. When drilling with fresh muds, deep invasion must always be suspected; and it is a safe practice to ascertain if additional correction is needed for invasion.

Normal curves as a rule may not be used to obtain R_t, as they probe only within the invaded zone of porous hard rocks.

The Tixier (RM) method finds its best field of application in this class of reservoirs. It has the advantage of not requiring the determination of formation factor, which is so highly variable in these rocks.

The Archie method is of course still applicable, but there is great danger that the R_o read at a particular level of 100 per cent water saturation may not apply to the level of interest precisely because of variations in lithology and of F.

2. Thin resistive beds offer a difficult problem of interpretation. If the thin beds are between low-resistivity beds, the $R_t = (R_{max}/R_{min}) R_{sh}$ rule is applicable and useful.

However, in the case of thin, porous zones within thick, hard zones, conventional tools are practically useless. The limestone curves will give R_i and the formation factor, porosity, and hole diameter; but there are no good safe ways of getting R_t. For this purpose, special logging techniques should be used:

1. In fresh mud, oil-base mud, and empty hole, the induction log will prove useful, especially in low resistivity. Oil and water zones can be distinguished by its use. If R_t is high, however, the accuracy of the induction log readings falls off very rapidly.

2. In salt muds, the salt-mud survey combination is to be advocated: gamma ray, microlaterolog, and laterolog. The neutron curve may be used for good measure as an additional check on porosity.

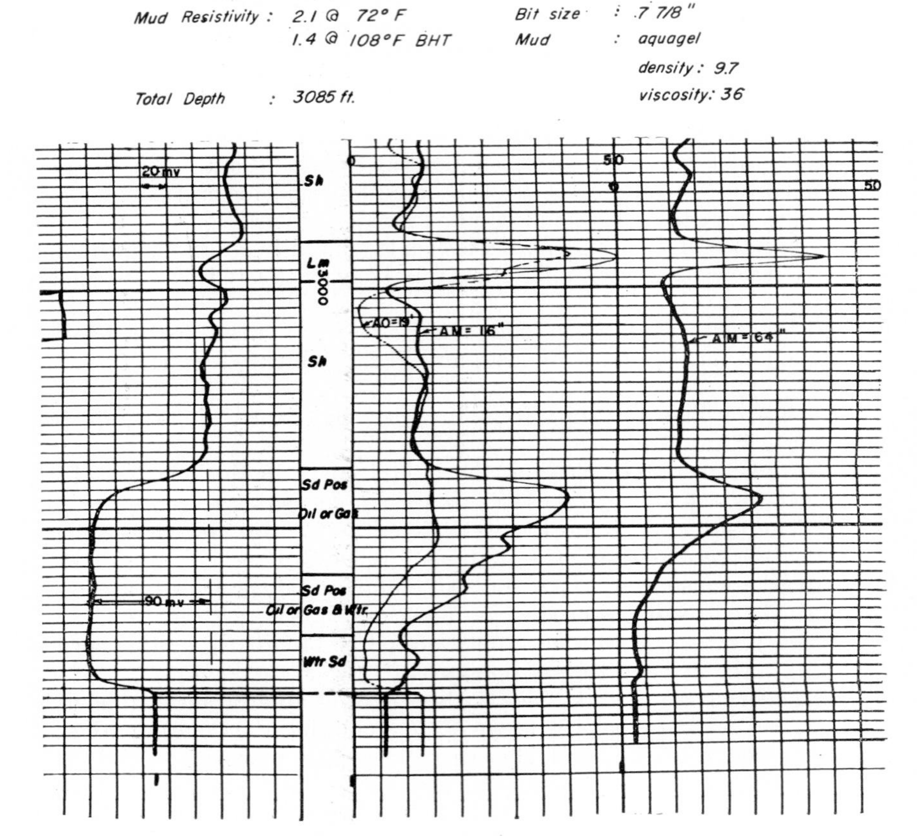

EXAMPLE LOG 1. Red Fork sand, Oklahoma.

Example 1. Example log 1 is from the Red Fork sand, Pawnee County, Oklahoma. This sand is known for its shalyness in the form of disseminated clay and production is obtained mostly through fracture treatment.

The log shows well-defined gradients on all resistivity curves. On the lateral curve, the gradient at the top of the sand is interrupted by a flat top because of the almost exact compensation of the continuous gradient in the transition zone by the decay characteristic of the lateral. That the gradient on the lateral should be continuous near the top of the sand is evidenced by the continuity of the gradient on the normal curves. The existence of a gradient on the short-normal curve is unusual and may be explained by the presence of a transition zone or decrease of water saturation with height; less and less residual oil is present toward the top of the sand. In addition, because of the shalyness of the sand, clay swelling has prevented a deep invasion of the sand and the short-normal curve responds to a certain degree to the uninvaded section of the rock. The lower section of the sand has all the earmarks of a water zone, 100 per cent water saturated.

The following information is pertinent to this well:

$d = 7\frac{7}{8}$ in.
$R_m = 2.1$ at 72°F
$R_m = 1.4$ at BHT = 108°F
$R_{wc} = 0.057$ at 70°F
$R_{wc} = 0.042$ at 108°F

No microlog is available from this well. The water-zone resistivity is 2.0 and no bore-hole correction is required. True formation factor is $F_t = 2/0.042 = 48$. Using $m = 1.8$, porosity figures out 12 per cent, which is somewhat low. The difficulty in obtaining a reasonable answer from a recorded R_o is the lack of precision. From the short-normal curve in the water zone a formation factor of 18 is obtained corresponding to 20 per cent porosity, which probably is somewhat high. An average porosity of 16 per cent is probably more likely, and a formation factor of 27. Computed R_o is 1.15, or about half the recorded value. Saturations at various levels in the log may be computed from the lateral:

Depth, ft	Lateral		Water saturation (%) $= \sqrt[2]{1.15/R_t}$
	Actual	Corrected	
3,060	10	10	35
3,050	17	17	27
3,040	24	22.4	23

In completing a well of this type, one should avoid perforating casing in a zone more water-saturated than 40 per cent for water-free production, and preferably higher in order to avoid water coning.

Because of the resistivity gradient, an order of magnitude for the specific permeability may also be had. With API oil gravity of about 40° and a basic resistivity gradient of $\frac{1}{2} \times \frac{14}{20} = 0.35$, the Tixier chart gives 180 md permeability. This is a high value for this sand.

Using the permeability-tortuosity correlation chart, $t^2 = F\phi = 0.16 \times 27 = 4.3$ and a permeability of 10 md is obtained which is more in line with the known permeability of the Red Fork. This well was perforated from 3,041 to 3,050 ft and made 35 BOD after fracture treatment.

Example 2. Example log 2 is from the Springer section, Garvin County, Oklahoma, and includes conventional log and microlog. The section from 9,410 to 9,441 ft is of special interest. It is delineated by the inflection points on the SP curve and by the short-normal curve. The SP curve

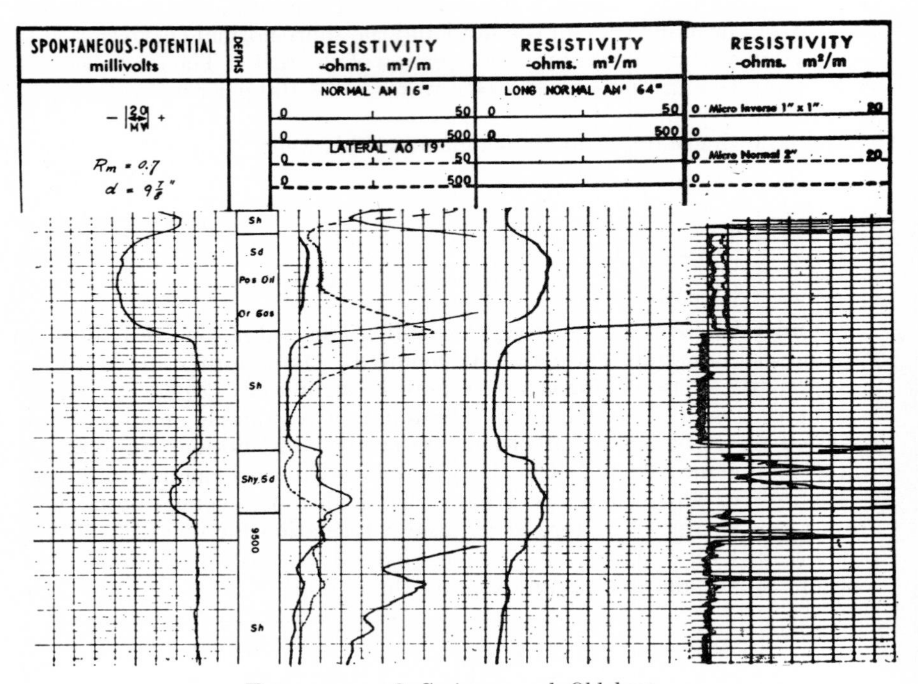

EXAMPLE LOG 2. Springer sand, Oklahoma.

shows a well-rounded appearance with inflection points near the shale base line, indicating a high value for R_t.

The apparent resistivity values are as follows:

AM 16 in. = 70
AM 64 in. = 150
AO 19 ft = 240 (as read by the two-thirds rule since the bed thickness is comprised between 1.5 AO and 2.5 AO)

The normal curve readings need to be corrected for bore-hole effect, invasion, bed thickness, and the like. For the lateral, only a bore-hole correction is needed, unless invasion proves too deep.

Bore-hole corrections by departure curves using $d = 9\frac{7}{8}$ in. and $R_m = 0.7$ at BHT of 140°F result in the following values:

AM 16 in. = 112
AM 64 in. = 105
AO 19 ft = 112

All three curves give substantially the same answer. Since they all probe to different depths, the formation must be but slightly invaded. Similar results are obtained by plotting the normal-curve values on departure curves for thin beds. There is, however, enough invasion for the microlog to respond normally. This microlog was run using the D-type pad.

$$R_{1.5\text{in.}} = 2.5 \qquad R_{2\text{in.}} = 4.0 \qquad R_{mc} = 1.0 \qquad R_{mf} = 0.50$$

We find

$$e_{mc} = \tfrac{3}{8}\text{ in.} \qquad \text{(Fig. 5-4)}$$

Because the mud-cake thickness is rather large, the empirical chart of Fig. 5-5*a* is used, yielding 17 per cent porosity and $F = 28$. Calculating porosity from the short-normal curve would be unreliable in view of the fact that there is relatively little invasion in this sand.

To determine water saturation, formation-water resistivity must be known. Investigating the SP approach, it is observed that static SP is probably not read by the SP curve (−80 mv) because of the high resistivity of the formation. Using the SP correction chart (Fig. 4-16), it is seen that the recorded SP is only 87 per cent of the static value. Hence static SP = −92 mv. Using a K factor of 70 and adjusting it to formation temperature, we find $R_{wc} = 0.033$ ohm-meter from Fig. 4-9. Water resistivity catalogues of this region give $R_{wc} = 0.06$ at 70°F or 0.03 at 140°F, which is a reasonable check.

Computing water saturation, we have

$$R_o = FR_{wc} = 28 \times 0.033 = 0.92 \text{ ohm-meter}$$

Since $R_t = 112$, the water saturation is

$$\sigma_{wc} = \sqrt{\frac{0.92}{112}} = 9.0\%$$

This horizon is an oil and gas producer in this well.

This example log gives a good illustration of the pitfalls which may be encountered in the Tixier (RM) method. Plotting SP = −92 mv vs. $R_i/R_t = 1$ on Fig. 5-13, we find $\sigma_{wc} = 17$ per cent. Although this is not an unreasonable answer, because there is little invasion, the Tixier method is not applicable. The discrepancy is, however, more marked when the porosity is computed by means of the chart of Fig. 5-3 where we obtain 15 per cent porosity by plotting $(R_t/R_m)(R_m/R_w) = 112 \times 11 = 1{,}600$ vs. 17 per cent.

Example 3. Example log 3 is again from the Springer section of southern Oklahoma and includes conventional log and microlog. The section of interest is from 8,832 to 8,898 ft. It is delineated by the short-normal

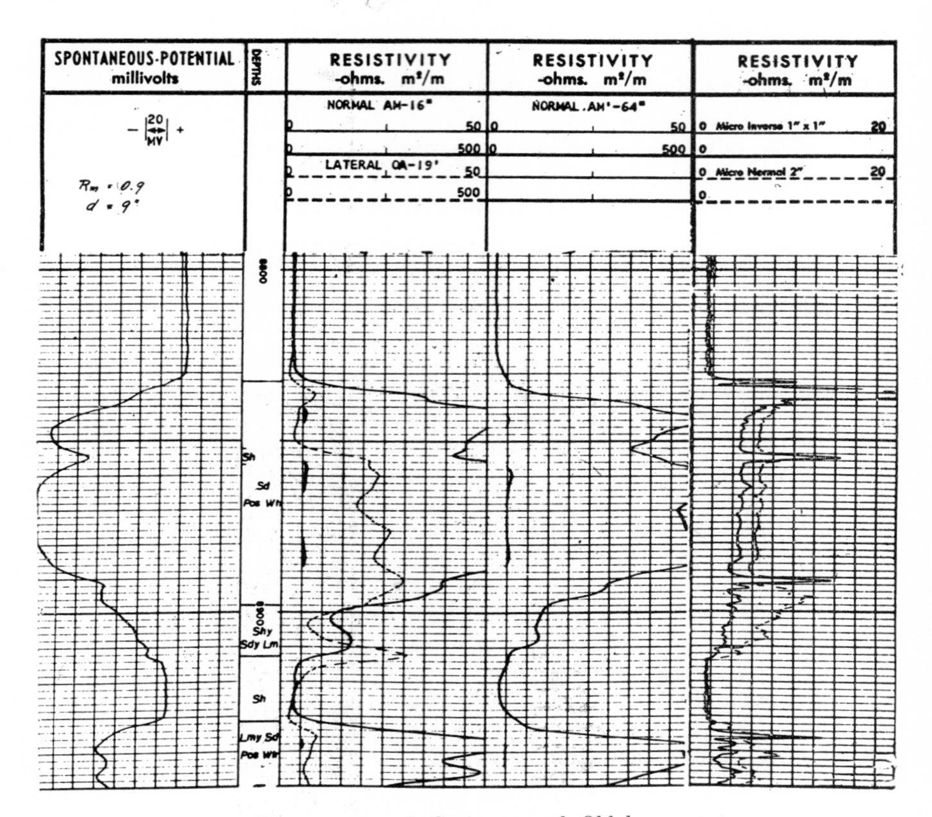

EXAMPLE LOG 3. Springer sand, Oklahoma.

curve since the SP inflection points are not well marked in view of gradational lithologic changes at bed boundaries.

The apparent resistivity values are as follows:

AM 16 in. = 50
AM 64 in. = 50
AO 19 ft = 22.5

By plotting these data on departure curves it may be observed that the formation is highly invaded and, therefore, probably of low porosity.

Bore-hole corrections using $d = 9$ in. and $R_m = 0.9$ at 140°F give:

AM 16 in. = 54
AM 64 in. = 40
AO 19 ft = 20

The trend of these values as the probing distance of the logging curves increases is another indication that invasion is present.

Connate water resistivity calculations from the SP curve without correction do not give a reasonable answer, being $R_{wc} = 0.011$ at 140°F, which is much above the point of NaCl saturation. The discrepancy is due to the presence of a substantial streaming-potential effect which may be evaluated from Fig. 4-8 and is found to be -30 mv.

The static SP would therefore be -110 mv and $R_{wc} = 0.027$.

Using the short normal to calculate porosity, we find:

SP = -110 mv, $R_{mf} = 0.68$
Porosity = ϕ = 7.5%
Formation factor = F = 200
$R_o = 0.027 \times 200 = 5.4$

$$\text{Connate water saturation} = \sqrt{\frac{5.4}{20}} = 50\%$$

Obviously, the well does not have any possibility of being an oil producer and indeed it makes water.

The microlog approach to determine porosity gives:

$R_{1.5\text{in.}} = 4.5$, $R_{2\text{in.}} = 6.5$
$R_{mc} = 1.1$, $R_{mf} = .68$
$e_{mc} = \frac{1}{4}$ in.

Because of the thickness of the mud cake, the empirical chart of Fig. 5-5*a* is used giving a porosity of 13 per cent and $F = 50$.

Using these results, the water saturation would be 26 per cent. This is a more optimistic value, but in the Springer sand this is too high a value of water saturation to expect oil production because of its oil-wet characteristics.

The above calculations must be considered as estimates only because when deep invasion is suspected there is danger that the lateral may not be read directly and may need departure-curve correction for invasion. This is indeed the case, yielding:

$$\frac{D_i}{d} = 5 \qquad \frac{R_t}{R_m} = 10 \qquad R_t = 9$$

The sand would definitely be interpreted as water producing regardless of the value of R_o selected.

An application of the Tixier (RM) method should be satisfactory here because of the deep invasion; it gives

$$\text{SP corrected} = -110 \text{ mv}$$

$$\frac{R_i}{R_t} = \frac{54}{9} = 6$$

$$\sigma_{wc} = 70\%$$

Computing the porosity by the same method,

$$\frac{R_t}{R_m}\frac{R_m}{R_{wc}} = 10 \times 14 = 140$$

$$\phi = 12\%$$

Example 4. Example log 4 is from the McLish sand, Simpson formation of Oklahoma. The well produces from one section only 7,981 to 7,996 ft, although the porous sections immediately above should be of much more interest. In fact, it is probable that production might be coming from the upper two sections: 7,912 to 7,920 ft and 7,896 to 7,905 ft.

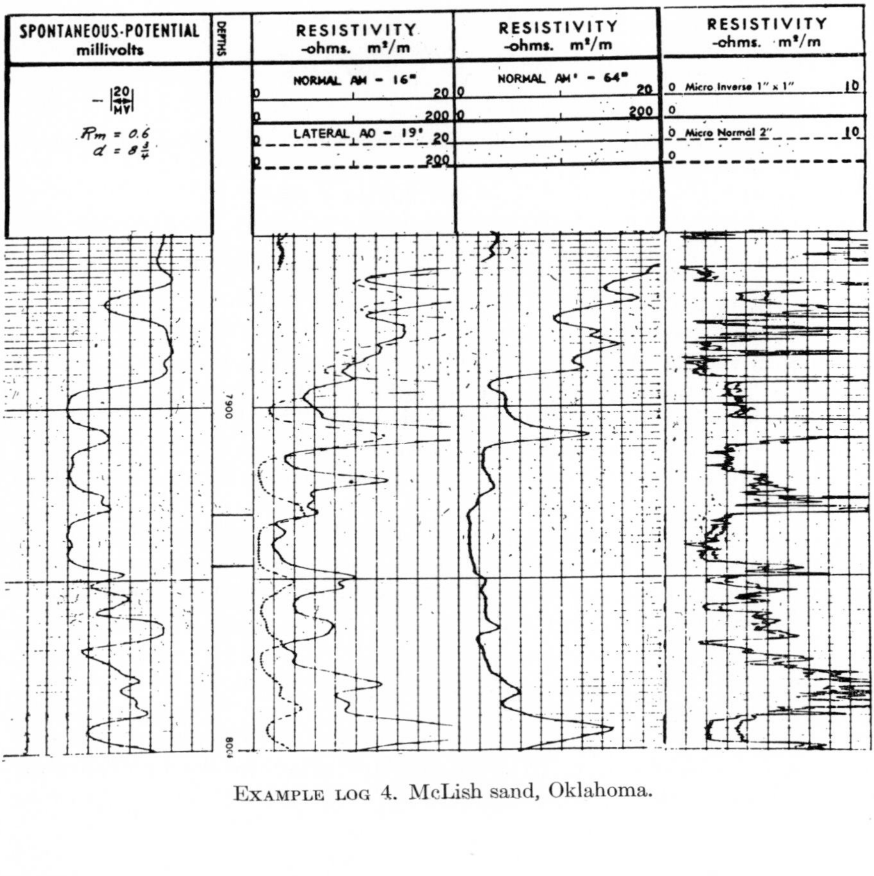

EXAMPLE LOG 4. McLish sand, Oklahoma.

This log is particularly difficult to interpret because of the following conditions:

1. The lateral curve is shielded in all three intervals of interest and no reading of significance can be made on this curve in these intervals.
2. The three intervals have almost no invasion; even the micrologs read almost true resistivity in the three intervals.
3. The McLish sand is a glauconitic rock which exhibits always a low-resistivity curve at high oil saturation.
4. The zones of interest are enclosed by high-resistivity shales; for such a situation it is not possible to apply safely departure-curve calculations.

There is one saving feature in this log; i.e., the long-normal curve reads true resistivity as follows:

7,981–7,996 ft, 1 ohm-meter
7,912–7,920 ft, 2.5 ohm-meters
7,896–7,905 ft, 4.5 ohm-meters

A well-defined resistivity gradient is exhibited between the various sections under discussion. In view of the fact that the lithology is substantially the same in all zones, this in itself is sufficient evidence for the existence of oil in the upper two zones. The lower zone, which is the only one perforated and oil productive, is difficult to interpret because of the noninvaded nature of the sand. From other logs of the water-bearing McLish sand in the same general area, it is known that $R_o = 0.25$ ohm-meter. The water saturation in the lower zone would therefore be 50 per cent. This figure is said to be the "critical water saturation" of the McLish sand; i.e., no water will be produced. Because of the noninvaded nature of this sand it is impossible to determine from the available logs whether or not the connate water is movable.

Example 5. Example log 5 is from the S. E. Luther field, Howard County, Texas, where oil production is obtained from the Fusselman lime at 9,854 to 9,880 ft. A number of different type logs were obtained through the producing section:

SP–gamma ray; 10 in. normal; 32 in. limestone; 19 ft lateral
Microlog (H pad)
Microlaterolog
Laterolog

No water-resistivity information is available from formation samples and the SP curve is used to compute R_{wc}. The SP deflection as read directly by the curve is -70 mv. When corrected for bore hole, thickness, and resistivity, SSP $= -100$ mv is obtained. $K = 70$ corrected to 164°F gives $R_{mf}/R_{wc} = 17$. $R_{mf} = 0.33$ and $R_{wc} = 0.02$ ohm-meter.

Various means for determining porosity are available: microlog, microlaterolog, and $AM = 10$ in.–LS 32 in. combination. From the microlog (H pad), calculations give $\phi = 16.5$ per cent and $F = 30$ for a residual-oil saturation of 15 per cent. The empirical chart gives $\phi = 12$ per cent, $F = 60$. From the microlaterolog which reads an average of 30 ohm-

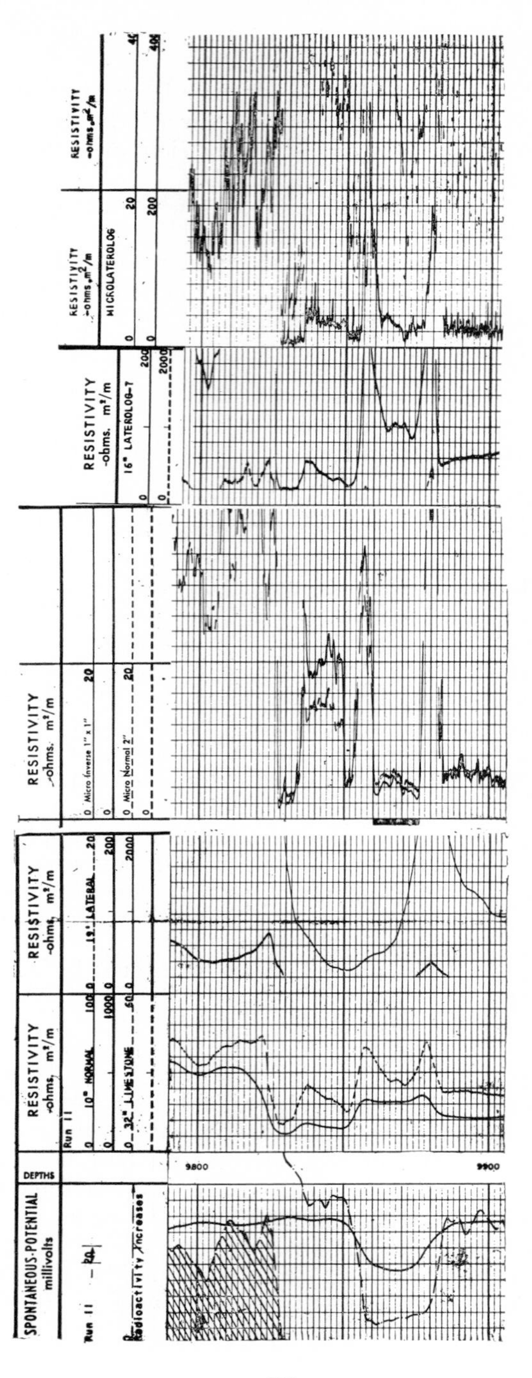

Example log 5. Fusselman lime, Texas.

meters, $\phi = 11.5$ per cent and $F = 70$ for ROS = 15 per cent, a reasonable check with the microlog. However, when using the $AM = 10$ in.–LS 32 in. combination in Fig. 5-2 it is observed that the hole is enlarged to 10.5 in. and that the porosity is only 6 per cent and $F = 280$ at ROS = 15 per cent. The reason for the discrepancy is that the enlarged section of the hole is filled with mud cake and therefore both the microlog and microlaterolog interpret this low-resistivity material as due to porosity. Core analysis in this well indicates that the porosity determined from the normal-limestone curve combination is more nearly correct. Hence, $R_o = 0.02 \times 280 = 5.6$ ohm-meters. The value of R_t may be determined from the lateral curve by the two-thirds rule as 200 ohm-meters by direct reading, and when corrected for bore-hole effect, $R_t = 125$. A check on this value is obtained from the laterolog, which reads directly 100 ohm-meters; when the log is corrected by means of a departure curve for invasion, $R_t = 120$.

Water saturation in this reservoir rock is computed to be

$$\sqrt{\frac{5.6}{125}} = 21\%$$

Example 6. Example log 6 is from the Frio sand, Fulton Beach Field, Aransas County, Texas. This area is notorious for the shalyness of its producing horizons which are characterized by highly reduced SP deflections.

The interval of interest is 7,077 to 7,083 ft. Actual SP is −20 mv, whereas the computed static SP from the known formation-water resistivity is

$$\text{SSP} = -70.7 \frac{620}{538} \log \frac{0.42}{0.06} = -69 \text{ mv}$$

$$\text{SP reduction factor} = \alpha = \frac{20}{69} = 0.29$$

The two shaly-sand approaches will be reviewed in more detail. The Schlumberger shaly-sand technique (Fig. 5-16) gives $R_{xo}/R_t = 1$; total water saturation at intersection of R_{xo}/R_t vs. ASP is 70 per cent. With such a high total water saturation, the oil in place would be rather small and this water saturation figure is likely to be too high. When reduced for static SP, the water saturation in the effective pore space is 28 per cent and it is concluded that the horizon should produce oil; this conclusion is verified by production tests.

Calculating porosity from Fig. 5-17, one finds $\phi = 24$ per cent, which is lower than the core-analysis results of 32 per cent. The log-derived figure is, however, the effective value of porosity.

The other approach suggested for shaly-sand interpretation gives the following results:

The apparent formation factor computed from the microlog when ROS = 25 per cent is $F_a = 2.98$.

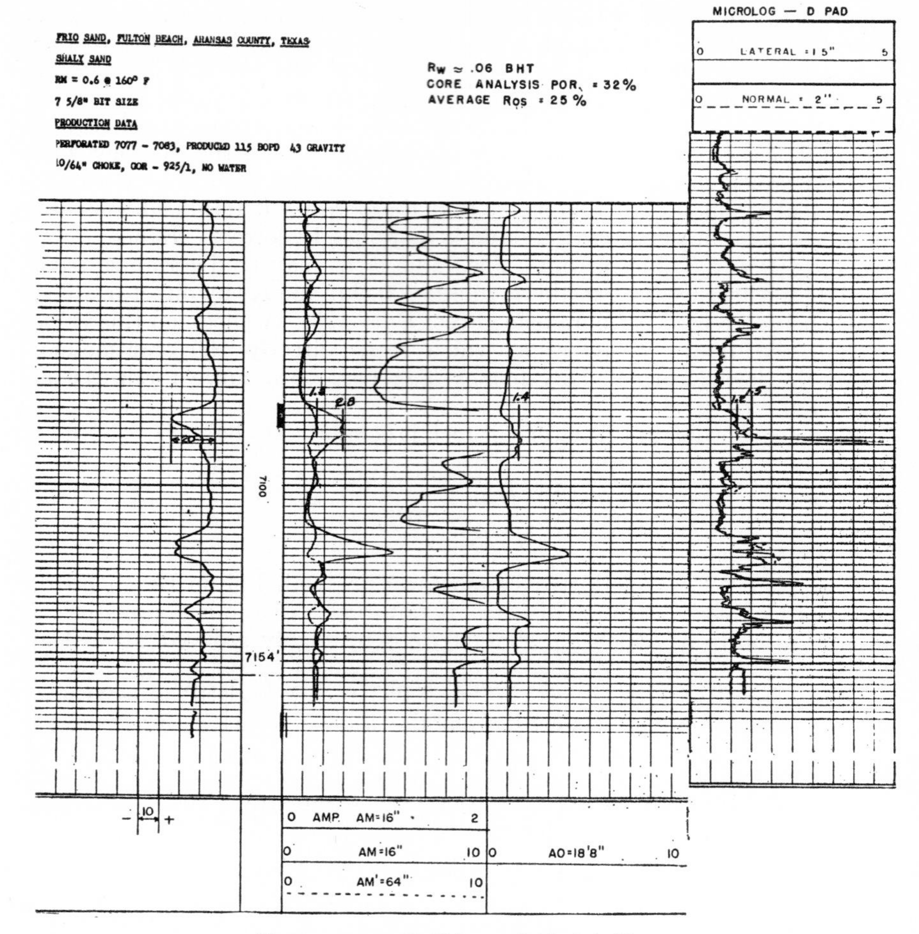

EXAMPLE LOG 6. Frio sand (shaly), Texas.

We have, by Eq. (5-26),

$$\frac{F_t}{F_a} = \left(\frac{0.42}{0.06}\right)^{1-.29} = 3.98$$

Hence

$$F_t = 11$$

$$\phi = 24\% \qquad \text{(Humble formula)}$$

Water of hydration is obtained by Eq. (5-24):

$$\frac{F_t}{F_a} = 3.98 = 1 - \phi_h + \phi_h \frac{0.42}{0.06} = 1 + 6\phi_h$$

$$\phi_h = 49.6\%$$

ϕ_h is a fraction of pore space not occupied by movable water (it may be called the water of hydration retained in a mechanically nonmovable status).

Total water saturation (σ_{wc}) is calculated by Archie's formula:

$$\sigma_{wc} = \sqrt{\frac{F_t R_{wc}}{R_t}} \sqrt{\frac{11 \times 0.06}{2.25}} = 54.2\%$$

$$\text{Movable water saturation} = 4.6\%$$

Permeability estimated from the tortuosity-permeability correlation in Fig. 5-18 is 200 md and critical movable water saturation (irreducible) calculated from the Fig. 5-19 relation is 32 per cent. Hence the well should produce clean oil and the relative ability of oil and water to flow (WOR) need not be evaluated.

SELECTED REFERENCES ON QUANTITATIVE ELECTRIC-LOG INTERPRETATION

1932

Sundberg, Karl: Effect of Impregnating Waters on Electrical Conductivity of Soils and Rocks, *Trans. AIME*, pp. 367ff.

1934

Pirson, S. J.: Interpretation of Three Layer Resistivity Curves, *Trans. AIME*, pp. 148ff.

Tagg, G. F.: Interpretation of Resistivity Measurements, *Trans. AIME*, pp. 135ff.

1937

Gillingham, W. J.: Electrical Logging in the Appalachian Fields, *Penn. State Coll. Mineral Inds. Expt. Sta. Bull.* 21.

Jakosky, J. J., and R. H. Hopper: The Effect of Moisture on the Direct Current Resistivities of Oil Sands and Rocks, *Geophysics*, vol. 2, no. 1, pp. 33ff.

1938

Martin, M. G., et al.: Determination of the Potential Productivity of Oil-bearing Formations by Resistivity Measurements, *Geophysics*, vol. 3, no. 3, pp. 258ff.

1942

Archie, G. E.: The Electrical Resistivity Log as an Aid in Determining Some Reservoir Characteristics, *AIME Tech. Pub.* 1422.

1945

Guyod, H.: Electric Log Interpretation, *Oil Weekly*, series of four articles, December.

1947

Archie, G. E.: Electrical Resistivity—An Aid in Core Analysis Interpretation, *Bull. Am. Assoc. Petroleum Geol.*, no. 2, pp. 350ff.

Pirson, S. J.: Electric Logging, *Oil Gas J.*, series of five articles, October to December.

1949

Doll, H. G.: The S.P. Log in Shaly Sands, *AIME Tech. Pub.* 2912.

Dunlap, H. F., et al.: The Relation between Electrical Resistivity and Brine Saturation in Reservoir Rocks, *AIME Tech. Pub.* 2711.

Patnode, H. W.: Relationship of Drilling Mud Resistivity to Mud Filtrate Resistivity, *AIME Tech. Pub.* 2512.

——— and M. R. J. Wyllie: The Presence of Conductive Solids in Reservoir Rocks as a Factor in Electric Log Interpretation, *AIME Tech. Pub.* 2797.

Tixier, M. P.: Evaluation of Permeability from a Determination of the Resistivity Gradient on the Electric Log, *Oil Gas J.*, June 16, pp. 113ff.

———: Electric Log Analysis in the Rocky Mountains, *Petroleum Engr. Ref. Ann.*, pp. B34ff.; *Oil Gas J.*, June 23, pp. 143ff.

Williams, M.: Estimation of Interstitial Water from the Electric Log, *AIME Tech. Pub.* 2936.

Wyllie, M. R. J.: A Quantitative Analysis of the Electrochemical Component of the S.P. Curve, *AIME Tech. Pub.* 2511.

1950

Barber, R. C.: Porosity Permeability Check by Electric Log, *World Oil*, August, pp. 165ff.

Chombart, L. G.: Factors Involved in Practical Electrical Log Analysis, University of Oklahoma Symposium on Subsurface Methods.

De Witte, L.: Resistivity and Saturation Distribution in Infiltrated Zones of Porous Formations around Drill Holes, *Oil Gas J.*, July 27, pp. 246ff.

———: Relations between Resistivities and Fluid Content of Porous Rocks, *Oil Gas J.*, Aug. 24, pp. 120ff.

Lyle, H. N.: Well-site Interpretation of Electric Logs, *Oil Gas J.*, Nov. 23, pp. 77ff.

Young, J. W., and R. Pot: Resistivity Measurements on Limestone Cores, *Petroleum Engr.*, January, pp. B50ff.

1951

Jones, P. H., and T. B. Buford: Electric Logging Applied to Ground-water Exploration, *Geophysics*, vol. 16, no. 1, pp. 115ff.

Jones, Park J.: Electric Log Resistivity, Porosity and Water Saturations for Clean and Shaly Sandstone, *World Oil*, Feb. 1, pp. 140ff.

Pirson, S. J.: Review of Quantitative Methods of Electric Log Interpretation, *Oil Gas J.*, May 24, pp. 102ff.

Tixier, M. P.: Porosity Index in Limestone from Electric Logs, *Oil Gas J.*, Nov. 15, pp. 140ff.; Nov. 22, pp. 63ff.

——— and R. L. Forsythe: Application of Electric Logging in Canada, *Can. Mining Met. Bull.*, September.

Walstrom, J. E.: The Quantitative Aspect of Electric Log Interpretation, *AIME Tech. Pub.* 3280.

1952

Archie, G. E.: Classification of Carbonate Reservoir Rocks and Petrophysical Considerations, *Bull. Am. Assoc. Petroleum Geol.*, vol. 36, no. 2, pp. 273ff.

Hamilton, R. G.: Common Fallacies in Electric Log Interpretation, *World Oil*, April, pp. 141ff.

Summers, G. C., and R. A. Broding: Continuous Velocity Logging, *Geophysics*, vol. 17, no. 3, pp. 598ff.

Winsauer, W. O., et al.: Resistivity of Brine-saturated Sands in Relation to Pore Geometry, *Bull. Am. Assoc. Petroleum Geol.*, vol. 36, no. 2, pp. 253ff.

Wright, T. R., and S. J. Pirson: Porosity Profile Determination from Electric Logs, *Bull. Am. Assoc. Petroleum Geol.*, vol. 36, no. 2, pp. 299ff.

Wyllie, M. R. J., and M. B. Spangler: Application of Electrical Resistivity Measurements to the Problem of Fluid Flow in Porous Media, *Bull. Am. Assoc. Petroleum Geol.*, vol. 36, no. 2, pp. 359ff.

1953

Howell, B. F., Jr.: Electrical Conduction of Fluid Saturated Rocks, *World Oil*, February, pp. 113ff.; March, pp. 142ff.

Keller, G. V.: Effect of Wettability on the Electrical Resistivity of Sand, *Oil Gas J.*, Jan. 5, pp. 62ff.

Whiting, R. L., E. T. Guerrero, and R. M. Young: Electrical Properties of Limestone Cores, *Oil Gas J.*, July 17, pp. 309ff.

1954

Birks, J.: An Evaporation Method for Measuring the Resistivity—Water Saturation Characteristics of Cores, *J. Inst. Petroleum*, January, pp. 14ff.

Doll, H. G., and M. Martin: How to Use Electrical Log Data to Determine Maximum Producible Oil Index, *Oil Gas J.*, July 5, pp. 120ff.

Poupon, A., M. E. Loy, and M. P. Tixier: A Contribution to Electrical Log Interpretation in Shaly Sands, *Trans. AIME Petroleum Div.*, June, pp. 27ff.

Smith, H. D., and H. A. Blum: MicroLaterolog versus Microlog for Formation Factor Calculations, *Geophysics*, vol. 19, no. 2, pp. 310ff.

1955

Blum, H. A., and J. L. Martin: Log Interpretation Problem in Low Resistivity Sands, *J. Petroleum Technol.*, vol. 7, no. 8, pp. 10ff.

De Witte, L.: A Study of Electric Log Interpretation Methods in Shaly Formations, *AIME Tech. Pub.* 4076.

Kunz, K. S., and M. P. Tixier: Temperature Surveys in Gas Producing Wells, *AIME Tech. Pub.* 4077.

Martin, M.: With the MicroLog You Can Be Sure, *Oil Gas J.*, Sept. 19, pp. 109ff.; Oct. 24, pp. 106ff.

1956

Grynberg, J.: Quantitative Electric Log Interpretation of "D" and "J" Sands—Denver Basin, Symposium Oil and Gas Fields in Nebraska.

Heim, A. H., and H. W. True: Low Resistivity on Electric Log Could Mean "Chert," *World Oil*, March, pp. 126ff.

Hill, H. J., and J. D. Milburn: Effect of Clay and Water Salinity on Electrochemical Behavior of Reservoir Rocks, *J. Petroleum Technol.*, vol. 8, no. 3, pp. 65ff.

SELECTED REFERENCES ON QUANTITATIVE RADIOACTIVITY WELL LOGGING INTERPRETATION

1949

Bush, R. E., and E. S. Mardock: Some Preliminary Investigations of Quantitative Interpretations of Radioactivity Logs, *AIME Tech. Pub.* 2780.

1950

Bush, R. E.: Porosities Can Be Obtained from Radioactivity Logs in West Texas, *Oil Gas J.*, Apr. 27, pp. 153ff.

——— and E. S. Mardock: The Quantitative Application of Radioactivity Logs, *AIME Tech. Pub.* 3075.

1951

Fearon, R. E., and E. S. Mardock: The Quantitative Interpretation of Radioactivity Logs, *Proc. 3rd World Petroleum Congr.*, The Hague, May–June; *Oil Gas J.*, Mar. 24, 1952, pp. 188ff.

1952

Belcher, D. Y., and R. C. Herner: Use of Radioactive Material to Measure Soil Moisture and Density, *ASTM Bull.*

Russell, W. L.: Interpretation of Neutron Well Logs, *Bull. Am. Assoc. Petroleum Geol.*, vol. 36, no. 2, pp. 312ff.

Scotty, C. B., and E. F. Egan: Neutron Derived Porosity—Influence of Bore Hole Diameter, *AIME Tech. Pub.* 3377.

Trochinsky, B. B., Y. W. T. Spinks, and D. A. Lane: Soil Studies Using Nuclear Radiations, *ASTM Bull.*

1953

Dewan, J. T., and L. A. Allaud: Experimental Basis for Neutron Logging Interpretation, *Petroleum Engr.*, September, pp. B49ff.

1954

Long, D.: Determination of Yates Sand Porosities, *Tomorrow's Tools Today*, pp. 4ff., Midyear.

Russell, J. H., and B. O. Bishop: Quantitative Evaluation of Rock Porosities by Neutron-Neutron Method, *Petroleum Engr.*, April, pp. B76ff.

1955

Bishop, D.: Porosity Evaluation for Sands and Shaly Sands, *Tomorrow's Tools Today*, pp. 14ff.

Edwards, J. M., and A. L. Simpson: A New Method for Neutron Derived Porosity Determination for Thin Beds, *AIME Tech. Pub.* 4101.

Flagg, A. H., et al.: Radioactive Tracers in Oil Production Problems, *AIME Tech. Pub.* 3982.

1956

McLendon, D. H.: Interpretation of Radioactivity Logs in Gas-Drilled Wells, *Petroleum Engr.*, October, pp. B63ff.

CHAPTER 6

RESERVOIR-FLUID PROPERTIES

To understand and predict the behavior of oil and gas reservoirs, a knowledge of the physical and chemical characteristics of the fluids involved must be gained. These properties are measured on representative fluid samples obtained under prevailing reservoir conditions. They are solution gas-oil ratio; oil-reservoir-volume factor; gas-reservoir-volume factor; reservoir-oil compressibility; reservoir-gas compressibility; reservoir-oil, gas, and water viscosities; reservoir-oil, gas, and water densities. In addition it is necessary for the reservoir engineer to understand and be able to predict reservoir fluid-phase behavior, i.e., the expected changes in fluid-phase composition, in density, and in viscosity attendant to field-pressure reduction resulting from natural depletion operations or under fluid injection during pressure maintenance or pressure build-up operations.

HYDROCARBON GASES AND LIQUIDS

Oil and gas are organic compounds (carbon and hydrogen). However, only certain specific classes of hydrocarbon compounds are found in crude oils, whereas others are conspicuous by their absence.

The *organic compounds generally present in oils* may be listed as follows:

1. *Paraffin hydrocarbons* also called *saturated hydrocarbons.* These have the general formula C_nH_{2n+2} and are chemically stable. This series includes both the straight-chain hydrocarbons such as butane and the branched chain such as isobutane. A crude oil composed mostly of saturated hydrocarbon is termed a *paraffin-base crude,* a typical example of which is the Pennsylvania grade crude.

2. *Naphthenic hydrocarbons,* or *cycloparaffins.* These compounds have a ring or cyclic structure without double bond. They are, therefore, similar in properties to paraffins and chemically stable. Their generalized formula is C_nH_{2n}. An example is cyclopentane.

Cycloparaffins form a large percentage of certain crudes which are said to have a *naphthenic base,* typical examples of which are most mid-continent crudes.

3. *Aromatic hydrocarbons,* or *benzene series.* These compounds contain double bonds and are chemically active. In particular they are easily oxidized. Their general formula is C_nH_{2n-6}. Truly aromatic-base crudes are rare, although some exist in California and Sumatra. Aromatic hydrocarbons are found mostly in asphaltic- and mixed-base crudes.

In addition, oils contain certain minor accessory compounds which will be listed for completeness:

Chlorophyll derivatives and other porphyrins
Other nitrogenous compounds
Pigments

Although their bulk is of no consequence in crude oil, the accessory compounds may have an important bearing on the performance of a reservoir because of their polar and highly adsorbable nature. Polar compounds of crude oil when thoroughly coating the sand grains may render the reservoir rock completely oil-wet and water repellent. Reservoirs such as the Oklahoma City Wilcox are considered to be nearly completely oil-wet.

By contrast, *organic compounds which are almost totally absent* from crude oils will be listed:

1. Olefins, C_nH_{2n}, such as propylene
2. Diolefins, C_nH_{2n-2}, such as allene
3. Acetylenes, C_nH_{2n-2}, such as propine
4. Cycloolefins, C_nH_{2n-2}, such as cyclohexene

Methods and Apparatus for Subsurface Sampling. In order to prolong the life of a field through its most efficient productive stage, sound knowledge of the physical properties of oil and gas under reservoir conditions must be gained. Two of the most important instruments used for this purpose are the bottom-hole pressure gauge and the subsurface sampler.

Although the need for an adequate bottom-hole sampling apparatus has been recognized for a long time, the difficulties encountered have slowed down its development considerably and it was not until the early 1930's that considerable progress was made. Unless the sample is truly representative of the actual reservoir conditions and contains all the constituents of the fluid in their true proportions, the information gained from it can only be used with uncertainty.

The information desired from a sample of reservoir fluid should include the following physical characteristics, which will be defined in due course:

1. The amount of free gas present at the sampling point
2. The saturation pressure of the oil
3. The ratio of dissolved gas to oil
4. The solubility curve of the gas in oil as a function of pressure
5. The shrinkage curve of oil as a function of pressure
6. Compressibility of the oil
7. Thermal expansion of the oil

The requirements of a successful sampler are that it must fill itself with a representative reservoir sample without disturbing the conditions existing at the sampling point and must retain these conditions until laboratory tests are made on the sample. Obviously, perfect sampling is impossible to attain, for a slight disturbance will always be set up by any method of trapping the sample. In addition, the volume of the container must necessarily change slightly as the sampler is withdrawn from the well, because of the increasing pressure differential between the inside and outside of the sample container and the temperature change which occurs while the sample is withdrawn from the well.

In certain samplers the disturbing effect of the valving mechanism has been reduced to a minimum. The change in volume due to the pressure differential can be determined experimentally and corrected for by calculation. Although the temperature must necessarily change during sampling, the bottom-hole temperature can be restored by placing the sampler in a suitable heater jacket at the time of the tests.

A brief description will be given of several samplers. The earliest type is the *open-top bailer,* which, when lowered into the well, fills with fluid and is then withdrawn to the surface. The use of such a device is extremely limited, since all pressure will be lost through escape of solution gas. The bailer is still useful in determining water levels and fluid levels in low-pressure wells. In order to retain the solution gas, a mechanism for closing the sampler must be used.

The *Humble sampler* (Fig. 6-1) consists of a chamber closed at one end and provided with a valve at the other. The sampler is built with the valve at the bottom. To prevent fluid from entering the container at a point above the sampling point, a diaphragm is placed below the valve, which prevents entrance of fluid before a predetermined pressure is reached. A diaphragm can be constructed which bursts at the proper temperature and pressure, after it has been exposed to these conditions for a definite duration of time. The bursting pressures for tin disks of various thicknesses are given in Fig. 6-2 as a function of temperature. The chamber is evacuated before lowering, so that no air will be present in the sample. As the diaphragm is burst, fluid rushes into

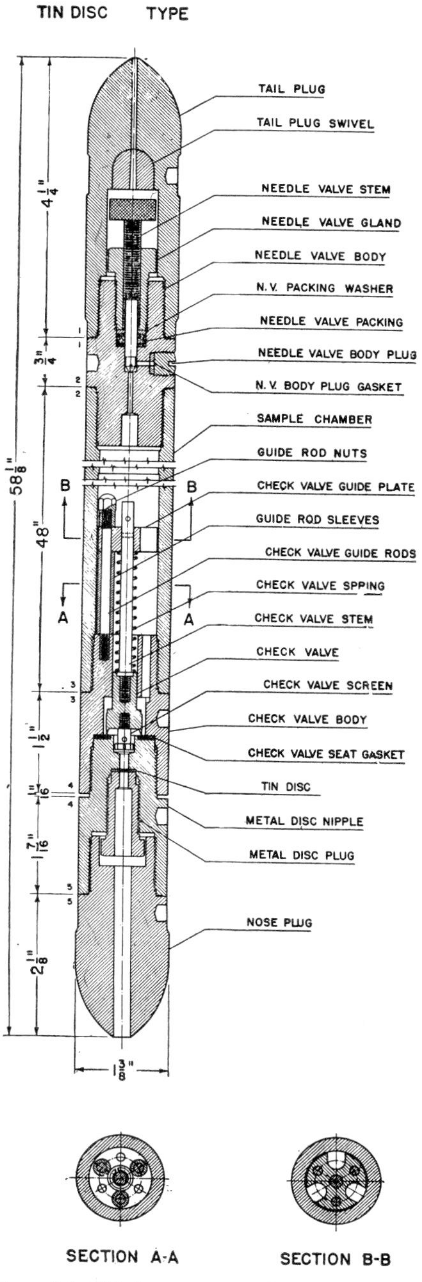

FIG. 6-1. High-pressure subsurface sampler, Humble design. (*Engineering Laboratories, Inc.*)

the evacuated space until the pressure is approximately the same as that existing in the well at the sampling point. The valve, which is lightly spring loaded, then closes and prevents loss of fluid. As the sampler is withdrawn from the well, the pressure difference across the valve increases and ensures additional sealing. Due to the sudden rush of oil into the evac-

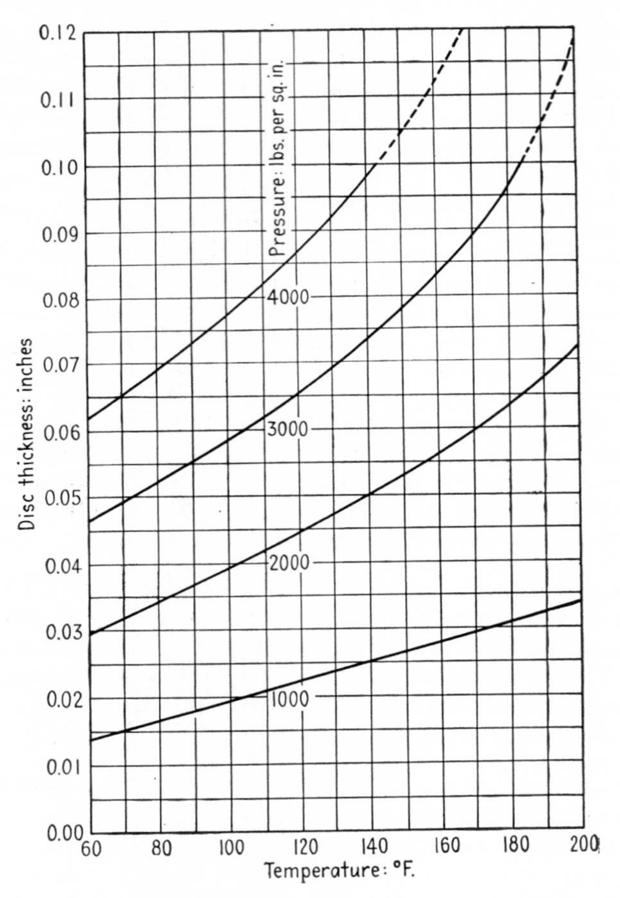

FIG. 6-2. Recommended tin-disk thickness for various pressures and temperatures for the Humble sampler. (*Engineering Laboratories, Inc.*)

uated space, gas is liberated from solution in the fluid, and because of the difficulty of returning this gas to solution, the sampler may be filled partly with fluid and partly with gas, although no free gas may be present at the sampling depth.

A sampler devised by Lindsly of the U.S. Bureau of Mines avoids, to a great extent, the possibility of solution gas liberation during sampling. This sampler is valved at both ends, the upper valve being held open during lowering, while the lower valve seats by gravity. As the sampler is lowered, the lower valve is raised by the velocity head of the oil which passes through the sampling chamber and out at the top, past the upper valve. Upon reaching the sampling point, the sampler is raised and lowered several times to secure a representative sample, and then it is held stationary until the top valve closes. This is accomplished by the force of a spring which pushes the valve firmly against its seat. The closing of the valve is slowed down by a heavy oil in a dashpot provided with a slow leak. The volume of this heavy oil and the size of the leak are adjusted so that closure takes place 15 to 20 min after the sampler has been introduced into the well. After closure of the upper valve, the sampler is withdrawn from the well. Upon starting its upward travel, the lower valve is closed only by its own weight. Whether this provides adequate sealing is a questionable point because spring loading is necessary to close a valve tightly against small pressure differentials. If the sampler is drawn up rapidly, the pressure differential soon becomes great enough to make a perfect seal. If any fluid is lost in the meantime, the chamber no longer contains a representative sample.

In order to obtain a true sample and keep it after it is once secured, both valves must be held open while collecting the sample and then must be tightly closed in such a manner as to cause no disturbance of the sample.

The sampler developed by the Gulf Oil Corporation has both valves spring loaded, and they are held open by mechanical means. In order to close them, it is necessary to send a messenger down the line which strikes a trigger, thus releasing both valves. It is necessary to provide a linkage between the two valves by a rod internal to the sampler.

The construction of the Gulf subsurface sampler is shown in Fig. 6-3. It consists essentially of a tubular chamber open at both ends with means for forcibly closing the valves at the ends of the chamber, thus trapping a sample of the fluid. The total length of the device is 61 in., with a diameter of 1¾ in., which permits it to be lowered into a tubing as small as 2 in. In the open position, the internal passages are designed to offer minimum obstruction to the flow of oil so that, as the sampler is lowered down the well, it passes through the fluid and causes minimum entrainment. The sample chamber is a single tube 42 in. in length and 1⅜ in. ID. This chamber is closed when the knife-edge valves are thrust against the soft fiber seats located on the end pieces. The seats are replaced by new ones after each run, in order to ensure perfect sealing. The upper valve is prevented from closing by the trigger bar, which is held in place by a bell crank until the trigger is depressed. The upper valve is forcibly held against the trigger bar by a push rod actuated by a heavy spring exerting a force of about 60 lb.

The lower valve is held open by a weak spring in the dashpot. The lower push rod cannot exert any force against the lower valve until the upper valve is completely closed, owing to construction of the interlock mechanism. Upon closure of the upper valve, the lower push rod is released and it closes the lower valve. In order to slow down its action, which would tend to disturb the sample, a dashpot, provided with a slow leak, dampens the valve action.

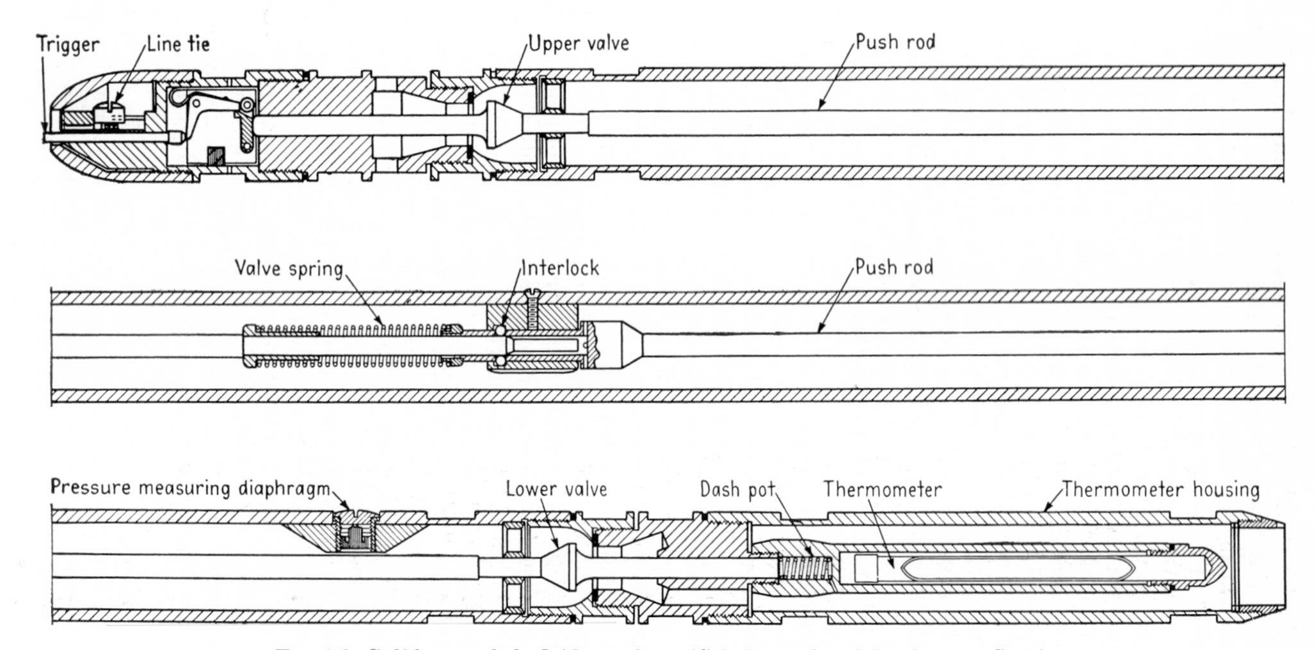

FIG. 6-3. Gulf bottom-hole fluid sampler. *(Gulf Research and Development Corp.)*

In order to carry out a sampling operation, the sampler is introduced into the well through a lubricator, as shown in Fig. 6-4. A steel measuring wire line is securely attached to the upper end of the sampler. A messenger, 1 in. OD by 8 in. long and weighing about 2 lb, is passed over the wire line and locked inside the lubricator. The lubricator is then assembled to the wellhead, the sampler is pulled against a constriction in the clamping attachment designed to prevent accidental tripping of the valve mechanism, the gate valve is then opened, and the sampler is lowered to the desired depth. After waiting 10 to 15 min in order to permit equilibrium fluid conditions to be established, the messenger is released, permitting it to slide down the wire until it strikes the projecting trigger on top of the sampler, thus closing both valves. The sampler is then withdrawn from the well, and it is subsequently taken to the laboratory where it is to be tested.

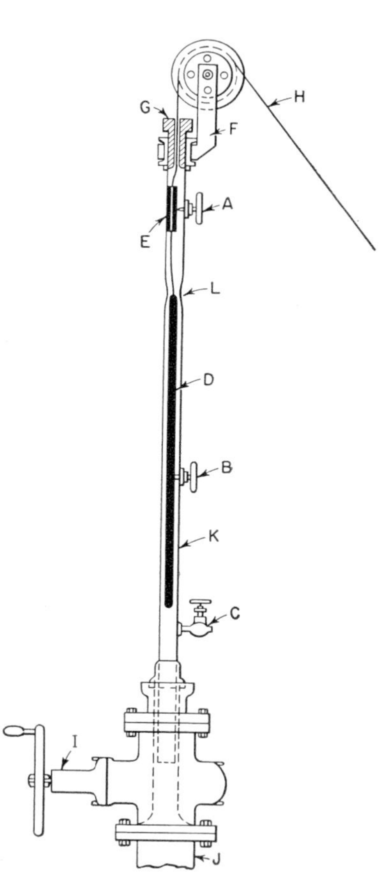

FIG. 6-4. Sampler lubricator assembly. *A*, messenger clamp; *B*, sampler clamp; *C*, bleeder valve; *D*, sampler; *E*, messenger; *F*, swivel pulley; *G*, stuffing box; *H*, wire line; *I*, gate valve; *J*, casing; *K*, lubricator body; *L*, restriction.

In order to measure the pressure in the sampler and thereby ascertain if a good sample has been obtained, the contact pressure measuring diaphragm shown in Fig. 6-5 is provided in the sampler wall. It consists of a thin steel diaphragm, chromium plated on both sides and clamped against a seat by a small plug. The face of the plug is lapped perfectly flat so that the diaphragm can rest against it at all times and undergoes no appreciable distortion due to the inner high pressures of the sampler. The free space behind the diaphragm is limited, so that even if excessive pressures are placed on the exterior of the diaphragm it suffers no permanent distortion. The plug contains a bakelite core which serves as insulation for a contact screw extending through the center. Holes are provided through the plug for transmitting pressure to the exterior face of the diaphragm. By applying external pressure through a suitable connection, the diaphragm is pushed away from the contact screw. The pressure at which contact is broken is indicated by a high-resistance voltmeter placed in series with a flashlight battery. By means of previous calibration, the pressure differential between the sample and the external pressure is determined.

In the laboratory, the sample should be tested at bottom-hole temperature. In order to enable the sample to be raised to this temperature, a heater jacket is placed around the sampler. This consists of a double-walled cylinder into which the sampler can slip leaving only a small clearance. Clamps are provided for holding the sampler in place. A hole is provided through the jacket wall through which the pressure measuring

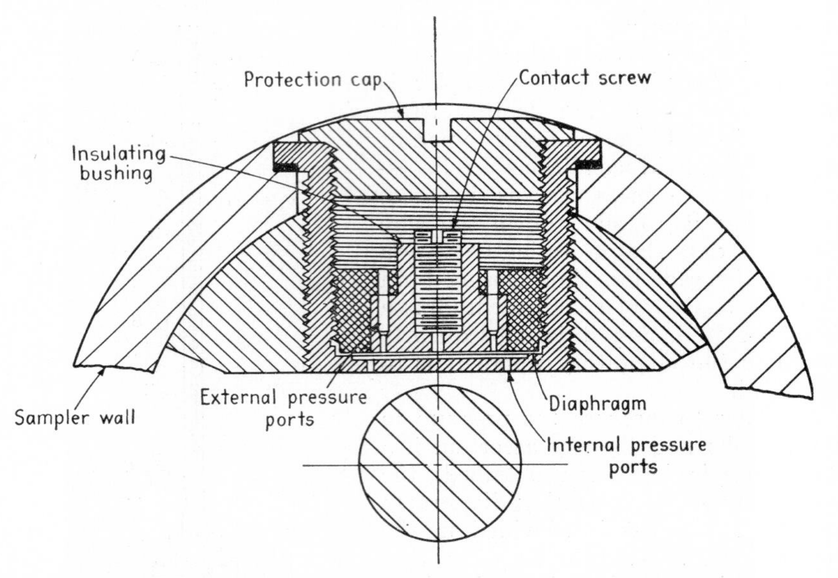

Fig. 6-5. Pressure-balancing diaphragm for measuring sampler pressures, Gulf design. (*After Exline Engineering Company.*)

adapter can be screwed into the wall of the sampler. The space between the two walls of the heater jacket is filled with a heated circulating fluid, the temperature of which is maintained at bottom-hole temperature by thermostatic control. The jacket is mounted on a support so that it can be swung end for end in order to stir up the sample. The thermostat can be set to give the temperature shown by the maximum indicating thermometer sent down with the sampler. All connections to the sampler are made through a coil of steel tubing, so that as the jacket is rotated there is no danger of breaking the connections.

The accessory apparatus needed is shown in Fig. 6-6. It consists of a reciprocating piston oil pump, which can pump oil either from a reservoir or from a measuring burette. A gauge is provided to indicate approximately the pressures obtained. For accurate pressure measurements, a dead-weight gauge is provided. Some of the accessory apparatus required is shown schematically in Fig. 6-16. A mercury gasometer for determining the quantity of gas bled off the sample and a glass fluid separator are shown.

In the laboratory the sampler is prepared for test by removing the lower protecting tube and the thermometer case. The valving device is then screwed on, making certain that the plunger is retracted so that there is no danger of accidentally pushing in the sampler valve. The protecting cap from the pressure contact is removed, and the sampler is inserted in

FIG. 6-6. Bottom-hole sample-testing apparatus showing sample container, glass separator, and mercury gasometer. (*Exline Engineering Company.*)

the heater jacket, lining up the pressure contact with the hole in the heater-jacket wall. The pressure plug is then screwed into the sampler wall and connection made to the dead-weight tester. The two leads from the voltmeter are connected to the binding post provided on the pressure plug. After a sufficient length of time has elapsed to ensure uniform temperature throughout the sampler, pressure measurement is made by piling weights on the dead-weight gauge until contact is broken, as indicated by the voltmeter. By properly adjusting the weights, a pressure may be reached where adding the smallest available weight breaks contact, while removing it causes contact to be made again. This smallest weight changes the pressure by ½ psi. Connection from the mercury reservoir is then made to the valve head, and, with the other head valve opened and the jacket swung so that the head is at the top, mercury is forced into the head by means of the mercury pump until it overflows from the open valve. This valve is then closed, and pumping is continued until the pressure on the mercury is equal to the pressure inside the sampler. The push rod is then screwed down to open the sampler valve. Then the valve in the head

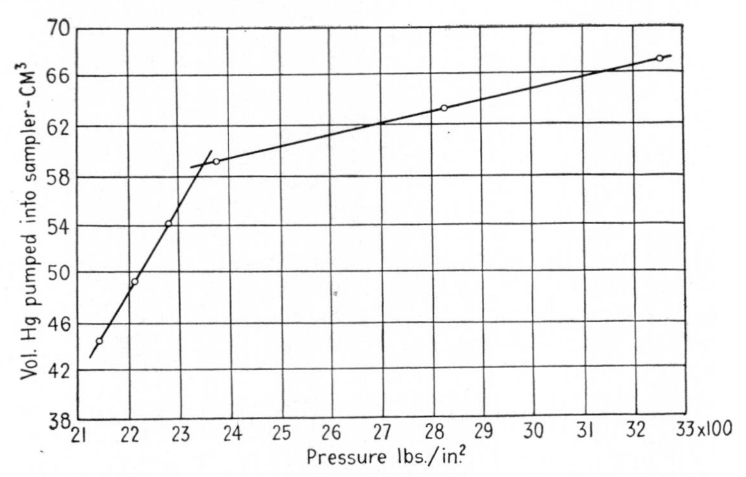

FIG. 6-7. Determination of saturation pressure of bottom-hole sample.

of the sampler is closed, the sampler is reversed five or six times to stir up the contents, and a pressure measurement is again made by adjusting the weights on the dead-weight gauge.

In order to test the physical status of the sample, mercury is injected in small increments. If free gas is present in the sample, there is a relatively small rise in pressure, since the addition of mercury to the sampler decreases its effective volume, forcing free gas into solution. If no free gas is present, the oil is compressed and shows a large increase in pressure of the order of several hundred psi. More mercury is injected in small quantities until several large increases in pressure indicate that all the gas has been put into solution, the pressure being measured after each injection. After all the gas has been placed in solution, a plot is made of the amount of mercury introduced into the sampler as a function of sampler pressure. Two intersecting straight lines can be drawn, the point of intersection showing the exact amount of mercury injected to achieve complete saturation and the pressure at which saturation is reached (saturation pressure). Such a plot, demonstrating the results from an actual test, is presented in Fig. 6-7.

A glass burette is then attached to the second valve on the valve head, and oil is bled into it from the sampler. The gas given off by the displaced oil is measured by means of the gasometer. After about 50 cc of oil has been displaced from the sampler, the valve is closed and time is allowed for all the gas to be liberated from solution in the oil. The volume of gas-free oil is noted, and the difference between the indicated volume and the oil volume when in the sampler shows the shrinkage due to the gas liberated. The oil in the burette is drained into a separate container, and, if desired, the gas may be saved for analysis. Knowing how much gas-saturated oil was originally in the sampler and how much gas was liberated from the oil withdrawn, the total gas remaining in solution in the sampler can be computed. About 10 per cent of this gas can be bled off through the meter in each test, care being taken to lose no oil during this process. The content of the sampler is then stirred to obtain equilibrium, and the pressure is measured. Mercury is again injected into the sampler to obtain saturation of the remaining oil, and the bleeding off of another oil fraction is made in the same manner as before. This process is repeated until all oil has been displaced from the sampler. Sufficient data are then available to calculate the reservoir oil information required on gas solubility and reservoir volume factor, with the exception of the thermal expansion of the oil. If this value is desired, it can be obtained for any degree of saturation by lowering the temperature of the heater jacket by a known amount and injecting mercury to secure resaturation. The volume of mercury pumped in to restore saturation is a measure of the decrease in oil volume due to the temperature change.

Very little error is encountered in the pressure measurements, provided that the dead-weight gauge is used for all measurements. The accuracy of these measurements is better than $\frac{1}{10}$ per cent for pressures above 500 psi. Below this pressure some difficulty is encountered in the use of the dead-weight gauge because of the small weight required. For measurements at low pressures, it is desirable to use a bourdon-type gauge which has an accuracy of 1 per cent. Owing to the expansion of the mercury reservoir and the compression of oil and mercury from the pump to the sampler connection, the amount of mercury actually introduced into the sampler is less than the oil pumped out of the burette. By the method described above, this difference can be accurately determined, and the proper corrections can be applied. Owing to the temperature difference between the mercury reservoir and the sampler, thermal expansion of mercury occurs. However, knowing the temperature difference and the volume of mercury in the sampler at any time, the proper correction can be made. In reversing the sampler to stir its content, the mercury falls down through the fluid, providing an excellent contacting means. However, the mercury tends to break up into small droplets, which will contain oil in the spaces between them. The sampler thus contains a coarse oil-mercury emulsion of known volume. Approximately 15 per cent of this emulsion is oil.

Some error is likewise incurred by oil clinging to the walls of the vessels used, but in view of the large volume of oil initially in the sampler this should be negligible.

Pressure-volume-temperature (PVT) Relationships. Before studying the bottom-hole sample testing methods, it is advisable to review briefly the physical behavior of hydrocarbon mixtures at the high temperatures and pressures encountered in the natural reservoirs. The presentation made by Dotterweich (1941) is adapted by courtesy of *The Petroleum Engineer*.

The study of binary mixtures of components exhibiting complete mutual solubility in all proportions leads to complex results, the details of which are beyond the scope of this work. In addition to variations in temperature, volume, and pressure, a fourth variable must be considered, namely, composition.

In order to introduce the nomenclature required to describe phase relationships, reference is made to Fig. 6-8*a*, which is a constant composition-

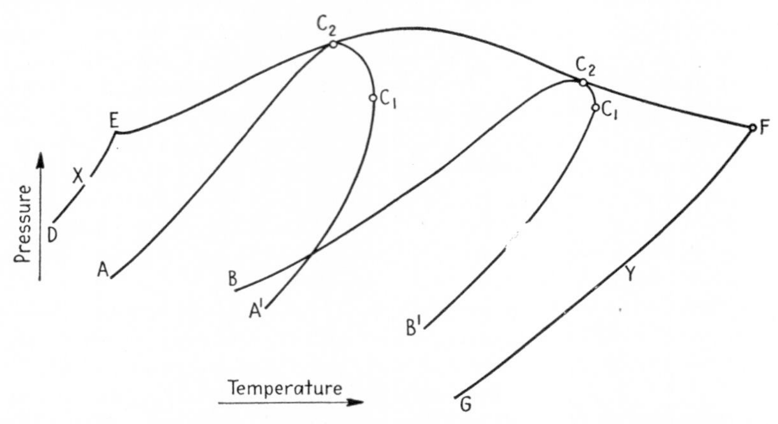

FIG. 6-8*a*. Pressure-temperature relations at constant composition for mixtures of components X and Y.

pressure-temperature chart for the two hypothetical components X and Y, mutually soluble in all proportions. The line DE represents the vapor-pressure curve for the component X and the line GF, the vapor pressure of component Y. When the two components are mixed in definite proportions, i.e., 60 per cent mole fraction X and 40 per cent mole fraction Y, and placed in a variable volume cell susceptible of variations in temperature and pressure, a curve such as AC_2C_1A' may result. If the experiment be repeated, beginning with 40 per cent mole fraction X and 60 per cent mole fraction Y, a curve BC_2C_1B' may be obtained.

An inspection of the curve AC_2C_1A' shows that the section $A'C_1$ represents the temperatures at which the components are just completely vaporized. This section of the line is referred to as the *dew-point curve*. The section AC_2 represents the various pressures and temperatures at which vapor formation begins and is referred to as the *bubble-point curve*. Similar description may be made for the curve BC_2C_1B'. The dew-point pressure of a fluid system is that pressure at which an infinitesimal amount of liquid is in equilibrium with an infinite amount of gas. The bubble-point pressure of a fluid system is that pressure at which an infinitesimal amount of vapor is in equilibrium with an infinite amount of liquid.

It may be noted on both curves that C_1 indicates the maximum temperature at which a liquid may be condensed from a vapor. This point is referred to as the *cricondentherm.* C_2 represents the point at which the liquid and vapor have identical qualities, and this point is referred to as the critical temperature and pressure. The critical point C of a mixture is defined as the temperature and pressure at which all physical properties of the phases merge and become continuously identical.

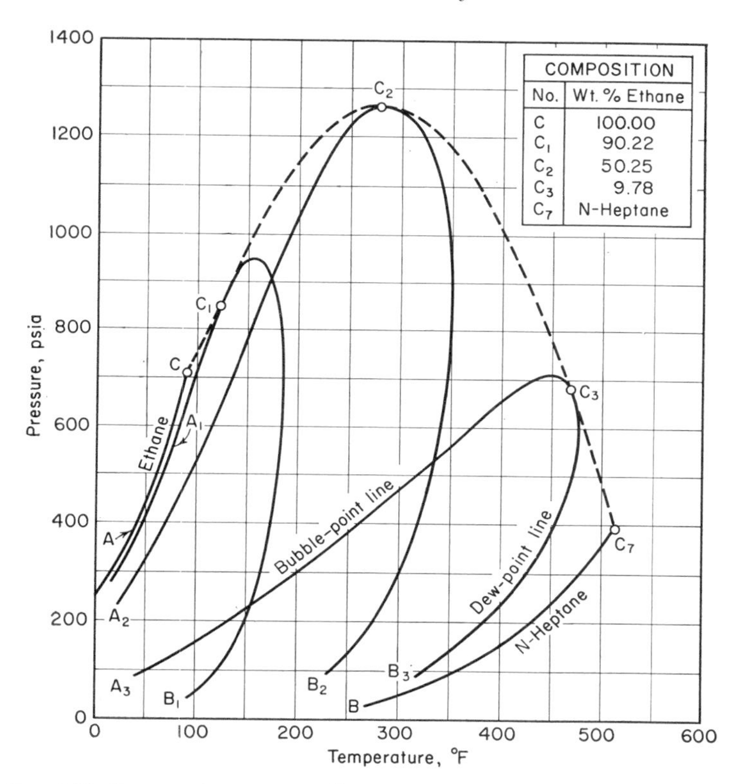

FIG. 6-8*b*. Pressure-temperature diagram for the ethane-*n*-heptane system.

Should the critical points obtained from mixtures of other molal composition be connected by the line EF, this line would be the *critical envelope curve* for the system investigated. The end points of the critical envelope are on the vapor-pressure lines of the pure components X and Y. In addition to this method of plotting the data, other procedures are available which have been reviewed by Weber (1939). By way of example of a binary system the pressure-temperature diagram for the ethane-heptane system is given in Fig. 6-8*b*.

Figure 6-9*a* shows the AA' section of Fig. 6-8*a* previously described. In addition, this diagram indicates the quality lines which represent the relative change in mole percentage of liquid between the dew-point and bubble-point curves. Beginning with a vapor at any temperature between C_1 and C_2, isothermal compression results in the precipitation of a liquid phase when line $A'C_1$ is crossed, the liquid phase increasing until the point E is reached. Further increase in pressure causes revaporization of this liquid phase until only the vapor phase is present when line C_1C_2 is crossed. Kuenen (1895) referred to this phenomenon as retrograde condensation of the first type. The crosshatched area represents the region in which the retrograde phenomenon takes place for the system under study. Retrograde condensation is a phenomenon of prime interest

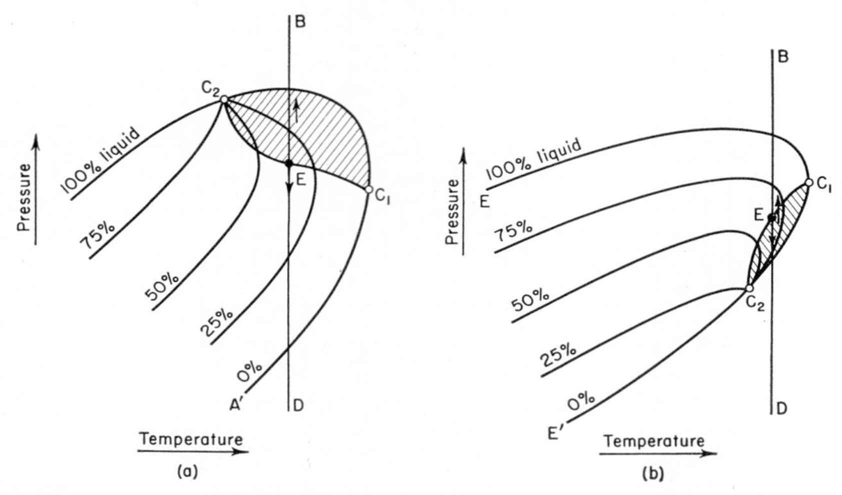

FIG. 6-9. Retrograde condensation and vaporization: (*a*) of the first type and (*b*) of the second type.

to the petroleum industry, especially in the production from condensate or distillate fields.

When the critical point is at a lower pressure than the cricondentherm C_1, retrograde condensation of the second type takes place. Figure 6-9*b* represents this phenomenon. Should a system be compressed isothermally between C_1 and C_2, a mixture separates with a density lower than that of the original system, the amount increasing at first (line DB), then decreasing until it entirely disappears. This condition possibly may be encountered when hydrocarbon systems are processed at extremely low temperature.

The previous discussion is limited to the phase behavior of components with mutual solubility. At high pressure, and especially when one component is polar, van der Waals has pointed out the possibility of the formation of two liquid layers. To distinguish a system forming one liquid layer from a system forming two liquid layers, the term "double retrograde" condensation was applied to the latter. Katz (1940) pointed out the probability of *double retrograde* condensation with high-pressure natural gases saturated with *both heavy hydrocarbons and water vapor*. Katz states:

"High pressure is known to increase the vapor pressure of water in the water–natural gas mixtures as the critical pressure for these mixtures is approached. Thus it may be expected that water will condense along with the hydrocarbons if the pressure is decreased isothermally."

The term retrograde suggests that the phenomena observed are reversed when compared with those of the accepted custom. Obviously depending upon temperature, pressure, and composition of the mixture, the behavior of hydrocarbon mixtures does not conform to the classical gas laws predicting vapor pressure and solubility relationships over the retrograde range.

Although the retrograde phenomena were known at the turn of the century, all the literature was originally in German. Research work by Sage and Lacey, sponsored by the American Petroleum Institute under research project 37, has produced valuable information relative to this subject. Kay et al. (1933) have contributed by their work with mixtures of ethane and heptane. Katz and Hachmuth (1937) have worked with mixtures of crude oil and natural gas, and Katz and Singleterry (1938) have noted the results of natural gas and crude oil containing tar. Katz and Kurata (1940) have published valuable information on retrograde condensation, including additional data on the phase relationship of methane and natural gas.

A possible explanation of the complex phenomena occurring in the condensate sand may be obtained from the work on light petroleum fractions by Sage, Lacey, and Schaafsma (1933).

Patten and Ivey (1938) have applied the data of Sage and others (1933) and constructed the graph of Fig. 6-10 in order to explain the probable behavior of hydrocarbons produced by condensate wells. Figure 6-10 is of a methane-propane system of constant composition as affected by changes in pressure and temperature. The curve AA' is for a 70 mole per cent methane, 30 mole per cent propane; curve BB' is for a 60 mole per cent methane, 40 mole per cent propane; curve CC' is for a 50 mole per cent methane, 50 mole per cent propane mixture.

Curve BB' reveals that the section $B'EH$ is the dew point for the gas phase of this mixture of 60 mole per cent methane and 40 mole per cent propane. The portion BH of the curve is the bubble-point pressure curve for the liquid phase.

Considering again the mixture of 60 mole per cent methane and 40 mole per cent propane, it is noted that if such a mixture at a constant temperature of 25°C (77°F) be compressed, the gas phase only exists until a pressure of 31.5 atm (460 psi) is reached, when a liquid phase appears. There is an increase in the liquid phase until the pressure of 97.5 atm (1,430 psi) is attained; above this pressure a uniform liquid phase will be present. If the experiment be repeated at 31.1°C (88°F), a uniform gaseous phase exists until a pressure of 38 atm is reached; then the liquid phase appears, and this phase increases until a pressure of 95.7 atm (1,410 psi) is attained, at which pressure the densities of the gaseous and liquid phases will be similar and the meniscus separating the two phases disappears. This pressure (95.7 atm) and temperature (31.1°C) are represented by point H, which is the critical pressure and temperature of the 60 mole per cent methane, 40 mole per cent propane mixture.

It should be noted that in a system containing two or more components it is possible to have a liquid phase above the critical pressure of the

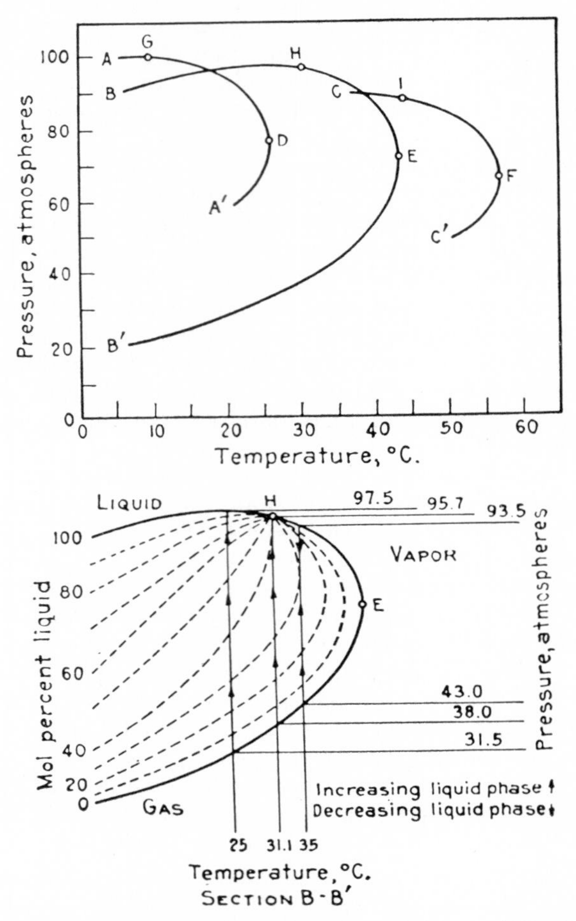

FIG. 6-10. Methane-propane system of constant composition. (*After Patten and Ivey, courtesy The Petroleum Engineer.*)

system. It should also be noted that the maximum temperature, or cricondentherm, at which a liquid phase may exist in the various mixtures is determined by the points D, E, and F, respectively, and that this temperature increases with increased per cent mole fraction of the heavier hydrocarbon. In addition, points G, H, and I determine the critical pressure and temperature points of the respective mixtures.

When the experiment is repeated with the same mixture at a temperature of 35°C (95°F), the liquid phase appears at a pressure of 43 atm (630 psi).

As the pressure increases, the liquid fraction will increase to a certain point after which point the liquid phase decreases until at a pressure of 93.5 atm (1,375 psi) it completely disappears and only the gaseous phase exists. The experiment at 35°C under variable pressure illustrates the phenomenon of retrograde vaporization of the first type.

Figure 6-11 is a phase diagram for a natural gas–natural gasoline mixture, as reported by Katz (1940), which represents the phase behavior in the critical region. The quality lines converge at a pressure of 2,730 psi

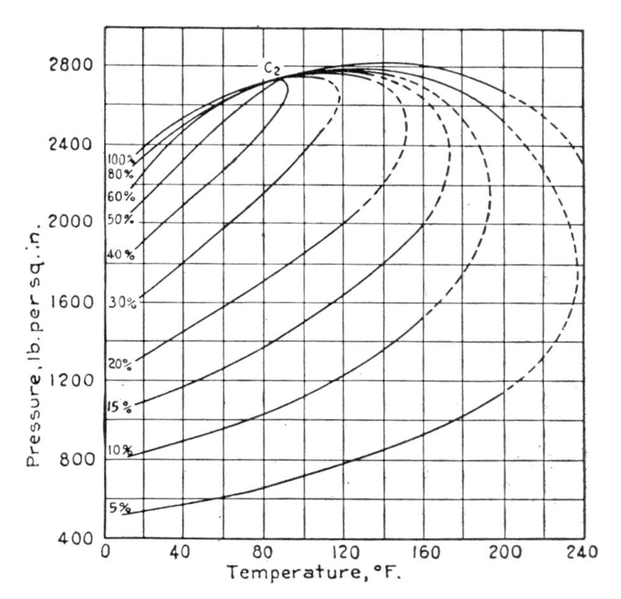

FIG. 6-11. Phase diagram of a natural gas–natural gasoline mixture. (*After Katz and Kurata, courtesy The Petroleum Engineer.*)

(185 atm) and 90°F (32.2°C), the respective critical pressure and temperature.

Another method of representing phase-behavior data consists in plotting the *equilibrium vaporization constant* as a function of pressure under isothermal conditions. The vaporization equilibrium constant may be defined as the ratio of the mole fraction of one component in the vapor phase to its mole fraction in the liquid phase. For a two-component system, two curves result, one for each component, the curves meeting at a value of unity for the equilibrium constant, at the critical temperature and critical pressure of the system.

Figure 6-12 (dotted portion) is for the 60 mole per cent methane, 40 mole per cent propane mixture plotted on the pressure-temperature-constant composition chart of Fig. 6-10. The ordinate is the vaporization constant, and the abscissa is the pressure in pounds per square inch. The equilibrium constant for methane decreases with increased pressure until its value is unity at 95.7 atm. The constant for propane first decreases, then increases until its value reaches unity at 95.7 atm also. This pressure (95.7 atm or 1,410 psi) is the critical pressure for the system and the prevailing isothermal condition of 31.1°C (88°F). This is also the critical temperature under the prevailing conditions of the system.

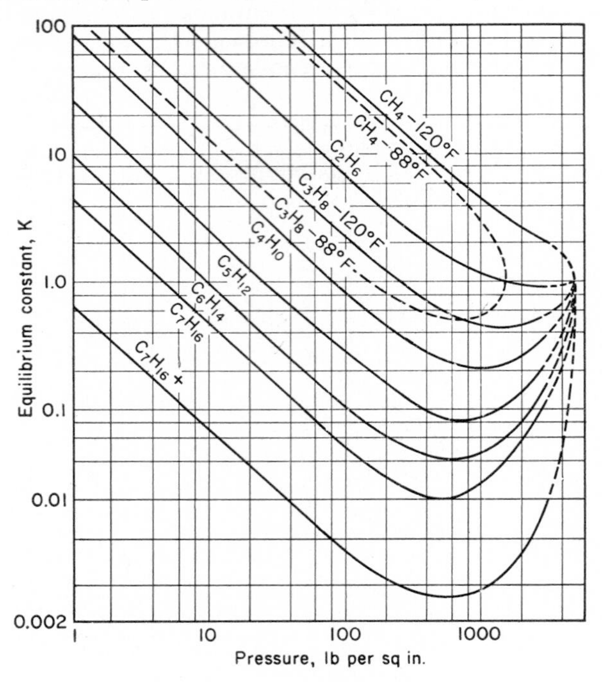

FIG. 6-12. Equilibrium vaporization constants. Solid lines represent data by Katz and Hachmuth based on 38.4° API crude oil–natural gas system at 120°F; dotted lines are data on methane-propane system by Patten and Ivey. (*Courtesy The Petroleum Engineer.*)

It should be noted that the *convergence pressure* for a binary mixture (the pressure at which the equilibrium constant is equal to unity) is the critical pressure of the mixture. In addition, the temperature of the system under isothermal conditions is the critical temperature of the system. The shapes of the equilibrium-constant curves as they diverge from the convergence pressure depend upon the composition of the system.

It has been observed for two-component systems, in which each component is a multicomponent mixture, that the equilibrium-constant curves still have similar characters. Figure 6-12 represents such a case (solid lines). It is based on data obtained by Katz and Hachmuth (1937) on mixtures of Oklahoma City crude oil (38.4°API) and natural gas at 120°F (49°C). The use of equilibrium constants obtained for one mixture may be used with a reasonable degree of accuracy for similar mixtures. At high pressure all equilibrium constants for mixtures are subject to deviation.

In Fig. 6-12 (data from Katz and Hachmuth) the equilibrium constants converge at about 5,000 psi (critical pressure) with a critical temperature of 120°F (49°C). In Fig. 6-11, the equilibrium constants would converge to unity at 2,730 psi and 90°F (32.2°C) should these data be plotted on an equilibrium-constant pressure chart such as Fig. 6-12.

The critical pressure of mixtures increases for compounds of higher molecular weight or with high percentage of heavy ends. Katz and Singleterry (1938) have reported that critical pressures of mixtures of natural gas and crude oil containing heavy tar may be above 25,000 psi.

Patten (1938) has determined experimentally a number of equilibrium constants for the products of condensate wells at various temperatures and at pressures up to 2,380 psi. Table 6-1 lists these values at the respective temperature and pressure. This table includes also the various constants as determined by Katz and Hachmuth (1937). It is noted that the equilibrium constants for the respective hydrocarbons are in fair agreement.

The PVT relationships of hydrocarbon gases and liquids are summarized in the composite diagram of Fig. 6-13, where the phase changes represented occur under constant volume. The terminology which characterizes the various phases is evidenced on the diagram.

TABLE 6-1

Hydrocarbon	Mole per cent contained in gas	Mole per cent contained in liquid	K, calculated	K (Katz and Hachmuth)
Pressure 2,000 psi; temperature 80°F (26.7°C)				
C_1	93.71	36.10	2.60	2.50
C_2	3.16	3.26	0.97	0.79
C_3	1.31	5.09	0.26	0.37
C_4	0.84	4.81	0.175	0.20
C_5	0.47	3.85	0.122	0.10
C_6	0.51	46.90	0.011	
Pressure 2,320 psi; temperature 90°F (32.2°C); mol wt C_6 = 119				
C_1	86.68	52.64	1.65	2.40
C_2	5.45	7.42	0.73	0.80
C_3	3.93	7.90	0.50	0.44
i-C_4	0.17	1.92	0.41 (for i-C_4 and n-C_4)	0.24
n-C_4	2.49	4.50		
C_5	0.42	4.18	0.10	0.13
C_6	0.86	21.44	0.04	

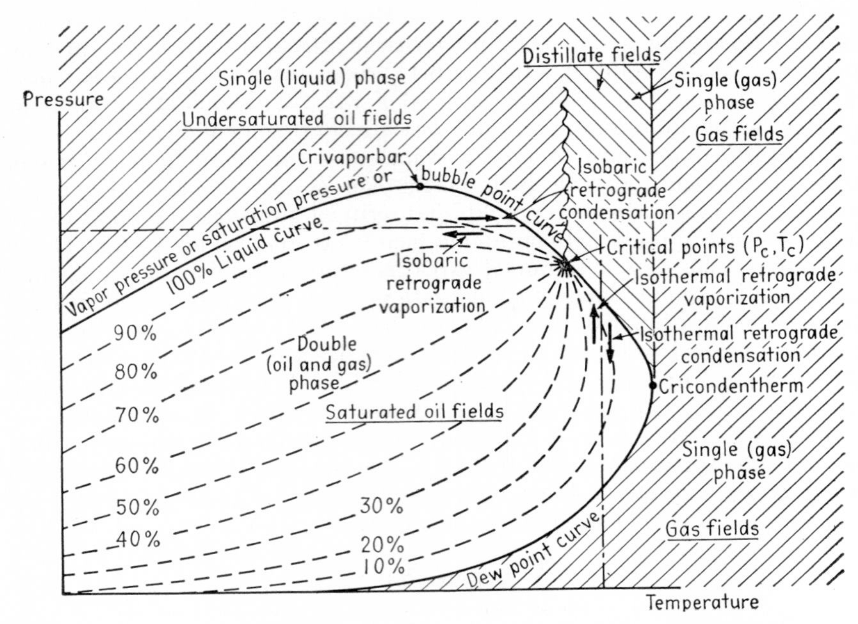

FIG. 6-13. Phase relationships and types of oil and gas fields possible with complex hydrocarbon systems.

Molecular Explanation of the Retrograde Phenomenon. A molecular explanation of the retrograde phenomenon has been given by Nielsen (1942), based on the interaction of van der Waals' forces between the molecules of a binary mixture. This theory is summarized here by courtesy of the *Oil Weekly*.

The explanation involves the assumption of attractive forces between molecules as governing the phase behavior of a system. In the case of nonpolar substances, such as hydrocarbons, the forces are entirely "van der Waals' forces," so-called because of their relation to the term a/V^2 in van der Waals' equation of state, $(P + a/V^2)(V - b) = nRT$. In this equation, a and b are constants for a given gas, n is the number of moles, and P, V, R, and T have the usual significance.

Although van der Waals' equation does not hold quantitatively at high pressures, it presents a simple explanation of the behavior of a gas. The term b is subtracted from the volume to allow for the space occupied by the molecules themselves. Thus, $V - b$ is the net space available for molecular motion. The term a/V^2 is often called the "internal pressure," since it is a correction applied to the pressure, due to the attraction between molecules. It is added to the pressure, since attraction between molecules acts in the same way as external pressure by reducing the volume. While a/V^2 measures the effect on the total pressure, a is a measure of the attraction of the individual molecules for each other at a given distance apart.

It is these forces which make a liquid surface act like an elastic membrane, on account of the one-sided attraction on the molecules in the surface. While the van der Waals forces tend to pull molecules together into the liquid state, the molecular motion (kinetic energy) associated with a given temperature tends to pull them apart. Under conditions where liquid and vapor can coexist, these opposing factors are balanced so that part of the substance is in each phase. When the temperature is above the critical, the attractive forces cannot maintain a liquid phase on account of the higher kinetic energies associated with the higher temperature. At pressures below the vapor pressure of the liquid, the attractive forces become lessened by the greater distance between molecules, so the liquid phase again cannot exist.

These same attractive forces cause one substance to be soluble in another and pull molecules into a given phase. There is an attraction between all molecules of a similar type, regardless of size, but the magnitude of the attraction depends on the molecule size, as shown by Table 6-2, which gives the values of a for a number of paraffin hydrocarbons. The smaller the molecular attraction, i.e., a, the more volatile the substance.

TABLE 6-2. VALUES OF THE VAN DER WAALS' CONSTANT a

Gas	a
Methane	0.0045
Ethane	0.0107
Propane	0.0170
n-Butane	0.0290
n-Pentane	0.0380
n-Hexane	0.0490

While normal processes of vaporization and condensation are associated mainly with the attraction of the heavier molecules for each other, the retrograde processes are associated with the attraction between the light and the heavy molecules. The former type of attraction tends to pull molecules into the liquid phase and the latter to pull the heavier molecules into the gaseous phase, when the gaseous phase is sufficiently dense, i.e., at high pressures.

Geological Factors Involved in the Characteristics of Reservoir Fluids. In a given field and reservoir, bottom-hole samples taken under identical pressure conditions do not necessarily exhibit the same saturation pressure, the latter being a measure of the amount of gas in solution per unit volume.

Normally the saturation pressure of a crude increases with temperature. This results from the increased vapor pressure of the gas in solution in the oil, which pressure causes the gas to be released in larger volumes when the sample is subjected to lower static pressures.

The type of geologic reservoir and its characteristic porosity and permeability, as well as its degree of fissuring and folding, may be responsible for the rapidity with which solution-gas equilibrium may be established throughout the reservoir.

There is no such thing as a leakproof roof over an oil reservoir. Gas seepages especially take place over geologic time, and the rate of escape of gases from solution in the oil depends on whether the overburden is mainly relatively impermeable formations such as shales, limestones, and water-saturated layers or more permeable sections such as unconsolidated sands. Other factors such as thickness of overburden, erosion, folding, fracturing, and fissuring also influence the rate of gas escape over geologic time.

Captain Comins (1933) has given a very illustrative example of what might happen over geologic time and during the production history of a Persian oil field. While Comins' theory of reservoir-oil evolution will be largely followed, certain modifications of the basic assumptions are made, namely, that (1) at a certain period during geologic time, the generation, migration, and accumulation of oil and gas into the structure ceased, (2) oil production is altogether from the oil zones of the reservoir, and (3) no water encroachment exists.

The structure composed of two domes separated by a saddle occupied the configuration represented on Fig. 6-14 at the close of the maximum sedimentation cycle. Before subsequent erosion it is postulated that oil and gas convection currents within the reservoir could take place at a faster rate than the rate at which the over-all gas leakage from the structure actually occurred. In view of the difference in level between the two domes, the lower dome was under a rock pressure too high and the gas diffusion path was too long to permit the formation of a gas cap, whereas in the higher dome the gas leakage rate was increased owing to a greatly facilitated gas diffusion. This permitted the formation of a gas cap. All the oil in the reservoir was accordingly saturated at the original gas-cap pressure in the higher dome.

It is possible to visualize geologic conditions of continued sedimentation and arrested oil accumulation where the overburden pressure was such that all the gas available in the reservoir was put into solution and the oil was then *undersaturated.* This may also occur when the oil is under a high hydrostatic pressure such as in the East Texas field.

It is generally observed that few undersaturated oil fields have been discovered at shallow depths unless they were under a very active water drive which maintained pressure over the saturation point.

Such oil fields when discovered are found to contain oil saturated to the prevailing hydrostatic pressure ($h \times 1/2.31$, where h is the reservoir depth, in feet) and not to overburden pressure ($h \times \delta \times 1/2.31$, where $\delta \cong 2.4$, the average rock density in oil fields). However, oil fields discovered at greater depth, i.e., larger than 10,000 ft, on the Gulf Coast are found to be saturated to overburden pressure (Cannon and Craze, 1938).

Generally it may be observed that:

1. Fields under active water drive contain undersaturated oil under hydrostatic bottom-hole pressure.

2. Fields with gas cap contain saturated oil, the saturation pressure of which is the gas-cap pressure. For shallow fields the gas-cap pressure is equal to or less than hydrostatic.

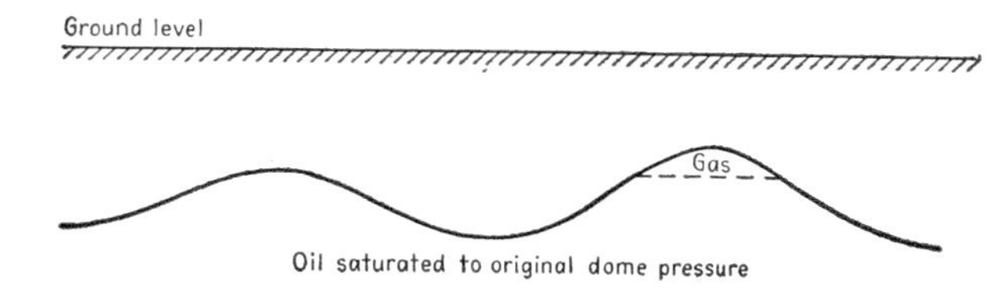

● *Stage a* shows a virgin reservoir in solution-equilibrium before seepages started. In geological time the whole of the oil in the reservoir has become saturated to original dome pressure in the higher gas dome. There is, therefore, no accumulation of gas in the lower dome. Earth pressures at all points are higher than dome or reservoir pressures and there are no seepages of gas or oil.

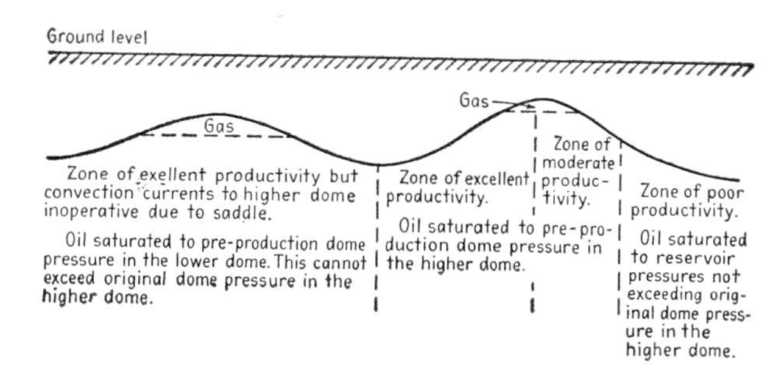

● *Stage b* shows disturbance of solution-equilibrium by seepages consequent upon erosion (position immediately before production). As a result of erosion the earth pressure on the higher gas dome has fallen below the original dome pressure, causing a gas seepage there and reducing the dome pressure and the volume of the free gas there. Owing to the saddle between the two domes, solution-equilibrium between them has not been maintained by convection. The saturation pressure of the oil in the lower dome therefore remained at original dome pressure in the upper dome until reservoir pressures in the lower dome fell to that pressure. Gas was then evolved from solution and accumulated there, but owing to the higher earth pressure there is no seepage.

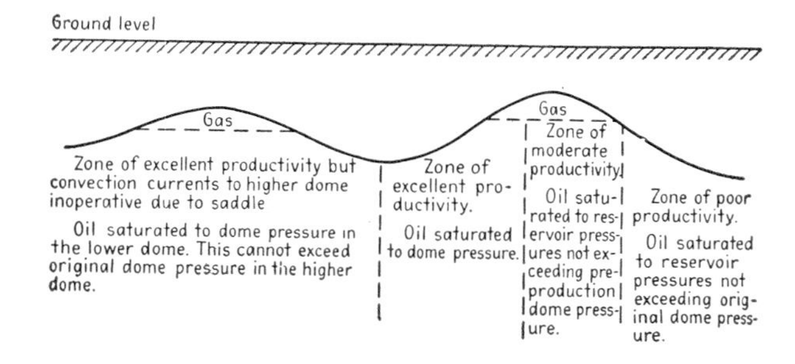

● *Stage c* shows a further disturbance of solution-equilibrium by production. As a result of production, dome pressure in the higher dome has fallen more rapidly and only in zones of excellent productivity favorable to convection currents has true solution-equilibrium been maintained. Owing to the increased rate of gas evolution gas has again accumulated in the higher as well as the lower dome. Also the rate of gas seepage from the higher dome has decreased as dome pressure has now fallen below earth pressure.

FIG. 6-14. Postulated history of fluid-saturation status in an Iranian field. (*After Comins.*)

Under the conditions assumed in Fig. 6-14*a*, the reservoir fluids are in equilibrium with the natural seepages.

In Fig. 6-14*b* a certain amount of erosion is assumed to have taken place over geologic time. As a result of erosion the over-all permeability to gas of the overburden was increased, hydrostatic and rock pressures were reduced, and a more active gas leakage ensued. This reduced the pressure in the higher dome, and the gas cap was enlarged. More rapid leakage also prevailed from the lower dome as well as convection currents to the higher dome. Pressure in the lower dome dropped, and a gas cap was formed. However, solution equilibrium between the higher and lower dome did not exist, owing to the presence of a saddle.

Figure 6-14*b* represents the conditions of the reservoir as they existed just before production started. Because of differential permeabilities between the various sections of the reservoir as shown, differential states of saturation for the oil existed as indicated.

Figure 6-14*c* indicates the disturbance produced by production. The pressure in the gas cap fell rapidly as production progressed, and, in zones of good or high permeability, true solution equilibrium was maintained. Increased gas evolution created larger gas caps. Gas leakage to the surface was considerably decreased because earth pressure exceeded gas-cap pressure. Saturation equilibrium within the oil zone was controlled during production by the relative degrees of permeability within the various sections of the field. In high-permeability zones, the oil was saturated to prevailing gas-cap pressure. In medium- and low-permeability sections equilibrium with gas-cap pressure was not achieved, and the oil remained saturated to preproduction gas-cap pressure in the first instance and to preerosion gas-cap pressure in the second instance. The presence of the saddle prevented saturation equilibrium between the two domes, even though the reservoir is of high permeability.

Testing of Bottom-hole Samples. For the purpose of ascertaining PVT relations of reservoir fluids, it is necessary to let gas evolve from solution in the oil. This may be accomplished by two distinct modes, namely, *flash* and *differential* vaporizations.

Flash vaporization, illustrated in Fig. 6-15*a*, is a process which is operative at constant temperature and which brings all the liquid into equilibrium with all the vapor either in a batch process or in a continuous-flow process. In this operation the fluid system remains at constant composition and weight, the liquid and vapor phases being in equilibrium with one another. The operation takes place in a variable volume and at variable pressure.

Differential vaporization is illustrated in Fig. 6-15*b* and is a process operative at constant temperature whereby the vapor is continuously removed from the liquid as soon as it is formed by continuous lowering of pressure. Vaporization of a gaseous constituent from a liquid causes the liquid to shrink in volume. Therefore, true differential vaporization requires a reduction of the volume of the container which may be achieved by the introduction of an inert fluid such as mercury in the laboratory and water in the field. In this operation, the fluid system is of variable composition and weight.

The attainment of equilibrium conditions between liquid and vapor phases requires intimate contact between the phases. Under agitation and extensive contact surface, the duration of the contact need not be long, but under quiescent contact long periods of time are needed for equilibrium to be established.

It is difficult to establish which vaporization process is operative in the reservoir itself. Very likely a combination of the two is involved.

The differential vaporization adopted by Lindsly (1936) deviates from

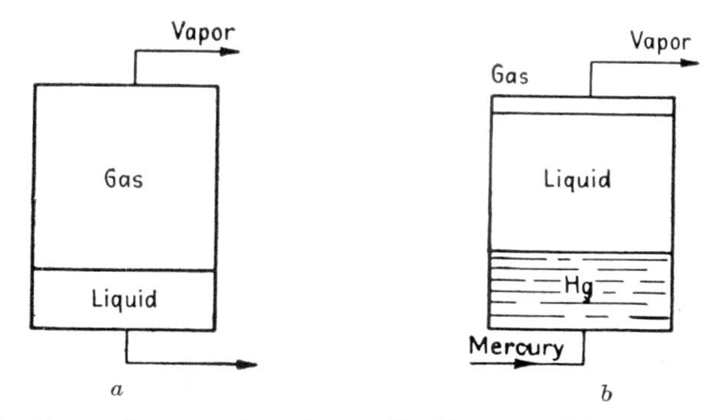

FIG. 6-15. Two types of vapor release from a liquid are possible: (*a*) flash vaporization and (*b*) differential vaporization. In flash vaporization both vapor and liquid are withdrawn continuously while equilibrium is maintained, whereas in differential vaporization the vapor only is withdrawn in a continuous manner while the volume shrinkage is made up by the injection of an inert liquid.

the true differential process because the tests are made in a constant volume cell; therefore, a large vapor space or gas cap is formed, due to liquid shrinkage. The *constant volume differential* vaporization of Lindsly may give close approximation to the fluid conditions operative in depletion and gas-cap expansion drives.

Another variant of differential vaporization is a process where the vapor space developed in the chamber due to volume shrinkage during the several pressure decrements is replaced by mercury at the end of each pressure decrement and the gas is forced back into solution, thus bringing the content of the chamber to a single phase. This is the procedure proposed by Exline (1936). For very small pressure decrements, the fluid characteristics obtained would be those of a true differential vaporization.

Katz (1939) has shown that there is no appreciable difference between the results obtained by the constant volume (Lindsly) and the approximate (Exline) differential vaporization methods of testing bottom-hole samples.

The required hook-up for the testing of bottom-hole samples by the Gulf method is shown in Fig. 6-16.

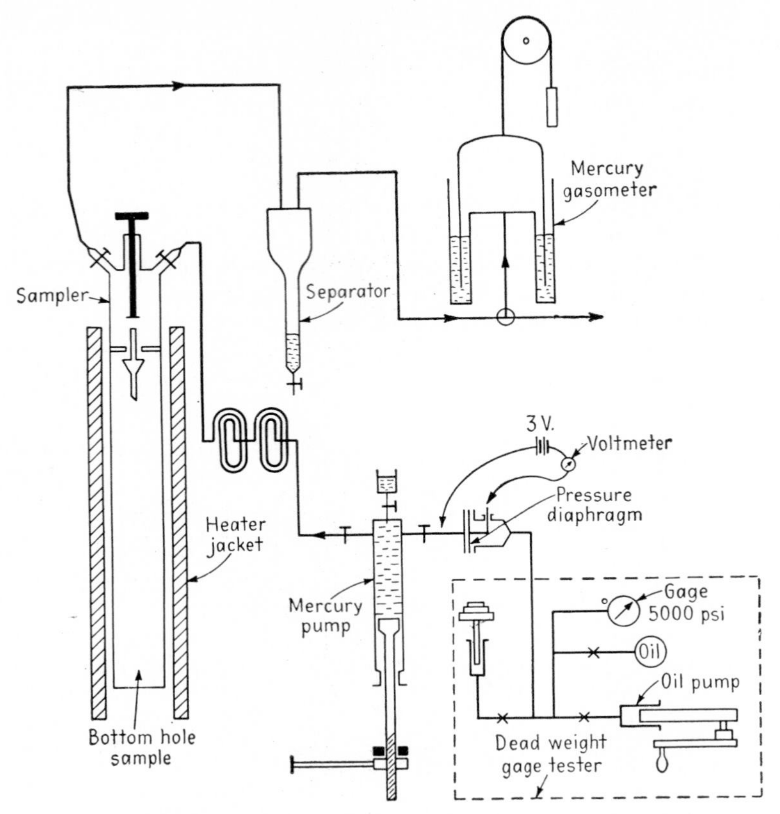

FIG. 6-16. Schematic diagram hook-up for bottom-hole sample testing by the Gulf method.

First of all the saturation or bubble-point pressure (SP_0) of the original sample is determined. This requires a mercury injection of volume h_0.

Test 1: Flash a certain volume from the sampler when the fluid is above SP_0. Read the residual oil O_1 in the burette and the gas G_1 evolved in the gasometer.

Resaturate the sample, and determine the new saturation pressure (SP_1) by a mercury injection of volume h_1.

Test 2: Flash a new volume of fluid from the sampler when the pressure is above SP_1. Read O_2 and G_2 as well as the new saturation pressure (SP_2) and mercury injection h_2.

Test n: Flash volumes On and Gn when saturation pressure is SP_{n-1}. Read new saturation pressure (SP_n) for mercury injection h_n.

Test f (final): Flash the last volume of gas necessary for the sample to reach atmospheric pressure. The largest volume of gas is normally liberated in this last step. Read O_f and G_f. The saturation pressure of the oil (O_r) remaining in the sampler is atmospheric (or nonexistent) since there is no more solution gas. The residual oil (O_r) in the sampler is measured by injecting sufficient mercury (h_f) into the sampler to fill it. This is observed when a drop of oil appears at the separator. Hence

$$O_r = V - \sum_{i=0}^{f} h_i$$

where V is the volume of the sampler at bottom-hole temperature.

The reservoir-fluid characteristics are readily calculated by filling Table 6-3, in which the operations are symbolically indicated.

TABLE 6-3. COMPUTATION OF BOTTOM-HOLE SAMPLE DATA

Saturation pressure (1)	Saturated oil volume (2)	Gas in solution in saturated oil (3)	Residual oil (4)	Gas solubility, S (3)/(4) (5)	Reservoir volume factor β (2)/(4) (6)
SP_0	$V - h_0$	$\sum_{i=f}^{1} G_i$	$O_r + \sum_{i=1}^{f} O_i$		
SP_1	$V - h_0 - h_1$	$\sum_{i=f}^{2} G_i$	$O_r + \sum_{i=2}^{f} O_i$		
SP_2	$V - h_0 - h_1 - h_2$				
SP_3	$V - \sum_{i=0}^{3} h_i$				
SP_n	$V - \sum_{i=0}^{n} h_i$	$\sum_{i=f}^{n+1} G_i$	$O_r + \sum_{i=n+1}^{f} O_i$	$\dfrac{\sum_{i=f}^{n+1} G_i}{O_r + \sum_{i=n+1}^{f} O_i}$	$\dfrac{V - \sum_{i=0}^{n} h_i}{O_r + \sum_{i=n+1}^{f} O_i}$
SP_{f-2}	. . . .	$G_{f-1} + G_f$	$O_r + O_f + O_{f-1}$		
SP_{f-1}	$V - \sum_{i=0}^{f-1} h_i$	G_f	$O_r + O_f$		
$SP_f = P_a$	$V - \sum_{i=0}^{f} h_i$	0	O_r		

Example. An example of computation of bottom-hole sample characteristics, the basic data of which are those of Table 6-4, is given in Tables 6-5 to 6-8.

TABLE 6-4. EXAMPLE OF COMPUTATION OF RESERVOIR-FLUID CHARACTERISTICS FROM BOTTOM-HOLE SAMPLE TESTING

(Data Pertaining to Gulf Judge 82, East Texas Field, Texas *)

Date of test	Sept. 4, 1943
Closed tubing pressure	175 psi
Closed casing pressure	10 psi
Choke size	1/4 in.
Flowing tubing pressure	95 psi
Flowing casing pressure	10 psi
Oil production, bbl per day	234
Gas production per day	89 MCF
Gas-oil ratio	380:1
Corrected gravity of oil	40°API
Temperature of oil in tank	87°F
Specific gravity of gas	1.03
Sample taken at	3,500 ft
Static bottom-hole pressure at 3,500 ft	1,024 psi
Flowing bottom-hole pressure at 3,500 ft after flowing well for 1 hr and 20 min and producing 17 bbl of oil	1,018 psi
Flowing temperature at 3,500 ft	145°F
Separator pressure	54 psi
Separator temperature	83°F

* Courtesy of the Gulf Research and Development Corporation.

TABLE 6-5. DATA USED TO DETERMINE THE INITIAL SAMPLE PRESSURE *

Mercury pump reading	Volume injected, cc	Observed pressure, psi	Corrected pressure, psi	Sampler temperature, °F
38	0	0	10	145
241	4.06	100	110	
259	4.42	215	225	
269	4.62	412	422	
274	4.72	610	620	
279	4.82	827	837	
284	4.92	965	975	
287	4.98	1,000	1,010	
254	5.00 †	976	986	
224	4.40	904	914	
204	4.00	859	869	
154	3.00	746	756	
54	1.00	670	680	

* Courtesy of the Gulf Research and Development Corporation.

† At this point a correction of 0.68 cc was applied to account for the introduction of a volume of steel caused by insertion of the valve stem of the bleeder head.

Table 6-6. Data Taken during the Six Mercury-injection Runs *

Run no.	Pump reading	Mercury volume pumped, cc	Mercury † volume injected, cc	Observed pressure, psi	Sample pressure, psi	Sampler tempera-ture, °F
1	54	0.32	−3.10	692	680	145
1	59	0.42	−3.00	693	681	
1	69	0.62	−2.80	701	689	
1	89	1.02	−2.40	702	690	
1	109	1.42	−2.00	702	690	
1	159	2.42	−1.00	703	691	
1	209	3.42	0	706	694	
1	229	3.82	0.40	754	742	
1	239	4.02	0.60	780	768	
1	249	4.22	0.80	790	778	
1	269	4.62	1.20	827	815	
1	289	5.02	1.60	895	883	142
1	109	1.42	−2.00	695	683	145
2	109	1.42	−2.00	640	628	144
2	209	3.42	0	645	633	145
2	259	4.42	1.00	650	638	145
2	309	5.42	2.00	651	639	144
2	359	6.42	3.00	652	640	145
2	409	7.42	4.00	653	641	145
2	509	9.42	6.00	658	646	144
2	559	10.42	7.00	752	740	145
2	609	11.42	8.00	870	858	145
2	659	12.42	9.00	985	973	145
2	209	3.42	0	645	633	145
3	209	3.42	0	521	509	146
3	264	4.52	1.10	524	512	145
3	314	5.52	2.10	528	516	145
3	364	6.52	3.10	533	521	145
3	414	7.52	4.10	533	521	145
3	814	15.52	12.10	543	531	145
3	914	17.52	14.10	545	533	
3	1,214	23.52	20.10	662	650	145
3	1,264	24.52	21.10	786	774	144
3	1,314	25.52	22.10	890	878	145
3	814	15.52	12.10	543	531	145
4	814	15.52	12.10	392	380	145
4	1,214	23.52	20.10	399	387	145
4	1,614	31.52	28.10	407	395	145
4	2,014	39.52	36.10	420	408	145

See p. 332 for footnotes.

TABLE 6-6. DATA TAKEN DURING THE SIX MERCURY-INJECTION RUNS * (*Continued*

Run no.	Pump reading	Mercury volume pumped, cc	Mercury † volume injected, cc	Observed pressure, psi	Sample pressure, psi	Sampler temperature, °F
4	2,054	40.32	36.90	517	505	145
4	2,114	41.52	38.10	632	620	145
4	2,214	43.52	40.10	845	833	145
4	1,214	23.52	20.10	399	387	145
5	1,214	23.52	20.10	269	257	145
5	1,614	31.52	28.10	272	260	
5	2,014	39.52	36.10	276	264	145
5	2,414	47.52	44.10	279	267	
5	2,714	53.52	50.10	308	296	145
5	2,764	54.52	51.10	400	388	
5	3,814	55.52	52.10	502	490	145
5	2,864	56.52	53.10	606	594	
5	2,014	39.52	36.10	276	264	145
6	2,014	39.52	36.10	163	151	145
6	2,414	47.52	44.10	166	154	
6	2,814	55.52	52.10	168	156	145
6	3,214	63.52	60.10	169	157	145
6	3,614	71.52	68.10	243	231	145
6	3,664	72.52	69.10	335	323	145
6	3,714	73.52	70.10	435	423	145
6	2,814	55.52	52.10	168	156	145
6	2,814	55.52	52.10		0	
6	8,214	163.52	160.10		0	
	Mercury pump refilled					
6	4,000	163.52	160.10		0	
6	4,600	175.42	172.10		0	

* Courtesy of the Gulf Research and Development Corporation.

† The volume of mercury pumped to obtain the initial saturation pressure was 3.42 cc. This value was subtracted from the values listed in column 3 to obtain those given in column 4.

TABLE 6-7. VOLUMES OF GAS BLED OFF FROM SAMPLE *

Run (1)	Observed volume, cu ft (2)	Gas temperature, °F (3)	Baro., in. Hg (4)	Gas † volume, 60°F cu ft (5)	Gas ‡ volume, 60°F 30 in. Hg cu ft (6)	Oil in separator, cc (7)	Oil volume, 60°F cc (8)
1	0.0200	79	29.2	0.01929	0.01880		
1	0.0300	79	29.2	0.02894	0.02820	1.7	1.69
2	0.1010	79	29.2	0.09744	0.09496		
2	0.0503	79	29.2	0.04853	0.04730	0.8	0.79
3	0.1000	79	29.2	0.09647	0.09402		
3	0.1000	79	29.2	0.09647	0.09402	3.1	3.07
4	0.1040	72	29.4	0.10165	0.09974		
4	0.1000	72	29.4	0.09774	0.09591	0.2	0.20
5	0.1001	72	29.4	0.09784	0.09600		
5	0.0999	72	29.4	0.09765	0.09582	2.8	2.78
6	0.1001	72	29.4	0.09784	0.09600		
6	0.1001	74	29.4	0.09784	0.09565		
6	0.1000	77.4	29.4	0.09676	0.09494		
6	0.1055	77	29.4	0.10216	0.10024		
6	0.1500	77.5	29.4	0.14512	0.14240		
6	0.1500	77.5	29.4	0.14512	0.14240		
6	0.1500	77.5	29.4	0.14512	0.14240	8.8	8.73
6	0.0609	78	29.4	0.05886	0.05776		
6	0.0065	78.5	29.4	0.00628	0.00616	10.5	10.41

* Courtesy of the Gulf Research and Development Corporation.
† Column 5 is obtained by applying factors of Table 6-9 to column 2.
‡ Column 6 is obtained by applying factors of Table 6-10 to column 5.

TABLE 6-8. VOLUME OF RESIDUAL OIL *

Volume of sampler No. 4	911.00 cc
Total mercury pumped in	172.10 cc
Volume of residual oil left in sampler	738.90 cc at 131°F
API gravity of oil left in sampler	38.4° at 60°F
Volume at 60°F of residual oil left in sampler	709.79 cc
Volume at 60°F of residual oil from separator	27.67 cc
Total volume of residual oil at 60°F	737.46 cc

* Courtesy of the Gulf Research and Development Corporation.

The data of Table 6-6 are graphically represented on Fig. 6-17 from which the saturation pressures at various stages of testing are obtained at the intersection points 1, 2, 3, 4, 5, and 6 corresponding to the various run numbers.

The results of Table 6-11 are graphically represented on Figs. 6-18 and 6-19 which, respectively, indicate the variations of volumetric shrinkage and of solution gas as a function of the sample's saturation pressure.

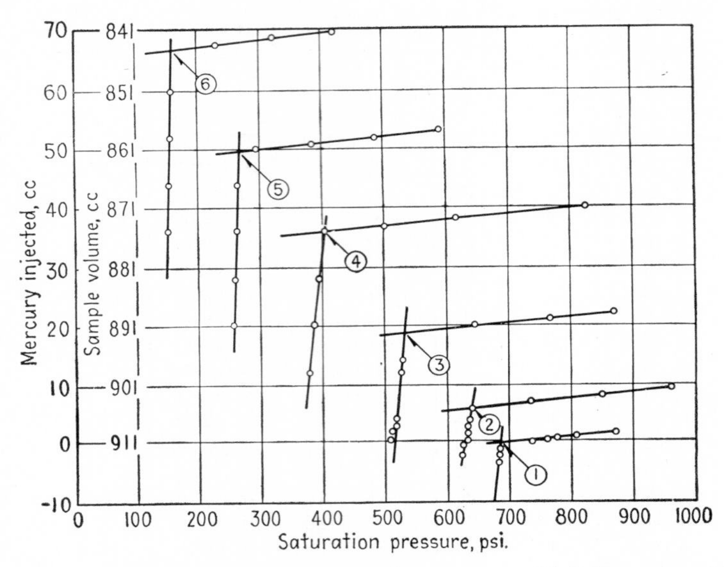

FIG. 6-17. Graphical determinations of saturation pressure. (*Gulf Research and Development Corp.*)

TABLE 6-9. FACTORS FOR CONVERTING OBSERVED GAS VOLUMES AT 60°F *

°F	0	1	2	3	4	5	6	7	8	9
50	1.01960	1.01761	1.01562	1.01364	1.01167	1.00970	1.00775	1.00580	1.00386	1.00193
60	1.00000	0.99808	0.99616	0.99426	0.99237	0.99047	0.98859	0.98671	0.98484	0.98298
70	0.98113	0.97928	0.97744	0.97560	0.97378	0.97196	0.97014	0.96834	0.96654	0.96474
80	0.96296	0.96118	0.95940	0.95764	0.95588	0.95412	0.95238	0.95063	0.94890	0.94717
90	0.94543	0.94371	0.94200	0.94030	0.93860	0.93691	0.93522	0.93354	0.93187	0.93020
100	0.92854	0.92688	0.92523	0.92359	0.92195	0.92031	0.91869	0.91707	0.91545	0.91384

* Courtesy of the Gulf Research and Development Corporation.

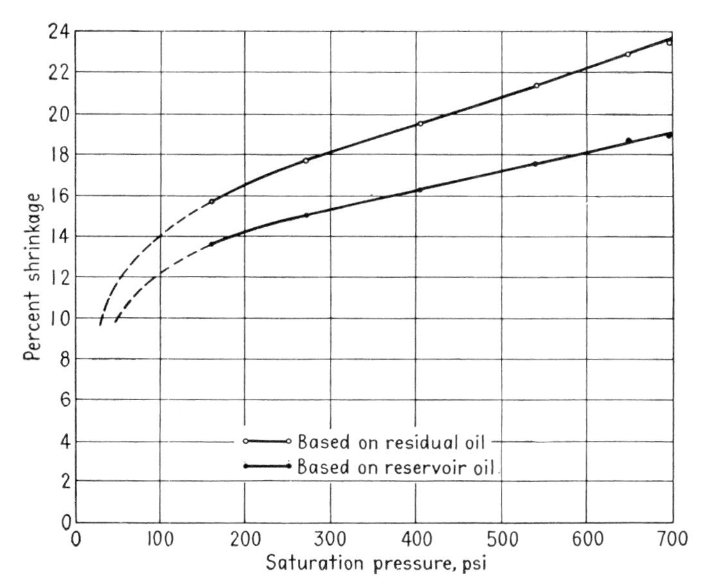

FIG. 6-18. Volume shrinkage from differential liberation. *(Gulf Research and Development Corp.)*

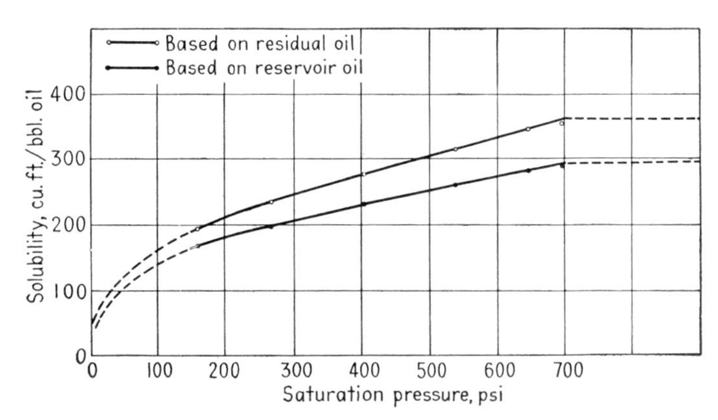

FIG. 6-19. Gas solubility from differential liberation. *(Gulf Research and Development Corp.)*

TABLE 6-10. CONVERSION FACTORS FOR REDUCING GAS VOLUME AT PRESSURE *B* TO VOLUME AT 30 IN. MERCURY *

B	0.00	0.01	0.02	0.03	0.04	0.05	0.06	0.07	0.08	0.09
28.0	0.93456	0.93489	0.93523	0.93556	0.93589	0.93623	0.93656	0.93689	0.93723	0.93756
28.1	0.93789	0.93823	0.93856	0.93889	0.93923	0.93956	0.93989	0.94023	0.94056	0.94089
28.2	0.94123	0.94156	0.94189	0.94223	0.94256	0.94289	0.94323	0.94356	0.94389	0.94423
28.3	0.94456	0.94489	0.94523	0.94556	0.94589	0.94623	0.94656	0.94689	0.94723	0.94756
28.4	0.94789	0.94823	0.94856	0.94889	0.94923	0.94956	0.94989	0.95023	0.95056	0.95089
28.5	0.95123	0.95156	0.95189	0.95223	0.95256	0.95289	0.95323	0.95356	0.95389	0.95423
28.6	0.95456	0.95489	0.95523	0.95556	0.95589	0.95623	0.95656	0.95689	0.95723	0.95756
28.7	0.95789	0.95823	0.95856	0.95889	0.95923	0.95956	0.95989	0.96023	0.96056	0.96089
28.8	0.96123	0.96156	0.96189	0.96223	0.96256	0.96289	0.96323	0.96356	0.96389	0.96423
28.9	0.96456	0.96489	0.96523	0.96556	0.96589	0.96623	0.96656	0.96689	0.96723	0.96756
29.0	0.96789	0.96823	0.96856	0.96889	0.96923	0.96956	0.96989	0.97023	0.97056	0.97089
29.1	0.97123	0.97156	0.97189	0.97223	0.97256	0.97289	0.97323	0.97356	0.97389	0.97423
29.2	0.97456	0.97489	0.97523	0.97556	0.97589	0.97623	0.97656	0.97689	0.97723	0.97756
29.3	0.97789	0.97823	0.97856	0.97889	0.97923	0.97956	0.97989	0.98023	0.98056	0.98089
29.4	0.98123	0.98156	0.98189	0.98223	0.98256	0.98289	0.98323	0.98356	0.98389	0.98423
29.5	0.98456	0.98489	0.98523	0.98556	0.98589	0.98623	0.98656	0.98689	0.98723	0.98756
29.6	0.98789	0.98823	0.98856	0.98889	0.98923	0.98956	0.98989	0.99023	0.99056	0.99089
29.7	0.99123	0.99156	0.99189	0.99223	0.99256	0.99289	0.99323	0.99356	0.99389	0.99423
29.8	0.99456	0.99489	0.99523	0.99556	0.99589	0.99623	0.99656	0.99689	0.99723	0.99756
29.9	0.99789	0.99823	0.99856	0.99889	0.99923	0.99956	0.99989	1.00023	1.00056	1.00089

* These factors include the correction for the pressure under the gasometer bell (0.50 in. water). Courtesy of the Gulf Research and Development Corporation.

TABLE 6-11. RESULTS OF DIFFERENTIAL LIBERATION OF SUBSURFACE SAMPLE FROM GULF JUDGE 82 *

Pressure, psi	Saturated oil volume		Gas in solution, cu ft	Residual oil			Shrinkage, per cent based on		Solution ratio based on	
	cc	bbl × 1,000		cc	Bbl × shrinkage		Residual oil	Reservoir oil	Residual oil, cu ft per bbl	Reservoir oil, cu ft per bbl
					1,000	cc				
(1)	(2)	(3)	(4)	(5)	(6)	(7)	(8)	(9)	(10)	(11)
694	911.00	5.730	1.6427	737.46	4.639	173.54	23.5	19.0	354	287
645	905.00	5.692	1.5957	735.77	4.628	169.23	23.0	18.7	345	280
538	891.92	5.610	1.4535	734.98	4.623	156.94	21.4	17.6	314	259
402	874.92	5.503	1.2654	731.91	4.604	143.01	19.5	16.3	275	230
268	861.22	5.417	1.0698	731.71	4.602	129.51	17.7	15.0	232	197
158	843.62	5.306	0.8780	728.93	4.585	114.69	15.7	13.6	191	165

* Courtesy of the Gulf Research and Development Corporation.

TABLE 6-12. SEPARATOR GAS ANALYSIS CORRESPONDING TO BOTTOM-HOLE SAMPLE OF GULF JUDGE 82, EAST TEXAS FIELD, TEXAS *

Composition	*Present sample, per cent*
CH_4	69.5
C_2H_6	17.5
C_3H_8	9.9
C_4H_{10}	2.1
C_5 +	1.0
	100.0
Mol wt	22.6
Sp gr	0.782

* Courtesy of the Gulf Research and Development Corporation.

The compressibility factor Z of the liberated solution gas collected in the gasometer was tested in the bottom-hole sampler with the results indicated in Fig. 6-20.

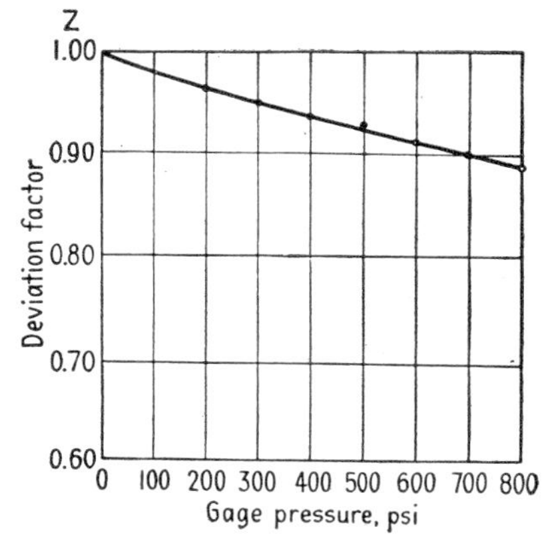

FIG. 6-20. Separator-gas deviation factor at 100°C. *(Gulf Research and Development Corp.)*

Prediction of the Density and Shrinkage of Crude Oils. In many instances the necessary bottom-hole sample data are unavailable for obtaining the physical characteristics of reservoir fluids. Katz (1942) has proposed a method by which the shrinkage of crudes may be calculated when the following ordinary field data are available: reservoir pressure and temperature, gas solubility in oil, stock-tank oil API gravity, and gas specific gravity with respect to air.

The shrinkage calculations do not depend upon the separation process, i.e., flash or differential vaporization of the gas, because the properties of the resulting gas and liquid, as well as the quantity of gas liberated, compensate for any changes in the shrinkage value.

The first step requires the computation of the density of liquids saturated with natural gas. A method by which this can be achieved has been presented by Standing and Katz (1942). The method consists in computing the density of the liquid at 60°F and 1 atm pressure; then it is corrected to the desired pressure and temperature. The densities of all constituents heavier than ethane are taken as the normal density in grams per milliliter or pounds per cubic feet of the pure constituent at 60°F and atmospheric pressure. For methane and ethane, it is necessary to devise an apparent density chart which gives the density of methane and of ethane as a function of the constituents other than methane or ethane. In most cases the method will compute the density of the crude oil saturated with natural gas to about ±2 per cent.

The calculations of the density of a crude oil saturated with natural gas require the analysis of the gas which is liberated when the crude oil is reduced in pressure, such as to atmospheric, along with the density of the remaining crude oil at the lower pressure. The quantity of gas liberated is added to the final crude oil, and the total volume of the crude oil saturated with this gas is computed at the saturation temperature and pressure. This volume minus that of the residual crude oil gives the shrinkage caused by vaporization.

Table 6-13 is an example calculation of the density and shrinkage for the Crescent crude and is based upon the data from Lindsly (1936), as presented by Standing and Katz (1942) and adapted here by courtesy of the *Oil Weekly*. The procedure consists in calculating the density of the propane and heavier material of the gas plus crude oil from Fig. 6-21 in order to find the apparent density of the ethane to be used in the tabulation. Likewise, the density of the ethane and heavier material must be computed to find the apparent density of methane for the particular calculation. Figure 6-21 gives the apparent densities of methane and ethane as a function of their weight per cent in the liquid and of the density at 60°F and 1 atm for the remainder of the material present. Figure 6-22 presents the correction to be made for the density at high pressure compared to the density at 1 atm, both at 60°F. The correction is obtained as an incremental density which results from compression to a higher pressure. Figure 6-23 is the chart which corrects the density of the material at the saturation pressure from 60°F to the saturation temperature. The density at 60°F may not fall on one of the lines given but may be interpolated between the relatively parallel lines. The units have been converted from grams per milliliter into pounds per cubic feet because of the convenience in shrinkage calculations.

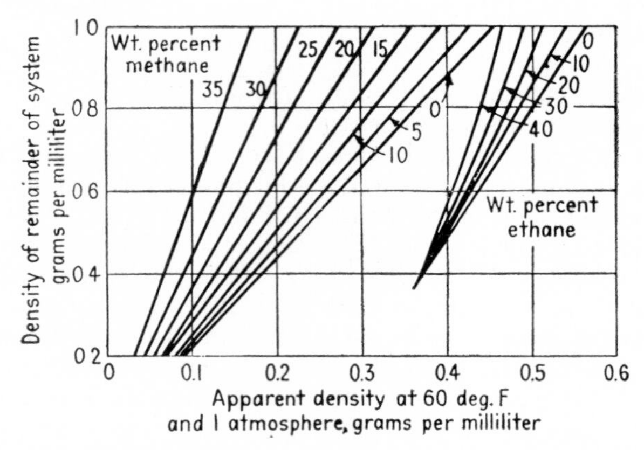

FIG. 6-21. Apparent density of ethane and methane. (*After Katz, courtesy Oil Weekly.*)

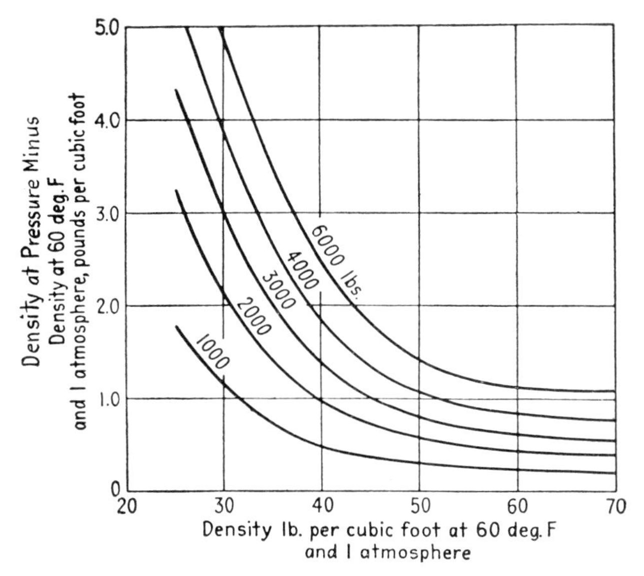

Fig. 6-22 Density correction of crude oils with pressure. (*After Katz, courtesy Oil Weekly.*)

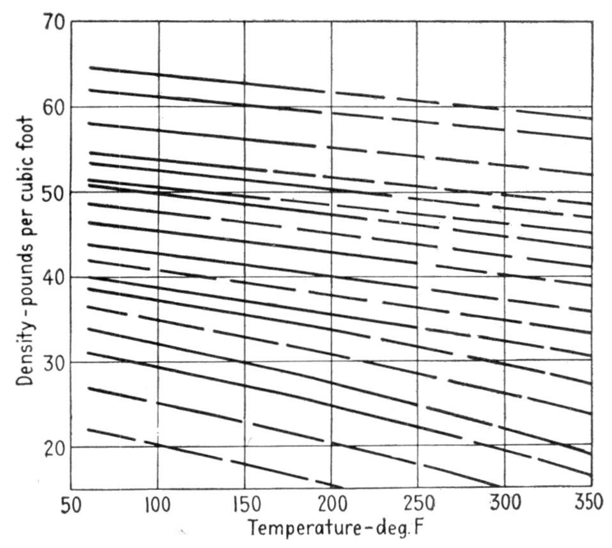

Fig. 6-23. Density change of crude oils with temperature. (*After Katz, courtesy Oil Weekly.*)

TABLE 6-13. EXAMPLE CALCULATION OF SHRINKAGE FACTOR FOR CRESCENT CRUDE

Given:

Gas liberated, cu ft per bbl of residual oil	814.0
Crude gravity (from Bureau of Mines) °API	41.7
Saturation temperature, °F	149.0
Saturation pressure, psia	2,575

Gas Analysis

Component	*Volume per cent*
Methane	75.33
Ethane	10.09
Propane	6.96
Butanes	5.58
Pentanes	1.56
Hexanes plus	0.48

Calculation of Shrinkage

Component	Volume per cent	Cubic feet	Molecular weight	Pounds	Liquid, lb per cu ft at 60°C and 14.7 psi	Liquid, cu ft
Methane	75.33	612.0	16	25.8	20.1	1.283
Ethane	10.09	82.0	30	6.5	30.9	0.210
Propane	6.96	56.6	44	6.6	31.8	0.208
Butanes	5.58	45.4	58	6.9	36.1	0.191
Pentanes	1.56	12.7	72	2.4	39.2	0.061
Hexanes plus	0.48	3.9	86	0.8	41.5	0.019
Crude oil	.....	5.61	..	286.0	51.0	5.610
Total	.....	.....	..	335.0	....	7.582
Propane plus	.....	.....	..	302.7	....	6.089
Ethane plus	.....	.....	..	309.2	....	6.329

Density of propane plus $= \dfrac{302.7}{6.089} = 49.8$ lb per cu ft $= 0.799$ g per cc

Wt per cent ethane $= \dfrac{6.5}{309.2} = 2.1$ in ethane plus fraction

Wt per cent methane $= \dfrac{25.8}{335.0} = 7.7$ in whole mixture

From Fig. 6-21: Apparent density of ethane $= 0.496$ g per cc $= 30.9$ lb per cu ft

Density of ethane plus $= \dfrac{309.2}{6.300} = 49.1$ lb per cu ft $= 0.788$ g per cc

From Fig. 6-21: Apparent density of methane $= 0.322$ g per cc $= 20.1$ lb per cu ft

Density of reservoir fluid at 60°F and 1 atm $= \dfrac{335.0}{7.582} = 44.2$ lb per cu ft

TABLE 6-13. EXAMPLE CALCULATION OF SHRINKAGE FACTOR FOR CRESCENT CRUDE (*Continued*)

Density of reservoir fluid at 60°F and 2,575 psia, using correction from Fig. 6-22, is 44.2 + 0.9 = 45.1 lb per cu ft

Density of reservoir fluid at 149°F and 2,575 psia, using Fig. 6-23, is 42.8 lb per cu ft

Cu ft of reservoir fluid per bbl of residual oil $= \frac{335}{42.8} = 7.82$ cu ft

Volume of dissolved gas = 7.82 − 5.61 = 2.21 cu ft

Shrinkage based on residual oil $= \frac{2.21}{5.61} = 39.4$ per cent

Shrinkage reported by Lindsly = 40.7 per cent

Calculated formation-volume factor = 1.394

Shrinkage based on reservoir oil $= \frac{2.21}{7.82} = 28.3$ per cent

Calculation of apparent density of dissolved gas at 60°F and 1 atm:

7.582 cu ft total at 60°F and 1 atm	335.0 lb total
5.61 cu ft residual oil at 1 atm	286.0 lb crude oil
1.972 cu ft dissolved gas at 1 atm	49.0 lb dissolved gas

Apparent density of dissolved gas $= \frac{49.0}{1.972} = 24.9$ lb per cu ft

The foregoing procedure for computing the shrinkage of reservoir oil is convenient if the analysis of the gas vaporized, the resultant gravity of the oil, and the saturation temperature and pressure are available. In most cases, if the analysis of the gas is available, the actual shrinkage measurement may have been made. The need for shrinkage predictions is for cases wherein the analysis of the gas is not known, although the quantity of gas and its gravity or molecular weight may be available.

Fluid Characteristics from Recombination Samples. In the eventuality that representative bottom-hole samples cannot be obtained, PVT relationships may be obtained by recombining oil and gas separator samples in their proper gas-oil ratios. Obviously such a procedure is dependable only when the surface gas-oil ratio is identical with the solution gas, such as is the case for instance in the early producing history of a depletion-drive field or when undersaturated oil is produced under a very active water drive.

Should recombination samples be obtained in the later life of the field when a free-gas phase has been produced in the reservoir by pressure depletion, a single phase will not exist in the bottom-hole sampler when pressured to bottom-hole pressure and temperature. In order to determine the reservoir fluid properties under such conditions, the free-gas phase must be removed. It represents the amount of free gas flowing in the reservoir with the oil. The original saturation conditions must be obtained by extrapolation to the original bubble-point pressure.

Composition and Properties of Evolved Gas. The methods of analysis of gas for their constituent hydrocarbons is beyond the scope of this study, but the following available processes are listed for the sake of completeness: low-temperature fractionation such as by the Podbielniak apparatus, fractional adsorption over activated charcoal, mass spectrographic, and partition chromatographic methods.

The density of the gas with respect to air is readily determined by means of the Edwards, or ACME, gravity balances.

The viscosity of natural gas varies with composition, pressure, and temperature, but in general there is no appreciable error involved in reservoir performance computations when an average viscosity is used for natural gas and solution gases throughout the life history of a field. The average viscosity of natural gas may be computed from its composition and the viscosity of each of its constituents by using the principle of additive fluidity (reciprocal of viscosity). If more accuracy is desired concerning the viscosity of gases under reservoir conditions, the relationships given by Bicher and Katz (1943) may be used, which indicate that at low pressures gas viscosity decreases as the molecular weight increases but at constant low pressure will increase with temperature. At high pressures, the gas viscosity increases with molecular weight but at constant high pressure decreases with temperature. In the absence of sufficient data the correlations of Beal (1946) may be used.

Of importance in reservoir engineering are the deviations of natural gas from Boyle's law according to composition, temperature, and pressure. These deviations are included in the *compressibility factor* (Z), which may be determined experimentally by means of the pressure-volume (PV) cell but may also be computed from a knowledge of the gas composition according to the method proposed by Brown (1940) and adapted here by courtesy of *The Petroleum Engineer*.

Numerous equations of state have been proposed, but the most convenient method for computing the PVT relationships of natural gas is by use of the so-called compressibility factor, which represents the deviation of the gas in question from the ideal gas laws as expressed in the following equation:

$$PV = ZNRT \tag{6-1}$$

where P = pressure, psia
V = volume, cu ft
Z = compressibility factor
N = no. of lb moles, or $\dfrac{\text{lb wt}}{\text{mol wt}}$
R = 10.73 for all gases and for the units stated herein
T = absolute temperature, °R

The compressibility factor Z is a dimensionless intensive factor independent of the extent or weight of the gas and determined by the composition of the gas, the temperature, and pressure. Once Z is known or determined, the calculation of PVT relationships may be made with as much ease at high pressure as at low pressure.

Like all correction factors the value of Z depends upon experimental data for its determination. Therefore, when applied to a particular gas such as methane, it would seem simpler to make a plot of density vs. pressure for lines of constant temperature than to go through the process of determining Z obtained in Eq. (6-1) in order to find the volume. Graphs such as Fig. 6-24 can be prepared for only those gases that have been

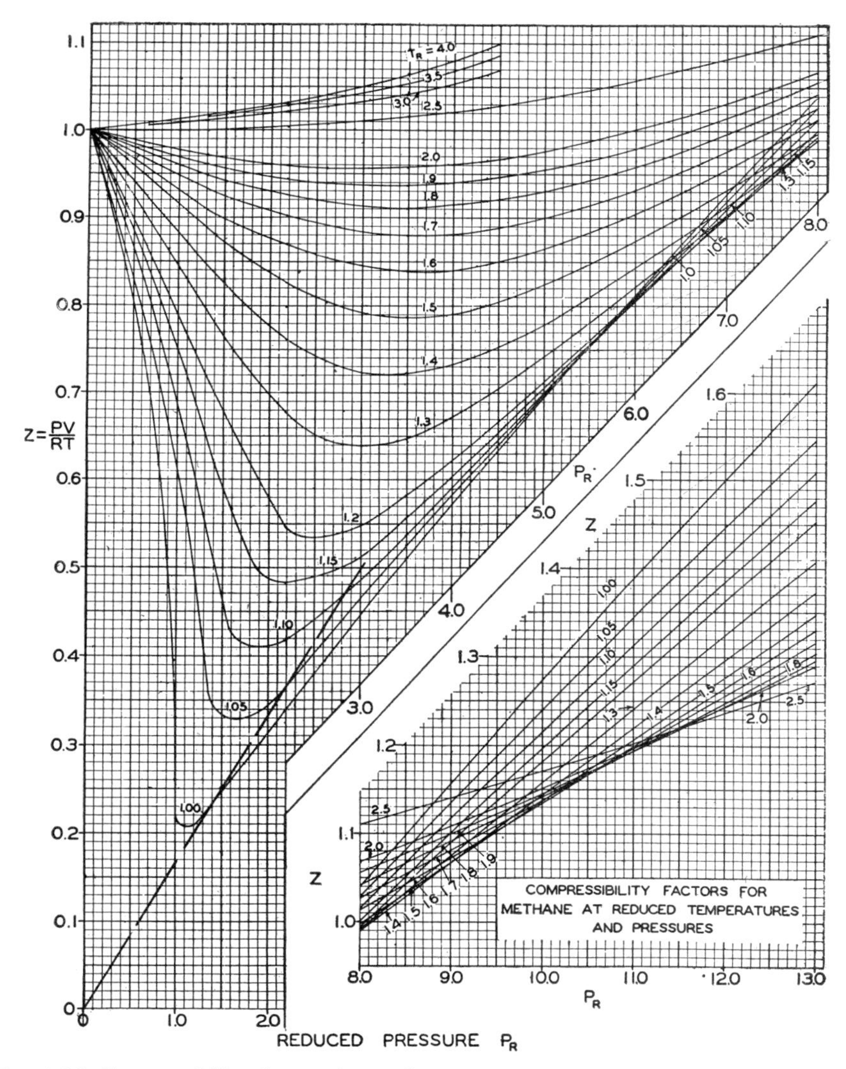

FIG. 6-24. Compressibility factors for methane at reduced temperatures and pressures. (*After Brown, courtesy The Petroleum Engineer.*)

thoroughly investigated, and diagrams such as Fig. 6-25, in which Z is plotted as a function of *reduced pressure* and *reduced temperature*, can be used for other similar gases to compute their unknown PVT properties, provided that their reduced pressure and temperature are known or can be calculated.

According to the *theorem of corresponding states*, the deviation of an actual gas from the ideal-gas law is the same for different gases when

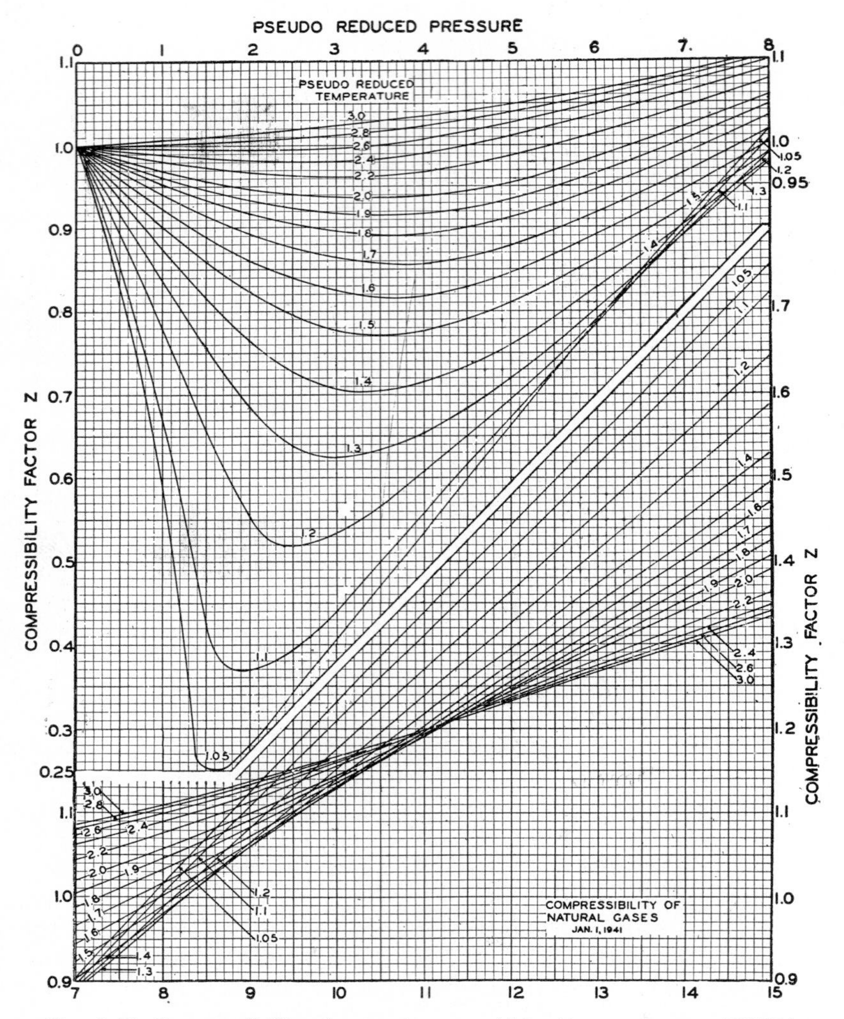

FIG. 6-25. Compressibility of natural gases. (*After Brown, courtesy AIME.*)

under identical corresponding states. Identical corresponding states are found at the same ratio value of the actual absolute temperature and pressure to the absolute critical temperature and pressure. They are defined, respectively, as follows:

$$\text{Reduced temperature} = T_r = \frac{T}{T_c}$$

$$\text{Reduced pressure} = P_r = \frac{P}{P_c}$$

where T_c = absolute critical temperature
P_c = absolute critical pressure
T = absolute temperature
P = absolute pressure

Therefore, if the theorem of corresponding states can be applied without appreciable error, all gases would have the same value for Z at the same reduced temperature and pressure, and a plot of Z for methane, as given in Fig. 6-24 as a function of reduced temperature and pressure, can be applied to determine the unknown value of Z for some other gas if we know or can determine the critical temperature and pressure of the second gas. This is a most important relationship, which appears to be reasonably accurate for similar gases and, when properly used, for gaseous mixtures.

The values of the compressibility factor in the case of single component gases can be extended to gaseous mixtures by use of the *pseudocritical temperature* and *pseudocritical pressure* of the gaseous mixture in place of the critical temperature and critical pressure for the single component gas. The molecular average critical temperature of the natural-gas mixture is the pseudocritical temperature, and the molecular average critical pressure of the mixture is the pseudocritical pressure, which are used in the same manner as the critical temperature and critical pressure of a pure gas to determine the values of Z from Fig. 6-24 or Fig. 6-25. Equation (6-1) may then be used with the molecular weight of the gaseous mixture M in the same manner as has been described for a pure gas.

An example will illustrate the method of calculating the average molecular weight of a gas the composition of which is set forth in Table 6-15.

The specific gravity of the gas referred to air is computed by dividing the molecular weight of the gas by the molecular weight of air, and we obtain

$$\frac{M \text{ for gas}}{M \text{ for air}} = \frac{20.36}{28.9} = 0.703$$

The molecular weight of a gas may be computed readily by multiplying its specific gravity (air = 1) by the molecular weight of air.

By analogy with pure substances, using the absolute critical temperatures and pressures for the individual components as given in Table 6-14, the pseudocritical temperature and the pseudocritical pressure for the same natural gas may be computed as set forth in Table 6-16.

The pseudocritical temperature T_c of this natural gas is 393.2°R absolute and its pseudocritical pressure P_c is 667.83 psia. These two values are constant for all computations involving the PVT relationship of this natural gas.

Table 6-14. Presently Accepted Physical Properties of Natural-gas Hydrocarbons

Compound	Formula	Molecular weight	Density of liquid, 60°F, grams per cc	Normal boiling point, °F	Critical temperature		Critical pressure, psia
					°F	°R	
Methane	CH_4	16.04	......	−258.5	−116	344	673
Ethane	C_2H_6	30.07	......	−127.5	89	549	712
Propane	C_3H_8	44.09	0.510	− 43.9	206	666	617
n-Butane	C_4H_{10}	58.12	0.584	31.1	306	766	551
Isobutane	C_4H_{10}	58.12	0.564	13.6	272	732	544
n-Pentane	C_5H_{12}	72.15	0.6304	96.9	386	846	485
Isopentane	C_5H_{12}	72.15	0.6241	82.3	369	829	483
n-Hexane	C_6H_{14}	86.17	0.6634	155.8	454	914	435
n-Heptane	C_7H_{16}	100.20	0.6875	209.1	512	972	397
n-Octane	C_8H_{18}	114.22	0.7064	258.2	564	1,024	362

Table 6-15. Computation of Molecular Weight of a Natural Gas

Component	*Per cent by gaseous volume, or molecular per cent*		*Molecular weight of component*		*Sum of the products is the average molecular weight*
Methane CH_4	83.19	×	16.04	=	13.31
Ethane C_2H_6	8.48	×	30.07	=	2.54
Propane C_3H_8	4.37	×	44.09	=	1.92
Isobutane i-C_4H_{10}	0.76	×	58.12	=	0.44
Normal butane n-C_4H_{10}	1.68	×	58.12	=	0.97
Isopentane i-C_5H_{12}	0.57	×	72.15	=	0.41
Normal pentane n-C_5H_{12}	0.32	×	72.15	=	0.23
Hexane C_6H_{14}	0.63	×	86.17	=	0.54
			Av mol wt	=	20.36

For this gas at a temperature of 100°F and 2,000 psia, the pseudoreduced temperature is

$$\frac{T}{T_c} = \frac{460 + 100}{393.2} = 1.425 = T_r$$

Similarly, the pseudoreduced pressure for the same conditions is

$$\frac{P}{P_c} = \frac{2{,}000}{667.83} = 2.994 = P_r$$

In order to determine the compressibility factor Z for this natural gas, the above pseudoreduced temperature and pressure are read on Fig. 6-24 (which correctly indicates the compressibility factor for pure methane), and a value of $Z = 0.740$ is obtained.

TABLE 6-16. COMPUTATION OF PSEUDOCRITICAL TEMPERATURE AND PRESSURE OF A NATURAL GAS

Component (1)	Mole fraction (2)	Individual absolute critical temperature T_c, °R (3)	Absolute pseudocritical temperature T_c, °R (4) = (2) × (3) (4)	Individual absolute critical pressure P_c, psia (5)	Absolute pseudo-critical pressure P_c, psia (6)
CH_4	0.8319	344	286	673	560
C_2H_6	0.0848	549	46.5	712	60.4
C_3H_8	0.0437	666	29.1	617	27.0
i-C_4H_{10}	0.0076	732	5.56	544	4.13
n-C_4H_{10}	0.0168	766	12.86	551	9.26
i-C_5H_{12}	0.0057	829	4.72	483	2.75
n-C_5H_{12}	0.0032	846	2.71	485	1.55
C_6H_{14}	0.0063	914	5.75	435	2.74
			393.2		667.83

Reservoir Oil Viscosity. One of the important characteristics which controls the movement of oil through the reservoir is viscosity, or internal resistance to fluid flow.

Oil viscosity is dependent upon two main factors: reservoir temperature and solution gas. The former may be assumed constant throughout the production history of a field, but the latter is changing constantly as solution gas evolves from the oil. It is, therefore, necessary to ascertain the viscosity of reservoir oils at bottom-hole temperature and pressure under a variable solubility of gas. Special instruments have been designed to this end, namely, the Gulf and Humble pressure viscosimeters, which are both of the rolling-ball type. Accordingly, only one type will be described, namely, the Humble viscosimeter.

This apparatus (Fig. 6-26) consists essentially of a removable, accurately bored cylindrical barrel of ¼-in. nominal internal diameter, 8 in. long, in which a closely fitting steel ball rolls through the oil with the barrel inclined at a definite angle. The ball makes contact at one end of the barrel with an insulated electrode, closing an electrical circuit which actuates a buzzer. The measurements consist essentially in determining the time required for the ball to travel the length of the barrel.

The barrel in which the ball rolls is made from stainless steel, specially bored to an exact uniform diameter and polished. For extreme corrosive

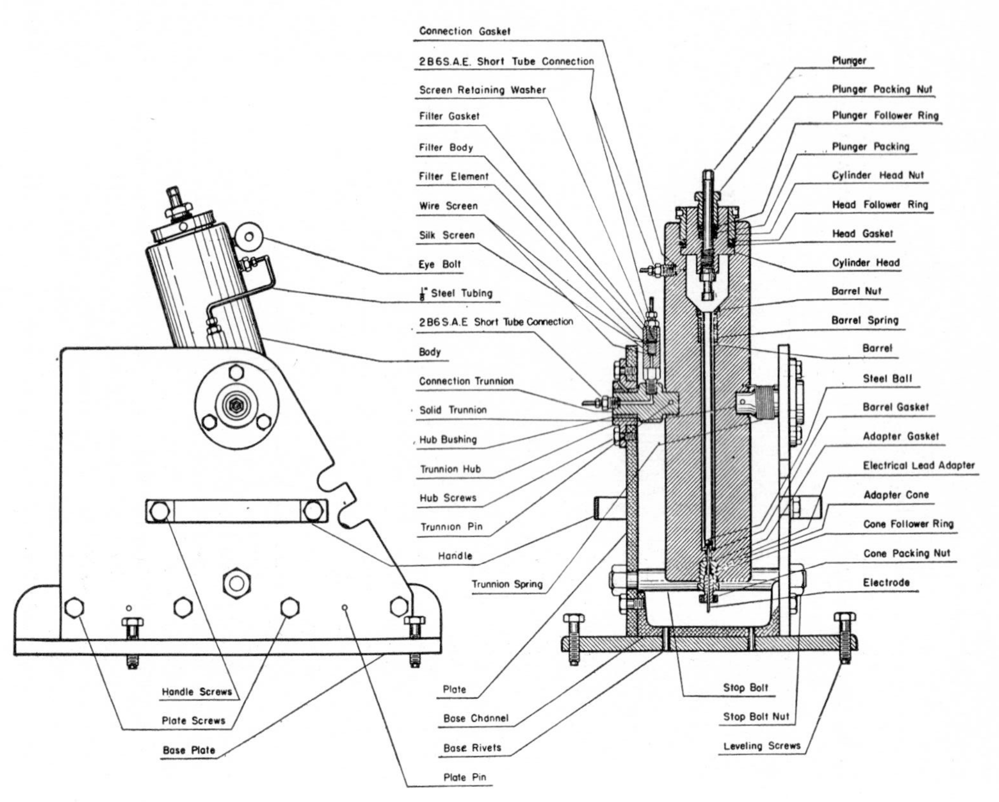

FIG. 6-26. Pressure viscosimeter assembly. (*Engineering Laboratories, Inc.*)

conditions a monel barrel is recommended. The barrel slides snugly into a hole bored in a solid stainless-steel cylinder and is held in place by a hollow nut. The spring prevents the barrel from seating against the bottom of the bored hole in the cylinder, while narrow external longitudinal slots in the barrel permit fluid to flow around it and through the bottom.

The upper part of the recess in the steel cylinder is enlarged to form a tapered chamber, which acts as a reservoir for the oil and affords space for agitation to ensure equilibrium between the gas and oil The taper permits the ball to roll readily into the barrel when the instrument is at an angle of inclination of 75 deg. The upper end of the chamber is sealed by a polished piston seated on a shoulder, and the closure is made with a neoprene gasket of area smaller than that of the lower surface of the piston. The primary gasket compression is effected by means of a hollow nut which slips over the piston.

A retractable plunger with a polished lower surface is screwed through the cylinder head in such a fashion that it is accessible and may be turned with a small wrench while the instrument is immersed in a high-temperature bath. While the viscosimeter is being charged with oil or the content is being agitated to bring about equilibrium, the plunger is kept partly or fully retracted. During the course of a measurement, however, the plunger is screwed into the cylinder, sealing the upper end of the barrel and simultaneously sealing the lower end of the barrel by pressing it against a gasket in the bottom of the bored recess in the cylinder. Since the pressure is at all times equal inside and outside of the roll barrel, the instrument has no pressure coefficient, and the double sealing of the barrel adequately prevents leakage during a measurement.

The steel cylinder is mounted on trunnions in such a manner that it may be rotated through an angle of approximately 330 deg.

The trunnion plates are equipped with one fixed stop, consisting of a cylindrical bar, which gives the barrel an angle of inclination of approximately 75 deg from the horizontal and two removable positive stops at angles of inclination of approximately 23 and 11 deg, permitting the roll time to be varied in the ratios of approximately 4:2:1 for any given viscosity and size of barrel and ball.

Viscosity determinations can readily be made on as little as 20 cc of liquid.

The results of viscosity determinations at reservoir temperatures and at various pressures are shown in Fig. 6-27. The curves show the results from four different oil fields.

The portion of the curve above saturation pressure represents the increase of viscosity with compression of the homogeneous saturated oil with all the available gas dissolved. This increase of viscosity of the saturated oil with pressure is characteristic of all liquids. The saturation pressure, or bubble point, is the pressure at which gas is first released from solution. At pressures below the saturation pressure, the escape of gas from solution increases the viscosity of the residual oil to a greater extent than it is reduced by volumetric expansion; the result is a net increase in viscosity. The saturation pressure of the oil is thus identified in the viscosimeter through the minimum in the viscosity-pressure curve. The saturation pressures determined in this manner check with those determined by the pressure-volume measurements on separate portions of the same subsurface sample. The increasing slope of the viscosity-pressure curve as the pressure approaches atmospheric reflects in part the increasing

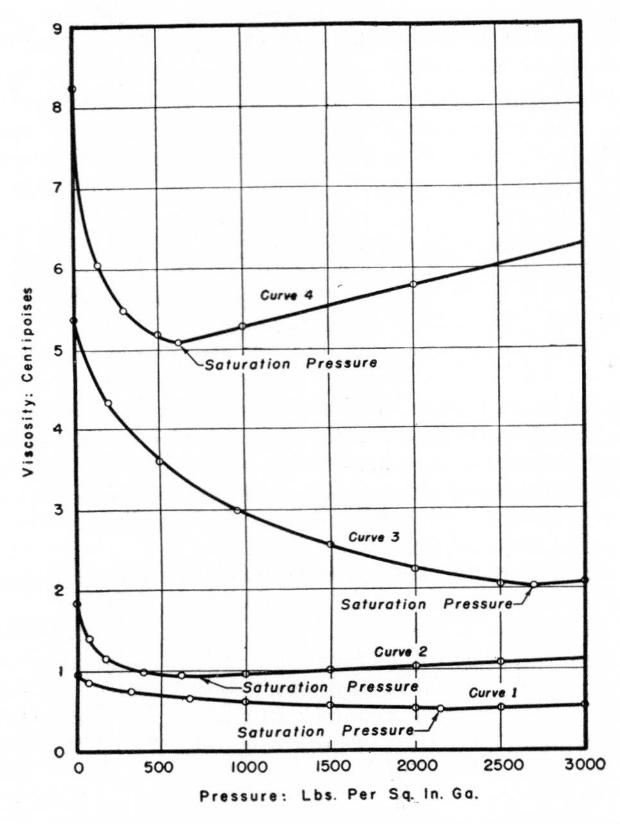

FIG. 6-27. Viscosity of reservoir oils. (*Engineering Laboratories, Inc.*)

richness of the liberated gas and loss of the more volatile fractions of the oil. The slopes of the viscosity-pressure curves vary from field to field with the nature of the oil and its dissolved gas.

Information on oil-viscosity relationship under reservoir conditions is often lacking in practice, and in view of the importance of this information in reservoir-behavior forecast it is imperative in many instances to resort to estimates. An approximate relationship between reservoir oil viscosity and solution gas may be derived from the following considerations:

Most natural hydrocarbons are nonpolar, and accordingly their fluidities are nearly additive terms in a mixture. Hence

$$\varphi_{\text{mixture}} = \sum_{i=1}^{n} m_i \varphi_i \tag{6-2}$$

where m_i is the mole fraction of any component of fluidity φ_i.

For simplification, two fluids only are involved in the calculations: oil and gas. The mole fraction of each will be assumed to be nearly equivalent to volumetric fraction in the solution.

Knowing the fluidities of the stock-tank oil φ_o and that of the liquefied gas φ_g at reservoir temperature, we have

$$\varphi_{\text{mixture}} = \frac{1}{\beta}\varphi_o + \frac{\beta - 1}{\beta}\varphi_g \tag{6-3}$$

where β is the reservoir-volume factor.

As a first approximation, let the viscosity of dissolved gas be 0.25 centipoise. Then $\varphi_g = 4.0$, and the following approximate relation is obtained for the viscosity of the reservoir oil μ with its gas in solution:

$$\mu = \frac{\beta\mu_o}{1 + 4(\beta - 1)\mu_o} \tag{6-4}$$

where μ_o is the stock-tank oil viscosity at reservoir temperature.

Formula (6-4) is valid only for the range of pressure varying from atmospheric to the saturation pressure, because it does not include the effect of oil compressibility above the saturation pressure.

CONNATE WATER PROPERTIES

Connate water, as the name indicates, is fossil sea water trapped in the interstices of the sediments during their deposition. It is also called interstitial or formation water.

Connate water by its movements and geochemical transformations over geologic time is held responsible for rock cementation and induration.

Geophysical evidence has established that the composition of sea or ocean waters has changed little over geologic time. Yet connate waters are found to be much more saline, by factors varying from 3 to 10, than sea waters. Normal sea water contains on the average 3.5 per cent, or 35,000 ppm by weight of NaCl. Various theories have been advanced to explain the salinity enrichment of connate waters over geologic time. One of the most plausible theories explains the process by evaporation of water molecules by entrainment of leaking gases from geologic structures. Another theory calls for the evaporation of water owing to the geothermal gradient of the earth. Possibly both processes operate simultaneously. The dissolved salts and ions are predominantly the following: Na^+, K^+, Mg^{++}, Ca^{++}, Ba^{++}, Li^+ and Cl^-, NO_3^-, $CO_3^=$, HCO_3^-, $SO_4^=$.

Many oil-field waters are notably lacking in sulfates ($SO_4^=$) but high in carbonates ($CO_3^=$). This is because of the reducing condition of the environment in which oil fields are found, and sulfates are therefore transformed into sulfides ($S^{=}$). This is further substantiated by the fact that connate waters are predominantly oxygen free and are even reducing in character.

Connate waters are often found to be weakly alkaline to neutral. They have also the important property of flocculating clays. Therefore, when clays are present within the reservoir together with highly saline connate water, they occupy a minimum of space within the pores. Should connate water be replaced by fresh waters, the clays swell and reduce or even prohibit fluid permeability.

According to its stratigraphic position in a field, connate water may be designated by the following self-explanatory terminology: edge, bottom, intermediate, or top water. However, it is now known that the distribution of water within a reservoir is controlled by the various capillary-pressure curves of the individual layers within the sand. A coarser and more permeable seam has a lower displacement pressure and requires a smaller water saturation in order to provide equilibrium of pressure between the various fluid phases.

An important point in reservoir studies is the areal extent of the aquifer. This is a geologic problem which must be solved in each individual case. In lenticular sands (graywacke sediments), the aquifer is limited in extent, and the connate water can supply very little energy to the reservoir. On the other hand, in quartzose-type sediments, the aquifer may extend over large areas and supply reservoir energy by volumetric expansion when field pressure declines. The aquifer may even outcrop, in which case the connate water is under the hydrostatic pressure of a column of water which extends to the surface of the earth. In certain regions this hydrostatic pressure may vary with regional rainfall.

The movement of water into an oil field is controlled by two of its physical characteristics, namely, viscosity and compressibility. The compressibility of water changes little within the range of temperature, pressure, and salinity encountered in oil-field practice. The compressibility may be taken to be 44×10^{-6} unit volume per atm, or 3.0×10^{-6} per psi within the range of bottom-hole pressures normally encountered in oil fields.

As a valid approximation for the viscosity of connate water to be used in reservoir calculations, the value in centipoises may be interpolated from Table 6-17 for the actual bottom-hole temperature.

TABLE 6-17. VISCOSITY OF WATER

Temperature, °F	*Viscosity, centipoises*
50	1.30
75	0.92
100	0.68
125	0.53
150	0.43
175	0.36
200	0.30

SELECTED REFERENCES ON RESERVOIR FLUIDS

1888

Van der Waals, J. D.: "Die Kontinuität des Gasförmiges und Flüssiges Zustandes," Johann Ambrosius Barth, Munich.

1893

Kuenen, J. P.: Messungen über die Oberflache von van der Waals für Gemische von Kohlensaüre und Chlormethyl, *Z. physik. Chem.*, vol. 11, pp. 38ff.

1895

Kuenen, J. P.: On the Condensation and the Critical Phenomena of Mixtures of Ethane and Nitrous Oxides, *Phil. Mag.*, vol. 40, pp. 173ff.

1901

Duhem, P.: Liquefaction of a Gaseous Mixture, *J. Phys. Chem.*, vol. 5, pp. 91ff.

Roozeboom, H. W. B.: "The Heterogeneous Equilibria from the Standpoint of the Phase Rule," vols. 1, 2, and 3, Friedrig Vieweg und Söhne, Brunswick.

1931

Lacey, W. N.: Testing Rates of Solution of Oil and Gas, *Oil Gas J.*, July 9, pp. 15ff.; July 16, pp. 68ff.

1932

Brown, G. G., et al.: Fundamental Design of High Pressure Equipment Involving Paraffin Hydrocarbons—Pressure-Volume-Temperature Relations of Paraffin Hydrocarbons, *Ind. Eng. Chem.*, May, pp. 513ff.

1933

Bromiley, E. C., and D. Quiggle: Vapor Liquid Equilibria of Hydrocarbon Mixtures, *Ind. Eng. Chem.*, October, pp. 1136ff.

Comins, D.: Gas Saturation Pressure of Crude under Reservoir Conditions as a Factor in the Efficient Operation of Oil Fields, *World Petroleum Congress*, vol. 1, pp. 458ff.

Lindsly, B. E.: A Study of Bottom-hole Samples of East Texas Crude Oil, *U.S. Bur. Mines Rept. Invest.* 3213.

———: Solubility and Liberation of Gas from Natural Oil Gas Solutions, *U.S. Bur. Mines Tech. Pub.* 554.

Sage, B. H.: Measurement of Viscosities of Liquids Saturated with Gases at High Pressures, *Ind. Eng. Chem., Anal. Ed.*, pp. 261ff.

———, et al.: Behavior of Hydrocarbon Mixtures Illustrated by a Simple Case, *API Prod. Bull.* 212, pp. 219ff.

1934

Hill, E. S., and W. N. Lacey: Rate of Solution of Methane in Quiescent Liquid Hydrocarbons, *Ind. Eng. Chem.*, December, pp. 1327ff.

Katz, D. L.: Effect of Gas Liberation upon the Properties of Crude Oil, *Oil Weekly*, Oct. 22, pp. 19ff.

1935

Sage, B. H., and W. N. Lacey: Formation Volume and Viscosity Studies for Dominguez Field, *API Drill. and Prod. Pract.*, pp. 141ff.

Sage, B. H., et al.: Viscosity of Hydrocarbon Solutions—Solution of Ethane and *n*-Butane in Crystal Oil, *API Prod. Bull.* 216, pp. 40ff.

———: Viscosity of Hydrocarbon Solutions: Solutions of Four Hydrocarbon Gases in a Crude Oil, *API Prod. Bull.* 216, pp. 45ff.

1936

Bertraum, E. A., and W. N. Lacey: Rates of Solution of Gases in Oils, *Ind. Eng. Chem.*, March, pp. 316ff.

Exline, P. G.: New Apparatus for Securing and Examining Subsurface Samples of Oil, *API Drill. and Prod. Pract.*, pp. 126ff.

Kay, W. B.: Density of Hydrocarbon Gases and Vapors, *Ind. Eng. Chem.*, September, pp. 1014ff.

Lindsly, B. E.: A Bureau of Mines Study of a Bottom Hole Sample from the Crescent Pool, Oklahoma, *Petroleum Engr.*, July, pp. 34ff.

Sage, B. H., and W. N. Lacey: Formation Volumes and Energy Characteristics of Gas-cap Material from Kettleman Hills Field, *API Drill. and Prod. Pract.*, pp. 158ff.

Schilthuis, R. J.: The Technique of Securing and Examining Subsurface Samples of Oil, *API Drill. and Prod. Pract.*

1937

Katz, D. L., and K. H. Hachmuth: Vaporization Equilibrium Constants in a Crude Oil, Natural Gas System, *Ind. Eng. Chem.*, vol. 29, pp. 1072ff.

1938

Buckley, S. E.: Calculations of Equilibria in Hydrocarbon Mixtures, *Trans. AIME*, pp. 178ff.

Katz, D. L.: Subsurface Sampling, *API Drill. and Prod. Pract. Bull.* 225, pp. 135ff.

Katz, D. L.: Application of Vapor Equilibrium Constants to Production Engineering Problems, *Trans. AIME*, pp. 159ff.

Katz, D. L., and C. E. Singleterry: Significance of the Critical Phenomena in Oil and Gas Production, *AIME Tech. Pub.* 971.

Kay, W. B.: Liquid Vapor Phase Equilibrium Relations in the Ethane *n*-Heptane System, *Ind. Eng. Chem.*, April, pp. 459ff.

Kimmell, G. O., and R. L. Huntington: Stage Separation of Crude Oil Gas Mixtures, *Oil Weekly*, Oct. 17, pp. 40ff.

Patten, F. V. L., and D. C. Ivey: Phase Equilibria in High Pressure Condensate Wells, *Oil Weekly*, Dec. 12, pp. 20ff.

Sage, B. H., and W. N. Lacey: Effect of Pressure upon Viscosity of Methane and Two Natural Gases, *Trans. AIME*, pp. 118ff.

——— and ———: Viscosity of Hydrocarbon Solutions: Viscosity of Liquid and Gaseous Propane, *Ind. Eng. Chem.*, July, pp. 829ff.

——— et al.: Tentative Equilibrium Constants for Light Hydrocarbons, *API Drill. and Prod. Pract.*, pp. 386ff.

Stephenson, E. A.: Behavior of Contents of High-pressure Reservoirs, *Trans. AIME*, pp. 189ff.

1939

Eilerts, K., et al.: Properties of a Petroleum Reservoir Liquid and Its Residua with Applications of the Data to Production Problems, *U.S. Bur. Mines Rept. Invest.* 3474.

Sage, B. H., and W. N. Lacey: "Volumetric and Phase Behavior of Hydrocarbons," Stanford University Press, Stanford, Calif.

——— et al.: Effect of Pressure on Viscosity of *n*-Butane and Iso-Butane, *Ind. Eng. Chem.*, February, pp. 223ff.

Vitter, A. L., Jr.: Hydrocarbon Mixtures in Condensate Production, *Oil Gas J.*, Oct. 19, pp. 491ff.

Weber, G.: Testing and Sampling Methods Used in Condensate Wells, *Oil Gas J.*, Oct. 12, pp. 51ff.

Weber, H. C.: "Thermodynamics for Chemical Engineers," John Wiley & Sons, Inc., New York.

1940

Brown, G. G.: "Deviation of Natural Gas from Ideal Gas Laws," Circular, Clark Bros. Co., Inc., Olean, New York.

Eilerts, K.: Equilibrium Cell for Investigating Properties of Fluids from Petroleum and Natural-gas Reservoirs, *U. S. Bur. Mines Rept. Invest.* 3514.

Katz, D. L., and F. Kurata: Retrograde Condensate, *Ind. Eng. Chem.*, vol. 32, pp. 817ff.

Lavender, H. M., et al.: Gas Equilibrium Constants—Methane Decane Systems, *Oil Gas J.*, July 11, pp. 48ff.

1941

Dotterweich, F. H.: Physical Properties of Hydrocarbon Mixtures in Condensate Production, *Petroleum Engr.*, February, pp. 98ff.

1942

Katz, D. L.: Prediction of the Shrinkage of Crude Oils, *Oil Weekly*, Nov. 30, pp. 17ff.

Nielsen, R. F.: Molecular Explanation of Retrograde Condensation, *Oil Weekly*, Jan. 5, pp. 28ff.

Standing, M. B., and D. L. Katz: Density of Crude Oils Saturated with Natural Gas, *Trans. AIME*, pp. 159ff.

1943

Bicher, L. B., Jr., and D. L. Katz: Viscosity of Natural Gases, *AIME Tech. Pub.* 1599.

Olds, R. H., et al.: Volumetric and Viscosity Studies of Gas and Oil from the Santa Maria Valley Field, *AIME Tech. Pub.* 1588.

1945

Brownscombe, E. R., and D. R. Conlon: Precision in Bottom-hole Pressure Measurements, *AIME Tech. Pub.* 1942.

Olds, R. H., et al.: Volumetric and Phase Behavior of Oil and Gas from Paloma Field, *AIME Tech. Pub.* 1861.

1946

Beal, C.: Viscosity of Air, Water, Natural Gas, Crude Oil and Its Associated Gases at Oil Field Temperatures and Pressures, *AIME Tech. Pub.* 2018.

1947

Billman, G. W., B. H. Sage, and W. N. Lacey: Phase Behavior in the Methane Ethane —*n*-Pentane System, *AIME Tech. Pub.* 2232.

McKetta, J. J., and D. L. Katz: Phase Relations of Hydrocarbon-Water Systems, *AIME Tech. Pub.* 2123.

Sage, B. H., and W. N. Lacey: Apparatus for Determination of the Volumetric Behavior of Fluids, *AIME Tech. Pub.* 2269.

———, and R. H. Olds: Volumetric Behavior of Oils and Gas from Several San Joaquin Valley Fields, *AIME Tech. Pub.* 2153.

1948

Olds, R. H., B. H. Sage, and W. N. Lacey: Volumetric and Viscosity Studies of Oil and Gas from a San Joaquin Valley Field, *AIME Tech. Pub.* 2412.

Weinaug, C. F., and J. C. Cordell: Revaporization of Butane and Pentane from Sand, *AIME Tech. Pub.* 2467.

1949

Barr, K. W., F. Morton, A. R. Richards, and R. O. Young: The Crude Oil of Trinidad, 3 parts, *J. Institute Petroleum*, August, September, October.

Brokaw, A. D.: Correction of Gas Volumes for Compressibility and Temperatures, *AIME Tech. Pub.* 2698.

Elfrink, E. B., et al.: A New Compressibility Correlation for Natural Gases and Application to Estimates of Gas-in-place, *AIME Tech. Pub.* 2642.
Sage, B. H., and W. N. Lacey: Behavior of Binary, Ternary, and Multicomponent Systems at States Similar to Those Encountered in Condensate Fields, *AIME Tech. Pub.* 2631.

1950

Culberson, O. L., and J. J. McKetta, Jr.: Phase Equilibria in Hydrocarbon-Water Systems, *AIME Tech. Pub.* 2932.
Reamer, H. H., and B. H. Sage: Volumetric Behavior of Oil and Gas from a Louisiana Field I, *AIME Tech. Pub.* 2950.
Rzasa, M. J., and G. Borden, Jr.: Correlation of Bottom Hole Sample Data, *AIME Tech. Pub.* 2931.
Rzasa, M. J., and D. L. Katz: The Coexistence of Liquid and Vapor Phases at Pressure above 10,000 PSI, *AIME Tech. Pub.* 2809.

1951

Espach, R. H., and J. Fry: Variable Characteristics of the Oil in the Tensleep Sandstone Reservoir, Elk Basin Field, Wyoming and Montana, *AIME Tech. Pub.* 3018.
Records, L. R., and D. H. Seely, Jr.: Low Temperature Dehydration of Natural Gas, *AIME Tech. Pub.* 3022.

1954

Carr, N. L., et al.: Viscosity of Hydrocarbon Gases under Pressure, *AIME Tech. Pub.* 3915.
Cook, A. B., et al.: Changes in Gas-Oil Ratios with Variations in Separator Pressures and Temperatures, *Petroleum Engr.*, vol. 26, no. 3, pp. B77ff.
Salmon, R.: Vapor Liquid Calculations, *Petroleum Refiner*, vol. 3, no. 3, pp. 156ff.

1955

Sage, J. F.: Water Analyses Help Identify Formations, *World Oil*, January, pp. 75ff.

1956

Bonham, L. C.: Geochemical Investigation of Crude Oils, *Bull. Am. Assoc. Petroleum Geol.*, vol. 40, pp. 897ff., May.
Stevens, N. P.: Origin of Petroleum, *Bull. Am. Assoc. Petroleum Geol.*, vol. 40, pp. 51ff., January.

CHAPTER 7

RESERVOIR FORCES AND ENERGIES

The fluids under reservoir conditions are subjected to the action of a number of natural forces which are active in driving oil and gas to the producing wells or in retaining oil within the reservoir. These forces are variable both over the producing life history of the field and according to the type of reservoir rock and structure. Similarly, the available stored energies responsible for the natural producing processes vary with reservoir conditions, and their mode of dissipation is a function of the producing histories and processes.

The forces active in the reservoir are the following:

1. Body forces
2. Static pressure
3. Static interfacial tension between the fluids

BODY FORCES

There are three fundamental physical body forces in nature, namely, gravitational attraction, magnetic, and electrical forces.

Only the first-named body force is of consequence in our problem inasmuch as the reservoir fluids involved are neither sufficiently magnetic nor are electrically charged.

However, owing to differences in the density between free gas, oil, and water, represented respectively by δ_g, δ_o and δ_w, the various fluids are subjected to the following gravitational forces per unit volume:

$$g\delta_g, \; g\delta_o, \; g\delta_w$$

where g is the acceleration of gravity. Differential gravitational forces have generally a negligible effect on the performance of high-pressure fields, except in the segregation-drive process (to be discussed later) and in fields where there exists a large vertical permeability such as in vuggy and fissured limestone. However, when field pressure is depleted and the geologic structures are of sufficient relief, the recovery of oil by gravity drainage may become all important, as was illustrated by the Wilcox-sand reservoir at Oklahoma City.

RESERVOIR OR STATIC FLUID PRESSURE (BOTTOM-HOLE PRESSURE)

The static fluid pressure in a reservoir is that which exists in the absence of mechanical or flow disturbances. It denotes the pressure existing in a well at the face of an oil-bearing stratum when production has been shut in for a sufficient length of time in order to build up a gas and liquid column pressure in the bore hole equal to the pressure existing in the oil-bearing stratum.

Reservoir pressure is, therefore, that pressure which exists under equilibrium conditions in advance of or after the establishment of production.

Reservoir pressure increases with depth in an almost linear manner. This is interpreted as being the result of the outcropping, at some more or less remote distance, of the geologic formations which constitute the reservoir rock. These formations, saturated with water, accumulate a hydrostatic pressure corresponding to the difference in elevation of the outcrop and the oil reservoir. In many fields the approximate reservoir pressure may be predicted in advance of discovery by multiplying the depth in feet below the ground-water table by the factor 0.435.

However, there are many exceptions to this rule, especially at greater depths than about 7,000 ft. This appears to be the result of the state of flux of the rocks under the weight of the overburden. Some constituents of the rocks at these depths have passed the elastic limit and are subjected to plastic deformations. As a result, the pore spaces of shales in particular are reduced to a very small fraction of bulk volume. This in turn reduces the over-all permeability to the leakage gases of the overburden. Cannon and Craze (1938) have submitted bottom-hole pressure data of deep Gulf Coast oil fields where this relationship is indicated. Further evidence that the overburden pressure at great depth is responsible for rock flowage may be seen in surface subsidence which at times results from the removal of oil. The additional bottom-hole pressure over hydrostatic pressure in a deep field may be termed "rock pressure."

There are also some outstanding cases of subnormal bottom-hole pressures, in particular in the Permian basin of West Texas, the explanation for which may be found in excessive gas leakage over geologic time.

Determination of bottom-hole pressure requires instruments of extreme accuracy when it is considered that the desired measurable pressure changes in a relatively long period of time during the life history of a field may be of the order of 1 to 4 psi at a bottom-hole pressure of 2,000 psi. Accordingly, we find ouselves confronted with a situation demanding accuracies of at least 0.1 per cent. The accuracies attained with the finest test gauges on the market do not nearly meet this demand.

Together with this requirement for high precision, there is just as definite a demand for a rugged construction. Ordinarily, the more rugged an instrument, the less precise it will be. The reason for this lies chiefly in the fact that in most instruments the energy available for the required motion is very limited and greater friction drag follows as a result of more rugged construction.

A high energy is necessary in a precision gauge in order that the random friction forces inherent in the mechanical movement be a very small proportion of the total force. All the bourdon-type gauges necessarily have a small total energy since the movement is obtained by the straightening of a heavy bent tube with pressure applied internally. The Amerada gauge is an example of this type of construction applied to a bottom-hole gauge. In order to avoid mechanical multiplication with its consequent frictional effects, which would be fatal to a gauge of this type, the bourdon tube is made quite long and coiled lengthwise into a helix of 25 turns. The open end of the tube is attached to the base while the closed end is fastened to a rotatable shaft which carries the stylus. In this gauge, there are but three points of friction, the two shaft bearings and the contact of the stylus with the paper. However, the tube has been made so long that it acts as a weak spring, and the stylus can remain a certain distance below or above the true position for a given pressure when the stylus friction is not properly adjusted.

Description of the Gulf Gauge. The Gulf bottom-hole pressure gauge, which was designed by Exline (1937), has the external appearance of a 1¾-in. OD tube with rounded ends (Fig. 7-1). This barrel serves to hold the pressure sensitive element, consisting of a string of bellows fastened to a header at the top of the barrel and to a powerful instrument spring at the bottom. The chamber between the barrel and the string of bellows is filled with a clean noncorrosive oil which serves as a medium for the transmission of pressures. The lower end of the chamber is positively

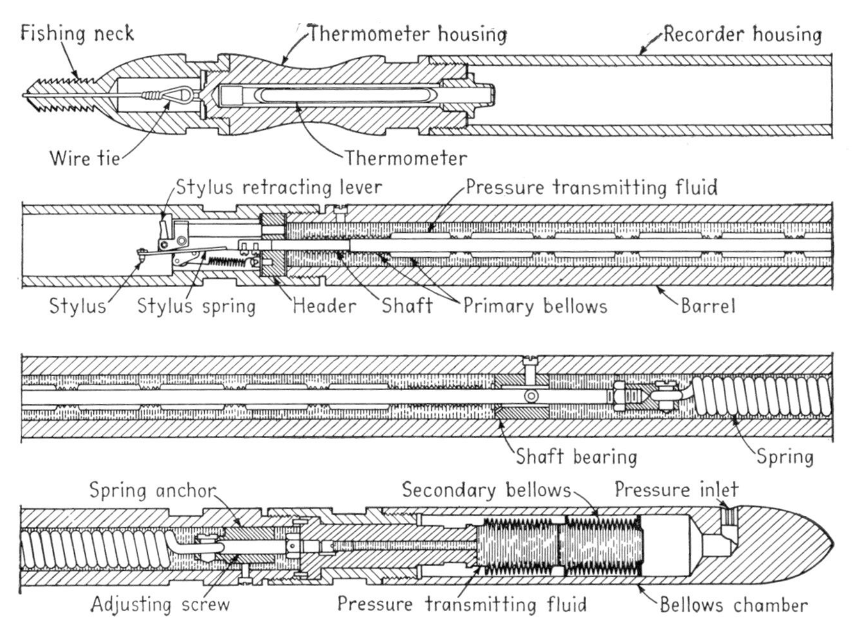

FIG. 7-1. Details of precision subsurface pressure gauge, Gulf design. (*Gulf Research and Development Corp.*)

sealed by a pair of secondary bellows, acting merely to maintain separation between the inner oil and the well fluid. This bellows system is made of brass and is gold-plated on the outside as a protection against corrosion. It is 1¼ in. in diameter and is very flexible and soft, which permits instant response to small changes of pressure. It is enclosed in the secondary bellows chamber which, at its lower end, has an opening for the entrance of crude oil at bottom-hole pressure. The lower end of the primary bellows string is sealed to a shaft which is attached to the main spring and passes loosely through the bellows and header to give an indication of the motion. The bellows act as a packless piston of cross-sectional area equal to that of the effective area of the bellows. If a hydrostatic pressure is admitted to the bellows chamber, the bellows are compressed. The compressive force developed equals approximately 450 lb at 3,000 psi. Such a force would necessarily compress the string of bellows excessively if its motion were not restrained by a strong spring. This spring is designed to give 1-in. motion at the maximum force of the pressure range, i.e., approximately 450 lb for the 3,000-lb gauge. The bellows used in the Gulf gauge are made of beryllium copper tubing. They have a 9⁄16-in. OD and a length of 1⅜ in. between the ends of convolutions. Nine such bellows are used in series resulting in a string approximately 14 in. long.

The bellows are placed in the gauge in a half-stretched position at zero pressure, the stretch being supplied by the tension of the main spring. For maximum motion of 1 in., the bellows are gradually compressed until they pass through the unstretched position and eventually reach their maximum compression. In this way, the bellows move about their neutral position, ½ in. in tension and ½ in. in compression. This has proved to be a very effective means of increasing their fatigue life.

In the annealed state, beryllium copper is a soft material which can be drawn and formed without great difficulty. Proper heat-treatment of beryllium copper brings about precipitation hardening, which results in a material almost comparable to steel. The heat-treatment is very simple and consists of heating the annealed bellows at 325°C for 2 or 3 hr in a nonoxidizing atmosphere. This treatment results in a bellows of great strength, able to withstand pressures of 3,000 psi. In addition, beryllium copper bellows possess desirable elastic properties.

Besides acting as a packless piston, the bellows develop their own force. In the extended position, they counteract the main spring. In the middle position, the spring force due to the bellows becomes zero, and, in the state of compression, the spring force due to the bellows supports the main spring.

Another important element of the gauge is the main instrument spring which serves to restrain the motion of the bellows, due to the force exerted by the pressure on the bellows. This spring is closely coiled and made of chrome vanadium steel. In order to obtain good repetition and straight-line response of the gauge, it is essential that it be designed for low combined stresses so as to eliminate hysteresis effects. Aging is another effect likely to cause inaccuracies. The aging of a spring material is oftentimes a considerable source of error, especially when pressure measurements are made over a considerable interval of time. Both hysteresis and aging can be minimized by proper heat-treatment.

Most bottom-hole pressure measurements are made at elevated temperatures of 150 to 180°F, and sometimes higher. The change of the modulus of elasticity of the spring and bellows must be considered. Therefore, bottom-hole temperatures must be taken into consideration when making bottom-hole pressure measurements. Errors of the order of 30 to 60 psi, depending on the temperature response of the gauge, will be encountered by overlooking this important factor. For this reason a maximum indicating thermometer is supplied with each gauge. If the temperature gradient of a given well is not known, it has to be obtained by a a number of measurements at different levels. In many wells, a linear increase of temperature with depth is observed, and the intermediate temperatures are obtained by linear interpolation.

The Gulf gauge is of the continuous direct-recording type. The direct recorder carries a stylus spring attached directly to the shaft, which in turn carries the stylus on its free end. Its maximum motion is only 1 in. The stylus pointer is held back by means of a retracting mechanism during insertion and removal of the clock in order to protect it from damage due to rubbing against the drum housing. Whenever the recorder clock mechanism is placed into the drum housing, it automatically releases the stylus spring which in turn is pushed against the chart, ready to scribe the record.

The pressure lines are measured across the chart from the zero line as reference, while the time coordinate is scribed along the chart. A 24-hr clock supplies the driving torque of the drum. A gear train which permits two different speeds transmits the torque of the clock.

The chart material used is aluminum foil, 0.003 in. thick and highly polished. The stylus described is made of steel. The line thus obtained is extremely fine, approximately 0.001 in., and easily visible on the chart. Aluminum foil is used as chart material because of the high accuracy required. It must be remembered that with a 3,000-psig the entire pressure range is compressed in the small linear space of 1 in. An error of just 0.001 in. results in an error of 3 psi. The ability of scribing accurate fine lines and of preserving these lines on aluminum charts without distortion due to temperature or hygroscopic effects results in a very reliable record. The chart material is preformed at the factory in such a way as to assume almost exactly the curvature of the inside surface of the drum. The chart is then easily slipped into the drum and held securely in position by means of especially designed snap rings. The snap rings are made so as to exert a constant pressure along the entire circumference of the drum, thereby assuring a perfect cylindrical shape of the chart.

In order to read the bottom-hole pressure charts with an accuracy comparable to that of the gauge, an optical comparator or microscope is required. The measuring accuracy is 0.001 in. Charts of 4 × 7 in. can be accommodated. Distances are measured directly on a scale in 0.025-in. divisions with a vernier affording a reading to 0.001 in. For reading and measurement purposes, the chart is placed on the base plate and held under a piece of plate glass, which in turn is held down by two spring clips. The microscope is held on crossbars directed by a V-shaped guide bearing moving along a carefully ground rod.

In order to secure reliable data from recorder charts, a convenient method has been worked out for calculating the true bottom-hole pressures from the measured deflections obtained from the charts by applying the necessary temperature corrections. This requires calibration.

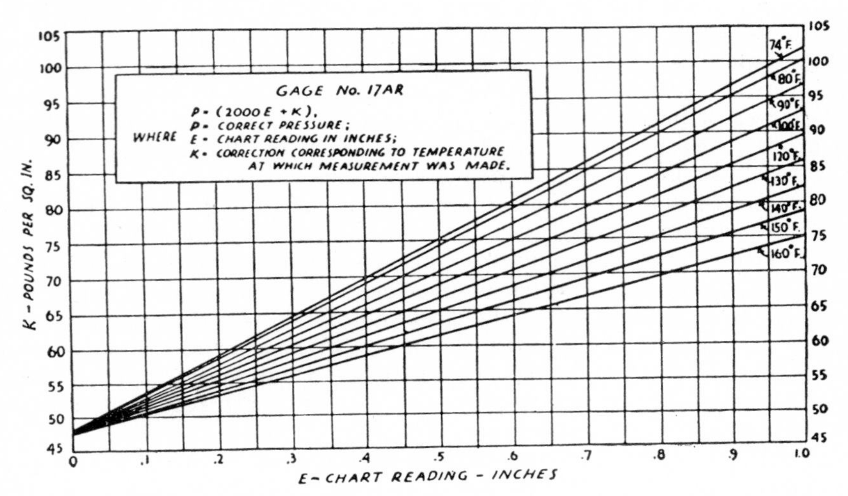

FIG. 7-2. Sample calibration sheet for subsurface pressure gauge. *(Gulf Research and Development Corp.)*

The recorder is calibrated in a manner similar to ordinary indicating gauges. Pressure measurements are made at 100-psi intervals in sets of measurements at varying temperature. The charts are then read under the microscope. A set of data is thereby obtained representing chart deflections. All deflections are reduced to a common zero. On the assumption that the stylus motion is an almost linear function of the pressure at a given temperature, the equations of the straight lines representing these data are set up. These straight lines represent the temperature deviation of the gauge for the temperature rise between any base temperature and actual bottom-hole temperature. A typical calibration chart for a recorder is shown in Fig. 7-2.

Geological and Production Engineering Uses of Bottom-hole Pressure Data. In addition to the reservoir-engineering uses of bottom-hole pressure data, they find application to geological field studies and in production problems. Inasmuch as these problems are outside the field of interest of the present study, they will be listed for reference only:

1. Determination of faulting in a reservoir and of the sealing effectiveness of the fault system between the various reservoir blocks.

2. Productivity tests and determination of drawdown curves. Determination of well potential from drawdown curves.

3. Density of fluid column in a well and presence of water at the bottom of the well.
4. Required minimum flowing pressure.
5. Determination of size of pumping equipment.
6. Control of efficiency of repressuring and of gas bypassing.
7. Testing efficiency of acidizing.
8. Allocation and reallocation of allowable production under proration schedules.
9. Prevention of oil migration across property lines.
10. Determination of drainage area of a well and of well interference.
11. Productivity-index tests on individual wells.
12. Determination of formation plugging by decrease of productivity index.
13. Determination of optimum rate of production.
14. Determination of the type of driving mechanism in a field by establishing the isobaric maps at various intervals of time during the production history of the field. Steep-pressure gradients generally indicate a predominance of depletion drive but may also indicate areas of low permeability. Low-pressure gradients may indicate the presence of active water drive, especially if associated with sustained high bottom-hole pressures. However, areas of high permeability may also be indicated by low-pressure gradients.

CAPILLARY FORCES

Capillary forces in an oil and gas reservoir are the result of the combined effect of surface and interfacial liquid tensions, pore size and shape, and the wetting properties of the reservoir rock.

Surface and interfacial tension of fluids results from molecular properties occurring at their surface or interface. Surface tension is the tendency of a liquid to expose a minimum free surface. It is a "skin effect" at the surface or interface similar to the tension of a stretched membrane. Surface tension may be defined as the contractile tendency of a liquid surface exposed to gases. The interfacial tension is a similar tendency which exists when two nonmiscible liquids are in contact.

Methods of Surface-tension Measurements. A number of methods have been devised for measuring surface tension with respect to gases, namely, the capillary-rise, the sessile-drop, and the captive-bubble method. For the measurement of surface as well as of interfacial tensions, the du Noüy tensiometer is a most convenient instrument.

Capillary-rise Method. Let us consider a circular capillary tube of radius r, wetted by the liquid to be tested. It is plunged vertically in a vessel containing the liquid (Fig. 7-3). The latter immediately rises to a height h above the free liquid level in the vessel.

Let γ be the surface tension of the liquid with respect to air, i.e., the force in dynes per centimeter exerted by the contractile tendency of the liquid surface. The column of liquid in the capillary must be held up against the gravity pull by a force, the so-called capillary suction or capillary-pressure characteristic of the tube and fluid. We may write

$$\text{Capillary suction} = \text{gravity pull}$$

or

$$2\pi r\gamma \cos\theta = g\delta\pi r^2 h \tag{7-1}$$

where θ = angle of contact between liquid and glass tube
δ = density of liquid
g = acceleration of gravity
h = fluid capillary rise

Hence the value of the surface tension is readily calculated:

$$\gamma = \frac{g\delta hr}{2\cos\theta} \tag{7-2}$$

The value $g\delta h$ is also the hydrostatic pressure (ΔP) exerted by the column of liquid in the capillary. Hence

$$\gamma = \frac{r\,\Delta P}{2\cos\theta} \tag{7-3}$$

The significance of ΔP may be gained from the following considerations. Hydrostatic equilibrium requires pressures at the surface of a liquid in the vessel to be equal, say, to atmospheric pressure. Yet we have atmospheric pressure over the fluid meniscus in the capillary. Considering the pressure variation along the height of the capillary, we see that a sharp pressure discontinuity of value $\Delta P = g\delta h = 2\gamma \cos\theta/r$ must exist through the meniscus' interface. This is the *capillary pressure* of the tube, which can also be interpreted as the capillary resistance to the penetration into the tube, saturated with a wetting fluid, of a liquid which does not wet the substance of the tube. As such, it is also called the *displacement pressure* of the tube. As the experiment indicates, a liquid which wets the substance of the tube will be pulled or sucked into the tube.

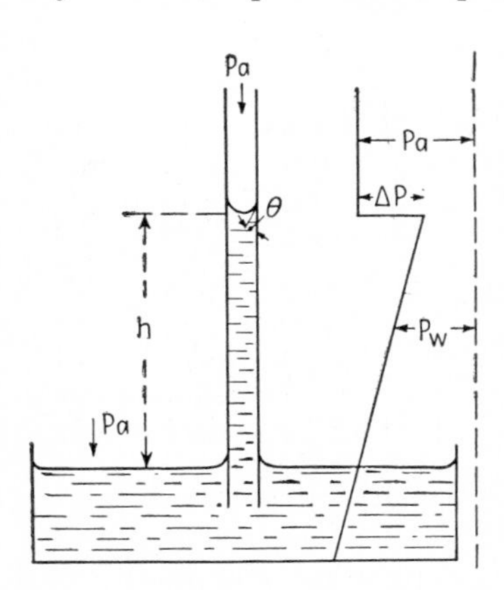

FIG. 7-3. Capillary-rise method of measuring surface tension.

The measurement of the surface tension by the capillary-rise method requires the measurement of the angle of contact θ, at best a difficult problem. Hence the method is generally used with liquids which fully wet the surface of the tube substance for which $\theta = 0$ and $\cos\theta = 1$.

A further important observation concerning capillary pressure is that the pressure is higher inside the concave boundary than outside, the differential pressure being the capillary pressure. This relation has been generalized by Gardescu (1930) for those interfaces other than spherical having two main radii of curvature, r_1 and r_2, the relation being as follows:

$$\Delta P = \gamma \left(\frac{1}{r_1} + \frac{1}{r_2} \right) \tag{7-4}$$

Sessile-drop Method. The sessile-drop method of measuring the surface tension of liquids with respect to air makes use of an instrument called the stalagmometer (Fig. 7-4). This method consists in determining the number of drops falling from the capillary end of the stalagmometer while the surface of the liquid within the bulb is lowered from the upper to the lower mark. The principle of the method resides in the observation that the size of a drop falling from a capillary tube depends on the surface tension of the liquid. The apparatus consists of a capillary tube, the end of which is flattened out to give a larger dropping surface and is further ground flat and polished. A bulb is blown in the tube near the center so as to hold more liquid. The capillary ends are etched with divisions so as to facilitate reading the volumes of the drops by noting how many scale divisions correspond to one drop. The instrument is calibrated with liquids of known surface tensions. The surface tension can be read from charts giving in abscissa the number of liquid drops corresponding to the calibrated volume. This method is susceptible of adaptation to the measurement of surface and interfacial tensions of liquids under high pressure and temperature.

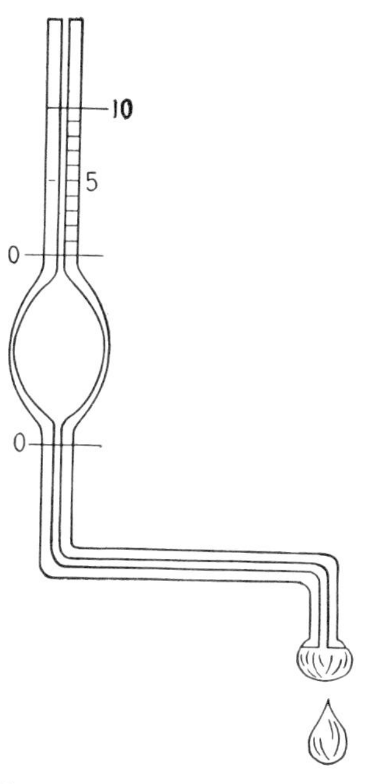

FIG. 7-4. Sessile-drop method of measuring surface tension.

Captive-bubble Method. The captive-bubble method is devised to measure surface and interfacial tension as well as the angle of contact of a liquid with a solid.

The instrument consists of a glass tube through which the liquid of interest is admitted. A bubble is forced out of the tube and placed in contact with the solid surface of interest, such as a core sample of the reservoir, mineral face, and the like (Fig. 7-5). A microscope is focused on the bubble. A graduated vernier mounted on the rotating cross hairs permits the angle measurements. The cross hairs are successively rotated to be parallel to the solid surfaces and then to the tangent at the contact point of the meniscus with the solid surface.

The angle of contact is a function of the directional tendency to displacement; we have the advancing angle of contact when water has a tendency to advance through oil and receding angle of contact when oil has a tendency to advance through water. The two conditions are represented in Fig. 7-5. Bartell and associates (1938) attempted to use a

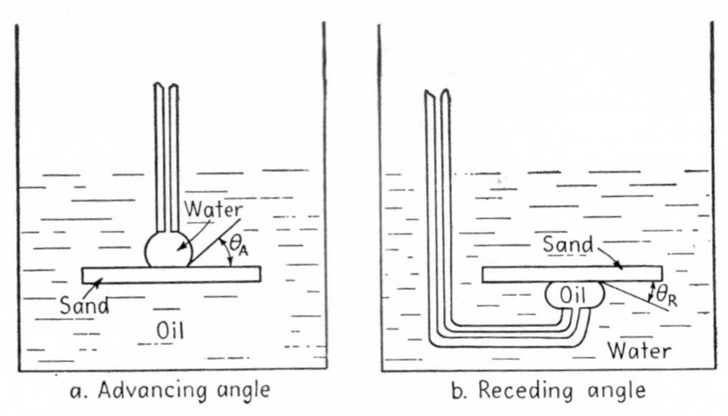

FIG. 7-5. Captive-bubble method of measuring contact angle and wettability.

similar method to determine the preferential wetting properties of certain oils for pure silica. Their results are given in Table 7-1. The conclusion

TABLE 7-1. ANGLE OF WETTING OVER PURE SILICA FOR VARIOUS RESERVOIR CRUDES

Crude	θ Advancing	θ Receding
Bradford	77°	36°
Oklahoma City (Wilcox)	165°	36°
California	156°	43°

drawn by Bartell was that when both angles are less than 90 deg, the solid surface is water-wet. It is oil-wet in the opposite case. Silica is therefore water-wet in the presence of Bradford crude and oil-wet in the presence of Wilcox and California crudes. The difference in wetting properties can be attributed to the variations in polar-compounds content of the various crudes.

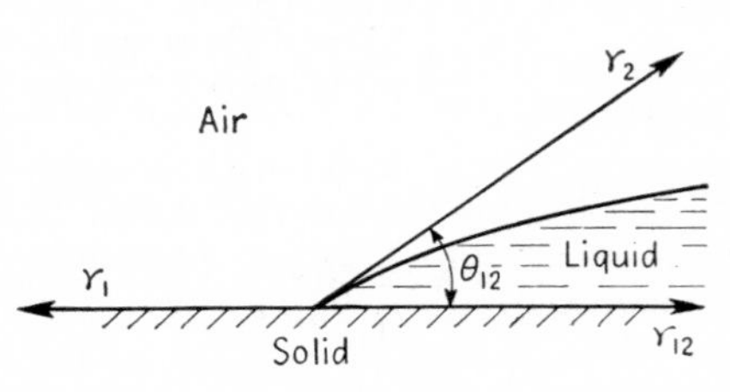

FIG. 7-6. Wetting liquid meniscus over solid.

A knowledge of the interfacial tension between two liquids permits us to calculate the other components of tension at the various interfaces according to the well-known Antonow equilibrium equation:

$$\gamma_1 - \gamma_{12} = \gamma_2 \cos \theta_{12} \tag{7-5}$$

corresponding to the conditions of Fig. 7-6. The value $\gamma_1 - \gamma_{12}$ is called the "*adhesion tension*" of the liquid for the surface and is a measure of wetting. If the liquid wets the solid, $\theta_{12} < 90°$ and the adhesion tension is positive (Fig. 7-6). The converse is true for a nonwetting fluid. Wettability is therefore characterized by a contact angle. It is also a measurement of the spontaneous tendency which a liquid has to displace another. This may be measured in a Bartell cell illustrated in Fig. 7-7. Assuming that water wets the sand packed in the horizontal part of the cell and that the sand was originally saturated with oil, the instant water comes in contact with the sand, the water-oil interface in the sand is such that a greater pressure exists on the oil than on the water side owing to the concave shape of the oil interface. Originally oil and water were at atmospheric pressure. In order to restore equilibrium, oil is displaced in the

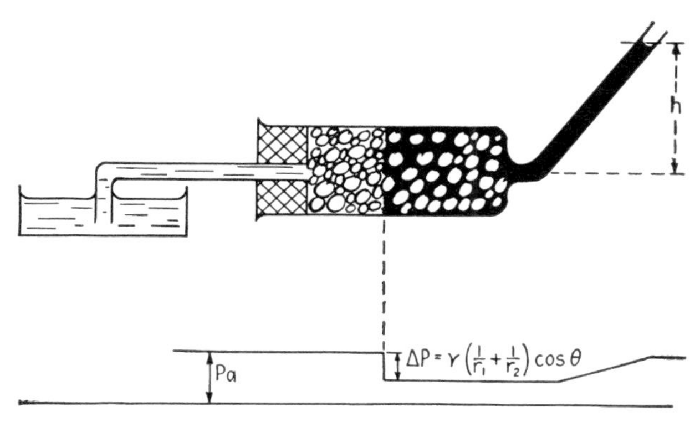

FIG. 7-7. Bartell cell illustrating capillary drive and pressure distribution in a porous medium.

vertical tube to a height h so that the interfacial capillary pressure between oil and water will be equilibrated. The equilibrium position is shown in Fig. 7-7, which also indicates the pressure distribution profile through the various fluids. An experiment of the type just described, when carried out on reservoir samples, permits us to obtain information on how effective spontaneous capillary displacement by a wetting fluid may be in removing oil.

Tensiometer Method. The *ring*, or *du Noüy*, method of measuring surface and interfacial tension is the practical laboratory means most commonly used. The instrument, also called a tensiometer, is represented in Fig. 7-8.

The ring is made of platinum-iridium wire. It is supported by a bail, or vertical loop, and in use the ring is held parallel to the surface of the liquid. To measure surface tension, the ring is placed in the liquid surface and the force necessary to withdraw it from the liquid is determined. For interfacial measurements, the ring is placed in the interface, and the force necessary to break the interfacial film with the ring is measured. This force may be measured by any suitable device. For example, an analytical balance has been used for this purpose, but it has obvious limitations. Du Noüy used a modified torsion balance because of its convenience, reliability, and suitability.

The Cenco–du Noüy tensiometer, as shown in Fig. 7-8, consists of a main frame and support on which is mounted the taut torsion wire W. The torsion arm K, which supports the ring H, is attached to the torsion wire at its mid-point. As the wire is twisted, the torsional force raises the ring. The amount of twist is a measure of the torsion and of the lifting force. The force exerted on the ring is translated into appropriate units by scale S and vernier V.

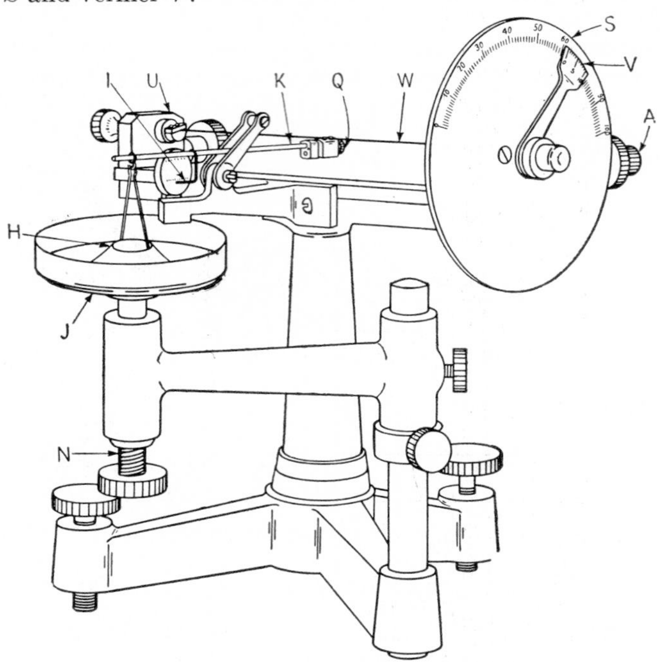

Fig. 7-8. Du Noüy tensiometer. (*Courtesy Cenco News Chats.*)

To calibrate the instrument, the vernier is set at zero on the scale and the dry ring H is attached to the lever arm. At this point the index arm must be set in the neutral position as indicated by index I. This is done by rotating the knob which is part of unit U. The calibration is done by adding known weights (approximately 500 to 1,000 mg) to the ring. Upon restoring the index arm to the neutral position by means of knob A, the scale reading should be the value obtained by dividing the added weights by twice the circumference of the ring, expressed in dynes per centimeter. If this is not the case, the length of the lever arm must be altered until this condition is obtained.

To make a measurement of surface tension, the cleaned ring is attached to the lever arm. The liquid to be measured is placed in the clean container, such as an evaporating dish, watch glass, or beaker. The dish with the liquid is raised until the ring is immersed about 5 mm in the liquid. The liquid is lowered by means of screw N until the ring is in the surface of the liquid and the index is in approximately the neutral position. The torsion of the wire is increased by rotating knob A to bring the vernier near the expected reading on the dial. Then the dish is lowered by means of screw N; the knob A is turned slowly with a steady movement to increase the torsion on the wire. At the same time the dish is lowered proportionately so that at all times the index is kept in the neutral position. This position is held even though the surface of the liquid is distended as shown in Fig. 7-9.

This double-movement procedure is continued until the film breaks. The scale reading at the breaking point of the film is the apparent surface

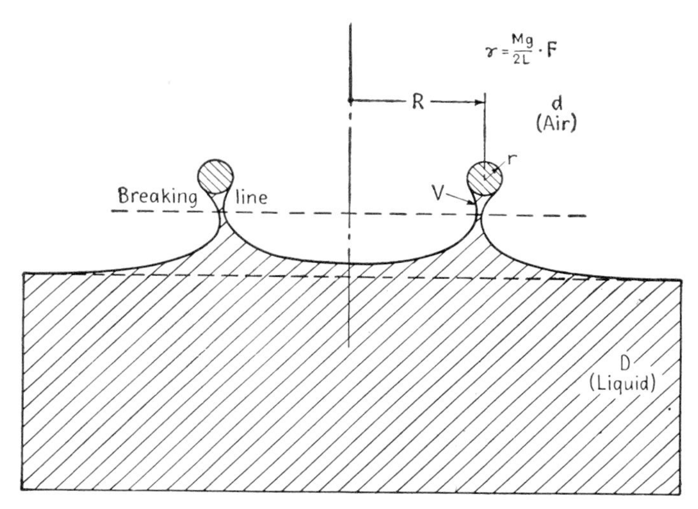

FIG. 7-9. Condition of liquid surface film at breaking point. (*Courtesy Cenco News Chats.*)

tension γ, where $\gamma = Mg/2L$, Mg being the pull on the ring expressed in dynes and L the length of the periphery of the ring in centimeters. The factor 2 enters into the expression because 2 films are involved, as shown in Fig. 7-9, above and below the breaking line. The distention of the surface film indicates there are several factors affecting the pull on the ring which contribute to the apparent surface tension γ. Obviously a correction has to be made to obtain the true surface tension (γ). Only two of the unwanted forces are of sufficient magnitude to require correction. There is a large amount of experimental evidence to support this statement. One force is the weight of liquid clinging to the ring after the film breaks. The separation occurs at the breaking line. This volume is represented by V and is a function of the radius of the ring R and density of the liquid D. The other force, the elevation of the surface of the liquid inside the ring to a higher level than the surface outside, is a function of R/r. These two effects result in a correction factor F, so that γ, the true surface tension, is equal to $(Mg/2L)F$.

The apparent surface tension may differ, according to Harkins and Jordan (1930) and Freud and Freud (1930), from the true surface tension by as much as 30 per cent in extreme cases. For most measurements the difference is probably less than 5 per cent.

Zuidema and Waters (1941) have published an empirical formula, with universal constants, which gives correction factors agreeing with accepted results within very close limits. Figure 7-10 shows curves constructed, using this formula, which apply to both interfacial and surface-tension measurements.

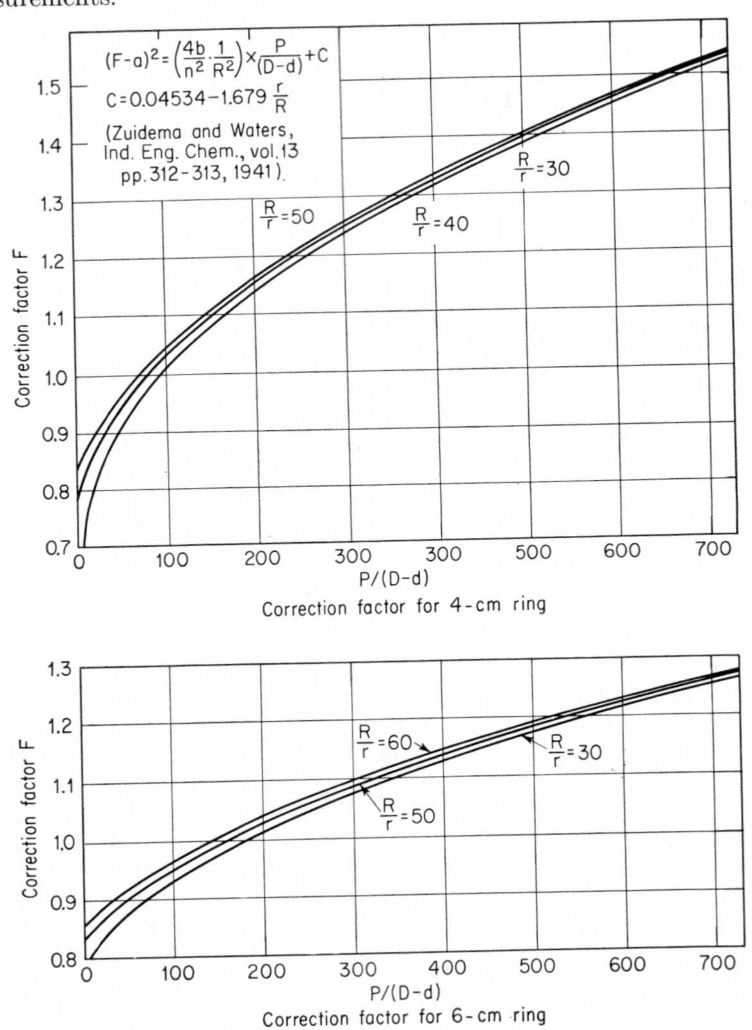

FIG. 7-10. Correction charts for ring size in surface-tension measurements. (*Courtesy Cenco News Chats.*)

When the measurement to be made is on the interface between water and a liquid lighter in density than water, the ring pull is upward and the procedure is as follows: Preliminary adjustments are the same as described for surface-tension measurement. With water only in the clean dish, the platform is raised until the ring is immersed from 5 to 7 mm in the water. A quantity of the liquid is then poured on the surface of the water. This should be to a depth of 5 to 10 mm, depending upon the liquid. The height of the dish is adjusted until the ring is in the interface and the lever arm in approximately the neutral position; then the dish is lowered

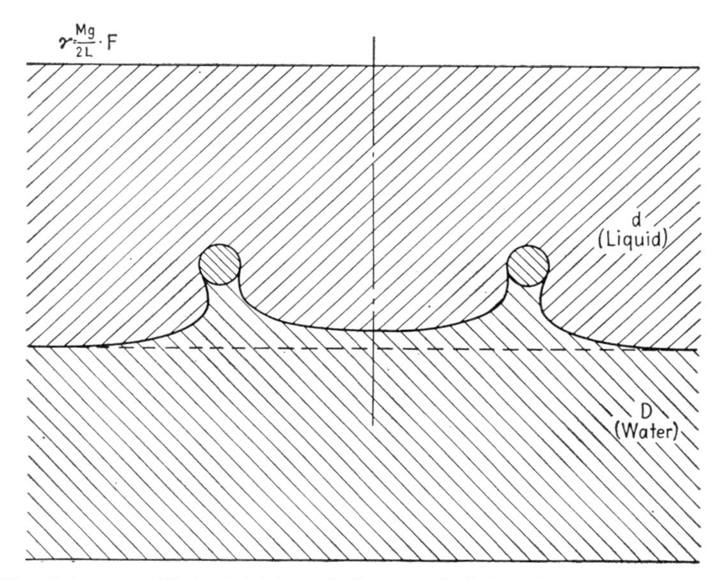

Fig. 7-11. Distention of interfacial film during interfacial-tension measurement. (*Courtesy Cenco News Chats.*)

in proportion to the increased torsion of the wire, keeping the index of the lever arm at zero. The reading when the film breaks is the apparent interfacial tension. By applying correction factor F, the true interfacial tension may be computed.

Figure 7-11 shows the distention of the interfacial film during the early part of the interfacial-tension measurement.

To make an interfacial measurement between water and a liquid with a density greater than water, it is necessary to have an instrument which will exert a downward force on the ring. This instrument has a double-armed parallelogram structure which affords stability for keeping the ring aligned during downward movement. The adjustment of the instrument is very similar to that described above except that there are two arms to be adjusted in length instead of one. The procedure of measurement is similar.

One of the most important considerations in surface-tension measurements is the cleanliness of the vessels as well as the ring. The ring is cleaned by rinsing in a naphtha, rinsing with distilled water, and flaming in the reducing flame of an ordinary burner. In practice, when interfacial measurements are made, the ring is moved from water into the other liquid. Some observers follow the practice of aging the film for 30 sec before taking the final measurement. Surface tension is dependent upon temperature; thus, the temperature at which the measurement is made should be noted.

Capillary Pressure of Reservoir Rocks. The interfacial phenomena described above for a single capillary tube also exist when bundles of interconnected capillaries of varying sizes exist in a porous medium. The capillary-pressure difference which exists within a porous medium between two immiscible phases will again be a function of the interfacial tension and of the average size of the capillaries, which size controls the curvature of the interface. In addition, the curvature is also a function of the saturation distribution of the fluids involved.

The capillary pressure of a porous rock may be defined in various manners:

It is the pressure differential between the various mobile and interlaced fluid phases within the porous network of the rock.

It is the suction capacity of the rock for a fluid phase that will wet the rock.

It is a measure of the tendency of the rock to suck in the wetting fluid phase or to repel the nonwetting phase.

It is a measure of the curvature of the interfaces between the various fluids.

It may help to visualize capillary pressure if we consider two spherical sand grains in contact with one another (Fig. 7-12). Consider them water-wet (hydrophilic) and oil-repellent. When a large saturation in water exists within the pores, the fluid distribution may be as shown by interface 1. The curvature of the interface is relatively small, and the capillary pressure is small. Should water be removed from the system and oil saturation increased, the fluid interface would be such as shown by curve 2; the capillary pressure between the phases will be greater owing to the large interfacial curvature. The variations in capillary pressure for this system may be represented by a curve plotted vs. saturation, as shown in Fig. 7-12. It will help if we consider the absolute pressure within each phase. The oil phase is at atmospheric pressure, whereas the water phase will have an absolute pressure less than atmospheric since it is terminated by a concave surface. The absolute water-pressure curve is asymptotic to the irreducible water saturation.

In practice the capillary-pressure curve is inverted and plotted above the abscissa. Yet it is well to bear in mind that the curve represents negative values of pressure for the wetting phase. In order to obtain the pressure in the wetting phase, the capillary pressure must be subtracted from the pressure in the nonwetting phase.

The capillary pressure–fluid saturation relationship of rock aggregates, serving as oil reservoirs, will be discussed presently. Admittedly, the capillary pressure of reservoir-rock specimen can be measured by finding out how much pressure must be applied on a nonwetting fluid in order to reach a certain saturation in that fluid. If the largest capillary opening be considered as circular, of radius r, the pressure needed for forcing the nonwetting fluid will be $\Delta P = 2\gamma \cos \theta / r$. It is the minimum pressure at which the nonwetting fluid starts to enter the core because any capillary of smaller radius will require a higher pressure application. This minimum pressure is called the *displacement pressure* of the core.

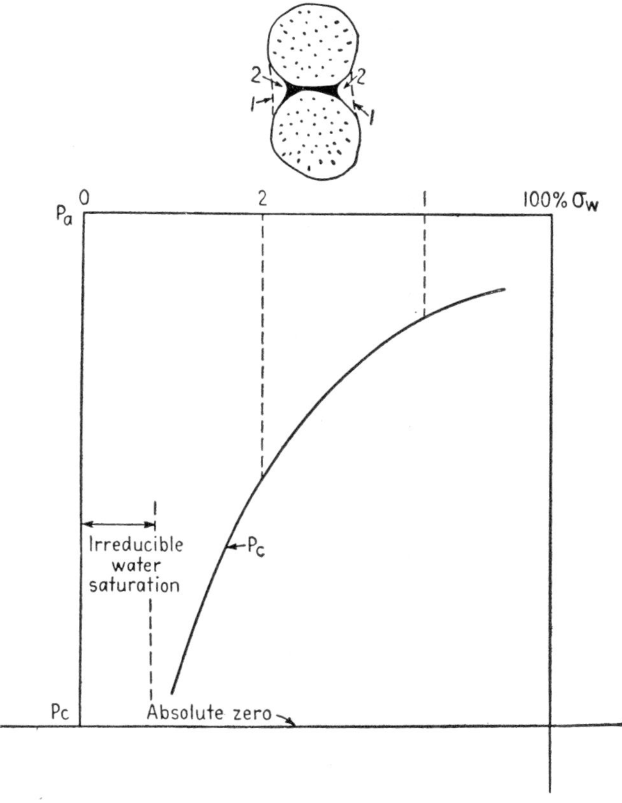

FIG. 7-12. Capillary pressure as a function of fluid saturation in a reservoir rock.

As the driving pressure upon the nonwetting fluid is increased, capillaries of smaller and smaller radii are penetrated by the nonwetting fluid.

Should the capillaries of the specimen be highly uniform in size, no excess pressure would be required to saturate them in nonwetting fluid and the plot of pressure applied vs. fluid saturation would be very flat until the irreducible saturation is reached. This is illustrated in curve 1, Fig. 7-13. On the contrary, should the capillaries be of very heterogeneous size, the capillary-pressure curve would be very steep such as curve 3. Curve 2 is the capillary pressure for capillary size distribution of medium heterogeneity.

It may be summarized that the capillary pressure of a reservoir rock as a function of fluid saturation is a measure of *capillary size distribution*, which in turn is a measure of the *rock texture.* Fine textured rocks made up of small cemented grains, closely packed, exhibit a higher capillary

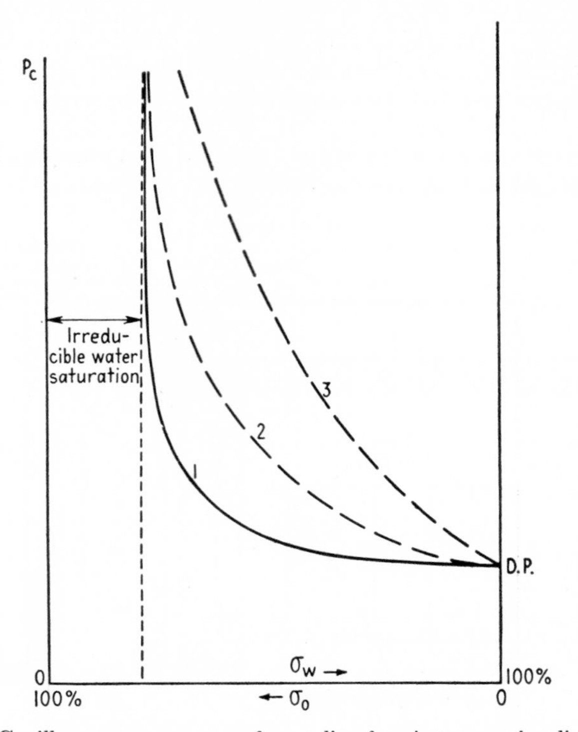

FIG. 7-13. Capillary-pressure curves for media of various pore-size distributions.

pressure at a given saturation than coarse textured rocks made up of large grains, poorly cemented and loosely packed.

It is possible from the capillary-pressure curve to calculate the average size of the pores making up a stated fraction of the total pore space. Let P_c be the average capillary pressure for the 10 per cent between saturations of 40 and 50 per cent. The average capillary radius is obtained from

$$r = \frac{2\gamma \cos \theta}{P_c} \tag{7-6}$$

which equation may be solved provided that the interfacial tension γ and the angle of contact θ may be evaluated.

Methods of Capillary-pressure Measurements. The various means of measuring the capillary pressure of reservoir-rock samples will now be reviewed briefly:

Desorption of Saturated Cores over a High-displacement Pressure Diaphragm. The procedure is best illustrated by referring to Fig. 7-14 where the cores are initially fully saturated in wetting fluid (generally water but preferably connate water). The base of the cores must be terminated by a flat and polished surface. A diaphragm of porous material (unglazed ceramic) serves as the support for the cores. However, the average pore size of this diaphragm must be much smaller than that of the cores in order to ensure proper results. Biological filters have proved excellent for the purpose.

In order to ensure proper fit of the cores and diaphragm surfaces, various finely divided ingredients are inserted in between, such as pulverized talc,

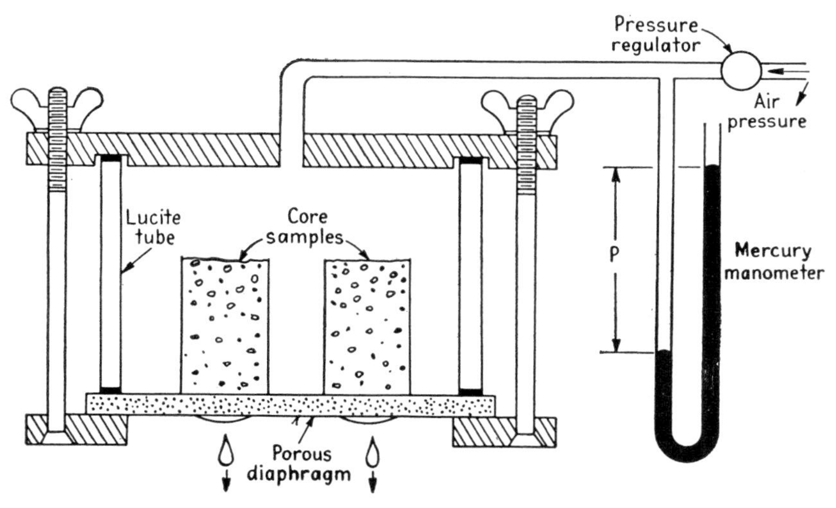

FIG. 7-14. Desaturation apparatus for the measurement of capillary pressure in core samples.

galena, or flour, wetted with the cores' saturating fluid. A sheet of tissue paper has also proved to be very effective. When a pressure of nonwetting fluid (gas, air, oil) is applied within the vessel clamped over the core assembly, the saturating fluid is driven through the porous diaphragm and the fluid displacement is measured in a graduated tube.

A complete capillary-pressure curve has to be run in steps. First, pressure will be applied in small steps so as to determine the displacement pressure or point at which the nonwetting fluid starts to penetrate. When this pressure is determined, a slight excess pressure is applied and left for a sufficient length of time to ensure that no further flow takes place out of the core. The pressure is then raised another increment, and the fluid outflow is again measured.

The maximum driving pressure which can be reached by this method is the displacement pressure of the diaphragm, at which point the driving phase will break through and ruin the experiment. The range of operation possible with a diaphragm of known displacement pressure is indicated on Fig. 7-15.

The procedure described above is slow, at best, but many such tests may be made simultaneously in a battery of pressuring vessels. Another simplification used in many routine tests where the determination of connate water saturation is the aim consists in applying but one single pressure step high enough to attain the irreducible water saturation. This practice appears to be of doubtful value, as will be seen later, inasmuch as equilibrium of pressure must be established at all levels within the water phase of a reservoir in place. The irreducible water saturation is not necessarily that corresponding to the equilibrium, especially within the transition zone.

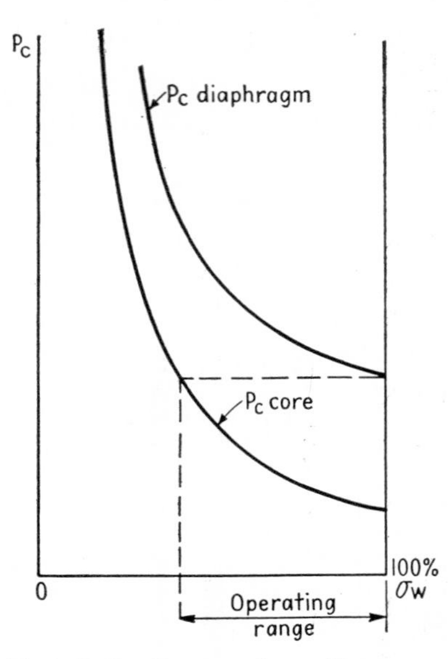

FIG. 7-15. Range of capillary-pressure tests over a porous diaphragm.

A distinction must be made between the *displacement* and *threshold* pressures. The former refers to the entrance pressure of a nonwetting fluid into a porous medium fully saturated with a wetting fluid. However, if the medium is partially saturated with nonwetting fluid, the entrance pressure is reduced to a point below the displacement pressure. If the saturation in the nonwetting fluid is the equilibrium saturation to this fluid phase, the threshold pressure is now zero since the porous network starts to show conductivity to the nonwetting phase at this point. The state of saturation in which a threshold pressure exists is known as insular.

The capillary-pressure curve is asymptotic to the vertical drawn through the wetting-phase equilibrium saturation or point at which the porous medium fails to show conductivity to the wetting phases.

The relationships between the various saturation conditions in the different fluids, their equilibrium saturation, and the corresponding capillary- and threshold-pressure curves are illustrated in Fig. 7-16.

A different procedure of using a displacement pressure diaphragm in capillary-pressure measurements was originated by Hassler and Brunner (1945). It makes use of suction to desaturate the cores, as indicated in the illustration, Fig. 7-17. It is reported that this method of operation often leads to experimental difficulties because of gas breaking through the diaphragm. Another disadvantage resides in the maximum range of measurements, which is limited to 1 atm.

Gravity Drainage of Long Vertical Cores. This method is not essentially different from the diaphragm method. It is applicable to long packed

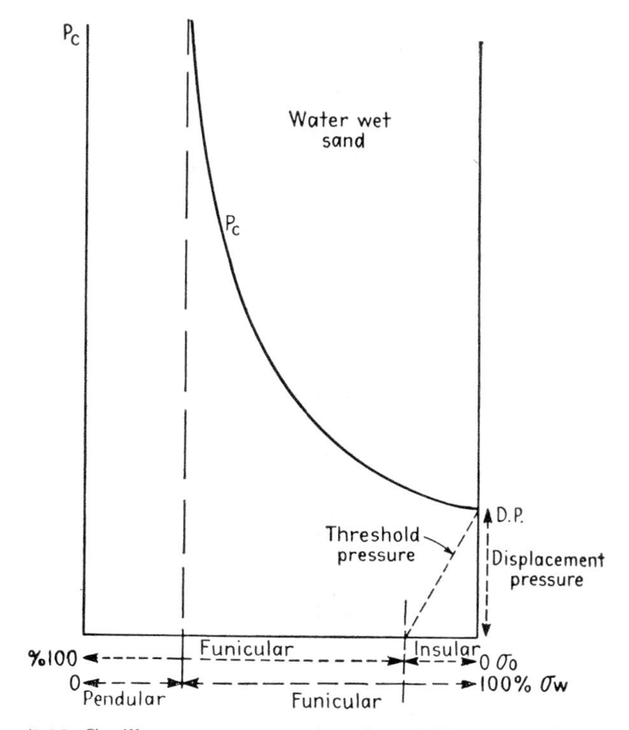

Fig. 7-16. Capillary pressure as a function of fluid-saturation stages.

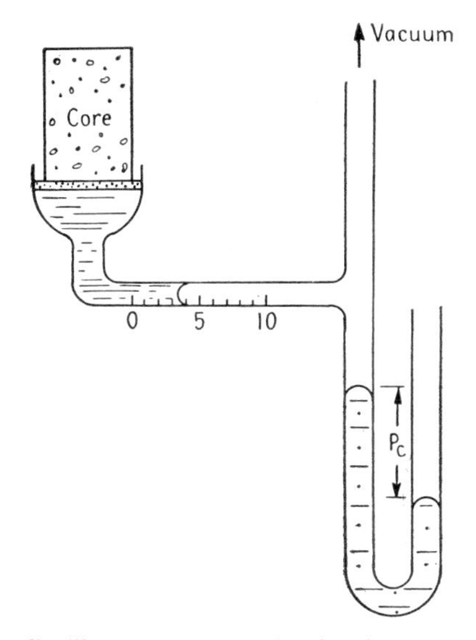

Fig. 7-17. Capillary-pressure testing by the vacuum method.

tubes of unconsolidated sands as well as to long cores of consolidated sands. As the name indicates, the desaturation force comes from the differential density $\Delta\delta$ of the fluids involved. The capillary pressure P_c at any level h in the drainage column may be computed by

$$P_c = gh\,\Delta\delta = \gamma\left(\frac{1}{r_1} + \frac{1}{r_2}\right)\cos\theta \tag{7-7}$$

For best results a high-displacement pressure diaphragm should be placed at the bottom of the drainage column.

In order to obtain the capillary pressure vs. fluid saturation, the latter must be determined at each level. This may be done in the case of water drainage by electrical-conductivity measurements. In the case of oil drainage, a column built by sections can be dismantled rapidly upon completion of the experiment, and the individual sections weighed. The oil volume and saturation are obtained by difference.

The limitations of this method are quite evident: a high-driving pressure requires a very high column, the drainage process is very slow at best, inaccuracies are encountered in the determination of saturation, etc. Accordingly, this method is used only for special problems and not as a routine procedure.

Mercury-injection Method. This method developed by Drake and Ritter (1945) was originally devised to measure the capillary size distribution of catalysts. It consists in injecting mercury under very high pressure into solid porous substance. Mercury will generally be nonwetting for reservoir rocks. In addition it has a very high surface tension (480 dynes per cm). A further advantage of the method comes from the fact that it can be used on dried cores, unsaturated by liquid. A disadvantage of the method is that the cores are spoiled by the test and are unusable for further experiments owing to their mercury content.

The operational procedure is indicated in Fig. 7-18 and is as follows: The core is placed in the mercury reservoir A; the lid B is adapted thereto; vacuum is applied for a sufficient length of time to remove air; mercury is pumped into the reservoir until an excess mercury appears over stopcock C; the latter is then closed. A high-pressure mercury pump D of the type employed in testing bottom-hole samples is used to inject mercury further into the system. Pressure is measured for each incremental mercury volume injected, the measuring system being again identical with the technique of testing bottom-hole samples. The mercury increments used presumably penetrate the core and may be expressed in saturation percentages which are plotted vs. mercury pressure.

In order to obtain the capillary pressure corresponding to water, various assumptions must be made. Purcell (1948), who studied the method in some detail, assumes an angle of wetting for water of 0 and 140 deg for mercury. Then the capillary pressures to mercury and water are in the approximate ratio of 5:1. It must be further assumed that no change occurs in the surface tension of mercury when in very small capillaries. Henderson (1947) has shown that this last assumption may not always be verified

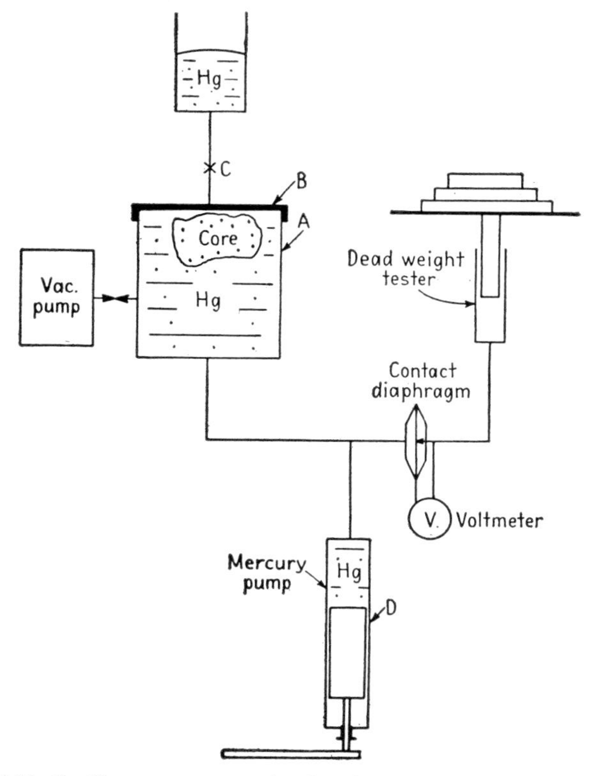

FIG. 7-18. Capillary-pressure testing by the mercury-injection method.

as the surface tension of mercury varies with the curvature of its interface. The advantages of the mercury method are twofold. It is extremely rapid, a complete test being possible in about 30 to 60 min. In addition, the method is applicable to small core samples of irregular shape as well as drill cuttings.

Centrifuge Method. Hassler and Brunner (1945) have reported a fast though more complex procedure for measuring capillary pressures. In principle it makes use of a greatly increased gravity drainage effect by submitting the saturated cores to variable multiples of the acceleration of gravity g obtained in a high-speed centrifuge.

It is necessary that a centrifuge for measurement of capillary pressure shall run smoothly even when considerably out of balance. This requirement was met in Hassler's apparatus by the use of a centerless rotor, i.e., one suspended on a shaft flexible enough to bend while the rotor takes whatever center the constantly shifting liquid masses require. The damping forces required to avoid the damaging resonance vibration to which this type of construction normally gives rise are supplied by a rubber damping bearing below the rotor, consisting of a leather bearing enclosed in a metal cup A surrounded by a ring of sponge rubber B which is held in a steel ring C (Fig. 7-19). This bearing does not support any of the weight of the rotor, which is suspended from a ball bearing D. The suspension represents a compromise between flexibility and strength; it consists of

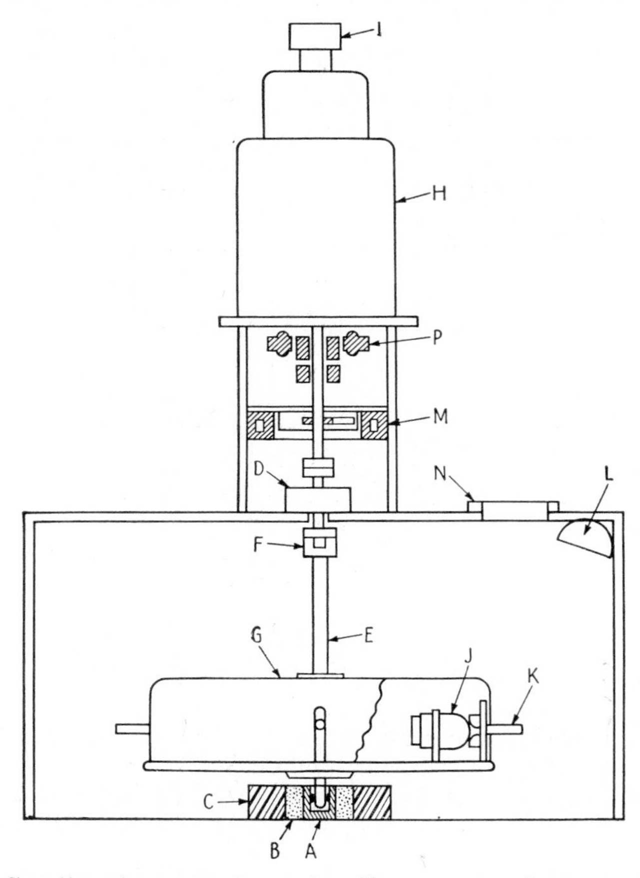

FIG. 7-19. Centrifuge for measurement of capillary pressure of core samples. (*After Hassler, courtesy AIME.*)

a rigid shaft E provided with two universal joints, one of which is shown at F and the other hidden by the streamlined rotor cover G. The rotor is driven at speeds up to 4,000 rpm by a ⅛-hp variable-speed a-c motor H. The motor is provided with an adjustable centrifugal governor which actuates an electronic relay. The core is held in a metal container J, which is provided with a graduated glass pipette K to collect the liquid pulled from the core. Provision is made for four core holders on the rotor, and the pipettes are read by means of a stroboscope lamp L operated by a contact device M on the motor shaft. The contact device M is provided with four contacts, and a selector switch enables any one of the four pipettes to be viewed as desired through the window N. The speed of the centrifuge is obtained by measuring the voltage of a small a-c generator P on the motor shaft. This tachometer is calibrated by means of a stroboscope disk on the rotor.

To measure capillary pressures with this apparatus, the extracted cores are saturated and placed in their core holders after their dry and saturated weights have been obtained. The centrifuge is then started and run at successively greater speeds, the speed being held constant at each chosen value until the cores have all attained equilibrium, as indicated by no further increase with time of the quantity of liquid contained in the pipettes. When equilibrium is attained, which takes from a few minutes to ½ hr or more, the quantity of liquid in each of the pipettes is read with the aid of the stroboscope and the speed of the centrifuge is increased. When the run is over, the cores are removed from the centrifuge and weighed to give a check on the saturation determined from the last pipette reading.

The simplified theory for the computation of the capillary pressure, which Hassler has shown to be sufficiently accurate for practical purposes, is as follows.

It was shown above that capillary pressure is a function of the fluid saturation along the core. Conversely it may be said that saturation is a function of capillary pressure: $\sigma = \sigma(P_c)$. But P_c in the centrifuge is given by

$$P_c = a\,\delta h \tag{7-8}$$

where a = acceleration produced by rotation of centrifuge at an angular velocity ω
δ = fluid density
h = distance of any fluid element from core outlet where capillary pressure is zero owing to its contact with fluid of zero curvature in the measuring pipette

The average saturation $\bar{\sigma}$ in the core at a definite constant speed may be obtained from the following expression:

$$\bar{\sigma} = \frac{1}{L}\int_0^L \sigma(P_c)\,dP_c = \frac{1}{a\,\delta L}\int_0^L \sigma(h)\,dh \tag{7-9}$$

where L is the total length of the core and where h varies from O to L. It may be written

$$a\,\delta L\,\bar{\sigma} = \int_0^L \sigma(h)\,dh \tag{7-10}$$

Taking the derivative of both sides with respect to L, we obtain

$$a\,\delta\bar{\sigma} = \sigma(L) \tag{7-11}$$

Hence the saturation $\sigma(L)$ at the face of the core closest to the axis of rotation of the centrifuge may be calculated from a knowledge of the average fluid saturation $\bar{\sigma}$, the fluid density δ, and the acceleration a

produced at an average distance r of the core from the axis of the centrifuge rotor. Saturation $\sigma(L)$ corresponds to a capillary pressure $P_c = a\,\vartheta L$.

Knowing the angular velocity ω or the speed of rotation in rpm, the acceleration a may be evaluated from the following expression:

$$a = \omega^2 r = \left(\frac{2\pi \text{ rpm}}{60}\right)^2 r \tag{7-12}$$

where ω = radians per sec
r = cm
in order to obtain a in centimeters per second per second.

Some Engineering and Laboratory Applications of Capillary-pressure Data. *Boundary Effect between Two Homogeneous Porous Media.* Let two media, 1 and 2, be in intimate contact along a surface (Fig. 7-20). The

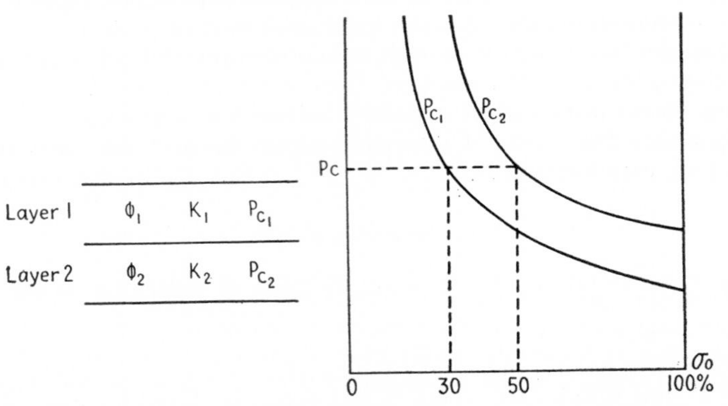

FIG. 7-20. Fluid-saturation discontinuity between formations of different capillary-pressure characteristics.

media have, respectively, the porosities ϕ_1 and ϕ_2 and the absolute permeabilities K_1 and K_2. Their capillary-pressure curves are as shown on the right of the figure, indicating medium 1 to be made up of larger capillaries than medium 2. Let a two-phase fluid mixture (i.e., oil and water) flow parallel to the surface of contact. The two media are assumed to be water-wet. Let the saturation in medium 1 be 30 per cent in oil It is desired to know the saturation in medium 2.

Equilibrium is assumed between the various phases and media. No further transfer of fluid takes place from one medium to the other. Hence there must be continuity of pressure across the boundary. In particular at any one point along the boundary, the pressure measured in any phase must be the same on both sides of the boundary because both phases are in the funicular saturation region. Hence there must also be continuity of capillary pressure across the boundary. Since the saturation in medium 1 is 30 per cent, the value of P_c in both media is P_c, and the saturation in medium 2 must necessarily be 50 per cent.

This shows that a discontinuity of saturation exists when two media of different displacement pressure are placed in contact with one another provided that the saturations are funicular in both media.

Determination of Connate Water Saturation by Capillary-pressure Method. The procedure is as follows:

1. Run the air-water capillary-pressure curves on selected and representative cores from the well.
2. Correct to oil-water capillary pressure, assuming that for identical fluid distribution where oil takes the place of air we have the same radius of curvature and the same angle of contact of the meniscus. Hence the capillary-pressure values determined by testing must be changed by the ratio of the interfacial tensions $= \dfrac{\gamma \text{ oil-water}}{\gamma \text{ air-water}}$, which Hocott (1939) has determined to be of the order of $3/8$. A new curve is so obtained for each core which represents the oil-water capillary pressure.
3. Evaluate the height h of each core above the water level (edge water or bottom water). This must be done from an evaluation of dry-hole data, drill stem tests, electric and radioactive logs.
4. Calculate the value of the capillary pressure P_c for each core level by the following formula:

$$P_c = gh(\delta_{\text{water}} - \delta_{\text{oil}}) \tag{7-13}$$

5. Read the value of P_c so obtained on each corrected curve, and the corresponding connate water saturation is obtained in abscissa.

Thornton and Marshall (1947) have suggested an approximate method of obtaining connate water saturation by merely securing the lowest possible water saturation by means of a desaturation test in an apparatus of the type illustrated in Fig. 7-14, in which a relatively high gas pressure is applied. This, obviously, is correct only if it may be assumed that the core was obtained from a sufficiently high level above the water table. Should this requirement not be met, the connate water saturation may still be determined by the more accurate method just discussed.

End Effect in Laboratory Experiments. An application of capillary pressure to the study of the *end effect* and to its quantitative prediction will be studied under the detailed review of production mechanisms (Chap. 10).

Capillary Lining of Wells. For the purpose of improving production performance and in particular to reduce producing gas-oil ratios, Muskat (U.S. Patent No. 2,365,428) proposed the use of a capillary lining in wells. The procedure consists in introducing into the well bore at the sand face a porous lining with displacement pressure of higher value than the sand itself. The wetting properties should be the same as those of the sand. A discontinuity of saturation is thus created, resulting in a higher saturation in oil within the lining. Hence the effective permeability to gas is reduced, as is the gas-oil ratio.

An obvious disadvantage of the method is that it also reduces the oil-flow rate.

Optimum Water-encroachment Rate in Lensing Sands. This problem has been partially discussed by Leverett (1939). Assuming that the capillary-pressure curves for the lens and the main sand (Fig. 7-21*a*) are those shown in Fig. 7-20 for an oil-wet sand and that the residual oil saturation behind the advancing water-encroachment front is 30 per cent, the corresponding saturation in the tight section will be 50 per cent. Under a given rate of water advance, the water front in the lens will trail behind at a certain distance and capillary readjustment of fluids will result in counterflow of oil from the tight to the loose sand. Under very low rate of water encroachment, less oil will be lost by entrapment and counterflow from the tight sand into the watered-out loose sand. However, in

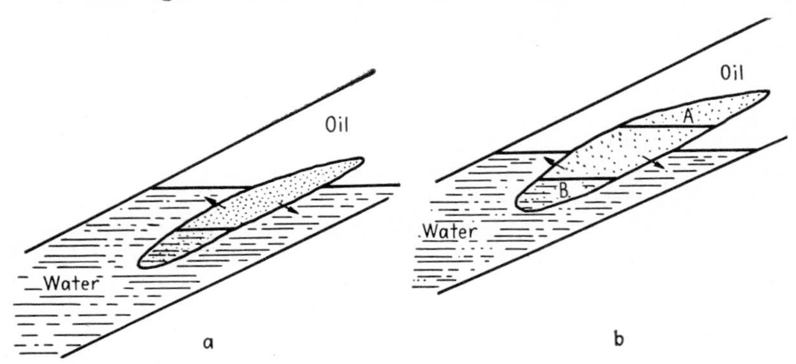

FIG. 7-21. Behavior of water-encroachment front as affected by wetting properties of reservoir rock in (*a*) an oil-wet sand and (*b*) a water-wet sand.

order to recover an appreciable amount of oil from the tight lens, a pressure differential must exist between water and oil which exceeds the displacement pressure of the tight sand.

In the case of a water-wet sand, the condition will be as shown in Fig. 7-21*b*. Should the rate of water encroachment be rapid, the water front in the tight lens would lag behind (*B*) and considerable oil would be lost from the tight sand to the watered-out loose sand as a result of capillary readjustment through oil counterflow. This is easily explained by means of the capillary-pressure diagrams. Assuming originally 100 per cent oil saturation and a residual oil saturation of 20 per cent in the watered-out loose sand, the oil saturation in equilibrium with this figure in the tight sand is 35 per cent (assuming that capillary-pressure curves such as those of Fig. 7-15 apply to the sands in question). Hence, behind the water front in the loose sand, the nonflooded tight sand will have a tendency to desaturate by losing its oil to the watered-out loose sand, as shown by the arrows. Hence a slow rate of advance of the water encroachment is again indicated, particularly if capillary suction could be taken advantage of to maintain the flood front in the tight lens at a position such as *A* in advance of the main front. This will be the case if the rate of capillary encroachment of water in the tight lens is greater than in the main sand. Under such conditions, the flood front in the tight sand will always be ahead of the front in the loose sand, and no entrapment of oil in the tight lens may result through encirclement of the lens by the flood front.

SELECTED REFERENCES ON RESERVOIR FORCES AND ENERGIES

1917

Versluys, J.: Die Kappillarität der Boden, Inst. Mitt. Bodenk., vol. 7, pp. 117ff.

1930

Freud, B. B., and H. Z. Freud: A Theory of the Ring Method for the Determination of Surface Tension, *J. Am. Chem. Soc.*, vol. 52, pp. 1772ff.

Gardescu, I. I.: Behavior of Gas Bubbles in Capillary Spaces, *AIME Tech. Pub.*, p. 306.

Harkins, W. D., and H. F. Jordan: A Method for the Determination of Surface and Interfacial Tension from the Maximum Pull on a Ring, *J. Am. Chem. Soc.*, vol. 52, pp. 1751ff.

1931

Millikan, C. V., and C. V. Sidwell: Bottom-hole Pressures in Oil Wells, *Trans. AIME*, pp. 194ff.

Richards, L. A.: Capillary Conduction of Liquids through Porous Media, *Physics*, vol. 1, pp. 318ff.

1932

Millikan, C. V.: Geological Applications of Bottom Hole Pressures, *Bull. Am. Assoc. Petroleum Geol.*, vol. 16, no. 9, pp. 891ff.

1933

Hawthorn, D. W.: Sub-surface Pressures in Oil Wells and Their Field of Applications, *Trans. AIME Petroleum Development and Technol.*, pp. 148ff.

Millikan, C. V.: Reservoir and Bottom-hole Producing Pressures as a Basis for Proration, *AIME Tech. Pub.* 103.

1934

Parks, E. K., and C. W. Gibbs: Instruments and Equipment for Recording Subsurface Pressures, *Trans. AIME Petroleum Development and Technol.*, pp. 42ff.

1935

Garrison, A. D.: Selective Wetting of Reservoir Rock and Its Relation to Oil Production, *API Drill. and Prod. Pract.*, pp. 130ff.

Schilthuis, R. J., and W. Hurst: Variations in Reservoir Pressure in the East Texas Field, *Trans. AIME Petroleum Development and Technol.*, pp. 164ff.

1936

Exline, P. G.: Precision Gage for Sub-surface Pressure Measurements, *Oil Gas J.*, June 4, pp. 32ff.

1937

Miller, H. C., et al.: Oil Well Behavior Based upon Subsurface Pressures and Production Data, *Trans. AIME Petroleum Development and Technol.*, pp. 97ff.

Muskat, M.: Use of Data on Build Up of Bottom-hole Pressures, *Trans. AIME Petroleum Development and Technol.*, pp. 44ff.

1938

Benner, F. C., et al.: Nature and Importance of Surface Forces in Production of Petroleum, *API Drill. and Prod. Pract.*, pp. 442ff.

Buckley, S. E.: Pressure Production Relationship in the East Texas Field, *API Drill. and Prod. Pract.*, pp. 140ff.

Cannon, G. E., and R. C. Craze: Excessive Pressures and Pressure Variation with Depth of Petroleum Reservoirs in the Gulf Coast Region of Texas and Louisiana, *Trans. AIME Petroleum Development and Technol.*, pp. 31ff.

Livingston, H. K.: Surface and Interfacial Tension between Water and Oil under Reservoir Conditions, *AIME Tech. Pub.* 1001.

Millikan, C. V.: Bottom Hole Pressures in Current Oil Well Operations, *Oil Weekly*, May 30, pp. 41ff.

1939

Hocott, C. R.: Interfacial Tension between Water and Oil under Reservoir Conditions, *AIME Tech. Pub.* 1006.

Livingston, H. K.: The Effects of Surface Phenomena on the Production of Oil, *Petroleum Engr.*, January, pp. 84ff.

1940

Jones, N. N.: Practical Use of Subsurface Pressure Measurements in East Texas, *Oil Weekly*, Dec. 16, pp. 18ff.

Perdum, J. F.: Subsurface Pressure and Temperature Gauges and Samplers, *Mines Mag. Colo.*, August, pp. 435ff.

1941

Abadic, H. G.: Subsurface Pressure Recorders and Equipment, *Petroleum Engr.*, November, pp. 69ff.

Benner, F. C., and F. E. Bartell: The Effect of Polar Impurities upon Capillary and Surface Phenomena in Petroleum Production, *API Drill. and Prod. Pract.*, pp. 341ff.

Carman, P. C.: Capillary Rise and Capillary Movement of Moisture in Fine Sands, *Soil Sci.*, vol. 52, pp. 1ff.

Leverett, M. C.: Capillary Behavior in Porous Solids, *AIME Tech. Pub.* 1223.

Zuidema, H. H., and G. W. Waters: Ring Method for the Determination of Interfacial Tension, *Ind. Eng. Chem.*, vol. 13, pp. 312ff.

1942

Benner, F. C., et al.: Evaluation of Effective Displacement Pressures for Petroleum Oil-Water Silica Systems, *Oil Gas J.*, Nov. 12, pp. 199ff.

Katz, D. L.: Possibilities of Secondary Recovery for Oklahoma City Wilcox Sand, *AIME Tech. Pub.* 1400.

Kemler, E. N.: Applying Bottom Hole Pressure Data to Production Problems, *Oil Weekly*, series of four articles, August–September.

Livingston, H. K.: Surface Energy Relationships in Petroleum Reservoirs, *AIME Tech. Pub.* 1526.

1943

Hassler, G. L., et al.: The Role of Capillarity in Oil Production, *AIME Tech. Pub.* 1623.

Katz, D. L., et al.: Surface Tension of Crude Oils Containing Dissolved Gases, *AIME Tech. Pub.* 1624.

1945

Brownscombe, E. R., and D. R. Conlon: Precision in Bottom Hole Pressure Measurements, *AIME Tech. Pub.* 1942.

Drake, L. C., and H. L. Ritter: Pore-size Distribution in Porous Materials, *Ind. Eng. Chem., Anal. Ed.*, vol. 17, pp. 782ff.

Drake, L. C., and H. L. Ritter: Macro-pore Size Distributions in Some Typical Porous Substances, *Ind. Eng. Chem., Anal. Ed.*, vol. 17, pp. 787ff.

Hassler, G. L., and E. Brunner: Measurement of Capillary Pressures in Small Core Samples, *AIME Tech. Pub.* 1817.

McCullough, J. J., et al.: Determination of Interstitial Water Content of Oil and Gas Sands by Laboratory Tests of Core Samples, *API Drill. and Prod. Pract.*, pp. 180ff.

1947

Bruce, W. A., and H. J. Welge: The Restored State Method for Determination of Oil in Place and Connate Water, *API Drill. and Prod. Pract.*, May, pp. 166ff.

Popovich, M. J.: A Study of the Relationship between Grain Size and Capillary Pressure, *Producers Monthly*, October, pp. 27ff.

Thornton, O. F., and D. L. Marshall: Estimating Interstitial Water by the Capillary Pressure Method, *AIME Tech. Pub.* 2126.

1949

Calhoun, J. C., Jr., et al.: Experiments on the Capillary Properties of Porous Solids, *AIME Tech. Pub.* 2640.

Dale, C. R.: Bottom Hole Flow Surveys for Determination of Fluid and Gas Movements in Wells, *AIME Tech. Pub.* 2644.

Haymaker, E. R., et al.: Method of Establishing a Stabilized Back-pressure Curve for Gas Wells Producing from Reservoirs of Extremely Low Permeability, *AIME Tech. Pub.* 2545.

Purcell, W. R.: Capillary Pressures—Their Measurement Using Mercury and the Calculation of Permeability Therefrom, *AIME Tech. Pub.* 2544.

Rose, W.: A Note on the Application of the Capillary Pressure Method for the Determination of Oil Recovery, *AIME Tech. Note.*

Rose, W.: Theoretical Generalizations Leading to the Evaluation of Relative Permeability, *AIME Tech. Pub.* 2563.

Rose, W., and W. A. Bruce: Evaluation of Capillary Character in Petroleum Reservoir Rock, *AIME Tech. Pub.* 2594.

1950

Douglas, H. W.: A Pendant-drop Apparatus for Surface and Interfacial Tensions, *J. Sci. Instr.*, vol. 27, no. 3, pp. 67–69.

Purcell, W. R.: Interpretation of Capillary Pressure Data, *AIME Tech. Note* 60.

Rose, W., and B. Greifer: Anomalies in the Measurement of Wetting Liquid Pressure Gradients, *AIME Tech. Note* 57.

Schellinger, A. K.: Calorimetric Method for the Determination of the Surface Energy of a Brittle Crystalline Solid, *Science*, vol. 111, pp. 693ff.

Weyl, W. A.: Wettability, a Function of Polarizability of the Surface Ions, *J. Appl. Phys.*, April, pp. 338ff.

1951

Hough, E. W., et al.: Interfacial Tensions at Reservoir Pressures and Temperatures; Apparatus and the Water-Methane System, *AIME Tech. Pub.* 3019.

1953

Dickinson, G.: Reservoir Pressures in Gulf Coast Louisiana, *Bull. Am. Assoc. Petroleum Geol.*, vol. 37, no. 2, pp. 410ff.

Killins, C. R., et al.: Capillary Desaturation and Imbibition in Porous Rocks, *7th Ann. Tech. Conf., Penn. State Univ.*, October 28–30, pp. 55–56.

1954

Kennedy, H. T., and E. T. Guerrero: The Effect of Surface and Interfacial Tensions on the Recovery of Oil by Water-flooding, *J. Petroleum Technol.*, vol. 6, no. 5, pp. 41–47ff.

Matthews, C. S., et al.: A Method for Determination of Average Pressure in a Bounded Reservoir, *Trans. AIME Petroleum Div.*, vol. 201, pp. 182ff.

1955

Ainsworth, W. J., and M. F. Hawkins, Jr.: Two Errors in Pressure Measurement Using Subsurface Gauges, *AIME Tech. Note* 302; *J. Petroleum Technol.*, vol. 7, no. 9, pp. 80ff.

Sukkar, Y. K., and D. Cornell: Direct Calculation of Bottom-hole Pressures in Natural Gas Wells, *AIME Tech. Pub.* 4010; *J. Petroleum Technol.*, vol. 7, no. 3, pp. 43ff.

1956

Coley, F. H., et al.: A Study of the Effect of Wettability on the Behavior of Fluids in Synthetic Porous Media, *Producers Monthly*, vol. 20, no. 8, pp. 28ff.

Marx, J. W.: Determination of Gravity Drainage Characteristics on the Centrifuge, *J. Petroleum Technol.*, vol. 8, no. 4, pp. 88ff.

Reisberg, J., and T. M. Doscher: Interfacial Phenomena in Crude-oil–water Systems, *Producers Monthly*, vol. 20, no. 11, pp. 28ff.

CHAPTER 8

MECHANICS OF FLUID FLOW IN POROUS MEDIA

The tools of the reservoir engineer are mathematical in nature and it behooves him to learn the use of these tools proficiently and accurately. Basically, the equations of fluid flow in porous and permeable media are applications of the empirical Darcy's law. As originally derived, this law included only the effect of gravity and was used by Darcy in the prediction of water flow in filtering water-supply plants under gravity flow. With the application of external pressure to the fluid by means of pumps or otherwise, it was recognized that both pressure and gravity as driving force must enter the equations of flow. For single fluid-phase flow in space, i.e., in any direction with respect to the horizontal, the generalized form of Darcy's law becomes

$$Q = A\frac{K}{\mu}\left(-\frac{dP}{du} + \frac{\vartheta}{1{,}033}\sin\alpha\right) \tag{8-1}$$

where Q = rate of flow (a directional quantity), cc per sec
A = cross-sectional area of flow, sq cm
K = permeability, darcys
μ = fluid viscosity, centipoises
$\frac{dP}{du}$ = pressure gradient, atm per cm in direction u
ϑ = fluid density, g per cu cm
u = direction of flow
α = angle of dip; $\alpha > 0$ if the flow direction u is up-dip
$\frac{\delta \sin\alpha}{1{,}033}$ = atm per cm in direction of flow

The study of fluid-flow equations is conveniently divided as follows:

I. Horizontal flow: The force of gravity is ineffectual as a source of driving energy and the gravity term drops out of the flow equation.
  A. Steady-state flow: The conditions of flow are nonchangeable with time; i.e., time as a factor is not present in the equation of flow.
    1. Single-phase flow: Only one fluid at a time is flowing within the porous structure of rock, such as water, oil, or gas. However, a fixed and nonmoving phase may be present and often is, as is the case for oil flow in a rock containing irreducible water saturation, or in the case of oil flow with a nonmovable gas phase of saturation less than critical gas saturation.

a. Incompressible fluid flow: The changes in unit volume of the flowing phase due to pressure variations are negligible for practical purposes. This is the case for the flow of oil or water under steady-state conditions but obviously not for gas flow. The flow lines may be geometrically complex, depending on the pattern of wells. We may have linear, radial, and pattern flow lines.

2. Multiple-phase flow: Two or more fluids at a time are flowing within the porous structure of rock, such as water-oil, gas-oil, and water-oil-gas. The fluid phases interfere with one another and the concept of relative permeability must be called upon to study the simultaneous fluid flow of the various phases. Some of the fluids are compressible and others incompressible. Flow-line distribution may be linear, radial, or pattern.

B. Transient fluid flow: The conditions of flow are changeable with time; i.e., time as a factor is now present in the equation of flow. In essence, all reservoir-engineering flow problems are transient, but some may be considered as a succession of steady-state conditions.

1. Single-phase flow: Only one fluid at a time is flowing in the porous structure of the rock. A simple type of transient flow is the fill-up history of a water-injection well in a water flooding operation. Most transient conditions, however, originate because of fluid compressibility. The flow lines may again be linear, radial, or pattern. Of more importance in transient behavior is the physical size of the system in which it takes place, infinite or finite.
2. Multiple-phase flow: The problem of transient flow to several fluids has not yet been solved. Some empirical relationships of limited usefulness have been proposed.

II. Flow in space: The force of gravity is effectual as a source of driving energy and the gravity term must be included in the flow equation. Steady-state flow only will be considered. The solution of problems by the flow equation containing a gravity term becomes complex and only some elementary examples will be treated.

A. Single-phase flow:

1. Radial gravity flow
2. Tilting of interface
   - *a.* One fluid moving: tilting of water table
   - *b.* Two fluids moving: fingering of water-encroachment front and of gas cap and water and gas coning.

B. Multiple-phase flow:

1. General equation of flow
2. Gravity segregation by counterflow

HORIZONTAL STEADY-STATE SINGLE-PHASE FLOW OF INCOMPRESSIBLE FLUID

The differential flow equation is as follows:

$$Q = -A \frac{K}{\mu} \frac{dP}{du} \tag{8-2}$$

Linear Flow. Let a fluid of viscosity μ flow from a region of pressure P_1 to one of pressure P_2 over a distance L. Integrating Eq. (8-2), we find

$$Q = A \frac{K}{\mu} \frac{P_1 - P_2}{L} \tag{8-3}$$

This expression is written in the fundamental units that defined the "darcy unit." Transforming it into practical units such that:

Q = bbl per day
A = sq ft
P = psi
L = ft

we have

$$Q \left(\frac{5.61 \times 30.5^3}{24 \times 60 \times 60} \right) = (A \times 30.5^2) \frac{K}{\mu} \frac{(P_1 - P_2) \times 1/14.7}{L \times 30.5}$$

or

$$Q_{\text{bbl/day}} = 1.127 A_{\text{sq ft}} \frac{K_D}{\mu_{\text{cps}}} \frac{(P_1 - P_2)_{\text{psi}}}{L_{\text{ft}}} \tag{8-4}$$

Radial Flow. Let the flow of a fluid take place into a well of radius $(r_w)_{\text{cm}}$ from an external radius $(r_e)_{\text{cm}}$ under the influence of a pressure difference $P_e - P_w$, where P_e is the pressure in atmospheres at the external radius and P_w is the pressure in atmospheres at the well. Let the thickness of the permeable rock be constant and be of value h_{cm}.

Applying Eq. (8-2) to a circle of radius r where $r_w < r < r_e$, we have

$$Q = (2\pi r h) \frac{K}{\mu} \frac{dP}{dr}$$

It is to be noted that dP/dr is positive since P increases with r.

Under steady-state conditions, the rate of flow Q is the same through circles of radii r, r_e, or r_w; the differential equation may be integrated by separation of the variables:

$$Q \int_{r_w}^{r_e} \frac{dr}{r} = 2\pi h \frac{K}{\mu} \int_{P_w}^{P_e} dP$$

or

$$Q = 2\pi h \frac{K}{\mu} \frac{P_e - P_w}{\ln (r_e/r_w)} \tag{8-5}$$

where ln represents natural logarithm.

Equation (8-5) is written in the fundamental units defining the *darcy*. Converting into practical units,

$$Q_{\text{bbl/day}}\left(\frac{5.61 \times 30.5^3}{24 \times 60 \times 60}\right) = 2\pi(h_{\text{ft}} \times 30.5)\,\frac{K}{\mu}\,\frac{(P_e - P_w)_{\text{psi}} \times 1/14.7}{\ln\,(r_e/r_w)}$$

or

$$Q_{\text{bbl/day}} = 7.07\,\frac{h_{\text{ft}}K_D}{\mu_{\text{cps}}}\,\frac{(P_e - P_w)_{\text{psi}}}{\ln\,(r_e/r_w)} \tag{8-6}$$

or

$$Q_{\text{bbl/day}} = 3.07\,\frac{h_{\text{ft}}K_D}{\mu_{\text{cps}}}\,\frac{(P_e - P_w)_{\text{psi}}}{\log\,(r_e/r_w)} \tag{8-7}$$

where log is logarithm to base 10. The units of r_e and r_w are immaterial but must be the same for both: centimeters, feet, inches, etc.

Pattern Flow. For the flow in a five-spot pattern flood, Muskat (1937) has derived the following equations:

In fundamental units:

$$Q = \frac{hK}{\mu}\,\frac{P_e - P_w}{\ln\,(d/r_w) - 0.619} \tag{8-8}$$

where d is the distance between unlike wells (injection to producer).

In practical units:

$$Q_{\text{bbl/day}} = 3.535\,\frac{h_{\text{ft}}K_D}{\mu_{\text{cps}}}\,\frac{(P_e - P_w)_{\text{psi}}}{\ln\,(d/r_w) - 0.619} \tag{8-9}$$

or

$$Q_{\text{bbl/day}} = 1.535\,\frac{h_{\text{ft}}K_D}{\mu_{\text{cps}}}\,\frac{(P_e - P_w)_{\text{psi}}}{\log\,(d/r_w) - 0.269} \tag{8-10}$$

HORIZONTAL STEADY-STATE SINGLE-PHASE FLOW OF COMPRESSIBLE FLUID

The differential flow equation is again (8-2). Because of the expansion of the fluid as a result of pressure reduction, the rate of flow Q_1 at the higher pressure P_1 is no longer the same as at the lower pressure P_2. Under the assumption of isothermal expansion, which in the reservoir is always verified except perhaps very close to the well bore, we have, by applying Boyle's law during a unit time interval,

$$P_1Q_1 = P_2Q_2 = PQ \tag{8-11}$$

where P and Q are, respectively, variable pressure and flow rate at any distance inside the system.

We have, by substitution,

$$Q = \frac{Q_2 P_2}{P} = -A \frac{K}{\mu} \frac{dP}{du} \tag{8-12}$$

Linear Flow. Integrating (8-12) linearly between P_1 and P_2, after separating the variables,

$$Q_2 P_2 \int_0^L du = -A \frac{K}{\mu} \int_{P_1}^{P_2} P\,dP$$

or

$$Q_2 = A \frac{K}{\mu} \frac{1}{P_2} \frac{P_1^2 - P_2^2}{2L} \tag{8-13}$$

However, we have

$$\frac{P_1^2 - P_2^2}{2} = \frac{P_1 + P_2}{2} (P_1 - P_2)$$

$(P_1 + P_2)/2 = P_m$ will be called the mean pressure. Substituting in (8-13),

$$Q_2 = A \frac{K}{\mu} \frac{P_m}{P_2} \frac{P_1 - P_2}{L} \tag{8-14}$$

Writing Eq. (8-14) in practical units generally used for gas flow,

$$Q_{2_{\text{cu ft/day}}} \left(\frac{30.5^3}{24 \times 60 \times 60} \right) = A_{\text{sq ft}} (30.5)^2 \frac{K}{\mu} \frac{P_m}{P_2} \frac{(P_1 - P_2)_{\text{psi}} \times 1/14.7}{L_{\text{ft}} \times 30.5}$$

or

$$Q_{2_{\text{cu ft/day}}} = 6.33 A_{\text{sq ft}} \frac{K_D}{\mu_{\text{cps}}} \frac{P_m}{P_2} \frac{(P_1 - P_2)_{\text{psi}}}{L_{\text{ft}}} \tag{8-15}$$

It is to be noted that Q_2 is the measured volume flow rate under a pressure P_2, which is generally atmospheric pressure P_a, in which case Q_2 takes on the subscript a.

Radial Flow. A circle of variable radius r will be considered such that

$$r_w < r < r_e$$

and

$$Q_a P_a = QP = Q_e P_e$$

Applying Darcy's law in horizontal flow to express Q,

$$Q = \frac{Q_w P_w}{P} = (2\pi r h) \frac{K}{\mu} \frac{dP}{dr}$$

Separating the variables and integrating,

$$Q_w P_w \int_{r_w}^{r_e} \frac{dr}{r} = 2\pi \frac{hK}{\mu} \int_{P_w}^{P_e} P\, dP$$

or

$$Q_w = 2\pi \frac{hK}{\mu} \frac{1}{P_w} \frac{P_e^2 - P_w^2}{2 \ln (r_e/r_w)}$$

Substituting

$$\frac{P_e^2 - P_w^2}{2} = \frac{P_e + P_w}{2} (P_e - P_w) \text{ by } P_m(P_e - P_w)$$

$$Q_w = 2\pi \frac{hK}{\mu} \frac{P_m}{P_w} \frac{P_e - P_w}{\ln (r_e/r_w)} \tag{8-16}$$

Writing Eq. (8-16) in practical units generally used for gas flow,

$$Q_{w\text{cu ft/day}} = 39.6 \frac{h_{\text{ft}} K_D}{\mu_{\text{cps}}} \frac{P_m}{P_w} \frac{(P_e - P_w)_{\text{psi}}}{\ln (r_e/r_w)} \tag{8-17}$$

where Q_w is the volume rate measured at the prevailing well pressure P_w.

In the study of gas flow it is desirable to obtain the flow rate at a preassigned base pressure P_a and base temperature T_a, base conditions which are generally those of gas sales. Where the gas pressure declines from a well pressure P_w to P_a, it is necessary to take into account the compressibility coefficient Z. Equation (8-17) becomes

$$Q_{a\text{cu ft/day}} = 39.6 \frac{h_{\text{ft}} K_D}{Z \mu_{\text{cps}}} \frac{T_a}{T_f} \frac{1}{P_{a\text{psi}}} \frac{(P_e^2 - P_w^2)_{\text{psi}}}{2 \ln (r_e/r_w)}$$

If the base conditions are such that $P_a = 14.7$ psi and $T_a = 60°\text{F}$,

$$Q_{a\text{cu ft/day}} = 703 \frac{h_{\text{ft}} K_D}{Z \mu_{\text{cps}} T_f} \frac{P_e^2 - P_w^2}{\ln (r_e/r_w)} \tag{8-18}$$

Another practical formula is

$$Q_{a\,\mathrm{cu\,ft/day}} = 10{,}320 \frac{h_{\mathrm{ft}} K_D}{Z \mu_{\mathrm{cps}} T_f P_{a\,\mathrm{psi}}} \frac{P_e^2 - P_w^2}{\ln (r_e/r_w)} \tag{8-19}$$

which is to be used when the base pressure P_a is different from 14.7 psia.

Of some practical interest is the pressure distribution in a linear and in a radial flow system.

Pressure Distribution in a Linear-flow System. In the case of an incompressible fluid, Eq. (8-2) is integrated from a fixed point of known pressure P_1 to a variable point x of variable pressure P under a constant steady-state flow rate Q:

$$Q \int_0^x du = -A \frac{K}{\mu} \int_{P_1}^P dP$$

or

$$P_1 - P = \frac{Q}{A} \frac{\mu}{K} x$$

Since

$$Q = A \frac{K}{\mu} \frac{P_1 - P_2}{L}$$

where $P_1 - P_2$ is the total pressure drop over distance L, we may write

$$\frac{P_1 - P}{P_1 - P_2} = \frac{x}{L} \tag{8-20}$$

Equation (8-20) indicates that the pressure decline vs. distance is a straight line for the linear flow of an incompressible fluid and that it is independent of the permeability of the porous medium and of the viscosity of the fluid.

Considering now the flow of a compressible fluid that follows Boyle's law and integrating Eq. (8-12),

$$P_1^2 - P^2 = 2 \frac{Q}{A} \frac{\mu}{K} x$$

and

$$\frac{P_1^2 - P^2}{P_1^2 - P_2^2} = \frac{x}{L} \tag{8-21}$$

This pressure decline vs. distance follows the parabolic law and indicates that pressure is maintained near the inlet because of the release of energy stored in the gas, but it is still independent of permeability.

Figure 8-1 shows comparative pressure decline for linear flow of incompressible and compressible fluids.

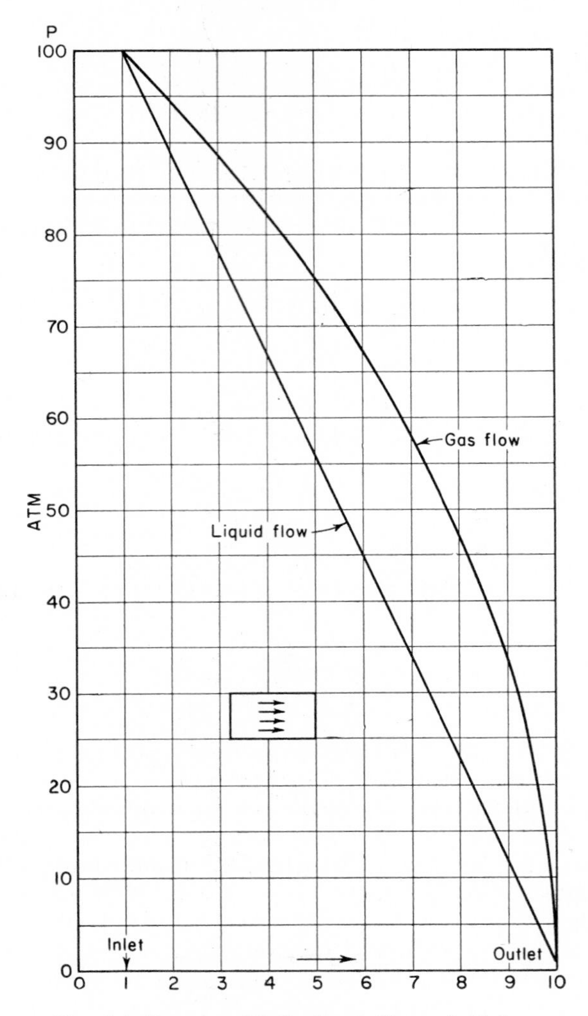

FIG. 8-1. Pressure distribution in linear fluid flow.

Pressure Distribution in a Radial-flow System. Considering now radial flow and the pressure distribution along a radial line, we find by integrating Eqs. (8-5) and (8-16) that it is different, depending on whether we have centripetal or centrifugal flow.

For the flow of *incompressible* fluid in a radial system the pressure distribution is given by the following equations:

For inward flow

$$P = P_e - \Delta P \frac{\ln (r_e/r)}{\ln (r_e/r_w)} = P_w + \Delta P \frac{\ln (r/r_w)}{\ln (r_e/r_w)} \tag{8-22}$$

For outward flow

$$P = P_e + \Delta P \frac{\ln (r/r_w)}{\ln (r_e/r_w)} = P_w - \Delta P \frac{\ln (r_e/r)}{\ln (r_e/r_w)} \tag{8-23}$$

For the flow of *compressible* fluid in a radial system the pressure distribution is given by

For inward flow

$$P^2 = P_e^2 - (P_e^2 - P_w^2) \frac{\ln (r_e/r)}{\ln (r_e/r_w)} = P_w^2 + (P_e^2 - P_w^2) \frac{\ln (r/r_w)}{\ln (r_e/r_w)} \tag{8-24}$$

For outward flow

$$P^2 = P_e^2 + (P_w^2 - P_e^2) \frac{\ln (r_e/r)}{\ln (r_e/r_w)} = P_w^2 - (P_w^2 - P_e^2) \frac{\ln (r/r_w)}{\ln (r_e/r_w)} \tag{8-25}$$

Figures 8-2 and 8-3 give the results of such calculations for a radial system where the radius of the well bore r_w is 0.1 the external radius. For the case of inward radial flow (Fig. 8-2) (centripetal), the pressure profile for incompressible fluid flow is curved above the straight line, because as the fluid advances toward the well it must flow through a decreasing cross-sectional area and it must move at constantly increasing velocity until it reaches the well bore, therefore requiring greater and greater gradients. For compressible fluid flow in the same direction, pressure is again maintained above the incompressible case because of the release of energy as pressure declines.

Figure 8-3 shows the pressure decline for outward flow (centrifugal). Incompressible flow shows a rapid decline in pressure away from the well bore because of the rapidly increasing cross-sectional area available to the flow. For compressible fluid, the pressure drop is less rapid because of the release of stored energy.

Table 8-1 gives a useful summary of steady-state flow equations for homogeneous fluids.

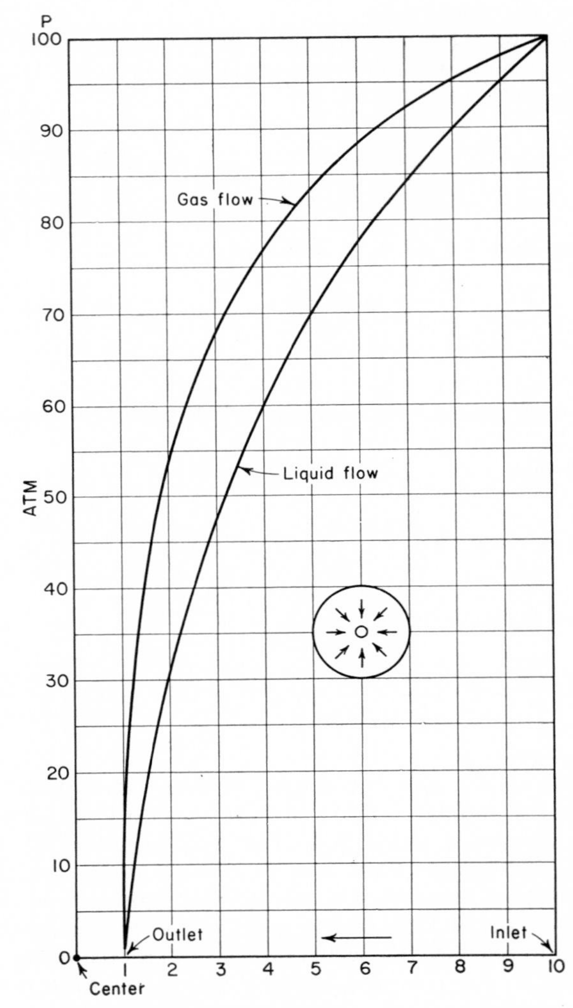

FIG. 8-2. Pressure distribution in centripetal radial flow.

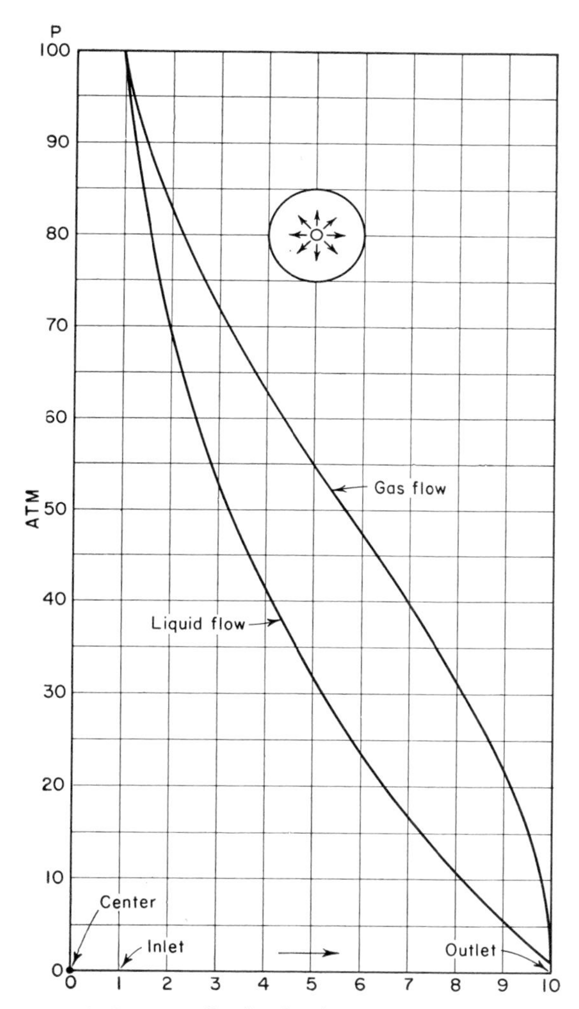

FIG. 8-3. Pressure distribution in centrifugal radial flow.

TABLE 8-1. STEADY-STATE FLOW EQUATIONS FOR HOMOGENEOUS FLUIDS

	Conventional units	Practical units	
Flow rate Pressure Length Viscosity	cc per sec atm cm cps	barrels per day psi ft cps	cu ft per day psi ft cps
Linear flow	$Q = A \frac{K}{\mu} \frac{\Delta P}{L}$ † $Q_a = A \frac{K}{\mu} \frac{P_m}{P_a} \frac{\Delta P}{L}$ ‡	$Q = 1.127A \frac{K}{\mu} \frac{\Delta P}{L}$ $Q_a = 1.127A \frac{K}{\mu} \frac{P_m}{P_a} \frac{\Delta P}{L}$	$Q = 6.33A \frac{K}{\mu} \frac{\Delta P}{L}$ $Q_a = 6.33A \frac{K}{\mu} \frac{P_m}{P_a} \frac{\Delta P}{L}$
Radial flow	$Q = 2\pi \frac{hK}{\mu} \frac{\Delta P}{\ln (r_e/r_w)}$ † $Q_w = 2\pi \frac{hK}{\mu} \frac{P_m}{P_w} \frac{\Delta P}{\ln (r_e/r_w)}$ ‡	$Q = 7.07 \frac{hK}{\mu} \frac{\Delta P}{\ln (r_e/r_w)}$ $Q = 3.07 \frac{hK}{\mu} \frac{\Delta P}{\log (r_e/r_w)}$ $Q_w = 7.07 \frac{hK}{\mu} \frac{P_m}{P_w} \frac{\Delta P}{\ln (r_e/r_w)}$ $Q_w = 3.07 \frac{hK}{\mu} \frac{P_m}{P_w} \frac{\Delta P}{\log (r_e/r_w)}$	$Q = 39.6 \frac{hK}{\mu} \frac{\Delta P}{\ln (r_e/r_w)}$ $Q = 17.19 \frac{hK}{\mu} \frac{\Delta P}{\log (r_e/r_w)}$ $Q_w = 39.6 \frac{hK}{\mu} \frac{P_m}{P_w} \frac{\Delta P}{\ln (r_e/r_w)}$ $Q_w = 17.19 \frac{hK}{\mu} \frac{P_m}{P_w} \frac{\Delta P}{\log (r_e/r_w)}$

Five-spot	$Q = \pi \frac{hK}{\mu} \frac{\Delta P}{\ln \frac{d}{r_w} - 0.619}$ †	$Q = 3.535 \frac{hK}{\mu} \frac{\Delta P}{\ln \frac{d}{r_w} - 0.619}$ $Q = 1.535 \frac{hK}{\mu} \frac{\Delta P}{\log \frac{d}{r_w} - 0.269}$	$Q = 19.8 \frac{hK}{\mu} \frac{\Delta P}{\ln \frac{d}{r_w} - 0.619}$ $Q = 8.60 \frac{hK}{\mu} \frac{\Delta P}{\log \frac{d}{r_w} - 0.269}$
	$Q_w = \pi \frac{hK}{\mu} \frac{P_m}{P_w} \frac{\Delta P}{\ln \frac{d}{r_w} - 0.619}$ ‡	$Q_w = 3.535 \frac{hK}{\mu} \frac{P_m}{P_w} \frac{\Delta P}{\ln \frac{d}{r_w} - 0.619}$ $Q_w = 1.535 \frac{hK}{\mu} \frac{P_m}{P_w} \frac{\Delta P}{\log \frac{d}{r_w} - 0.269}$	$Q_w = 19.8 \frac{hK}{\mu} \frac{P_m}{P_w} \frac{\Delta P}{\ln \frac{d}{r_w} - 0.619}$ $Q_w = 8.60 \frac{hK}{\mu} \frac{P_m}{P_w} \frac{\Delta P}{\log \frac{d}{r_w} - 0.269}$

† Incompressible flow.
‡ Compressible flow.

HORIZONTAL STEADY-STATE MULTIPLE-PHASE FLOW

When several fluid phases are flowing simultaneously through the porous rock framework, the concept of relative permeability to each phase must be introduced in studying fluid flow.

Since the flow lines are horizontal, the effect of gravity is neglected and the equations of flow to the various phases in the x direction are the following:

$$Q_o = -A \frac{K_o}{\mu_o} \frac{dP_o}{dx}$$

$$Q_g = -A \frac{K_g}{\mu_g} \frac{dP_g}{dx} \qquad (8\text{-}26)$$

$$Q_w = -A \frac{K_w}{\mu_w} \frac{dP_w}{dx}$$

where Q_o, Q_g, Q_w = volumetric rates of flow for oil, gas, and water, respectively, cc per sec
A = cross-sectional area, sq cm
K_o, K_g, K_w = the effective permeability to oil, gas, and water, respectively, darcys
μ_o, μ_g, μ_w = viscosities of oil, gas, and water, respectively, cps
P_o, P_g, P_w = pressure within oil, gas, and water phases, respectively, atm
x = distance, cm

Water-Oil Ratio (WOR). By the application of the generalized Darcy law to horizontal flowing conditions, the effect of gravity may be neglected and the following relationships, valid within the reservoir itself for linear flow, are obtained:

$$Q_o = A \frac{K_o}{\mu_o} \frac{P_i - P_o}{L} \qquad (8\text{-}27)$$

$$Q_w = A \frac{K_w}{\mu_w} \frac{P_i - P_o}{L} \qquad (8\text{-}28)$$

where Q_o = volumetric rate of oil flow
Q_w = volumetric rate of water flow
K_o = effective permeability to oil
K_w = effective permeability to water
μ_o = oil viscosity at reservoir conditions
μ_w = water viscosity at reservoir conditions
A = cross-sectional area of reservoir rocks available to tne flow Q
L = length along which the pressure drop $P_i - P_o$ takes place

It is assumed that we consider a sufficiently large bulk volume of the reservoir so that the same pressure differential $P_i - P_o$ exists within the oil and water phases. This may be done because the capillary pressure P_c

is negligible compared with the total pressure differential. We shall, therefore, obtain from the following deductions a bulk equation rather than a local equation. Dividing Eqs. (8-27) and (8-28) by one another, we obtain

$$\mathrm{WOR}_{\text{reservoir}} = \frac{Q_w}{Q_o} = \frac{\mu_o}{\mu_w}\frac{k_w}{k_o} \tag{8-29}$$

If one is interested in obtaining the surface WOR, it is necessary to take into account the shrinkage of oil caused by gas released from solution when the oil is depressured from reservoir conditions to separator or atmospheric pressure. The shrinkage is inversely proportional to β, the reservoir volume factor. Accordingly

$$\mathrm{WOR}_{\text{surface}} = \beta \frac{\mu_o}{\mu_w}\frac{k_w}{k_o} \tag{8-30}$$

Gas-Oil Ratio (GOR). Let us apply similarly the generalized Darcy law to the horizontal flow of oil and gas, making assumptions similar to those for the calculation of water-oil ratios. We have

$$Q_o = A \frac{K_o}{\mu_o} \frac{P_i - P_o}{L} \tag{8-31}$$

$$Q_g = A \frac{K_g}{\mu_g} \frac{P_i^2 - P_o^2}{2LP_m} \tag{8-32}$$

where Q_g = volumetric rate of gas flow calculated under average reservoir conditions of pressure and temperature
μ_g = gas viscosity at reservoir conditions
K_g = effective permeability to gas
P_m = mean pressure = $(P_i + P_o)/2$, or average between inlet and outlet pressure, and other notations have the same significance as above

Dividing Eqs. (8-31) and (8-32) by one another, we obtain

$$\text{Gas-oil ratio}_{\text{reservoir}} = \frac{Q_g}{Q_o} = \frac{\mu_o}{\mu_g}\frac{k_g}{k_o} \tag{8-33}$$

If we are interested in obtaining the surface gas-oil ratio, it is necessary to make the following reductions:

1. For the liberation of gas from solution in the oil. Oil shrinks by a factor β and releases a volume of gas S at normal temperature and pressure. This is assuming that there is no fluid-phase composition change when passing from one temperature and pressure condition to another.

2. The reservoir gas stream expands from a reservoir pressure P_m to atmospheric pressure P_a, and from reservoir temperature T_f to atmospheric temperature T_a. In so doing, the compressibility factor Z must be included.

The surface gas-oil ratio becomes

$$\text{Gas-oil ratio}_{\text{surface}} = S + \beta \frac{\mu_o}{\mu_o} \frac{k_g}{k_o} \frac{P_m}{P_a} \frac{T_a}{T_f} \frac{1}{Z} = S + \frac{\beta}{\alpha_m} \frac{k_g}{k_o} \frac{\mu_o}{\mu_g} \tag{8-34}$$

where $\alpha_m = \dfrac{P_a}{P_m} \dfrac{T_f}{T_a} Z$ is the reservoir volume at the mean pressure P_m of one unit volume of surface gas.

HORIZONTAL TRANSIENT SINGLE-PHASE FLOW

In order to introduce the concept of transient flow, the behavior of a water-injection well in secondary recovery by water flooding will be studied.

Behavior of a Water-injection Well. *Case* I. One stratum only of uniform permeability and porosity is present and it is laterally continuous. The pore space is empty and water injection eventually will completely fill it. Reservoir pressure is originally atmospheric and air or gas present offers no resistance to displacement. No residual gas is present and no oil bank is formed ahead of the flood front.

We have

$$Q = 2\pi \frac{hK}{\mu} \frac{\Delta P}{\ln (r/r_w)} \tag{8-35}$$

$$V = \text{fill-up volume} = \pi(r^2 - r_w{}^2)h\phi$$

$$Q = \frac{dV}{d\theta} = 2\pi r h \phi \frac{dr}{d\theta} \tag{8-36}$$

Equating (8-35) and (8-36),

$$\frac{K}{\mu} \frac{\Delta P}{\ln (r/r_w)} = \phi r \frac{dr}{d\theta}$$

Separating the variables and integrating,

$$\frac{K \, \Delta P}{\mu \phi} \int_0^\theta d\theta = \int_{r_w}^r \ln \frac{r}{r_w} r \, dr \tag{8-37}$$

Integrating by part,

$$\frac{K \, \Delta P}{\mu \phi} \theta = \frac{1}{2} \left[r^2 \left(\ln \frac{r}{r_w} - \frac{1}{2} \right) + \frac{1}{2} r_w{}^2 \right] \tag{8-38}$$

The time required for the flood front to reach a radius r is obtained by

$$\theta_{\text{sec}} = \frac{\mu_{\text{cps}} \phi}{2K_D \, \Delta P_{\text{atm}}} \left[r_{\text{cm}}{}^2 \left(\ln \frac{r}{r_w} - \frac{1}{2} \right) + \frac{1}{2} r_{w\text{cm}}{}^2 \right] \tag{8-39}$$

Converting to practical units,

$$\theta_{\text{days}} = 0.079 \frac{\mu_{\text{cps}}\phi}{K_D \, \Delta P_{\text{psi}}} \left[r_{\text{ft}}^2 \left(\ln \frac{r}{r_w} - \frac{1}{2} \right) + \frac{1}{2} r_{w_{\text{ft}}}^2 \right] \tag{8-40}$$

The above formula applies until about halfway between an input well and a producer in a five-spot flooding pattern.

To calculate break-through time:

1. Calculate injection rate at halfway mark $Q_{1/2}$, where $r = \frac{1}{2}d$
2. Calculate injection rate at break-through by Muskat's five-spot conductivity formula: $Q_5 = 3.535 \dfrac{hK}{\mu} \dfrac{\Delta P}{\ln (d/r_w) - 0.619}$
3. Evaluate area unswept

$$A = (\text{area of five-spot} \times \text{pattern efficiency} - \pi r_{1/2}^2)$$

The pattern efficiency of a five-spot = 72.26 per cent for a mobility ratio $M = 1$. For other mobility ratios, see graph of Fig. 8-4.

4. Additional required time to break through in days =

$$\frac{A_{\text{ft}}^2 h_{\text{ft}} \phi}{\frac{1}{2}(Q_{1/2} + Q_5)_{\text{bbl/day}} \times 5.61}$$

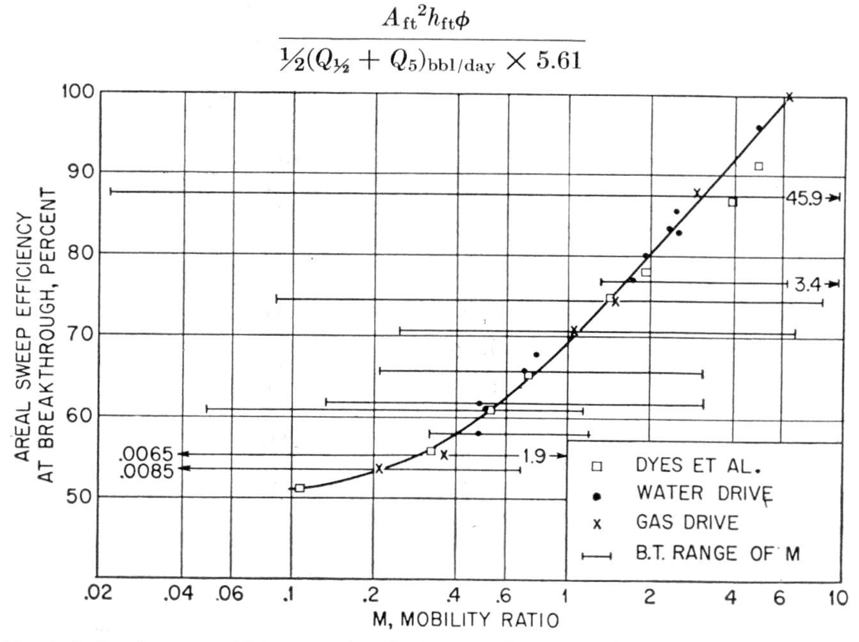

FIG. 8-4. Areal sweep efficiency at break-through (five-spot well pattern). (*After Craig et al., courtesy AIME.*)

Case II. *Stratified Reservoir.* If a reservoir is composed of different and laterally continuous porous and permeable strata which are not presumably in communication with one another—i.e., under water flood they perform independently of one another—the combined water-injection performance of the system is obtained by superposition of the various instantaneous injection rates calculated at a given time for each. The time of break-through in each layer is different for all strata and if after break-through at the most permeable layer a maximum permissible water-oil ratio is imposed, the manner in which differential break-through occurs controls the ultimate expected recovery.

In general, there are four sources of inefficiencies in water flooding:

1. Pattern efficiency or areal sweep efficiency of the drive. It depends on the geometric pattern of wells, but to a greater extent it is a function of the mobility ratio M of the driven to driving fluid.

$$M = \frac{K_o/\mu_o}{K_w/\mu_w}$$

where o stands for the driven fluid and w for the driving fluid. K_o and K_w are the effective permeabilities to oil and water, respectively, which should be evaluated at the mean fluid saturation ahead of the front for the former and back of the front for the latter.

2. Vertical fluid segregation because of gravity effects; this leads to the concept of vertical sweep efficiency. It depends on the differential density between the driven and driving fluids and is also a function of rate of drive and to a certain extent of the geometric well pattern.

3. Displacement efficiency is a measure of how effectively the driven fluid is replaced by the driving fluid; it is expressed by the residual driven fluid saturation that remains in the pore space. Displacement efficiency by a frontal drive may be determined by techniques to be studied in Chap. 11.

4. Differential break-through is a source of inefficiency and depends on the inhomogeneity of the reservoir rock, especially with respect to permeability. The degree of inhomogeneity of a reservoir rock may be expressed in terms of Lorenz coefficients (Chap. 2). Inefficiency because of differential break-through could be considered as a factor in vertical sweep efficiency.

Problem. Transient Behavior of a Water-injection Well. Calculate the water-input-rate history in a five-spot flooding project in a primary depleted sand of the following characteristics:

K = 10 md
ϕ = 14 per cent
h = 10 ft
ΔP = 1,000 psi (constant injection pressure)
μ_w = 1.0 cps

Two cases will be investigated: Case I: Filling of empty pore space; no oil bank is formed. Case II: An oil bank is formed ahead of the water front.

Case I. Comparative performances will be investigated for two input well radii:

a. Well radius = 4 in.
b. Effective shot well radius = 15 ft

Water well to water-well spacing = 300 ft.

Initial transient input rate is to be tied arbitrarily to the steady-state rate as given by the Muskat's five-spot conductivity formula. The effect of the oil bank is neglected.

I. *Time calculations*
(*a*) $r_w = 0.333$ ft

$$\theta_{\text{days}} = 0.079 \frac{0.14 \times 1}{0.01 \times 1{,}000} \left(\ln \frac{r}{r_w} - \frac{1}{2} \right) r^2 + \frac{{r_w}^2}{2}$$

$$\theta_{\text{days}} = 11.06 \times 10^{-4} \left(\ln \frac{r}{r_w} - \frac{1}{2} \right) r^2 + \frac{{r_w}^2}{2}$$

Assuming different values of r up to radial flow limit:

r, ft	$\frac{r}{r_w}$	$\ln \frac{r}{r_w}$	θ, days
10	30	3.40	0.321
25	75	4.32	2.660
50	150	5.00	12.450
75	225	5.41	30.500
100	300	5.70	57.600
106	318	5.78	65.600

(*b*) $r_w = 15$ ft

r, ft	$\frac{r}{r_w}$	$\ln \frac{r}{r_w}$	θ, days
25	1.67	0.511	0.132
50	3.33	1.200	2.060
75	5.00	1.610	7.050
100	6.67	1.900	15.640
106	7.07	1.950	18.180

II. *Rate calculations*
(*a*) $r_w = 0.333$ ft

$$Q_{\text{bbl/day}} = 7.07 \frac{hK}{\mu} \frac{\Delta P}{\ln (r/r_w)}$$

$$Q_{\text{bbl/day}} = 7.07 \times \frac{10 \times 0.01}{1} \times \frac{1{,}000}{\ln (r/r_w)} = \frac{707}{\ln (r/r_w)}$$

r, ft	$\frac{r}{r_w}$	$\ln \frac{r}{r_w}$	Q, bbls/day
10	30	3.40	208.0
25	75	4.32	163.5
50	150	5.00	141.2
75	225	5.41	130.5
100	300	5.70	124.0
106	318	5.78	122.0

(*b*) $r_w = 15$ ft

r, ft	$\frac{r}{r_w}$	$\ln \frac{r}{r_w}$	Q, bbls/day
25	1.67	0.511	1,380
50	3.32	1.20	589
75	5.00	1.61	440
100	6.67	1.90	372
106	7.07	1.91	371

III. *Break-through calculations*

$$Q_{\text{bbl/day}} = 3.535 \frac{hK}{\mu} \frac{\Delta P}{\ln (d/r_w) - 0.619}$$

where $d = 212$ ft.

(*a*) $r_w = 0.333$ ft

$$Q_{\text{bbl/day}} = 3.535 \frac{10 \times 0.01 \times 1{,}000}{1} \times \frac{1}{\ln (212/0.333) - 0.619}$$

$$= 60.8 \text{ bbl/day}$$

(*b*) $r_w = 15$ ft

$$Q_{\text{bbl/day}} = 3.535 \frac{10 \times 0.01 \times 1{,}000}{1} \times \frac{1}{\ln (212/15) - 0.619} = 176 \text{ bbl/day}$$

$$\text{Sweep efficiency} = 72.26\%$$

Mean flow rate at $r_w = 0.333$ ft $\quad \bar{Q} = \frac{122 + 60.8}{2} = 91.4$ bbl/day

at $r_w = 15$ ft $\quad \bar{Q} = \frac{362 + 176}{2} = 269$ bbl/day

Additional time to break-through:

$$\theta_{\text{B.T.}} = \frac{(0.7226A - \pi r_{1/2}^2)h\phi}{Q_{\text{av}} \times 5.61}$$

$$(a)\ r_w = 0.333 \text{ ft} \qquad \theta = \frac{0.7226(300)^2 - \pi(106)^2 \cdot (10) \cdot (0.14)}{91.4 \times 5.61} = 80.6 \text{ days}$$

$$(b)\ r_w = 15 \text{ ft} \qquad \theta = \frac{0.7226(300)^2 - \pi(106)^2 \cdot (10) \cdot (0.14)}{269 \times 5.61} = 27.5 \text{ days}$$

Results of performance calculations for the assumed two cases of water-input well radius are shown in Fig. 8-5.

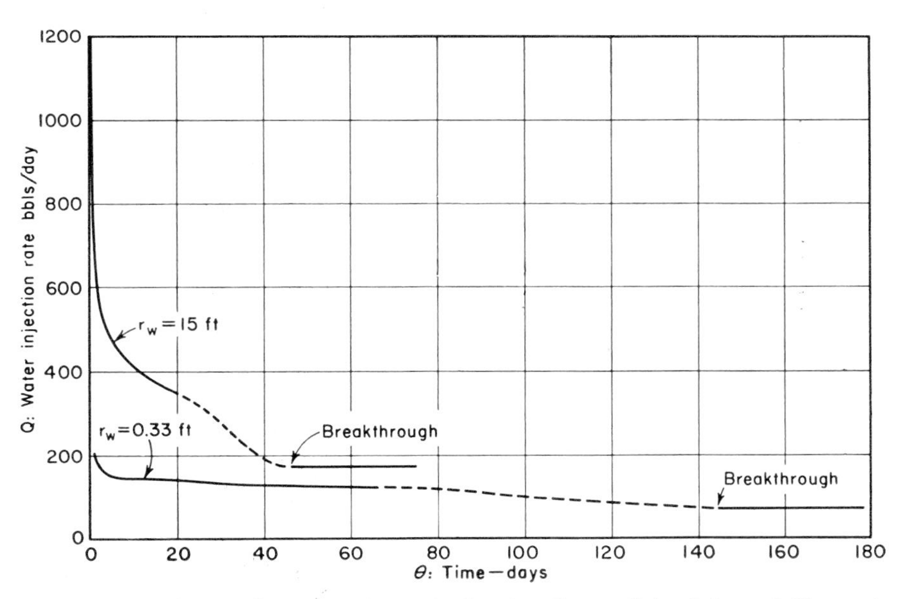

FIG. 8-5. Transient performance of a water-input well; no oil bank formed (five-spot water flooding).

Case II. Taking into account the formation of an oil bank in a depleted oil reservoir made up of one uniform layer, assume:

1. The free-gas phase goes in solution in the oil bank.
2. The relative permeability characteristics are known for the reservoir rock.

Let the applied pressure difference ΔP be partitioned according to

$$\Delta P = \Delta P_w + \Delta P_o \tag{8-41}$$

where ΔP_w is within the water zone and ΔP_o is within the oil bank.

$$Q_{\text{bbl/day}} = 7.07h \frac{\Delta P}{\dfrac{\mu_o}{K_o} \ln \dfrac{r}{r_1} + \dfrac{u_w}{K_w} \ln \dfrac{r_1}{r_w}} = 7.07h \frac{\Delta P_w}{\dfrac{\mu_w}{K_w} \ln \dfrac{r_1}{r_w}} \tag{8-42}$$

$$\theta_{\text{day}} = 0.079 \frac{\mu_w \phi (1 - \sigma_{wi} - \sigma_{or})}{K_w \, \Delta P_w} \left[r_1^2 \left(\ln \frac{r_1}{r_w} - \frac{1}{2} \right) + \frac{1}{2} r_w^2 \right] \tag{8-43}$$

To calculate ΔP_w, the following formula is used:

$$\frac{\Delta P}{\dfrac{u_w}{K_w} \ln \dfrac{r_1}{r_w} + \dfrac{\mu_o}{K_o} \ln \dfrac{r}{r_1}} = \frac{\Delta P_w}{\dfrac{\mu_w}{K_w} \ln \dfrac{r_1}{r_w}} \tag{8-44}$$

To calculate r_1, a volumetric balance is made:

Oil removed from flooded-out section = oil displaced into oil bank

$$\pi(r_1^2 - r_w^2) h\phi(\sigma_o - \sigma_{or}) = \pi(r^2 - r_1^2) h\phi(1 - \sigma_{wi} - \sigma_o) \tag{8-45}$$

$$1 - \sigma_{wi} - \sigma_o = \sigma_g$$

To solve simultaneously the various equations step by step:

1. Assume r_1.
2. Calculate r from (8-45).
3. Calculate the pressure partition from (8-44).
4. Calculate Q and θ from (8-42) and (8-43).

(A sweep-efficiency factor should be included to take care of various sources of inefficiences.) This calculation is good to about halfway between the input and the producing well.

Calculate the injection rate for the five-spot after break-through, using K_w as a function of water saturation and the break-through rate by a modified five-spot formula

$$Q_5 = 3.535h \frac{\Delta P}{\dfrac{\mu_o}{K_o} \ln \dfrac{d}{r_1} + \dfrac{\mu_w}{K_w} \ln \dfrac{r_1}{r_w} - 0.619} \tag{8-46}$$

This assumes that the water bank is still circular when oil breaks through r_1 may be calculated at oil break-through from reservoir fill-up, using the applicable sweep-efficiency coefficient.

Calculation of *water* break-through flow rate:

$$Q_5 = 3.535 \frac{hK_w}{\mu_w} \frac{\Delta P}{\ln (d/r_w) - 0.619} \tag{8-47}$$

Problem. Transient Behavior of a Water-injection Well (an oil bank being formed).

Given: A water flooding pattern such as that shown in Fig. 8-6, where

$K = 10$ md
$\phi = 14\%$
$\Delta P = 1{,}000$ psi
$\mu_w = 1$ cp
$\mu_o = 3$ cp
$h = 10$ ft

The relative-permeability curves are given in (Fig. 8-7). The saturation profile is given in (Fig. 8-8).

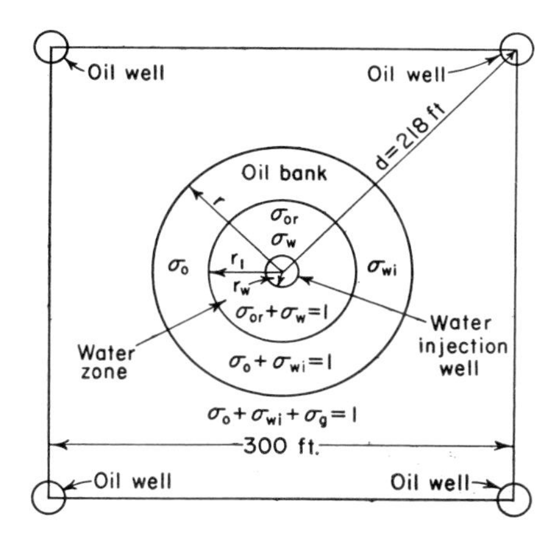

FIG. 8-6. Layout for a five-spot water flood.

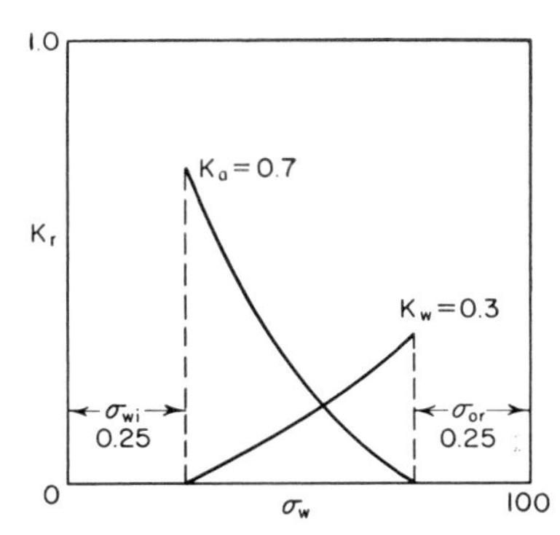

FIG. 8-7. Relative-permeability curves applicable to flooding.

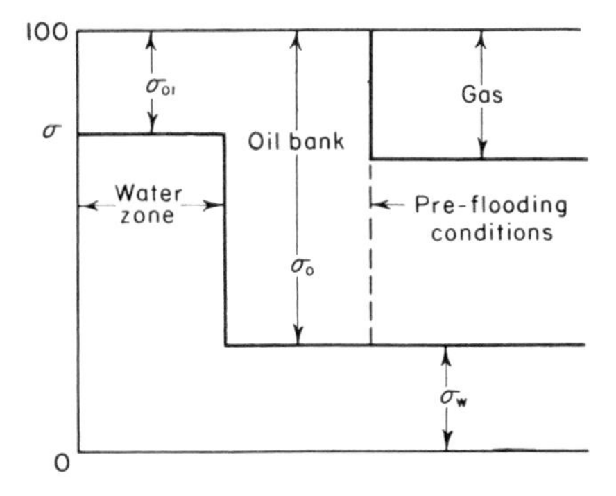

FIG. 8-8. Distribution of fluid saturation in the flood front.

The following *assumptions* are made in solving this problem:

1. The end relative permeabilities are those which prevail in the oil zone (K_o) and in the water zone (K_w).

2. All free gas goes in solution in the oil bank. This is generally the case when flooding is in a depleted oil reservoir unless gas pressuring is resorted to in advance of water flooding.
3. σ_{wi} is irreducible water saturation.
4. Oil displaces no water.
5. In the water zone, $\sigma_{or} + \sigma_w = 1.0$.
6. In the oil bank, $\sigma_{wi} + \sigma_o = 1.0$.
7. $\Delta P = \Delta P_o + \Delta P_w =$ constant.

The unknowns of the problem are:

1. Time, θ
2. Radius of oil front, r
3. Radius of water zone, r_1
4. Injection rate, Q_w
5. Pressure drop in the water zone, ΔP_w

Equations used in the problem:

$$(1)\quad Q_{\text{bbl/day}} = 7.07h \frac{\Delta P}{\dfrac{\mu_o}{K_o}\ln\dfrac{r}{r_1} + \dfrac{\mu_o}{K_w}\ln\dfrac{r_1}{r_w}}$$

$$(2)\quad \theta_{\text{days}} = 0.079\frac{\mu_w Q(1 - \sigma_{wi} - \sigma_{or})}{K_w(\Delta P_w)}\left[r_1^2\left(\ln\frac{r_1}{r_w} - \frac{1}{2}\right) + \frac{r_w^2}{2}\right]$$

(3) Oil displaced from water zone = oil gained by oil bank

$$(r_1^2 - r_w^2)(\sigma_o - \sigma_{or}) = (r^2 - r_1^2)\sigma_g$$

$$(4)\quad \frac{\Delta P_w}{\dfrac{\mu_w}{K_w}\ln\dfrac{r_1}{r_w}} = \frac{\Delta P}{\dfrac{\mu_w}{K_w}\ln\dfrac{r_1}{r_w} + \dfrac{\mu_o}{K_o}\ln\dfrac{r_1}{r_1}}$$

$$(5)\quad \Delta P = \Delta P_w + \Delta P_o$$

To solve the problem:

1. Assume that r_1 takes successively the values 10, 25, 50, 75, 100, and 105 ft.
2. Solve by Eq. (3) for r.
3. Solve by Eq. (4) for ΔP_w.
4. Solve by Eq. (1) for Q and by (2) for time.
5. Plot Q vs. time.

I. *r calculations*

(*a*) $r_w = 0.333$ ft

$$(r_1^2 - r_w^2)(\sigma_o - \sigma_{or}) = (r^2 - r_1^2)\sigma_g$$

$$\sigma_o = 0.45 \qquad \sigma_{or} = 0.25 \qquad \sigma_g = 0.3 \qquad \sigma_{wi} = 0.25$$

r_1	$r_1^2 - r_w^2$	$\frac{\sigma_o - \sigma_{or}}{\sigma_g}$	$r^2 - r_1^2$	r
10	99	0.666	66.5	12.90
25	624	0.666	416.0	32.30
50	2,499	0.666	1,665.0	64.60
75	5,624	0.666	3,750.0	96.70
100	10,000	0.666	6,660.0	129.50
125	15,625	0.666	10,420.0	161.50
164	26,900	0.666	17,900.0	212.00

(*b*) $r_w = 15$ ft

r_1	$r_1^2 - r_w^2$	$\frac{\sigma_o - \sigma_{or}}{\sigma_g}$	$r^2 - r_1^2$	r
25	400	0.666	266.4	29.8
50	2,375	0.666	1,580.0	64.0
75	5,400	0.666	3,600.0	96.1
100	9,775	0.666	6,520.0	128.5
125	15,400	0.666	10,260.0	161.0
164	26,775	0.666	17,800.0	212.0

II. ΔP_w *calculations*

(*a*) $r_w = 0.333$ ft

$$\Delta P_w = \left(\frac{\mu_w}{K_w}\right) \ln \frac{r_1}{r_w} \frac{\Delta P}{\frac{\mu_w}{K_w} \ln \frac{r_1}{r_w} + \frac{\mu_o}{K_o} \ln \frac{r}{r_1}}$$

$$\mu_w = 1 \text{ cps} \qquad K_w = 0.3$$

$$\mu_o = 3 \text{ cps} \qquad K_o = 0.7 \qquad P = 1{,}000 \text{ psi}$$

$\frac{r_1}{r_w}$	$\ln \frac{r_1}{r_w}$	$\frac{\mu_w}{K_w}$	$\frac{r}{r_1}$	$\ln \frac{r}{r_1}$	$\frac{\mu_o}{K_o}$	ΔP_w, psi
30	3.41	3.33	1.290	0.253	4.3	912
75	4.33	3.33	1.290	0.253	4.3	930
150	5.02	3.33	1.290	0.253	4.3	940
225	5.41	3.33	1.290	0.253	4.3	949
300	5.72	3.33	1.290	0.253	4.3	950
375	5.92	3.33	1.290	0.253	4.3	950
492	6.20	3.33	1.290	0.253	4.3	952

(b) $r_w = 15$ ft

$\frac{r_1}{r_w}$	$\ln \frac{r_1}{r_w}$	$\frac{\mu_w}{K_w}$	$\frac{r}{r_1}$	$\ln \frac{r}{r_1}$	$\frac{\mu_o}{K_o}$	ΔP_w, psi
1.67	0.51	3.33	1.19	0.174	4.3	694
3.34	1.20	3.33	1.29	0.253	4.3	735
5.00	1.61	3.33	1.29	0.253	4.3	830
6.67	1.89	3.33	1.29	0.253	4.3	850
8.33	2.12	3.33	1.29	0.253	4.3	865
10.10	2.31	3.33	1.29	0.253	4.3	885

III. *Rate calculations*

(a) $r_w = 0.333$ ft

$$Q_{\text{bbl/day}} = 7.07Kh \frac{\Delta P}{\frac{\mu_o}{K_o} \ln \frac{r}{r_1} + \frac{\mu_w}{K_w} \ln \frac{r_1}{r_w}}$$

r_1	$\frac{\mu_o \ln (r/r_1)}{K_o}$	$\frac{\mu_w \ln (r_1/r_w)}{K_w}$	Q, bbl/day
10	1.09	11.35	56.8
25	1.09	14.40	45.6
50	1.09	16.70	39.7
75	1.09	18.00	37.0
100	1.09	19.00	35.1
125	1.09	19.70	34.0
164	1.09	20.64	32.5

(b) $r_w = 15$ ft

r_1	$\frac{\mu_o \ln (r/r_1)}{K_o}$	$\frac{\mu_w \ln (r_1/r_w)}{K_w}$	Q, bbl/day
25	0.75	1.71	287.0
50	1.09	4.00	139.0
75	1.09	5.36	109.0
100	1.09	6.30	95.5
125	1.09	7.06	86.5
164	1.09	7.73	80.1

IV. *Time calculations*

(*a*) $r_w = 0.333$ ft

$$\theta_{\text{days}} = 0.079 \frac{\mu_w Q(1 - \sigma_{wi} - \sigma_{or})}{K_w\,(\Delta P_w)} \left[r_1^2 \left(\ln \frac{r_1}{r_w} - \frac{1}{2} \right) + \frac{r_w^2}{2} \right]$$

r_1	$\frac{r_1}{r_w}$	$\ln \frac{r_1}{r_w}$	r_1^2	$\frac{r_w^2}{2}$	θ, days
10	30.3	3.41	100	0.055	0.588
25	75.8	4.33	625	0.055	4.74
50	151.6	5.02	2,500	0.055	22.10
75	227.0	5.41	5,625	0.055	53.50
100	303.0	5.72	10,000	0.055	101.00
125	379.0	5.92	15,625	0.055	164.00
164	497.0	6.20	26,400	0.055	297.00

(*b*) $r_w = 15$ ft

r_1	$\frac{r_1}{r_w}$	$\ln \frac{r_1}{r_w}$	r_1^2	$\frac{r_w^2}{2}$	θ, days
25	1.67	0.51	625	112.5	0.334
50	3.34	1.20	5,000	112.5	8.47
75	5.00	1.61	5,625	112.5	14.10
100	6.67	1.84	10,000	112.5	30.60
125	8.33	2.12	15,625	112.5	54.00
164	10.10	2.31	26,900	112.5	108.00

The following is a summary of the results of calculations.

(*a*) $r_w = 0.333$ ft

r_1	r	ΔP_w, psi	Q, bbl/day	θ, days
10	12.85	912	56.8	0.588
25	33.30	930	45.6	4.74
50	64.00	940	39.7	22.10
75	96.70	949	37.0	53.50
100	128.80	950	35.1	101.00
125	161.50	950	34.0	164.00
164	212.00	952	32.5	297.00—break-through to oil

(b) $r_w = 15$ ft

r_1	r	ΔP_w, psi	Q, bbl/day	θ, days
25	29.8	654	252	0.334
50	64.0	784	139	8.47
75	96.0	830	109	14.10
100	128.5	850	95.5	30.60
125	161.0	865	86.5	54.00
164	212.0	880	78.0	107.00—break-through to oil

Results of performance calculations for the assumed two cases of water-input well radius when an oil bank is formed are shown in Fig. 8-9.

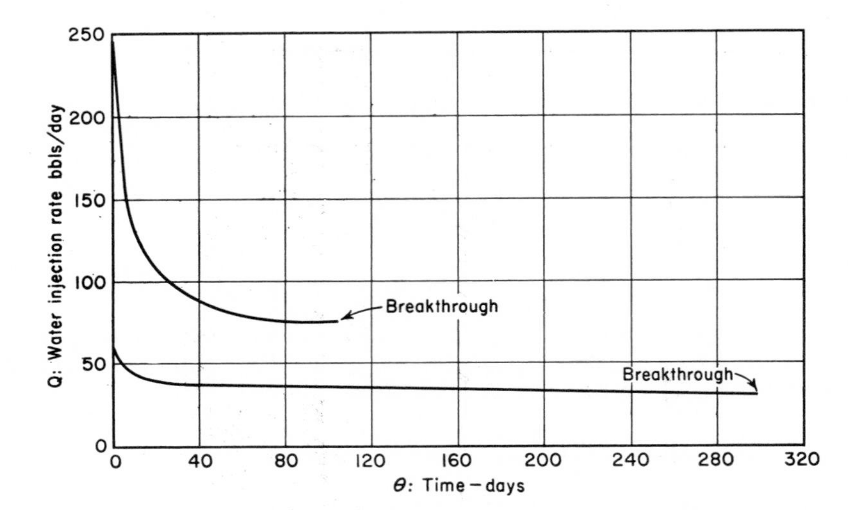

FIG. 8-9. Transient performance of water-input well; oil bank formed (five-spot water flooding).

HORIZONTAL TRANSIENT SINGLE-PHASE FLOW OF A SLIGHTLY COMPRESSIBLE FLUID

The Diffusivity Equation. The density of a slightly compressible fluid is represented by

$$\vartheta = \vartheta_0 e^{-c(P_o - P)} \tag{8-48}$$

where ϑ_0 = density at P_o and c = compressibility, per atm.

It is assumed in the above formula that the fluid pressure is above the bubble point at all times.

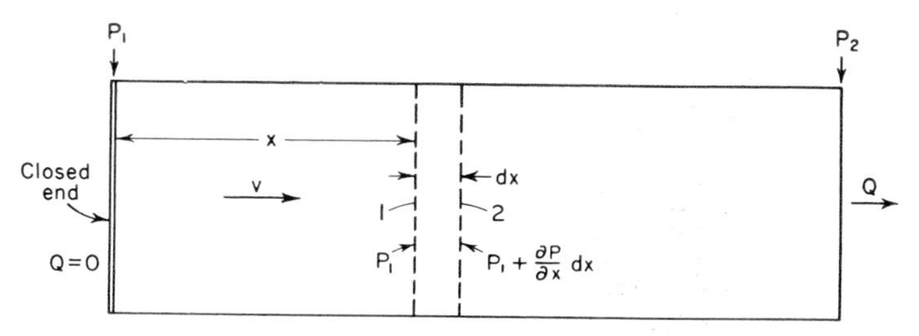

FIG. 8-10. Conditions existing in transient flow by fluid expansion.

Horizontal Linear Flow. Consider horizontal linear flow resulting from the expansion of a fluid originally at pressure P_o (Fig. 8-10). Applying Darcy's law,

$$v = -\frac{K}{\mu}\frac{dP}{dx} \tag{8-49}$$

Let ϑ = mean fluid density in the corresponding intervals dx and $d\theta$

m_1 = mass passing through plane 1 in $d\theta = \left(-A\frac{K}{\mu}\frac{dP}{dx}\right)\vartheta\,d\theta$

m_2 = mass passing through plane 2 in $d\theta$

$$= -A\frac{K}{\mu}\left[\frac{dP}{dx} + \frac{\partial}{\partial x}\left(\frac{\partial P}{\partial x}\right)dx\right]\vartheta\,d\theta$$

Net actual mass flowing out of $dx = A\frac{K}{\mu}\frac{\partial^2 P}{\partial x^2}dx\,\vartheta\,d\theta$

Weight loss of fluid by the elementary volume comprised between planes 1 and 2 when pressure drops by dP is $(A\,dx\,\phi)d\vartheta$. Equating the net actual weight flowing to the weight loss of the fluid in interval dx,

$$(A\,dx\,\phi)\,d\vartheta = A\frac{K}{\mu}\frac{\partial^2 P}{\partial x^2}dx\,\vartheta\,d\theta$$

$$\vartheta\frac{\partial^2 P}{\partial x^2} = \frac{\phi\mu}{K}\frac{d\vartheta}{d\theta} \tag{8-50}$$

But

$$d\vartheta = \vartheta_o e^{-c(P_o-P)}(-c\,dP)$$

or

$$d\vartheta = -c\vartheta\,dP$$

and

$$\frac{d\vartheta}{d\theta} = -c\vartheta\frac{\partial P}{\partial\theta}$$

Substituting $d\vartheta/d\theta$ by its value in (8-50),

$$\frac{\partial^2 P}{\partial x^2} = \frac{\phi\mu c}{K}\frac{\partial P}{\partial\theta} \tag{8-51}$$

This equation is known as the diffusivity equation for linear flow.

Horizontal Radial Flow. Equation (8-51) becomes

$$\frac{\partial^2 P}{\partial x^2} + \frac{\partial^2 P}{\partial y^2} = \frac{\phi \mu c}{K} \frac{\partial P}{\partial \theta} \tag{8-52}$$

Changing the coordinates from cartesian to radial by standard procedure, the diffusivity equation for radial flow becomes

$$\frac{1}{r} \frac{\partial}{\partial r} \left[r \frac{\partial P}{\partial r} \right] = \frac{\phi \mu c}{K} \frac{\partial P}{\partial \theta}$$

or

$$\nabla^2 P = \frac{\phi \mu c}{K} \frac{\partial P}{\partial \theta} \tag{8-53}$$

where $\nabla^2 P$ is the Laplacian of P. Let

$$\bar{t} = \frac{K_D}{\phi \mu_{\text{cps}} c_{\text{atm}^{-1}}} \frac{1}{r_{w,\text{cm}}^2} \theta_{\text{sec}}$$

where $\bar{t}$ is dimensionless time. After substitution, the diffusivity equation becomes

$$\nabla^2 P = \frac{\partial P}{\partial \bar{t}} \tag{8-54}$$

Various solutions have been proposed for the above equation of flow. The rigorous solution (Van Everdingen and Hurst) is

$$P(\bar{t}) = \frac{4}{\pi^2} \int_0^\infty \frac{(1 - e^{u^2 t})\, du}{u^3[J_1^2(u) + Y_1^2(u)]} \tag{8-55}$$

For $\bar{t}$ large (Muskat)

$$P(\bar{t}) = \frac{1}{2} \left[-E_i \left(-\frac{1}{4\bar{t}} \right) \right] \qquad \text{where } E_i = \int_{\frac{1}{4\bar{t}}}^{\infty} \frac{e^{-n}}{n}\, dn \tag{8-56}$$

For $\bar{t} \geq 100$ (Van Everdingen and Hurst)

$$P(\bar{t}) = \tfrac{1}{2}[\ln \bar{t} + 0.80907] \tag{8-57}$$

Figure 8-11 gives a comparison of the pressure values obtained by the rigorous solution [Eq. (8-55)] and the approximate solution [Eq. (8-57)].

Graphic Solution of the Diffusivity Equation. The graphic method for the solution of the diffusivity equation consists in replacing the differential equation by an equation of finite differences.

Linear Flow. Let $\alpha^2 = K/\phi c \mu$ and the diffusivity equation (8-51) is written

$$\frac{\partial^2 P}{\partial x^2} = \frac{1}{\alpha^2} \frac{\partial P}{\partial \theta} \tag{8-58}$$

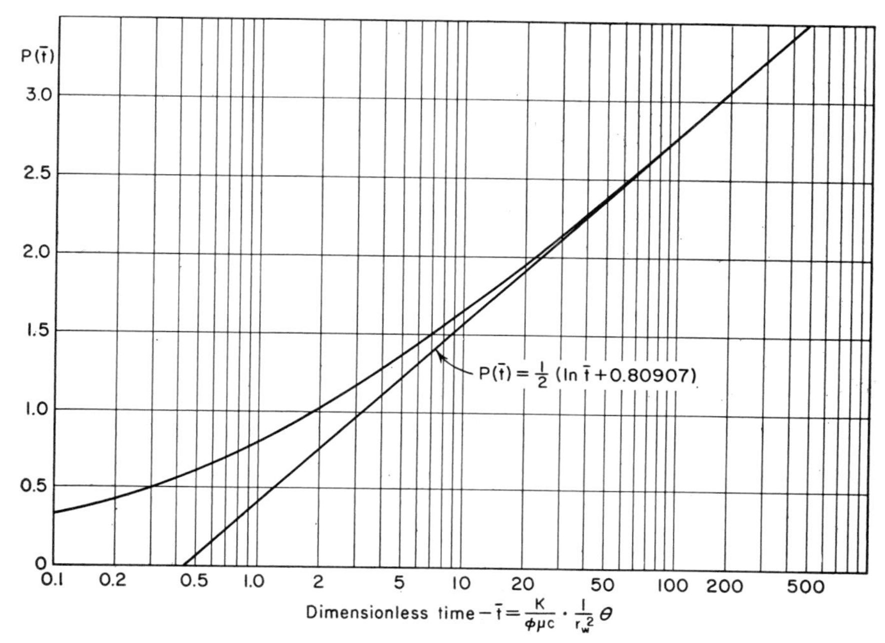

FIG. 8-11. Plot showing deviations between exact and approximate solution of the diffusivity equation in radial flow.

Consider a space interval Δx corresponding to a time interval $\Delta\theta$. By definition of partial differentials, we have

$$\frac{\Delta P}{\Delta x} = \frac{P(x, \theta) - P(x - \Delta x, \theta)}{\Delta x} \quad \text{in interval } x - \Delta x \text{ to } x$$
$$\frac{\Delta P}{\Delta x} = \frac{P(x + \Delta x, \theta) - P(x, \theta)}{\Delta x} \quad \text{in interval } x \text{ to } x + \Delta x \tag{8-59}$$

when $\Delta x \to 0$.

However, in order to lead to a practical engineering solution, Δx and $\Delta\theta$ will be considered to be small finite differences. Similarly we have for the second partial differential

$$\frac{\Delta^2 P}{\Delta x^2} = \frac{\dfrac{P(x + \Delta x, \theta) - P(x, \theta)}{\Delta x} - \dfrac{P(x, \theta) - P(x - \Delta x, \theta)}{\Delta x}}{\Delta x} = \frac{P(x + \Delta x, \theta) - 2P(x, \theta) + P(x - \Delta x, \theta)}{(\Delta x)^2} \tag{8-60}$$

$$\frac{\Delta P}{\Delta \theta} = \frac{P(x, \theta + \Delta\theta) - P(x, \theta)}{\Delta\theta} \tag{8-61}$$

Substituting in Eq. (8-58) and rearranging terms,

$$P(x, \theta + \Delta\theta) = P(x, \theta) + \frac{\alpha^2 \Delta\theta}{(\Delta x)^2}[P(x + \Delta x, \theta) - 2P(x, \theta) + P(x - \Delta x, \theta)] \quad (8\text{-}62)$$

It is to be noted that Δx and $\Delta\theta$ were arbitrarily chosen and it may be permitted to select any appropriate relationship which is convenient to simplify the problem. Such a relation is

$$\Delta\theta = \frac{1}{2}\frac{(\Delta x)^2}{\alpha^2} \quad (8\text{-}63)$$

Then the equation in finite differences becomes

$$P(x, \theta + \Delta\theta) = \tfrac{1}{2}[P(x + \Delta x, \theta) + P(x - \Delta x, \theta)] \quad (8\text{-}64)$$

This means that if the interval of time $\Delta\theta$ is selected to correspond to the interval of distance Δx according to Eq. (8-63), the pressure after any succeeding time interval $\Delta\theta$ at a particular point $P(x)$ is obtained by taking the mean values of the pressures at the two neighboring points $P(x - \Delta x)$ and $P(x + \Delta x)$ which prevailed at the preceding time θ.

If the pressures are represented graphically along the linear system, the pressure at any point X is obtained by merely joining by a straight line the pressure values at points $(X - \Delta X)$ and $(X + \Delta X)$ obtained in the preceding interval.

Example. Let a pipe of length 1,000 ft, filled with sand of porosity $\phi = 0.3$ and permeability $K = 0.1$ darcy, contain an oil of viscosity $\mu_o = 5$ cps and compressibility $c_o = 2 \times 10^{-5}$ psi^{-1}. This pipe is decompressed to 500 psi from 3,000 psi by withdrawing oil at a maximum rate of 0.01 bbl reservoir oil per hour. When will the first pressure decline arrive at the end of the pipe?

Divide the pipe in 10 equal segments: $\Delta x = 100$ ft. The corresponding $\Delta\theta$ is

$$\Delta\theta = \frac{1}{2}\frac{0.3 \times 5 \times 2 \times 10^{-5} \times 14.7}{0.1} \times (100 \times 30.5)^2$$

$$= 20{,}300 \text{ sec} = 0.237 \text{ day}$$

The production rate of 0.01 bbl per hr produces a pressure gradient in the section of pipe near the outlet, of

$$\frac{dP}{dx} = 0.01 \times 24 \times \frac{1}{1.127} \times \frac{5}{0.1} = 10.63 \text{ psi/ft}$$

Over the 100 ft of the first pipe section, the pressure drop is initially 1,063 psi and the pressure profile after the first increment of time of 0.237 day is substantially represented by a straight line joining a point of pressure of 1,937 psi at the outlet with a value of 3,000 psi at the end of 200 ft of pipe. The solution of the problem must be looked upon as a series of steady states occurring after discrete increments of time numbered successively 0, 1, 2, 3, ... The initial or zero time increment requires that a pressure gradient of 1,063 psi be established in the first section. At the end of the increment and beginning of increment 1, the outlet pressure is still 1,937 psi and the pressure wave reaches to a distance of 200 ft.

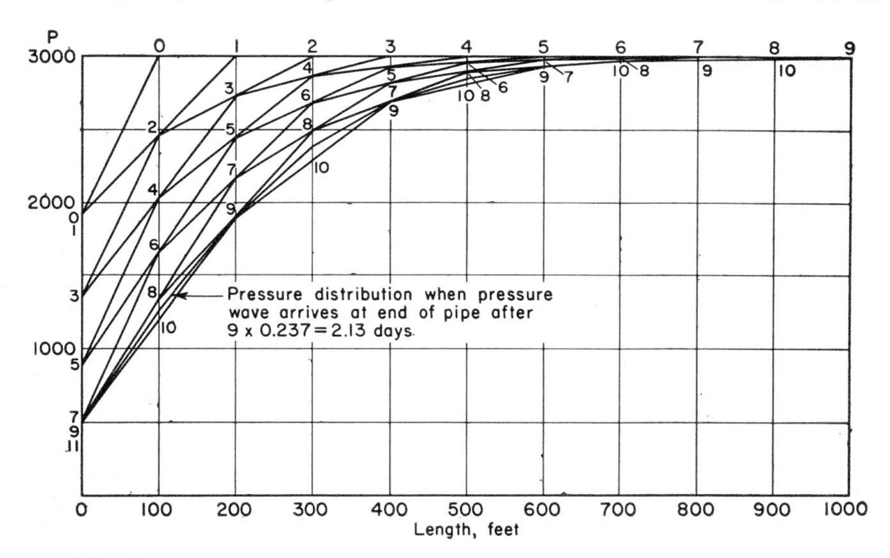

FIG. 8-12. Graphic solution of diffusivity equation in a linear system of finite extent.

Both points are numbered 1. At the end of increment 2 and at the end of 100 ft of the first segment of pipe, the pressure is 2,410 psi obtained by drawing a straight line 11. The construction of Fig. 8-12 is self-explanatory concerning the graphic solution, and it is seen that the pressure wave will reach the end of the pipe after nine increments of time. By joining the points having the same order numbers a pressure profile is obtained which represents the pressure distribution in time and space.

Radial Flow. In transient radial flow, the graphic solution procedure is carried in a similar manner, using semilog paper.

Example. An oil field has an average radius of 1 mile and is bounded by a circular aquifer limited in extent to 10 miles in radius. The original field pressure is 3,000 psig. The oil field was developed very rapidly (instantaneously for the purpose of the problem) and the field pressure reached 1,000 psig, at which it is intended to maintain it by adjusting fluid withdrawals. Assuming that this is achieved, calculate for 2 months:

1. The pressure distribution in the aquifer as a function of time, i.e., at successive intervals of time
2. The daily rate of water influx into the field

Additional required data are as follows:

$K = 100$ md
$c_w = 3 \times 10^{-6}$ psi^{-1}
$\mu_w = 0.5$ at BHT
$\phi = 20$ per cent
$h = 30$ ft

The distance increment Δx is chosen as being 1 mile. Accordingly the time increment is

$$\Delta\theta = \frac{1}{2} \times \frac{0.2 \times 0.5 \times 3 \times 10^{-6}}{6.33 \times 0.1} \times (5{,}280)^2 = 6.61 \text{ days}$$

The rate of water influx is obtained from

$$Q_{w,\text{ bbl/day}} = 3.07 \frac{0.1 \times 30}{0.5} \frac{\Delta P}{\log 2/1}$$

where ΔP is the pressure drop in the first circle 1 mile wide within the aquifer. The pressure differentials across this first circle are read at each successive interval of time on the graph of Fig. 8-13. The following water influx history is obtained:

Time units, 6.61 days	ΔP, psi	Q_w, bbls/day
1	1,260	77,000
3	1,065	65,100
5	960	58,600
7	900	55,000
9	850	52,000
11	815	49,800

Well Application of Transient Flow. *Determination of Reservoir Capacity (ΣKh) and Skin Effect Due to Well Completion from Pressure Build-up Curves.* This method is altogether based on the Van Everdingen and Hurst equation:

$$P_{\text{atm}} = q(\bar{t})(\tfrac{1}{2} \ln \bar{t} + 0.4045) \tag{8-65}$$

which expresses the pressure drop in a radial-flow system for a single-phase fluid. It is an application of Eq. (8-57) to the evaluation of the pressure drop ΔP created by a flow rate $q(\bar{t})$. $\bar{t}$ is in dimensionless units (d.u.) derived as follows:

$$\bar{t}_{\text{d.u.}} = \frac{k_D}{\phi\mu_{\text{cps}}c_{\text{atm}}{}^{-1}} \frac{1}{r_{w,\text{cm}}{}^2} \theta_{\text{sec}} \tag{8-66}$$

$q(\bar{t})$ = influx rate; cc per cm length of well bore or unit thickness per dimensionless unit of time

This ΔP equation form should be applied only when $\bar{t}_{\text{d.u.}} > 100$.

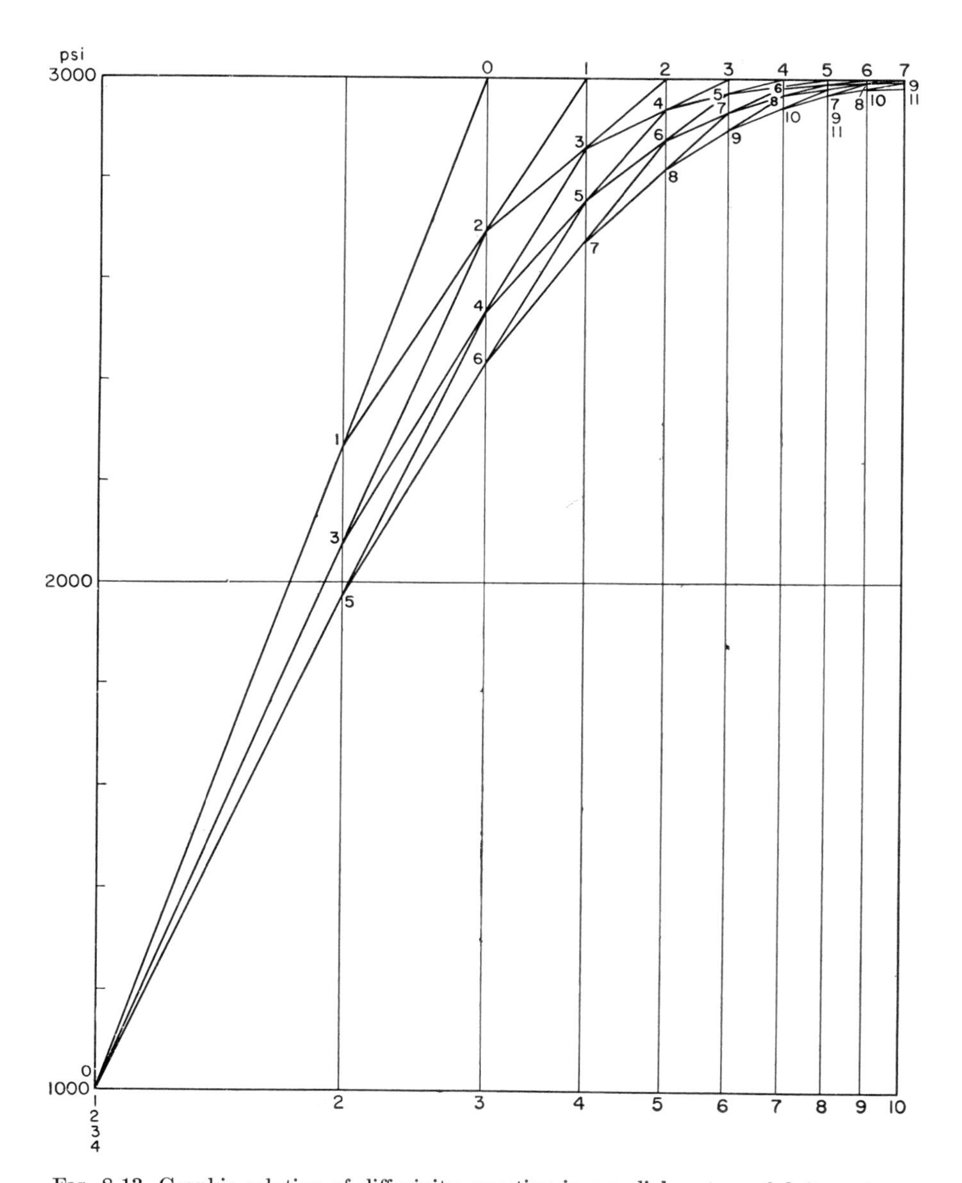

FIG. 8-13. Graphic solution of diffusivity equation in a radial system of finite extent.

Suppose that there is an extra resistance S around the well bore due to completion damage (which is named the "skin effect"); the flow equation would be written

$$P = q(\bar{t})(\tfrac{1}{2} \ln \bar{t} + 0.4045 + S)$$

Rigorously, this equation is applicable only when $q(\bar{t})$ = constant, but in practice, the variations in flow rate that are encountered make very little difference.

The skin effect may be computed from well pressure build-up tests, a history of which may be represented by Fig. 8-14:

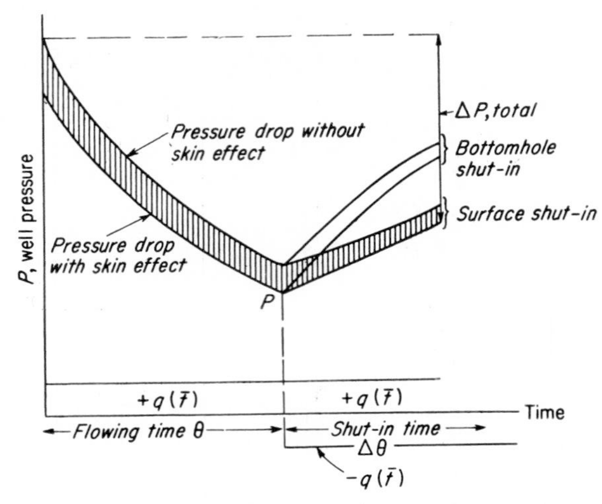

FIG. 8-14. Variation of pressure vs. time in a pressure build-up test for various assumptions.

After a certain build-up time ($\Delta\bar{t}$), the total pressure difference $(\Delta P)_{\text{total}}$ may be considered to be the sum of two canceling fluid flows, $+q(\bar{t})$ and $-q(\bar{t})$; we have

$$(\Delta P)_{\text{total}} = q(\bar{t})[(\tfrac{1}{2} \ln (\bar{t} + \Delta\bar{t}) + 0.4045 + S) - (\tfrac{1}{2} \ln \Delta\bar{t} + 0.4045 + S)]$$

$$= q(\bar{t}) \frac{1}{2} \ln \frac{\bar{t} + \Delta\bar{t}}{\Delta\bar{t}}$$

$$P = \text{well pressure} = P_{st} - q(\bar{t}) \frac{1}{2} \ln \frac{\bar{t} + \Delta\bar{t}}{\Delta\bar{t}}$$

$$P = P_{st} + q(\bar{t}) \frac{1}{2} \ln \frac{\Delta\bar{t}}{\bar{t} + \Delta\bar{t}} \tag{8-67}$$

where P_{st} = static pressure, from which it is seen that the skin effect is canceled out.

The pressure build-up tests are plotted on semilog coordinates (Fig. 8-15) where BHP on linear scale is plotted vs. $\Delta\bar{t}/(\bar{t} + \Delta\bar{t})$ on log scale. The curve so obtained is extrapolated to $\Delta \bar{t} = \infty$ or to

$$\frac{\Delta \bar{t}}{\bar{t} + \Delta \bar{t}} = 1$$

This is a straight line in the latter part of the build-up test, the slope of which is a measure of the millidarcy times feet (ΣKh) capacity of the reservoir. This part of the curve depends also on the structural features

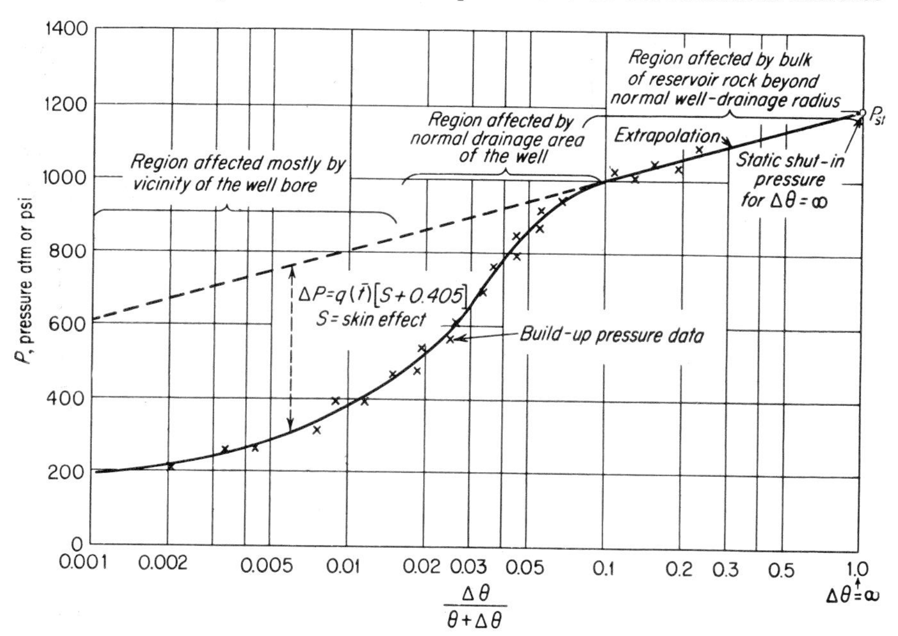

FIG. 8-15. Pressure build-up test in a well.

of the reservoir, such as the existence of a faulted reservoir and limited aquifer.

Actually, the slope of the curve measures the *flow capacity* or cumulative effective oil permeability of the reservoir times net pay thickness:

$$\Sigma(K_{o_{\text{md}}} h_{\text{ft}}) = 162.5 \frac{Q_{o_{\text{STB/day}}} \beta \mu_{cps}}{\begin{bmatrix}\text{pressure build-up, psi, per} \\ \text{cycle on straight-line part} \\ \text{of logarithmic plot}\end{bmatrix}} \qquad \text{md-ft} \qquad (8\text{-}68)$$

The other important contribution of this study is to evaluate well-completion methods, since a value of the skin effect S may be obtained by projecting the straight line back and measuring $P = q(\bar{t})(S + 0.4045)$ for $\Delta \bar{t} = 1$, from which S is calculated.

Tests made in wells drilled with certain muds, and particularly with oil-base muds, show that the skin effect was only 15 per cent of drawdown, whereas it was much larger for water-base mud wells. After "hydrafrac" treatment, a negative skin effect is often found, the absolute value of which is a measure of the effectiveness of this well-completion treatment. The skin-effect calculation should permit the evaluation of well treatments such as acidizing, water-block removal, clay flocculation, etc.

Proof of Graphic Construction to Obtain Skin Effect of a Well. The pressure increment per cycle on the straight part of the extrapolated curve up to static pressure is

$$q(t)\left[\frac{1}{2}\ln 10\right] = q(\bar{t})\left[\frac{2.3}{2}\log 10\right] = 1.15q(\bar{t})$$

In order to determine the skin effect, it is necessary to obtain the transient pressure drop created in the neighborhood of the well for a small increment of time ($\Delta\bar{t}$), that is, small compared with $\bar{t}$, which must be larger than 100. We have

$$\frac{\Delta\bar{t}}{\bar{t}+\Delta\bar{t}} \cong \frac{\Delta\bar{t}}{\bar{t}}$$

when $\Delta\bar{t}$ is small. Calculating the well pressure P_1 which would prevail when $\Delta\bar{t} = 1$, which is, when no skin effect is present,

$$P_1 = P_{st} - \log\frac{\bar{t}}{\Delta\bar{t}} \times \text{(pressure drop per cycle)}$$

$$P_1 = P_{st} - \frac{1}{2.3}\ln\bar{t} \times 1.15q(\bar{t})$$

$$P_1 = P_{st} - \tfrac{1}{2}q(\bar{t})\ln\bar{t}$$

Calculating the well pressure P_2 which prevails just prior to shut-in,

$$P_2 = P_{st} - q(\bar{t})(\tfrac{1}{2}\ln\bar{t} + 0.4045 + S)$$

Subtracting P_2 from P_1,

$$\Delta P = q(\bar{t})(0.4045 + S)$$

The skin effect expressed as a pressure differential is $q(\bar{t})S$. Hence

$$\text{Skin effect} = \Delta P - q(\bar{t}) \times 0.4045$$

But $$q(\bar{t}) = \frac{1}{1.15}\text{(pressure drop per cycle on straight line)}$$

$$(\text{Skin effect})_{\text{psi}} = (\Delta P)_{\text{psi}} - \frac{0.4045}{1.15}(\text{psi/cycle}) = (\Delta P)_{\text{psi}} - 0.352\,(\text{psi/cycle})$$

The method reviewed here for determining static pressure, reservoir capacity, and skin effect is general; it works equally well for gas wells, two-phase flow, variable flow rate, and stratified reservoirs. The theory on well skin effect is adapted from Arps (1955).

FLUID FLOW IN SPACE WHEN GRAVITY FORCES PROVIDE A CONTRIBUTION TO THE FLOW POTENTIAL

In this class of problems the force of gravity, as a body force, provides part of the driving energy in addition to other external forces that may be applied to the moving fluids.

Single-phase Flow

Steady-state Radial Gravity Flow of Incompressible Fluid. A simple case of flow under the influence of gravity alone is provided by radial flow of a liquid toward a well under the influence of its own gravity head. The overlying gas is assumed to exert no flow potential. In this case the original form of Darcy's law applies without modification, for it was derived for gravity flow only:

$$v = -\frac{K}{\mu} g\vartheta \frac{dH}{dr} \tag{8-69}$$

where v = horizontal velocity in free space
r = radial coordinate
H = fluid flow potential. $H = z + (P/g\vartheta)$ where z is the height of the free surface of the fluid above a reference plane and P is the reservoir pressure
ϑ = fluid density

Let the flow take place between two levels of the free surface; z_w at the well and z_e at the external boundary. Let z be the height at any distance r. Since the reservoir pressure is zero, the flow rate Q through a cylinder of radius r and height z is

$$Q = 2\pi rz \frac{K}{\mu} g\vartheta \frac{dz}{dr}$$

Separating the variables and integrating between the well and the external boundary,

$$Q = \pi \frac{K}{\mu} g\vartheta \frac{z_e^2 - z_w^2}{\ln (r_e/r_w)} \tag{8-70}$$

When converting into practical units,

$$Q_{\mathrm{bbl/day}} = 1.535 \frac{K_D}{\mu_{\mathrm{cps}}} \vartheta \frac{z_e^2 - z_w^2}{\ln (r_e/r_w)} \tag{8-71}$$

where z_e and z_w are expressed in feet, and ϑ is now specific gravity.

Tilting of Fluid Interface. The surfaces of separation within reservoirs between oil and gas, oil and water, and gas and water are not always horizontal. While the most common reason for such tilting under static conditions is found in the capillary properties of reservoir rocks because of lithologic factors, in certain cases tilting of interfaces may occur even when the formations are homogeneous and isotropic.

Tilting as a Result of Only One Fluid in Motion. The most common case of this type is that of a tilted water table or surface of separation between oil and water zones. The density effect of the overlying fluid may no longer be neglected. Under stabilized flow conditions of the underlying water (the differential gravity head responsible for the fluid movement results from a change of elevation dz of the water-oil contact), it is $g(\vartheta_w - \vartheta_o)\, dz$.

The horizontal gravity-head gradient is

$$g\vartheta \frac{dH}{dx} = g(\vartheta_w - \vartheta_o) \frac{dz}{dx} \tag{8-72}$$

where $dz/dx = \tan \beta$ is the slope of the interface with respect to the x axis. Introducing this relation into Darcy's law [Eq. (8-69)] for linear flow,

$$Q_w = -A \frac{K}{\mu} g(\vartheta_w - \vartheta_o) \frac{dz}{dx} \tag{8-73}$$

or

$$\tan \beta = -\frac{Q_w}{A} \frac{\mu}{K} \frac{1}{g(\vartheta_w - \vartheta_o)} \tag{8-74}$$

if flow-potential H_w measurements are available within the water zone, we have also

$$Q_w = -A \frac{K}{\mu} g\vartheta_w \frac{dH_w}{dx} \tag{8-75}$$

where

$$H_w = z + \frac{P}{g\vartheta_w} \tag{8-76}$$

and after substitution in (8-74) we find for the slope of the oil-water interface:

$$\tan \beta = \frac{\vartheta_w}{\vartheta_w - \vartheta_o} \frac{dH_w}{dx} \tag{8-77}$$

Equation (8-77) was first derived by Hubbert (1940) and its importance was further stressed by him (1952) in a discussion of oil accumulation under hydrodynamic conditions. $\tan \beta$ may be expressed directly in feet per mile; dH_w/dx is also expressed in feet per mile; dH_w/dx may be considered as the horizontal gradient of a *potentiometric surface* within the water zone. A potentiometric surface within a fluid is that on which the potential energy is constant. In this instance the potential energy of the water is made up of two parts, namely the *energy of position* (due to height above a reference level) and the *energy of injection* (due to pressure). It is assumed in flow problems considered here that a third source of energy, the energy of motion, or *kinetic energy*, is negligible.

The sum of the energies of position and of injection per unit mass of the fluid is called the *flow potential* (H) of that fluid and is given by Eq. (8-76).

The tilting of interfaces discussed here is of special importance before the discovery and during the development of an oil and gas accumulation, but the tilting is maintained for long periods of time after production is initiated, even though all fluids may be set in motion during recovery operations.

Tilting as a Result of Two Fluids in Motion. This case is of special engineering significance, for it gives rise to water and gas coning, fingering of expanding gas cap, fingering of encroaching water up-structure, and to segregation of fluids of different density when one is injected into the reservoir.

GAS-CAP FINGERING. In a uniform and isotropic permeable medium, consider a surface of constant capillary pressure or of constant saturation in one fluid in the transition zone between the oil and gas zones (Fig. 8-16).

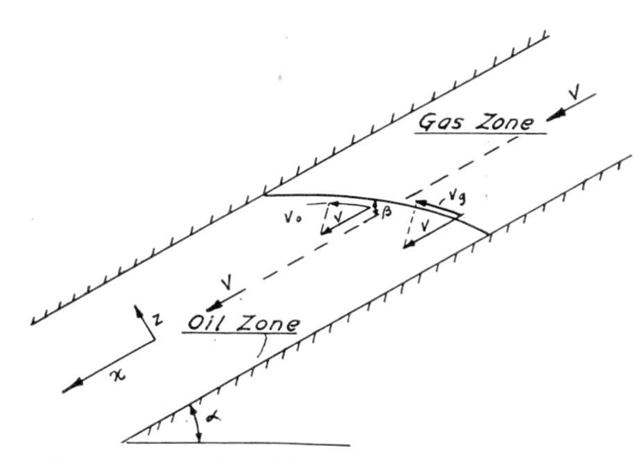

FIG. 8-16. Gas-cap expansion with fluid-flow deflections at gas-oil contact.

Consider that dynamic equilibrium has been reached and that the velocity of the drive is constant and uniform throughout the medium; this may be termed "planar flow," with flow lines parallel to the structure.

Let β be the angle made by the surface of liquid separation with the direction x of drive. The constant velocity of the drive gives components of flow parallel to the interface, v_g and v_o, respectively, in the gas and oil phases.

At the interface, the velocity vectors v_g and v_o are parallel to one another and are given by the generalized form of Darcy's law:

$$v_g = -\frac{K_g}{\mu_g}\left[\frac{\partial P_g}{\partial u} + g\vartheta_g \sin(\alpha - \beta)\right] \tag{8-78}$$

or

$$v_o = -\frac{K_o}{\mu_o}\left[\frac{\partial P_o}{\partial u} + g\vartheta_o \sin(\alpha - \beta)\right] \tag{8-79}$$

where u is the direction of the interface. Because of the constancy of the capillary pressure along the interface, we have $\partial P_g/\partial u = \partial P_o/\partial u$ and, from (8-78) and (8-79), we may write immediately

$$v_g \frac{\mu_g}{K_g} + g\vartheta_g \sin(\alpha - \beta) = v_o \frac{\mu_o}{K_o} + g\vartheta_o \sin(\alpha - \beta) \tag{8-80}$$

or

$$v_o \frac{\mu_o}{K_o} - v_g \frac{\mu_g}{K_g} = -g(\vartheta_o - \vartheta_g) \sin(\alpha - \beta) \tag{8-81}$$

Since the drive is at constant input rate, the inlet and outlet velocities must be equal because there is no accumulation or source in the system. Let this velocity be v. Because of the tilt β of the interface on the direction x, the stream flow-line components parallel to this surface of separation are

$$v_g = v \cos \beta \tag{8-82}$$

$$v_o = v \cos \beta \tag{8-83}$$

Substituting (8-82) and (8-83) into (8-81) and rearranging the terms, we obtain

$$v\left(\frac{\mu_o}{K_o} - \frac{\mu_g}{K_g}\right) = -g(\vartheta_o - \vartheta_g)(\sin \alpha - \cos \alpha \tan \beta) \tag{8-84}$$

But $\tan \beta = dz/dx$, and (8-84) may be rewritten

$$\frac{dz}{dx} - \tan \alpha = -v\left[\frac{(\mu_o/K_o) - (\mu_g/K_g)}{g(\vartheta_o - \vartheta_g) \cos \alpha}\right] \tag{8-85}$$

A tendency for the gas cap to finger into the oil zone exists when the slope of the interface tends to become parallel to the structure or when $dz/dx = 0$. The velocity of drive at which this occurs is termed the *critical velocity* v_c of the gas-cap expansion; it is attained when it satisfies the following relation:

$$v_c = g(\vartheta_o - \vartheta_g) \frac{\sin \alpha}{\dfrac{\mu_o}{K_o} - \dfrac{\mu_g}{K_g}} = \frac{\vartheta_o - \vartheta_g}{1{,}033} \frac{\sin \alpha}{\dfrac{\mu_o}{K_o} - \dfrac{\mu_g}{K_g}} \tag{8-86}$$

v_c is positive since $\sin \alpha < 0$ for down-dip gas flow. The mobilities K_o/μ_o and K_g/μ_g should be calculated for saturation conditions that prevail at the expanding gas front. The smaller the difference in mobilities, the larger may be the rate of gas-cap expansion.

In order to maintain a horizontal interface between the oil and gas phases, the velocity of expansion should be such that the condition $dz/dx = -\tan \alpha$ is satisfied; i.e., it may be attained only under rest conditions.

For a horizontal drive, Eq. (8-85) becomes

$$\frac{dz}{dx} = -v\left[\frac{(\mu_o/K_o) - (\mu_g/K_g)}{g(\vartheta_o - \vartheta_g)}\right] \tag{8-87}$$

where dz/dx is the slope of the interface defined by a line of constant saturation between the driving gas and the driven oil. It is of interest to change Eq. (8-87) in terms of the flow potential in one of the fluids, i.e., oil, for which we have

$$v = -\frac{K_o}{\mu_o} g\vartheta_o \frac{dH_o}{dx} \tag{8-88}$$

where H_o, the oil flow potential, is

$$H_o = z + \frac{P_o}{g\vartheta_o} \tag{8-89}$$

Substituting (8-88) in (8-87),

$$\frac{dz}{dx} = \frac{(\mu_o/K_o) - (\mu_g/K_g)}{\mu_o/K_o} \frac{\vartheta_o}{\vartheta_o - \vartheta_g} \frac{dH_o}{dx} \tag{8-90}$$

Equation (8-90) shows that the slope of dz/dx of the surface separating two fluids in horizontal motion is a function of

$$\frac{(\mu_o/K_o) - (\mu_g/K_g)}{\mu_o/K_o} = \text{reciprocal mobility-ratio difference}$$

$$\frac{\vartheta_o}{\vartheta_o - \vartheta_g} = \text{density difference}$$

$$\frac{dH_o}{dx} = \text{flow-potential gradient in one phase}$$

It is also of interest to see what happens to Eq. (8-90) when one of the fluids is immobile, such as the gas phase. Then there is no flow in the gas phase and Eq. (8-90) reduces to

$$\frac{dz}{dx} = -\frac{\vartheta_o}{\vartheta_o - \vartheta_g} \frac{dH_o}{dx} \tag{8-91}$$

Equation (8-91) is Hubbert's relation for the tilted water table if one substitutes subscripts w for o and o for g. When there is only one fluid in motion, the viscosity and mobility effects drop out from Eq. (8-90) and the angle of tilt of the interface is only a function of density and flow-potential gradient.

WATER-TABLE FINGERING. A derivation in all respects similar to that made above for gas-cap fingering may be made for water-table fingering during water encroachment up-dip, with the following results:

$$\frac{dz}{dx} - \tan\alpha = v \frac{\dfrac{\mu_w}{K_w} - \dfrac{\mu_o}{K_o}}{g(\vartheta_w - \vartheta_o)\cos\alpha} \tag{8-92}$$

For a horizontal water drive, the tilt of the interface between the oil and water is given by

$$\frac{dz}{dx} = \frac{\vartheta_w}{\vartheta_o - \vartheta_w} \frac{\dfrac{\mu_o}{K_o} - \dfrac{\mu_w}{K_w}}{\mu_w/K_w} \frac{dH_w}{dx} \qquad \text{where } H_w = z + \frac{P_w}{g\vartheta_w}$$

The critical velocity for up-dip water encroachment, i.e., beyond which the front becomes unstable and bypasses the oil at the base of the reservoir rock, is given by

$$v_c = g(\vartheta_w - \vartheta_o) \frac{\sin\alpha}{\dfrac{\mu_w}{K_w} - \dfrac{\mu_o}{K_o}} = \frac{\vartheta_w - \vartheta_o}{1{,}033} \frac{\sin\alpha}{\dfrac{\mu_w}{K_w} - \dfrac{\mu_o}{K_o}} \tag{8-93}$$

Equation (8-92) for water-table fingering was originally derived by Dietz (1953) but developing a somewhat different reasoning concerning the behavior of fluids at the interface.

Gas Coning. Gas coning occurs around a well bore when the well produces from an oil zone overlain by a free-gas zone. The oil-gas contact is

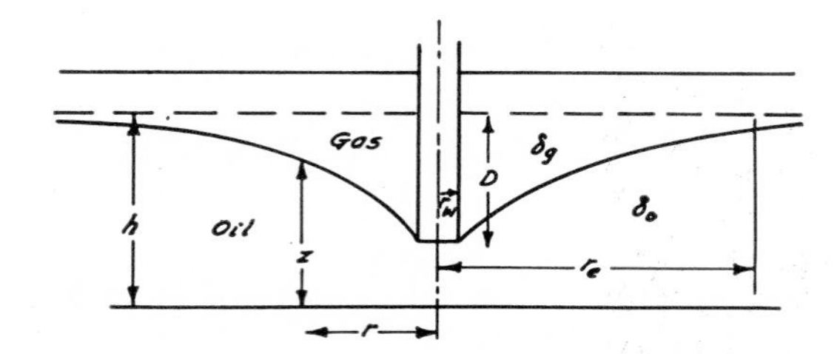

FIG. 8-17. Gas coning (conditions at gas break-through).

depressed around the well bore by virtue of the radial flow of oil and the pressure differential which results from it. To counterbalance the differential pressure caused by oil flow in the gas zone, a taller gas column must exist near the well bore than at a distance from it. The following derivations are adapted from a paper by Meyer and Garder (1954).

Consider a well (Fig. 8-17) which penetrates a depth D into a horizontal oil zone of thickness h. Let H_g and H_o be, respectively, the flow potentials of gas and oil; they are given by the following expressions:

$$H_g = z + \frac{P_g - P'}{g\vartheta_g} \tag{8-94}$$

$$H_o = z + \frac{P_o - P'}{g\vartheta_o} \tag{8-95}$$

where z is the elevation above an arbitrary reference level and P' is a reference pressure. P_g and P_o are, respectively, the pressures in the gas and oil zones; ϑ_g and ϑ_o are their phase densities. For the limiting flow case under study, flow in the gas zone is nonexistent and H_g is constant throughout the zone (H_g = constant). The value of P' may then be substituted as a function of H_g into H_o, and, neglecting capillary pressure ($P_g = P_o$),

$$H_o = H_g \frac{\vartheta_g}{\vartheta_o} + \frac{\vartheta_o - \vartheta_g}{\vartheta_o} z \tag{8-96}$$

Equation (8-96) is the oil-flow potential function within the oil zone.

Applying Darcy's law to the radial flow of oil into the well bore,

$$Q_o = 2\pi g \vartheta_o \frac{K_o}{\mu_o} zr \frac{dH_o}{dr} \tag{8-97}$$

and substituting H_o by its value and observing that the variations of fluid density with distance are negligible,

$$Q_o = 2\pi g(\vartheta_o - \vartheta_g) \frac{K_o}{\mu_o} zr \frac{dz}{dr} \tag{8-98}$$

This differential equation may now be integrated by separating the variables:

$$Q_o \int_{r_w}^{r_e} \frac{dr}{r} = 2\pi g(\vartheta_o - \vartheta_g) \frac{K_o}{\mu_o} \int_{h-D}^{h} z\,dz \tag{8-99}$$

or

$$Q_{o,\mathrm{max}} = \pi \frac{g(\vartheta_o - \vartheta_g)}{\ln (r_e/r_w)} \frac{K_o}{\mu_o} [h^2 - (h - D)^2] \tag{8-100}$$

In practical units

$$Q_{o,\mathrm{max}_{\mathrm{bbl/day}}} = 1.535 \frac{\vartheta_o - \vartheta_g}{\ln (r_e/r_w)} \frac{K_o}{\mu_o} [h^2 - (h - D)^2] \tag{8-101}$$

where h and D are expressed in feet. Formula (8-101) is nothing but the radial flow of oil under its own gravity head.

Water Coning. Water coning occurs around a well bore (Fig. 8-18) when the latter produces from an oil zone underlaid by bottom water, even when the point of entry of oil into the well bore is removed from the oil-water contact. The derivation of the formula for the maximum permissible oil-flow rate without water production from the underlying aquifer is similar in all respects to the coning of gas.

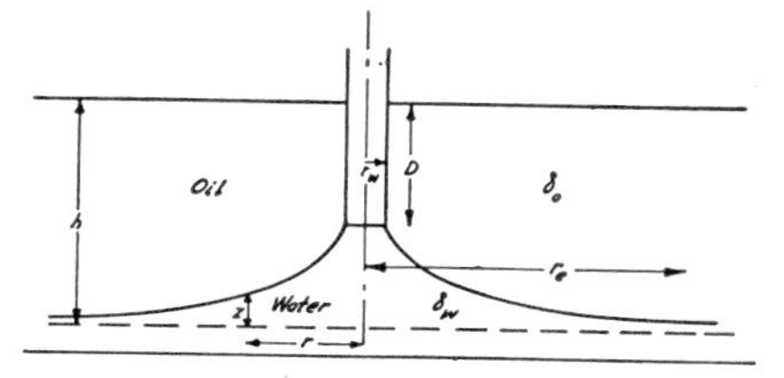

FIG. 8-18. Water coning (conditions at water break-through).

Let the flow potentials in oil and water be, respectively, H_o and H_w and expressed by

$$H_o = z + \frac{P_o - P'}{g\vartheta_o} \tag{8-102}$$

$$H_w = z + \frac{P_w - P'}{g\vartheta_w} \tag{8-103}$$

For the limiting case under study, no water flows to the well in the aquifer and H_w is a constant. Using this observation to eliminate the reference pressure P' from Eqs. (8-102) and (8-103), and neglecting capillary pressure ($P_o = P_w$),

$$H_o = H_w \frac{\vartheta_w}{\vartheta_o} + \left(\frac{\vartheta_o - \vartheta_w}{\vartheta_o}\right) z \tag{8-104}$$

Applying Darcy's law to the radial flow of oil into the well bore,

$$Q_o = 2\pi g \vartheta_o \frac{K_o}{\mu_o} (h - z) r \frac{dH_o}{dr} \tag{8-105}$$

and substituting H_o by its value,

$$Q_o = 2\pi_g (\vartheta_o - \vartheta_w) \frac{K_o}{\mu_o} (h - z) r \frac{dz}{dr} \tag{8-106}$$

Separating the variables and integrating,

$$Q_o \int_{r_w}^{r_e} \frac{dr}{r} = 2\pi g (\vartheta_o - \vartheta_w) \frac{K_o}{\mu_o} \int_0^{h-D} (h - z)\, dz \tag{8-107}$$

or

$$Q_{o,\max} = \pi \frac{K_o}{\mu_o} \frac{g(\vartheta_w - \vartheta_o)}{\ln (r_e/r_w)} (h^2 - D^2) \tag{8-108}$$

In practical units

$$Q_{o,\max_{\text{bbl/day}}} = 1.535 \frac{\vartheta_w - \vartheta_o}{\ln (r_e/r_w)} \frac{K_o}{\mu_o} (h^2 - D^2) \tag{8-109}$$

where h and D are expressed in feet.

Simultaneous Gas and Water Coning. If the effective oil-pay thickness h is comprised between a gas cap and a water zone (Fig. 8-19), the completion interval h_c must be such as to permit maximum oil-production rate without having gas and water simultaneously produced by coning, gas breaking through at the top of the interval and water at the bottom. This case is of particular interest in the production from a thin column underlaid by bottom water and overlaid by gas.

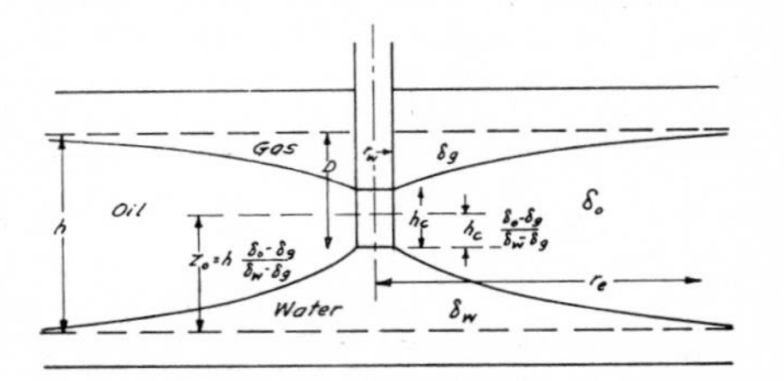

FIG. 8-19. Simultaneous gas and water coning (conditions for simultaneous gas and water break-through).

To secure maximum oil-production rate there must be a relation between the depth of well penetration D into the pay thickness h and the completion interval h_c.

Writing the equation for the flow potential of oil at the well bore and at the gas-oil contact,

$$H_o = H_g \frac{\vartheta_g}{\vartheta_o} + (h - D + h_c) \frac{\vartheta_o - \vartheta_g}{\vartheta_o} \tag{8-110}$$

Similarly, at the water-oil contact,

$$H_o = H_w \frac{\vartheta_w}{\vartheta_o} + (h - D) \frac{\vartheta_o - \vartheta_w}{\vartheta_o} \tag{8-111}$$

These two equations must be the same; and introducing the relation,

$$H_g \vartheta_g = H_w \vartheta_w - h(\vartheta_o - \vartheta_g) \tag{8-112}$$

which is valid at the drainage radius, we obtain

$$D = h - (h - h_c) \frac{\vartheta_o - \vartheta_g}{\vartheta_w - \vartheta_g} \tag{8-113}$$

D is the optimum penetration of the well into the oil zone below the gas-oil contact for a specified completion interval h_c, and for maximum oil-production rate. It may be considered that there will be a horizontal plane intersecting the interval h_c over which the oil-flow lines are horizontal. Let the vertical coordinate of this plane be z_o. Its value may be determined from the following considerations.

The oil-flow potential evaluated on this plane using the oil-gas boundary or the oil-water boundary must be the same:

$$H_{o-w} = H_w \frac{\vartheta_w}{\vartheta_o} + z_0 \frac{\vartheta_o - \vartheta_w}{\vartheta_o} \tag{8-114}$$

$$H_{o-g} = H_g \frac{\vartheta_g}{\vartheta_o} + z_0 \frac{\vartheta_o - \vartheta_g}{\vartheta_o} \tag{8-115}$$

Equating relations (8-114) and (8-115) and using again the flow-potential continuity equation (8-112) at the drainage radius, we find

$$z_o = h \frac{\vartheta_o - \vartheta_g}{\vartheta_w - \vartheta_g} \tag{8-116}$$

The maximum oil-flow rate to the well (Q_o) may be divided into two parts, one, Q_{og}, which takes place above the plane z_o and is the maximum rate in the absence of gas breaking to the well from the gas cone, the other, Q_{ow}, which takes place below the plane z_o and is the maximum rate in the absence of water production from the water cone. We have $Q_o = Q_{og} + Q_{ow}$.

$$Q_{og} = \pi \frac{g(\vartheta_o - \vartheta_g)}{\ln (r_e/r_w)} \frac{K_o}{\mu_o} \left[h^2 \left(1 - \frac{\vartheta_o - \vartheta_g}{\vartheta_w - \vartheta_g}\right)^2 - h_c^2 \left(1 - \frac{\vartheta_o - \vartheta_g}{\vartheta_w - \vartheta_g}\right)^2 \right] \tag{8-117}$$

$$Q_{ow} = \pi \frac{g(\vartheta_w - \vartheta_o)}{\ln (r_e/r_w)} \frac{K_o}{\mu_o} \left[h^2 \left(\frac{\vartheta_o - \vartheta_g}{\vartheta_w - \vartheta_g}\right)^2 - h_c^2 \left(\frac{\vartheta_o - \vartheta_g}{\vartheta_w - \vartheta_g}\right)^2 \right] \tag{8-118}$$

After addition and simplification, the expression for maximum oil flow without gas and water coning is

$$Q_{o,\max} = \pi \frac{gK_o(h^2 - h_c^2)}{\mu_o \ln (r_e/r_w)} \times \left[(\vartheta_o - \vartheta_g) \left(1 - \frac{\vartheta_o - \vartheta_g}{\vartheta_w - \vartheta_g}\right)^2 + (\vartheta_w - \vartheta_g) \left(\frac{\vartheta_o - \vartheta_g}{\vartheta_w - \vartheta_g}\right)^2 \right] \tag{8-119}$$

Example. An example will illustrate the computation technique.

Let a horizontal oil column 20 ft in thickness be overlaid by a uniform gas-saturated layer. The oil column is underlaid by bottom water. The reservoir is a horizontal layer uniform in its physical properties. $K = 0.1$ darcy, $\mu_o = 3$ cps, $\vartheta_o = 0.8$, $\vartheta_w = 1.05$, $\vartheta_g = 0.25$, $r_w = 0.5$ ft, $r_e = 660$ ft. Perforated interval desired is 5 ft. How should the well be completed for maximum oil-production rate without gas or oil coning and what is this rate?

We find

Well penetration:

$$D = 20 - 15 \frac{0.80 - 0.25}{1.05 - 0.25} = 9.7 \text{ ft}$$

Equilibrium level:

$$z_o = 20 \frac{0.80 - 0.25}{1.05 - 0.25} = 13.75 \text{ ft}$$

$$h - D + h_c - z_o = 20 - 9.7 + 5 - 13.75 = 1.55 \text{ ft}$$

$$z_o - h + D = 13.75 - 20 + 9.7 = 3.45 \text{ ft}$$

Maximum oil-flow rate above equilibrium level:

$$Q_{og} = 1.535 \frac{0.8 - 0.25}{\ln \frac{660}{0.5}} \times \frac{0.1}{3} \times [(20 - 13.75)^2 - 1.55^2] = 0.144 \text{ bbl/day}$$

Maximum oil-flow rate below equilibrium level:

$$Q_{ow} = 1.535 \frac{1.05 - 0.8}{\ln \frac{660}{0.5}} \times \frac{0.1}{3} [13.75^2 - 3.45^2] = 0.318 \text{ bbl/day}$$

Maximum total permissible production rate:

$$Q_{o,\max} = Q_{og} + Q_{ow} = 0.462 \text{ bbl/day}$$

It may be observed, as was expected, that greater maximum permissible oil-production rates are obtained, other conditions remaining unchanged, when the completion or perforation interval is as thin as possible.

Multiple-phase Flow

When various fluid phases are flowing in space simultaneously through the porous rock structure, the flow equations in their most general form must be used to study fluid flow.

In addition to considering external forces and gravity forces as a source of driving energy on the fluids, one might also consider the effect of other body forces such as electric and magnetic forces.

Gravity effects exert, per unit volume of fluid flowing, a force given by

$$F_g = g\vartheta \sin \alpha$$

where g = acceleration of gravity, or 980 cm per sec per sec
ϑ = density, or mass per unit volume of flowing fluid
α = angle made by direction of flow and horizontal direction

Gravity effects are always present for any flowing fluid, but, as in the case of gas, they are often of negligible magnitude.

Magnetic effects can be neglected in oil-field work as the fluids involved have very low or negligible magnetic susceptibility contrast. Connate waters rich in $FeCl_3$ may be under the restraining effect of the earth's magnetic field, but such waters are unknown in ordinary oil-field practice.

Electric effects occur during the displacement of a charged fluid with respect to a fixed framework also electrically charged. This gives rise to the streaming potential E_s and if the electric-charge density of the flowing fluid is e per unit volume, the electric restraining effect is obtained from $F_e = E_s e$, which must be included in the dynamic equation. In this case, we need not include an angle of dip because the restraining electric force is always parallel to the direction of flow.

Darcy's law in its most generalized form will then be written as follows:

$$v_u = -\frac{K}{\mu}\left(\frac{\partial P}{\partial \mu} + g\vartheta \sin \alpha + E_s e\right) \tag{8-120}$$

where u = direction of flow
v_u = linear velocity of flowing fluid in free space, cm per sec
K = absolute fluid permeability, darcys
μ = fluid viscosity, centipoises
$\frac{\partial P}{\partial u}$ = pressure gradient in direction of flow, atm per cm
α = angle of dip of flow direction with respect to the horizontal (α is taken as positive up-dip)

This generalized equation assumes a homogeneous fluid flowing in a reservoir fully saturated by that fluid.

If we have more than one fluid simultaneously flowing, effective permeabilities must be used. For oil, gas, and water flows, we have

$$v_{ou} = -\frac{K_o}{\mu_o}\left(\frac{\partial P_o}{\partial u} + g\vartheta_o \sin\alpha + E_s e_o\right)$$

$$v_{gu} = -\frac{K_g}{\mu_g}\left(\frac{\partial P_g}{\partial u} + g\vartheta_o \sin\alpha\right) \qquad (8\text{-}121)$$

$$v_{wu} = -\frac{K_w}{\mu_w}\left(\frac{\partial P_w}{\partial u} + g\vartheta_w \sin\alpha + E_s e_w\right)$$

In these equations, no electric restraining effect is assumed for gas, which is most certainly not ionized in the earth. However, both oil and water may be electrically charged. Electric charges within connate water should be dissipated rapidly, but not so readily in oils which generally contain polar compounds such as asphalt and paraffin. In practice, electric effects are neglected in flow problems, but they may be the cause of troublesome paraffin problems. However, electric restraining forces may not be of negligible magnitude in water flooding operations where relatively fresh water is introduced and an appreciable streaming potential is created. In laboratory flooding experiments they may also be of considerable magnitude.

Accordingly, the generalized forms of Darcy's law which will find application are the following:

$$v_{ou} = -\frac{K_o}{\mu_o}\left(\frac{\partial P_o}{\partial u} + g\vartheta_o \sin\alpha\right)$$

$$v_{gu} = -\frac{K_g}{\mu_g}\left(\frac{\partial P_g}{\partial u} + g\vartheta_g \sin\alpha\right) \qquad (8\text{-}122)$$

$$v_{wu} = -\frac{K_w}{\mu_w}\left(\frac{\partial P_w}{\partial u} + g\vartheta_w \sin\alpha\right)$$

The pressure gradients which appear in the above formulas are within single-fluid phases and are designated by the subscripts.

SELECTED REFERENCES ON MECHANICS OF FLUID FLOW IN POROUS MEDIA

1937

Muskat, M.: "The Flow of Homogeneous Fluids through Porous Media," McGraw-Hill Book Company, Inc., New York.

1940

Hubbert, M. King: The Theory of Ground Water Motion, *J. Geol.*, vol. 48, nos. 8 and 9, pp. 785ff.

1941

Evinger, H. H., and M. Muskat: Calculation of Theoretical Productivity Factor, *AIME Tech. Pub.* 1352.

1942

Evinger, H. H., and M. Muskat: Calculation of Productivity Factors for Oil-gas-water Systems in the Steady State, *AIME Tech. Pub.* 1416.

Hetherington, Charles R., D. T. MacRoberts, and R. L. Huntington: Unsteady Flow of Gas through Porous Media, *AIME Tech. Pub.* 1398.

Lewis, James A., W. L. Horner, and Marion Stekoll: Productivity Index and Measurable Reservoir Characteristics, *AIME Tech. Pub.* 1467.

Rodd, Charles C.: Determination of Oil-well Capacities from Liquid-level Data, *AIME Tech. Pub.* 1475.

Travers, W. J., Jr.: Completion Practices Related to Well Productivity, *AIME Tech. Pub.* 1465.

1944

Arthur, M. G.: Fingering and Coning of Water and Gas in Homogeneous Oil Sand, *AIME Tech. Pub.* 1723.

1949

Clark, J. B.: A Hydraulic Process for Increasing the Productivity of Wells, *AIME Tech. Pub.* 2510.

MacRoberts, D. T.: Effects of Transient Conditions in Gas Reservoirs, *AIME Tech. Pub.* 2547.

Van Everdingen, A. F., and W. Hurst: The Application of the Laplace Transformations to Flow Problems in Reservoirs, *Trans. AIME*, pp. 305ff.

1950

Howard, Robert A., and Marsh S. Watson, Jr.: Relative Productivity of Perforated Casing-I, *AIME Tech. Pub.* 2851.

Howard, Robert A., and Marsh S. Watson, Jr.: Relative Productivity of Perforated Casing-II, *AIME Tech. Pub.* 2933.

Miller, C. C., et al.: The Estimation of Permeability and Reservoir Pressures from Bottom Hole Pressure Build-up Characteristics, *Trans. AIME*, pp. 91ff.

1951

Brownscombe, E. R., and L. R. Kern: Graphical Solution of Single Phase Flow Problems, *Petroleum Engr.*, February, pp. B-7ff.

Horner, D. R.: Pressure Build-up in Wells, *Proc. 3rd World Petroleum Congr.*, Sec. II, pp. 503ff.

1953

Chatas, A. T.: A Practical Treatment of Non-steady State Flow Problems in Reservoir Systems, *Petroleum Engr.*, May, pp. B-42ff.; June, pp. B-38ff.; August, pp. B-44ff.

Dietz, D. N.: A Theoretical Approach to the Problem of Encroaching and By-passing Edge Water, *Proc. Koninkl. Ned. Akad. Wetenschap.*, series B, vol. 56, pp. 83ff.

Hubbert, M. K.: Entrapment of Petroleum under Hydrodynamic Conditions, *Bull. Am. Assoc. Petroleum Geol.*, vol. 37, pp. 1954ff.

Hurst, W.: Establishment of the Skin Effect and Its Impediment to Fluid Flow into a Well Bore, *Petroleum Engr.*, October, pp. B-6, B-16.

Thomas, G. B.: Analysis of Pressure Build-up Data, *Trans. AIME*, pp. 125ff.

Van Everdingen, A. F.: The Skin Effect and Its Influence on the Productive Capacity of a Well, *Trans. AIME*, pp. 171ff.

1954

Meyer, H. I., and A. O. Garder: Mechanics of Two Immiscible Fluids in Porous Media, *J. Appl. Phys.*, vol. 25, no. 11, pp. 1400ff.

Nielsen, R. F.: How to Calculate Unsteady State Flow, *Oil Gas J.*, July 26, pp. 253ff.

Timmerman, E. H.: Figure Your Chances Before Fracturing, *Oil Gas J.*, June 7, pp. 94ff.

1955

Arps, J. J.: How Well Completion Damage Can Be Determined Graphically, *World Oil*, April, pp. 255ff.

Nowak, T. J., and G. W. Lester: Analysis of Pressure Fall-off Curves Obtained in Water-injection Wells to Determine Injective Capacity and Formation Damage, *AIME Tech. Pub.* 4057.

1956

Groeneman, A. R., and F. F. Wright: Analysis of Fluid Injection Wells by Shut-in Pressures, *J. Petroleum Technol.*, vol. 8, no. 7, pp. 21ff.

Meyer, H. I., and D. F. Searcy: Analog Study of Water Coning, *J. Petroleum Technol.*, vol. 8, no. 4, pp. 61ff.

Van Meurs, P.: The Use of Transparent Three-dimensional Models for Studying the Mechanism of Flow Processes in Oil Reservoirs, *AIME Tech. Paper* 678G.

CHAPTER 9

VOLUMETRIC EVALUATION OF OIL-IN-PLACE AND EMPIRICAL RESERVE ESTIMATES

A fundamental prerequisite to reservoir performance prediction is a satisfactory knowledge of the volume of oil originally in place in the reservoir rock and of the energy which will be effective in expelling oil and gas to the producing wells. An oil reservoir in the earth is necessarily confined by certain geologic and fluid boundaries which it is necessary to establish with a sufficient degree of accuracy. Within the confine of such boundaries, oil is contained in what is commonly referred to as "gross pay." "Effective pay" is that part of the reservoir thickness which contributes to oil recovery and is defined by lower limits of porosity and permeability and upper limits of water saturation. All available measurements performed on reservoir samples and in wells such as core analysis and well logs are made full use of in this evaluation. Knowing the pore-space volume, the computation of hydrocarbon in place becomes a simple matter when reservoir fluid properties are known.

THE RESERVOIR BOUNDARIES

An underground oil reservoir is confined by impermeable geologic strata or boundaries and, in many instances, between features such as the water-oil contact and the gas-oil contact.

1. *Definition of geologic boundaries.* The geologic features which limit the oil and gas accumulations may be impermeable shales or massive limestones, anhydrite, igneous, and metamorphic rocks structurally deformed into anticline, monocline, syncline, or fault block, or they may be the result of lithologic changes such as by lensing of porosity development or by facies changes. Formation pinch-out and unconformities may also be considered as possible geological confining factors. The upper and lower boundaries of oil- and gas-bearing reservoir rocks may be established by correlation of drill-cutting sample logs, core logs, electric and radioactivity logs, etc. The most common practice is to use such logs to establish geological cross sections in a grid pattern across the field. A first evaluation of the development and lateral extension of porous and nonporous development may be made at this stage. This study should be extended beyond the limits of the oil accumulation because it may establish the possible existence and extent of an aquifer and permit passing judgment at a later date upon the activity of water drive.

2. *Definition of water-oil contact.* The water-oil contact is at best a loose terminology, for there may not be a sharp demarcation level across which one passes from 100 per cent water to 100 per cent oil saturation. Owing to the capillary forces between the two fluids when contained in a porous medium, the boundary may be sharp (if the capillary pressure of the rock is flat) or it may be very diffuse and vertically extended (if the capillary pressure of the rock is steep at high nonwetting-phase saturation values). In addition, for practical engineering purposes, the water-oil contact as defined here is that at which 100 per cent water production would be obtained just below it by means of a selective production test on packers such as in drill-stem tests. In fact, a good and reliable means of establishing the producing water-oil contact is by drill-stem tests with successive packer settings at various levels in the vicinity of the expected contact. The analysis of cores and the examination of formation samples are other means of determining the level of the oil-water contact.

A more reliable and less expensive way to make this determination is by well logs of one sort or another. Such logs are almost always available. From conventional electric logs the water-oil contact level may be evaluated by making fluid content and, more specifically, water-saturation determinations and by evaluating the level at which 100 per cent water will be produced. Similar determinations may be made from focused current logs. Of interest in picking the level of the water-oil contact is the behavior of the contact log and micrólog in high-porosity formations, the water-oil contact being often characterized by a reversal in the departure between the 1½- and 2-in. curves. Also of interest in this respect is the behavior of the neutron log, especially when the formation lithology is relatively homogeneous and when there is a relatively large hydrogen richness contrast between reservoir oil and formation water, for then there is a sharp change in the neutron deflection at the water-oil contact. In general, crude oils different in gravity from 40° API give such a reaction, the heavier oils showing less deflection and the lighter oils more deflection than at the water level.

With the advent of scintillation detectors for gamma-ray and neutron-gamma logging of wells, it is possible to determine the water-oil contact by means of gamma-ray energy selector. If the formation water is very saline, it is rich in chlorine; this chemical element under bombardment by neutrons gives off a gamma ray of capture of 5-mev energy. By setting the secondary gamma-logging discriminator at a level above normal gamma-ray energy of capture and thereby selecting only those given off by chlorine, it is possible to locate the water-oil contact level.

3. *Definition of gas-oil contact.* Drill-stem tests performed while the well is drilling or selective production tests with straddle packers after drilling through a formation, may establish the level of the gas-oil contact, i.e., the level where 100 per cent gas production is obtained. The contact between oil and gas in the reservoir should be viewed as a zone of transition rather than as a sharp boundary.

Somewhat less expensive is the determination of the gas-oil contact from core analysis, for frequently a level may be found in the core above which no trace of oil may be visually observed or measured, although the prevailing water saturation indicates the presence of hydrocarbons. Electric logs are very inadequate for picking the level of a gas-oil contact except under the most ideal conditions when the reservoir rock is of uniform lithology. Then, owing to the difference in interfacial tension between oil-water and gas-water saturation, a lesser formation-water saturation exists in the gas zone than in the oil zone. This change of saturation is reflected by a small increment in true resistivity above the gas-oil contact.

Of more interest in this respect is the reaction of the neutron curve at the gas-oil contact, for there is often enough difference in the hydrogen richness of oil and gas to give sharp deflection changes. This change may even be enhanced by varying the spacing between source and detector in the neutron logging device employing multiple spacing (MS log of Lane-Wells).

THE EFFECTIVE PAY

In the previous section, techniques for delineating the upper and lower limits of the geologic strata or rocks containing hydrocarbons were studied. The interval may be termed "gross pay." But the whole of this section may not be an effective reservoir fluid container, nor is all the pore space filled with oil and gas. Hence, it is necessary to determine an effective or net pay thickness.

Coregraph Method. The most common method of determining effective pay is by means of coregraph techniques. The values of porosity, permeability, and water saturation measured at successive levels are plotted horizontally, as shown in Fig. 9-1. To each parameter a cutoff value is assigned, i.e., a value below which it is presumed that no hydrocarbon production will be obtained. As may be surmised, the selection of cutoff values is a matter calling for a great deal of experience with the type of reservoir rock under study. Only a few guiding principles may be given which may help select cutoff values for each of the above parameters. It may also be inferred that quite often only one and perhaps two parameters may be used instead of three in eliminating nonpay from the gross section.

The two most important parameters that determine pay are fluid saturation and permeability, and of these two permeability is by far the controlling one. Yet it is difficult to select with assurance a permeability cutoff value; and its range in magnitude varies between 0.1 to 100 md, depending on the most common or average permeability value in the section, for the presence of high-permeability channels adjacent to otherwise tight zones may render the latter effective in yielding their oil. A suggested possibility for determining the permeability cutoff value is to determine the interwell flow capacity of the reservoir rock by means of flow build-up tests. Under favorable conditions, a dependable value for the rock flow capacity (Kh) in millidarcy-feet may be obtained. Then assume a value h_e for the effective-pay thickness and calculate the corresponding mean effective permeability K_e from $K_e = Kh/h_e$. On the permeability coregraph, locate a cutoff permeability K_c such that the mean permeability of the crosshatched diagram (Fig. 9-1) is equal to K_e. Several values for h_e may be assumed, including a maximum and a minimum one, thereby determining the maximum and minimum cutoff permeabilities that determine the effective pay. A reasonable value for K_c may then be selected.

It may be objected that the procedure outlined above considers as pay only that part of the reservoir rock which is effective in conducting fluids to the well, whereas adjacent tight zones may act as feeders to the more

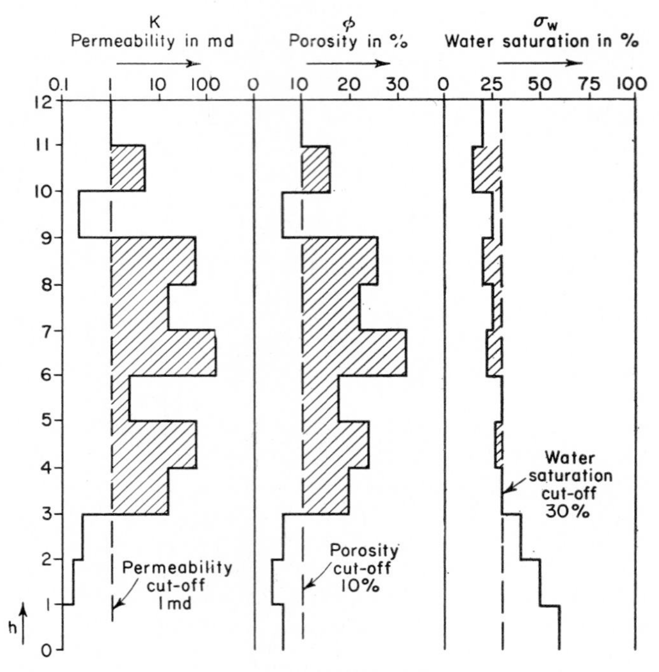

FIG. 9-1. Principle of core-graph method of determining effective pay.

permeable sections and thereby contribute to the effective pay. These views are valid and the above procedure must be considered as giving a pessimistic or conservative solution to the problem. Having established this very minimum for the value of the effective pay, personal preferences, circumstances, and beliefs may then come into play to increase its value in a reasonable measure.

The cutoff permeability and porosity values may also be influenced by the expected type of drive, for in depletion recovery finer-sized pores may be expected to produce oil than in water-drive recovery.

In carbonate reservoirs, the pore structure is no longer uniform as in sands and sandstones where the pore structure is intergranular. Although the porosity of limestones is at times simply intergranular, it is more commonly made up of various systems of channels connected in parallel.

According to Archie (1952) the porosity of carbonates may be divided into three main types.

Type 1: *Compact-crystalline Limestones.* These rocks have a shiny appearance on a fresh fracture surface and the rock is hard, dense, has a resinous appearance, and is sharp on its edges. The carbonate crystals which form this rock type are tightly interlocked and no pore space is visible to the naked eye. This type of rock becomes a commercial reservoir when its porosity attains 7 to 10 per cent and its permeability exceeds 0.1 md. However, should secondary porosity have developed, commercial reservoirs are possible when as little as 5 per cent porosity exists.

Type 2: *Chalky Limestones.* These rocks have a dull and earthy appearance. The carbonate crystals have an imbricated packing and join one another at random angles. Fine powdered crystals are present in the interstices and give this type of rock its chalky appearance. It becomes a commercial reservoir rock when 15 per cent porosity exists, at which point a permeability of 0.1 md is often developed. The reason why chalky limestones require more porosity development in order to be a commercial reservoir is because of the pore-filling nature of the fine chalk or powdered carbonates.

Type 3: *Granular or Saccharoidal Limestones.* This type of rock also includes oölitic limestones. These rocks have a sugary appearance because of the coarsely crystalline nature of the grains. They become commercial reservoir rocks when 5 to 6 per cent porosity exists, at which point a permeability of 0.1 md is developed. From a pore-size distribution standpoint, granular limestones are intermediate between the compact-crystalline types (which are very uniform in pore sizes of small diameters) and the chalky types (which are heterogeneous in pore sizes).

As a general remark, it may be said that the lithology of carbonate reservoirs is a controlling factor in determining pay and nonpay.

Micrologand Contact-log Methods. The use of wall-resistivity measuring devices (microlog, contact log, etc.) in evaluating effective pay is somewhat arbitrary and is based upon the belief that, if a mud cake is formed while drilling on the walls of a well, the formation facing it must have sufficient porosity and permeability to produce hydrocarbons, provided that fluid-saturation conditions in such rocks are otherwise favorable. The devices cited are, in fact, nothing else but mud-cake detectors. Of course such devices do not have a sufficiently fine resolution to pick up fracture porosity.

In an oil- and gas-bearing section, the departure of the microlog tools is generally positive because of the residual hydrocarbons in the flushed zone. The procedure to evaluate effective pay is to color such area of departure, thereby indicating vividly the amount and location of pay sections. However, effective pay may also be indicated by zero or negative departure, especially in high-porosity formations. Accurate selection of effective pay from the microlog must be made in conjunction with SP deflection studies.

Again the use of these devices for the purpose at hand may be considered as pessimistic and conservative, but it gives a safe minimum value on which to base the economics of a new field development.

Microlaterolog and Limestone Curves. These devices permit the location of porous zones and the determination of the porosity values; however, they do not respond greatly to mud-cake thickness like other micro tools.

Self-potential Deflection Method. A technique for determining the effective pay of a porous–nonporous rock sequence is by the use of SP deflections. It is known that the boundary between porous and nonporous rocks is located at the point of inflection on the SP curve. By careful inspection of the SP curve, it is possible to locate all such points, provided the laminations are, in general, thicker than the bore-hole diameter. In fresh muds, all sections on the SP curve having a negative trend are considered as porous and permeable, whereas those having a positive trend are considered as nonporous. In muds which are more saline than formation water, this relationship is reversed.

The total thickness of all porous and permeable sections is the effective pay.

In a laminated sand-shale sequence as reservoir formation where shale laminations are considerably thinner than hole diameter, other SP curve techniques have been suggested for the evaluation of the effective pay. The theory was originally derived by Doll (1948) for a sequence of clean sand laminations and shale. Later it was extended to shaly sands of the clay-disseminated type.

Method of the Area under the Self-potential Curve. This method was suggested by H. G. Doll in his paper "The S.P. Log: Theoretical Analysis and Principles of Interpretation" (1948). This method requires that the shale resistivity be equal to that of the sand and, therefore, it is mostly valid for shaly sands containing water and for sands containing a large fraction of conductive colloids. The method consists of planimetering the area between a shale base line and the SP curve, to express this area in millivolt-feet and to divide this area by the static SP expressed in millivolts obtained from a clean water sand, stratigraphically close to the object sand, and in which it is fairly certain that equivalent formation waters are present. If formation-water salinity is known, the static SP may be computed by means of the SP formula.

When the above assumptions may no longer be made, as when the sand contains oil in commercial quantities ($R_t > R_{sh}$), the above approach gives a *lower limit* to the effective pay thickness. An *upper limit* may be obtained by dividing the area under the SP curve by the maximum SP recorded through the shale-sand interval. It is, therefore, possible to bracket the effective pay thickness between two figures.

Method of the Pseudostatic Self-potential. This method is again derived from a study of H. G. Doll: "The SP Log in Shaly Sands" (1949). One must be able to read the pseudostatic SP or SP which results from the shaly water sand. The static SP for a clean sand must also be known, either from observation or by calculation. The following formulas are at the basis of the method:

$$\alpha = \frac{\text{pseudostatic SP}}{\text{static SP}}$$

$$u = \frac{R_t}{R_i} \tag{9-1}$$

$$q = \frac{p}{1 - p} \frac{R_t}{R_{sh}}$$

The method consists in solving for q from Fig. 9-2, reproduced from Doll's paper, from which the shale fraction p may be derived. The method requires an unusual degree of skill in interpreting logs in shaly sands.

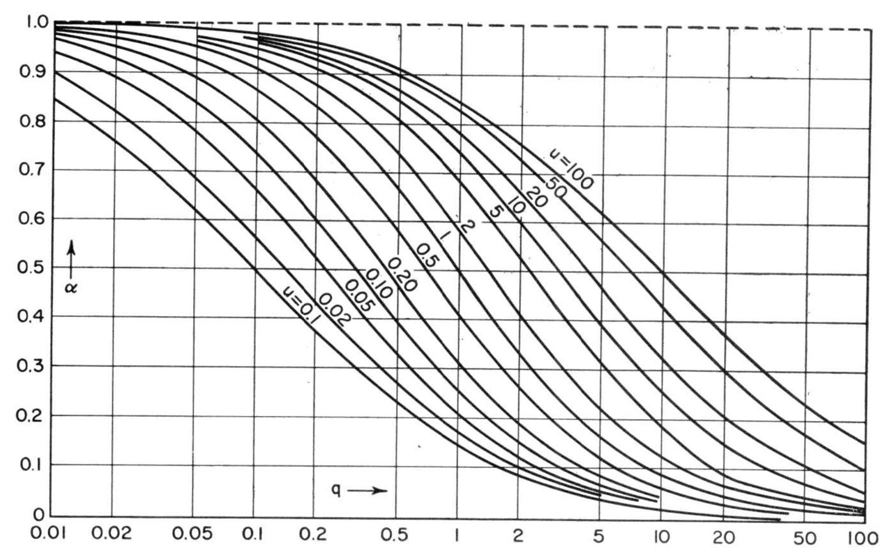

Fig. 9-2. Method of determination of effective pay from electric log for laminated sand-shale reservoir. (*After Doll, courtesy AIME.*)

For shaly sands of the clay-disseminated type, it is necessary to know the formation-water resistivity and to compute a static SP value, then to evaluate the area under the actual SP curve, and then to proceed by one of the above techniques.

Gamma-ray–Neutron Method. The neutron curve responds to fluid-filled porosity but does not discriminate between pay and nonpay. The use of the gamma-ray curve has been suggested as the discriminator on the basis that it detects the presence of clay filling the pore space of rocks. The producing potentialities of a formation could then be determined from gamma-ray logs, provided the natural radioactivity of shale and clay contamination responsible for the permeability reduction is constant. This principle is used by McCullough in Canada to determine effective pay in the Cardium sand (Pembina field). The technique is, of course, empirical and arbitrary; it requires calibration in a specific area and horizon.

Examples of Log Techniques of Effective-pay Determination. The previous discussion has shown that the microlog is a fairly reliable method of evaluating the effective pay, at least to the extent that flow capacity is concerned. It will be used as the standard to which to compare the results of the "area under the SP curve" method.

Example log 1: Fig. 9-3, sec. 2,596 to 2,654 ft.

For the application of this technique it is necessary to know the static SP. In this instance the log does not give it, and it must be calculated from known formation-water resistivity. It is calculated as −104 mv. The planimetered area under the SP curve is 2,040 mv × feet. Therefore, the effective pay is 2,040/104 = 19.5 ft. From the microlog, the effective pay is 19.5 ft. A perfect check is obtained.

Example log 2: Fig. 9-4, sec. 6,530 to 6,597 ft.

The static SP is presumably recorded by this log as −125 mv. The area under the SP curve is 6,800 mv × feet. Effective pay is 6,800/125 = 54.2 ft. The microlog gives 48 ft of pay. A satisfactory check is obtained.

Example of Application of the Doll Method (1949). The interval 2,596 to 2,654 in Example log 1 will be used to illustrate the technique and the use of Fig. 9-2.

The gross interval is 68 ft in thickness, but much of it is nonporous and permeable, as was already seen above.

The following values are read directly from the conventional log for this interval:

$$R_t = 18 \text{ ohm-meters}$$
$$R_i = 28 \text{ ohm-meters}$$
$$R_{sh} = 10 \text{ ohm-meters}$$
$$\text{Actual SP} = -40 \text{ mv}$$
$$\text{Static SP} = -104 \text{ mv}$$

We have

$$u = \frac{R_t}{R_i} = 0.645$$

$$\frac{R_t}{R_{sh}} = 1.8$$

$$\alpha = 0.385$$

Reading α and u in Fig. 9-2, we obtain $q = 4$. Solving for p from

$$q = \frac{p}{1 - p} \frac{R_t}{R_{sh}} = 4$$

we find

$$p = 0.69$$

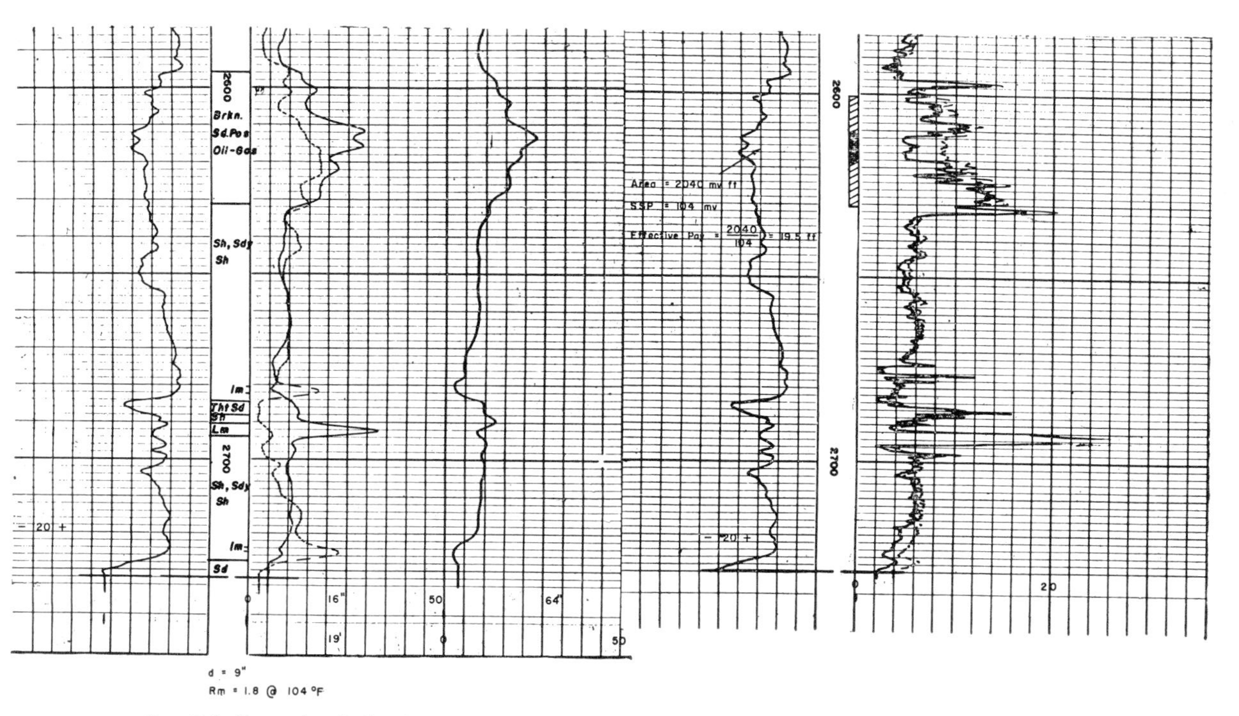

FIG. 9-3. Example of effective-pay calculation by microlog and area under the SP-curve methods.

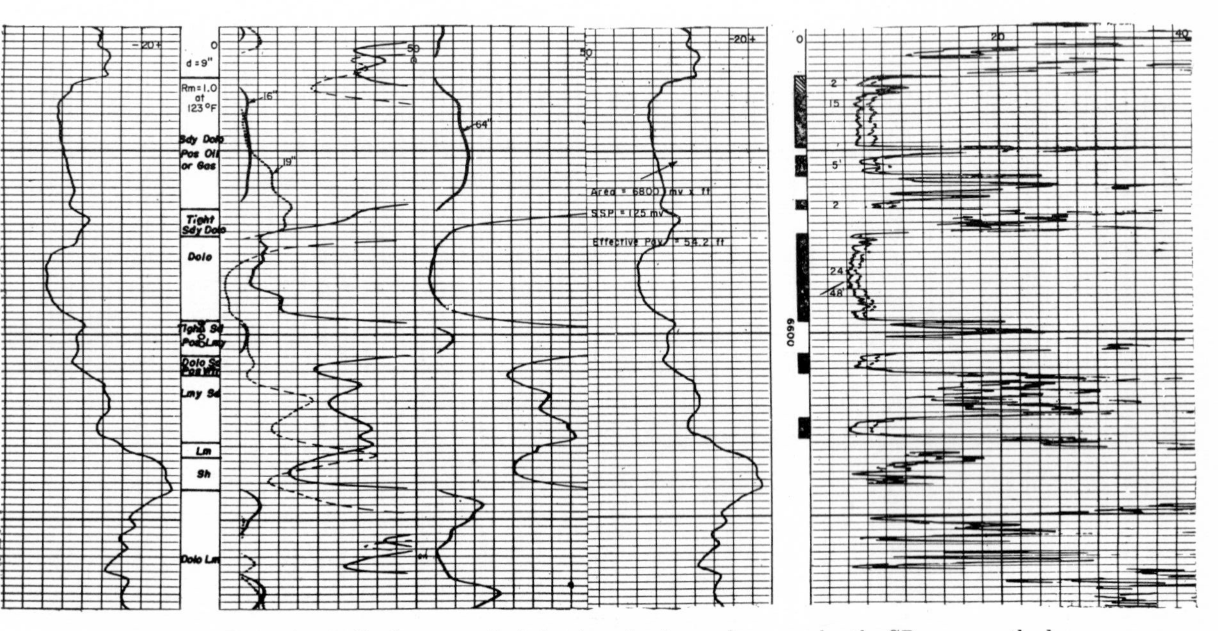

Fig. 9-4. Example of effective-pay calculation by microlog and area under the SP-curve methods.

p is the fraction of the gross interval represented by nonporous and nonpermeable sections. Hence the effective pay is $(1 - 0.69)68 = 21$ ft. Value of the effective pay found by the other technique was 19.5 ft; a satisfactory check is obtained.

VOLUMETRIC CALCULATIONS

The methods reviewed up to this point permit the determination of the available void space within the reservoir rock and the geometric extent of the formations susceptible of containing oil and gas. The geometric extent is normally represented by field and lease maps, coupled with contouring of the effective-pay thickness at an appropriate interval in order to picture the structure, relief, or reservoir thickness.

For the purpose of reservoir pore-volume calculations, two types of maps are particularly desirable, namely, the isopach and the isovol maps.

The isopach map, as the name indicates, is that which is represented by lines of equal effective-pay thickness h_e. However, this representation may not give an exact idea of the reservoir volume available as an oil and gas container owing to the possibility of porosity variations between wells, as indicated by core analysis and electric and radioactivity logging. In such a case, a better idea of the reservoir volume will be obtained from a map contoured on the basis of equal values of the product $h_e\phi$, in which ϕ is the porosity for each zone. An isovol map is thus obtained.

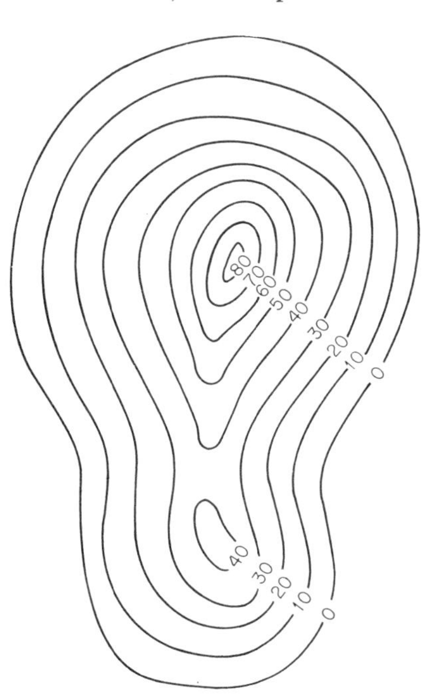

FIG. 9-5. Reservoir isopach map.

The next problem is to compute the reservoir volume available to oil and gas from such a map. The author is indebted to J. Tarner for the following method whereby planimetering of the areas between contours is resorted to in conjunction with the use of graphical integration methods by either the trapezoidal rule or Simpson's rule.

The area enclosed by each contour is most easily obtained by using a planimeter. The planimeter should be calibrated for each map, as map scales are sometimes distorted. This may be done by determining the planimeter reading of a known area. On many oil-company land maps, the area of each lease is printed under the landowner's name. Such an area or a 640-acre section (1 square mile) may be used for calibrating the planimeter.

After the areas enclosed by the contour lines have been found, the determination of reservoir pore volumes is reduced to reading, to a proper scale, the area under the curve obtained by plotting the area between two contours vs. the average height of the same contours. For example, consider a field as shown in Fig. 9-5. This may be considered an isopach or an isovol map; in either case the area enclosed by each contour is determined. This has been done by using a planimeter, and the results are

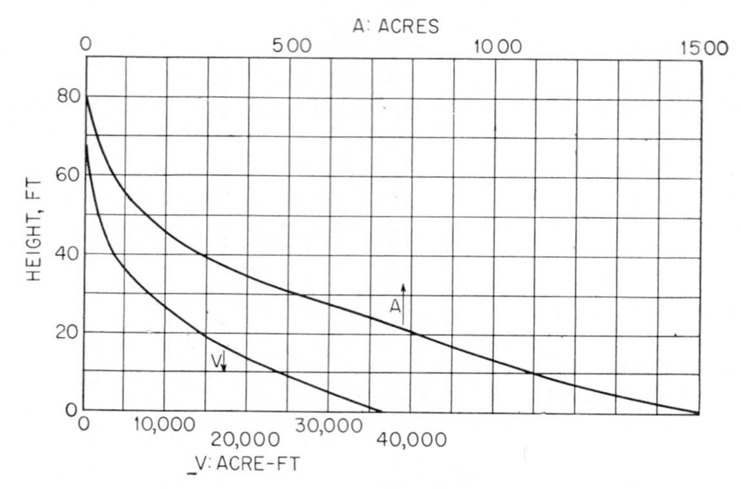

FIG. 9-6. Structure volume and cross-sectional area vs. height.

shown in Fig. 9-6 as a plot of intercontour areas vs. height. The volume V_o of the reservoir can now be obtained by the following integration:

$$V_o = \int_0^H f(h_e)\, dh_e \tag{9-2}$$

where H equals the total thickness or closure of reservoir and $f(h_e)$ is the equation of curve V of Fig. 9-6.

Since an analytical expression for this curve would be practically impossible to obtain, the area under the curve must be determined by graphic integration.

Two methods for evaluating this area are known, namely, the trapezoidal and Simpson's rules. The trapezoidal rule is as follows:

$$V_o = h(\tfrac{1}{2}a_0 + a_1 + a_2 + a_3 + \cdots + a_{n-1} + \tfrac{1}{2}a_n) \tag{9-3}$$

where V_o = volume of reservoir, acre-ft
a_0 = area enclosed by zero contour, such as when drawn at the water-oil contact, acres
a_1 = area enclosed by first contour, acres
a_n = area enclosed by the nth contour, acres
h = contour interval, ft

In the example,

$$V_o = 10 \times \left(\frac{1{,}560.32}{2} + 1{,}130.24 + 812.80 + 533.76 + 284.8 + 144.64 + 71.04 + 26.24 + \frac{4.48}{2}\right)$$
$$= 37{,}859 \text{ acre-ft}$$

Simpson's rule obtains the area under irregular curves more closely than the trapezoidal rule but has the disadvantage of requiring the division of the interval along the abscissa into an even number of equal intervals (i.e., an odd number of areas). However, the final area may be zero.

Simpson's rule is as follows:

$$V_o = \frac{h}{3}(a_0 + 4a_1 + 2a_2 + 4a_3 + \cdots + 2a_{n-2} + 4a_{n-1} + a_n)$$

or in the example at hand,

$$V_o = 10/3\ (1{,}560.32 + 4 \times 1{,}130.24 + 2 \times 812.80 + 4 \times 533.76 + 2 \times 284.8 + 4 \times 144.64 + 2 \times 71.04 + 4 \times 26.24 + 4.48) = 37{,}472 \text{ acre-ft}$$

The thickness of the interval between the top of the structure and the uppermost contour is, at the most, equal to, and generally is much less than, the thickness of the regular contour interval. This volume must be evaluated separately. If the regular contour intervals are small enough, very little error results in assuming the same interval to apply between the top of the structure and the uppermost contour.

In the example at hand, the greatest average thickness that the top segment could have is 5 ft. As the area enclosed by this contour is 4.48 acres, it results in an additional volume of approximately 20 acre-ft in both calculations, giving 37,879 acre-ft by the trapezoidal rule and 37,492 acre-ft by Simpson's rule.

There is a difference of about 387 acre-ft between the two calculations. Since Simpson's rule more closely approximates areas under irregular curves, the true reservoir volume for the example is chosen as that given by Simpson's rule.

It is evident that the smaller the contour level, the more closely the true volume is approximated.

Either method gives a sufficiently accurate measurement of volumes when enough contour intervals are drawn or when the ratio of the areal coverage is large in comparison with structural closure.

Knowing the reservoir volume V_o in acre-ft occupied by oil and the average reservoir porosity ϕ, the reservoir oil in place $N\beta_o$ may readily be calculated, provided that information on the average connate water saturation σ_w is known. The expression for the oil in place $N\beta_o$ includes a reservoir volume factor β_o which multiplies the stock-tank oil volume N in order to take into account the shrinkage of the reservoir oil when depressured to atmospheric conditions. The original stock-tank content N of the reservoir in barrels is expressed by the following volumetric relation:

$$N = 7{,}758 \frac{V_o\phi(1 - \sigma_w)}{\beta_o} \tag{9-4}$$

The volume of the gas cap V_g, if present, may similarly be evaluated by planimetering operations. The available gas-cap gas G in cubic feet at NTP is then readily calculated from

$$G = 43{,}560V_g\phi(\sigma_g)\frac{460 + 60}{460 + T_f}\left(\frac{P_o}{14.4}\frac{1}{Z_o} - \frac{P_a}{14.4}\frac{1}{Z_a}\right) \tag{9-5}$$

where σ_g = gas saturation
Z_o = gas compressibility factor at initial reservoir pressure P_o
Z_a = 1 at atmospheric pressure P_a
T_f = formation temperature, °F

In addition a considerable amount of gas is present in solution in the reservoir oil, which is readily computed by the product $5.61NS_o$, where S_o is the original solution gas in cubic feet per cubic foot of stock-tank oil. However, following depletion, a certain gas saturation remains in the reservoir volume not occupied by oil. This residual gas saturation depends upon the oil-recovery efficiency of the prevailing producing mechanisms.

Another rule for the evaluation of reservoir volume is the *pyramidal rule:* This rule is based upon the consideration that each segment or horizontal slice of the reservoir may be considered as the frustrum of a pyramid or cone, the height of which is h, and the lower and upper surfaces are, respectively, a_1 and a_2; the volume is given by

$$V = \frac{h}{3}(a_1 + \sqrt{a_1a_2} + a_2) \tag{9-6}$$

For a succession of n slices through the structure and separated from one another by equal spacing h, the total volume is

$$V = \frac{h}{3}(a_1 + \sqrt{a_1a_2} + 2a_2 + \sqrt{a_2a_3} + 2a_3 + \cdots + \sqrt{a_{n-1}a_n} + a_n) \tag{9-7}$$

Regardless of the rule used, it is necessary to take into account the small upper volume of the structure. An approximation to this volume is to consider it a pyramid, the base area of which is a_n and the height of which

(h_n) must be evaluated by interpolation. This volume, considered to be a pyramid, is

$$V = \tfrac{1}{3} h_n a_n \tag{9-8}$$

Because of the surface curvature in the upper part of most geologic structure, a closer approximation for the upper volume is obtained by considering it as a spherical segment of base area a_n and height h_n, the volume of which is

$$V = \frac{\pi h_n^3}{6} + \frac{a_n h_n}{2} \tag{9-9}$$

The true volume of the upper structural segment will be found comprised between these two formulas, which may be considered as lower and upper limits, respectively.

EMPIRICAL RESERVE ESTIMATES

As a guide to future production operations of a reservoir at large and in property evaluation, it is often desirable to make recovery estimates in the early life of a field soon after its discovery, even before the limits of the accumulation have been determined by drilling or before there is enough production history for a safe extrapolation into the future by reservoir-engineering forecasting techniques.

Expected recoveries are naturally dependent on the prevailing pressures, on the types of fluids involved, and on the expected type of drive.

If field pressure is above the bubble point, i.e., the reservoir holds undersaturated oil, recovery is made in two parts: first, by expansion of a single phase until bubble-point pressure is reached; second, production by one of the fundamental recovery mechanisms operating singly or in combination: depletion drive, water drive, or segregation drive.

Reserve estimates may also be made on a field-wide basis or on a lease basis. In the latter instance, consideration of structural position and fluid migration in or out of the lease confines must also be allowed for, in addition to allowing for the type of drive.

Calculation of Stock-tank Oil Recoverable by Expansion from Undersaturated Oil. When reservoir pressure is larger than bubble-point pressure by a substantial amount, reservoir-oil volume is reduced, owing to its compressibility as a single-phase fluid. Because of rock and connate water compressibility when field pressure is reduced, additional oil is expulsed as a result of their expansion. Using the acre-foot as the unit of reservoir-rock volume, the recovery (ER) in barrels of stock-tank oil by expansion of reservoir oil when decompressed from field pressure to bubble-point pressure is obtained by

$$\mathrm{ER} = 7{,}758 \frac{\phi}{\beta_b} (P_0 - P_b) \left[(1 - \sigma_w) c_o + \sigma_w c_w + \frac{1 - \phi}{\phi} c_r \right] \tag{9-10}$$

where ϕ = porosity fraction
β_b = reservoir volume factor at the bubble-point pressure
P_0 = original field pressure, psi
P_b = bubble-point pressure, psi
σ_w = connate water saturation, fraction
c_o = compressibility of oil, per psi
c_w = compressibility of water, per psi
c_r = compressibility of rock, per psi

The compressibility of oil, c_o, is normally obtained from bottom-hole sample tests and depends on the type of oil and amount of solution gas. c_w may be taken as 3×10^{-6} per psi. Bulk compressibility of rock c_r varies with the type of rock and its degree of cementation and induration as well as with its porosity and should be determined for a specific reservoir. However, in the absence of such determination, the compressibility figures determined by Carpenter and Spencer (1940) and by Hall (1953) may be used as a guide. These investigators show that the pore-space reduction owing to increased pressure on a rock is proportionately greater for low-porosity rocks, being 10×10^{-6} per psi for 2 per cent porosity and reaching an asymptotic value of 3×10^{-6} per psi for porosity values of 20 to 30 per cent.

In most cases c_w may be taken to be 4×10^{-7} per psi. Formula (9-10) shows that, for rock of very low porosity, a large fraction of the oil recovered by expansion results from rock compressibility.

Depletion-drive Recovery. The unit recovery (DR) in barrels of stock-tank oil by depletion drive may be calculated from

$$\mathrm{DR} = 7{,}758\phi\left(\frac{1-\sigma_w}{\beta_0} - \frac{1-\sigma_w-\sigma_g}{\beta_2}\right) \qquad \text{STO per acre-ft} \qquad (9\text{-}11)$$

where β_0 is the original reservoir volume factor at the bubble point and β_2 is the final reservoir volume factor at abandonment ($\beta_2 \cong 1.03$).

An estimate must be made of the ultimate free gas saturation σ_g. σ_g is to be evaluated by Arps' (1954) correlation of the Craze and Buckley API data (1945), where the average σ_g is shown to be 30 per cent. But adjustments are needed according to prevailing original solution gas S_o and oil viscosity μ_o. σ_g is taken to be 30 per cent for an oil viscosity of 2.2 cps and 400 cu ft per bbl original solution gas.

For each doubling of the solution gas, add 3 per cent to σ_g.

For each doubling of oil viscosity, subtract 3 per cent from σ_g.

Water-drive Recovery. The recovery (WR) on a unit basis is obtained from

$$\mathrm{WR} = 7{,}758\phi\left(\frac{1-\sigma_w}{\beta_0} - \sigma_{or}\right) \qquad \text{STO per acre-ft} \qquad (9\text{-}12)$$

where σ_{or} is the residual stock-tank oil as pore-space fraction by water drive. This residual oil is obtained empirically according to Arps (1954) from the Craze and Buckley API data (1945) as a function of oil viscosity and permeability, as follows:

Correction for viscosity trend for $K = 400$ md

Oil viscosity, $\mu_{o,cps}$	*Residual reservoir oil, $\beta\sigma_{or}$*
0.2	0.30
0.5	0.32
1.0	0.345
2.0	0.37
5.0	0.405
10.0	0.435
20.0	0.465

Correction for permeability trend

Average permeability, md, K_{av}	*Deviation of $\beta\sigma_{or}$ from viscosity trend*
50	0.12
100	0.09
200	0.06
400	0.00
500	−0.02
1,000	−0.01
2,000	−0.045
5,000	−0.085

Segregation-drive Recovery. The recovery (SR) on a unit basis is obtained from

$$\text{SR} = 7{,}758\phi\left(\frac{1 - \sigma_w}{\beta_0} - \sigma_{or}\right) \qquad \text{STO per acre-ft} \qquad (9\text{-}13)$$

where σ_{or} is the residual stock-tank oil as pore-space fraction by segregation drive.

The residual oil at the abandonment pressure is $\beta_a\sigma_{or}$, where β_a is the reservoir-volume factor at abandonment; its value depends on the type of operation conducted, whether with or without gas counterflow, or depending on the gas-injection ratio into the gas cap. However, residual oil is generally so low by this type of operation that a fair estimate is generally arrived at by letting $\beta_a\sigma_{or} = 10$ per cent.

Recovery from Heterogeneous Reservoirs. In a layered reservoir where the physical properties of reservoir rock are widely variable, oil recoveries are affected by the degree of heterogeneity of the reservoir. This is true of all recovery mechanisms but it is of particular importance in water-drive fields and in water flooding operations. At least this is the problem which has received the most attention. Various authors have given considerations to this effect in the displacement of oil by water in a heterogeneous permeability profile.

Stiles (1949) presented a method of predicting recovery from water flooding operations which makes use of permeability variation and vertical distribution of productive capacity. The method permits calculating the produced water cut vs. cumulative oil recovery; therefore, if a preassigned water cut exists as economic limit, it is possible to determine expected recovery to this limit. The basic concept on which the Stiles method is based is that injected or encroaching water sweeps the zones of higher permeability first and that break-through at the producing wells first occurs in the zones of high permeability.

It is concluded that the distance of penetration of a water front in each layer varies according to individual permeability variation, as if such variations were continuous from input to producing well. This concept admittedly is not correct if there is lensing, but the method makes no allowance for this factor.

The basic technique of calculation consists in determining a permeability- and a capacity-distribution curve from the measurements of permeability within short intervals of the reservoir rock. The permeability values are rearranged in order of decreasing permeability regardless of their structural position in the reservoir rock. For the purpose of comparison between wells, it is convenient to express the distribution curves in terms of dimensionless permeability and capacity as well as dimensionless thickness of the formation. To this end a tabulation such as Table 9-1 is made, where the headings have the following meaning:

$$h = \frac{h_i}{\Sigma h_i} = \text{fraction of dimensionless cumulative thickness}$$

$$\Delta C = hk = \text{increment of total fluid-flow capacity}$$

$$C = \text{cumulative flow capacity}$$

The results of Table 9-1 are plotted in Fig. 9-7. Further tabulation is made in Table 9-2 in which a dimensionless permeability is calculated, and its value is similarly plotted in Fig. 9-7.

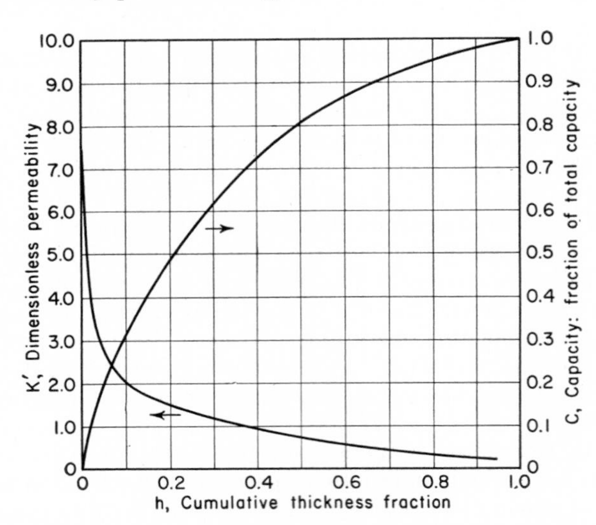

FIG. 9-7. Permeability and capacity distribution. (*After Stiles, courtesy AIME.*)

TABLE 9-1. CALCULATION OF CAPACITY DISTRIBUTION
(*After Stiles, courtesy AIME*)

Cumulative thickness, ft	h = fraction of cumulative thickness	K = permeability, md	ΔC = increment of total capacity	C = cumulative capacity, fraction
1	0.0345	776	0.153	0.153
2	0.0690	454	0.089	0.242
3	0.1034	349	0.069	0.311
4	0.1380	308	0.061	0.372
5	0.1724	295	0.058	0.430
6	0.2070	282	0.056	0.486
7	0.2414	273	0.054	0.540
8	0.2759	262	0.052	0.592
9	0.3103	228	0.045	0.637
10	0.3448	187	0.037	0.674
11	0.3793	178	0.035	0.709
12	0.4138	161	0.032	0.741
13	0.4483	159	0.031	0.772
14	0.4828	148	0.029	0.801
15	0.5172	127	0.025	0.826
16	0.5517	109	0.021	0.847
17	0.5862	88	0.017	0.864
18	0.6207	87	0.017	0.881
19	0.6552	87	0.017	0.898
20	0.6897	77	0.015	0.913
21	0.7241	71	0.014	0.927
22	0.7586	62	0.012	0.939
23	0.7931	58	0.011	0.950
24	0.8276	54	0.011	0.961
25	0.8621	50	0.010	0.971
26	0.8966	47	0.009	0.980
27	0.9310	47	0.009	0.989
28	0.9655	35	0.007	0.996
29	1.000	16	0.004	1.000
		5,075		

TABLE 9-2. CALCULATION OF PERMEABILITY DISTRIBUTION
(*After Stiles, courtesy AIME*)

h = fraction of cumulative thickness	Δh = increment of cumulative thickness	C = cumulative capacity, fraction	ΔC = increment of cumulative capacity	$K' = \frac{\Delta C}{\Delta h}$ dimensionless permeability	h' = average cumulative thickness, fraction
0.01	0.01	0.065 *	0.065	6.50	0.005
0.02	0.01	0.110	0.045	4.50	0.015
0.05	0.03	0.200	0.090	3.00	0.035
0.10	0.05	0.308	0.108	2.16	0.075
0.20	0.10	0.476	0.168	1.68	0.150
0.30	0.10	0.620	0.144	1.44	0.250
0.40	0.10	0.731	0.111	1.11	0.350
0.50	0.10	0.812	0.081	0.81	0.450
0.60	0.10	0.870	0.058	0.58	0.550
0.70	0.10	0.917	0.047	0.47	0.650
0.80	0.10	0.952	0.035	0.35	0.750
0.90	0.10	0.980	0.028	0.28	0.850
0.95	0.05	0.991	0.011	0.22	0.925
1.00	0.05	1.000	0.009	0.18	0.975

* From capacity distribution curve.

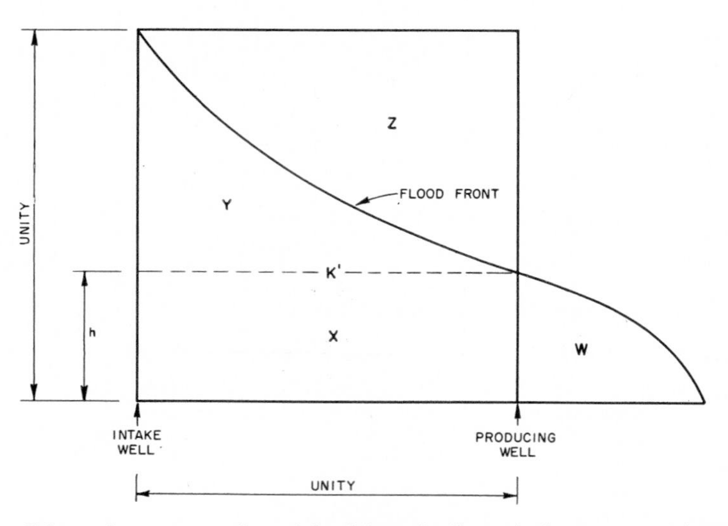

FIG. 9-8. Schematic representation of flood front in dimensionless space. (*After Stiles, courtesy AIME.*)

Let the flood front be advanced a sufficient distance and break through at the producing wells within a certain number of the more permeable layers such that their dimensionless thickness is h and their dimensionless permeability is K'. The linear advance of the flood is presumed proportional to permeability. On the schematic representation of the flood front of Fig. 9-8 in dimensionless space, to a value h corresponds a value K' read at the spacing between wells.

Certain areas W, X, Y, Z are designated in Fig. 9-8. Since the total flow capacity in dimensionless space is unity and is represented by the area under the front, we have

$$X + Y + W = 1$$

Similarly, since the volume to be flooded is unity, we have

$$X + Y + Z = 1$$

Hence

$$W = Z$$

Let the flow capacity corresponding to thickness h be represented by C; we have

$$C = W + X$$

Therefore

$$Y = 1 - (W + X) = 1 - C$$

X and Y represent fractions of the reservoir volume from which oil has been displaced from the total volume $X + Y + Z = 1$. Oil recovery expressed as a fraction of recoverable oil is therefore

$$\text{Recovery} = \frac{X + Y}{X + Y + Z} = \frac{K'h + (1 - C)}{1 \times K'} = h + \frac{1 - C}{K'}$$

For the flood-front position represented in Fig. 9-8, the water cut in the flow stream at the producing well is calculated as follows:

$$\text{Rate of water production} = C \frac{K_w}{\mu_w}$$

$$\text{Rate of oil production} = (1 - C) \frac{K_o}{\beta\mu_o}$$

$$\text{Total rate of fluid production} = C \frac{K_w}{\mu_w} + (1 - C) \frac{K_o}{\beta\mu_o}$$

$$\text{Water cut} = \frac{C \dfrac{K_w}{\mu_w}}{C \dfrac{K_w}{\mu_w} + (1 - C) \dfrac{K_o}{\beta\mu_o}} = \frac{CM}{CM + \dfrac{1 - C}{\beta}}$$

where $M = \dfrac{K_w}{K_o} \dfrac{\mu_o}{\mu_w}$, or mobility ratio

β = reservoir-volume factor of the oil

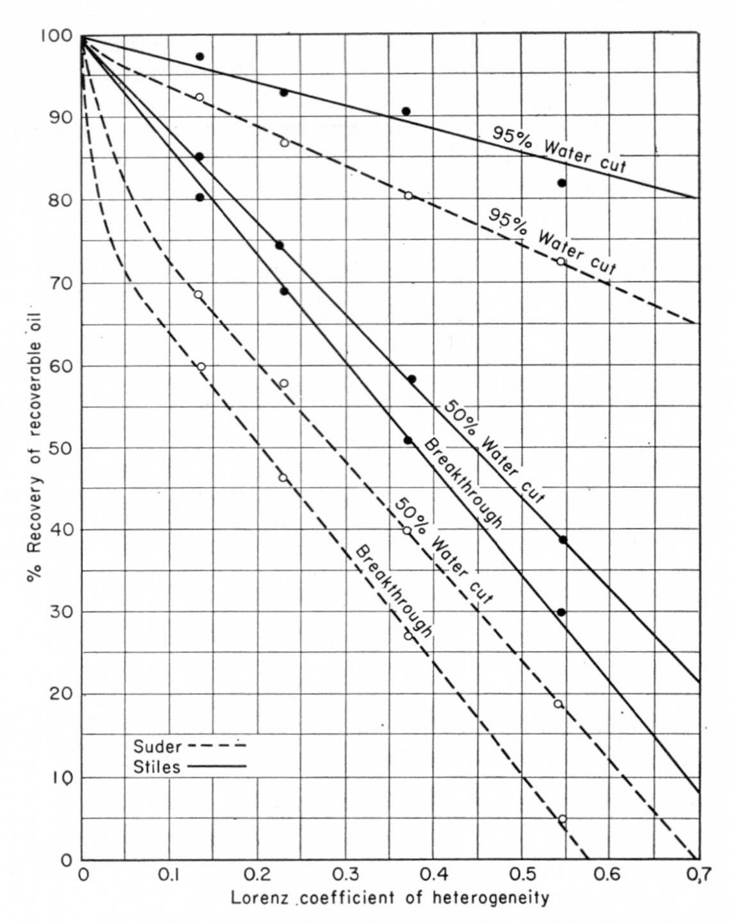

FIG. 9-9. Recovery vs. Lorenz coefficient of heterogeneity. (*After Schmalz and Rahme, courtesy Producers Monthly.*)

Examples of recovery and water-cut calculations are shown in Tables 9-3 and 9-4.

The Stiles method of calculating recovery and water cut should be satisfactory in water-encroachment problems or where no gas phase has developed. In water flooding of depleted fields, the method does not take into account the pressure of a gas phase and fluid fill-up requirements.

Schmalz and Rahme (1950) presented a simplified method of calculating recovery by water flooding in heterogeneous permeability profiles which makes use of the Lorenz coefficients to characterize the permeability distribution within a rock formation (Chap. 2). These writers calculated recoveries at various water cuts in a variety of permeability profiles according to two manners of determining the differential advance of the flood front. One, by the Stiles method, just reviewed, where the flood-front penetration is proportional to permeability and, in essence, presumes the existence of a constant injection rate and variable injection pressures. The other hypothesis is that of Suder which assumes constant injection pressure and variable flow rates.

The Schmalz and Rahme results are shown in Fig. 9-9 from which recovery at a specified water cut may be read directly as a function of the Lorenz coefficient of heterogeneity.

Dykstra and Parsons (1949) proposed another method of predicting recovery from water flooding a heterogeneous permeability profile which

TABLE 9-3. CALCULATION OF RECOVERY
(*After Stiles, courtesy AIME*)

h = fraction of cumulative thickness	K' = dimensionless permeability	C = cumulative capacity, fraction	$K' \cdot h$	$K'h + (1 - C)$	$\frac{[K'h + (1 - C)]}{K'}$ = recovery, fraction of total recovery
0.00	7.50 *	0.000 *	0.000	1.000	0.133
0.01	5.32	0.065	0.053	0.988	0.186
0.02	3.83	0.110	0.076	0.966	0.252
0.05	2.69	0.200	0.135	0.935	0.348
0.10	2.03	0.308	0.203	0.895	0.441
0.20	1.55	0.476	0.310	0.834	0.538
0.30	1.19	0.620	0.357	0.737	0.619
0.40	0.92	0.731	0.368	0.637	0.692
0.50	0.71	0.812	0.355	0.543	0.765
0.60	0.55	0.870	0.330	0.460	0.836
0.70	0.41	0.917	0.287	0.370	0.902
0.80	0.31	0.952	0.248	0.296	0.955
0.90	0.25	0.980	0.225	0.245	0.980
0.95	0.20	0.991	0.190	0.199	0.995
1.00	0.00	1.000	0.000	0.000	1.000

* From permeability and capacity distribution curves.

TABLE 9-4. CALCULATION OF WATER CUT
(*After Stiles, courtesy AIME*)

h = fraction of cumulative thickness	C = cumulative capacity, fraction	$C \cdot A$	$C \cdot A + (1 - C)$	$\frac{C \cdot A}{C \cdot A + (1 - C)}$ = water cut, fraction
0.00	0.000 *	0.000	1.000	
0.01	0.065	0.092	1.027	0.090
0.02	0.110	0.156	1.046	0.149
0.05	0.200	0.284	1.084	0.262
0.10	0.308	0.437	1.129	0.387
0.20	0.476	0.676	1.200	0.563
0.30	0.620	0.880	1.260	0.698
0.40	0.731	1.038	1.307	0.794
0.50	0.812	1.153	1.341	0.860
0.60	0.870	1.235	1.365	0.905
0.70	0.917	1.302	1.385	0.941
0.80	0.852	1.352	1.400	0.966
0.90	0.980	1.392	1.412	0.986
0.95	0.991	1.408	1.417	0.994
1.00	1.000	1.420	1.420	1.000

* From capacity distribution curve.

$$A = \frac{K_{rw}}{K_{ro}} \times \frac{\mu_o}{\mu_w} \times u = \frac{0.20}{0.80} \times \frac{4.34}{0.82} \times 1.073 = 1.42$$

makes use of statistical parameters derived from the probability theory, namely, the permeability variation derived from the profile by a technique explained in Chap. 2. Knowing the variation v and the mobility ratio $M = K_w/K_o\ (\mu_o/\mu_w)$, where K_w/μ_w, the mobility of water, is determined back of the front and K_o/μ_o, the mobility of oil, is determined ahead of the front. These two values, when read on Fig. 9-10 or 9-11, respectively computed for water-oil ratios of 1 and 25, determine a coverage factor or sweep efficiency C which is a measure of the total reservoir volume affected by the flood. C is a recovery factor to be applied to the expected recovery under homogeneous conditions.

Depletion Recovery from Gas-distillate Field. In a gas-distillate field, it is necessary not only to evaluate recovery of gas by methods already discussed, but also to predict the recovery of distillate. The latter depends on the field pressure and on operating conditions.

For the solution of such a problem it is necessary to know the compressibility factor Z of the reservoir fluid mixture as a function of pressure and also the composition of the fluid effluent from the well, generally gpm content (gallons of condensate per thousand cu ft of gas).

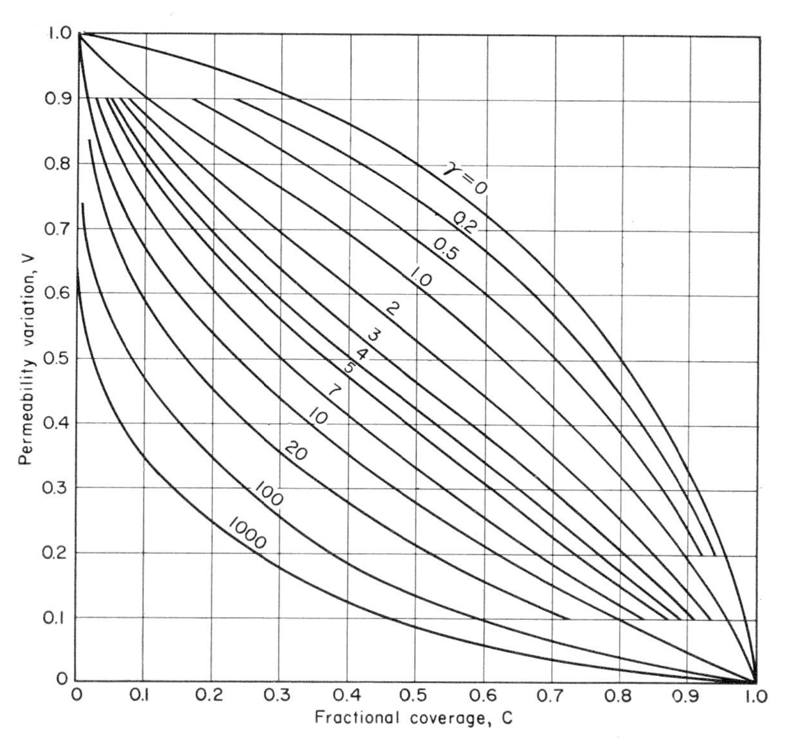

FIG. 9-10. Fractional coverage as a function of permeability variation and mobility ratio for a producing water-oil ratio of 1. (*After Parsons and Dykstra, courtesy API.*)

Recovery calculations are based on the following simple theory. By the gas law we have

$$\frac{P_0}{Z_0} V_g = nRT_f \tag{9-14}$$

where P_0 = original field pressure
Z_0 = original compressibility coefficient
V_g = reservoir pore volume occupied by hydrocarbons in vapor phase
n = moles of gas in place
R = gas constant
T_f = reservoir temperature, $R°$

When a certain production Δn moles has taken place, the field pressure becomes P and the following relation applies:

$$\frac{P}{Z} V_g = (n - \Delta n)RT_f \tag{9-15}$$

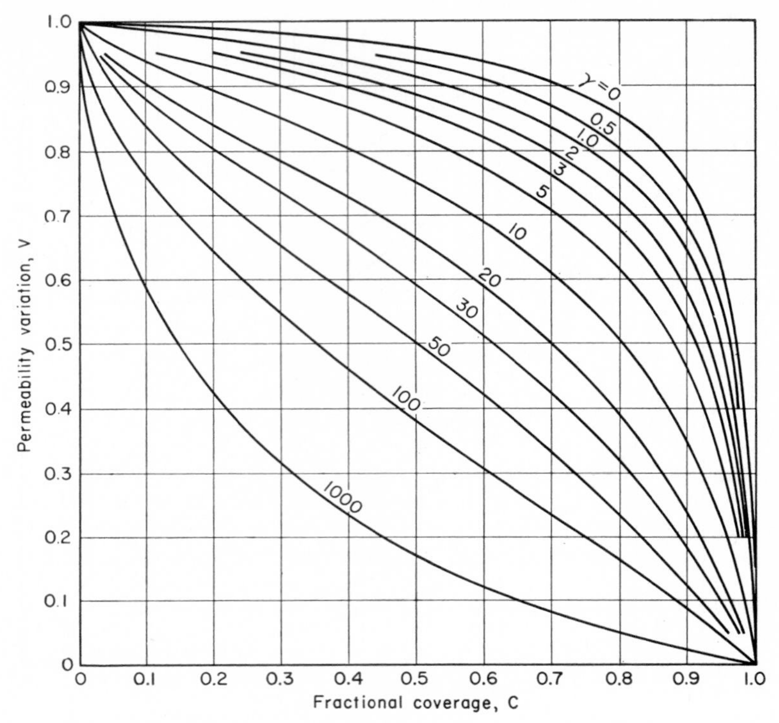

FIG. 9-11. Fractional coverage as a function of permeability variation and mobility ratio for a producing water-oil ratio of 25. (*After Parsons and Dykstra, courtesy API.*)

Subtracting,

$$\frac{P_0}{Z_0} - \frac{P}{Z} = \Delta n \, RT_f \tag{9-16}$$

Dividing Eq. (9-16) by Eq. (9-14),

$$\frac{\Delta n}{n} = 1 - \frac{P/Z}{P_0/Z_0} \tag{9-17}$$

which is the equation of a straight line on coordinate paper when $\Delta n/n$ is plotted vs. P/Z. $\Delta n/n$ is the mole fraction of gas removed from the reservoir. The first task in evaluating gas and distillate reserves is to draw such a graph for the cases at hand.

The next information which is needed is the liquid content of the wet gas at various pressures; generally this includes butanes and pentanes and heavier gases expressed in gpm as a function of pressure. This information is available from bottom-hole sample analysis, recombination separator sample analysis, or from phase behavior computations of the reservoir fluids.

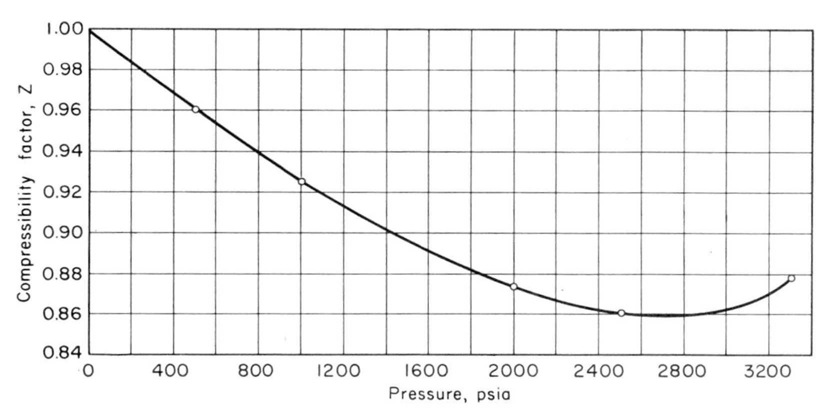

Fig. 9-12. Compressibility of gas vs. pressure.

An example of calculation will illustrate the procedure. In a gas-distillate field, all production is going to a gasoline plant that recovers 100 per cent pentanes and heavier, and 85 per cent butanes. Shrinkage and fuel losses average 8 per cent of intake gas. Original reservoir pressure was 3,100 psia;

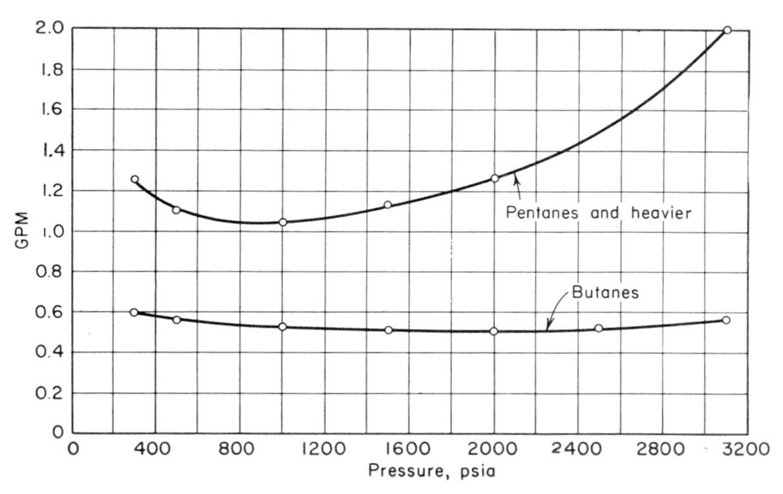

Fig. 9-13. The content in gallons per minute of vapor phase by differential vaporization vs. pressure.

the reservoir temperature was 213°F. Pertinent reservoir fluid properties, as obtained from laboratory analysis of recombined separator samples, are summarized by Figs. 9-12 to 9-14. Other field data are:

Average porosity = 17.0 per cent
Connate water = 30 per cent
Pay thickness = 10 ft

Developed acres = 3,200
Current reservoir pressure = 2,500 psia
Current cumulative production = 8,750,000 Mcf gas sold
479,000 bbl liquid products

Determine ultimate recovery to 500-psia reservoir pressure at abandonment. Equation (9-17) applied to this field is plotted in Fig. 9-15.

The recovered liquefied gases in gpm vs. pressure are calculated from Fig. 9-14 and Fig. 9-15 on an incremental basis by means of the following tabulation:

Reservoir pressure	Wet-gas production		Average liquid content			Gallons cumulative	
	Interval	Cumulative	C_{5+}	$0.85C_{4+}$	Total	Produced	gpm
3,100	...	...	1.90	0.47	2.37		
2,900	5.5	5.5	1.80	0.46	2.26	12.40	2.26
2,700	6.0	11.5	1.65	0.45	2.10	12.60	2.17
2,500	6.0	17.5	1.54	0.45	1.99	11.95	2.11
2,300	6.6	24.1	1.43	0.44	1.87	12.32	2.04
2,100	6.7	30.8	1.34	0.44	1.78	11.91	1.98
1,900	6.7	37.5	1.27	0.43	1.70	11.38	1.94
1,700	6.7	44.2	1.21	0.43	1.64	10.98	1.89
1,500	6.8	51.0	1.15	0.43	1.58	10.74	1.85
1,300	6.6	57.6	1.10	0.43	1.53	10.10	1.82
1,100	6.5	64.1	1.06	0.43	1.49	9.69	1.78
900	6.4	70.5	1.04	0.44	1.48	9.48	1.75
700	6.5	77.0	1.04	0.45	1.49	9.69	1.73
500	6.6	83.6	1.06	0.46	1.52	10.03	1.72
300	6.6	90.2	1.15	0.49	1.64	10.83	1.71

$$\text{Wet-gas production} = \frac{\text{gas sold}}{1 - \text{shrinkage}} = \frac{8{,}750{,}000}{1 - 0.08} = 9{,}520{,}000 \text{ Mcf}$$

From Fig. 9-15, it is observed that 17.5 per cent of gas in place will be produced at 2,500 psia. Hence, for gas in place originally, $n = \dfrac{9{,}520{,}000}{175}$ = 54,400,000 Mcf.

From Fig. 9-15, it may be observed that wet-gas recovery at 500 psia will be 0.836, or 54,400,000 × 0.836 = 45,400,000 Mcf wet gas or 41,800,000 Mcf salable gas.

Plant product recovery = average recovered gpm to 500 psia: 1.72

$$\text{Distillate recovery} = 45{,}400{,}000 \times \frac{1.72}{42} = 1{,}860{,}000 \text{ bbl}$$

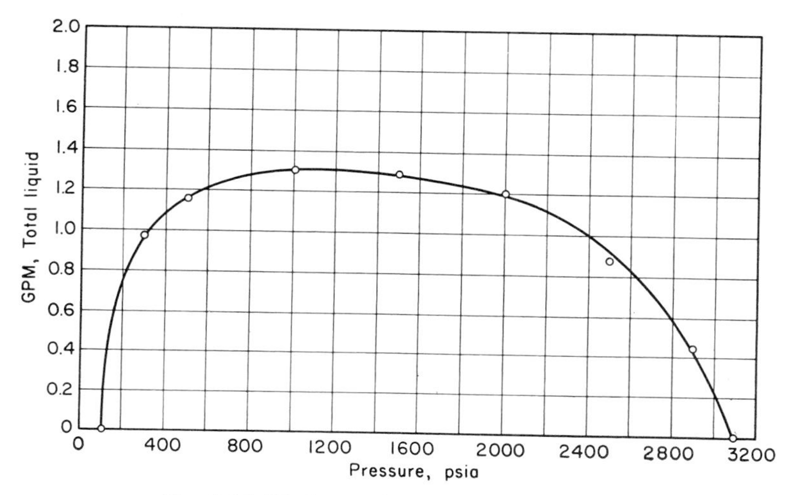

FIG. 9-14. Flash vaporization of composite fluid.

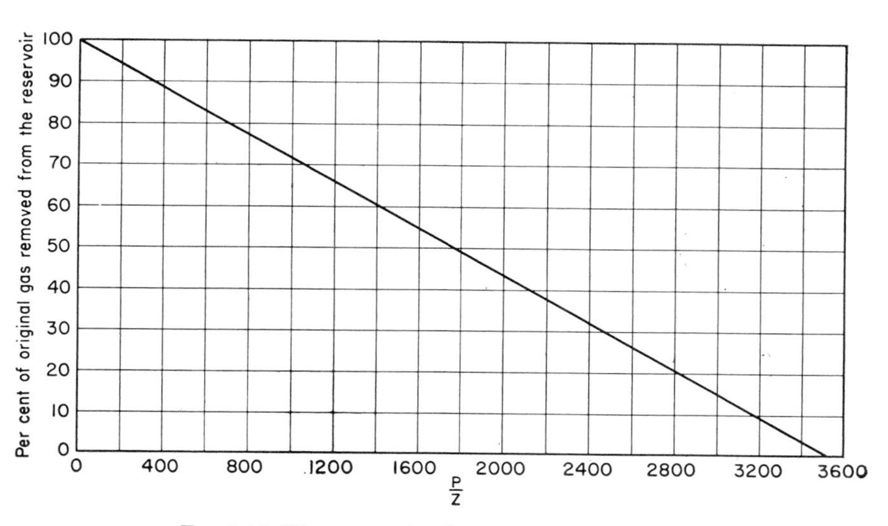

FIG. 9-15. Wet-gas production vs. corrected pressure.

Hydrocarbon pore volume may be calculated from

$$V_g = \frac{nZRT}{379P} = \frac{54{,}400{,}000 \times 1{,}000 \times 0.877 \times 10.73 \times (460 + 213)}{379 \times 3{,}100}$$

$$= 293{,}000{,}000 \text{ cu ft}$$

$$\text{Reservoir acreage} = \frac{\text{pore volume}}{\text{net pay thickness} \times \text{porosity} \times (1 - \sigma w)43{,}560}$$

$$= \frac{293{,}000{,}000}{10 \times 0.17 \times (1 - 0.3)43{,}560} = 5{,}640 \text{ acres}$$

Should the well spacing be one well per square mile, the required number of wells for a complete drilling development is

$$\frac{5{,}640}{640} = 9 \text{ wells}$$

Should there have been only five wells currently drilled from which production was obtained, it may be suspected that an areal extension exists to this field on which four additional wells could be drilled.

SELECTED REFERENCES ON VOLUMETRIC EVALUATION OF OIL-IN-PLACE AND EMPIRICAL ESTIMATES OF RESERVES

1921

Beal, C. H.: Essential Factors in Valuation of Oil Properties, *Trans. AIME*, vol. 65, pp. 245ff.

McLaughlin, R. P.: "Oil Land Development and Valuation," McGraw-Hill Book Company, Inc., New York.

1924

Brown, R. W.: "Valuation of Oil and Gas Lands," McGraw-Hill Book Company, Inc., New York.

Cutler, W. W.: Estimation of Underground Oil Reserves by Oil Well Production Curves, *U.S. Bur. Mines Bull.* 228.

1928

Johnson, R. H., and P. Ruedeman: Appraisal of Oil and Gas Properties, Reprinted from *National Petroleum News.*

1930

Huntington, R. L.: Estimation of Oil and Gas Reserves, *Oil Gas J.*, Oct. 15, pp. 124ff.

Stephenson, E. A.: Valuation of Flood Oil Properties, *AIME Tech. Pub.* 323.

1932

Biddison, P. M.: Estimation of Natural Gas Reserves, "Geology of Natural Gas," American Association of Petroleum Geologists' Symposium, pp. 1035ff.

Stephenson, E. A.: Valuation of Natural Gas Properties, "Geology of Natural Gas," American Association of Petroleum Geologists' Symposium, pp. 1011ff.

1935

Gregory, P. P.: Estimation of Reserves in Prorated Limestone Fields, *Oil Weekly*, Oct. 21, pp. 33ff.

Judson, S. A., et al.: Estimation of Petroleum Reserves in Prorated Fields, *Trans. AIME Petroleum Development and Technol.*, vol. 14, pp. 11ff.

Schilthuis, R. J.: Reservoir Energy and Oil Production Data Used in Estimating Reserves, *Oil Gas J.*, Oct. 17, pp. 34ff.

1936

Albertson, M.: Estimation of Developed Petroleum Reserves, *Trans. AIME*, vol. 118, pp. 13ff.

Katz, D. L.: Method of Estimating Oil and Gas Reserves, *Trans. AIME Petroleum Development and Technol.*, vol. 118, pp. 10ff.

Schilthuis, R. J.: Active Oil and Reservoir Energy, *Trans. AIME Petroleum Development and Technol.*, vol. 118, pp. 33ff.

1937

Ginter, R. L.: Influence of Connate Water on Estimation of Oil Reserves, *Oil Gas J.*, Oct. 7, pp. 97ff.

1940

Carpenter, C. B., and G. B. Spencer: Measurements of Compressibility of Consolidated Oil-bearing Sandstones, *U.S. Bur. Mines Rept. Invest.* 3540.

1941

Dodge, J. F., et al.: Estimation by Volumetric Methods of Recoverable Oil and Gas from Sands, *Bull. Am. Assoc. Petroleum Geol.*, vol. 25, no. 7, pp. 1302ff.

1942

Paine, P.: "Oil Property Valuation," John Wiley & Sons, Inc., New York.

1945

Craze, R. C., and S. E. Buckley: A Factual Analysis of the Effect of Well Spacing on Oil Recovery, *API Drill. and Prod. Practice*, pp. 144ff.

1946

Pirson, S. J.: Mathematical Methods of Decline Curve Extrapolation and Reserve Calculation, *Oil Weekly*, vol. 123, no. 2, pp. 45ff.

1948

Doll, H. G.: The S.P. Log: Theoretical Analysis and Principles of Interpretation, *AIME Tech. Pub.* 2463.

Wharton, J. B., Jr.: Isopachous Maps of Sand Reservoirs, *Bull. Am. Assoc. Petroleum Geol.*, vol. 32, no. 7, pp. 1331ff.

1949

Doll, H. G.: The S.P. Log in Shaly Sands, *AIME Tech. Pub.* 2912.

Stiles, W. E.: Use of Permeability Distribution in Water Flood Calculation, *AIME Tech. Pub.* 2513.

1950

Dykstra, H., and R. L. Parsons: The Prediction of Oil Recovery by Water Flood, "Secondary Recovery of Oil in the United States," 2d ed., pp. 160ff., American Petroleum Institute.

Schmalz, J. P., and H. S. Rahme: The Variation in Water Flood Performance with Variation in Permeability, *Producers Monthly*, July, pp. 9ff.

1952

Archie, G. E.: Classification of Carbonate Reservoir Rocks and Petrophysical Considerations, *Bull. Am. Assoc. Petroleum Geol.*, vol. 36, no. 2, pp. 273ff.

1953

Guthrie, R. K., et al.: Computation of Sand Volumes from Isopach Maps Using Punched Cards Instead of a Planimeter, *Oil Gas J.*, Feb. 2, pp. 65ff.

Hall, H. N.: Compressibility of Reservoir Rocks, *Trans. AIME Petroleum Div.*, vol. 198, pp. 309ff.

Harrison, R. W.: Valuation of Oil and Gas Properties, *Petroleum Engr.*, vol. 25, no. 7, pp. A-41ff.

Terry, L. F., and K. E. Hill: Valuation of Producing Properties for Loan Purposes, *J. Petroleum Technol.*, vol. 5, no. 7, pp. 22–26.

1954

Arps, J. J.: Estimating Oil Reserves, *Trans. AIME*, July, pp. 55ff.

1955

Shearin, H. M., and S. R. Latimer: Advantage of a Coordinated Formation Evaluation Program, *J. Petroleum Technol.*, vol. 7, no. 7, pp. 11ff.

1956

Arps, J. J.: Estimation of Primary Oil Reserves, *J. Petroleum Technol.*, vol. 8, no. 8, pp. 182ff.

CHAPTER 10

OIL PRODUCTION BY DEPLETION DRIVE

Under the influence of pressure reduction brought about by well completion into a reservoir rock, solution gas is liberated, forms bubbles which eventually coalesce, and forms continuous flow channels which permit simultaneous flow of oil and gas to such wells. Oil production is brought about by the volumetric expansion of solution gas and by volumetric expulsion of oil. In the early stages of depletion, the replacement of reservoir oil by the expanding gas is on an equal-volume basis, but as pressure declines and as a larger gas phase develops, more gas expansion is required per unit volume of oil produced because of the free-flow ability of the gas phase. The ability of free gas to flow simultaneously with oil in a reservoir rock greatly limits the efficiency of the recovery process by pressure depletion. In a large measure, the numerical efficiency of the recovery process is controlled by the k_g/k_o characteristics of the reservoir rock and also by the fluid properties at reservoir conditions. Simple depletion-drive production presupposes the nonexistence of water encroachment or of an expanding gas cap.

Reservoir performance predictions require a dependable knowledge of the original stock-tank oil in place. The latter may be determined by volumetric evaluation of the oil in place but should be confirmed for dependable predictions by material-balance calculations.

THE MATERIAL-BALANCE EQUATION

Let us consider Fig. 10-1, where an oil reservoir is schematically represented. Figure 10-1*a* indicates the original conditions of the reservoir with its oil zone and gas cap at the original pressure P_0, whereas Fig. 10-1*b* represents the same reservoir after n units of *stock-tank* oil have been produced and a net water encroachment of W-w units has taken place. The following notations will be used:

Let N = number of units of stock-tank oil (no dissolved gas), cu ft originally present in the reservoir

n = number of units of stock-tank oil, cu ft, produced up to a given time

m = fraction of reservoir oil volume ($N\beta_0$) originally occupied by gas

P_0 = original absolute bubble-point pressure, psia, before any production began

P = absolute bottom-hole pressure, psia, at the time when n units of stock-tank oil have been produced

β_0 = initial reservoir volume of 1 unit of stock-tank oil with its complement of dissolved gas at P_0

β = reservoir volume of 1 unit of stock-tank oil with its complement of dissolved gas at P

α_0 = reservoir volume of 1 unit of gas at standard conditions of temperature (60°F) and pressure (14.7 psia) when subjected to reservoir pressure (P_0) and formation temperature (T_f) Thus

$$\alpha_0 = \frac{14.7}{P_0} \frac{T_f}{520} Z_0$$

where Z_0 = compressibility coefficient of the produced gas under a pressure of P_0

α = reservoir volume of 1 unit of gas at standard conditions of temperature (60°F) and pressure (14.7 psia) when subjected to reservoir pressure (P) and formation temperature (T_f)

Thus

$$\alpha = \frac{14.7}{P} \frac{T_f}{520} Z$$

since it is assumed that the production process is isothermal and that no appreciable temperature change occurs when oil and gas are removed from the reservoir. Z is the compressibility coefficient for the produced gas under a pressure P.

S_0 = solubility of gas in oil on a unit per unit basis (standard cu ft of gas per cu ft of stock-tank oil) at pressure P_0

S = solubility of gas in oil on a unit per unit basis (standard cu ft of gas per cu ft of stock-tank oil) at pressure P

r_n = net average cumulative gas-oil ratio in standard cu ft of gas per unit (cu ft) of stock-tank oil; net gas-oil ratio is the difference between gross or produced gas-oil ratio and injected or recycled gas-oil ratio $r_n = \frac{1}{n} \Sigma \Delta nR$

W = total number of units (cu ft) of water which encroached into the reservoir during production of n units of stock-tank oil

w = total number of units (cu ft) of water produced with n units of stock-tank oil

$W - w$ = net water encroachment into the reservoir

The reservoir fluid properties are generally available in the form of graphs such as those represented by Figs. 10-2 and 10-3.

The material-balance equation expresses the relationship which must exist at all times in an oil and gas reservoir produced under or near equilibrium conditions. Figure 10-1a shows the conditions as they originally existed in the reservoir under pressure P_0 where $N\beta_0$ is the reservoir volume occupied by all the original stock-tank oil containing its complement

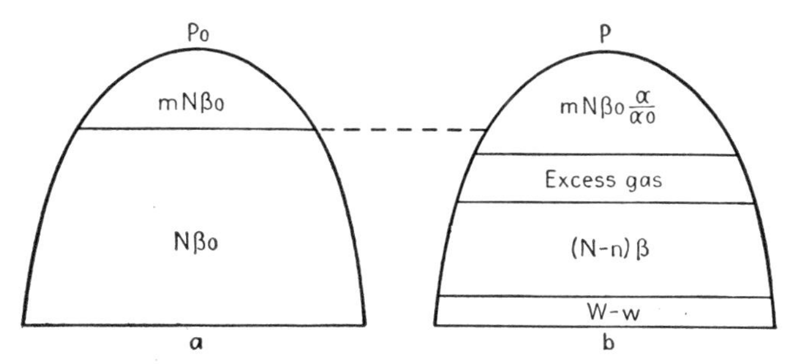

FIG. 10-1. Schematic representation of reservoir conditions (*a*) at original bottom-hole pressure P_0 and (*b*) at pressure P after production of n units of stock-tank oil.

of dissolved gas. $mN\beta_0$ is the reservoir volume occupied by the gas cap under pressure P_0. After n units of stock-tank oil have been produced, the field pressure is reduced to P and the conditions have become those represented by Fig. 10-1*b*, where $W - w$ is the net reservoir volume in-

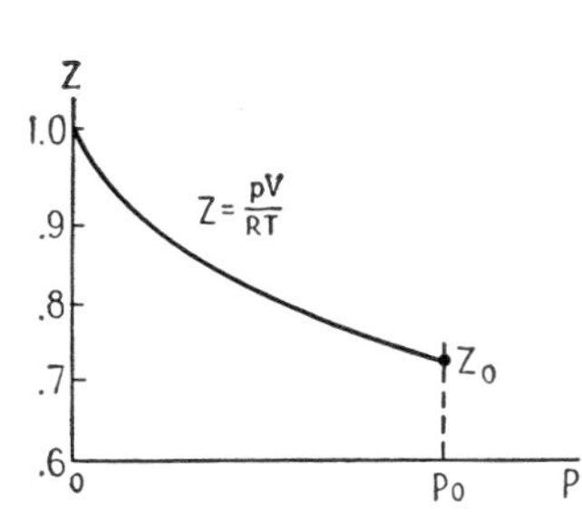

FIG. 10-2. Gas compressibility factor vs. reservoir pressure.

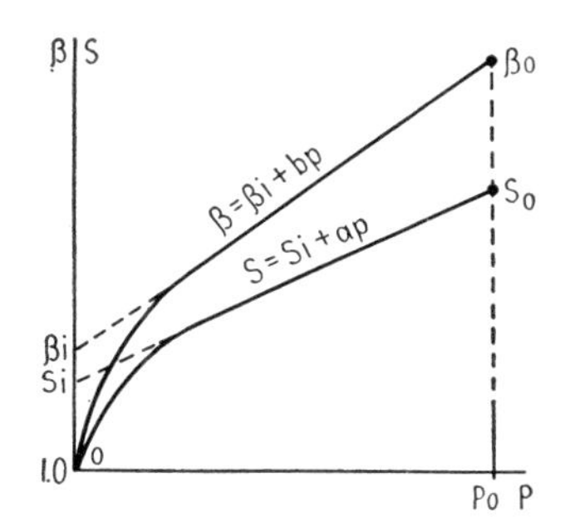

FIG. 10-3. Variations of solution gas S and reservoir volume factor β as a function of reservoir pressure.

vaded by water, $(N - n)\beta$ is the reservoir volume of the remaining stock-tank oil including its complement of dissolved gas under pressure P, and $mN\beta_0 \dfrac{\alpha}{\alpha_0}$ is the new volume of the gas cap obtained by expansion of the gas between pressure P_0 and P under the assumption that no free gas was produced from the gas cap. Such conditions should prevail if modern, accepted production practices are adhered to.

Considering a material balance on gas and that the net space vacated by the oil and gas produced must be exactly filled by gas that came out of solution in excess of the net gas produced, we have the evident relation that the net vacated space is equal to the reservoir space vacated by the reservoir oil produced, $n\beta_0$, plus the volumetric shrinkage of the oil remaining, $(N - n)(\beta_0 - \beta)$, minus the volumetric expansion of the gas cap,

$mN\beta_0\left(\frac{\alpha}{\alpha_0} - 1\right)$, and minus the net water encroachment $(W - w)$. Expressed in mathematical terms, this reads

$$\text{Net vacated space} = n\beta_0 + (N - n)(\beta_0 - \beta) - mN\beta_0\left(\frac{\alpha}{\alpha_0} - 1\right) - (W - w) \quad (10\text{-}1)$$

The volume of gas at standard conditions that came out of solution in excess of the net gas produced is equal to the sum of the gas in solution in the n units of oil produced (nS_0) and of the gas that came out of solution from the oil remaining in the reservoir, $(N - n)(S_0 - S)$, minus the net gas produced (nr_n). When expressed in mathematical form, we obtain

$$\text{Volume of excess liberated gas at standard conditions} = nS_0 + (N - n)(S_0 - S) - nr_n \quad (10\text{-}2)$$

The volume of gas, as given by (10-2), when reduced by the volumetric factor α must be equal to the net vacated space as given by (10-1) if no gas is to remain unaccounted for, giving

$$n\beta_0 + (N - n)(\beta_0 - \beta) - mN\beta_0\left(\frac{\alpha}{\alpha_0} - 1\right) - (W - w) = \alpha[nS_0 + (N - n)(S_0 - S) - nr_n] \quad (10\text{-}3)$$

which, when simplified and solved for N, yields

$$N = \frac{n[\beta + \alpha(r_n - S)] - (W - w)}{m\beta_0\left(\frac{\alpha}{\alpha_0} - 1\right) + \alpha(S_0 - S) - (\beta_0 - \beta)} \quad (10\text{-}4)$$

This equation is equivalent to that originally derived by Schilthuis (1936), though in a somewhat different form. The equivalence may be verified by introducing in Eq. (10-4) the expression $\mathbf{u} = \beta + \alpha(S_0 - S)$ and $\mathbf{u}_0 = \beta_0$. Schilthuis' equation in its original form is then obtained, which reads as follows:

$$N = \frac{n[(\mathbf{u} + \alpha(r_n - S_0)] - (W - w)}{m\mathbf{u}_0\left(\frac{\alpha}{\alpha_0} - 1\right) + (\mathbf{u} - \mathbf{u}_0)} \quad (10\text{-}5)$$

The symbol **u** has a physical significance; it is the flash reservoir volume of a stock-tank oil unit when pressure drops from P_0 to P.

Simultaneously with Schilthuis' work, Katz (1936) proposed a tabulation means for the evaluation of oil in place. Pirson (1944) showed the two methods to be equivalent and pointed out the advantage of using the material balance in equation form, inasmuch as it can be subjected to analytical studies.

A short discussion of the material-balance equation will bring out some of its interesting features.

1. Material-balance methods of estimating original oil in place are derived from a consideration of the reservoir as a whole. However, they can be applied to limited portions of a field, such as a lease or block of leases, under special restrictions; there must not be any movement of fluids across property lines (no regional migration), and the field as a whole must be under internal gas drive. Active water drive and gas-cap expansion drive generally lead to errors when applying the material balance to a limited lease.

2. The material-balance method of estimating oil in place is based on the assumption that the oil and gas fluids perform in the field in a manner similar to the laboratory performance during the testing of bottom-hole samples. However, there is considerable doubt that this is the case under certain sand or reservoir-rock conditions, particularly when reservoir permeability is small. It is probable, under these conditions, that during vaporization because of pressure reduction more gas remains in solution in the oil when in the porous rock formation than for the same oil when in the bottom-hole sampler under the same pressure. In addition there is the strong possibility that more gas remains in solution under high drawdowns and excessive withdrawal rates. This may be termed "vaporization hysteresis." It is believed that under certain conditions, equivalent reservoir-rock vaporization is only attained when the pressure has dropped several hundred psi below the pressure at which the same vaporization was obtained in the laboratory.

3. The practice of "stage separation" of crude oil from the gas has an important bearing on the calculation of reserves. Stage separation is practiced for the purpose of keeping more gas in solution in the produced oil. Therefore, the lease gas does not have the same properties as that on which the solubility-shrinkage tests were performed in the laboratory.

4. Should the field be the object of repressuring or recycling by injection of gas into the gas cap and should the field pressure be increased thereby over the pressure existing at the start of the repressuring operations, it is normal to expect that the injected gas does not go immediately (if ever) in solution in the remaining reservoir oil, owing to the absence of sufficient mixing of the oil and gas phases. Under these conditions one must enter into the equation gas deviation factors for the gas-cap gas which correspond to actual gas-cap pressures, whereas the shrinkage and solubility factors for oil should be those corresponding to the pressure existing at the start of the repressuring program.

5. When gas first starts to come out of solution in the reservoir, it is composed mostly of the more volatile hydrocarbons, e.g., methane and ethane. Hence the compressibility factors which should be used in the reserve computation vary not only with pressure but also with the age of the field.

6. If in a field the water drive is sufficiently active or the rates of oil withdrawal are so adjusted that the bottom-hole pressure does not change

$(P = P_0)$ at any time during the producing life of the field, the following relations are verified:

$$\begin{aligned} r_n &= S_0 = S \\ n\beta_0 &= W - w \\ \beta &= \beta_0 \\ \alpha &= \alpha_0 \\ P &= P_0 \end{aligned}$$

A substitution of these relations into the material equation (10-4) discloses that both the numerator and denominator vanish. Accordingly, the estimation of reserves becomes undetermined, and independent means must be used in order to determine the oil in place, for example, through the application of volumetric methods based on the estimate of the available pore space within the reservoir (Chap. 9).

Rates of oil withdrawal are seldom adjusted so that no pressure drop takes place, but it is important to realize that the more active the water drive is, the closer to vanishing small quantities will be the numerator and denominator of the material-balance equation. Consequently, any slight error made in reading pressures, shrinkage, solubility, etc., will have a disproportionate effect on the final results of reserve and field-performance calculations.

7. Another convenient manner of writing the material-balance equation is obtained by dividing both numerator and denominator of Eq. (10-4) by α and regrouping the terms, yielding

$$N = \frac{n\left(\frac{\beta}{\alpha} - S\right) + \Sigma\, \Delta nR - \frac{1}{\alpha}(W - w)}{m\beta_0\left(\frac{1}{\alpha_0} - \frac{1}{\alpha}\right) + \left(\frac{\beta}{\alpha} - S\right) - \left(\frac{\beta_0}{\alpha} - S_0\right)} \qquad (10\text{-}6)$$

The expression $\Sigma\, \Delta nR$ is the cumulative gas produced. All forms of the material-balance equations are simply a different manner of expressing the following fundamental relation:

Oil originally in place in STO units

$$= \frac{\text{net volumetric reservoir fluid withdrawals}}{\text{volumetric gas expansion of reservoir fluid per unit STO}}$$

8. No reservoir geometry factor is involved in the material-balance equation, for it gives no information about the fluid distribution in the structure or in the pore texture, or about the possibility of fluid migration, whether vertical or horizontal.

9. The material balance, in effect, contains three unknowns, i.e., three quantities which it is difficult to evaluate, namely, the original oil in place N, the original relative size of the gas cap m, and the cumulative water encroachment W.

N to a certain extent may be estimated by pore-volume calculations based on core-analysis results, well logs, and other mapping tools. The uncertainty is large, however, and it is desirable to improve the accuracy of the evaluation of N; this is provided by the material balance, provided that complete statistical production data are available on all produced fluids: oil, water, and gas. m may be evaluated from core analysis and well-log interpretation, but is more readily available from well tests and mud logs which have a finer definition on the level of the oil-gas contact. W must be evaluated from past performance statistics; the techniques used will be discussed in Chap. 12.

10. Engineering uses of the material-balance equation are listed:
    a. To perform depletion-drive calculations
    b. To determine the original oil in place and confirm volumetric estimates
    c. To verify possible extensions to a partially developed oil field where oil in place calculated is much larger than volumetric estimates
    d. To determine the existence of water encroachment and its rate of influx
    e. To verify the existence of a gas cap

11. It is well to stress the assumptions made in the derivation of the material-balance equation which, in effect, are its limitations:
    a. Its derivation presupposes a constant-volume container, closed on all sides, and though there is a pressure decline there is no connate water expansion, no rock expansion, and no geostatic compression. These assumptions do not offer large limitations except when the reservoir pressure is above the bubble-point pressure of the oil. The field is fully developed and there is no extension possible according to geologic information.
    b. It is assumed that pressure equilibrium prevails throughout the reservoir volume and at all times during production history and without existence of supersaturation. This implies that no large pressure differential exists across the field, that laboratory PVT data apply to the reservoir fluids, and that no fluid composition changes take place except that reflected in the PVT data. Such fluid properties are assumed constant even in fields with large structural relief.
    c. Differential vaporization rather than flash prevails in the reservoir especially in the early stages of depletion; in the latter stages, flash vaporization may take effect, but generally it is not a very large factor.
    d. No gas segregation takes place under the influence of gravity and no gas-cap gas is produced; these assumptions are necessary for the purpose of derivation only.
    e. Reliable production statistics are available for the past production history, especially concerning the cumulative production n, the instantaneous gas-oil ratio R, the water production w, and the field pressure P. Since field pressure is seldom constant, it is necessary to compute an average representative value. A volumetrically weighted average pressure based on effective

pay appears to be a satisfactory solution to this problem, provided the properties of the reservoir fluids are those of normal crudes, i.e., where solution gas and reservoir volume factor are essentially linear with pressure. For volatile crudes, i.e., where this relation is no longer linear, another basis for pressure averaging may be needed.

Particular Cases of the Material-balance Equation

Depending on the field conditions prevailing, the material-balance equation may take different simplified forms more appropriate to the situation at hand:

Undersaturated Reservoir. *Reservoir at a pressure above the bubble-point pressure of the reservoir oil.* The original field pressure is still represented by P_0, whereas the bubble-point pressure is represented by P_b. The corresponding reservoir volume factors are β_0 and β_b, respectively.

For any pressure P between the above values and neglecting rock and connate water compressibility, the material-balance equation becomes

$$N\beta_0 = (N - n)\beta + (W - w) \tag{10-7}$$

By definition, oil compressibility is $c_o = -1/\beta \; d\beta/dP$ and $\beta - \beta_0 \cong c_o\beta_0(P_0 - P)$, since c_o is essentially a constant above the bubble-point pressure. By substitution in (10-7), we obtain

$$Nc_o\beta_0(P_0 - P) = n\beta - (W - w) \tag{10-8}$$

When rock and connate water compressibilities are no longer negligible, and this is the general case for undersaturated reservoirs, an effective oil compressibility must be used which is obtained from

$$c_{o\text{effective}} = c_o + c_w \frac{\sigma_w}{1 - \sigma_w} + c_r \frac{1 - \phi}{\phi(1 - \sigma_w)} \tag{10-9}$$

where c_w = water compressibility $\cong 3 \times 10^{-6}$ per psi
c_r = rock compressibility $\cong 3 \times 10^{-7}$ per psi
σ_w = connate water saturation
ϕ = porosity

Rock compressibility is made out of two factors, namely, the compressibility of the minerals and geostatic compressibility owing to the weight of the overburden.

Highly Compressible Fluid (Gas or Distillate Field). In the case of a highly compressible fluid, rock and water compressibility may be safely neglected. Applying the laws of gas compressibility with corrections for deviation from Boyle's law and writing that the container volume remains constant,

$$G_0 \left(\frac{P_a}{P_0}\frac{T_f}{T_a} Z_0\right) = (G_0 - \Delta G)\left(\frac{P_a}{P}\frac{T_f}{T_a} Z\right) + (W - w) \tag{10-10}$$

where G_0 is the original volume of gas in place measured at standard conditions and ΔG is the volume of gas produced.

Using the notation α_o and α for the reservoir volume of one unit of gas,

$$G_0\alpha_o = (G_0 - \Delta G)\alpha + (W - w) \tag{10-11}$$

Solving for ΔG,

$$\Delta G = G_0 \frac{\alpha - \alpha_o}{\alpha} + \frac{W - w}{\alpha} = G_0 \frac{P_0/Z_0 - P/Z}{P_0/Z_0} + \frac{W - w}{\alpha} \tag{10-12}$$

When there is no water encroachment or water produced,

$$G = G_0 \frac{\alpha - \alpha_o}{\alpha} = G_0 \frac{P_0/Z_0 - P/Z}{P_0/Z_0} \tag{10-13}$$

This relation was used in Chap. 9 for evaluation of condensate reserves and leads to a simple graphic construction for the solution of such problems.

Volumetric Reservoir. This is the usual case of simple depletion-drive performance because there exists no water drive, no original gas cap, and none is formed by gravity segregation during production.

The material balance is written immediately:

$$N = \frac{n[\beta + \alpha(r_n - S)]}{\alpha(S_0 - S) - (\beta_0 - \beta)} = \frac{n[\mathbf{u} + \alpha(r_n - S_0)]}{\mathbf{u} - \mathbf{u}_o} \tag{10-14}$$

When a new field is discovered, one of the first tasks of the reservoir engineer is to ascertain whether or not performance follows this simple form of the material balance, i.e., to determine if the reservoir is volumetric. To this end, dependable past-performance statistical data are needed. For each fixed time at which a mean reservoir pressure is available, the oil originally in place N is calculated. If a reasonably constant value is obtained and more particularly if this figure checks with the volumetric evaluation of oil in place, it is concluded that the field will have a volumetric performance; i.e., will produce strictly by *pressure* or *gas* depletion.

If, on the other hand, it is found that the value of N is increasing constantly with time, it is a safe indication of the existence of a water drive. It is then possible also to evaluate the rate at which water influx into the reservoir takes place. Techniques for making such evaluations will be studied in Chap. 12.

However, if there has been an unrecognized gas cap and calculations have been made on this assumption, the values of N obtained at successive times will also be found to increase with time. It is therefore impossible to conclude whether or not an active water drive, a gas cap, or both, are present. The indetermination may only be lifted when cores, well logs, and well tests are conclusive as to the nonpresence of a gas cap.

Another case of interest may be encountered, that is, when reasonably constant values of N are calculated but are substantially larger than pore-volume estimates of the oil in place. This may be considered as proof of the existence of an unrecognized and undrilled field extension whose reservoir oil is in good communication with the developed portion of the field.

THEORY OF DEPLETION-DRIVE CALCULATIONS

Prediction of the expected performance of a volumetric reservoir consists in predetermining *pressure decline* and *gas-oil ratio* vs. cumulative production. A time relationship is also desired and for this purpose it is necessary to ascertain the mean productivity of the wells, i.e., to determine the *productivity index* (PI) decline vs. pressure. A conversion of the field performance to a time basis becomes possible under conditions of unrestricted flow at the wells or under preassigned restricted production under known future proration schedules.

The main part of the problem is the computation of pressure decline and gas-oil ratio vs. cumulative production. This is accomplished by the solution of five simultaneous equations:

Material-balance equation:

$$N = \frac{n[\beta + \alpha(r_n - S)]}{\alpha(S_0 - S) - (\beta_0 - \beta)}$$

Instantaneous gas-oil-ratio equation:

$$R = S + \frac{\beta}{\alpha}\frac{k_g}{k_o}\frac{\mu_o}{\mu_g}$$

Cumulative gas production:

$$G = \Sigma\Delta n\, R = nr_n \tag{10-15}$$

Fluid saturation equation:

$$\sigma_l = \sigma_w + (1 - \sigma_w)\frac{(N - n)\beta}{N\beta_0}$$

PI equation:

$$\text{PI} = (\text{PI})_0 K_o \frac{(\beta\mu_o)_0}{\beta\mu_o}$$

Determination of Appropriate k_g/k_o Characteristics. The first task with which the reservoir engineer is faced when he plans a calculation of future reservoir performance by depletion drive is the selection of the appropriate relative flow abilities of gas and oil as a function of reservoir fluid saturation, i.e., the selection of the appropriate k_g/k_o curve vs. total liquid saturation σ_l.

Techniques for determining such curves from cores have been reviewed in Chap. 2, and the methods evolved from laboratory research are relatively sound. However, because of the sampling problem, it is seldom that laboratory tests and field performance give satisfactory verification.

The present practice is still to determine a k_g/k_o curve from past performance history and to use laboratory data as a guide for its extrapolation toward lower fluid saturation. In fact, it is not uncommon to find tenfold discrepancies between the laboratory and the field k_g/k_o curve, the latter giving high values for the ratio.

Example. From the following past performance history of a field it is desired to establish a valid k_g/k_o curve.

PAST PERFORMANCE HISTORY

Date	P, wtd. av. BHP, psia	β	α	n, cum. oil prod. 10^3 STO bbl	S, cu ft/cu ft	R, wtd. av. inst. GOR, cu ft/bbl	μ_o, cps
6-30-36	2,050	1.262		(Discovery)		535	
	1,690 = BPP	1.265	0.0064		96.25		1.18
3-31-42	1,480	1.238	0.00745	1,785	86.50	825	1.20
3-31-43	1,425	1.232	0.00777	2,150	84.00	920	1.22
3-31-48	1,050	1.186	0.01120	4,400	66.00	1,750	1.31

The following steps are needed:

1. Compute the indicated original oil in place using the material balance at the above dates. Calculations should be made with the bubble-point pressure as the original pressure P_0. Estimate the most probable value of original oil in place in this field.

2. Calculate the stock-tank oil produced when pressure is lowered from 2,050 psia to the bubble-point pressure of 1,690 psia.

3. Calculate a k_g/k_o curve for this field from the production data, and extrapolate to lower liquid saturation. Assume that there is no gas cap, and assume a probable value for the original oil in place. Use a gas viscosity of 0.02 centipoise. Assume an equilibrium gas saturation of 5 per cent in drawing the k_g/k_o curve. For extrapolation, follow the trend indicated by Fig. 2-18.

The results of the calculations are as follows:

1. Original oil in place calculated at the various dates is:

March 31, 1942	N = 52,250,000 bbl STO
March 31, 1943	N = 48,900,000 bbl STO
March 31, 1948	N = 43,000,000 bbl STO

No apparent trend is indicated by the results. An average of the two closest figures, or 50,575,000 bbl STO, may be considered as the probable oil in place. The results of oil-in-place calculations are considered sufficiently constant to indicate the field to be volumetric.

2. Stock-tank oil produced when pressure declines from 2,050 psia to the bubble point is

$$n = 50{,}575{,}000 \times \frac{(1.265 - 1.262)}{1.265} = 120{,}000 \text{ bbl}$$

3. The k_g/k_o values are obtained from the instantaneous gas-oil ratio equation as follows: 0.006037, 0.008255, and 0.035455, respectively, at the

above three dates. The corresponding values of the fluid saturation are obtained by solving the saturation equation, yielding the following values: 0.945, 0.934, and 0.837, respectively. The k_g/k_o curve so obtained is plotted in Fig. 10-4.

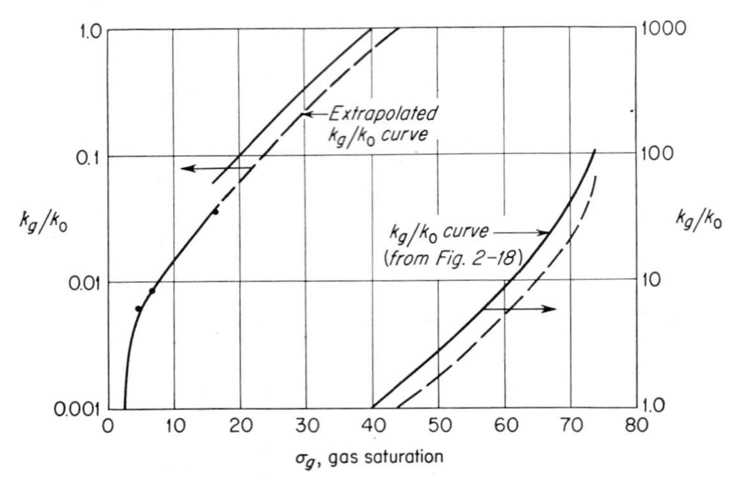

FIG. 10-4. Computed k_g/k_o curve extrapolated to follow the trend of results in Fig. 2-18.

Computation Techniques

The difficulties involved in the problem of forecasting performance of depletion-drive fields have been adequately treated in the literature. The first to propose a solution to this problem is Babson (1944), who suggested a rather laborious trial-and-error procedure in which increments of oil production are first assumed. Several gas-oil ratios are further assumed to correspond to the production increments postulated, and, by means of the material-balance equation and of the instantaneous gas-oil ratio formula, field pressures and average gas-oil ratios are calculated. The answer that corresponds best to the original assumption is taken as the solution for the production increment assumed. The procedure is repeated successively for new production increments until the field pressure reaches atmospheric, at which time the sum of the production increments gives the cumulative oil production expected by solution gas drive. In the main, Babson's method is a roundabout process which requires tedious computations. The main merit of the method consists in having awakened the reservoir engineers to the possibility of predicting future reservoir performance by depletion drive under various assumed reservoir conditions.

Tarner's Method of Depletion-drive Prediction. Almost simultaneously with Babson's work, Tarner (1944) made a contribution to the solution of this problem which is much more direct in its approach. As an illustration of the method of Tarner, the same problem solved by its author in the original paper referred to will be repeated under one slightly different assumption, namely, the existence of an equilibrium saturation for gas

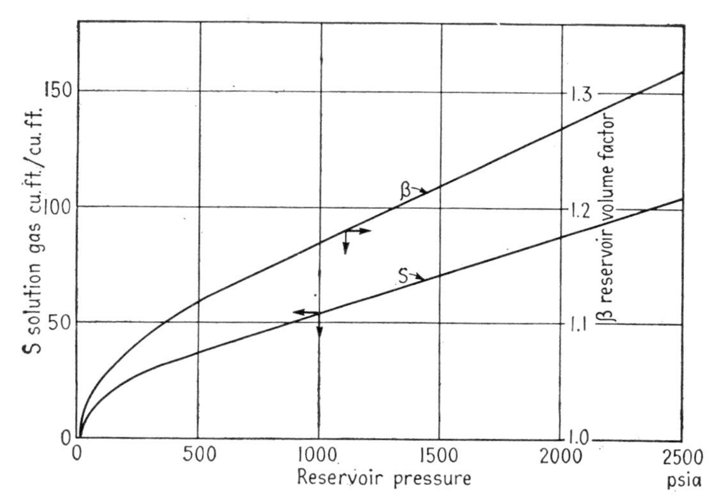

FIG. 10-5a. Reservoir-oil characteristics: gas solubility and reservoir volume factor.

at about 90 per cent oil saturation, whereas Tarner's original example had an equilibrium saturation at about 97 per cent oil.

The fluid characteristics are given in Figs. 10-5a, b, c, d, and the relative-permeability ratio k_g/k_o is given in Fig. 10-6.

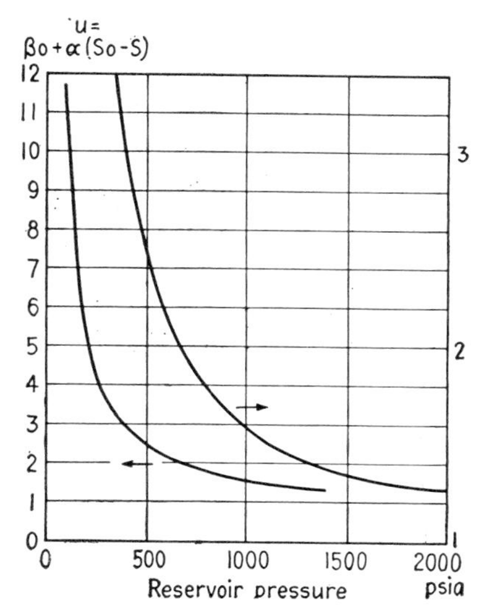

FIG. 10-5b. Reservoir fluid expansion from initial pressure P_0 = 2,000 psia.

The line of reasoning followed by Tarner is essentially as follows: Given the material-balance equation and the instantaneous gas-oil ratio formula, it should be possible to find the field pressure attained for each assumed

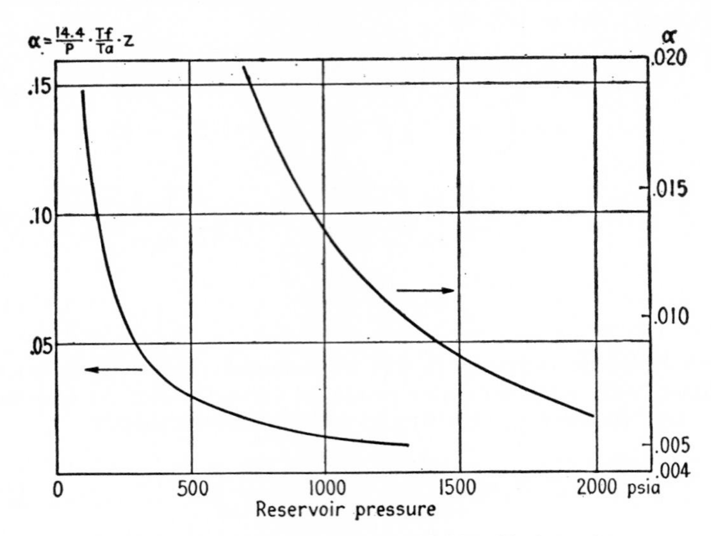

FIG. 10-5c. Reservoir volume of 1 NTP cubic foot of gas.

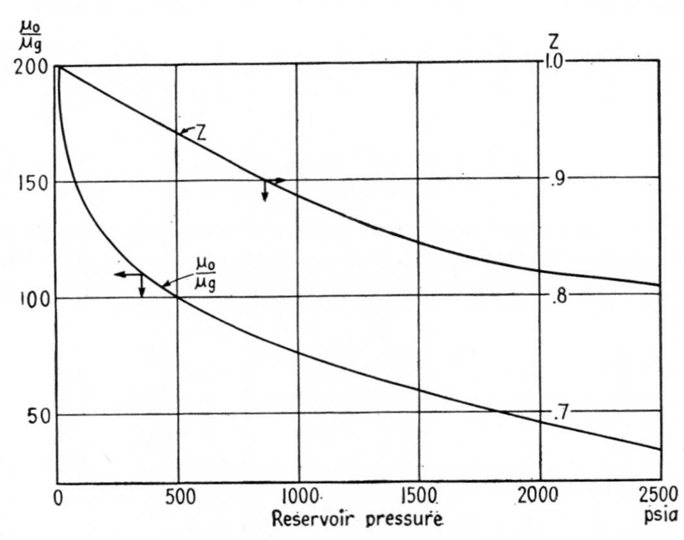

FIG. 10-5d. Reservoir-gas compressibility and viscosity ratio of fluids.

increment of stock-tank oil production. These equations, in the notations used previously, are as follows:

$$N = \frac{n[\beta + \alpha(r_n - S)] - (W - w)}{m\beta_0\left(\dfrac{\alpha}{\alpha_0} - 1\right) + \alpha(S_0 - S) - (\beta_0 - \beta)} \tag{10-16}$$

$$R = S + \beta \frac{k_g}{k_o} \frac{\mu_o}{\mu_g} \frac{P}{P_a} \frac{T_a}{T_f} \frac{1}{Z} = S + \beta \frac{k_g}{k_o} \frac{\mu_o}{\mu_g} \frac{1}{\alpha} \tag{10-17}$$

where

$$\alpha = \frac{P_a}{P} \frac{T_f}{T_a} Z \tag{10-18}$$

For simplification purposes it will be assumed that there is no water encroachment ($W = 0$), no water produced ($w = 0$), and no original gas cap ($m = 0$). Hence Eqs. (10-16) and (10-17) may be written

$$N = \frac{n[\beta + \alpha(r_n - S)]}{\alpha(S_0 - S) - (\beta_0 - \beta)} \tag{10-19}$$

$$R = S + \beta \frac{k_g}{k_o} \frac{\mu_o}{\mu_g} \frac{1}{\alpha} \tag{10-20}$$

For a stated cumulative production n, the cumulative produced gas G may be calculated by each of Eqs. (10-19) and (10-20) as follows:

$$G = nr_n = N\left[(S_0 - S) - \frac{1}{\alpha}(\beta_0 - \beta)\right] - n\left(\frac{\beta}{\alpha} - S\right) \tag{10-21}$$

and

$$G = \int_0^n R\, dn \tag{10-22}$$

However, we are more concerned with the gas-production increment $(G_2 - G_1)$ between two cumulative oil productions, n_2 and n_1. The gas-production increment takes two different forms derived from Eqs. (10-21) and (10-22):

$$G_2 - G_1 = N\left(S_1 - S_2 - \frac{\beta_0 - \beta_2}{\alpha_2} + \frac{\beta_0 - \beta_1}{\alpha_1}\right) - n_2\left(\frac{\beta_2}{\alpha_2} - S_2\right) + n_1\left(\frac{\beta_1}{\alpha_1} - S_1\right) \tag{10-23}$$

$$G_2 - G_1 = \frac{R_1 + R_2}{2}(n_2 - n_1) \tag{10-24}$$

Equation (10-24) is valid, provided that it may be assumed that the variation of G is linear, or nearly so, in the cumulative production interval n_1 to n_2.

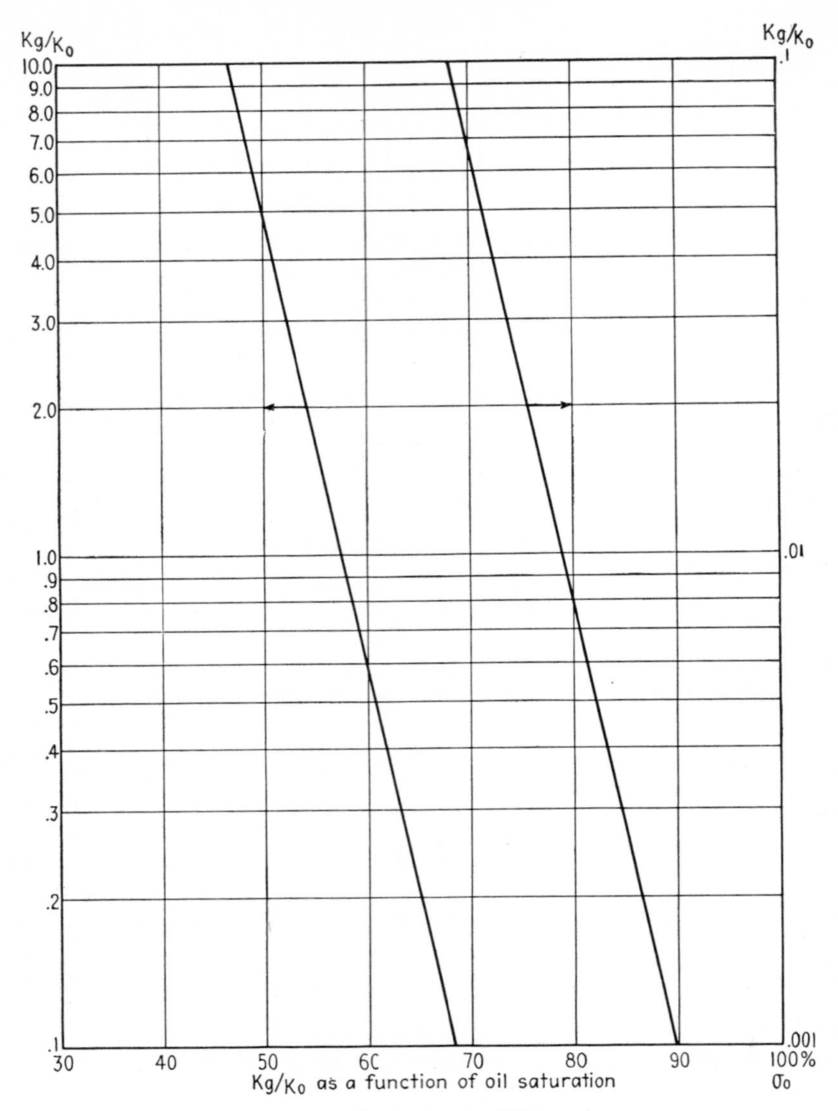

FIG. 10-6. Relative-permeability ratio.

The calculation of the instantaneous gas-oil ratio R requires the knowledge of fluid saturation within the reservoir. These may be established as follows:

Assuming that there exists a connate water saturation σ_w uniformly distributed, the reservoir saturation in oil σ_o reached after a cumulative production n is obtained by

$$\sigma_o = (1 - \sigma_w)\frac{(N - n)\beta}{N\beta_0} \tag{10-25}$$

and the total liquid saturation σ_l is obtained by

$$\sigma_l = \sigma_w + (1 - \sigma_w)\frac{(N - n)\beta}{N\beta_0} \tag{10-26}$$

From a knowledge of the total fluid saturation, one may readily determine the value of k_g/k_o from relative permeability–saturation relationships such as Fig. 10-6. This preassumes a constant shift of the k_g/k_o curve for a constant connate water saturation increment.

The general calculation procedure devised by Tarner for the calculation of the field pressure P_2 and gas-oil ratio R_2, corresponding to an oil-production increment $(n_2 - n_1)$ from initial conditions n_1, P_1, is as follows:

1. Assume that field pressure P_2 prevails.
2. Make three judicious guesses as to the production of stock-tank oil that might result from the assumed field pressure drop: n_2', n_2'', n_2'''.
3. Calculate the total gas produced in these three eventualities by both the material-balance and the instantaneous gas-oil ratio equations [formulas (10-23) and (10-24)]. The calculations by means of Eq. (10-23) are straightforward and give $G_2' - G_1$, $G_2'' - G_1$, and $G_2''' - G_1$, whereas a combination of Eqs. (10-20) and (10-24) is needed to calculate the incremental gas production by means of the gas-oil ratio equation. The new values for the gas increments produced are designated as $(G_2 - G_1)'$, $(G_2 - G_1)''$, and $(G_2 - G_1)'''$. From the six values of the gas production increment, a good solution for the true value may be found by plotting them as shown on Fig. 10-7. This is a graphic method of obtaining the values of n_2 and the true gas increment $G_2 - G_1$ which correspond to the originally assumed pressure P_2.

The process may now be carried out for sufficiently numerous pressure decrements so that the assumptions made at the outset will not be invalidated. Pressure decrement steps should not be so large as to require more than 2 to 3 per cent production of the oil originally in place. A slight peculiarity occurs in these calculations in the early life of the field, namely, before a gas saturation is reached which will exceed the equilibrium saturation; for within this saturation region the relative permeability to gas is zero or nearly so. Yet the method is still applicable with the following remarks.

Let us assume that we start producing a field at its original field pressure P_0 and solution gas S_0, the reservoir rock having an equilibrium saturation of 90 per cent in oil. If a production increment of 3 per cent of the reservoir oil in place is reached when the pressure drops to P_1, there will be no conductivity to gas within the sand, and the producing gas-oil ratio will be equal to the solution gas at that pressure. Yet, the material-balance equation must be verified at all times under the assumed conditions of the problem. Therefore, the production increment n_1 may be calculated

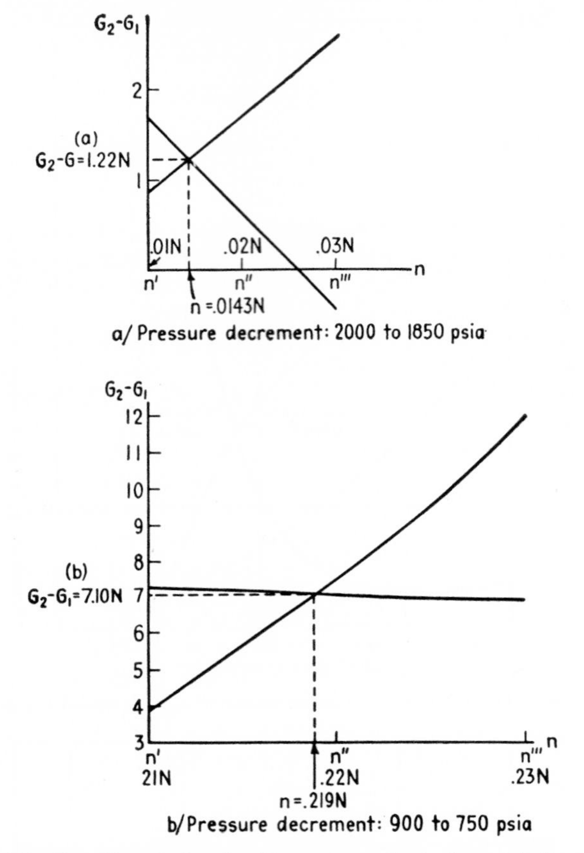

FIG. 10-7*a* and *b*. Graphic solution by Tarner's method of cumulative stock-tank oil and incremental gas produced.

directly from Eq. (10-16). These conditions will prevail until the equilibrium gas saturation is reached, following which point the gas-oil ratio will start to rise. Accordingly, an internal gas-drive field exhibits at first a decreasing gas-oil ratio below original solution gas corresponding to the solution gas at prevailing reservoir pressure until the equilibrium gas saturation is reached.

The performance of the example is represented in Fig. 10-8. It may be noted that the gas-oil ratio reaches a maximum value following which it drops rapidly until complete depletion. The increasing part of the gas-oil ratio curve is the result of greater gas saturation as pressure decreases, whereas the decreasing part results from the reduced solution gas per unit of stock-tank oil at the lower field pressures.

The initial minimum in the gas-oil ratio curves predicted by theory has been observed in but a few instances in actual practice, probably because field production data are seldom properly kept in the early life of the field.

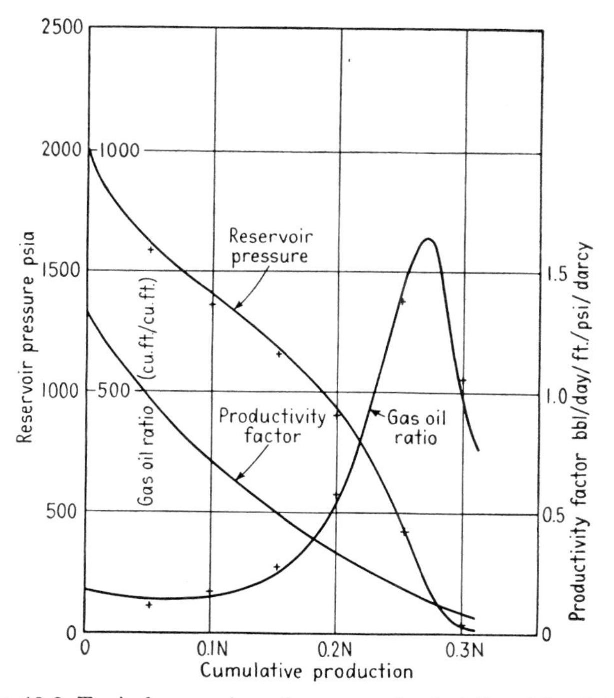

FIG. 10-8. Typical reservoir performance of a depletion-drive field.

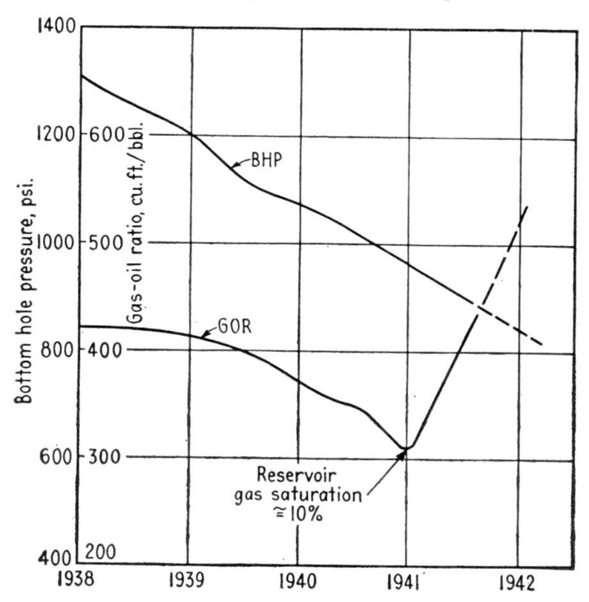

FIG. 10-9. Reservoir performance, Zenith pool, Kansas, in early stage of depletion. (*Pan American Petroleum Corporation.*)

Figure 10-9 gives the early performance history of the Zenith field, Kansas, where the theoretical gas-oil ratio performance was actually observed. The production history is available for the years 1938 to 1942, during which time the produced gas-oil ratio dropped from the solution gas of 420 cu ft per bbl to 305 cu ft per bbl, or by 27.5 per cent. The equilibrium saturation to gas was reached during the early part of 1941, when it was estimated that 10 per cent of the reservoir volume was occupied by gas. In the meantime the bottom-hole pressure dropped from 1,280 psi to 960 psi at the gas-oil-ratio minimum point.

The following example of calculation, according to Tarner's method, assumes an initial reservoir pressure of 2,000 psia. Atmospheric pressure is assumed to be 14.4 psia and surface temperature 60°F. Formation temperature is 140°F.

1. Initial production stage when production results in a pressure decrement from 2,000 psia to 1,850 psia. From Fig. 10-5 we read

At 2,000 *psia:*	*At* 1,850 *psia:*
$S_0 = 88$ cu ft per cu ft	$S = 83$ cu ft per cu ft
$\beta_0 = 1.269$	$\beta = 1.254$
$\alpha_0 = 6.1 \times 10^{-3}$	$\alpha = 6.65 \times 10^{-3}$
$\dfrac{\mu_o}{\mu_g} = 46$	$\dfrac{\mu_o}{\mu_g} = 49$
	$n = 0.0143N$

Differential gas production is obtained by means of material-balance equation (10-21)

$$G_2 - G_1 = 2.74N - 105.5n$$

Assuming three values for n as fraction of N: $0.01N$, $0.02N$, $0.03N$, we calculate the following differential gas productions as a function of N:

$$G_2' - G_1 = 2.74N - 1.06N = 1.68N$$
$$G_2'' - G_1 = 2.74N - 2.11N = 0.63N$$
$$G_2''' - G_1 = 2.74N - 3.17N = -0.43N$$

Now, calculating the total gas production by the gas-oil-ratio formula:

Production assumed, n	Total, liquid saturation, $\sigma_w + (1 - \sigma_w)\dfrac{(N-n)\beta}{N\beta_0}$	k_g/k_o	Gas-oil ratio		Total gas production, $\dfrac{S_0 + R_1}{2}n$
			Instantaneous, $83 + \beta\dfrac{k_g}{k_o}\dfrac{\mu_o}{\mu_g}\dfrac{1}{\alpha}$	Average, $\dfrac{S_0 + R_1}{2}$	
$0.01N$	0.978	0	83	85.5	$0.855N$
$0.02N$	0.969	0	83	85.5	$1.710N$
$0.03N$	0.959	0	83	85.5	$2.565N$

The above results are now plotted as shown on Fig. 10-7a, which indicates that a cumulative oil production $n = 0.0143N$ should result when the field pressure drops from 2,000 to 1,850 psia, the corresponding instantaneous gas-oil ratio being 83 cu ft per cu ft and the cumulative gas production $1.22N$. This example of calculation illustrates how the theory accounts for a gas-oil ratio lower than initial solution gas in the region where k_g/k_o is zero or negligible and until the equilibrium saturation to gas is reached within the reservoir.

2. Calculations between the field pressures 950 and 800 psia will be illustrated also. We have the following characteristics:

At 800 *psia* (P_2)	*At* 950 *psia* (P_1)
$S = 48$	$S = 53$
$\beta = 1.149$	$\beta = 1.164$
$\frac{\mu_o}{\mu_g} = 84$	$\frac{\mu_o}{\mu_g} = 77.5$
$\alpha = 1.7 \times 10^{-2}$	$\alpha = 1.4 \times 10^{-2}$
	$n = 0.197N$

Assuming the following three values for n as a fraction of N: $0.21N$, $0.22N$, and $0.23N$, we obtain from Eq. (10-23)

$$G_2' - G_1 = 11.39N - 4.09N = 7.30N$$
$$G_2'' - G_1 = 11.39N - 4.29N = 7.10N$$
$$G_2''' - G_1 = 11.39N - 4.38N = 7.01N$$

By the gas-oil-ratio formula, we obtain

Stock-tank oil in place, $N - n$	Oil saturation, $\frac{(N-n)\beta}{N\beta_0} x(1-\sigma_w)$	$\frac{k_g}{k_o}$	Gas-oil ratio: Instantaneous, $48 + \frac{k_g}{k_o}\frac{1.149 \times 84}{1.7 \times 10^{-2}}$	Gas-oil ratio: Average, $\frac{R_1 + R_2}{2}$	Production increment, $n_2 - n_1$	Differential gas production, $(n_2 - n_1) \times \frac{R_1 + R_2}{2}$
$0.79N$	0.715	0.051	337	295	$0.013N$	$3.83N$
$0.78N$	0.706	0.063	405	329	$0.023N$	$7.57N$
$0.77N$	0.697	0.076	478	365	$0.033N$	$12.03N$

From the plot on Fig. 10-7b it is seen that the correct solution for the pressure drop between 950 and 800 psia is

$$n_{800} = 0.219N$$
$$(G_2 - G_1)_{800} = 7.1N$$
$$R_{800} = 399 \text{ cu ft per cu ft instantaneous}$$

Table 10-1 summarizes the calculations made for the example at hand, and the field performance is plotted on Fig. 10-8.

TABLE 10-1. SUMMARY OF CALCULATIONS FOR DEPLETION-DRIVE PERFORMANCE

(Tarner's Method)

Assumed pressure, psia	Instantaneous gas-oil ratio, cu ft per cu ft	Differential gas produced, fraction of N	Cumulative stock-tank oil produced, fraction of N
2,000	88	0	0
1,850	83	1.22	0.0143
1,700	78	1.57	0.0336
1,550	73	1.89	0.062
1,400	86.2	2.64	0.095
1,250	99.3	4.37	0.139
1,100	159	3.92	0.168
950	253	5.85	0.197
800	399	7.10	0.219
650	535	7.30	0.234
500	658	8.15	0.247
350	772	9.09	0.260
200	826	10.73	0.273
100	726	8.96	0.284
14.4	385	14.60	0.311

The third element of reservoir performance is the *productivity factor*, which may be defined as stock-tank oil production per unit time (day) per foot of sand per darcy unit of permeability (absolute) per pound pressure drop, when the producing differential pressure between the reservoir and producing wells tends to be very small. Technological field practice makes frequent use of a well-test measurement known as *productivity index*, or PI. This is defined as stock-tank oil production per unit time (day) per pound pressure drop at vanishing pressure differential. The *specific productivity index* is a similar quantity referred to a foot of sand or reservoir rock. Symbolically, the productivity factor may be written

$$\mathrm{PF} = \left(\frac{Q_o}{hK\,\Delta P}\right)_{\Delta P \to 0} \tag{10-27}$$

where Q_o = total stock-tank production at one well
h = producing zone thickness, ft
K = absolute reservoir permeability, darcys
ΔP = producing differential pressure, psi

Considering a producing well of radius r_w draining a reservoir area of radius r_e where the field pressure is P_e, we have the following relation by the radial-flow formula:

$$Q_o = 2\pi r h \frac{K_o}{\beta\mu_o}\frac{dP}{dr} \tag{10-28}$$

which expresses the volumetric stock-tank oil flow in cubic centimeters per second across an area of the sand in the form of a cylinder of circumference $2\pi r$ in centimeters and height h in centimeters. K_o is the effective oil permeability of the sand and μ_o the oil viscosity in centipoises at reservoir conditions. The pressure gradient dP/dr is expressed in atmospheres per centimeter.

By integration of Eq. (10-28) between the well and the radius of the drainage area we obtain after separation of the variables

$$\frac{Q_o}{2\pi h K}\int_{r_w}^{r_e}\frac{dr}{r} = \int_{P_w}^{P_e}\frac{K_o/K}{\beta\mu_o}\,dP$$

or

$$\frac{Q_o}{2\pi h K}\ln\frac{r_e}{r_w} = \int_{P_w}^{P_e}\frac{K_o/K}{\beta\mu_o}\,dP$$

or

$$\frac{Q_o}{hK} = \frac{2\pi}{\ln(r_e/r_w)}\int_{P_w}^{P_e}\frac{K_o/K}{\beta\mu_o}\,dP \tag{10-29}$$

In order to satisfy the definition of the productivity factor in Eq. (10-29), we need only make the differential producing pressure $(P_e - P_w)$ equal to 1 lb and determine the values of β and μ_o at the average pressure, $(P_e + P_w)/2$. Numerically, the productivity factor is obtained from

$$\text{PF} = \frac{Q_o}{hK} = \frac{2\pi}{\ln(r_e/r_w)}\frac{K_o/K}{\beta\mu_o} \tag{10-30}$$

The calculations are best carried out by means of a tabulation as shown in Table 10-2, where the coefficient 1.127 takes care of the reduction to practical units according to the productivity-factor definition.

TABLE 10-2. TABULATION FORM FOR THE CALCULATION OF THE PRODUCTIVITY FACTOR

P, psia	Gas-oil ratio, cu ft per cu ft	n	σ_o, oil saturation	K_o/K	β	μ_o	$\text{PF} = 1.127\frac{2\pi}{\ln\frac{r_e}{r_w}}\frac{K_o/K}{\beta\mu_o}$
1,500	75	$0.075N$	0.89	0.75	1.221	1.109	0.837

The above calculations have been carried out for the example at hand, assuming a well radius $r_w = 3$ in., a drainage radius $r_e = 330$ ft, and an absolute reservoir permeability of 1 darcy.

The transformation constant required to obtain the productivity factor on a barrel per day basis per foot of sand per pound pressure drop is directly calculated from $\frac{30.5 \times 24 \times (60)^2}{5.61 \times (30.5)^3 \times 14.7} = 1.127$. The effective-permeability ratio K_o/K may be read from the curves of Leverett. The PF values obtained for the problem at hand are plotted on Fig. 10-8.

A more involved method of calculating the productivity factor has been proposed by Evinger and Muskat (1942). Starting with Eq. (10-29), it is integrated for three differential pressures $\Delta P = P_e - P_w$ (say of 50, 100, and 150 psi). The values of Q_o/hK are calculated and plotted on graph paper vs. the assumed ΔP. The tangent to the curve at the origin ($\Delta P = 0$) is then drawn, and the value of the tangent's slope gives the productivity factor when read on a pound per square inch unit basis.

The calculations obtained by the above simplified method and that of Evinger and Muskat generally agree sufficiently well for practical purposes so that the more involved method may be dispensed with. In view of the uncertainties encountered in evaluating reservoir permeability in certain fields, predicted productivity factors have seldom agreed with those observed by well testing. The disagreement between theory and practice is particularly serious in the California fields as reported by Johnston and Sherborne (1943), where deviations from actual values may be by factors of 10 to 100. Obviously, there must be something fundamentally inadequate in the assumptions made, and most of the discrepancy can probably be traced to the disagreement between laboratory values for permeability and the actual field values owing to differences in mineralogical behavior of core samples and the reservoir rock in place. Such differences are likely to be most important in reservoir rocks made of highly reactive minerals such as feldspar, mica, and clays [Arkosic Sediments (Chap. 1)], whereas a better correspondence between theory and practice may be expected in clean sands [Quartzose Sediments (Chap. 1)].

Depletion-drive Performance Prediction by Trial-and-error Solution of Schilthuis' Equation. The Schilthuis form of the material-balance equation (10-5) may conveniently be used for a trial-and-error solution of depletion-drive problems. In addition, the method about to be reviewed is highly flexible and lends itself to modifications in the performance calculations which otherwise are not readily introduced either into the Tarner or the Muskat method. This is more particularly the case when gravity segregation occurs simultaneously with the depletion mechanism or when studying the effect of gas injection and cycling under the assumption that only part of the reservoir oil is contacted by the injected gas as may be evidenced by the results of pilot injection programs in advance of full-scale operations. In this last instance the gas-contacting efficiency is represented by a *conformance factor*, such as suggested by Patton (1946), which represents the departure from uniform dissemination of the injected gas throughout the actual reservoir. The conformance factor in a reservoir depends upon various characteristics such as (1) the sweep efficiency of the input–output well network, (2) the permeability profile variations or stratification in clastic-type reservoirs, and (3) the porosity distribution, especially in carbonate reservoirs, among the various types of pore openings: intercrystalline, intergranular fissures, vugs, solution channels, etc. Quantitatively, the conformance factor e is defined as the ratio of the net effective pore space affected by the injected gas to the total net effective pore space of the entire productive reservoir.

For illustration purposes the method will be applied to the example previously solved by Tarner's method. It makes use of the usual equations for the material balance, for the instantaneous gas-oil ratio, and for fluid saturation but expressed in more convenient form for this purpose.

It is assumed that there is no connate water saturation, no gas cap, and no water encroachment. The equations are written as follows:

Schilthuis' equation:

$$N = \frac{n[\mathbf{u} + \alpha(r_n - S_0)]}{\mathbf{u} - \mathbf{u}_0}$$

where r_n = cumulative average gas-oil ratio.

Gas-oil-ratio equation (cu ft per cu ft):

$$R = S + F\left(\frac{k_g}{k_o}\right)$$

where $F = \beta \frac{\mu_o}{\mu_g} \frac{P}{14.4} \frac{T_a}{T_f} \frac{1}{Z} = \frac{\beta}{\alpha} \frac{\mu_o}{\mu_g}$

Reservoir-oil saturation:

$$\sigma_o = \frac{N - n}{N} \frac{\beta}{\beta_0}$$

The values $\mathbf{u}$ and α represent reservoir-fluid characteristics as a function of pressure:

$$\mathbf{u} = \beta + \alpha(S_0 - S)$$

$$\alpha = \frac{14.4}{P} \frac{T_f}{T_a} Z$$

and are given by Fig. 10-5 for the example at hand.

For the purpose of reservoir-performance calculations, it is unnecessary to know the value of the initial stock-tank oil in place (N), and the calculations may be carried out on the basis of $N = 1$ cu ft. Therefore, the cumulative oil production n will be represented by a fraction of 1.

The trial-and-error method consists in making successive judicious assumptions for the increment of oil produced (Δn) for an assumed field pressure decrement such that all three equations above will be simultaneously satisfied. The calculations are best performed by means of a tabulation such as represented in Table 10-3, which gives in succession, by column numbers, the steps to be carried out. The aim of the tabulation and cal-

Table 10-3. Depletion-drive Calculations by Means of Schilthuis' Equation

Pressure P, psia (1)	Cumulative stock-tank oil production, n (fraction of 1) (2)	Reservoir stock-tank oil, $1 - n$ (3)	β (4)	$(1 - n)\beta$ (5)	Oil saturation, $\sigma_o = \frac{(1-n)\beta}{\beta_0}(1 - \sigma_w)$ (6)	Total liquid saturation, $\sigma_l = \sigma_o + \sigma_w$ (7)	$\frac{k_g}{k_o}$ (from graph) (8)	$F = \frac{\beta}{\alpha}\frac{\mu_o}{\mu_g}$ (9)	$F\frac{k_g}{k_o}$ (10)	S, cu ft per cu ft (11)	Instantaneous gas-oil ratio $S + F\frac{k_g}{k_o}$, cu ft per cu ft (12)	Average gas-oil ratio, $\frac{R_i + R_{i-1}}{2}$ (13)
2,000	0	1	1.269							88		
1,850	0.0142	0.9868	1.254	1.238	0.976	0.976	0	9,300	0	83	83	85.5
1,700	0.034	0.966	1.239	1.197	0.943	0.943	0	9,100	0	78	78	80.5
1,550	0.06	0.94	1.224	1.151	0.908	0.908	0	8,820	0	73	73	75.5
1,400	0.093	0.907	1.210	1.098	0.865	0.865	0.002	8,350	16.7	68	84.7	78.8
1,250	0.13	0.87	1.194	1.04	0.819	0.819	0.0054	7,750	41.8	63	104.8	94.7
1,100	0.166	0.834	1.180	0.984	0.776	0.776	0.0138	7,120	98.3	58	156.3	130.5
950	0.196	0.804	1.164	0.937	0.738	0.738	0.0305	6,420	195.7	53	248.7	202.5
800	0.218	0.782	1.149	0.898	0.708	0.708	0.060	5,920	355	48	403	326
650	0.233	0.767	1.134	0.870	0.686	0.686	0.1	4,860	486	43	529	466
500	0.247	0.753	1.119	0.841	0.663	0.663	0.155	3,950	612	38	650	589
350	0.260	0.74	1.100	0.814	0.641	0.641	0.25	2,980	745	32	777	713
200	0.2735	0.7265	1.075	0.780	0.615	0.615	0.44	1,800	792	24	816	796
100	0.286	0.714	1.052	0.751	0.592	0.592	0.70	960	672	16	688	752
14.4	0.311	0.689	1	0.689	0.543	0.543	2.0	192.5	385	0	385	536

Table 10-3. Depletion-drive Calculations by Means of Schilthuis' Equation (*Continued*)

Oil-production increment, $\Delta^i_{i-1}n$ (14)	Gas-production increment, $\Delta^i_{i-1}G = R\,\Delta n$ (15)	Cumulative gas production, $G = \sum_0^i \Delta G$ (16)	Cumulative average gas-oil ratio, $r_n = \frac{G}{n}$ (17)	$r_n - S_0$ (18)	$\alpha \times 10^3$ (from graph) (19)	$(r_n - S_0)\alpha$ (20)	$\mathbf{u}$ (from graph) (21)	$\mathbf{u} + (r_n - S_0)\alpha$ (22)	$n[\mathbf{u} + (r_n - S_0)\alpha]$ (23)	$\mathbf{u} - \mathbf{u}_0$ (24)	$\frac{n[\mathbf{u} + (r_n - S_0)\alpha]}{\mathbf{u} - \mathbf{u}_0}$ (25)
							1.269				
0.0142	1.21	1.21	85.5	−2.5	6.65	−0.0167	1.287	1.270	0.01802	0.018	1.001
0.0198	1.59	2.81	82.6	−5.4	7.30	−0.039	1.312	1.273	0.0433	0.043	1.007
0.026	1.962	4.77	79.6	−8.4	8.15	−0.069	1.346	1.277	0.0766	0.077	0.994
0.033	2.60	7.37	79.3	−8.7	9.10	−0.079	1.392	1.313	1.222	0.123	0.994
0.037	3.51	10.88	83.8	−4.2	10.3	−0.043	1.452	1.409	1.83	1.83	1.000
0.036	4.71	15.59	93.9	5.9	11.9	0.070	1.534	1.604	0.266	0.265	1.003
0.030	6.08	21.67	110.7	22.7	14.0	0.318	1.654	1.972	0.3865	0.385	1.003
0.022	7.17	28.84	133	45	17.0	0.765	1.829	2.594	0.565	0.560	1.009
0.015	6.98	35.82	154	66	21.0	1.387	2.079	3.466	0.807	0.810	0.997
0.014	8.25	44.07	179	91	28.0	2.55	2.520	5.07	1.252	1.251	1.001
0.013	9.27	53.34	205	117	41.0	4.795	3.395	8.19	2.13	2.126	1.002
0.0135	10.75	64.09	234	146	73.0	10.65	5.745	16.40	4.48	4.476	1.002
0.0125	9.40	73.49	257	169	148.0	25.20	11.702	36.90	10.53	10.433	1.009
0.025	13.40	86.89	280	192	1038.0	199.2	92.4	291.6	90.8	91.1	0.997

culations is to arrive at a material balance, or to arrive at figures in column 25 which are as close to 1.0 as possible. In view of the sensitivity of the material-balance equation to small errors, it is necessary to satisfy it with a precision of ±0.5 per cent or better. Accordingly calculations should preferably be made by means of a mechanical calculator, although careful slide-rule calculations may be sufficiently accurate.

The instantaneous gas-oil ratio is obtained from column 12 on a cubic feet per cubic foot basis. In order to obtain the results on a cubic feet per barrel basis, it is necessary to multiply the figures by 5.61.

As a matter of interest the results of the present calculations are compared with those obtained by Tarner's method and are plotted in Fig. 10-8 by means of crosses.

Modification when a constant percentage (I) of the produced gas is injected back into the reservoir and is uniformly dispersed throughout the reservoir fluids. In this eventuality the calculations are carried out as usual but with the insertion of the following columns between columns 15 and 17:

15*a*	15*b*	16
Fraction of produced gas injected, $\Delta G\, I$	Net gas production increment, $\Delta G(1 - I)$	Net cumulative gas production, $G = \Sigma\, \Delta G(1 - I)$

Modification for the presence of a gas cap. In this case it is necessary to know the original volume of said gas cap and the ratio (m) of this volume to that of the original oil in place. The term $m\beta_o(\alpha/\alpha_0 - 1)$ is then added to the denominator in column 25.

Modification for gas-cap injection of a fraction of the produced gas without dispersion into the oil zone. In this eventuality the injected gas is not dispersed throughout the liquid phases and only provides for a more rapid expansion of the gas cap in the ratio of the reservoir volume of the injected gas to the volume of the original gas cap.

The term

$$m\beta_o\left(\frac{\alpha}{\alpha_0} - 1\right) + \alpha \sum_0^i \Delta G\, I$$

is then added to the denominator in column 25. I is the fraction of the produced gas injected, but because of the fact that it is not in equilibrium with reservoir oil, columns 15*a* and 15*b* are not used.

Modification for water encroachment W and water production w. In this case it is necessary to evaluate the rate of water encroachment by methods to be studied in Chap. 12. When this rate is known, it is necessary to introduce the value of the net water encroachment ($W - w$) in columns 23 and 25.

Modification for sweep efficiency and conformance factor in gas-injection projects. If the conformance factor (e) has been established for the reservoir under study, the needed modifications are introduced by considering that the total production from the reservoir oil is divided into two sections, one said to be *conformable* and the other *noncomformable.*

Production from the nonconformable oil section ($1 - e$) is assumed to take place according to the normal depletion process without gas injection. Accordingly, the first step is to carry out a calculation of this nature down to the abandonment pressure.

At each pressure decrement, a gas-production increment of $R_n \Delta n$ $(1 - e)$ is entered in column 15, where R_n stands for the normal gas-oil ratio. It is now assumed that the conformable oil fraction needs only to satisfy the gas-oil-ratio equation, and accordingly in the second step a new gas-production increment ($R_e \Delta n$) is calculated to correspond to the oil increment produced from the conformable oil section $(1 - n)e$. R_e stands for the gas-oil ratio in the conformable section. The two gas-production increments are added in column 15. Columns 15a, 15b, and 16 must now be used taking into account the injected gas fraction I. The rest of the columns are now filled in as usual, and a material-balance equation based on all the oil in the reservoir must exist to a sufficient approximation. Otherwise, a new production increment is assumed and the process is repeated until a balance is attained.

Modification for heterogeneous permeability system in a reservoir. In certain reservoirs, particularly carbonate reservoirs, where an extensive channel or fracture system is the main fluid-conductive medium to the wells, whereas the bulk of the oil is contained in intergranular spaces, two fluid-conductive systems prevail, each with its characteristic relative-permeability ratio (k_g/k_o). If this behavior is known from core laboratory determinations, the future performance of the reservoir may be calculated.

An additional complication may take place owing to gravitational effects, which tend to force oil toward the lower part of the reservoir, especially when the horizontal driving pressure gradients are less than the differential gravity pull on the oil and gas phases.

To calculate this type of performance, it is necessary to know the relative pore volume between the intergranular and fissured reservoirs.

The first step is to calculate a normal depletion performance for the intergranular reservoir, using the appropriate k_g/k_o curve.

The second step is to apply trial-and-error material-balance calculation to the fissures system under the assumption that the oil and gas produced from the intergranular pore spaces are now present within the fissure system. A different and appropriate k_g/k_o curve must be used in this instance.

As one may foresee, performance and recoveries from a heterogeneous reservoir will depend on the relative shape of the k_g/k_o curve and the relative volume of the two porous systems. A technique for calculating depletion-drive performance in such complex porosity systems has been proposed by Pirson (1953).

Muskat's Derivation of Depletion-drive Prediction. Muskat's treatment (1945) for the derivation of the depletion history for internal gas-drive reservoirs makes use of the material-balance equation expressed in differential form, as applied to elementary volumes of the reservoir between which pressure gradients are assumed negligible. Therefore, the reservoir is considered as a homogeneous medium with uniform field pressure throughout, "as if the reservoir were equivalent to a tank provided with continuously distributed outlets for fluid withdrawal" and without fluid interchange between the neighboring differential elements. Each volume element of the reservoir is treated independently and is required to satisfy conservation requirements of the oil and gas contents as well as the constancy of the reservoir volume. In practice, the reservoir is produced at a limited number of wells rather than at closely spaced and uniformly distributed outlets. The effect that well-spacing distances may have on recovery will be discussed later.

The present derivation will be consistent with notations previously used and will follow Muskat's treatment.

In the present derivation no gas injection is assumed to take place. Let us express the fluid content of the reservoir per unit volume of pore space. We have

$$\text{Stock-tank oil content} = \frac{\sigma_o}{\beta}$$

$$\text{Gas content measured at standard conditions} = \frac{S\sigma_o}{\beta} + (1 - \sigma_o - \sigma_w)\frac{1}{\alpha}$$

where σ_o and σ_w are, respectively, the reservoir oil and water saturations. The stock-tank-oil content of a unit of pore-space volume is obtained by dividing the oil saturation σ_o by the reservoir volume factor β. The gas content of a similar volume is composed of the gas in solution in the oil $S(\sigma_o/\beta)$ and the free gas expanded to standard conditions $(1 - \sigma_o - \sigma_w)$ $1/\alpha$.

The oil- and gas-production increments Q_o and Q_g out of the unit reservoir volume may be expressed as differentials of the fluid contents.

$$Q_o = d\frac{\sigma_o}{\beta}$$
$$Q_g = d\left[\frac{S\sigma_o}{\beta} + (1 - \sigma_o - \sigma_w)\frac{1}{\alpha}\right] \tag{10-31}$$

which actually are the expressions of the material-balance equation in differential form.

The instantaneous gas-oil ratio R may be derived immediately from Eqs. (10-31) as follows:

$$R = \frac{Q_g}{Q_o} \tag{10-32}$$

which may also be expressed by the gas-oil-ratio equation derived in Chap. 8:

$$R = S + \beta \frac{k_g}{k_o} \frac{\mu_o}{\mu_g} \frac{P}{P_a} \frac{T_a}{T} \frac{1}{Z} = S + \beta \frac{k_g}{k_o} \frac{\mu_o}{\mu_g} \frac{1}{\alpha} \tag{10-33}$$

Equation (10-32) postulates the desaturation of the elementary volume in gas and oil to be in a ratio which satisfies the gas-oil-ratio equation for the prevailing fluid saturations. In addition to this requirement the material balance in the elementary volume should be verified.

After equating relations (10-32) and (10-33), we obtain

$$\frac{Q_g}{Q_o} = S + \beta \frac{k_g}{k_o} \frac{\mu_o}{\mu_g} \frac{1}{\alpha} \tag{10-34}$$

In the differential expression for Q_g, Eq. (10-31), one may assume σ_w to remain constant which means that we deal with a two-fluid flow system and that no connate water is produced. Therefore

$$\begin{aligned} Q_o &= \frac{1}{\beta} d\sigma_o - \sigma_o \frac{d\beta}{\beta^2} \\ Q_g &= \frac{S\, d\sigma_o}{\beta} + \frac{\sigma_o\, dS}{\beta} - \sigma_o S \frac{d\beta}{\beta^2} + (1 - \sigma_o - \sigma_w) d\left(\frac{1}{\alpha}\right) - \frac{d\sigma_o}{\alpha} \end{aligned} \tag{10-35}$$

and Eq. (10-34) becomes

$$\frac{\dfrac{S\, d\sigma_o}{\beta} + \dfrac{\sigma_o\, dS}{\beta} - \sigma_o S \dfrac{d\beta}{\beta^2} + (1 - \sigma_o - \sigma_w) d\left(\dfrac{1}{\alpha}\right) - \dfrac{d\sigma_o}{\alpha}}{\dfrac{d\sigma_o}{\beta} - \sigma_o \dfrac{d\beta}{\beta^2}} = S + \beta \frac{k_g}{k_o} \frac{\mu_o}{\mu_g} \frac{1}{\alpha} \tag{10-36}$$

During the production process there is only one independent variable, namely, pressure. Therefore, the differentials of Eq. (10-36) may be expressed in terms of pressure variations. This permits formulating the reservoir desaturation process $d\sigma_o/dp$, which is also the volumetric withdrawal of reservoir oil per unit reservoir volume of pore space and per unit pressure decrement. Solving Eq. (10-36) for $d\sigma_o/dp$, we obtain

$$\frac{d\sigma_o}{dp} = \frac{\dfrac{\alpha\sigma_o}{\beta} \dfrac{dS}{dp} + \dfrac{\sigma_o}{\beta} \dfrac{\mu_o}{\mu_g} \dfrac{k_g}{k_o} \dfrac{d\beta}{dp} + \alpha(1 - \sigma_o - \sigma_w) \dfrac{d}{dp}\left(\dfrac{1}{\alpha}\right)}{1 + \dfrac{\mu_o}{\mu_g} \dfrac{k_g}{k_o}} \tag{10-37}$$

Equation (10-37) is Muskat's differential equation for the production history of depletion gas drive, but expressed in somewhat different notations.

The integration of this equation as a function of pressure p gives the value of σ_o, the reservoir saturation in oil containing its solution gas. Hence between the initial pressure P_0 and the reservoir pressure p, the produced reservoir oil on a pore-space basis is $1 - \sigma_w - \sigma_o$, whereas the produced stock-tank oil on a pore-space basis is obtained from

$$\frac{1 - \sigma_w}{\beta_0} - \frac{\sigma_o}{\beta}$$

and as a fraction of original stock-tank oil in place by

$$\frac{\Sigma \Delta n}{N} = 1 - \frac{\sigma_o}{1 - \sigma_w} \frac{\beta_0}{\beta}$$

Once the reservoir oil saturation σ_o at any pressure is known, the instantaneous gas-oil ratio R may be calculated by means of Eq. (10-33).

In order to predict the desaturation process vs. pressure decline and inasmuch as Eq. (10-37) is not an analytic expression, the integration must be carried out numerically or step by step under the assumption of finite pressure decrements Δp. The corresponding oil-saturation decrements are calculated by inserting in the numerator and denominator of Eq. (10-37) the proper values for each of the quantities, most of which are functions of pressure. The derivatives with respect to pressure of the solution gas dS/dp, of reservoir volume factor $d\beta/dp$ and $d/dp(1/\alpha)$ must also be computed by graphic methods. Other quantities entering Eq. (10-37) are functions of the reservoir oil saturation, such as k_g/k_o and $1 - \sigma_o - \sigma_w$. Their determination requires a knowledge of the average oil saturation at each pressure decrement, which obviously may be obtained only by trial and error. If the pressure decrements assumed are small, the error which results from the assumption of an oil saturation equal to that existing at the start of the pressure decrement will be small. However, it is well to bear in mind that such an error exists.

In practice, the numerical integration of Eq. (10-37) is best carried out by combining a certain number of terms which are functions of pressure only into single functions. The notations of Muskat will be used in this instance:

$$\lambda(p) = \frac{\alpha}{\beta} \frac{dS}{dp} \tag{10-38}$$

$$\epsilon(p) = \alpha \frac{d}{dp} \left(\frac{1}{\alpha}\right) \tag{10-39}$$

$$\eta(p) = \frac{1}{\beta} \frac{\mu_o}{\mu_g} \frac{d\beta}{dp} \tag{10-40}$$

$$\omega(\sigma_o,p) = 1 + \frac{\mu_o}{\mu_g} \frac{k_g}{k_o}$$

The differential equation may then be written, on an incremental basis, as follows:

$$\Delta\sigma_o = \Delta p \left[\frac{\sigma_o \lambda(p) + \sigma_o \dfrac{k_g}{k_o} \eta(p) + (1 - \sigma_o - \sigma_w)\epsilon(p)}{\omega(\sigma_o p)} \right] \tag{10-41}$$

The method of Muskat is advantageous when a large number of computations are planned, as is the case in theoretical studies of the influence of various factors on depletion-drive performance where the fluid and reservoir-rock characteristics remain unchanged in each case. In this case the graphs $\lambda(p)$, $\epsilon(p)$, $\eta(p)$, and $\omega(\sigma_o,p)$ may be computed once for all, and the values which enter Eq. (10-41) are read directly from the curves.

The cumulative recovery in stock-tank oil may be calculated as a fraction of pore space by the following relation:

$$\text{Stock-tank oil cumulative recovery} = \sum_{P_o}^{p} \frac{\Delta\sigma_o}{\beta} \tag{10-42}$$

in which p is the prevailing field pressure and β is read at that pressure.

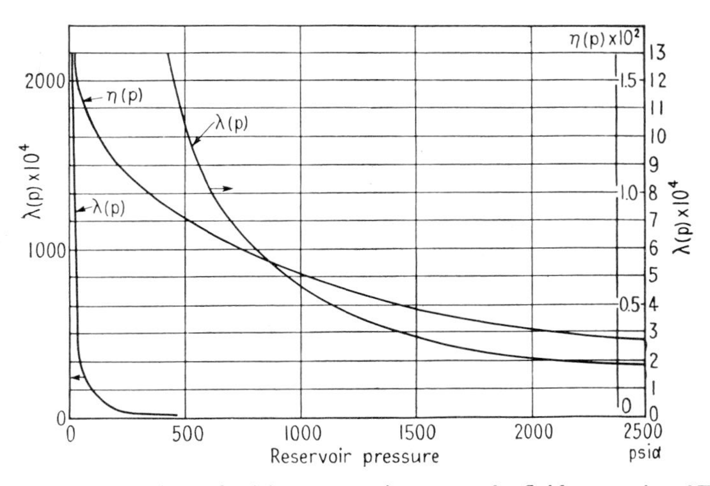

FIG. 10-10. Functions η (p) and λ (p) vs. reservoir pressure for fluid properties of Fig. 10-5.

For comparative purposes, the example solved previously by the method of Tarner was repeated by Muskat's method. The results are plotted on Fig. 10-10 for the 2,000-psi initial pressure. The fluids and relative-permeability characteristics used were those of Figs. 10-5, and 10-6, whereas the derived functions η, λ, and ϵ are shown, respectively, on Figs. 10-11 and 10-12.

Depletion-drive Prediction by the Method of Finite Differences. A great deal of time is consumed in making reservoir performance calculations and it is desirable to have at hand means that are simple, accurate, and rapid.

Such a means was developed by writing the material-balance equation in finite difference form. All depletion-performance calculation methods (based on differential equations) determine increments of oil production;

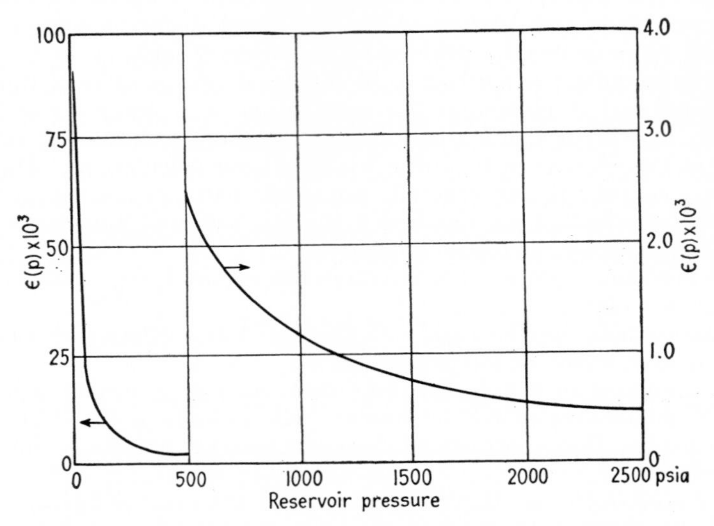

FIG. 10-11. Function ϵ (p) vs. reservoir pressure for fluid properties of Fig. 10-5.

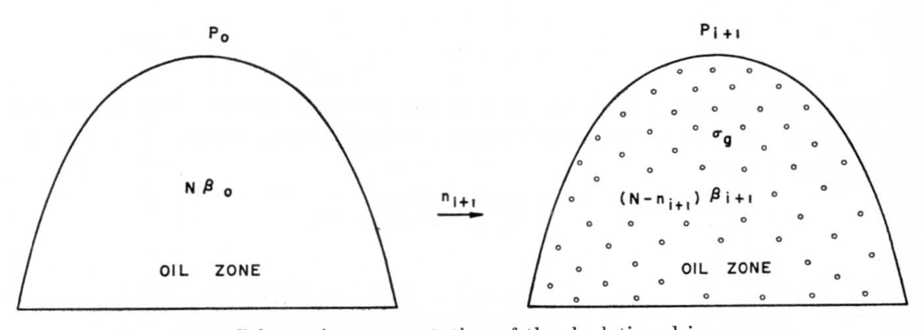

FIG. 10-12. Schematic representation of the depletion-drive process.

they have the disadvantage of not being self-correcting or self-adjusting when computational errors are inadvertently introduced. If it is desired to ascertain the accuracy of the answer, it is necessary to provide a checking procedure by means of the finite form of the material balance, or to provide a foolproof calculation technique, or a quick checking procedure.

Another shortcoming of differential methods resides in the basic assumptions made concerning the linear continuity of trend of the fluid properties or performance characteristics within a selected interval of pressure decline. In order for these assumptions to be approximately verified when using the Muskat technique, it is necessary to select pressure-decline intervals as short as possible and yet compatible with the time allocated for such computations. Nevertheless, the performances obtained by the two techniques are not identical because of the cumulative errors introduced by the basic assumptions. On the other hand, the method of Muskat necessitates no trial-and-error procedure. In view of the numerous calculations it requires, it is best performed on high-speed digital computers; it is definitely not a method for field use by the ordinary engineer.

The finite difference method to be discussed retains some of those disadvantages but it eliminates the assumption of a linear continuity of property and performance trend within the pressure decrement selected; this is at the expense of requiring trial-and-error calculations. However, these are converging and generally not more than two guesses on the incremental production are required if the first one was judiciously made. The method makes the following claims:

1. A minimum number of calculations are required; i.e., a tabulation in 21 columns suffices.
2. Calculations may be made with great accuracy using a slide rule only.

The disadvantages of the method are:

1. Trial-and-error calculations (although converging) are needed.
2. Cumulative errors may be present if checks by finite material balance are not made. Hence, occasional checks by material balance in finite form are advisable.

The Finite Difference Material Balance. In the usual symbols, the material balance may be written on the basis of one unit of oil originally in place ($N = 1$).

$$1 = \frac{n[\beta + \alpha(r_n - S)]}{\alpha(S_0 - S) - (\beta_0 - \beta)}$$

when there is neither gas cap ($m = 0$) nor water drive ($W = 0$), nor water produced ($w = 0$). Dividing numerator and denominator by α and regrouping terms,

$$1 = \frac{n\left[\left(\frac{\beta}{\alpha} - S\right)\right] + nr_n}{\left(\frac{\beta}{\alpha} - S\right) - \left(\frac{\beta_0}{\alpha} - S_0\right)}$$

where nr_n may be replaced by $\Sigma\, \Delta n\, R_{av}$ = the cumulative gas produced G, in which R_{av} is the *average* flowing gas-oil ratio in a selected interval of pressure decline. Let us consider two successive pressures P_i and P_{i+1} during which pressure decrement a production increment $\Delta_i^{i+1}n$ occurred. We may write the material balance at these successive pressures:

At P_i:

$$\left(\frac{\beta}{\alpha} - S\right)_i - \left(\frac{\beta_0}{\alpha_i} - S_0\right) = n_i\left(\frac{\beta}{\alpha} - S\right)_i + \sum_0^i \Delta n R_{av} \qquad (10\text{-}43)$$

At P_{i+1}:

$$\left(\frac{\beta}{\alpha} - S\right)_{i+1} - \left(\frac{\beta_0}{\alpha_{i+1}} - S\right) = (n_i + \Delta_i^{i+1}n)\left(\frac{\beta}{\alpha} - S\right)_{i+1} + \sum_0^{i+1} \Delta n R_{\text{av}} \qquad (10\text{-}44)$$

Subtracting (10-43) from (10-44) and introducing the following functions:

$$\Delta_i^{i+1}\left(\frac{\beta}{\alpha} - S\right) = \left(\frac{\beta}{\alpha} - S\right)_{i+1} - \left(\frac{\beta}{\alpha} - S\right)_i$$

$$\Delta_i^{i+1}\left(\frac{1}{\alpha}\right) = \frac{1}{\alpha_{i+1}} - \frac{1}{\alpha_i}$$

we obtain

$$\Delta_i^{i+1}\left(\frac{\beta}{\alpha} - S\right) - \beta_0\,\Delta_i^{i+1}\frac{1}{\alpha} = n_i\,\Delta_i^{i+1}\left(\frac{\beta}{\alpha} - S\right) + \Delta_i^{i+1}n\left(\frac{\beta}{\alpha} - S\right)_{i+1} + \Delta_i^{i+1}nR_{\text{av}}$$

Solving for $\Delta_i^{i+1}n$,

$$\Delta_i^{i+1}n = \frac{(1 - n_i)\,\Delta_i^{i+1}\left(\frac{\beta}{\alpha} - S\right) - \beta_0\,\Delta_i^{i+1}\frac{1}{\alpha}}{\left(\frac{\beta}{\alpha} - S\right)_{i+1} + R_{\text{av}}} \qquad (10\text{-}45)$$

Equation (10-45) is the basic relation of the simplified finite difference method; it must be combined with the saturation and gas-oil-ratio equations to provide a solution of the depletion-drive performance of a field.

The basic equation (10-45) may readily be modified to take care of a constant fraction I of the produced gas which may be returned to the reservoir as dispersed gas injection; it becomes

$$\Delta_i^{i+1}n = \frac{(1 - n_i)\,\Delta_i^{i+1}\left(\frac{\beta}{\alpha} - S\right) - \beta_0\,\Delta_i^{i+1}\frac{1}{\alpha}}{\left(\frac{\beta}{\alpha} - S\right)_{i+1} + R_{\text{av}}(1 - I)} \qquad (10\text{-}46)$$

Should the use of a conformance factor e be advisable in the calculation, the procedure to be followed is readily devised. A primary balance would first be calculated in the usual manner and a calculation would then be performed with gas injection, wherein the gas-oil ratio is controlled by the fluid saturation in the conformable zone.

An example of calculation will illustrate the new technique.

Hypothetical Problem on Depletion-drive Performance

An oil reservoir is known to have neither water drive nor gas cap nor a sufficient vertical permeability to cause fluid segregation by gravity. No gas cap will be formed during production. It is expected to produce oil entirely by solution gas drive.

The structural and isopach map is that of Fig. 10-13 for which the reservoir volume was computed in Chap. 9. The structure is entirely closed at the base and might be considered to be a reef. A uniform irreducible water saturation of 0.20 is assumed present throughout. Hence, no water is produced. Reservoir-rock properties are given in Table 10-4 and plotted in Fig. 10-14. Reservoir-fluid properties are given in Table 10-5.

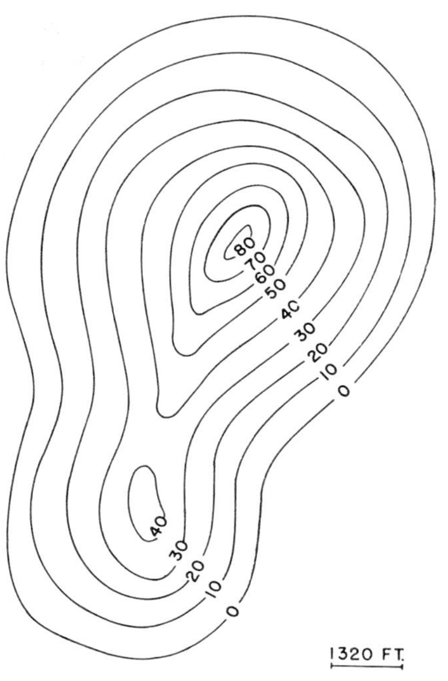

FIG. 10-13. Reservoir isopach map of the hypothetical field under study.

1. Calculate the stock-tank oil originally in place by the volumetric method, together with the oil produced by expansion when the field pressure declines to the bubble point.

2. Calculate the primary depletion-drive performance of this field. Depletion-drive calculation should start at the bubble-point pressure. In plotting the performance, however, the curves should begin at 2,000 psia and the initial production obtained by oil expansion should be calculated and included in the performance curves.

The calculation of a primary depletion-drive performance consists essentially in solving the following system of simultaneous equations:

Saturation equation:

$$\sigma_l = \sigma_w + \frac{(1-n)\beta}{\beta_0}(1-\sigma_w)$$

Gas-oil-ratio equation:

$$R = S + \frac{\beta}{\alpha}\frac{k_g}{k_o}\frac{\mu_o}{\mu_g} \tag{10-47}$$

Material-balance equation in finite difference form:

$$\Delta_i^{i+1}n = \frac{(1 - n_i)\,\Delta_i^{i+1}\left(\frac{\beta}{\alpha} - S\right) - \beta_0\,\Delta_i^{i+1}\,\frac{1}{\alpha}}{\left(\frac{\beta}{\alpha} - S\right)_{i+1} + R_{\text{av}}}$$

This is done by a trial-and-error procedure, choosing successive pressure decrements $\Delta P = P_i - P_{i+1}$ and calculating the corresponding production increment $\Delta_i^{i+1}n$. In this process a judicious increment Δn is first

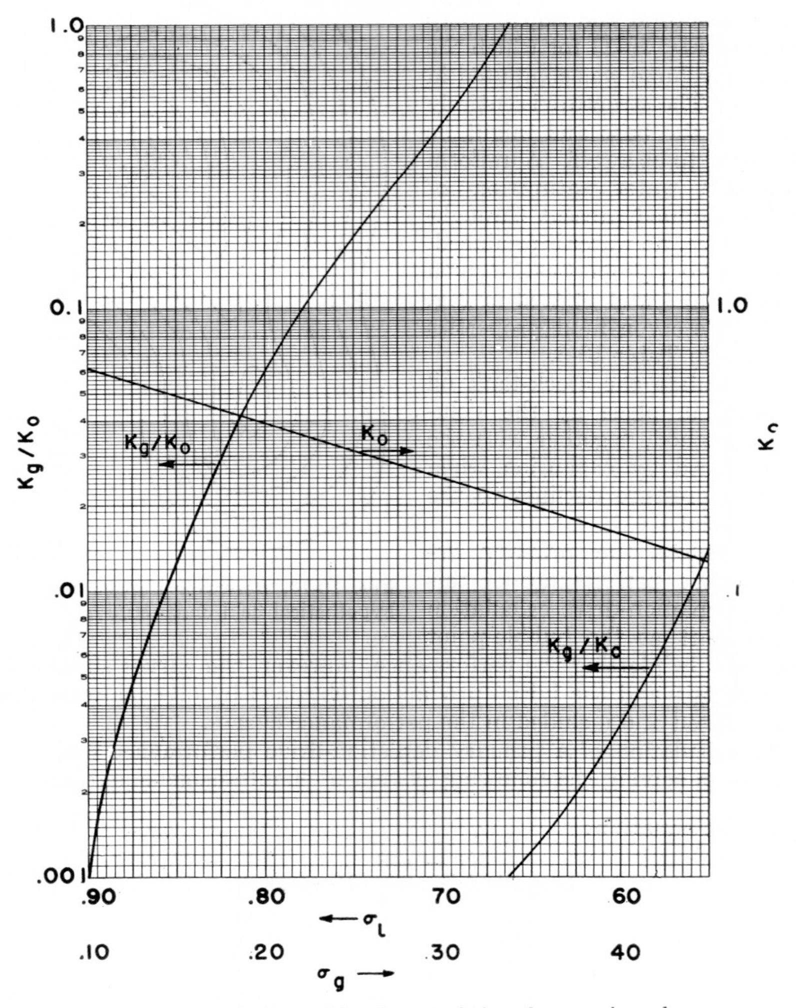

Fig. 10-14. k_g/k_o and k_o characteristics of reservoir rock.

TABLE 10-4. RESERVOIR-ROCK PROPERTIES

Porosity = 24%
Permeability = 0.5 darcy to air (dry); 0.4 darcy to oil at irreducible water

Capillary pressure (oil-formation water)

P, psi	σ_w, %
0.50	100 †
0.60	88
0.75	60
1.00	40
2.00	28
5.00	22
10.00	20 ‡

k_g/k_o relation at irreducible water saturation

σ_g	$\frac{k_g}{k_o}$	k_o
10	0.001	0.61
12.5	0.005	
15	0.0135	
17.5	0.03	
20	0.06	0.39
22.5	0.11	
25	0.18	
27.5	0.28	
30	0.45	0.25
32.5	0.73	
35	1.20	0.20
37.5	2.00	
40	3.40	0.15
42.5	6.30	
45	14.00	
50	. . .	0.06
60	. . .	0.02
70	. . .	0.00
80	. . .	0.00
90	. . .	0.00

Oil-brine relative permeability

σ_w	k_o	k_w
0.20	1.0	0
0.30	0.7	0.001
0.40	0.41	0.005
0.45	0.29	0.010
0.50	0.17	0.015
0.55	0.07	0.027
0.60	0.01	0.05
0.62	0	0.07
0.65	0	0.09
0.70	0	0.14
0.80	0	0.33
0.90	0	0.62
1.00	0	1.00

† Displacement pressure. ‡ Irreducible.

Table 10-5. Tabulation of Reservoir-fluid Data

P, pressure, psia	β, oil-reservoir-volume factor, vol/vol	S, solution gas surface, cu ft/cu ft STO	$\frac{\beta}{\alpha} - S$	$\Delta\left(\frac{\beta}{\alpha} - S\right)$	Z, compressibility	$\alpha = \frac{14.7}{P}\frac{T_f}{T_a}Z$ $T_f = 95°F$ $T_a = 60°F$ Gas-reservoir-volume factor, reservoir vol/surface vol	$\frac{1}{\alpha}$	$\Delta\frac{1}{\alpha}$	μ_o, reservoir-oil viscosity, cps	μ_g, reservoir-gas viscosity, cps	$F = \frac{\beta}{\alpha}\frac{\mu_o}{\mu_g}$
2,000(P_0)	1.237	...	...	...	...	...	...	...	1.35		
1,500(BPP)	1.241 = β_0	87.4 = s_0	80.4	...	0.708	0.00741 = α_0	135.10	...	1.21	0.0160	12,679
1,400	1.229	82.8	69.2	−11.2	0.717	0.00811	123.85	−11.25	1.23	0.0158	11,830
1,300	1.217	78.4	58.8	−10.4	0.730	0.00890	112.85	−11.00	1.25	0.0154	11;147
1,200	1.205	74.1	48.8	−10.0	0.740	0.00981	102.15	−10.70	1.27	0.0150	10,400
1,100	1.192	69.7	39.8	−9.0	0.752	0.01089	91.80	−10.35	1.30	0.0147	9,677
1,000	1.180	65.6	31.1	−8.7	0.768	0.01220	81.80	−10.00	1.33	0.0144	8,935
900	1.168	60.8	23.4	−7.7	0.786	0.01388	72.05	−9.75	1.37	0.0139	8,294
800	1.155	55.1	17.3	−6.1	0.807	0.01595	62.65	−9.40	1.43	0.0134	7,738
700	1.143	50.5	10.8	−6.5	0.828	0.01865	53.55	−9.10	1.51	0.0130	7,109
600	1.131	45.6	5.1	−5.7	0.850	0.0223	44.80	−8.75	1.62	0.0125	6,567
500	1.118	40.2	0.3	−4.8	0.872	0.0276	36.20	−8.60	1.77	0.0120	5,969
400	1.106	34.9	−3.7	−4.0	0.898	0.0355	28.15	−8.05	1.97	0.0115	5,340
300	1.093	29.0	−6.6	−2.9	0.922	0.0489	20.45	−7.70	2.27	0.0110	4,612
200	1.077	22.4	−8.2	−1.6	0.948	0.0760	13.15	−7.30	2.70	0.0105	3,640
100	1.056	14.7	−8.5	−0.3	0.975	0.1708	5.85	−7.30	3.37	0.0100	2,082
14.7(P_a)	1.000	0.0	0.94	+9.44	1.000	1.0650	0.94	−4.91	4.40	0.0095	435

REMARK: The above property functions were computed with a slide rule, except F. All results of computations are slide-rule results.

assumed, and it is verified if it fits the equation to an accuracy of ± 1 per cent. If not, the value Δn calculated is taken as the new choice of production increment and so on until verification is achieved.

3. Reduce the depletion-drive performance of this field calculated under part 2 to a time basis, knowing that the initial average productivity index of the wells was 0.5 bbl per day per psi and under the assumption that the wells will be abandoned when the production rate reaches 3 bbl per calendar day per well. Determine the abandonment pressure corresponding to this production rate.

Number of wells = 50
Well radius = 4 in.
Well allowable = 40 bbl per working day
20 working days = 30 calendar days = 1 month
Sand-face pressure = 100 psia, at producing wells
Assume 30 calendar days per month.

4. Repeat part 3, but assume that the field is divided into three productivity index areas for which the well distribution is as follows:

Original PI, bbl per day per psi	*No. of wells*
0.10	10
0.50	30
0.75	10

Postulate that the initial oil in place is allocated evenly between wells and that a constant allowable of 40 bbl per working day will be allocated to each well regardless of productivity index. Postulate complete equalization of pressure between the various productivity index areas.

5. Calculate the performance of this field, using the pertinent data given above but under the assumption that, beginning when the field pressure had declined to 900 psia, 60 per cent of the produced gas is reinjected. Assume that a conformance factor equals 1. Convert the results to a time basis, all wells having the same initial PI = 0.5 bbl per day per psi and an allowable of 40 bbl per working day. The calculations of a depletion-drive performance with gas injection (auxiliary or stimulation production method) consist essentially in solving the following system of simultaneous equations which apply to the conformable zone e of the reservoir:

Saturation equation in conformable zone:

$$(\sigma_l)_e = \sigma_w + \frac{(e - n_e)\beta}{e\beta_0}(1 - \sigma_w)$$

Instantaneous gas-oil ratio in conformable zone:

$$(R)_e = S + \frac{\beta}{\alpha}\left(\frac{k_g}{k_o}\right)_e \frac{\mu_o}{\mu_g} \qquad (10\text{-}48)$$

Differential material balance:

$$\Delta_i^{i+1}n = \frac{(1 - n_i)\,\Delta_i^{i+1}\left(\frac{\beta}{\alpha} - S\right) - \beta_o\,\Delta_i^{i+1}\frac{1}{\alpha}}{\left(\frac{\beta}{\alpha} - S\right)_{i+1} + R_{e,\text{av}}(1 - I)} = (1 - e)\,\Delta n_p + \Delta n_e$$

This may be done by the trial-and-error procedure.

In view of the higher operating cost, an economic limit of 5 bbl per calendar day per well is now assumed. Determine the abandonment pressure corresponding to this new economic limit.

6. Calculate the performance of this field, using the above pertinent data, but under the assumption that, beginning when the field pressure has declined to 900 psia, 60 per cent of the gas is reinjected. Assume a conformance factor of $e = 0.50$. Convert the results to a time basis, all the wells having the same initial productivity index = 0.5 bbl per day per psi and an allowable of 40 bbl per working day. In view of the higher operating cost, an economic limit of 5 bbl per calendar day is again assumed.

7. When cycling according to part 6, what is the abandonment pressure? What will the gas-injection requirement be in order to maintain this field pressure? A conformance factor of 0.5 is assumed. Sand-face pressure = 100 psia. Postulating an economic gas-oil-ratio limit of 40,000 cu ft per bbl what will be the ultimate field recovery and how long will it take to reach it? During this operation no shut-down days are required.

The k_g/k_o and k_o relations as a function of total liquid saturation (σ_l) are plotted in Fig. 10-14.

Solution. Part 1. At 2,000 psia the oil in place is computed to be

$$7{,}758 \times 37{,}472 \times 0.24(1 - 0.20) \times \frac{1}{1.237} = 45{,}121{,}500 \text{ bbl STO}$$

At 1,500 psi the oil in place is

$$7{,}758 \times 37{,}472 \times 0.24(1 - 0.20) \times \frac{1}{1.241} = 44{,}941{,}000 \text{ bbl STO}$$

The reservoir volume in acre-ft is 37,472.

Production above the bubble point is the difference between the above two figures or 180,500 bbl STO, which is 0.4 per cent of the oil in place at the bubble-point pressure.

Part 2. The results of the primary depletion calculations by the finite difference material balance are given in Table 10-6.

It is observed that for a field-pressure decline down to atmospheric pressure, 27.04 per cent of the oil originally present at the bubble-point pressure would be obtained.

The calculations were checked by means of the finite material balance and were found to be accurate within the specified limit of ±1 per cent. However, the verification calculations are not shown.

TABLE 10-6. DEPLETION-DRIVE CALCULATIONS BY THE FINITE DIFFERENCE MATERIAL BALANCE

Pressure, P (1)	Production increment, Δn (2)	Cumulative production, $n = \Sigma(\Delta n)$ (3)	$1 - n$ (4)	$\frac{\beta}{\beta_0}$ (5)	$\sigma_o = (1 - \sigma_w) \times (4) \times (5)$ (6)	$\sigma_l = \sigma_o + \sigma_w$ (7)	$F = \frac{\beta}{\alpha} \frac{\mu_o}{\mu_g}$ (8)	$\frac{k_g}{k_o}$ (9)	$(8) \times (9)$ (10)	S (11)
1,500	0	0	1	1	...	...	12,679	...	...	87.4
1,400 *	0.018	0.018	0.9820	0.990	0.776	0.976	11,830	0	0	82.8
1,300 *	0.0246	0.0426	0.9574	0.982	0.743	0.943	11,147	0	0	78.4
1,200 *	0.0309	0.0735	0.9265	0.972	0.721	0.921	10,400	0	0	74.1
1,100	0.0359	0.1094	0.8916	0.962	0.685	0.885	9,677	0.0029	28.0	69.7
1,000	0.0290	0.1384	0.8616	0.952	0.655	0.855	8,935	0.011	98.2	65.6
900	0.0230	0.1614	0.8386	0.942	0.631	0.831	8,294	0.025	207.4	60.8
800	0.0184	0.1808	0.8192	0.932	0.610	0.810	7,738	0.046	356.0	55.1
700	0.0125	0.1933	0.8067	0.921	0.595	0.795	7,109	0.067	476.0	50.5
600	0.0104	0.2037	0.7963	0.913	0.581	0.781	6,567	0.096	630.4	45.6
500	0.0092	0.2139	0.7861	0.902	0.568	0.768	5,969	0.13	776.0	40.2
400	0.0077	0.2206	0.7794	0.890	0.554	0.754	5,340	0.17	907.5	34.9
300	0.0077	0.2288	0.7717	0.881	0.544	0.744	4,612	0.20	923.0	29.0
200	0.0081	0.2369	0.7631	0.867	0.529	0.729	3,640	0.27	982.5	22.4
100	0.0102	0.2471	0.7529	0.850	0.512	0.712	2,082	0.36	750.0	14.7
14.7	0.0233	0.2704	0.7296	0.805	0.470	0.670	435	0.84	365.5	0

* As long as $k_g/k_o = 0$, Δn calculations are made directly without trial and error.

Table 10-6. Depletion-drive Calculations by the Finite Difference Material Balance (*Continued*)

$R_{inst} = (11) + (10)$	$R_{av} = \frac{R_i + R_{i+1}}{2}$	$\left(\frac{\beta}{\alpha} - S\right)$	$(13) + (14)$	$\Delta\left(\frac{\beta}{\alpha} - S\right)$	$(4)_i\,(16)$	$\Delta\left(\frac{1}{\alpha}\right)$	$\beta_0\,\Delta\frac{1}{\alpha}$	$(17) - (19)$	$\Delta n = \frac{(20)}{(15)}$
(12)	(13)	(14)	(15)	(16)	(17)	(18)	(19)	(20)	(21)
87.4	...	80.4							
82.8	85.1	69.2	154.3	−11.2	−11.2	−11.25	−13.98	2.78	0.018
78.4	80.6	58.8	139.4	−10.4	−10.2	−11.00	−13.64	3.44	0.0246
74.1	71.3	48.8	120.1	−10.0	−9.57	−10.70	−13.28	3.70	0.0309
97.7	85.9	39.8	125.7	−9.0	−8.33	−10.35	−12.85	4.52	0.0359
163.8	130.8	31.1	161.9	−8.7	−7.75	−10.00	−12.41	4.66	0.0288
268.2	216.0	23.4	239.4	−7.7	−6.63	−9.75	−12.11	5.48	0.0230
411.1	339.7	17.3	357.0	−6.1	−5.11	−9.40	−11.69	6.58	0.0184
526.5	468.8	10.8	479.6	−6.5	−5.32	−9.10	−11.30	5.98	0.0125
676.0	601.3	5.1	606.4	−5.7	−4.60	−8.75	−10.88	6.28	0.0104
816.2	746.1	0.3	746.4	−4.8	−3.82	−8.60	−10.69	6.87	0.0092
942.4	879.3	−3.7	875.6	−4.0	−3.15	−8.05	−9.99	6.84	0.0077
952.0	947.0	−6.6	940.4	−2.9	−2.26	−7.70	−9.55	7.29	0.0077
1,004.9	978.5	−8.2	970.3	−1.6	−1.23	−7.30	−9.06	7.83	0.0081
764.7	884.8	−8.5	876.3	−0.3	−0.23	−7.30	−9.06	8.83	0.0102
365.5	565.1	0.94	566.0	9.44	7.10	−4.91	−6.10	13.20	0.0233

It is to be noted that a tabulation in 21 columns only is required for the computations. Although only the final calculations at each pressure are shown, generally only two guesses were required at each chosen pressure decrement, and in some cases only one. When the gas-oil ratio reached its peak value, as many as three guesses on Δn were required. Results of the calculations are shown in Fig. 10-15.

Part 3. Table 10-7 shows the calculation of the productivity indices during primary production. The production rate per well q_o is plotted vs. field pressure in Fig. 10-16. The allowable rate of 26.7 bbl STO per day determines that the field will fail to make its permissible production when the

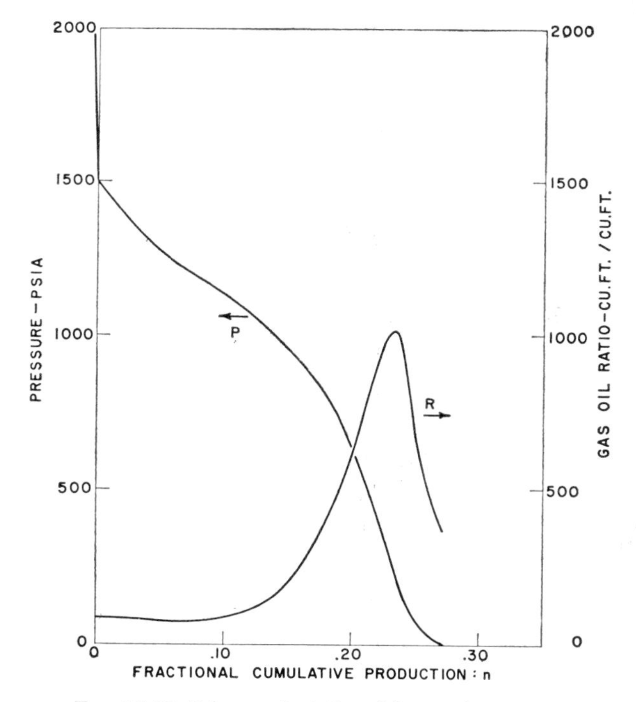

FIG. 10-15. Primary depletion-drive performance.

field pressure reaches 360 psia, at which time the cumulative production is $n = 0.221$ or 9,931,961 bbl STO. It will therefore take a time in months obtained from

$$\frac{9{,}931{,}961}{26.7 \times 30 \times 50} = 248.3 \text{ months}$$

for the field pressure to decline to 360 psia at the maximum allowable producing rate. The performance during the decline productivity period is computed in Table 10-8.

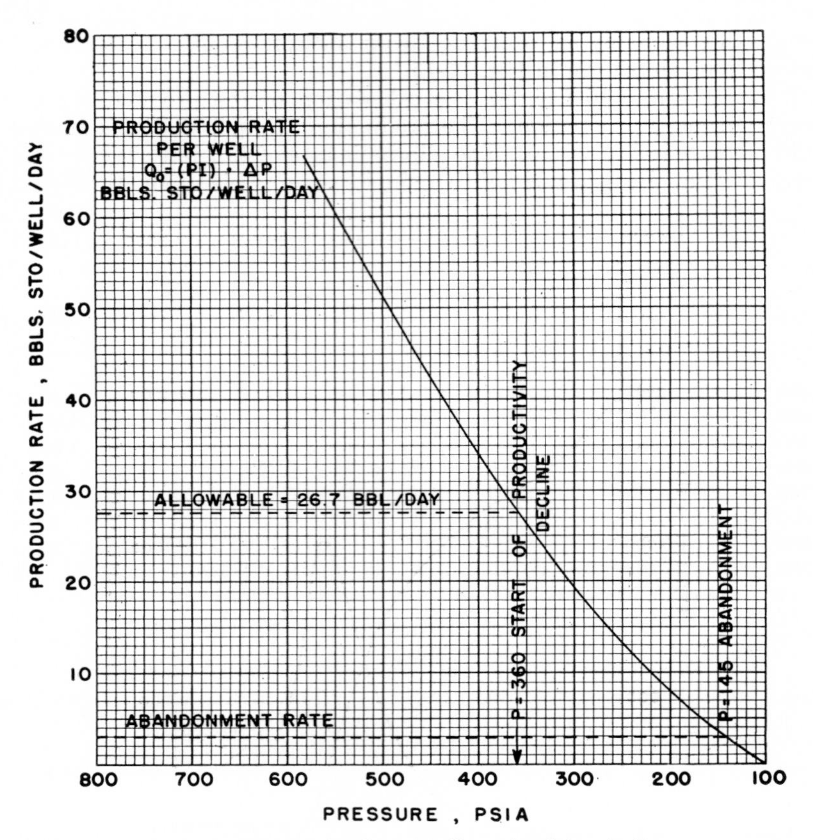

FIG. 10-16. Determination of well-productivity decline.

TABLE 10-7. TABULATION FOR PI AND WELL-PRODUCTION-RATE CALCULATIONS

$$PI = (PI)_0 k_0 \frac{(\mu_o \beta)_0}{\mu_o \beta}$$

$$(PI)_0 = 0.50; \; (\mu_o \beta)_0 = (1.21 \times 1.241) = 1.5016$$

P (1)	σ_l (2)	k_o (3)	μ_o (4)	β (5)	$\mu_o\beta$ (6)	$1.5016 \times k_o$ (7)	(7) ÷ (6) (8)	PI (9)	n (10)	$P - 100$ (11)	Q_o, bbl/day (9) × (11)
1,500	1.000	1.000	1.21	1.241	1.5016	1.5016	1.000	0.500	0	1,400	700
1,300	0.949	0.775	1.25	1.217	1.5213	1.1637	0.765	0.383	0.045	1,200	460
1,100	0.888	0.575	1.30	1.192	1.5496	0.8634	0.557	0.279	0.105	1,000	279
900	0.836	0.457	1.37	1.168	1.6002	0.6862	0.429	0.215	0.155	800	172
700	0.799	0.386	1.51	1.143	1.7259	0.5796	0.336	0.168	0.187	600	101
500	0.768	0.338	1.77	1.118	1.9789	0.5075	0.256	0.128	0.212	400	51
300	0.746	0.305	2.27	1.093	2.4811	0.4580	0.185	0.093	0.225	200	19
100	0.714	0.266	3.37	1.056	3.5587	0.3994	0.112	0.056	0.245	0	0
14.7	0.671	0.215	4.40	1.000	4.4000	0.3228	0.073	0.037	0.270		

TABLE 10-8. PERFORMANCE COMPUTATION DURING DECLINING PRODUCTIVITY PERIOD

(Time conversion)

Pressure interval (1)	Mean well-producing rate in pressure interval (2)	n (3)	Δn (4)	Time increment, $\Delta\theta = \frac{(4)N}{(2) \times 30 \times 50}$ (5)	Cumulative time, months (6)
360	22.4	0.221	. . .	. . .	248.3
300	22.4	0.225	0.004	4.4	253.7
200	12.3	0.232	0.007	16.9	270.8
150	5.1	0.238	0.006	25.3	306.1
100	1.5	0.245	0.007	39.8	445.9

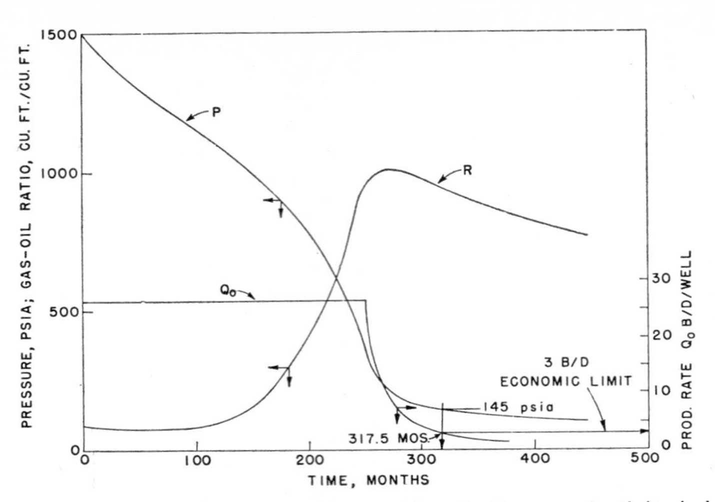

Fig. 10-17. Depletion-drive performance vs. time (uniform productivity index).

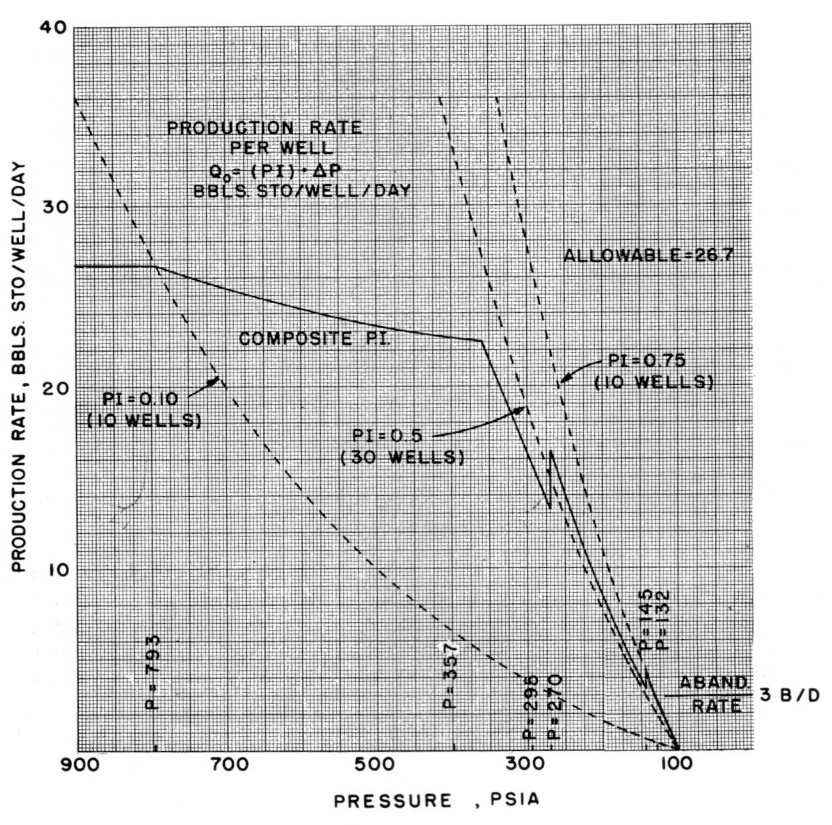

Fig. 10-18. Determination of composite productivity index.

The results of the conversion of the performance on a time basis are plotted in Fig. 10-17. Cumulative recovery is 0.239 of the oil originally in place.

Part 4. In this case there are various areas within the field exhibiting different productivities. Equalization of pressure throughout the field is not presumed to prevail; hence fluid migration between the various areas does not take place; the low PI wells will be abandoned first because they will reach the economic limiting rate of 3 bbl per day sooner than the high PI wells. In order to study the sequence of well abandonment and the pressure at which this occurs, Table 10-9 is computed and the results are plotted in Fig. 10-18.

TABLE 10-9. TABULATION OF PRODUCTIVITY INDEX AND WELL-PRODUCTION RATES ACCORDING TO INITIAL WELL PRODUCTIVITY INDEX

10 wells, $(PI)_0 = 0.10$
50 wells: 30 wells, $(PI)_0 = 0.50$
10 wells, $(PI)_0 = 0.75$

P	$K_o \frac{(\mu_o\beta)_0}{\mu_o\beta}$	PI *	Q_o*	PI †	Q_o†	PI ‡	Q_o‡
1,500	1.000	0.100	140	0.500	700	0.750	1,050
1,300	0.765	0.077	92	0.383	460	0.574	689
1,100	0.557	0.056	56	0.279	279	0.418	418
900	0.42	0.043	34	0.215	172	0.322	258
700	0.336	0.034	20	0.168	101	0.252	151
500	0.256	0.026	10	0.128	51	0.192	77
300	0.185	0.019	3.88	0.093	19	0.139	28
200	0.158	0.016	1.6	0.079	7.9	0.118	11.8
150	0.136	0.014	0.7	0.068	3.4	0.102	5.1
100	0.112	0.011	0	0.056	0	0.084	0

* Originally in place = 0.10.
† Originally in place = 0.50.
‡ Originally in place = 0.75.

The following abandonment schedule is observed:

10 wells of initial PI = 0.1, when P = 270 psia

30 wells of initial PI = 0.5, when P = 145 psia

10 wells of initial PI = 0.75, when P = 132 psia

A composite production rate per remaining wells is calculated as shown in Fig. 10-18 and the increments of production time are calculated in a manner similar to part 3. The results appear in Table 10-10.

TABLE 10-10. PERFORMANCE COMPUTATION DURING DECLINING PRODUCTIVITY PERIOD

(Time conversion)

P (1)	No. of wells producing (2)	n (3)	Δn (4)	Mean well-producing rate (5)	Time increment, $\Delta\theta = \frac{(3)\ \Delta n}{(5) \times (2) \times 30}$ (6)	Cumulative time, months (7)
793	50	0.174	. . .	26.70	. . .	195.5
700	50	0.187	0.013	25.36	15.0	210.5
600	50	0.200	0.013	24.20	15.7	226.2
500	50	0.210	0.010	23.36	12.6	238.8
357	50	0.221	0.011	22.40	14.4	253.2
295	50	0.225	0.004	16.86	7.6	260.8
270	40	0.227	0.002	13.22	4.0	264.8
225	40	0.230	0.003	10.20	8.4	273.2
175	40	0.235	0.005	5.88	23.3	296.5
145	10	0.239	0.004	4.20	31.9	328.4
132	10	0.241	0.002	0	164.2	492.6

The results of the conversion of the reservoir performance on a time basis are plotted in Fig. 10-19. Cumulative recovery is 0.241 of original oil in place when the last high productivity index wells are abandoned.

Part 5. This section of the problem calls for the injection of 60 per cent of the produced gas, starting when the field pressure has dropped to 900

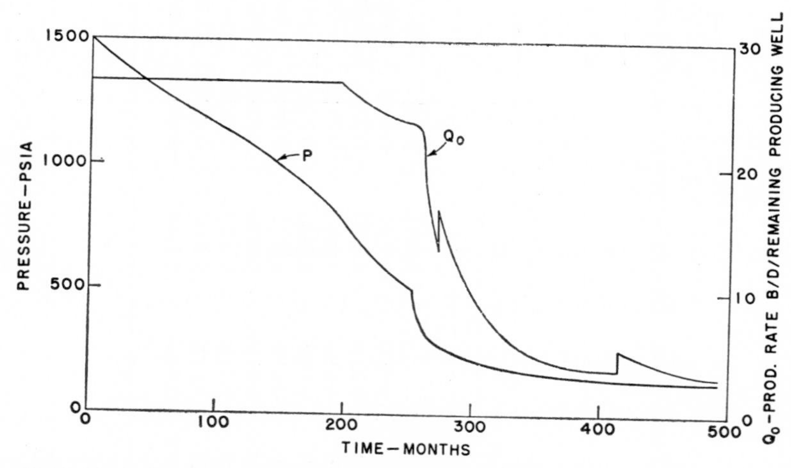

FIG. 10-19. Depletion-drive performance vs. time (three areas of different productivity index).

TABLE 10-11. DEPLETION-DRIVE CALCULATIONS BY THE FINITE DIFFERENCE MATERIAL BALANCE WITH DISPERSED GAS INJECTION

$I = 0.6$

P (1)	Δn (2)	$n = \Sigma \Delta n$ (3)	$1 - n$ (4)	$\frac{\beta}{\beta_0}$ (5)	$\sigma_o = (1 - \sigma_w) \times (4) \times (5)$ (6)	$\sigma_l = \sigma_o + \sigma_w$ (7)	$\frac{k_g}{k_o}$ (8)	F (9)	(8) × (9) (10)	S (11)
900	...	0.1614	0.8386	0.942	...	...	...	...	...	60.8
800	0.0377	0.1991	0.8009	0.932	0.598	0.798	0.06	7,738	463.7	55.1
700	0.0249	0.2240	0.7760	0.921	0.571	0.771	0.12	7,109	853.0	50.5
600	0.0155	0.2395	0.7605	0.913	0.555	0.755	0.17	6,567	1,118.0	45.6
500	0.0139	0.2534	0.7466	0.902	0.539	0.739	0.22	5,969	1,312.0	40.2
400	0.0118	0.2652	0.7348	0.890	0.522	0.722	0.30	5,340	1,602.0	34.9
300	0.0110	0.2762	0.7238	0.881	0.509	0.709	0.38	4,612	1,754.0	29.0
200	0.0110	0.2872	0.7128	0.867	0.494	0.694	0.50	3,640	1,820.0	22.4
100	0.0132	0.3004	0.6996	0.850	0.475	0.675	0.74	2,082	1,540.0	14.7
14.7	0.0306	0.3310	0.6690	0.805	0.430	0.630	1.18	435	513.0	0

TABLE 10-11. DEPLETION-DRIVE CALCULATIONS BY THE FINITE DIFFERENCE MATERIAL BALANCE WITH DISPERSED GAS INJECTION (*Continued*)

R_{inst} = (10) + (11) (12)	R_{av} (13)	$(1 - I)R_{av}$ (13*a*)	$\left(\frac{\beta}{\alpha} - S\right)$ (14)	(14) + (13*a*) (15)	$\Delta\left(\frac{\beta}{\alpha} - S\right)$ (16)	$(4)_i \times (16)$ (17)	$\Delta \frac{1}{\alpha}$ (18)	$\beta_0 \Delta \frac{1}{\alpha}$ (19)	(17) − (19) (20)	$\Delta n = \frac{(20)}{(15)}$ (21)
268.2	...	...	23.4	...	−7.8					
519.8	394.0	157.5	17.3	174.8	−6.1	−5.11	−9.40	−11.69	6.58	0.0377
903.5	585.9	234.2	10.8	245.0	−6.5	−5.21	−9.10	−11.31	6.10	0.0249
1,163.6	1,033.6	413.0	5.1	418.1	−5.7	−4.42	−8.75	−10.88	6.46	0.0155
1,352.2	1,257.9	503.0	0.3	503.3	−4.8	−3.65	−8.60	−10.69	7.04	0.0139
1,636.9	1,494.6	598.0	−3.7	594.3	−4.0	−2.98	−8.05	−9.99	7.01	0.0118
1,783.0	1,710.0	684.0	−6.6	677.4	−2.9	−2.13	−7.70	−9.55	7.42	0.0110
1,842.0	1,812.7	725.0	−8.2	716.8	−1.6	−1.16	−7.30	−9.06	7.90	0.0110
1,554.7	1,698.7	679.0	−8.5	670.5	−0.3	−0.21	−7.30	−9.06	8.85	0.0132
513.0	1,033.9	414.0	0.94	414.9	+9.44	+6.60	−4.91	−6.10	12.70	0.0306

psia by primary depletion. This operation is generally considered as being of a "secondary recovery" nature although it starts before the "primary phase" or complete depletion is terminated. The gas injection is of a dispersed nature and it is assumed that the fluid saturation remains uniform within the whole reservoir volume; i.e., there is no driving front

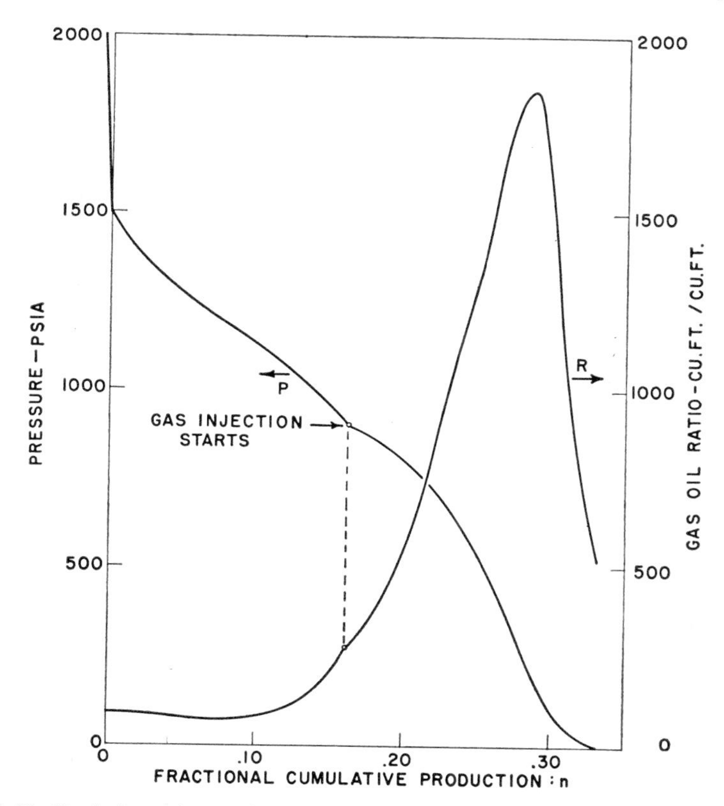

FIG. 10-20. Depletion-drive performance with gas injection ($I = 0.6$, $e = 1$, uniform productivity index).

produced and no saturation discontinuity or gradient is formed within the reservoir. It is also assumed for part 5 that the injected gas contacts the whole of the reservoir volume; i.e., the conformance factor is 1.0.

Table 10-11 gives a summary of the calculations by the differential material balance. The only additional column required over straight depletion is 13*a*.

It is observed that an additional 6 per cent of the original stock-tank oil is recovered by this "secondary recovery" operation when the field is depleted to atmospheric pressure.

Performance curves are plotted in Fig. 10-20 and reduction to a time basis is plotted in Fig. 10-21. The latter reduction was carried out by the

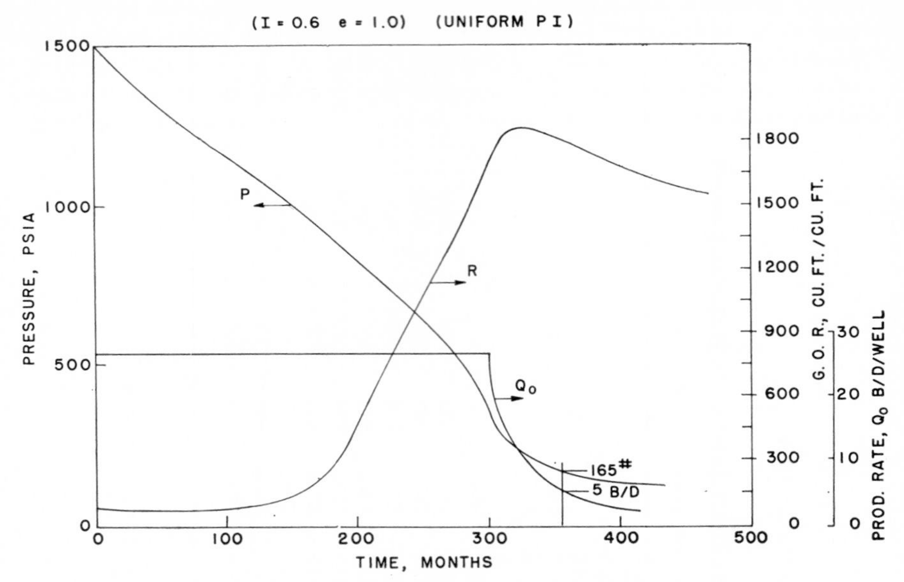

FIG. 10-21. Depletion-drive performance vs. time ($I = 0.6$, $e = 1$, uniform productivity index).

technique of part 3 where all well productivity indices are identical. Cumulative production is 0.291 of oil originally in place when the field pressure of 165 psia is reached, at which time all the wells reach their economic limit of 5 bbl per day.

Part 6. For this part of the problem the same injection ratio ($I = 0.6$) is used as in part 5, but it is presumed that the injected gas contacts only a fraction ($e = 0.5$) of the reservoir volume owing to the pattern distribution of the injection wells, to the postulated heterogeneous type of porosity (mixture of vuggy and intergranular), and to other structural elements of the reservoir.

The calculations are shown in Table 10-12. As the pressure declines, 50 per cent of the reservoir volume produces altogether by pressure depletion and is not swept by injection gas; the increments of primary production Δn_p so obtained are recorded in columns 3 and 4 and are derived directly from part 2. The increments of production derived from the volume of reservoir subject to injection Δn_e are calculated by trial and error and are recorded in column 5. A first increment Δn_e is assumed, and it is calculated in column 26 if this was a correct assumption. If not, the figure obtained in column 26 is tried in column 5 and this second trial will generally satisfy the problem. Cumulative production is recorded in column 7. It is observed that 3 per cent of the oil originally in place is obtained by this operation, a result which could have been readily predicted from part 5 since the injection characteristics are the same but only 50 per cent of the reservoir is affected.

TABLE 10-12. DEPLETION-DRIVE CALCULATION BY THE FINITE DIFFERENCE MATERIAL BALANCE

With dispersed gas injection ($I = 0.6$) and conformance factor ($e = 0.5$)

P (1)	$\Delta n =$ (4) + (5) (2)	Δn_p (3)	$\Delta n_p(1 - e)$ (4)	Δn_e (5)	$n_e = \Sigma(5)$ (6)	$n = \Sigma(2)$ (7)	$1 - n =$ 1 − (7) (8)	$\frac{e - n_e}{e}$ (9)	$\frac{\beta}{\beta_0}$ (10)	(9)·(10) (11)	(11)$(1 - \sigma_w)$ (12)	$(\sigma_l)_e =$ σ_w + (12) (13)	$\left(\frac{k_g}{k}\right)_e$ (14)
900	...	...	...	...	.0809	.1614	.8386	.839					
800	.03310	.0190	.0095	.0236	.1045	.1945	.8055	.791	.932	.735	.5896	.7896	.0762
700	.01765	.0127	.00625	.0113	.1153	.21215	.78785	.7694	.921	.7085	.5668	.7668	.133
600	.01392	.0105	.0051	.0089	.1242	.22607	.77393	.7524	.912	.6862	.549	.749	.185
500	.0125	.0092	.0046	.0079	.1321	.23857	.76143	.7366	.902	.6644	.5315	.7315	.251
400	.0103	.0080	.0040	.0063	.1384	.24887	.75113	.7232	.890	.6435	.5149	.7149	.338
300	.00965	.0075	.00375	.0059	.1454	.25858	.74142	.7112	.881	.626	.501	.701	.430
200	.0096	.0082	.0041	.0055	.1499	.26808	.73192	.7002	.867	.607	.485	.690	.590
100	.01135	.0098	.00495	.0064	.1563	.27945	.72055	.6871	.850	.584	.4675	.6675	.840
14.7	.0244	.0248	.0124	.0120	.1683	.30385	.69615	.664	.805	.534	.4275	.6275	2.050

Table 10-12. Depletion-drive Calculation by the Finite Difference Material Balance (*Continued*)

With dispersed gas injection ($I = 0.6$) and conformance factor ($e = 0.5$)

F (15)	(14)·(15) (16)	S (17)	$R_e =$ (17) + (16) (18)	$R_{e,\text{av}}$ (19)	(19)(1 − I) (20)	$\frac{\beta}{\alpha} - S$ (21)	(21) + (20) (22)	$\Delta\left(\frac{\beta}{\alpha} - S\right)$ (23)	$(8)_i$ (23) (24)	$\beta_0 \, \Delta \frac{1}{\alpha}$ (25)	(24) − (25) (26)	$\Delta n =$ (26)/(22) (27)
...	...	60.8	268.2	...	...	23.4	...	−7.8				
7,738	590	55.1	645.1	448	179.2	17.3	196.5	−6.1	−5.12	−11.69	6.57	.0334
7,109	945	50.5	995.5	820.3	[illegible]	10.8	339.0	−6.5	−5.24	−11.31	6.07	.0179
6,567	1,215	45.6	1,271	1,128	[illegible]51.2	5.1	456.0	−5.7	−4.48	−10.88	6.36	.0140
5,969	1,500	40.2	1,540.2	1,405.5	562.0	0.3	562.5	−4.8	−3.71	−10.69	6.98	.01238
5,340	1,808	32.9	1,840.9	1,691.4	676.6	−3.7	673.3	−4.0	−3.05	−9.99	6.94	.0103
4,612	1,985	29.0	2,010	1,928	770.0	−6.6	764.6	−2.9	−2.18	−9.55	7.37	.00965
3,640	2,150	22.4	2,172.4	2,091.2	836.5	−8.2	828.3	−1.6	−1.19	−9.06	7.87	.0095
2,082	1,751	14.7	1,765.7	1,968.5	787.4	−8.5	779.0	−0.3	−0.22	−9.06	8.84	.01135
435	891	0	891	1,328	31	0.94	532.0	9.44	6.80	−6.10	12.90	.0242

Performance curves and reduction to time of this operation are plotted, respectively, in Figs. 10-22 and 10-23. Cumulative recovery is 0.263 of the stock-tank oil originally present when the field pressure reaches 160 psia, at which all the wells fail to make the economic production rate of 5 bbl per day.

Part 7. In this part of the problem it is desired to maintain field pressure at the abandonment pressure of part 6, which was found to be 160

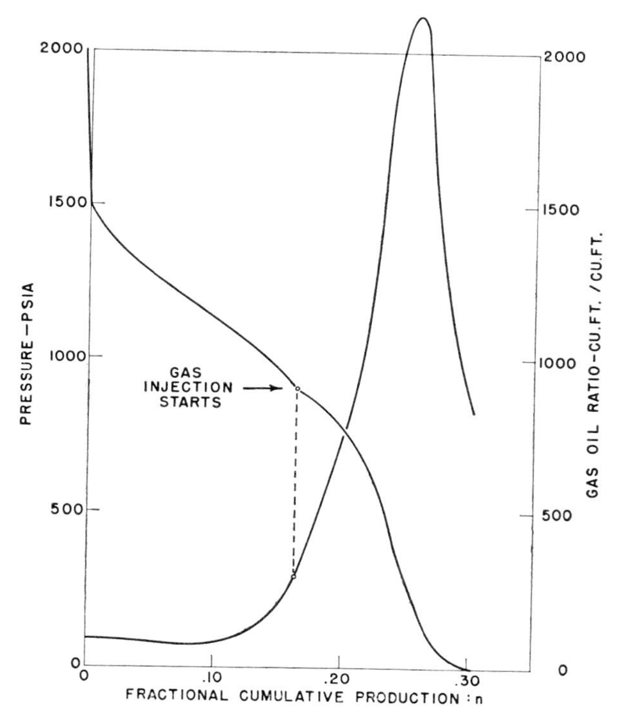

FIG. 10-22. Depletion-drive performance with gas injection (I = 0.6, e = 0.5, uniform productivity index).

psia by Fig. 10-23. Since the field pressure will be maintained, the numerator of Eq. (10-46) written for gas injection under part 5 will be zero for all Δn calculations. Yet Δn will have a definite value at all times, and this may occur only if the formula takes an indeterminate form; i.e., the denominator must also be zero.

$$\left(\frac{\beta}{\alpha} - S\right)_{i+1} + (1 - I)R_{av} = 0$$

or

$$I = 1 + \frac{(\beta/\alpha - S)_{i+1}}{R_{av}} \qquad (10\text{-}49)$$

Since there is no pressure decline, R_{av} may be replaced by R_e, which is the instantaneous gas-oil ratio during the pressure maintenance operation and which is altogether controlled by the fluid-flow characteristics of the conformable section of the reservoir.

Formula (10-49) is the equation of gas-injection requirement to maintain a given pressure. For the conditions of the problem, this pressure being 160 psia, $(\beta/\alpha - S)$ is a negative quantity: −8.8 cu ft per cu ft.

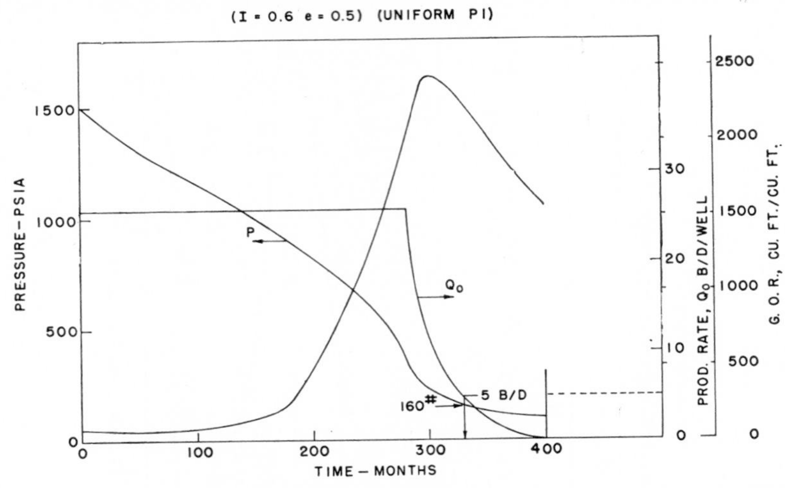

FIG. 10-23. Depletion-drive performance vs. time ($I = 0.6$, $e = 0.5$, uniform productivity index).

At the limiting gas-oil ratio of 40,000 cu ft per bbl or 7,130 cu ft per cu ft, the ultimate fluid saturation in the conformable zone is calculated by solving for $(k_g/k_o)_e$ from

$$7{,}130 = 19.6 + \frac{1.07}{0.099} \times \frac{2.94}{0.01303} \left(\frac{k_g}{k_o}\right)_e$$

$(k_g/k_o)_e = 2.296$ which corresponds to a total liquid saturation $(\sigma_l)_e = 0.618$ from the k_g/k_o curve (Fig. 10-14). Total recovery will then be obtained by adding recoveries from the nonconformable and conformable sections.

Recovery from nonconformable section to 160 psia $= (1 - e)n_p = 0.5 \times 0.238 = 0.119$.

In the conformable section at abandonment we have

$$(\sigma_l)_e = \sigma_w + \frac{e - n_e}{e} \frac{\beta}{\beta_0} (1 - \sigma_w)$$

$$0.618 = 0.2 + \frac{0.5 - n_e}{0.5} \frac{1.07}{1.241} \times 0.8$$

from which

$$n_e = 0.197$$

$$\text{Total recovery} = 0.119 + 0.197 = 0.316$$

TABLE 10-13. PRESSURE-MAINTENANCE CALCULATIONS

$P = 160$ psia

$(\Delta\sigma_l)_e$	$(\sigma_l)_e$	$\left(\frac{k_g}{k_o}\right)$	$F\left(\frac{k_g}{k_o}\right)_e$	R_e	$R_{\epsilon,av}$	$\frac{\frac{\beta}{\alpha} - S}{R}$	I	k_o	$Q_o = 14.5 \times k_o \times \Delta P$ BPD	$Q_{o,av}$, BPD	$\Delta\theta = e \frac{7,758 \times V \times \phi \times (\Delta\sigma_l)_e}{\beta\, 50 \times 30 \times Q_{o,av}}$, month
	0.7040	0.430	1,331.6	1,351.2	...	...	...	0.250	3.63		
0.0215	...	...	...	...	1,668	0.0053	0.9947	...	...	3.48	134
	0.6825	0.635	1,966.5	1,986.1	...	...	...	0.230	3.34		
0.0215	...	...	...	...	2,495	0.0035	0.9965	...	...	3.18	147
	0.6610	0.970	3,003.9	3,023.5	...	...	...	0.208	3.02		
0.0215	...	...	...	...	3,829	0.0023	0.9977	...	...	2.88	162
	0.6395	1.490	4,614.2	4,633.8	...	...	...	0.019	2.76		
0.0215	...	...	...	...	5,882	0.0015	0.9985	...	...	2.61	179
	0.6180	2.300	7,110.4	7,130.0	...	...	...	0.017	2.46		

Additional recovery by pressure maintenance is therefore only 0.316 − 0.268 = 0.048 of the oil originally in place.

Performance prediction during the pressure-maintenance stage of production may be made by choosing successive total liquid saturation decrements and calculating the corresponding instantaneous gas-oil ratios which in turn determine the injection requirements I. Because of the decrease in oil saturation, well productivity decreases constantly but at a very slow rate. Table 10-13 is a summary of the pressure-maintenance calculation.

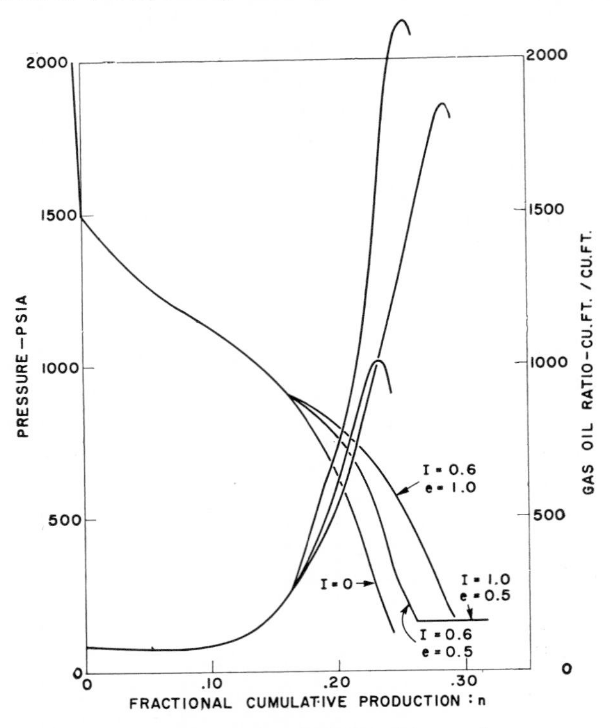

FIG. 10-24. Comparative depletion-drive performance.

It is observed that the daily rate of production per well has dropped to a value lower than the postulated economic limit of 5 bbl per day. This occurred, first, because the section of the reservoir untouched by the injected gas is no longer declining in pressure and no further production is obtained from it; second, decline in productivity is observed also because of the reduction in oil saturation in the conformable section.

The time required to produce the additional oil through pressure maintenance, i.e., 4.8 per cent of the original stock-tank oil, is 622 months. Such long deferred returns on the invested capital are without any significant present-day values. The operation is of doubtful economic interest.

Comparative performance of the various production techniques is shown in Fig. 10-24.

FACTORS INFLUENCING DEPLETION-DRIVE PERFORMANCE

The factors which modify depletion-drive performance and its ultimate recovery have been brought out by the calculations of various investigators, some of which are summarized herein. These factors are:

1. Reservoir pressure
2. Reservoir-fluid viscosity and API gravity
3. Gas in solution in reservoir oil
4. Shape of the relative-permeability ratio curve
5. Presence of a connate water phase
6. Presence and formation of a gas cap and its mode of expansion
7. Practice of gas cycling and injection ratio
8. Vaporization hysteresis within the reservoir
9. Well spacing
10. Rates of fluid withdrawal and pressure drawdowns
11. Gas saturation gradient in gas-injection projects
12. High volatility of reservoir oil

Reservoir-fluid Viscosity and Gravity. Muskat and Taylor (1946) have calculated the expected depletion performance under the assumption of an

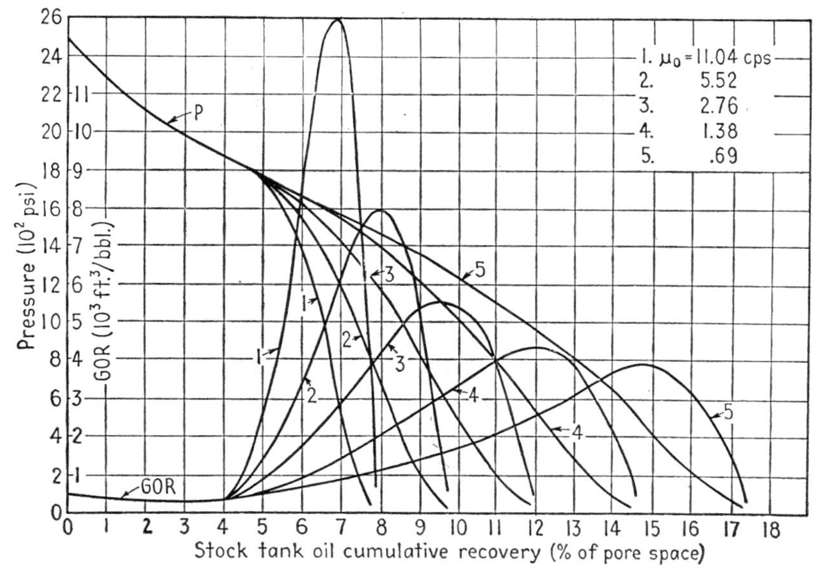

FIG. 10-25. Effect of oil viscosity on depletion-drive performance. (*After Muskat and Taylor.*)

original field pressure of 2,500 psi for crudes of stock-tank oil viscosities of 11.04, 5.52, 2.76, 1.38, and 0.69 centipoises. In each case the original gas solubility was assumed to be 534 cu ft per bbl. The performance curves are reproduced on Fig. 10-25 indicating, respectively, the following recoveries as a percentage of pore space (stock-tank oil basis): 7.8, 9.8,

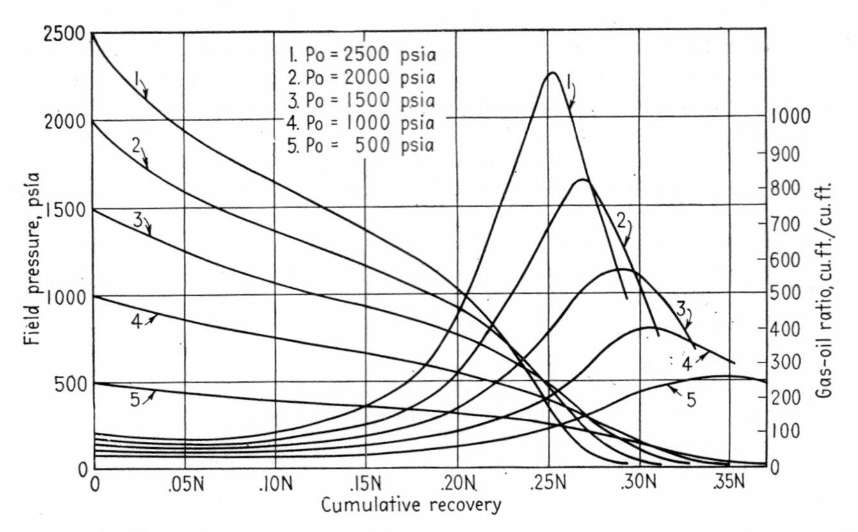

FIG. 10-26*a*. Theoretical reservoir performance at various initial pressures by Tarner's method; abandonment pressure 14.7 psia.

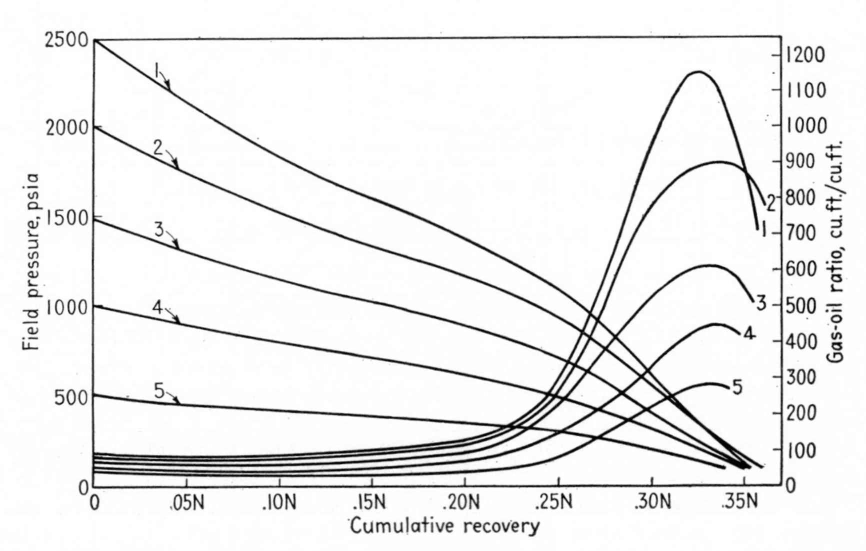

FIG. 10-26*b*. Theoretical reservoir performance at various initial pressures by Muskat's method; abandonment pressure 100 psia.

12.0, 14.5, and 17.4 per cent. This evidences the higher recoveries attainable with low-viscosity crudes, at constant solution gas.

Reservoir Pressure. For a stock-tank oil of specified physical properties, the amount of gas held in solution depends upon the prevailing field pressure as indicated by the solubility-pressure curve (Chap. 6). The effect of gas solubility as a function of pressure has been studied and the results are summarized in Figs. 10-26*a* and *b*, which indicate that there is a general increase in recovery with a decrease in initial bottom-hole pressure. The

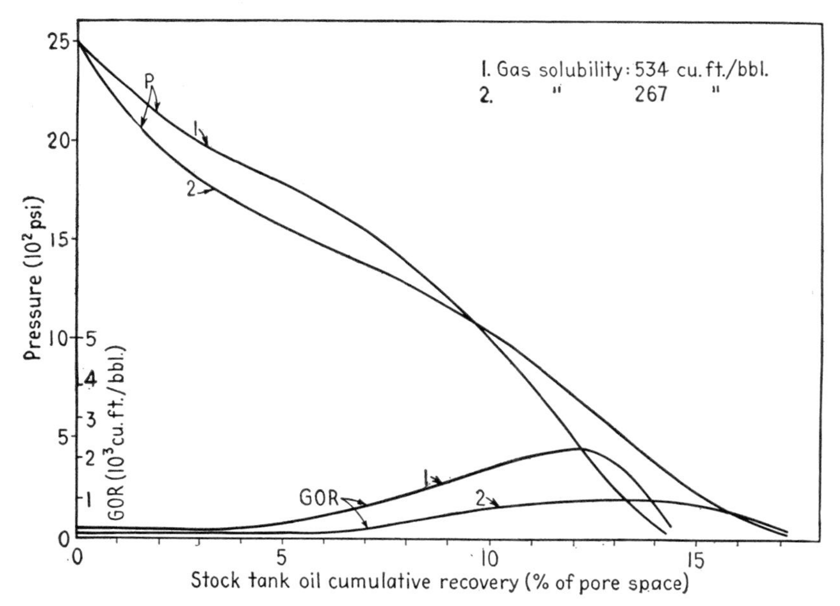

FIG. 10-27. Effect of gas solubility on depletion-drive performance. (*After Muskat and Taylor.*)

results also indicate that at high initial field pressure the gas-oil ratio curve is highly peaked in the later life of the field owing to high requirements in gas release from solution in order to produce a unit of oil. A large percentage of the reservoir energy is thus wasted uselessly for the purpose of creating channels for gas flow.

The lower recovery at high initial pressure is also the result of the associated higher reservoir oil shrinkage.

Gas Solubility in Reservoir Oil. Muskat and Taylor (1946) have calculated the performance data for a crude of stock-tank viscosity 1.38 centipoise and for solution gas of 534 and 267 cu ft per bbl at the saturation pressure of 2,500 psi. The results are shown on Fig. 10-27, where it is observed that the reservoir with the lesser solution gas recovers 17.5 per cent of pore space in stock-tank oil, whereas the oil with the greater amount of gas in solution at the same original pressure recovers only 14.5 per cent of pore space. This is an unexpected result which is explained by the required greater shrinkage of the reservoir oil with the smaller solution gas in the early stage of production in order to attain a saturation in the reservoir permitting conductivity to gas (the equilibrium saturation). This is also evidenced by a more rapid pressure decline in the early life of the field. In the case of the oil with the higher gas solubility, a moderate pressure decline permits sufficient voidage to attain the equilibrium saturation.

Further calculations made by Muskat and Taylor (1946) on the effect of crude gravities on depletion-drive performance indicate a reversion in recovery. Recovery increases at first for an increase in API gravity to about 40°API; then it decreases for a 50°API oil. This reversion is accounted for by the higher shrinkages of high-gravity oils. The results of these investigations indicate that oil recoveries from reservoirs exceeding 500 psi in pressure and 100 cu ft per bbl in solution gas are controlled more by fluid-flow characteristics than by reservoir energy.

Shape of the Relative-permeability Curve. Muskat (1945) studied this effect and calculated two performances, one under the assumption that

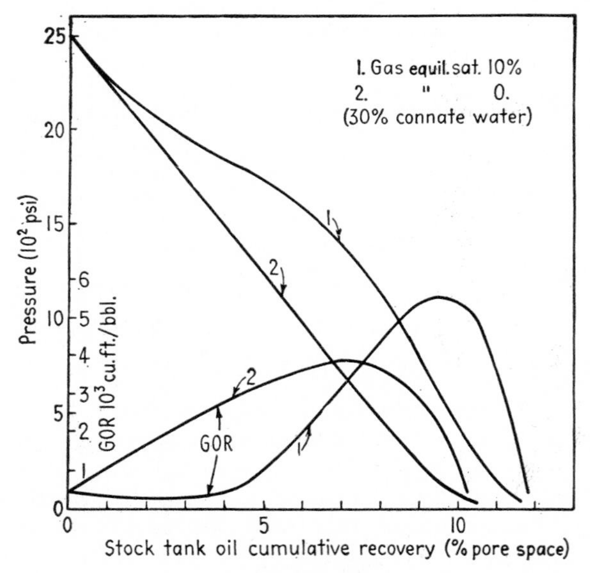

FIG. 10-28. Effect of shape of relative-permeability ratio curve on reservoir performance by depletion drive. (*After Muskat and Taylor.*)

equilibrium saturation to gas is not required before oil is expulsed and the other where a saturation of 10 per cent in gas is required before conductivity to gas becomes possible. The results of these calculations are shown in Fig. 10-28, where the lack of an initial gas-oil-ratio minimum is noticed in the absence of a gas equilibrium saturation, whereas a minimum exists in the other eventuality. This explains the divergence of results obtained by Tarner (no gas-oil-ratio minimum) and Babson (presence of gas-oil-ratio minimum) in the first theoretical studies made on depletion-drive performance. It is observed that the existence of an equilibrium gas saturation contributes to higher stock-tank oil recovery.

Correlation of k_g/k_o Relationship to Petrophysical Properties of Reservoir Rock. Empirical observations made by various laboratories indicate a shift of the k_g/k_o curve toward higher gas saturation (higher oil recoveries) for rocks of the same lithology but of greater and greater permeability. If one considers the gas saturation developed at $k_g/k_o = 1$, this may be considered as a "recovery index" by depletion drive. The higher the value of the recovery index, the higher the expected ultimate recovery by depletion. For rocks of the same lithology, greater ultimate recovery is therefore expected from the more permeable sands.

When the recovery index by depletion is plotted vs. the logarithm of air permeability, it is observed that the group of points so obtained may be classified according to rock porosity. For a given permeability the recovery index is greater at low porosities. In fact, this correlation is such that it may be represented by the formula

$$\text{Recovery index} \div \frac{\log K_{\text{air}}}{\phi}$$

For a given lithology, the product of the recovery index by ϕ plotted vs. $\log K$ is substantially a straight line.

This relationship has a singular resemblance to the Kozeny equation expressed on rock-volume basis:

$$\frac{1}{S_v{}^2} = t^2 \frac{K_{\text{air}}}{\phi}$$

In view of the similarity of these two expressions, it may be said that to a first approximation the recovery index by depletion is inversely proportional to the square of the rock's specific surface S_v on a rock-volume basis. S_v is naturally a function of the reservoir-rock lithology and it increases at equal rock permeability from clean sand, to shaly sand, to calcareous sand, to sandy conglomerate. Hence, at equal porosity and permeability the depletion recovery index decreases in the same sequence. This general conclusion has also been verified by correlation of laboratory and field data.

Presence of a Connate Water Phase. As observed, previously the presence of a connate water phase shifts the relative-permeability ratio curves toward the region of low oil saturation. Muskat's calculations indicate an additional recovery, on a stock-tank oil basis, of 1.7 per cent of pore space in the case of 30 per cent connate water saturation as against zero connate water saturation. On the basis of reservoir oil in place, the additional pore-space voidage is actually 14 per cent. The basis for these conclusions comes from the theoretical calculations of Muskat and Taylor (1946), the results of which are shown on Fig. 10-29.

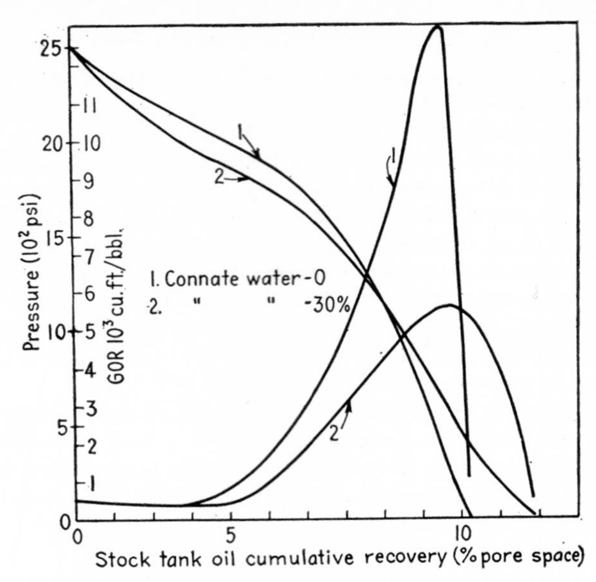

FIG. 10-29. Effect of connate water saturation on depletion-drive performance. (*After Muskat and Taylor.*)

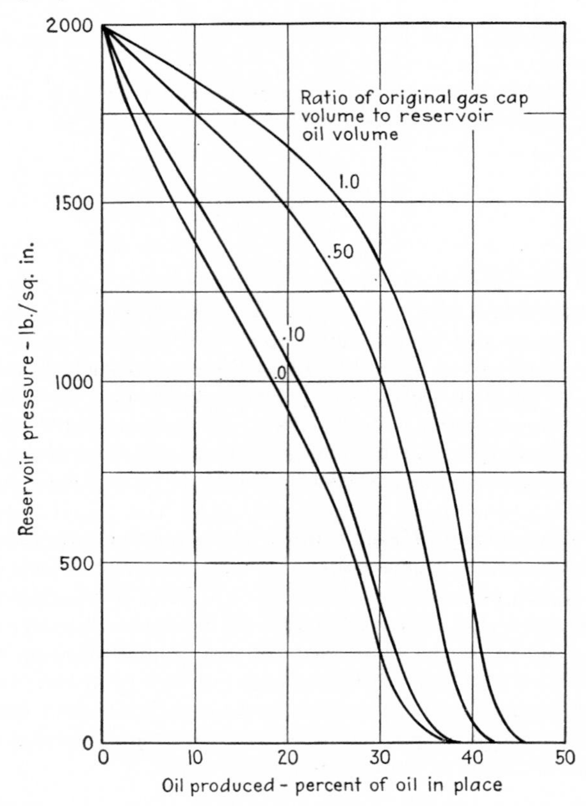

FIG. 10-30. Effect of presence of a gas cap on depletion-drive performance. (*After Tarner, courtesy Oil Weekly.*)

Presence and/or Formation of a Gas Cap and Its Mode of Expansion. The effect of a gas cap has been thoroughly discussed by both Tarner (1944) and Muskat (1945). Under the assumption that the gas-cap gas diffuses through the oil zone and is at all times in equilibrium with the reservoir oil, Tarner has shown that the oil recovery, on a pore-space voidage basis, increases from 37.5 to 45.5 per cent as the ratio of the original gas-cap volume passes from zero to one.

The performance curves are shown on Figs. 10-30 and 10-31. Muskat has made similar calculations in the case where the gas-oil ratio is not

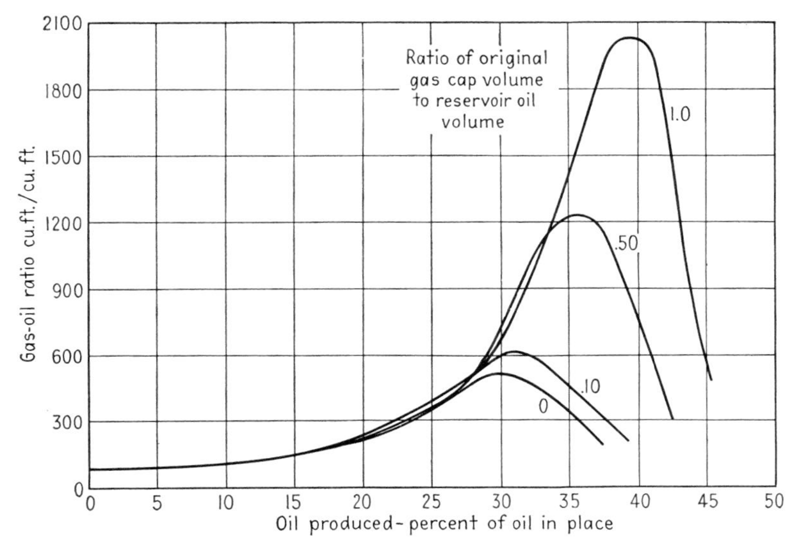

FIG. 10-31. Effect of presence of a gas cap on depletion-drive performance. (*After Tarner, courtesy Oil Weekly.*)

allowed to exceed a stated economic or stipulated gas-oil-ratio limit. The latter investigator also made calculations for withdrawals in gas-cap expansion-drive reservoirs with complete gravity segregation but without introduction of the beneficial action of gas counterflow on recovery.

Practice of Gas Cycling. Gas cycling may be practiced from the beginning of the life history of a field at discovery or at a later date. A specified fraction of the produced gas may be returned to the reservoir, and performance calculations may be carried out in the usual manner. Both Tarner (1944) and Muskat (1945) have presented theoretical results which illustrate the recovery benefits to be derived from cycling programs. Tarner has shown that, if there is no limit to the producing gas-oil ratio, injecting 100 per cent of the gas from the start can recover most of the oil in place, i.e., until the irreducible saturation is reached. In practice only a fraction of the gas can be returned, and a quantitative evaluation of the benefits to be derived from gas cycling may be had from Figs. 10-32 and 10-33. Similar deductions can be made for gas cycling started at a later date in the life of a field from Fig. 10-34.

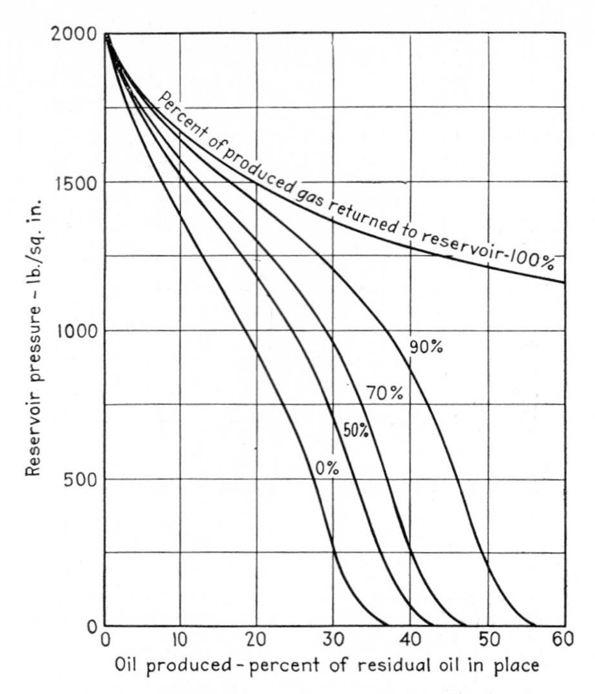

FIG. 10-32. Effect of gas injection on depletion-drive performance. (*After Tarner, courtesy Oil Weekly.*)

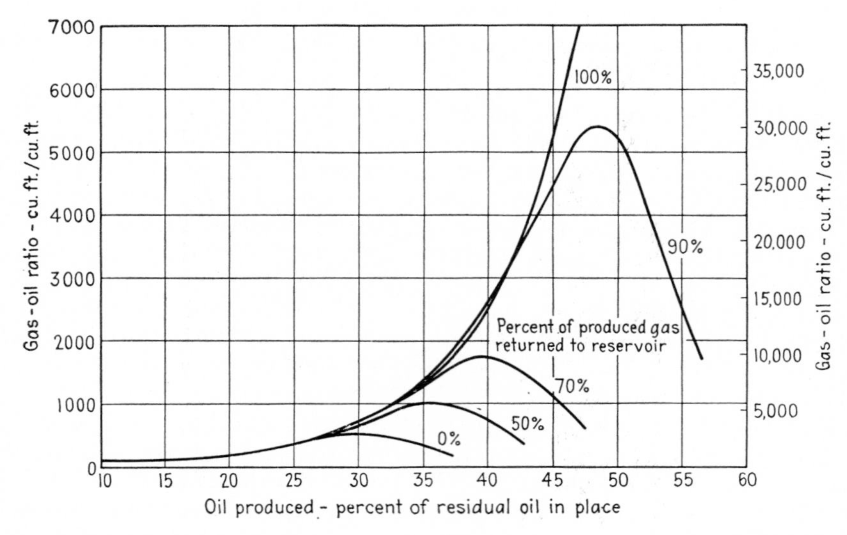

FIG. 10-33. Effect of gas injection on depletion-drive performance. (*After Tarner, courtesy Oil Weekly.*)

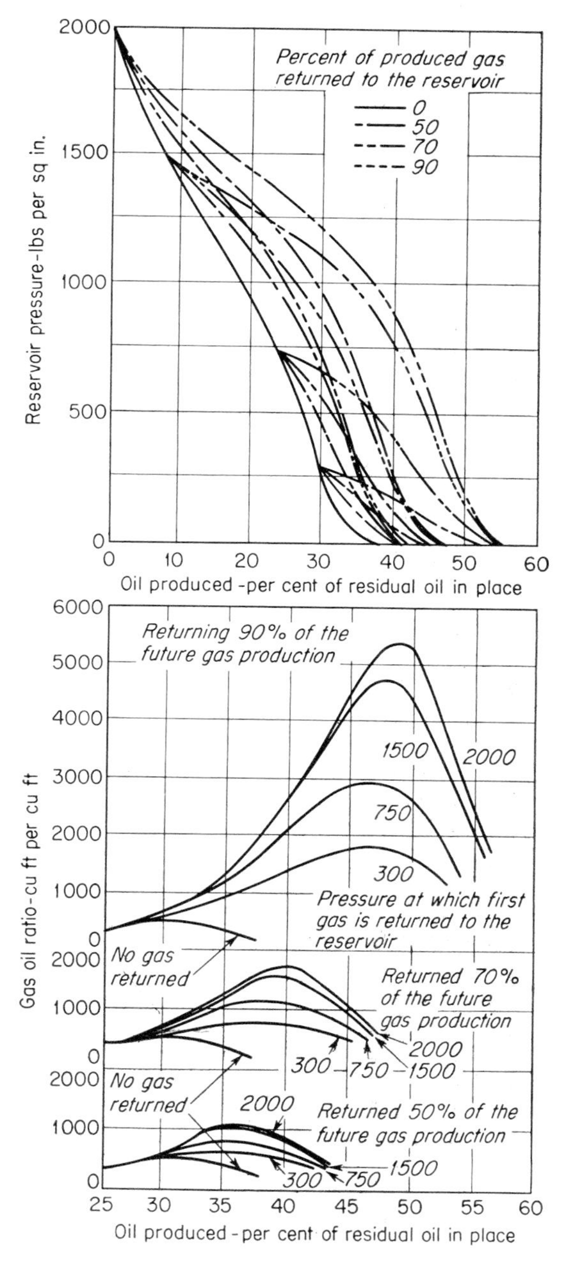

FIG. 10-34. Effect of gas injection on depletion-drive performance. (*After Tarner, courtesy Oil Weekly.*)

On the other hand, Muskat has shown that when economic restrictions are placed upon the maximum permissible gas-oil ratio, there may be advantages to inject but a fraction of the produced gas as illustrated in Fig. 10-35. It is seen that with 100 per cent gas cycling the ultimate recovery will be the same, when the permissible gas-oil ratio is reached and production must be discontinued, as when somewhat over 60 per cent of the produced gas is cycled. On the other hand, with a cycling ratio of 0.8, the economic gas-oil-ratio limit of 20,000 cu ft per bbl is never reached,

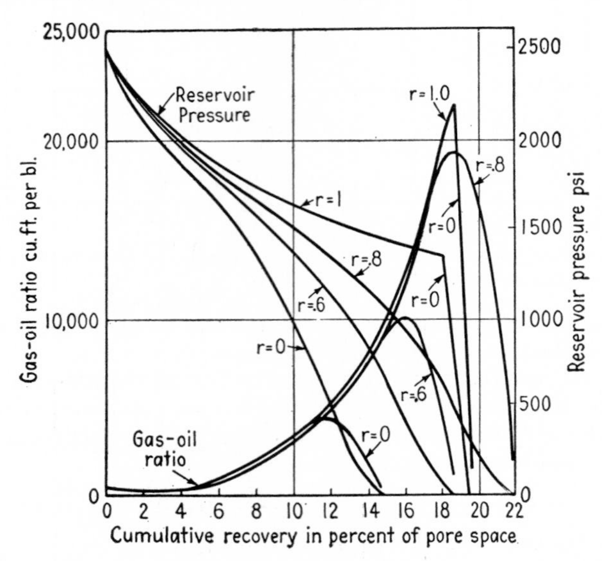

FIG. 10-35. Oil recoveries as a function of the gas-injection ratio with limiting gas-oil ratio of 20,000 cu ft per bbl. (*After Muskat.*)

and cycling operations may be continued until a cumulative recovery of 22 per cent of pore space is attained.

Vaporization Hysteresis within the Reservoir. It is expected that gas does not vaporize out of reservoir oil as readily within the reservoir rock as it does in the bottom-hole sample tester. Therefore, the oil remains supersaturated at the prevailing pressure and contains more gas in solution than expected under equilibrium conditions. In fact, when the bottom-hole pressure has reached abandonment or atmospheric pressure, the unrecovered oil may yet contain considerable solution gas.

In the absence of data, the sizes of the hysteresis loops were assumed in order to ascertain the magnitude of this effect on recovery. These loops are shown on Fig. 10-36. The method of Tarner was used for the computations together with the relative-permeability data of Fig. 10-6. The results of the computations shown in Fig. 10-37 indicate an inappreciable loss of recovery as a result of nonequilibrium liberation of solution gas for the assumed hysteresis in the reservoir-fluid properties. However, should the gas be released from solution in the produced oil, a shrinkage of about

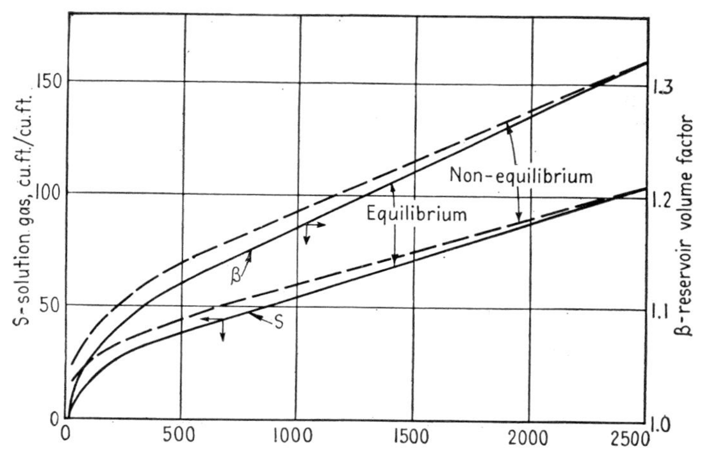

FIG. 10-36. Assumed vaporization-hysteresis loops resulting from nonequilibrium liberation of solution gas in the reservoir.

3 per cent would result, and the net recovery loss would be about 1 per cent of the original stock-tank oil in place.

Periodic testing of bottom-hole samples during the life of a field would ascertain the magnitude of the nonequilibrium vaporization for the production practice in effect. This would permit the adjustment of production rates to assure maximum recovery.

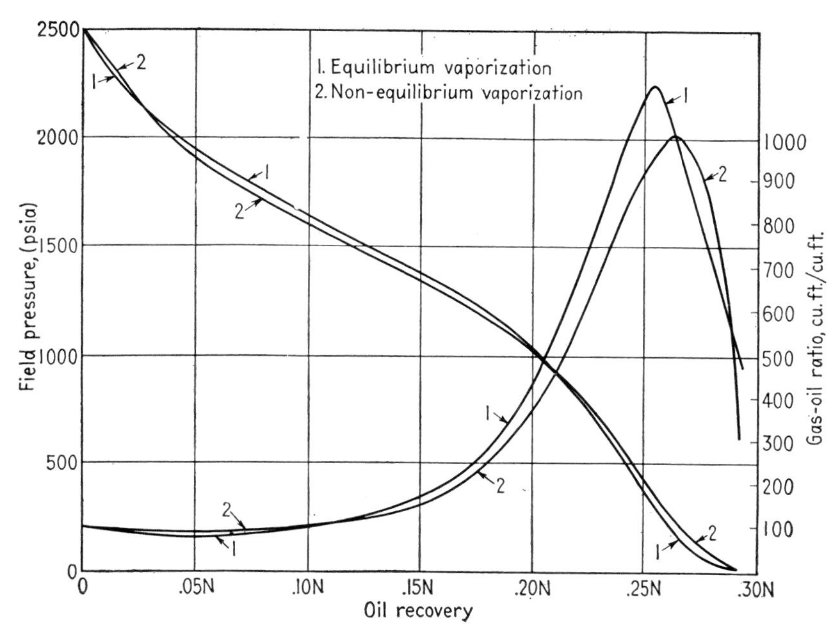

FIG. 10-37. Effect of vaporization hysteresis on reservoir performance and oil recovery.

Laboratory data which support the phenomenon of vaporization hysteresis in a reservoir and indicate it to be a function of pressure drawdown have been presented by Breston and Hughes (1948).

Well Spacing. Crego (1947) has attempted to verify experimentally the depletion-drive theory proposed by Muskat. He showed by internal gas drive of unconsolidated sand-packed tubes, saturated with water containing carbon dioxide under a pressure of about 1 atm, that the observed recoveries far exceeded (by factors of the order of 2) those predicted by the theory reviewed above. It appears that one important condition postulated in the theory of depletion drive, namely, a uniform distribution of outlets, was not approximated in Crego's experiments. The additional oil was presumably recovered by gas expulsion through the operation of the mechanism of external expansion drive. Crego's experiments are similar to field practice where the solution gas must travel long distances within the reservoir before it finds outlet to a well. Therefore, it appears that certain factors are missing from the theory and modifications must be introduced before the recovery from the depletion-drive mechanism may be predicted safely in laboratory experiments as well as in field operations. It is suggested that a combination of external- and depletion-drive mechanisms may give more reliable predictions. To this end the following theory is proposed.

Consider a unit volume of the reservoir containing a connate water saturation σ_w. Originally no free gas is assumed present. The original oil saturation is, therefore, $1 - \sigma_w$. Under a reservoir pressure P_0, the reservoir volume factor is β_0 and the solution gas is S_0. After production of a fraction of the oil, the pressure has dropped to p, the solution gas is S, and the reservoir volume factor is β. The saturation in reservoir oil is now σ_o. The total gas produced (A) from the unit reservoir volume is obtained from

$$A = \frac{1 - \sigma_w}{\beta_0} S_0 - (1 - \sigma_o - \sigma_w)\frac{1}{\alpha} - \frac{\sigma_o S}{\beta} \tag{10-50}$$

Within the reservoir unit volume, we may consider the following instantaneous fluid flows:

$$\text{Depletion oil-flow rate} = Q_o = d\left(\frac{\sigma_o}{\beta}\right) \tag{10-51}$$

$$\text{Depletion gas-flow rate} = Q_g = d\left[\frac{S\sigma_o}{\beta} + (1 - \sigma_w - \sigma_o)\frac{1}{\alpha}\right] \tag{10-52}$$

For simplification purposes it will be assumed that the area drained by a well is circular of external radius r_e, whereas the well radius is r_w. At any instant, the pressure distribution throughout the drainage area is assumed to be uniform, i.e., with negligible pressure gradient. Therefore, the fluid saturations in oil, gas, and connate water are also assumed constant at any one time during production.

Muskat (1945) has shown the passage of gas to be responsible for the instantaneous expulsion of oil per unit reservoir volume, which may be calculated by the following equation:

$$Q'_o = \frac{1}{\beta b} \frac{Q_g}{\int_0^\theta Q_g \, d\theta} = \frac{1}{\beta b} \frac{Q_g}{A'} \qquad (10\text{-}53)$$

where Q_g = instantaneous gas-flow rate
A' = total gas flow which has passed through the volume of the reservoir under study
b = slope of permeability-saturation curve on semilogarithmic paper

The reservoir volume factor β is introduced in Eq. (10-53) because of the pressure p prevailing in the reservoir at the time considered. For the circular reservoir considered, the total gas flow through a unit volume located at a distance r from the center of the well, may be calculated as follows:

$$A' = A \frac{\pi(r_e^2 - r^2)}{2\pi r} = A \frac{r_e^2 - r^2}{2r} \qquad (10\text{-}54)$$

A further simplification is introduced at this point as it would be impossible to solve the differential material-balance equation containing a variable radius. It will be postulated that the expulsion of oil by the gas flow can be averaged over the radius of drainage. Hence the total average gas flow is obtained by

$$A'_{\text{av}} = A \frac{\int_{r_w}^{r_e} \frac{r_e^2 - r^2}{2r} \, dr}{r_e - r_w} = A \frac{\frac{1}{2}\left(r_e^2 \ln \frac{r_e}{r_w} - \frac{r_e^2 - r_w^2}{2}\right)}{r_e - r_w} \qquad (10\text{-}55)$$

In practice, r_e is so much larger than r_w that r_w may be neglected in $r_e - r_w$ and r_w^2 in $r_e^2 - r_w^2$. Hence

$$A'_{\text{av}} = A \frac{r_e}{2}\left(\ln \frac{r_e}{r_w} - \frac{1}{2}\right) = AE \qquad (10\text{-}56)$$

where $E = \frac{r_e}{2}\left(\ln \frac{r_e}{r_w} - \frac{1}{2}\right)$ is a function of well spacing.

The differential material-balance equation may now be written

$$S + \beta \frac{\mu_o}{\mu_g} \frac{k_g}{k_o} \frac{1}{\alpha} = \frac{Q_g}{Q_o + \frac{1}{\beta b} \frac{Q_g}{A'_{\text{av}}}} = \frac{Q_g}{Q_o + \frac{1}{\beta b} \frac{Q_g}{A \frac{r_e}{2}\left(\ln \frac{r_e}{r_w} - \frac{1}{2}\right)}} \qquad (10\text{-}57)$$

Substituting the symbols Q_o, Q_g, and A by their values

$$S + \beta \frac{\mu_o}{\mu_g} \frac{k_g}{k_o} \frac{1}{\alpha} = \frac{d\left[\frac{S\sigma_o}{\beta} + (1 - \sigma_w - \sigma_o)\frac{1}{\alpha}\right]}{d\left(\frac{\sigma_o}{\beta}\right) + \frac{d\left[\frac{S\sigma_o}{\beta} + (1 - \sigma_w - \sigma_o)\frac{1}{\alpha}\right]}{\beta b\left[\frac{1-\sigma_w}{\beta_0}S_0 - (1 - \sigma_o - \sigma_w)\frac{1}{\alpha} - \frac{\sigma_o S}{\beta}\right]\frac{r_e}{2}\left(\ln\frac{r_e}{r_w} - \frac{1}{2}\right)}} \tag{10-58}$$

This equation may be compared to Eq. (10-36) of Muskat for the simple internal-drive mechanism. The difference resides in the expulsion term in the denominator, which includes the dimensions of the drainage area (r_e). Therefore, it is expected that this equation will permit the study of the influence of well spacing on the recovery mechanism by solution gas drive.

The total differentials may be replaced by the derivative with respect to pressure. When these calculations are carried out and the terms separated in order to solve for the variation of oil saturation in the reservoir as a function of pressure decline, the following expression is arrived at:

$$\frac{d\sigma_o}{dp} = \frac{\frac{\sigma_o}{\beta}\left(1 - \frac{R}{\beta AE}\right)\frac{dS}{dp} + (1 - \sigma_w - \sigma_o)\left(1 - \frac{R}{\beta AE}\right)\frac{d\frac{1}{\alpha}}{dp} + \sigma_o\left[-S + R\left(1 + \frac{S}{bAE\beta}\right)\right]\frac{d\beta/dp}{\beta^2}}{\frac{1}{\alpha}\left(1 + \frac{\mu_o}{\mu_g}\frac{k_g}{k_o}\right) + \frac{R}{\beta AEb}\left(\frac{S}{\beta} - \frac{1}{\alpha}\right)} \tag{10-59}$$

where R is the instantaneous gas-oil ratio.

As in the method of Muskat, the present equation must be integrated numerically, or point by point. The gas expulsion effect accounted for by the new depletion-drive equation will not take place until after the equilibrium saturation to gas has been reached, and the original equation of Muskat may be used up to that point.

There are certain limitations of the present equation which it is well to recognize:

1. The gas expulsion term is calculated and averaged for convenience, but it is realized that the transient effect is unaccounted for in the early stages of production when the pressure-decline wave travels to the limits of the drainage area.

2. The drainage area around a well has been assumed for convenience to be circular. Yet in a geometric array of wells, the drainage lines depart considerably from radial flow especially toward the edges of the area affected by each well.

The factor $E = \frac{r_e}{2}\left(\ln \frac{r_e}{r_w} - \frac{1}{2}\right)$ may be called the efficiency of the gas expulsion, and for a well radius of 3 in. and for the various well spacings normally used in depletion-drive fields E takes the following values:

Spacing well to well	E
40 acres location, or 1,320 ft.	2,435
10 acres location, or 660 ft.	1,105

The above figures are valid when the unit reservoir volume considered in the calculations is 1 cu ft and all the reservoir and fluid constants are referred to a cubic-foot basis. Owing to the large numerical value of E, some terms become negligible in the above equation, and the following simplified form will be found suitable:

$$\frac{d\sigma_o}{dp} = \frac{\dfrac{\sigma_o}{\beta}\dfrac{dS}{dp} + (1 - \sigma_w - \sigma_o)\dfrac{d\dfrac{1}{\alpha}}{dp} + \dfrac{\sigma_o}{\beta^2}\left[-S + R\left(1 + \dfrac{S}{bAE\beta}\right)\right]\dfrac{d\beta}{dp}}{\dfrac{1}{\alpha}\left(1 + \dfrac{\mu_o}{\mu_g}\dfrac{k_g}{k_o}\right)} \tag{10-60}$$

However, when numerical values are substituted in the equation it is found that spacing has no appreciable effect on recovery; yet in experiments such as Crego's the value of E becomes very small, and the gas expulsion term takes significance in the recovery mechanism.

Rates of Fluid Withdrawal and Pressure Drawdowns. Variations in withdrawal rates may have two effects:

1. A rapid production rate which results from high-pressure drawdown at the wells may not permit vaporization equilibrium to be established, and the reservoir oil may remain gas supersaturated. This phenomenon results in lower oil recovery as was shown under the study of vaporization hysteresis.

2. A high-pressure drawdown results in a higher pressure gradient within the drainage area of a well. This influences the value of the factor b in the gas expulsion effect. However, the sweeping action of gas is important only for very close well spacing.

Gas-saturation Gradient in Gas-injection Projects. When gas is injected in a depletion-drive field for the purpose of increasing recovery, the injected gas does not form a uniformly dispersed gas phase in the conformable section of the reservoirs; in fact, a fluid saturation gradient is established as a result of gas injection with a higher fluid saturation in the immediate vicinity of the producing well, which saturation in turn controls

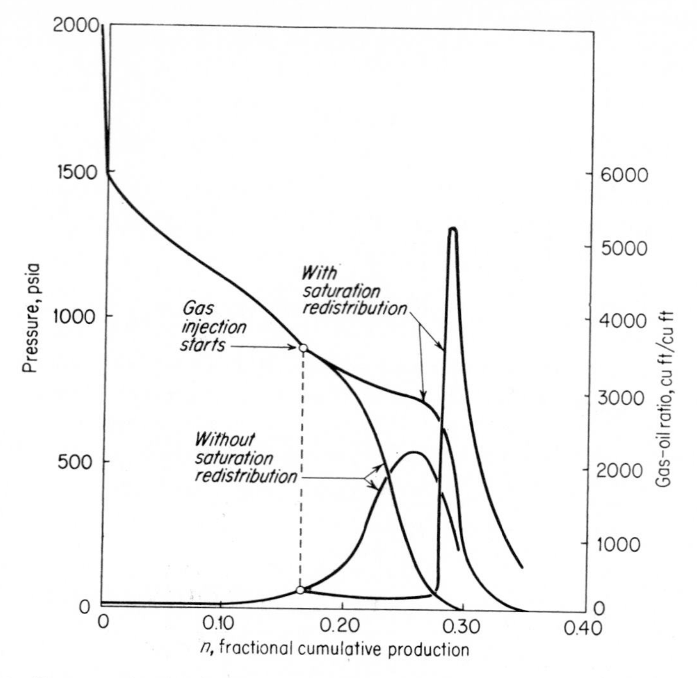

FIG. 10-38. Comparative performance of a depletion drive with gas injection in a conformable zone with and without fluid saturation gradient and redistribution.

the producing gas-oil ratio. As will be seen in Chap. 11, this effect may be taken into account by means of an equation proposed by Welge (1951), and a calculating technique has been advocated by Craig and Geffen (1955).

A feasible technique involves the use of the depletion-drive equations written in finite difference form:

$$\Delta_i^{i+1} n = \frac{(1 - n_i)\,\Delta_i^{i+1}\left(\dfrac{\beta}{\alpha} - S\right) - \beta_0\,\Delta_i^{i+1}\dfrac{1}{\alpha}}{\left(\dfrac{\beta}{\alpha} - S\right)_{i+1} + R_{e,\text{av}}(1 - I)}$$

$$R_e = S + \frac{\beta}{\alpha}\left(\frac{k_g}{k_o}\right)_e \frac{\mu_o}{\mu_g} \tag{10-61}$$

$$\bar{\sigma}_{le} = \sigma_w + (1 - \sigma_w)\,\frac{(e - n_e)\beta}{e\beta_0}$$

$$n = (1 - e)n_p + n_e$$

$$\Delta_i^{i+1} n = (1 - e)\,\Delta_i^{i+1} n_p + \Delta_i^{i+1} n_e$$

The symbols have their usual significance.

In order to take care of the effect of a saturation gradient between wells within the conformable section, the Welge equation must be complied with:

$$\Delta \bar{\sigma}_{ge} = \bar{\sigma}_{g_{ei+1}} - \sigma_{g_{wi+1}} = -Q_i \left(\frac{\Delta_i^{i+1} \bar{\sigma}_{oe}}{\Delta_i^{i+1} Q_i} \right) \tag{10-62}$$

where $\bar{\sigma}_{g_{ei+1}}$ = mean gas saturation = $1 - \bar{\sigma}_{l_{ei+1}}$

$\sigma_{g_{wi+1}}$ = gas saturation at producing well, which in turn controls flowing gas-oil ratio $R_{e_{i+1}}$

Q_i = cumulative gas injected = $\sum_0^i \alpha_{av} \, \Delta n R_{av} I \, \dfrac{1 - \sigma_w}{e\beta_0}$ expressed in pore-volume units of conformable section; each incremental volume is measured at mean injection pressure; a pore-volume unit of conformable section is $\dfrac{e\beta_0}{1 - \sigma_w}$

$\Delta_i^{i+1} Q_i$ = increment of gas injected = $\alpha_{av} \, \Delta_i^{i+1} n R_{av} I$, expressed in pore-volume units of conformable section, and measured at mean injection pressure

$\dfrac{\Delta \bar{\sigma}_{oe}}{\Delta Q_i}$ = value readily calculated from differential values of $\bar{\sigma}_{l_e}$ and Q_i

The step-by-step procedure for gas injection beyond break-through is as follows:

1. Assume a value for $R_{e_{i+1}}$; this value determines $\sigma_{g_{wi+1}}$ at the well bore.

2. Calculate the total increment of production $\Delta_i^{i+1} n$. $R_{e,av}$ is obtained from $\frac{1}{2}(R_{e_i} + R_{e_{i+1}})$.

3. Calculate $n_{i+1} = n_i + \Delta_i^{i+1} n$ and the mean liquid saturation $\bar{\sigma}_{l_e}$ in the conformable section of the reservoir. The decrement in mean oil saturation in the conformable section $\Delta_i^{i+1} \bar{\sigma}_{o_e}$ is then determined; it is equal to $\Delta \bar{\sigma}_{l_e}$ since the connate water saturation remains constant.

4. Calculate the reservoir volume (in pore-space unit volumes) of the increment of gas injected from $\Delta_i^{i+1} Q_i = \alpha_{av} \, \Delta_i^{i+1} n \, R_{e,av} I \, \dfrac{(1 - \sigma_w)}{e\beta_0}$

5. Solve Eq. (10-62) for $\Delta \bar{\sigma}_{g_e}$ and determine the value of $\bar{\sigma}_{g_{ei+1}}$ which should be equal to $1 - \bar{\sigma}_{l_{ei+1}}$. If this is not verified to a sufficient precision, assume a new value for $R_{e_{i+1}}$, and proceed anew until a satisfactory check is obtained (Table 10-4 and Fig. 10-38).

High Volatility of Reservoir Oil. In this case relative proportions of *liquid* and *vapor* (gas) flowing in the reservoir are not the same as those coming out of the separator because of wide difference in phase behavior at bottom-hole temperature and pressure and at separator temperature and pressure. In fact, for the type of crude discussed here in which the phase behavior is close to the critical of the reservoir-fluid mixture, the liquid of the separator acts as a solvent for the heavy ends of the vapor phase and

Table 10-14. Partial Pressure Maintenance by Finite Difference Material Balance

With dispersed gas injection ($I = 0.6$), conformance factor ($e = 0.5$), and fluid saturation gradient

P, psia (1)	R_e (assume) (2)	$R_{e,av}$ (3)	$1 - n$ = (1) − (12) (4)	$\Delta\left(\frac{\beta}{\alpha} - S\right)$ (5)	$(4)_i(5)$ (6)	$\beta_0 \Delta \frac{1}{\alpha}$ (7)	(6) − (7) (8)	$\frac{\beta}{\alpha} - S$ (9)	(9) + (3)(1 − I) (10)	Δn = (8)/(10) (11)	$n = \Sigma(\Delta n)$ (12)	$n_e = n - (1 - e)n_p$ (13)	$\bar{\sigma}_{oe} = (1 - \sigma_w) \times \frac{(e - n_e)\beta}{e\beta_0}$ (14)
900	252	...	0.840	...	...	...	...	...	...	...	0.160	...	0.631
800	240	246	0.7833	−6.1	−5.12	−11.68	6.56	17.3	115.7	0.0567	0.2167	0.1269	0.5564
700	220	230	0.7248	−6.5	−5.09	−11.18	6.09	10.8	102.8	0.0585	0.2752	0.1792	0.4748
650	3,200	1,710	0.7198	−3.05	−2.21	−5.525	3.315	7.75	691.75	0.00478	0.2802	0.1814	0.4664
600	5,200	4,700	0.718	−2.66	−1.913	−5.34	3.425	5.1	1,885	0.00182	0.282	0.1805	0.4652
500	4,600	4,900	0.7143	−4.8	−2.442	−10.68	7.238	0.3	1,960	0.00369	0.2857	0.1797	0.4612
400	4,200	4,400	0.7103	−4.0	−2.857	−10.00	7.143	−3.7	1,756	0.00406	0.2897	0.1797	0.4571
300	3,500	3,850	0.7054	−2.9	−2.06	−9.56	7.50	−6.6	1,533	0.0049	0.2946	0.1809	0.4494
200	2,900	3,150	0.6991	−1.6	−1.13	−9.06	7.93	−8.2	1,252	0.0063	0.3009	0.1803	0.4397
100	2,050	2,475	0.6901	−0.3	−2.097	−9.06	8.85	−8.85	981.5	0.0090	0.3099	0.1871	0.4255
14.7	650	1,350	0.6669	+9.44	+6.45	−6.09	12.54	0.94	541	0.0232	0.3331	0.1979	0.3831

TABLE 10-14. PARTIAL PRESSURE MAINTENANCE BY FINITE DIFFERENCE MATERIAL BALANCE (*Continued*)

$\Delta\bar{\sigma}_{oe} = \Delta(14)$ (15)	S (16)	$R_e - S =$ (2) − (16) (17)	$\frac{k_g}{k_o} =$ (17)/F (18)	σ_g well from (18) and k_g/k_o curve (19)	α (20)	$\alpha_{av} = \frac{\alpha_i + \alpha_{i+1}}{2}$ (21)	$\Delta Q_g =$ (21)(11)(3)$I \times \frac{1-\sigma_w}{e\beta_0}$ (22)	$Q_g = \Sigma \Delta Q_g$ (23)	$-Q_g \frac{\Delta\bar{\sigma}_{oe}}{\Delta Q_g} = (23)\frac{(15)}{(22)}$ (24)	$\bar{\sigma}_{ge} =$ (19) + (24) (25)	$1 - \bar{\sigma}_{oe} - \sigma_w =$ 1 − (14) − σ_w [must equal (25)] (26)
...	60.8	...	...	...	0.0139						
−0.076	55.1	184.9	0.0239	0.168	0.016	0.01495	0.1617	0.1617	0.076	0.244	0.245
−0.0816	50.5	169.5	0.0239	0.168	0.01868	0.01734	0.182	0.3437	0.154	0.3225	0.325
−0.0084	48.2	3,151.8	0.460	0.3023	0.02035	0.0195	0.123	0.468	0.0319	0.3342	0.3336
−0.0012	45.6	5,154	0.784	0.3294	0.02232	0.02133	0.142	0.610	0.00519	0.3346	0.3348
−0.0040	40.2	4,560	0.7625	0.328	0.02761	0.02496	0.350	0.960	0.0110	0.339	0.3388
−0.0041	30.9	4,215	0.800	0.3305	0.0355	0.03155	0.436	1.396	0.0131	0.3436	0.3429
−0.0077	29.0	3,470	0.7525	0.326	0.0489	0.0422	0.614	2.010	0.0250	0.3510	0.3506
−0.0097	22.4	2,877.6	0.790	0.3301	0.076	0.0624	0.965	2.975	0.0299	0.3600	0.3603
−0.0143	14.7	1,985	0.953	0.3395	0.1708	0.1234	2.136	5.111	0.0342	0.3737	0.3746
−0.0364	0	650	1.500	0.3616	0.1065	0.6179	15.00	20.111	0.0488	0.4103	0.4109

considerably more liquid is separated than the liquid volume flowing in the reservoir.

Actual performance in the reservoir is unchanged and may be calculated from PVT information obtained from a representative bottom-hole sample.

However, in order to predict the actual liquids obtained from the surface separator, it is necessary to know the composition of the fluid stream entering it and the operating temperature and pressure, and then to proceed with a *separator calculation*.

SELECTED REFERENCES ON OIL PRODUCTION BY DEPLETION DRIVE

1936

Hassler, G. L., et al.: Recovery of Oil from Sandstones by Gas Drive, *Trans. AIME Petroleum Development and Technol.*, pp. 120ff.

Katz, D. L.: A Method of Estimating Oil and Gas Reserves, *Trans. AIME*, vol. 118, pp. 18ff.

Schilthuis, R. J.: Active Oil and Reservoir Energy, *Trans. AIME*, vol. 118, pp. 33ff.

Wyckoff, R. D., and H. G. Botset: The Flow of Gas-Liquid Mixtures through Unconsolidated Sands, *Physics*, pp. 325ff.

1939

Leverett, M. C.: Flow of Oil-Water Mixtures through Unconsolidated Sands, *Trans. AIME Petroleum Development and Technol.*, pp. 149ff.

1940

Botset, H. G.: Flow of Gas-Liquid Mixtures through Consolidated Sand, *AIME Tech. Pub.* 1111.

Leverett, M. C., and W. B. Lewis: Steady Flow of Gas-Oil-Water Mixtures through Unconsolidated Sands, *AIME Tech. Pub.* 1206.

1941

Evinger, H. H., and M. Muskat: Calculation of Theoretical Productivity Factor, *AIME Tech. Pub.* 1352.

Leverett, M. C.: Capillary Behavior of Porous Solids, *Trans. AIME Petroleum Development and Technol.*, pp. 152ff.

1942

Evinger, H. H., and M. Muskat: Calculation of Productivity Factors for Oil-Gas-Water Systems in Steady State, *AIME Tech. Pub.* 1416.

Lewis, J. A.: Productivity Index and Measurable Reservoir Characteristics, *AIME Tech. Pub.* 1467.

1943

Cook, A. B.: Derivation and Application of Material Balance Equations, *U.S. Bur. Mines Rept. Invest.* 3720.

Hassler, G. L., et al.: The Role of Capillarity in Oil Production, *AIME Tech. Pub.* 1623.

Johnston, N., and J. E. Sherborne, Permeability as Related to Productivity Index, *Oil Gas J.*, Nov. 11, pp. 290ff.

1944

Babson, E. C.: Prediction of Reservoir Behavior from Laboratory Data, *AIME Tech Pub.* 1664.

Tarner, J.: How Different Size Gas Caps and Pressure Maintenance Programs Affect Amount of Recoverable Oil, *Oil Weekly*, June 12, pp. 32ff.

1945

Day, R. J., and S. T. Yuster: Predictions of Behavior in Air-Gas Drive, *Producers Monthly*, November, pp. 27ff.

Muskat, M.: The Production Histories of Oil Producing Gas-drive Reservoirs, *J. Appl. Phys.*, vol. 16, pp. 147ff.

———, and M. O. Taylor: Effect of Reservoir Fluid and Rock Characteristics on Production History of Gas Drive Reservoirs, *AIME Tech. Pub.* 1917.

Pirson, S. J.: The Engineering Approach to Oil Reservoir Controls, *Oil Weekly*, Dec. 31, pp. 22ff.

1946

Muskat, M.: Note on Gas Repressuring, *Producers Monthly*, February, pp. 23ff.

———, and M. O. Taylor: Effect of the Crude Gravity on the Performance of Gas Drive Reservoirs, *Petroleum Engr.*, December, pp. 88ff.

Patton, E. C., Jr.: Evaluation of Pressure Maintenance by Internal Gas Injection in Volumetric Controlled Reservoirs, *AIME Tech. Pub.* 2098.

1947

Crego, W. O.: Internal Gas Drive Production from Unconsolidated Sand, Pennsylvania State College M.Sc. Thesis (unpublished).

Hoss, R. L.: The Calculated Effect of Pressure Maintenance on Oil Recovery, *AIME Tech. Pub.* 2231.

Terwilliger, P. L.: A Study of Gas-drive Recovery on Unconsolidated Sands, Pennsylvania State College M.Sc. Thesis (unpublished).

1948

Breston, J. N., and R. V. Hughes: Long Core Experiments with Brine Floods Following Depletion with Gas Drive, *12th Ann. Tech. Meeting, Penn. State Coll.*

Elkins, L. F., et al.: Lance Creek Sundance Reservoir Performance—A Unified Pressure-maintenance Project, *AIME Tech. Pub.* 2401.

1949

Keller, W. O., et al.: Effect of Permeability on Recovery Efficiency by Gas Displacement, *API Tulsa Meeting*, Mar. 23–25.

Loper, R. G., and J. C. Calhoun, Jr.: The Effect of Spacing and Drawdown on Recovery from Internal Gas Drive Reservoirs, *AIME Tech. Pub.* 2592.

Miller, C. C., et al.: A Calculation of the Effect of Production Rate upon Ultimate Recovery by a Solution Gas Drive, *AIME Tech. Pub.* 2565.

1953

Pirson, S. J.: Performance of Fractured Oil Reservoirs, *Bull. Am. Assoc. Petroleum Geol.*, vol. 37, no.2, pp. 252ff.

Van Wingen, N.: The Use of the Material Balance Method in Reserve Estimation, *J. Petroleum Technol.*, vol. 5, no. 12, pp. 1ff.

1954

Higgins, R. V.: Study of Undersaturation during Repressuring and Supersaturation during Flow of Oil to Wells, *AIME Tech. Pub.* 3891; *J. Petroleum Technol.*, vol. 6, no. 9, pp. 117ff.

Stewart, C. R., et al.: The Role of Bubble Formation in Oil Recovery by Solution Gas Drives in Limestones, *AIME Tech. Pub.* 3962; *J. Petroleum Technol.*, vol. 6, no. 12, pp. 21ff.

1955

Arps, J. J., and T. G. Roberts: The Effect of the Relative Permeability Ratio, the Oil Gravity, and the Solution Gas-Oil Ratio on the Primary Recovery from a Depletion Type Reservoir, *AIME Tech. Pub.* 4103.

Bass, D. M., and P. B. Crawford: Predicting Reservoir Performance, *Petroleum Engr.*, June, pp. B59ff.

Hawkins, M. F., Jr.: Material Balances in Volumetric Unsaturated Reservoir above Bubble Point, *J. Petroleum Technol.*, vol. 7, no. 9, pp. 49ff.

Mueller, T. D., et al.: Analysis of Reservoir Performance K_g/K_o Curve Measured on a Core Sample, *AIME Tech. Pub.* 4102.

Pings, C. J., Jr., and W. Tempelaar-Lietz: Canal Field Gas Injection Project, *J. Petroleum Technol.*, vol. 7, no. 8, pp. 25ff.

Sturdivant, W. C., Jr.: A Simplified Method of Calculating Behavior in Closed Reservoirs, *Petroleum Engr.*, November, pp. B95ff.; December, pp. B105ff.; January, pp. B58ff.

Tracy, G. W.: Simplified Form of the Material Balance Equation, *AIME Tech. Note* 256.

Woods, R. W.: Case History of Reservoir Performance of a Highly Volatile Type Oil Reservoir, *J. Petroleum Technol.*, vol. 7, no. 9, pp. 156ff.

1956

Brinkman, F. H., and C. F. Weinaug: Calculated Performance of a Dissolved Gas Drive Reservoir by a Phase Behavior Method, *AIME Tech. Paper* 740G.

Craig, F. F., and T. M. Geffen: The Determination of Partial Pressure Maintenance Performance by Laboratory Flow Tests, *J. Petroleum Technol.*, vol. 8, no. 2, pp. 42ff.

Jacoby, R. H., and V. J. Berry, Jr.: A Method for Predicting Depletion Performance of a Reservoir Producing Volatile Crude Oil, *AIME Tech. Paper* 688G.

Reudelhuber, F. O., and R. F. Hinds: A Compositional Material Balance Method for Prediction of Recovery from Volatile Oil Depletion Drive Reservoir, *AIME Tech. Paper* 690G.

Smith, M. R., and J. H. Henderson: Performance of a Solution Gas Drive Reservoir, Rosenwald Pool, Oklahoma, *AIME Tech. Paper* 687G.

CHAPTER 11

THEORY OF OIL PRODUCTION BY FRONTAL DISPLACEMENT

In addition to displacement of oil from its reservoir-rock container through the expulsive agency of internally expanding solution gas (*depletion drive*), oil is recovered by a pistonlike displacement through external application of sources of energy either by water encroachment (*water drive*) or by an expanding gas cap or external gas drive which may operate with or without counterflow of oil and gas under the buoyancy effect of gravity forces (*segregation drive*).

The study of the fundamental oil-displacement mechanism by *water* or by *segregation drive* necessitates the establishment of mathematical relations which are valid at a point and at every point within the reservoir rock under the application of the driving forces resulting from external pressure application by water or gas. The relations to be studied are differential equations for the simultaneous flow of two phases, namely, the fractional-flow formula and the rate-of-frontal-advance formula.

THE FRACTIONAL-FLOW FORMULA

The derivation of this important equation will follow the outline originally proposed by Leverett (1940). Let us consider a mixture of fluids streaming in a direction u, making an angle α with the horizontal; α will be considered positive up-dip. Let the absolute permeability of the medium be K and the effective permeabilities to oil, gas, and water be K_o, K_g, and K_w, respectively. They are obtained from relative-permeability diagrams. Considering only the flow of a mixture of oil and water for the present, the generalized Darcy laws for the two fluids are written

$$q_{ou} = -\frac{K_o}{\mu_o}\left(\frac{\partial P_o}{\partial u} + g\delta_o \sin \alpha\right)$$
$$q_{wu} = -\frac{K_w}{\mu_w}\left(\frac{\partial P_w}{\partial u} + g\delta_w \sin \alpha\right) \qquad (11\text{-}1)$$

where $\partial P_o/\partial u$ and $\partial P_w/\partial u$ = pressure gradients within oil and water phases respectively, atm per cm

q_{ou} and q_{wu} = volumetric flow rates of oil and water per sec through a cross-sectional area of 1 sq cm

Hence it is preassumed that funicular saturation conditions prevail within both fluids. For the case assumed of up-dip flow, the effect of gravity is to retard the flow, which justifies the signs used. Equations (11-1) are transformed as follows:

$$q_{ou} \frac{\mu_o}{K_o} = -\frac{\partial P_o}{\partial u} - g\delta_o \sin \alpha \tag{11-2}$$

$$q_{wu} \frac{\mu_w}{K_w} = -\frac{\partial P_w}{\partial u} - g\delta_w \sin \alpha \tag{11-3}$$

Letting $\delta_w - \delta_o = \Delta\delta$ and $P_w - P_o = P_c$, the capillary pressure, we obtain after subtraction of (11-3) from (11-2) and dropping the subscript u

$$q_w \frac{\mu_w}{K_w} - q_o \frac{\mu_o}{K_o} = -\frac{\partial P_c}{\partial u} - g\, \Delta\delta \sin \alpha \tag{11-4}$$

Now let $q_o + q_w = q_t$ equal the total fluid flow, which when multiplied by μ_o/K_o becomes

$$q_w \frac{\mu_o}{K_o} + q_o \frac{\mu_o}{K_o} = q_t \frac{\mu_o}{K_o} \tag{11-5}$$

Dividing Eqs. (11-4) and (11-5) term by term, we obtain

$$\frac{q_w \dfrac{\mu_w}{K_w} - q_o \dfrac{\mu_o}{K_o}}{q_w \dfrac{\mu_o}{K_o} + q_o \dfrac{\mu_o}{K_o}} = \frac{-\dfrac{\partial P_c}{\partial u} - g\, \Delta\delta \sin \alpha}{q_t \dfrac{\mu_o}{K_o}} = \frac{-\dfrac{K_o}{q_t \mu_o}\left(\dfrac{\partial P_c}{\partial u} + g\, \Delta\delta \sin \alpha\right)}{1} \tag{11-6}$$

Using the well-known algebraic relation that if

$$\frac{A}{B} = \frac{C}{D}$$

then the following is true:

$$\frac{A + B}{B} = \frac{C + D}{D}$$

When applied to Eq. (11-6), we obtain

$$\frac{q_w \left(\dfrac{\mu_w}{K_w} + \dfrac{\mu_o}{K_o}\right)}{q_w \dfrac{\mu_o}{K_o} + q_o \dfrac{\mu_o}{K_o}} = \frac{1 - \dfrac{K_o}{\mu_o q_t}\left(\dfrac{\partial P_c}{\partial u} + g\, \Delta\delta \sin \alpha\right)}{1} \tag{11-7}$$

Now let

$$f_w = \frac{q_w}{q_w + q_o} = \frac{q_w}{q_t}$$

which is the fractional flow of water (q_w) in the total flow stream (q_t). Simplifying, and replacing the effective-permeability ratio K_o/K_w by the relative-permeability ratio k_o/k_w, we obtain

$$f_w = \frac{1 - \dfrac{K_o}{\mu_o q_t}\left(\dfrac{\partial P_c}{\partial u} + g\,\Delta\delta \sin\alpha\right)}{1 + \dfrac{k_o}{k_w}\dfrac{\mu_w}{\mu_o}} \tag{11-8}$$

This equation was published in 1940 by Leverett, but its practical significance was overlooked for several years.

The derivation of formula (11-8) is readily extended to express the ratio of gas flow to the total stream, as follows:

$$f_g = \frac{q_g}{q_o + q_g} = \frac{1 - \dfrac{K_o}{\mu_o q_t}\left(\dfrac{\partial P_c}{\partial u} + g\,\Delta\delta \sin\alpha\right)}{1 + \dfrac{k_o}{k_g}\dfrac{\mu_g}{\mu_o}} \tag{11-9}$$

provided that the following relations are set up:

$$\begin{aligned} P_c &= P_g - P_o \\ \Delta\delta &= \delta_g - \delta_o \\ \alpha &= \text{positive up-dip} \end{aligned}$$

Equation (11-8) differs from Leverett's formula by signs only inasmuch as he derived it for the following setup:

$$\begin{aligned} P_c &= P_o - P_w \\ \Delta\delta &= \delta_o - \delta_w \\ \alpha &= \text{positive down-dip} \end{aligned}$$

Since there are three quantities which may change sign according to the assumptions made, it is possible to write Eqs. (11-8) and (11-9) in four different forms equally valid. The author prefers the form of Eq. (11-8), where P_c represents a suction on the water in a water-wet reservoir rock; hence capillary action helps the movement of water, since P_c is negative and its gradient is positive in the direction of flow. For an oil-wet reservoir, we encounter reversed conditions.

It is seen also that gravity opposes the flow of water for up-dip flow, owing to the higher density of water with respect to oil. Hence its negative contribution to the numerator of f_w is evident. For down-dip flow, we have the reverse condition, with gravity helping the flow of water with respect to oil. The gravity relationships are completely reversed in the case of a gas- and oil-flowing mixture, for then the gas is lighter than oil, and $\Delta\delta$ in Eq. (11-9) is negative. It may be seen that the throughput q_t, or total rate of flow, has an effect on the fractional flow of a liquid within the pore spaces of a porous medium when the capillary-pressure gradient and the gravity pull bring about an appreciable contribution to the numerator of the equation. The total fluid throughput q_t is a function of *pressure gradient* within the reservoir and its effect upon recovery may be evaluated from the fractional-flow formulas. The denominator of the equations is affected only by the relative-permeability ratios of the reservoir rock and the viscosity ratios of the fluids involved. The ratios k_o/μ_o, k_w/μ_w, and k_g/μ_g are called the mobilities of oil, water, and gas, respectively.

Once the fluid characteristics, μ_o, μ_g, μ_w, δ_o, δ_g, δ_w, of the flow streams are fixed, the fractional flow is still a function of the throughput, q_t, of the formation dip, α, and of the fluid saturations, inasmuch as K_o, k_o/k_g, k_o/k_w, and P_c are functions of saturation at a selected point and at a given time. If throughput and dip are maintained constant, the fractional flow is a function of saturation only. If in addition it may be assumed that capillary-pressure gradient $\partial P_c/\partial u$ and gravity effects ($g\,\Delta\delta \sin\alpha$) may be neglected, the fractional-flow equation takes on a simpler form

$$f_w = \frac{1}{1 + \dfrac{k_o}{k_w}\dfrac{\mu_w}{\mu_o}} \tag{11-10}$$

for water and oil flow. For gas and oil flow it is

$$f_g = \frac{1}{1 + \dfrac{k_o}{k_g}\dfrac{\mu_g}{\mu_o}} \tag{11-11}$$

In discussing the fractional-flow formula, the following points are of interest:

1. The displacement mechanisms by frontal drive may be likened to the expulsion mechanism obtained by means of a loosely fitting piston that would penetrate the capillary openings within the rock. The degree of leakage or bypassing around the piston is represented by f_D, which at any point is the fraction of displacing fluid in the total flow q_t per unit area.

2. The mathematical representation of f_D applies only when oil is displaced by an external agent nonmiscible, nonsoluble in it. This implies that the displacement occurs substantially under equilibrium conditions; i.e., in the case of gas and oil, gas does not go into solution. Modifications will be introduced to the displacement theory when this condition is not fulfilled. Since the driving and driven fluids are nonmiscible, relative-permeability characteristics of the rock enter as factors in the displacement efficiency of the drive, and indirectly rock texture (grain size), rock structure (petrofabric, matrix, and cement), and rock composition (minerals), which control fluid wetting properties, do enter the formula.

3. The displacement considered is essentially one that takes place at constant temperature and pressure, at constant flux rate per unit area, and at constant composition of the fluid phases. However, modifications may be introduced when the fluid phases change in composition, as in the

case in high-pressure gas injection which causes retrograde vaporization of the reservoir oil (vaporization gas drive) or condensation of the heavy components of the gas phase into the reservoir oil (condensation gas drive).

4. The frontal-flow formula includes in one single relationship all factors which are of importance in affecting displacement efficiency by frontal drive:

a. Fluid properties:
Viscosities, μ_o, μ_D
Densities, ϑ_o, ϑ_D
Surface and interfacial tension, angle of contact and wetting through capillary-pressure relationship P_c
Fluid saturation, σ_D

b. Rock properties: effective and relative permeability

c. Structural properties: formation dip (α) and direction of displacement u with respect to structural relief

d. Pressure gradient and flow rate, q_t

5. The only independent variable is fluid saturation σ_D, all others being controlled by the conditions of the problem.

A point which needs further stress is the local nature of the equation; it indicates the value of the fluid ratio at a chosen point.

In practical problems, the question of units becomes of importance. In the denominator of the equation are present only relative-permeability and viscosity ratios; hence units need not be considered here, except that they must be in the same system. However, in the numerator, the effective permeability to oil, water, or gas must be in darcys, the viscosity in centipoises, and the total flow rate in cubic centimeters per square centimeter of cross-sectional area. The capillary-pressure gradient must be in atmospheres per centimeter, and the gravity effect ($g\ \Delta\vartheta \sin \alpha$) must similarly be in atmospheres per centimeter, which numerically becomes 0.00097 $\Delta\vartheta \sin \alpha$ where $\Delta\vartheta$ is now the differential specific gravity of the flowing fluids.

In practical field units the fractional formula becomes

$$f_D = \frac{1 - 1.127 \dfrac{K_o}{q_t \mu_o} \left(\dfrac{\partial P_c}{\partial u} + 0.434\ \Delta\vartheta \sin \alpha \right)}{1 + \dfrac{k_o}{k_D} \dfrac{\mu_D}{\mu_o}}$$

where q_t is in barrels per square foot per day and $\partial P_c/\partial u$ is in pounds per square inch per foot.

THE FRONTAL-ADVANCE RATE FORMULA

Buckley and Leverett (1941) are responsible for the derivation of this equation, although their publication does not indicate either the steps or the assumptions made. Let us consider a block of the reservoir rock (Fig. 11-1) of cross-sectional area A in square centimeters and of volumetric porosity ϕ. A total entering fluid throughput Q_t has a fractional content f_D in the displacing fluid D. At the output end, at a distance du from the input, the effluent throughput rate is assumed to be unchanged and of value Q_t, but the fractional content in displacing fluid is now $f_D - df_D$.

A further assumption made in the derivation is the equivalence of volumetric and surface porosity. Hence on the face of the block, a cross-sectional area ϕA is available to the passage of fluid. The linear rate of flow through the unit cross-sectional tube is, therefore, $Q_t/\phi A$ in centimeters per second. The constancy of flow rate Q_t, of pressure P, of temperature T_f, and of phase composition is also assumed. Only two fluid phases are assumed to be flowing, although a third may be present but is nonmovable. We can now write a material-balance equation for the reservoir block by expressing the law of conservation of matter within it by means of a local equation (i.e., a point or differential equation). We have

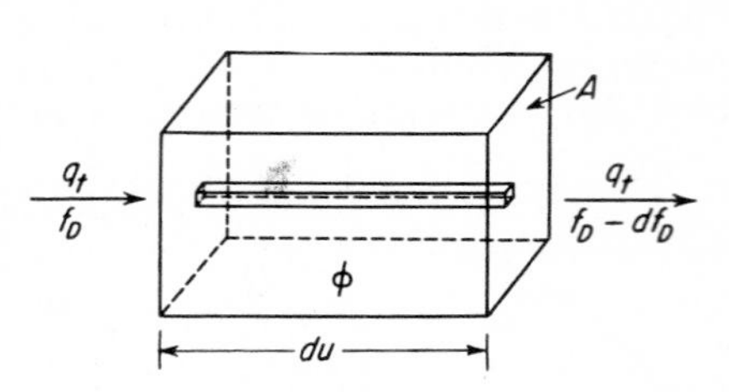

FIG. 11-1. Elementary reservoir block under the desaturation effect of a displacing fluid D.

$$(\phi A\ du)\ d\sigma_D = Q_t\ d\theta\ df_D \tag{11-12}$$

where the first term of the equation expresses the incremental change in saturation in the displacing fluid $d\sigma_D$ in the pore space $\phi A\ du$ of the rock volume considered. The second term of the equation is the decrement in displacing fluid in the volumetric efflux $Q_t\ d\theta$ that takes place in the increment of time $d\theta$.

Since the fractional-flow expression f_D contains only one independent variable, it is possible to write Eq. (11-12) as follows:

$$du = \frac{Q_t}{A\phi}\left(\frac{\partial f_D}{\partial \sigma_D}\right) d\theta \tag{11-13}$$

which expresses the linear advance du of a surface of constant saturation σ_D during an increment of time $d\theta$ under the application of a constant displacing fluid injection rate Q_t through a rock surface A. Fluid saturation σ_D being the only independent variable in a specified system, the rate of advance du is a function of saturation only.

The composition of the total fluid stream of rate Q_t is given by the fractional-flow formula (11-8) or (11-9) both of which are solely functions of saturation at a given position in the reservoir rock and at a given time. f_D may not be represented by an analytical expression and its derivative may not be obtained by analytical means. To obtain the derivative term that enters the rate-of-advance formula, it is necessary to compute the f_D curve point by point as a function of saturation from relative-permeability graphs representative of the reservoir rock under study.

The derivative of the fractional-flow formula is best obtained by graphic methods. This requires drawing a tangent to the f_D curve at various points and plotting the numerical values of the slopes to a suitable scale at the corresponding saturations. The tangent to a curve at a point may be drawn by sight but more accurately by means of a mirror and triangle combination or by means of a transparent cylindrical straight rod. The derivative curve obtained is a measure of the respective rate of advance of each saturation (Fig. 11-2). It is often a multiple-valued curve when capillary pressure is neglected and as such may be misleading. To rectify the results, Buckley and Leverett (1941) advocated balancing the areas

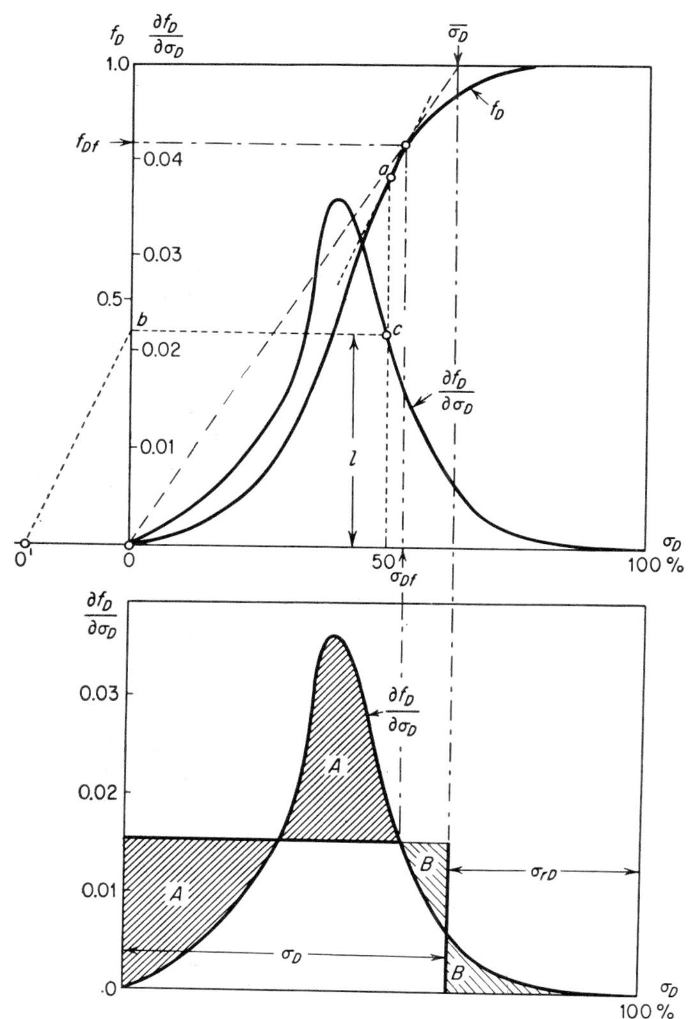

FIG. 11-2 (*top*). Fractional-flow relationship and method of graphic derivation.

FIG. 11-3 (*bottom*). Frontal-drive construction and break-through recovery.

under the derivative so as to get a single-valued curve. This also indicated the presence of a front in conformity with experimental observations, i.e., a surface separating two regions widely different in fluid saturation values (Fig. 11-3). For some time it was not realized that balancing the areas A of the derivative curve was equivalent to postulating that the corresponding part of the f_D curve is a straight line tangent to it and originating from the point of zero permeability to the displacing phase (irreducible saturation σ_{Di}). In the instance of Fig. 11-3, $\sigma_{Di} = 0$ and the tangent to the f_D curve is drawn from the origin. The former practice was also to balance the areas B of the derivative curve behind the front in order to obtain recovery at break-through. It is now

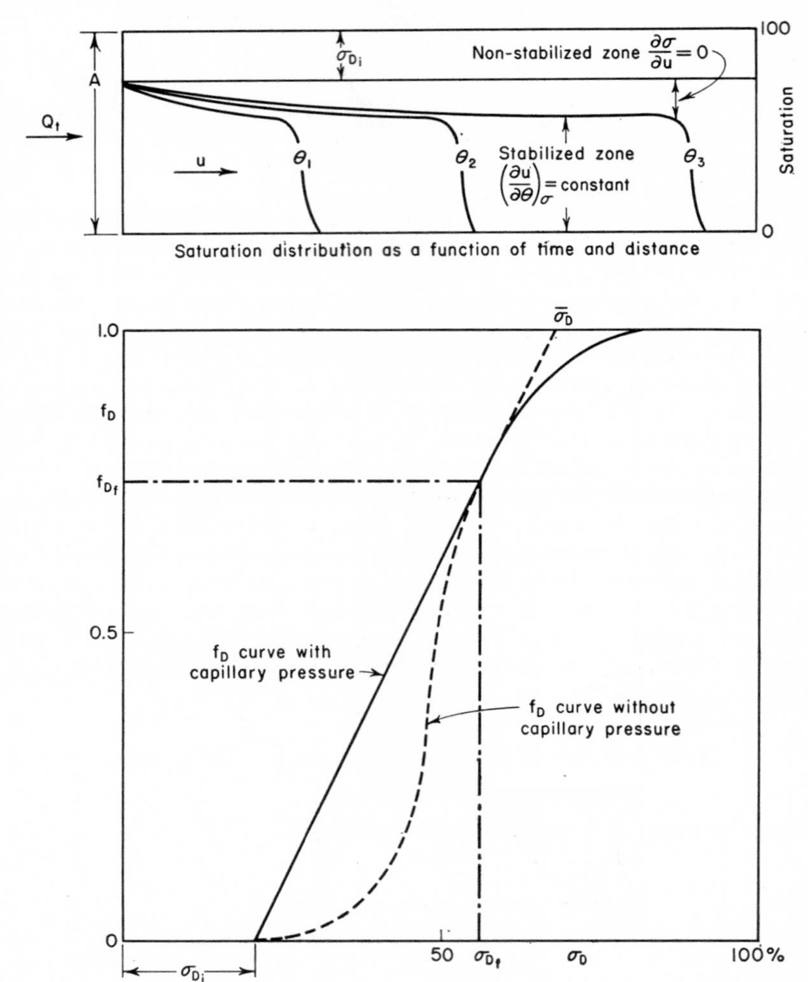

Fig. 11-4. Displacing-fluid saturation distribution and graphic method of displacement-efficiency calculation.

recognized that this is equivalent to extending the tangent to the f_D curve to a value of $f_D = 1$ and the saturation intercept so obtained indicates break-through recovery. The validity of these graphic calculations will be shown later.

A better understanding of the rate of advance formula and its significance may be had by a discussion of observations made during linear displacement experiments of oil by water or gas, as indicated on Fig. 11-4. One observes a zone behind the front in which the saturation distribution in either fluids changes relatively little with distance and for which one may write $\partial\sigma_D/\partial u \cong 0$. Since the capillary-pressure term of the fractional-flow formula may be written

$$\frac{\partial P_c}{\partial u} = \frac{\partial P_c}{\partial \sigma_D}\frac{\partial \sigma_D}{\partial u}$$

it ensues that for this zone the capillary-pressure term may be neglected. This zone is called also "nonstabilized" because *with time* it changes in saturation distribution, but as discussed above, it changes very little *with distance* at a given time.

By opposition, the frontal zone is called "stabilized," for its saturation distribution changes neither with time nor with distance. This is the zone in which the saturation distribution is in equilibrium with capillary forces; i.e., the wetting liquid saturation is sufficiently high to permit its readjustment faster than the imposed displacement by the external drive. In fact, the saturation distribution in the stabilized zone is identical with the corresponding portion of the static capillary-pressure saturation distribution. In this zone the rate of linear advance of a specified saturation is constant since the saturation distribution remains parallel to itself. Therefore the f_D curve is a straight line in this saturation interval.

Determination of Saturation at the Front. It may now be shown that the tangent from the origin (0) to the f_D curve determines the saturation at the displacement front when a driving nonwetting fluid is injected. Let Q_t be the steady-state total fluid flow rate through cross section A of the rock during time interval $\Delta\theta$. On the injection side, let the injected fluid be 100 per cent of the total flux. The injected displacing fluid is $Q_t\,\Delta\theta$ during $\Delta\theta$. Let $(du)_{\sigma_D}$ be the linear advance inside the rock of a plane of a certain saturation σ_D.

$$\text{Total injected displacing fluid} = A\phi\int_0^{1.0} (du)_{\sigma D}\, d\sigma_D$$

Writing the material balance in displacing fluid,

$$Q_t\,\Delta\theta = A\phi\int_0^{1.0} (du)_{\sigma_D}\, d\sigma_D$$

$$= A\phi\left[\Delta u\;\sigma_{Df} + \int_{\sigma_{Df}}^{1.0} (du)_{\sigma_D}\, d\sigma_D\right] \tag{11-14}$$

where Δu is the constant linear advance of the stabilized zone of width σ_{Df}. Substituting

$$\Delta u = \frac{Q_t}{A\phi}\left(\frac{\partial f_D}{\partial \sigma_D}\right)_f \Delta\theta \tag{11-15}$$

$$du = \frac{Q_t}{A\phi}\left(\frac{\partial f_D}{\partial \sigma_D}\right) \Delta\theta \tag{11-16}$$

and canceling common terms,

$$1 = \left(\frac{\partial f_D}{\partial \sigma_D}\right)_f \sigma_{Df} + \int_{\sigma_{D_f}}^{1.0} \frac{\partial f_D}{\partial \sigma_D}\, d\sigma_D \tag{11-17}$$

The integral in (11-17) is $1 - f_{Df}$. After simplification, we obtain

$$f_{Df} = \sigma_{Df}\left(\frac{\partial f_D}{\partial \sigma_D}\right)_f \tag{11-18}$$

Since the injected fluid is nonwetting with respect to the rock, free gas flow is controlled by the drainage relative-permeability curve and starts nearly at zero saturation. Hence the f_g curve originates from nearly zero saturation and Eq. (11-18) indicates that a tangent that originates from zero determines the saturation at the front.

Average Displacing Fluid Saturation behind Displacement Front (Recovery at Break-through). In a linear system of length L, when the front breaks through following an injection of duration $\Delta\theta$, we have

$$L = \frac{Q_t}{\phi A}\left(\frac{\partial f_D}{\partial \sigma_D}\right)_f \Delta\theta \tag{11-19}$$

$$\text{Total oil displaced} = Q_t\,\Delta\theta$$

$$\text{Fractional oil recovery} = \frac{Q_t\,\Delta\theta}{AL\phi} = \bar{\sigma}_D$$

where $AL\phi$ is total oil originally in place at 100 per cent oil saturation and $\bar{\sigma}_D$ is the mean saturation in displacing fluid D. Substituting L by its value and simplifying,

$$\text{Fractional oil recovery} = (\bar{\sigma}_D) = \frac{1}{\left(\dfrac{\partial f_D}{\partial \sigma_D}\right)_f} = \frac{\sigma_{Df}}{f_{Df}} \tag{11-20}$$

As formula (11-20) indicates, the oil-recovery figure may be obtained very simply by extending the tangent to the f_D curve to a value of 1.0. The tangent issues from the origin when the displacing fluid is nonwetting. In the case of a wetting displacing fluid, the tangent originates from the irreducible wetting-phase saturation (σ_{w_i}).

Modification for the Presence of a Preexisting (Connate) Saturation (σ_{Dc}) in the Displacing Fluid. The connate saturation is assumed to be larger than the irreducible wetting-phase saturation (σ_{w_i}).

Presently let the irreducible wetting phase be zero. Therefore, there exists in the total steady-state flow rate Q_t a fraction f_{Dc} of the injected volume which does not contribute to oil displacement, and we have the material balance

$$Q_t(1 - f_{Dc})\,\Delta\theta = A\phi \int_{\sigma_{Dc}}^{1.0} du\,d\sigma_D$$

$$= A\phi \left[(\sigma_{Df} - \sigma_{Dc})\,\Delta u + \int_{\sigma_{Df}}^{1.0} (du)_{\sigma_D}\,d\sigma_D \right] \tag{11-21}$$

After substitution of Δu and du by their respective values from Eqs. (11-15) and (11-16)

$$1 - f_{Dc} = (\sigma_{Df} - \sigma_{Dc}) \left(\frac{\partial f_D}{\partial \sigma_D} \right)_f + 1 - f_{Df}$$

and rearranging,

$$f_{Df} - f_{Dc} = (\sigma_{Df} - \sigma_{Dc}) \left(\frac{\partial f_D}{\partial \sigma_D} \right)_f \tag{11-22}$$

Graphic construction for this result is but slightly modified; the tangent is again drawn from the origin and it is simply required to draw a vertical at σ_{Dc} and to read as reservoir-oil recovery the distance $\bar{\sigma}_D - \sigma_{Dc}$ on the horizontal line $f_D = 1$.

Presence of a Finite Irreducible Connate Wetting-phase Saturation. The only modification is to draw the tangent from σ_{Di} rather than from the origin as shown on Fig. 11-4.

Critical Saturation in Displacing Fluid. This is the saturation $(\sigma_D)_{\text{crit}}$ for which the frontal construction is impossible. Therefore, no oil bank will be formed ahead of the displacing fluid and a frontal displacement mechanism is impossible.

$(\sigma_D)_{\text{crit}}$ is found at the point of the f_D curve where it starts to depart from a straight line or $(\sigma_D)_{\text{crit}} = \sigma_{Df}$.

Recovery at Break-through. At break-through the front has advanced a distance L, which is the full length of the system such that

$$L = \frac{Q_t(1 - f_{Dc})}{\phi A} \left(\frac{\partial f_D}{\partial \sigma_D} \right)_f \Delta\theta \tag{11-23}$$

$\Delta\theta$ being the time necessary to break-through.

$$\text{Displacement efficiency as a fraction of pore space} = \frac{\text{reservoir oil displaced}}{\text{total pore space}}$$

$$\text{Reservoir oil displaced} = Q_t(1 - f_{Dc})\,\Delta\theta$$

$$\text{Total pore space} = LA\phi$$

Pore-space-displacement efficiency as a fraction of pore space

$$= \frac{Q_t(1 - f_{Dc})\,\Delta\theta}{\dfrac{Q_t(1 - f_{Dc})}{\phi A} A\phi \left(\dfrac{\partial f_D}{\partial \sigma_D}\right)_f \Delta\theta}$$

$$= \frac{1}{\left(\dfrac{\partial f_D}{\partial \sigma_D}\right)_f} = \frac{\sigma_{Df} - \sigma_{Dc}}{f_{Df} - f_{Dc}} \tag{11-24}$$

Displacement efficiency as a function of reservoir oil originally in place

$$= \frac{\text{pore-space-displacement efficiency}}{1 - \sigma_{Dc}}$$

$$= \frac{1}{1 - \sigma_{Dc}} \frac{\sigma_{Df} - \sigma_{Dc}}{f_{Df} - f_{Dc}} \tag{11-25}$$

Displacing fluid saturation behind flood front as a fraction of pore space

$$= \sigma_{Dc} + \frac{\sigma_{Df} - \sigma_{Dc}}{f_{Df} - f_{Dc}} \tag{11-26}$$

Average Saturation Remaining in the Reservoir for Continued Injection beyond Break-through. For simplification in writing, let $\partial f_D/\partial \sigma_D = f'_D$.

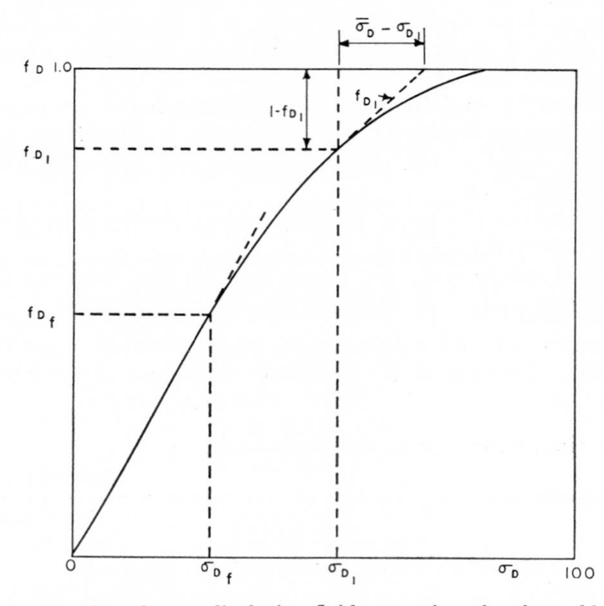

FIG. 11-5. Determination of mean displacing-fluid saturation after frontal break-through.

Consider that a saturation σ_{D1} has arrived at the end of the reservoir. $\bar{\sigma}_D$ is the average displacing saturation present in the reservoir (Fig. 11-5). It represents the average displacing fluid saturation in a volume of the reservoir swept out by the injected fluid wherein discrete saturation values comprised between σ_{D1} and 1.0 advance linearly according to Eq. (11-13). We have, after dropping the common factor $Q_t \, \Delta\theta / A\phi$,

$$\int_{\sigma_{D1}}^{\bar{\sigma}_D} (f'_{D1} - f'_D)\, d\sigma_D = \int_{\bar{\sigma}_D}^{1} f'_D \, d\sigma_D \qquad (11\text{-}27)$$

Noting that f'_{D1} is a constant in the interval σ_{D1} to $\bar{\sigma}_{D1}$, we have

$$\int_{\sigma_{D1}}^{\bar{\sigma}_D} f'_{D1}\, d\sigma_D = \int_{\sigma_{D1}}^{\bar{\sigma}_D} f'_D \, d\sigma_D + \int_{\bar{\sigma}_D}^{1} f'_D \, d\sigma_D = \int_{\sigma_{D1}}^{1} f'_D \, d\sigma_D = 1 - f\sigma_{D1}$$

$$f_{D1}(\bar{\sigma}_D - \sigma_{D1}) = 1 - f_{\sigma_{D1}} \qquad (11\text{-}28)$$

$$f'_{D1} = \text{slope at } \sigma_{D1} \text{ of the } f_D \text{ curve} = \frac{1 - f_{\sigma_{D1}}}{\bar{\sigma}_D - \sigma_{D1}}$$

Or written in a different manner:

$$\bar{\sigma}_D = \sigma_{D1} + \frac{1 - f_{\sigma_{D1}}}{f'_{D1}} \qquad (11\text{-}29)$$

This form of the relationship was given by Welge (1952) and relates the mean displacing fluid saturation in a porous medium after the passage of the front, i.e., during the subordinate phase of an external drive.

Application to Linear Drives

Linear Water Drive. Consider the case of a linear reservoir of length L and cross-sectional area A containing irreducible water saturation σ_{w_i} and an oil phase under bubble-point pressure P_0 containing solution gas S_0 per unit volume of stock-tank oil. Water is injected at a specified constant rate Q_t. Calculate the performance of this flood, i.e., stock-tank oil rate Q_o, water-oil ratio, and gas-oil ratio vs. time.

Relative permeabilities are known such that the f_w curve of Fig. 11-6 has been constructed and a tangent to it drawn from σ_{w_i}, this being a water-wet sand. Porosity is ϕ. Pertinent equations of the problems are

$$v_{\sigma_w} = \frac{Q_t}{A\phi}\left(\frac{\partial f_w}{\partial \sigma_w}\right) \qquad (11\text{-}30)$$

$$v_f = \frac{Q_t}{A\phi}\left(\frac{\partial f_w}{\partial \sigma_w}\right)_f \qquad (11\text{-}31)$$

where subscript f indicates that the functions are read at the front.

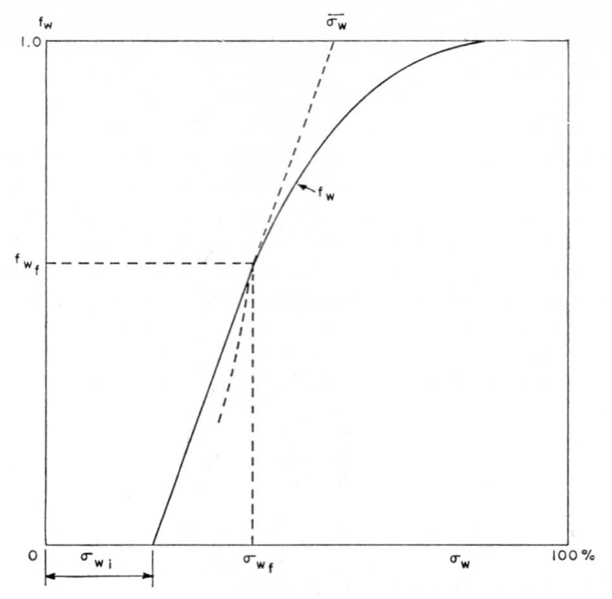

FIG. 11-6. Fractional-flow curve for a water drive.

Break-through time of the frontal advance of the flood is

$$\theta_b = \frac{L}{v_f} \tag{11-32}$$

or expressed in a different manner

$$\theta_b = \frac{AL\phi(\bar{\sigma}_w - \sigma_{wi})}{Q_t} \tag{11-33}$$

where $\bar{\sigma}_w$ is average water saturation behind the front obtained by extending the tangent to $f_w = 1$.

The above considerations are substantially correct, provided the width of the stabilized zone of the flood front is negligible with respect to the total length of the system. It is necessary to verify in practical cases that this is substantially so. It may be done in the following manner. By observation, the width of the stabilized zone is the distance necessary to create a pressure drop in the moving oil zone equal to the capillary pressure P_{cf} prevailing at the front under the saturation condition σ_{wf} prevailing at the front. P_{cf} is therefore the pressure differential across the stabilized portion of the front and it depends on the speed of flooding. If Q_t is small, it takes a long distance in the front to produce the required pressure drop and the stabilized zone is wide. If Q_t is large, the stabilized zone is narrow.

The approximate length L_f of the front may be obtained from

$$L_f = \frac{A}{Q_t} \frac{\overline{K}_o}{\mu_o} P_{cf} \tag{11-34}$$

where $\overline{K}_o$ is the mean effective permeability to oil in the stabilized zone.

If it is found that L_f is an appreciable fraction of the length of the system L, then it may be necessary to resort to a more complex analysis of the problem such as that proposed by Terwilliger et al. in gravity drainage (1951). While most of the oil in a water flood is recovered at break-through, it is of interest to investigate the performance beyond, in the so-called "subordinate phase" of the flood. The simplified theory in the absence of a capillary end effect (or wetting-fluid accumulation at the outlet) is first considered. The time of arrival of any saturation $\sigma_w > \sigma_{wf}$ at the end of the linear reservoir is given by

$$\theta = \frac{L}{v_{\sigma_w}} = \frac{LA\phi}{Q_t\left(\dfrac{\partial f_w}{\partial \sigma_w}\right)} \tag{11-35}$$

The prevailing water-oil ratio at that time is

$$\text{WOR} = \beta \frac{f_w}{1 - f_w} \qquad \text{or} \qquad f_w = \frac{\text{WOR}}{\beta + \text{WOR}} \tag{11-36}$$

Rate of stock-tank oil production at that time is

$$Q_o = \frac{Q_t}{\beta + \text{WOR}} = \frac{(1 - f_w)Q_t}{\beta} \tag{11-37}$$

Rate of water production at that time is

$$Q_w = Q_o(\text{WOR}) = \frac{\text{WOR}}{\beta + \text{WOR}} Q_t = Q_t f_w \tag{11-38}$$

The gas-oil ratio (GOR) is always equal to the solution gas (S_o). Complete performance beyond break-through may then be calculated point by point until a limiting value for the WOR.

Performance Calculations. The mechanism of a frontal water-drive process is best understood from an example of calculation.

Let us assume the following conditions in a simplified experiment in which we have a horizontal pipe 1,000 ft in length and 1 sq ft in cross section, packed with unconsolidated sand of porosity $\phi = 25$ per cent. The pipe, which will be called the reservoir, is fully saturated with oil at 2,000 psia. A solution gas of 600 cu ft (NTP) per bbl of stock-tank oil is present. The oil reservoir volume factor β is 1.5. A pressure sufficient to maintain a rate of water injection of 10 cu ft per hr is applied. The compressibility of water is neglected, and a compressibility figure $Z = 0.8$ is assumed to hold for the solution gas at the prevailing mean reservoir pressure. The experiment is performed at normal temperature ($T_f = 60°F$), and production is discharged at normal pressure ($P_a = 14.7$ psi). At reservoir conditions the viscosities of the fluids are respectively $\mu_o = 2.0$, $\mu_g = 0.018$, and $\mu_w = 1.0$ centipoise.

It is desired to calculate the *expected performance* of this experiment, a performance which may be defined by the following quantities as a function of time:

1. The stock-tank-oil production rate
2. The gas-oil ratio
3. The water-oil ratio

Since the experiment is to be performed at constant mean pressure, there will be no productivity index nor pressure-decline forecast.

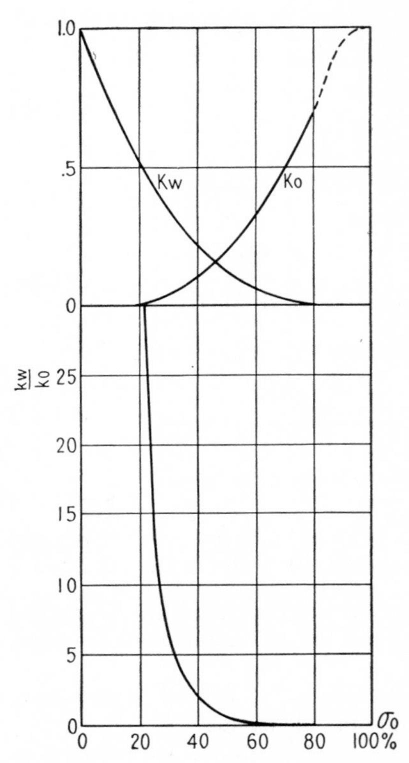

Fig. 11-7. (*top*) Relative permeability for oil-water flow (unconsolidated sand) $1.04 < K < 6.8$ darcys. (*After Leverett, courtesy AIME.*) (*bottom*) Relative-permeability ratio for oil-water flow.

There are obviously two phases in the experiments, namely, that which takes place before break-through of the water front and that which takes place after break-through. Buckley and Leverett (1941) have called the first, the *initial phase*, and the latter, the *subordinate phase*.

The *initial* phase of the experiment is the *frontal water drive* proper, i.e., the phase during which there is a sharp and moving discontinuity of fluid saturation. It represents typically the advancing water-encroachment front in a natural water-drive field. It is desired to calculate the *recovery at frontal break-through* as well as the *rate of frontal advance* and the *time of break-through.*

The *subordinate phase* of the experiment is that which takes place after break-through under the continued application of the driving fluid at the same injection rate. There is now no saturation discontinuity within the reservoir, and the oil desaturation process, which is responsible for additional oil production after frontal break-through, is actually an expulsion process during which oil production gradually becomes less and less and water production becomes greater and greater. Obviously there will be an economic limit to this process, and in the present experiment this will be when a water-oil ratio of 40:1 is attained.

The solution of this problem preassumes the availability of valid relative-permeability graphs applicable to the particular sand packing of the experiment. In the absence of specific relative-permeability tests on sand samples, the relative-permeability curves of Leverett (1939) are to apply to the case at hand (Fig. 11-7). From these curves, the ratio k_w/k_o has been computed and is given in the same figure.

The relative viscosity in the problem is $\mu_w/\mu_o = \frac{1}{2}$ from which the fractional water flow f_w is computed from (11-10), and the results are graphically represented in Fig. 11-8. The derivative of the f_w curve $\partial f_w/\partial \sigma_w$ has also been computed graphically and appears also on Fig. 11-8.

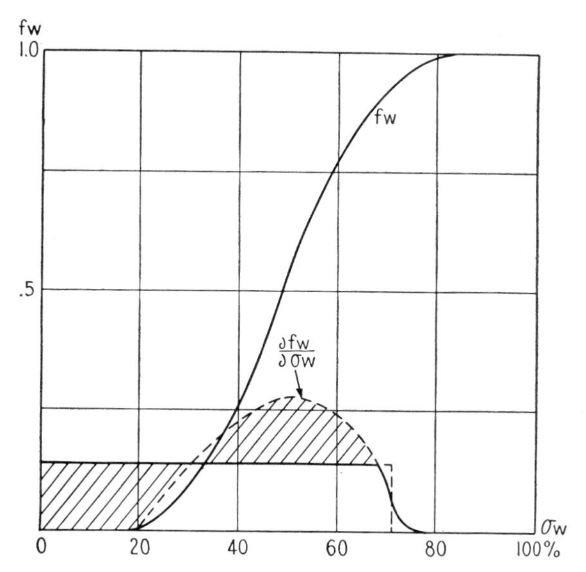

FIG. 11-8. Graphic computation of a water-drive front.

The water-drive front has been constructed as explained previously, and the residual oil saturation at reservoir conditions behind the advancing water front is found to be 29.5 per cent. The linear frontal-advance rate, which is proportional to $\partial f_w/\partial \sigma_w$, indicates that an injection of 10 cu ft of water per hour will advance a distance of

$$\frac{10 \text{ cu ft per hr}}{A\phi \times \text{per cent reservoir oil displaced}} = \frac{10}{0.25 \times 0.705}$$

$$= 56.7 \text{ ft per hr}$$

Therefore, it will take 1,000 ft/56.7 ft per hr = 17.7 hr for the front to reach the end of the pipe and break through.

During the initial recovery period, the rate of production of reservoir oil must necessarily be 10 cu ft per hr. However, when the oil is depressured to atmospheric conditions, it liberates 600 cu ft of gas at NTP and shrinks in volume by the reservoir volume factor $\beta = 1.5$. Therefore, the rate of stock-tank oil production is 6.66 cu ft per hr. The rate of gas production is 6.66 × 600/5.61 = 713 cu ft per hr. The gas-oil ratio all through this initial phase is 600 cu ft per bbl of stock-tank oil produced. Reservoir performance during this initial phase is represented by horizontal straight lines on Fig. 11-9. After break-through of the water front, the relative-permeability ratio, k_w/k_o, is 7.0 and the water-oil ratio passes suddenly from 0 to 21. Continued injection of water at the same rate during the subordinate production phase will recover more oil until a water-oil

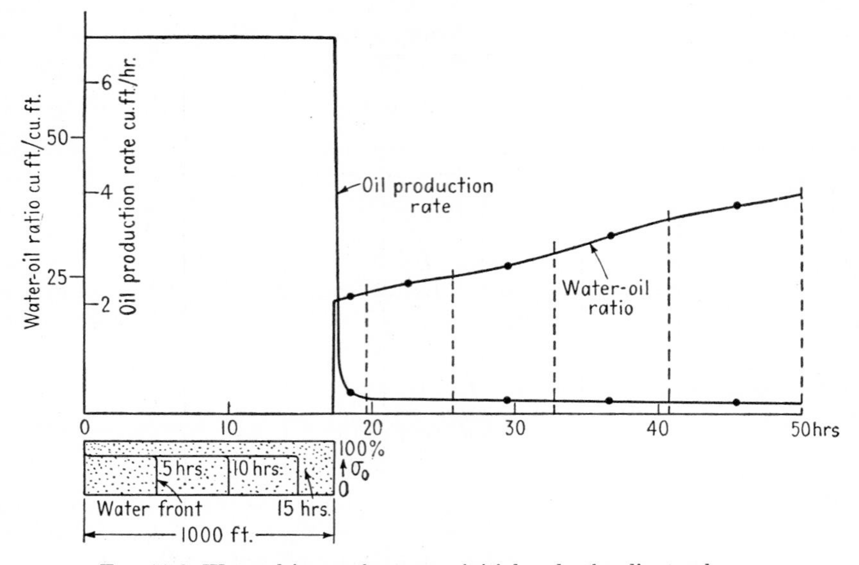

FIG. 11-9. Water-drive performance, initial and subordinate phases.

ratio of 40:1 is attained and a relative-permeability ratio, k_w/k_o, is reached, obtained by solving the following equation:

$$\frac{40}{1} = \frac{\mu}{\mu_w}\frac{k_w}{k_o}\beta = 2\frac{k_w}{k_o} \times 1.5$$

or for $k_w/k_o = 13.3$.

This will be reached when the sand is desaturated to an oil saturation of 25 per cent in reservoir oil. The performance after break-through may be obtained by calculating a certain number of intermediate points for the water-oil ratio and the oil production rate. The gas-oil ratio stays constant at 600 cu ft per bbl. To this end, the expected desaturation range between break-through recovery (70.5) and ultimate recovery (75.0) at the economic limit is divided into 4 equal parts of 1 per cent saturation and 1 part of ½ per cent. The time required to produce the additional ½ per cent by desaturation from 29.5 to 29 per cent is computed as follows:

Water-oil ratio at 29 per cent oil saturation = 2 × 7.4 × 1.5 = 22.2

Average water-oil ratio between break-through and

$$\text{the new saturation} = \frac{22.2 + 21}{2} = 21.6$$

Time required to desaturate packed pipe

$$= \frac{1{,}000 \text{ cu ft} \times 0.25 \times 0.5 \times (21.6 + 1.5)}{100 \times 10 \text{ cu ft per hr}}$$

$$= 2 \text{ hr, } 54 \text{ min}$$

The next step is to calculate the desaturation time for an additional recovery of 1 per cent of pore space, or for the desaturation step from 29 to 28 per cent oil saturation. The average water-oil ratio is then $\frac{22.2 + 25.2}{2} = 23.7$, and the desaturation time is computed to be 6 hr, 18 min. Similar computations for the desaturation steps 28 to 27 per cent, 27 to 26 per cent, and 26 to 25 per cent give, respectively, the average water-oil ratios of 27, 31.8, and 37.5 and the corresponding desaturation times of 6:45, 7:55, and 9:20 hr.

The stock-tank-oil production rate in cubic feet per hour is readily computed at each average water-oil ratio from the volumetric desaturation of the reservoir volume during the above intervals of time through the use of the general formula

Stock-tank-oil production rate

$$= \frac{\text{reservoir volume} \times \phi \times \text{desaturation step}}{\text{time interval required}} \frac{1}{\beta}$$

The performance data so obtained are plotted on Fig. 11-9, where the position of the advancing water front during the initial phase of the drive is also indicated within the schematic horizontal reservoir at the bottom of the figure. The subordinate phase starts at 17.7 hr, during which the oil-production rate decreases rapidly after break-through and settles down to a very low value while the water-oil ratio increases at almost a uniform rate.

According to the requirements of the problem, production is stopped at a water-oil ratio of 40:1, but it must be remembered that the system is still at a pressure of 2,000 psia. Should it be depressured at the end of the experiment, a small additional amount of oil will be produced by solution gas drive; however, this is a separate problem.

Factors That Influence Oil Recovery by Water Drive. The preceding theory lends itself to a study of the factors which influence recovery of oil by *pure water drive*, which factors may be listed as follows:

1. Relative-permeability ratio
2. Fluid-viscosity ratio
3. Presence of a connate water phase
4. Presence of a gas phase
5. Formation dip and rate
6. Capillary-pressure gradient in the direction of flow

Relative-permeability Ratio. In the study of permeability of porous media (Chap. 2), it was observed that relative permeability is a function of the wetting properties of the reservoir rock and of the fluid distribution within said rocks. Relative-permeability measurements in the laboratory, as shown by Morse (1947), do not always achieve a reproducible fluid distribution and, what is more serious, are not always performed under fluid-saturation distribution which duplicates reservoir conditions.

Ideal conditions require a dependable knowledge of relative permeabilities and of their ratios measured on samples of the reservoir rock itself.

The relative-permeability ratios give directly the *irreducible oil saturation* for continued water drive after break-through or for a prolonged subordinate phase until an uneconomic water-oil ratio is attained. However, the knowledge of this saturation is primarily useful in artificial water-drive (water-flooding) considerations, whereas in natural water-encroachment drive in *primary fields* it is the *residual saturation at break-through* which is of interest and which the reservoir engineer must strive to reduce to a minimum. The attainable break-through minimum is a function of the relative-permeability ratios and varies much as the irreducible saturation; yet it should be ascertained according to the theory developed here above.

Fluid-viscosity Ratio. In the simplified fractional-flow formula (11-10) for water, the viscosity ratio of the fluids involved appears as a multiplier to the relative-permeability ratio. To investigate the effect of viscosity, we postulate that the permeability ratio k_w/k_o calculated from Leverett's relative-permeability curves is applicable.

Water viscosity μ_w remains constant at 1 centipoise for the purpose of this study.

Oil viscosity μ_o under reservoir conditions may vary greatly from 0.1 centipoise for very light oils approaching distillate fluids in character to 2 centipoises for average grade oils and to as high as 10 centipoises for heavy crudes.

The amount of solution gas per unit of stock-tank oil and the reservoir temperature are controlling factors of reservoir oil viscosities.

On Fig. 11-10 the fractional-flow curves have been plotted for reservoir oil viscosities of 0.1, 1.0, 2.0, 6.0, and 10.0 centipoises. The break-through recoveries have been calculated in each case by the graphical methods just reviewed, and the results are plotted on Fig. 11-11, which indicates *quantitatively* a recovery trend which has been known *qualitatively* from the early days of petroleum engineering, namely, that oil recovery is increased by keeping gas in solution and the reservoir oil viscosity low. Similar results were reported by Buckley and Leverett (1942) and also by Heath (1943).

Modification Owing to the Presence of a Connate Water Phase. The study of frontal water drive has included thus far the presence of two phases, namely, the driving water phase and the driven oil phase. However, in practice, the virgin reservoir contains also connate water, and in secondary recovery projects it may contain fresh water as a result of casing leaks and surface or subsurface infiltrations of ground water.

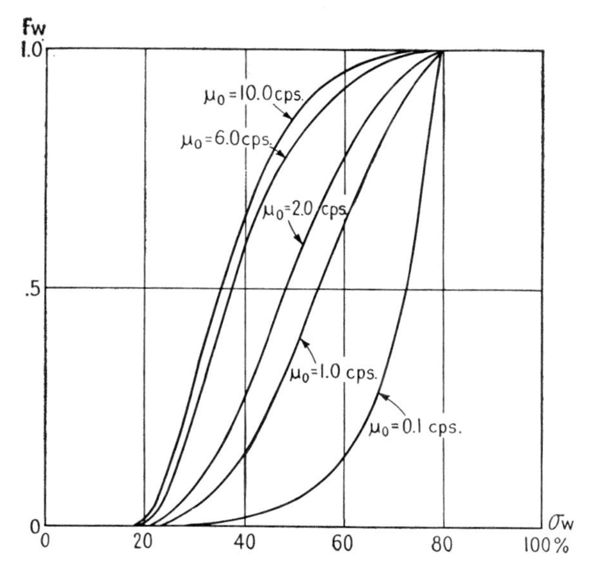

FIG. 11-10. Fractional flow of water as a function of oil viscosity.

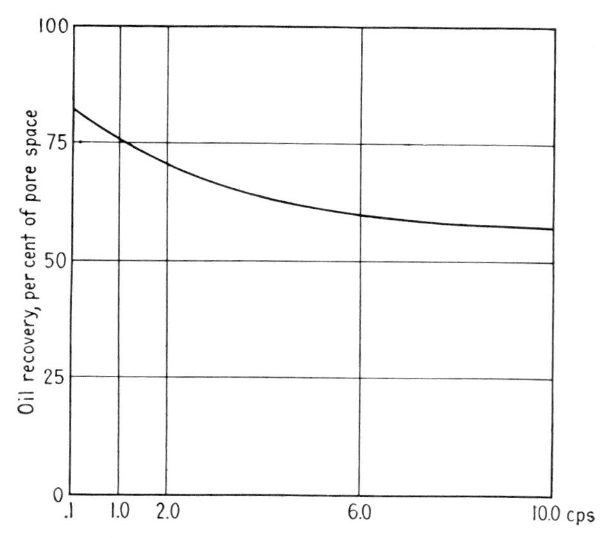

FIG. 11-11. Theoretical oil recovery at water-front break-through as a function of oil viscosity.

In this case, the calculation of oil recovery at break-through by means of the graphic construction of driving fronts necessitates a slight but obvious modification, as represented on Fig. 11-12, where a connate water of 30 per cent is presumed. The relative permeability and viscosity conditions of Fig. 11-8 are assumed to hold. Hence the same fractional-flow curve f_w is applicable to this problem. Though there exists theoretically a fluid conductivity to water from the start of the application of water pressure, the moment the water drive is applied to the reservoir the gathering of an oil bank ahead of the front justifies the use of the normal relative-

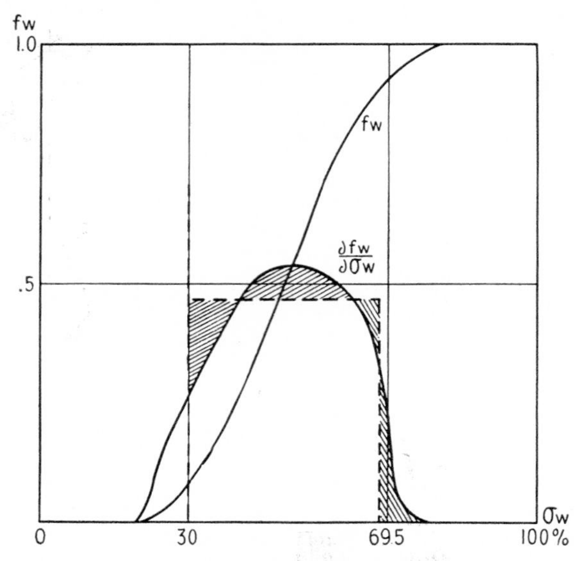

Fig. 11-12. Graphic construction of a water-drive front with 30 per cent connate water saturation.

permeability curves. Experiments by Sayre (1947) have shown that an oil bank forms ahead of the water front provided that the connate water saturation does not exceed a critical value. In his experiments, Sayre showed that an oil bank fails to form when connate water saturation reaches 51 per cent, which may be called the *critical connate water saturation*. Below this value, which, for a particular sand packing, consolidated or unconsolidated, should coincide with the maximum of the $\partial f_w/\partial \sigma_w$ curve, the two-phase relative-permeability and the f_w curves are valid as well as the derived f_w curve. In the case under consideration, a connate water saturation of 30 per cent exists (Fig. 11-12), and, therefore, this fraction of pore space does not yield recoverable oil. Hence the frontal construction must include only that part of the diagram occupied by oil, and the hachured areas shown on Fig. 11-12 are balanced out. Several observations may be made. Residual oil saturation on a percentage of original-oil-in-place basis behind the flood front is larger than in the absence of connate water. In the example at hand, it is 30.5 per cent instead of 29.5 per cent as originally found. But on a percentage of oil-in-place basis, the recovery with 30 per cent connate water present is $\frac{70 - 30.5}{70} = 56.5$ per cent, whereas it is only 39.5 per cent on a percentage of pore-space basis.

Similar graphic calculations were made for connate water saturations of 25, 35, 40, and 45 per cent, with the results that the recoveries on the basis of oil in place are respectively 60, 53, 48, and 40.5 per cent, whereas on the basis of pore space they are respectively 45, 34, 29, and 23 per cent.

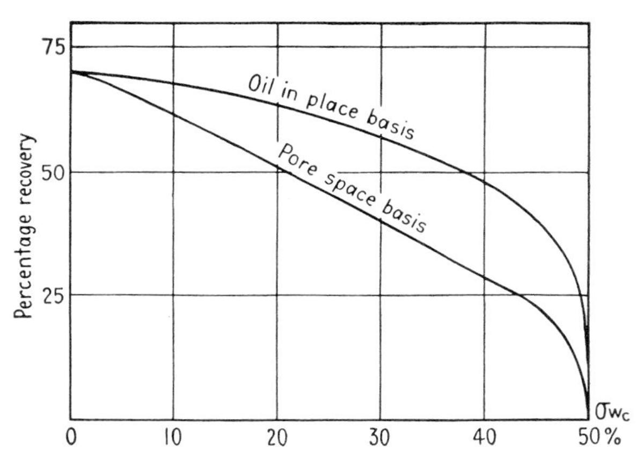

FIG. 11-13. Oil recovery at water break-through as a function of connate water saturation.

At 50 per cent connate water saturation, water breaks through immediately. The construction of a driving front becomes impossible, and no oil bank is formed ahead of the advancing drive. Therefore, recovery at break-through has no more meaning. The above results indicate recovery at frontal break-through of the water drive and are represented graphically on Fig. 11-13 as a function of connate water saturation. These theoretical recovery curves agree substantially with the trend shown by the experimental results of Sayre.

Modification Owing to the Presence of a Gas Phase. Modifications introduced as a result of the presence of a gas phase necessitate a further restriction on the problem, namely, the immobility of the gas phase (i.e., in an insular saturation state) or the prevention of its mobility by the presence of a high gas bubble-point capillary lining at the outlet or well. When all phases are mobile, relative-permeability values must then be obtained from three-phase diagrams such as originally determined by Leverett and Lewis (1940). Under these restrictions, the recovery and performance predictions are again straightforward according to the graphic procedures reviewed.

Modification Due to Reservoir Formation Dip and Flooding Rate. In the absence of the capillary-pressure gradient effect, the fractional-flow formula becomes

$$f_w = \frac{1 - \dfrac{K_o}{\mu_o q_t} g \, \Delta\delta \sin \alpha}{1 + \dfrac{k_o}{k_w} \dfrac{\mu_w}{\mu_o}} \tag{11-39}$$

where $\sin \alpha$ is positive for up-dip flow and $\Delta\delta = \delta_w - \delta_o$ is normally positive since oil is less dense than water. Hence for up-dip flooding and at a specific water saturation, the values of f_w are *smaller* than when there is

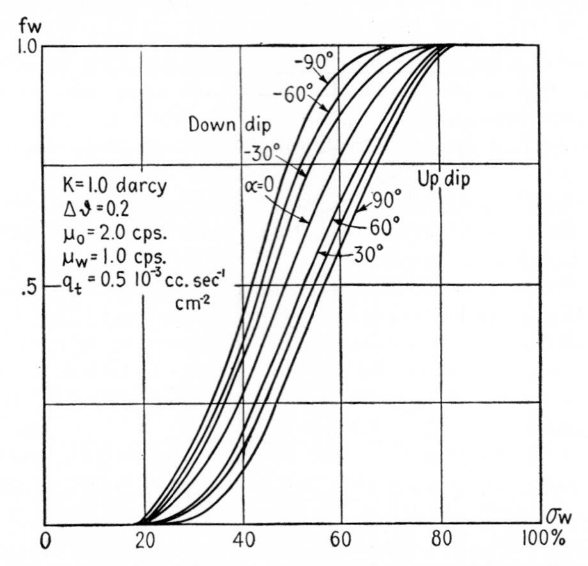

FIG. 11-14. Fractional flow of water as a function of formation dip.

no formation dip. The f_w curve is, therefore, displaced to the right, which results in higher oil recovery. For down-dip flooding, $\sin \alpha$ is negative and the f_w curve is displaced to the left toward lower saturations; this results in lower recoveries. These conditions are represented in Fig. 11-14 for a specific throughput $q_t = q_o + q_w$ and for varying values of the angle of dip: 30, 60, and 90 deg.

It is important to note that the recoveries are no longer independent of the throughput rate q_t. For up-dip flooding, the f_w curves can be displaced further to the right by very slow driving rates; this increases recovery further. There is naturally an optimum economic limit for up-dip water flooding rates below which the oil withdrawals become unattractive even though they are highly efficient.

For down-dip flooding, the f_w curves can similarly be displaced to the left toward the region of low recoveries for low throughput rates, obviously an undesirable practice. However, the recovery by down-dip flooding can be made to approach that from horizontal flooding by utilizing the maximum injection rate economically feasible.

These theoretical deductions have been partly verified by some experiments of Morse (1947) on down-dip and up-dip water flooding of long artificially consolidated sand cores, though the data were partly vitiated by some abnormal wetting phenomena. Morse found that the water-flooding process was more efficient at slow rates than at high rates when the flooding was vertically upward. However, there existed a critical low velocity below which little difference in recovery efficiency was noted. Conversely, in flooding vertically downward, higher flooding efficiencies were attained by increased rates of flooding until a critical velocity was again reached beyond which no further change in efficiency occurred.

Modification Due to Capillary-pressure Gradient and Wettability. Inasmuch as desaturation is not uniformly distributed throughout a reservoir and oil saturation is greater ahead of the water front and lower behind it, a capillary-pressure gradient exists which either favors or hinders oil recovery, depending upon the differential wetting properties of the reservoir rock.

In the normal water-wet sand, there exists a positive pressure differential in the direction of flow within the oil zone which results in a beneficial effect toward higher oil production.

In a truly oil-wet sand, the opposite effect occurs since the oil in the depleted section is under reduced pressure compared to the oil in the more saturated parts of the reservoir. The capillary pressure in this case is negative in the direction of the advancing drive. Hence the net result is to increase the values of f_w and displace the f_w curve toward the low water saturations and lower oil recoveries.

Again the throughput rate (q_t) has an important bearing on the recovery; in a truly water-wet sand, a slow advance of the water front favors the oil discharge ahead of the drive. In an oil-wet sand, a faster water frontal-advance rate should yield an oil recovery which approaches that expected from horizontal flooding in the absence of capillary and gravitational forces.

The various factors which have a bearing on the recovery efficiency of *water* drive, namely, the relative-permeability ratio curve, the fluid-viscosity ratio, the connate water and gas saturations, the formation dip, wetting and driving pressure gradient, have been reviewed separately, and methods have been indicated for ascertaining their *quantitative* effect. Oftentimes, several of these factors operate simultaneously, but their combined effect may yet be calculated by the application of the principles discussed.

Linear Frontal Gas Drive. Consider the same case as for the water flood but where gas injection at the rate Q_t is taking place.

Pertinent equations of the problem are

$$v_{\sigma g} = \frac{Q_t}{A\phi}\left(\frac{\partial f_g}{\partial \sigma_g}\right) \tag{11-40}$$

$$v_f = \frac{Q_t}{A\phi}\left(\frac{\partial f_g}{\partial \sigma_g}\right)_f \tag{11-41}$$

Break-through time of the gas frontal advance is

$$\theta_b = \frac{L}{v_f} = \frac{AL\phi(\bar{\sigma}_f)}{Q_t} \tag{11-42}$$

where $\bar{\sigma}_f$ is the mean gas saturation behind the front which is obtained by extending the tangent to the f_g curve to a value of 1.0.

For the above consideration to be correct, the length of the stabilized zone L_f must be negligible with respect to the length of the system. This is checked in a manner similar to the water-drive case by

$$L_f = \frac{A}{Q_t}\frac{\overline{K}_o}{\mu_o} P_{cf} \tag{11-43}$$

Investigating the performance beyond break-through, again in the absence of capillary end effect, we have the following relations for the performance calculation point by point:

The time of arrival of any saturation $\sigma_g > \sigma_{g_f}$ at the end of the linear reservoir is given by

$$\theta = \frac{L}{v_{\sigma g}} = \frac{LA\phi}{Q_t\left(\dfrac{\partial f_g}{\partial \sigma_g}\right)} \tag{11-44}$$

The gas-oil ratio at that saturation is

$$R = S + \frac{\beta}{\alpha}\left(\frac{f_g}{1 - f_g}\right) \tag{11-45}$$

in the case of a horizontal drive, because capillary pressure may be neglected beyond break-through.

The rate of stock-tank-oil production at that time is

$$Q_o = \frac{Q_t}{\beta}(1 - f_g) \tag{11-46}$$

and by substituting the value of f_g as a function of the producing gas-oil ratio R

$$Q_o = \frac{Q_t}{\left[\left(\dfrac{\beta}{\alpha} - S\right) + R\right]\alpha} \tag{11-47}$$

If a fraction I of the produced gas is injected back into the reservoir after break-through in addition to the available gas Q_t, a material balance gives

$$Q_o\left[\left(\frac{\beta}{\alpha} - S\right) + R\right]\alpha = Q_t + \alpha IRQ_o$$

or

$$Q_o = \frac{Q_t}{\left[\left(\frac{\beta}{\alpha} - S\right) + (1 - I)R\right]\alpha} \tag{11-48}$$

Complete performance beyond break-through may be calculated point by point until a limiting value for the gas-oil ratio is reached.

Performance Calculation. The mechanism of frontal gas drive will be illustrated by predicting the performance of a simplified experiment assuming the same physical characteristics for the reservoir and for the oil as in the frontal water drive but replacing the driving water by a driving gas of 0.018 centipoise viscosity at sufficient pressure to introduce 10 cu ft of gas per hr measured at the average pressure of 2,000 psia. The temperature of the reservoir is assumed to be the normal base temperature, and a gas compressibility coefficient of 0.8 is considered adequate.

It is desired to forecast the expected performance of this experiment, namely, to predict the variations as a function of time of the stock-tank-oil production rate and of the gas-oil ratio. We assume no connate water saturation to be present. The experiment is performed at the average pressure of 2,000 psia without allowing any pressure reduction; therefore, there will be no productivity index.

As in the case of a water drive, the experiment has two main phases: the *initial* or frontal gas drive proper and the *subordinate* phase, or desaturation by the driving pressure exerted by the gas on the oil. The experiment is carried out to an assumed economic limit for the gas-oil ratio of 40,000 cu ft per bbl of stock-tank oil. The time of oil recovery at gas front break-through and at the economic limit are again desired.

The solution of the problem preassumes the availability of valid relative-permeability graphs applicable to the particular sand packing of the experiment. In the absence of specific relative-permeability tests on reservoir samples, the curves of Wyckoff and Botset (1936) for unconsolidated sands are presumed to apply to the case at hand. From these curves, the ratios k_g/k_o for unconsolidated sand have been computed and are shown in Fig. 11-15*a*. When an immobile connate water phase is present in the sand, the k_g/k_o curves are shifted according to results of Leverett and Lewis (1940), as shown in Fig. 11-15*b*. The relative viscosity in the present problem is $\mu_o/\mu_g = 111.0$. The fractional flow (f_g) is computed from Eq. (11-11) in the absence of gravity and capillary-pressure effects, and the results are graphically represented in Fig. 11-16. The gas-drive front has been constructed as explained previously in the case of a water drive, and the residual oil saturation behind the advancing front is found to be 77.5 per cent. The oil recovery as a function of pore space is found to be 22.5 per cent, which is also the recovery to be had at gas break-through. The linear frontal-advance rate, which is proportional to $\partial f_g/\partial \sigma_g$, indicates that an injection of 10 cu ft of gas per hr will advance a distance of

$$\frac{10 \text{ cu ft}}{\phi \times \text{per cent reservoir oil displaced}} = \frac{10}{0.25 \times 0.225} = 177.5 \text{ ft per hr}$$

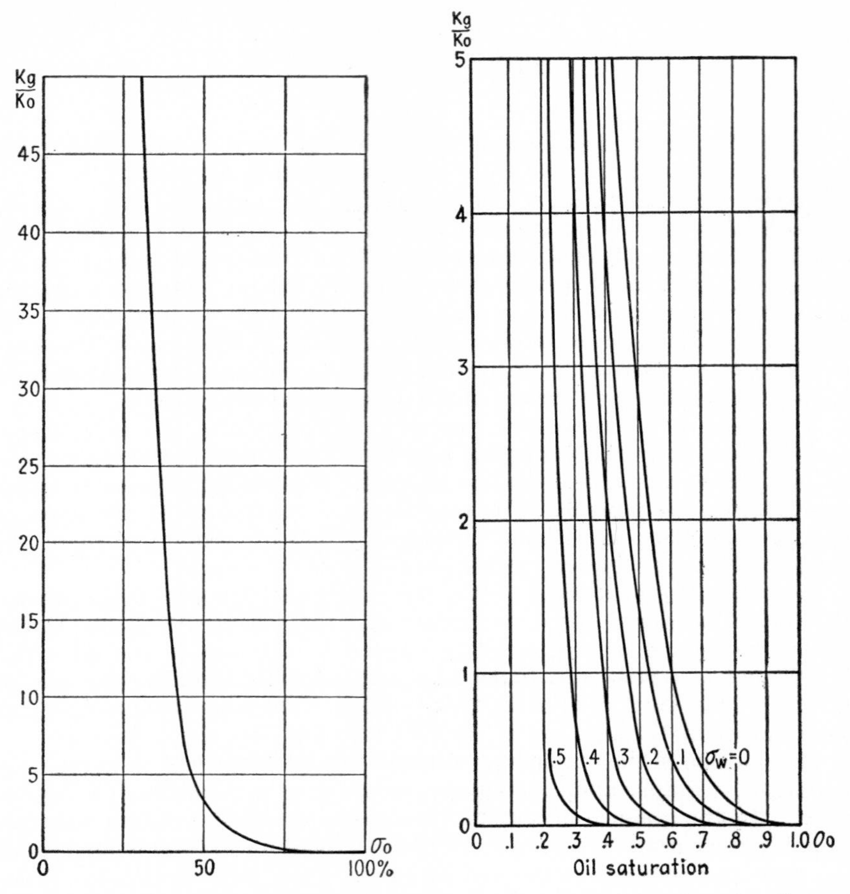

FIG. 11-15 (*a*). Relative-permeability ratio k_g/k_o for unconsolidated sand. Connate water absent. (*After Botset, courtesy AIME.*) (*b*). Relative-permeability ratio k_g/k_o as a function of connate water saturation.

Therefore, it will take $\dfrac{1{,}000}{177.5} = 5.63$ hr for the gas front to reach the end of the pipe and break through.

During the initial recovery period, the rate of production of reservoir oil must necessarily be 10 cu ft per hr. However, when the oil is depressured to standard conditions, it liberates 600 cu ft of gas at NTP per barrel of stock-tank oil, and the latter shrinks in volume by the reservoir volume factor $\beta = 1.5$. Therefore, the rate of stock-tank oil production is 6.66 cu ft per hr, the same as during the similar water-drive experiments. The rate of gas production is also 713 cu ft per hr. The gas-oil ratio all through this initial phase is again equal to the solution gas, or 600 cu ft per bbl of stock-tank oil. Reservoir performance is represented by horizontal straight lines on Fig. 11-17 during the initial phase of the drive. After

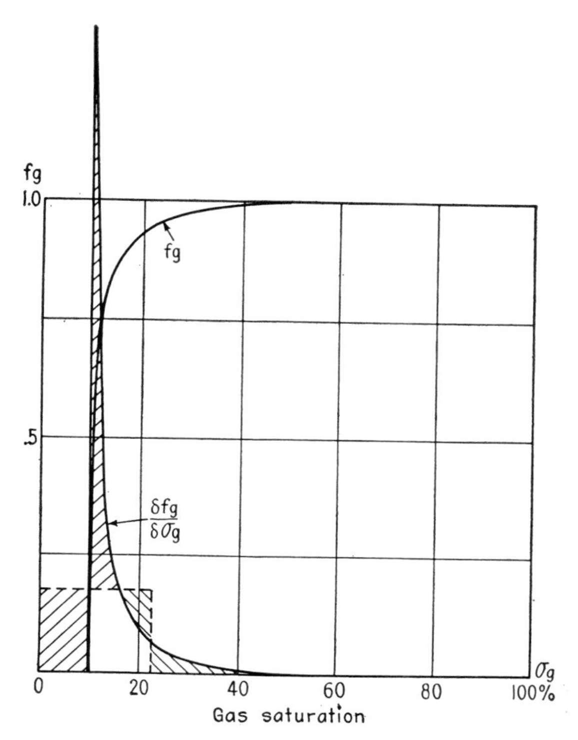

FIG. 11-16. Graphic construction of a gas-drive front.

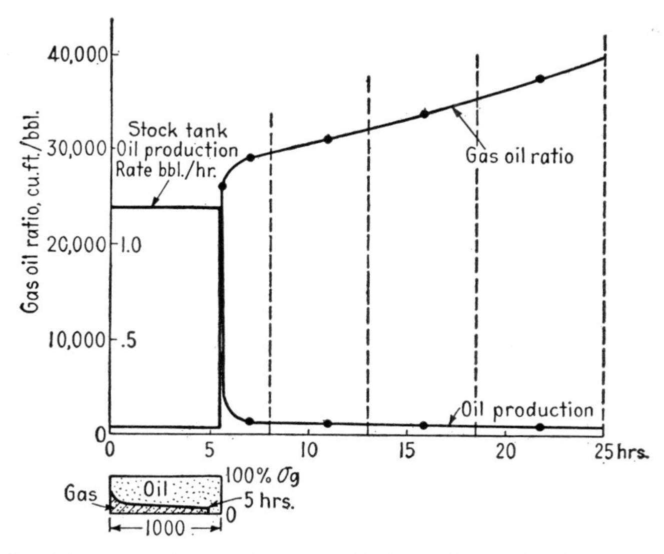

FIG. 11-17. Gas-drive performance, initial and subordinate phases.

the gas-front break-through, the relative-permeability ratio k_g/k_o is 0.16 and the gas-oil ratio passes suddenly from the solution gas, or 600 cu ft per bbl to

$$600 + 5.61\beta \frac{k_g}{k_o} \frac{\mu_o}{\mu_g} \frac{P_o}{P_a} \frac{T_a}{T_f} \frac{1}{Z} \text{ or } 600 + 5.61 \times 1.5 \times 0.16 \times \frac{2.0}{0.018} \times \frac{2{,}000}{14.7} \times \frac{1}{0.8} = 26{,}100 \text{ cu ft per bbl}$$

Continued injection of gas at the same rate during the subordinate phase of production will recover more oil until a gas-oil ratio of 40,000 cu ft per bbl is attained or at a relative-permeability ratio k_g/k_o obtained by solving the following equation for the value of k_g/k_o:

$$40{,}000 = S + 5.61\beta \frac{k_g}{k_o} \frac{\mu_o}{\mu_g} \frac{P_o}{P_a} \frac{T_a}{T_f} \frac{1}{Z}$$

or

$$40{,}000 = 600 + 5.61 \times 1.5 \frac{k_g}{k_o} \times \frac{2.0}{0.018} \times \frac{2{,}000}{14.7} \times \frac{1}{0.8}$$

from which it may be ascertained that a gas-oil ratio of 40,000 cu ft per bbl of stock-tank oil will be reached for a relative-permeability ratio k_g/k_o of 0.25, which corresponds on Fig. 11-15*b* to an oil saturation of 74 per cent.

The reservoir performance during the subordinate production phase is obtained by calculating the gas-oil ratios which correspond to a certain number of preassumed intermediary steps between break-through saturation and ultimate recovery. The production rates and required time intervals at each desaturation step are readily calculated from the following relations:

$$\text{Reservoir-oil production rate} = \frac{\text{gas-injection rate at NTP}}{\text{average GOR} - \text{solution gas}} \beta$$

$$\text{Desaturation time} = \frac{\text{reservoir volume} \times \text{porosity} \times \text{desaturation step}}{\text{reservoir-oil production rate}}$$

Table 11-1 is a record of the calculations:

TABLE 11-1. SUMMARY OF CALCULATIONS DURING THE SUBORDINATE GAS-DRIVE PHASE

Desaturation step, per cent of pore space	Average gas-oil ratio, cu ft per bbl	Reservoir-oil production rate, bbl per hr	Injection time, hr
77.5–77.0	29,300	0.0887	2.38
77.0–76.0	30,900	0.0843	5.04
76.0–75.0	32,500	0.0802	5.56
75.0–74.0	37,300	0.0695	6.40

The performance data so obtained are plotted on Fig. 11-17, where the position of the advancing gas front during the initial phase of the drive is indicated at the bottom of the figure after a 5-hr interval, followed thereafter by the subordinate phase during which the oil production rate decreases rapidly after break-through and settles down to a very low value while the gas-oil ratio increases at almost a uniform rate. Upon reaching a gas-oil ratio of 40,000 cu ft per bbl, at which time the gas drive is to stop, the system is still under a pressure of 2,000 psia. Should it be depressured at the end of the experiment, an additional small amount of oil will be produced by solution-gas drive. However, the amount so recovered will be insignificant.

Factors That Influence Oil Recovery by Frontal Gas Drive. The preceding theory lends itself to a study of factors which influence recovery of oil by *pure frontal gas drive*, which factors may be listed as follows:

1. Relative-permeability ratio
2. Fluid-viscosity ratio
3. Presence of a connate water phase
4. Presence of a gas phase
5. Formation dip and rate
6. Capillary-pressure gradient in the direction of flow

Relative-permeability Ratio. The ratio of relative gas permeability to the relative oil permeability as a function of oil saturation has been shown by Botset (1940) to be a function of the cementation or consolidation state of the reservoir rock. Very likely, it is also a function of the type of porosity: intergranular, fissure, vuggy, etc. Hence dependable laboratory measurements on representative samples of the reservoir rock are needed for accurate forecasting of frontal gas-drive recoveries. In the main, it can be said that the recovery of oil on a percentage of pore-space basis will be greater for unconsolidated granular rocks than for the same rocks when consolidated, both for the initial recovery phase of the drive and for the subordinate phase.

Fluid-viscosity Ratio. In the simplified fractional-flow formula for gas, Eq. (11-11), the viscosity ratio of the fluids involved appears as a multiplier to the relative-permeability ratio. In order to investigate the effect of the viscosity ratio, we shall use the relative-permeability ratio k_g/k_o obtained from the curves of Botset for unconsolidated reservoirs.

At the reservoir conditions of temperature and pressure and gas composition, a gas viscosity μ_g of 0.018 centipoise will be used.

Oil viscosity under the same reservoir conditions will be assumed to vary from 0.1 centipoise for distillate to 2.0 centipoises for average-grade oils and 10.0 centipoises for heavy crudes.

The fractional gas-flow curves have been plotted in Fig. 11-18 for the above viscosity relationships. Break-through recoveries have been calculated in each case by the graphical methods discussed, and the results have been plotted on Fig. 11-19, which indicates quantitatively the trend of recovery as a function of oil viscosity.

Modification Owing to the Presence of a Connate Water Phase. The study of frontal gas drive has included thus far the presence of only two phases, gas and oil. However, the reservoir contains often a certain fractional saturation in connate water. It shall be assumed for simplification purposes that the sand is water-wet and that interstitial water is immobile

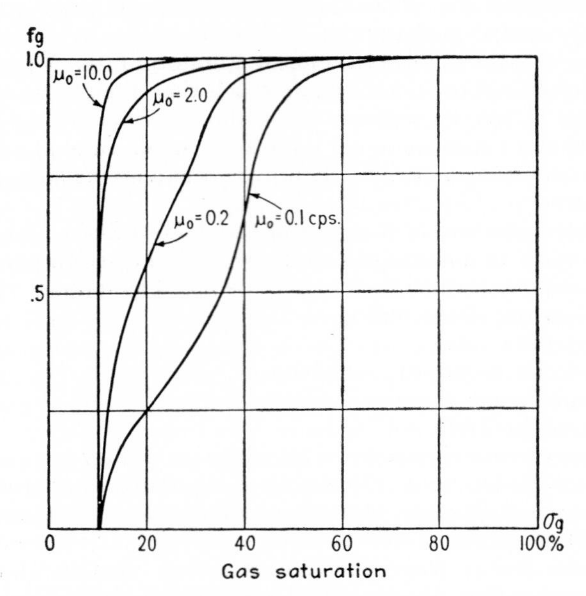

FIG. 11-18. Fractional flow of gas as a function of oil viscosity.

during the drive. The obvious modification required therefore is to use the relative permeabilities for gas and oil at the corresponding connate water saturation. Their ratio may be read directly from Fig. 11-15*b* for

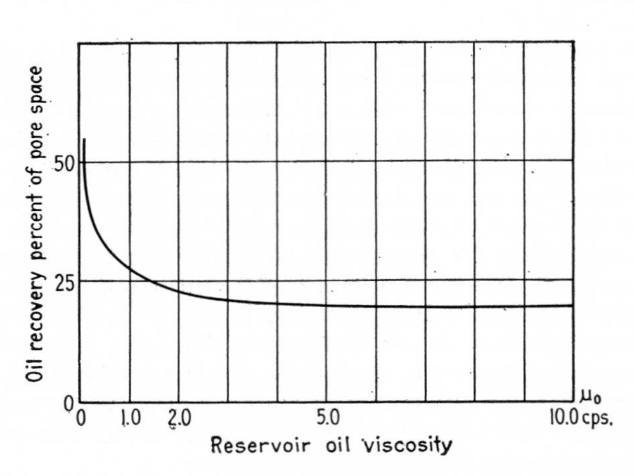

FIG. 11-19. Theoretical oil recovery at the gas-front break-through as a function of oil viscosity.

connate water saturations varying from 10 to 50 per cent in 10 per cent steps.

The various fractional gas-flow curves corresponding to these steps were computed as well as the recoveries at break-through as a function of pore space. The results indicated no well-defined trend of break-through recoveries for frontal gas drive as a function of connate water saturation. This could have been predicted from the shape of the relative-permeability curves of Fig. 11-15*b*, inasmuch as they all show a very similar trend and an almost constant shift for equal increments in connate water saturation.

Modifications Owing to the Presence of a Gas Phase. The graphic solution of this gas-drive problem should be similar in nature to the case of water drive with the presence of a water phase. However, a difficulty is encountered because of the sharpness of the f_g curve at the equilibrium saturation to gas, which is in the neighborhood of 10 per cent gas. The f_g curve's sharpness is greatly dependent upon the fluid-viscosity ratio as shown on Fig. 11-18, and it is sharpest for oils of viscosities of 1 centipoise and over. The maximum of the $\partial f_g/\partial \sigma_g$ curve occurs, therefore, in the neighborhood of the gas equilibrium saturation which is also the critical gas saturation above which no gas front will be found in a frontal gas drive. Hence the gas-front construction breaks down generally for gas saturations above the equilibrium saturation, and only the subordinate phase of the drive takes place with removal of oil by differential application of pressure from the gas phase to the oil phase.

Modifications Due to Reservoir Formation Dip. In the absence of the capillary gradient effect, the fractional gas-flow formula becomes

$$f_g = \frac{1 - \dfrac{K_o}{\mu_o q_t} g \, \Delta\delta \sin \alpha}{1 + \dfrac{k_o}{k_g} \dfrac{\mu_g}{\mu_o}} \tag{11-49}$$

in which $\sin \alpha$ is positive for up-dip flow and $\Delta\delta = \delta_g - \delta_o$ is normally negative since reservoir gas is less dense than reservoir oil. Hence at a specific formation saturation in gas, the values of f_g are all *larger* than when there is no formation dip for an up-dip frontal gas drive. The f_g curve is therefore displaced to the left, which results in lower oil recoveries. For a down-dip drive, $\sin \alpha$ is negative and the f_g curve is displaced to the right toward the higher gas saturations, which results in higher oil recoveries. These conditions are represented in Fig. 11-20 for a specific throughput $q_t = q_o + q_g$ and for varying values of the angle of dip: 30, 60, and 90 deg. However, as in the case of a frontal water drive, the recoveries are no longer independent of the throughput rate (q_t), i.e., the driving pressure gradient. For down-dip gas drive, the f_g curve can be displaced farther to the right by very slow driving rates, which will increase recovery further. There is naturally an economic limit below which the driving rate is so small as to be financially unattractive.

For up-dip gas drive, the f_g curve can be displaced to the left toward the region of low recoveries by low throughput rates, obviously an undesirable practice. However, the recovery by up-dip gas drive can approach that of a horizontal drive by utilizing the maximum gas injection rate economically feasible. Figure 11-21 is a plot of theoretical break-through re-

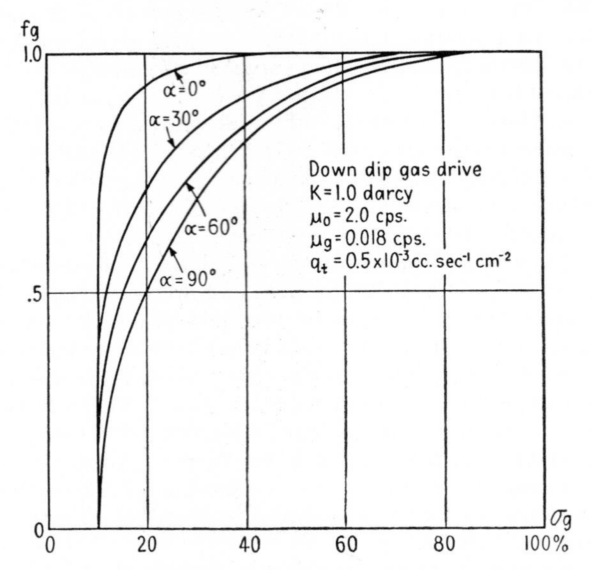

FIG. 11-20. Fractional flow of gas as a function of formation dip.

coveries by down-dip frontal gas drive as a function of the angle of dip and for the conditions shown in Fig. 11-20.

Modifications Due to Capillary-pressure Gradient. Inasmuch as reservoir desaturation is not uniformly distributed throughout a reservoir and oil

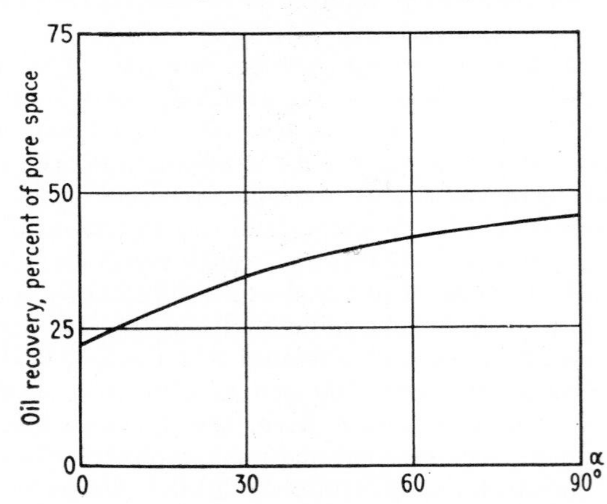

FIG. 11-21. Theoretical oil recovery at the gas-front break-through as a function of formation dip.

saturation is greater ahead of the gas front and lower behind it, a capillary-pressure gradient exists within the reservoir and across the driving gas front which is generally detrimental to recovery. This is because gas never wets the reservoir rock; hence there is always a capillary suction gradient $\partial P_c/\partial u$ on the oil which tends to reestablish saturation equilibrium across the front by pulling oil in a direction opposite to the direction of frontal advance u.

This effect can be evaluated by computing the expected capillary-pressure gradients at the expected rate of frontal advance and adding the values of $K_o/\mu_o q_t \, \partial P_c/\partial u$ at each corresponding value f_g. This displaces the f_g curve to the left, and graphic constructions of the frontal drive give the expected decrease in recovery.

The different factors which have a bearing on the recovery efficiency of *gas* drive, namely, the relative-permeability ratio curve, the fluid-viscosity ratio, the connate water and gas saturations, the formation dip, wetting and throughput rate, have been reviewed separately, and methods have been indicated for ascertaining their quantitative effect. In practice, several of these factors operate simultaneously, but their combined effect may yet be calculated by the application of the principles discussed.

Expulsion of Oil by External Gas Expansion. Gas compressed under high pressure releases energy during the process of volumetric expansion to a lower pressure according to well-known thermodynamic laws. Within the reservoir, gas expansion proceeds at isothermal conditions except perhaps in the immediate neighborhood of the producing wells. While the amount of energy released by expansion of a known volume of compressed gas can be calculated readily, the efficiency with which it expulses oil to the producing wells is a function of reservoir characteristics rather than of the amount of available energy and the mode of its release.

The expansive energy of gas may be obtained from two sources, namely, from an *external supply* such as used in *artificial gas drive* and *cycling operations* or from an *internal supply* from the gas liberated from solution in the oil. In this last instance it is called internal, solution, or depletion drive, the principles of which were given in Chap. 10.

To reduce the problem of external gas drive to its elementary concept, it is assumed that the oil to be produced contains no gas in solution and that none enters solution during the recovery process. For comparison purposes, a problem similar to that studied under frontal drives will be treated, namely, a reservoir 1,000 ft in length and 1 sq ft in cross section packed with unconsolidated sand of permeability equal to 1 darcy. The oil viscosity is 2.0 centipoises, and the constant driving pressure is 500 psi. The gas-compressibility factor is assumed to be unity throughout this pressure range. Starting with 100 per cent oil saturation (no connate water), the drive will have two phases: the *initial* and *subordinate* phases. The recovery at gas-front break-through will be 22.5 per cent of pore space as determined above by frontal gas drive under similar conditions. The main difference with the preceding case resides in the performance of the subordinate production phase as the present problem assumes a discharge to atmospheric pressure. This results in a volumetric expansion of the driving gas.

An ultimate economic gas-oil ratio of 20,000 cu ft per bbl is assumed, and the relative-permeability curves of Leverett are presumed applicable to the problem at hand.

It is desired to calculate the performance of the experiment, namely, the gas-oil ratio and production-rate history. Two equations are available for the solution of this problem:

1. The gas-oil-ratio equation:

$$R = \frac{k_g}{k_o} \frac{\mu_o}{\mu_g} \frac{P}{P_a} \tag{11-50}$$

which is a simplified form of Eq. (8-34), since $S = 0$, $\beta = 1$, and $T_a = T_f$.

2. Darcy's law applied to gas:

$$Q_g = A \frac{Kk_g}{\mu_g L} \frac{P_i^2 - P_a^2}{2P_a} = A \frac{Kk_g}{\mu_g L} \frac{P_m \, \Delta P}{P_a} \tag{11-51}$$

where Q_g = gas injection rate measured at atmospheric pressure P_a
P_i = inlet pressure
P_m = average pressure $\frac{1}{2}(P_i + P_a)$
$\Delta P = P_i - P_a$

Performance during the Primary Phase. During the primary or frontal-drive phase of the experiment, it may be assumed that the resistance to gas flow is negligible as compared to the resistance to oil flow, in view of the large ratio of oil to gas viscosity. Under a constant applied injection pressure, the gas injection rate will accordingly increase as the front advances closer to the outlet end. The variable gas injection rate has no effect on the residual oil saturation during the initial phase of the drive because the packing is horizontal and capillary-pressure gradient at the front is neglected. During this period, the rate of flow of oil Q_o is equal to the rate of gas injection measured at 500 psi.

The calculations for the performance during this initial period may be done, step by step, as follows:

Under a pressure differential of 500 psi, the oil-flow rate per hour for the full length of the pipe is obtained in cubic feet per hour, by

$$Q_o = 1.0 \text{ sq ft} \frac{1.0 \text{ darcy}}{2.0 \text{ centipoises}} \times \frac{500/14.7}{1{,}000 \times 30.5} \times \frac{1}{30.5} \times 3{,}600$$

$$= 0.0638 \text{ cu ft per hr}$$

Since the recovery is 22.5 per cent of oil in place and the reservoir porosity 25 per cent, the total frontal advance during a 50-hr period will be $\frac{50 \times 0.0638}{0.25 \times 0.225} = 56.7$ ft.

The next step is to calculate the oil-flow rate for the next 50-hr period under the application of a 500-psi pressure gradient over a length of 100 per cent oil saturation, or 1,000 − 56.7 = 943.3 ft.

The gas injection rate is then again equal to the hourly oil-flow rate:

$$Q'_o = 1.0 \text{ sq ft} \frac{1.0 \text{ darcy}}{2.0 \text{ centipoises}} \times \frac{500/14.7}{943.3 \times 30.5} \times \frac{1}{30.5} \times 3{,}600$$

$$= 0.0678 \text{ cu ft per hr}$$

and the linear frontal advance during this increment of time is now $\frac{50 \times 0.0678}{0.25 \times 0.225} = 60.2$ ft. These calculations were carried out until frontal break-through and are graphically shown on Fig. 11-22, which indicates the accelerated rate at which the front advances until break-through.

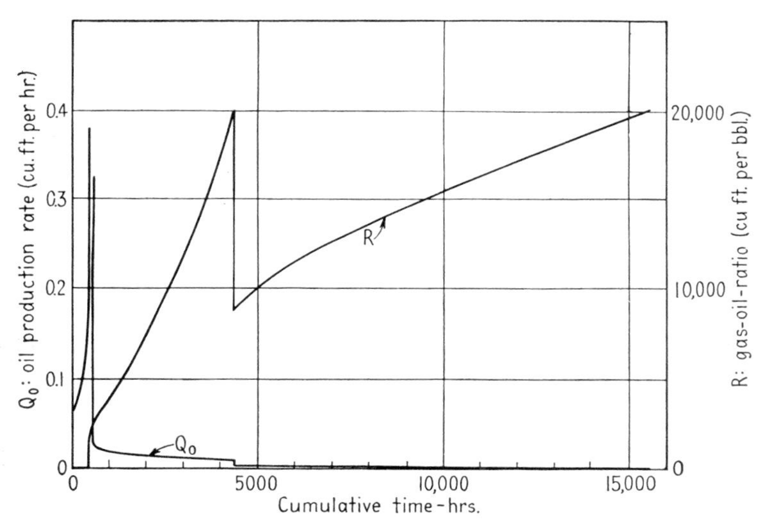

FIG. 11-22. Performance during primary and subordinate phases in an external gas-expansion drive.

Performance during Subordinate Phase. The subordinate phase of the experiment starts after frontal break-through, during which phase gas expands while flowing from 500 psi to atmospheric pressure.

It would be possible to carry out this experiment without regard to the gas-oil ratio reached, in which case the ultimate residual oil saturation would be the equilibrium saturation to the wetting phase (e.g., oil), namely, 30 per cent for the case of the k_g/k_o curve used in this example. Muskat (1946) has derived an equation which gives the history of oil-production rate decline under the basic assumption of a linear system of uniform pressure gradient in which the oil is produced by the stripping action of the expanding gas. In the problem considered here the gas volume produced is also equal to the gas volume injected because it is assumed that there is no initial solution gas and that none goes into solution during the drive.

Muskat's derivation is as follows:

In view of the linearity of the k_g/k_o relationship as a function of saturation on semilogarithmic coordinates, we may write

$$\frac{k_g}{k_o} = ae^{-b\sigma_o} \tag{11-52}$$

where a and b = constants which characterize the sand packing
σ_o = oil saturation

We have also by Darcy's law

$$Q_g = \frac{Kk_g}{\mu_g} A \frac{P_m}{P_a} \frac{\Delta P}{L} \tag{11-53}$$

$$Q_o = \frac{Kk_o}{\mu_o} A \frac{\Delta P}{L} \tag{11-54}$$

where P_m = average pressure
Q_g, Q_o = gas and oil throughput, respectively, measured at atmospheric conditions

Making the ratio of Eqs. (11-53) and (11-54), we obtain

$$\frac{k_g}{k_o} = \frac{\mu_g}{\mu_o} \frac{P_a}{P_m} \frac{Q_g}{Q_o} \tag{11-55}$$

However, the value of the oil throughput may also be obtained by considering that oil flow is the result of a desaturation process, which is quantitatively expressed by

$$Q_o = -V\phi \frac{d\sigma_o}{d\Theta} \tag{11-56}$$

where V = volume of reservoir
ϕ = its porosity
$d\sigma_o/d\Theta$ = time rate of change of oil saturation in the reservoir, a negative quantity

The value of $d\sigma_o/d\Theta$ may be obtained from (11-52):

$$\frac{d}{d\Theta} \frac{k_g}{k_o} = -bae^{-b\sigma_o} \frac{d\sigma_o}{d\Theta} = -b \frac{k_g}{k_o} \frac{d\sigma_o}{d\Theta} \tag{11-57}$$

whereas the value of $\frac{d}{d\Theta} \frac{k_g}{k_o}$ is obtained by taking the derivative of (11-55):

$$\frac{d}{d\Theta} \frac{k_g}{k_o} = \frac{\mu_g}{\mu_o} \frac{P_a}{P_m} \left(\frac{1}{Q_o} \frac{dQ_g}{d\Theta} - \frac{Q_g}{Q_o^2} \frac{dQ_o}{d\Theta} \right) \tag{11-58}$$

Equating (11-57) and (11-58), we obtain

$$-b\frac{d\sigma_o}{d\Theta} = \frac{k_o}{k_g}\frac{\mu_g}{\mu_o}\frac{P_a}{P_m}\left(\frac{1}{Q_o}\frac{dQ_g}{d\Theta} - \frac{Q_g}{Q_o^2}\frac{dQ_o}{d\Theta}\right) \tag{11-59}$$

Introducing the value of (11-55) in (11-59), we have

$$-b\frac{d\sigma_o}{d\Theta} = \frac{1}{Q_g}\frac{dQ_g}{d\Theta} - \frac{1}{Q_o}\frac{dQ_o}{d\Theta}$$

Therefore, (11-56) may be written

$$Q_o = \frac{V\phi}{b}\left(\frac{1}{Q_g}\frac{dQ_g}{d\Theta} - \frac{1}{Q_o}\frac{dQ_o}{d\Theta}\right) \tag{11-60}$$

which is a differential equation in Q_o and Q_g.

This equation is not readily integrable by ordinary methods, but if one let

$$A = \int_0^\theta Q_g\,d\Theta + a$$

it can be verified by substitution that the following equation is the solution of (11-60)

$$Q_o = \frac{V\phi}{b}\left(\frac{d\log A}{d\Theta}\right) = \frac{1}{b}V\phi\frac{Q_g}{A} \tag{11-61}$$

The physical significance of A is that it represents the cumulative gas injection plus an initial injection volume a corresponding to the initial oil production rate at $\Theta = 0$.

The cumulative oil recovery $\overline{Q_o}$ between the cumulative gas injection volumes A_1 and A_2 at times Θ_1 and Θ_2 is represented by

$$\overline{Q_o} = \frac{V\phi}{b}\int_{\theta_1}^{\theta_2}\frac{d\log A}{d\Theta}\,d\Theta$$

which becomes after integration

$$\overline{Q_o} = \frac{V\phi}{b}\log\frac{A_2}{A_1}$$

The preceding equations make no assumption concerning the possible variation in gas injection rates and are valid under all conditions.

If, however, the gas input rate Q_g is constant, then

$$A = Q_g\Theta + a$$

and

$$Q_o = \frac{V\phi}{b}\frac{Q_g}{Q_g\Theta + a} \tag{11-62}$$

Equation (11-62) indicates that if the reciprocal of the oil production rate $1/Q_o$ is plotted vs. time, a straight line should result. This relationship had already been established experimentally by Day and Yuster (1945) for gas-drive recovery on long cores, and Muskat's (1946) theory was a theoretical derivation inspired by the laboratory results of Day and Yuster.

The performance of the expulsion process by gas expansion may, however, be calculated more readily step by step through the use of Eqs. (11-50) and (11-51). To this end, desaturation steps are assumed starting from the residual oil saturation at break-through. The gas-oil ratio R is calculated at the end of desaturation by Eq. (11-50), and the corresponding gas-flow rate is calculated by Eq. (11-51). Then by the relation $Q_o = Q_g/R$, the oil-flow rate is calculated. Table 11-2 gives a summary of the calculations in the case at hand during the subordinate phases of the drive, initially under a driving pressure of 500 psi and later of 200 psi when the limiting gas-oil ratio of 20,000 cu ft per bbl had been reached.

TABLE 11-2. SUBORDINATE PHASE: SUMMARY OF CALCULATIONS FOR OIL EXPULSION BY EXTERNAL GAS EXPANSION

Desaturation step, per cent	Oil saturation, per cent	Gas-oil ratio, cu ft per bbl	Oil-flow rate, cu ft per hr	Time increment necessary for desaturation step, hr
		Injection pressure 500 psi		
0	77.5	1,665		
2.5	75.0	2,650	0.0214	292
2.5	72.5	3,550	0.0199	314
2.5	70.0	4,640	0.01795	348
2.5	67.5	6,060	0.01586	395
2.5	65.0	7,720	0.01426	439
2.5	62.5	9,700	0.0127	492
2.5	60.0	12,100	0.0113	553
2.5	57.5	15,350	0.00974	643
2.5	55.0	20,000	0.00824	759
		Injection pressure 200 psi		
0	55.0	8,660	0.001965	
1.5	53.5	11,500	0.00159	2,510
1.5	52.0	14,300	0.00135	2,960
1.5	50.5	17,100	0.00118	3,390
1.7	48.8	20,000	0.00107	3,970

Modification Owing to Capillary Pressure (End Effect). When two porous media are in contact along a boundary, the wetting-fluid distribution across this boundary requires continuity of pressure within the fluid. Owing to the curvature of the interface between the wetting and nonwetting fluid, a saturation discontinuity must exist in the wetting fluid. This is true also if one medium has 100 per cent porosity (such as the well bore) and the other is the reservoir sand. This is known as the *capillary end effect,* which was already recognized by Hassler and coworkers (1936) in some early air-drive experiments with oil-saturated cores. This effect was discussed more fully later by Leverett (1941) and by Hassler and coworkers (1943). The latter writers have shown that in a steady stream of a liquid and gas mixture through a sandstone body the liquid saturation increases to the wetting-phase equilibrium saturation near the outlet face. At that saturation, gas is just able to flow steadily. The liquid flows in a steady stream through the boundary, but the gas flow changes from steady stream within the sand to a flow condition as dispersed bubbles in the highly liquid saturated zone near the sand face. The capillary pressure, or difference in pressure across the curved interface between the liquid and gas phases, changes discontinuously at the boundary from the high value which exists at the equilibrium gas saturation to zero outside the sand body.

The effect on recovery introduced by the capillary-pressure end effect may be calculated from the following reasoning, according to a private and unpublished communication from L. F. Elkins (1943) and adapted here by courtesy of the Pan American Petroleum Corporation.

The flow of gas Q_g measured at the outlet pressure P_a may be obtained from

$$Q_g = -\frac{K_g A}{\mu_g}\frac{P_g}{P_a}\frac{dP_g}{dl} \tag{11-63}$$

where P_g is the pressure within the gas phase at any one point of the system.

The oil-flow rate Q_o is similarly obtained by

$$Q_o = -\frac{K_o A}{\mu_o}\frac{dP_o}{dl}$$

The capillary pressure P_c is obtained from

$$P_c = P_g - P_o$$

Hence

$$\frac{dP_c}{dl} = \frac{dP_g}{dl} - \frac{dP_o}{dl}$$

By means of the above equations it is possible to calculate the oil-saturation distribution profile at the end of the experiment when no more oil flows under the application of a specified gas pressure at the inlet end. This requires a knowledge of the curve of capillary pressure vs. oil saturation, which is a characteristic of the sand packing under consideration. In this instance, this curve is assumed to be given by Fig. 11-23.

Under the condition of nonexistent oil flow, the oil pressure, at the outlet face as well as within the sand, is the outlet pressure, or atmospheric pressure. If there were a pressure gradient within the oil, there would be an appreciable oil flow which is now nearly nonexistent after 15,000 hr of

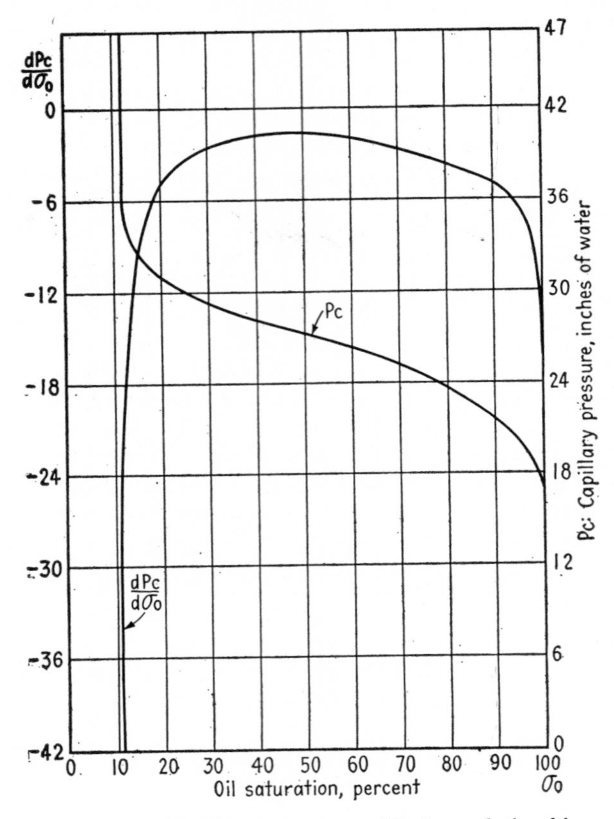

FIG. 11-23. Capillary-pressure equilibrium relationship.

gas injection (Fig. 11-22). Therefore, the pressure within the gas phase at any point is obtained by

$$P_g \cong P_a + P_c$$

and the gas-flow equation may be written

$$Q_g = -A \frac{K_g}{\mu_g} \frac{P_a + P_c}{P_a} \frac{dP_c}{dl} \tag{11-64}$$

It is now desired to predict the saturation distribution within the packing. To this end, Eq. (11-64) may be integrated after separation of the variables as follows:

$$\frac{Q_g}{A} \mu_g \, dl = -\frac{P_a + P_c}{P_a} K_g \, dP_c$$

where all the variables depending on oil saturation are on the right-hand side.

The distance l from the outlet end at which a saturation σ_o will exist may be obtained by integration between the equilibrium saturation σ_e at the outlet end and σ_o:

$$\frac{Q_g \, \mu_g}{A} l = -\int_{\sigma_e}^{\sigma_o} \frac{P_a + P_c}{P_a} K_g \, dP_c \tag{11-65}$$

This integration must be carried out numerically and graphically for various increments of saturation until either a saturation is reached where $P_a + P_c$ is equal to the injection pressure or a length l is reached equal to the length of the packing. The integration is most readily carried out by rewriting Eq. (11-65) and by expressing all functions under the integral sign as a function of saturation and in particular by taking the derivative of P_c with respect to saturation. We obtain

$$\frac{Q_g}{A} \mu_g l = -\int_{\sigma_e}^{\sigma_o} \frac{P_a + P_c}{P_a} K_g \frac{dP_c}{d\sigma_o} d\sigma_o \tag{11-66}$$

The integration of Eq. (11-66) is best carried out graphically. The graphic derivative $dP_c/d\sigma_o$ is first obtained, and the results are shown on Fig. 11-23. The integrand is then plotted graphically as shown on Fig. 11-24. A specific oil saturation σ_o is assumed, the area under the curve

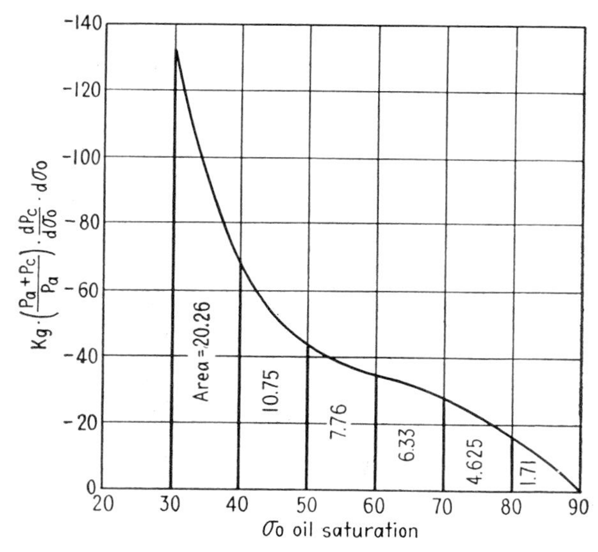

FIG. 11-24. Graphic integration for calculating the saturation end effect.

in Fig. 11-24 is planimetered, and the value of l is solved for from Eq. (11-66), at which the saturation σ_o is to be found in the sand packing.

The results of this calculation are illustrated on Fig. 11-25, which indicates an accumulation of oil at the outlet end of the packing extending only for a distance of 8 cm, in view of the high permeability of the reservoir and its low capillary pressures at the fluid saturations involved.

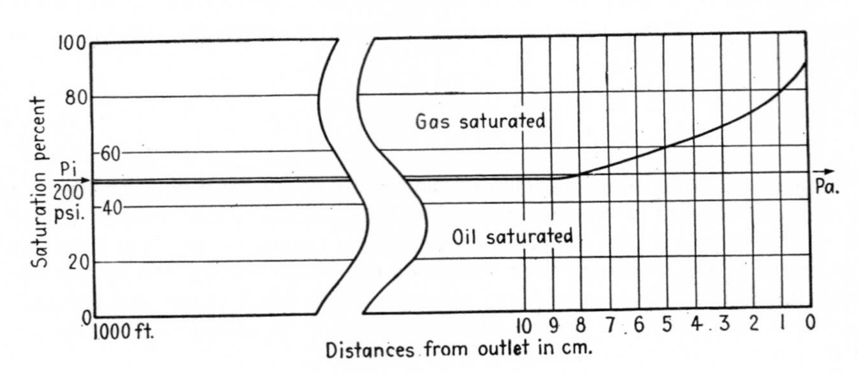

FIG. 11-25. Fluid-saturation profile under 200 psi inlet pressure.

It may readily be inferred that the application of a higher driving gas pressure gradient would have reduced further this outlet-end oil accumulation.

The capillary end effect here discussed is of little importance in actual field operations where the reservoir volumes involved are large compared to those affected by the end effect, but in laboratory model recovery experiments the results of desaturation such as carried out in flood pots and on long cores may be vitiated to a high degree by this capillary phenomenon.

Modification Owing to Driving Pressure Reduction. An interesting observation is made to the effect that additional oil may be recovered when the limiting gas-oil ratio of 20,000 cu ft per bbl is reached through the lowering of the injection pressure. In the present study, the pressure was reduced to 200 psi after 4,711.4 hr of injection under 500 psi. The production rate dropped sharply as shown on Fig. 11-22, while the gas-oil ratio was reduced to 8,660 cu ft per bbl. While such an operation would probably prove uneconomical in practice, it shows the possibility of maintaining the gas-oil ratio near the economic limit by a gradual or stepwise decrease of the injection pressure.

High-pressure Frontal Gas Drive. Two cases may be distinguished, depending on whether or not the possibility of phase change exists. For a normal crude with high-pressure gas injection at a pressure larger than its bubble point, gas goes into solution and increases its reservoir-volume factor as well as reduces its viscosity (*condensation gas drive*). For a volatile crude, gas not only goes into solution behind the front but it also vaporizes oil by retrograde vaporization further behind the front (*vaporization gas drive*). A combination of both processes is also possible.

High-pressure Gas Injection above the Bubble Point of a Normal Crude Oil (Condensation Gas Drive). Consider a linear gas drive as represented in

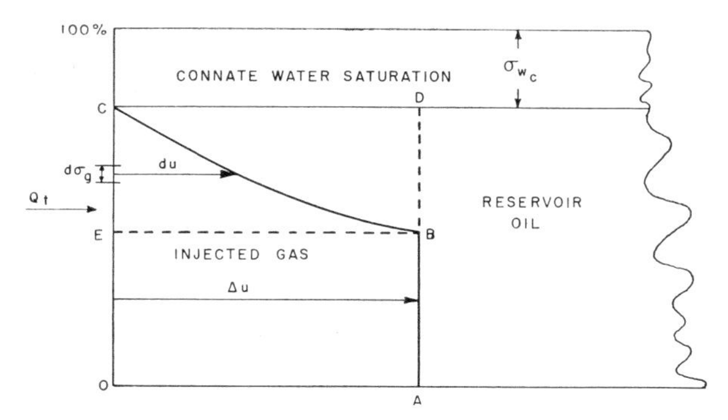

FIG. 11-26. Linear frontal gas drive at pressure higher than the reservoir oil's bubble-point pressure.

Fig. 11-26. The following gas balance is written for an increment of time $\Delta\theta$:

$$\text{Gas injected} = \text{free gas} + \text{gas in solution}$$

$$Q_t\,\Delta\theta = \text{free gas in area } OABC + \text{gas going in solution in area } (BECD - BCE) \qquad (11\text{-}67)$$

$$Q_t\,\Delta\theta = A\phi\left\{\left(\sigma_{g_f}\,\Delta u + \int_{\sigma_{gf}}^{1-\sigma_w} du\,d\sigma_g\right) + \frac{\alpha(S - S_o)}{\beta}\left[(1 - \sigma_w - \sigma_{g_f})\,\Delta u - \int_{\sigma_{gf}}^{1-\sigma_w} du\,d\sigma_g\right]\right\}$$

Substituting,

$$\Delta u = \frac{Q_t\,\Delta\theta}{A\phi}\left(\frac{\partial f_g}{\partial\sigma_g}\right)_f \qquad (11\text{-}68)$$

$$du = \frac{Q_t\,\Delta\theta}{A\phi}\left(\frac{\partial f_g}{\partial\sigma_g}\right) \qquad (11\text{-}69)$$

and canceling the common factors,

$$1 = \sigma_{gf}\left(\frac{\partial f_g}{\partial\sigma_g}\right)_f + \int_{\sigma_{gf}}^{1-\sigma_w}\frac{\partial f_g}{\partial\sigma_g}\,d\sigma_g + \frac{\alpha(S - S_0)}{\beta}\left[(1 - \sigma_w - \sigma_{gf})\left(\frac{\partial f_g}{\partial\sigma_g}\right)_f - \int_{\sigma_{gf}}^{1-\sigma_w}\frac{\partial f_g}{\partial\sigma_g}\,d\sigma_g\right] \qquad (11\text{-}70)$$

Carrying out the integration and rearranging terms,

$$f_{g_f} + \frac{\dfrac{\alpha(S - S_0)}{\beta}}{1 - \dfrac{\alpha(S - S_0)}{\beta}} = \left(\frac{\partial f_g}{\partial \sigma_g}\right)_f \left[\sigma_{gf} + \frac{(1 - \sigma_w)\dfrac{\alpha(S - S_0)}{\beta}}{1 - \dfrac{\alpha(S - S_0)}{\beta}}\right] \tag{11-71}$$

By comparison of Eq. (11-71) as written above with the standard formula obtained for gas drive without gas going into solution

$$f_{g_f} = \left(\frac{\partial f_g}{\partial \sigma_g}\right)_f \sigma_{gf} \tag{11-72}$$

one infers simple geometric construction for the recovery calculation at gas break-through, for only certain terms need be added to the coordinates of the f_g curve:

$$\left(\frac{\dfrac{\alpha(S - S_0)}{\beta}}{1 - \dfrac{\alpha(S - S_0)}{\beta}}\right) \text{ is added to the } f_g \text{ scale}$$

$$(1 - \sigma_w)\left(\frac{\dfrac{\alpha(S - S_0)}{\beta}}{1 - \dfrac{\alpha(S - S_0)}{\beta}}\right) \text{ is added to the } \sigma_g \text{ scale}$$

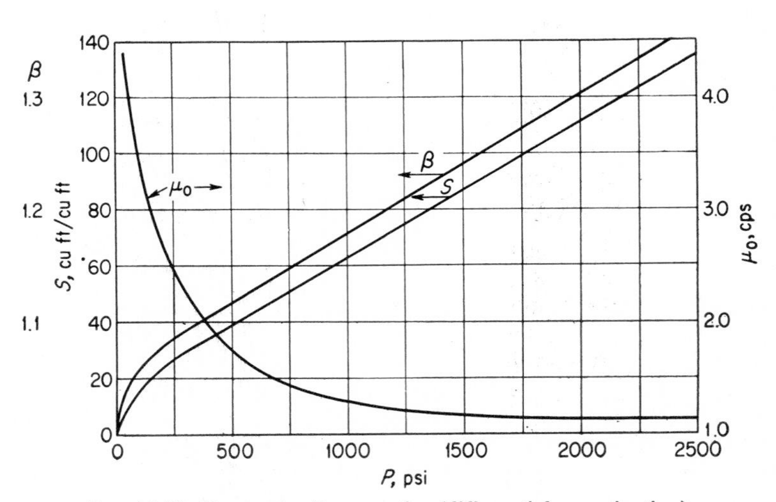

FIG. 11-27. Reservoir-oil properties (differential vaporization).

These two quantities are added below and to the left of the origin and determine a pole from which the tangent to the f_g curve is drawn and which determines saturation at the front and recovery at break-through in the usual manner.

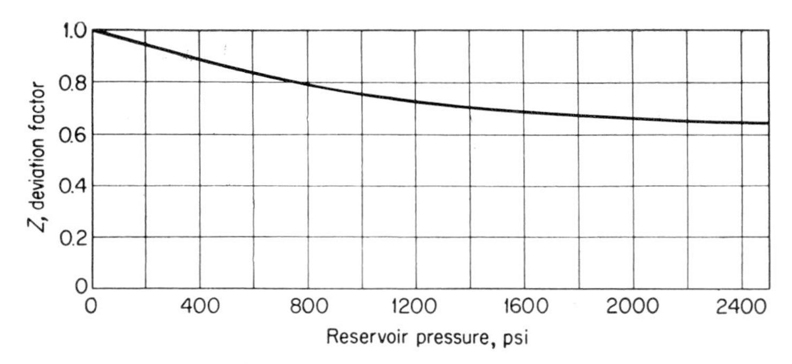

FIG. 11-28. Gas compressibility factor vs. reservoir pressure.

The f_g curve must be drawn using the viscosity ratios that will prevail under injection conditions of reservoir pressure and fluid composition. The following example illustrates the method:

The reservoir-fluid properties and relative-permeability properties assumed are represented in the attached Figs. 11-27 to 11-29.

Bubble point = 500 psi
Original solution gas = 39.2 cu ft/cu ft
Gas viscosity = 0.02 cps regardless of pressure

The summary of the calculations made is given in Table 11-3.

TABLE 11-3. RECOVERY CALCULATIONS FOR HIGH-PRESSURE GAS INJECTION

Injection pressure, psi	S, cu ft/cu ft	$S - S_0$	α	$\alpha(S - S_0)$	β	$\frac{\alpha(S - S_0)}{\beta}$	$1 - \frac{\alpha(S - S_0)}{\beta}$	$\frac{\frac{\alpha(S - S_0)}{\beta}}{1 - \frac{\alpha(S - S_0)}{\beta}}$
750	51.8	12.6	0.01675	0.211	1.150	0.184	0.816	0.225
1,000	64	24.8	0.0119	0.295	1.180	0.250	0.750	0.333
1,250	76	36.8	0.00905	0.333	1.210	0.276	0.724	0.382
1,500	87.4	48.2	0.00735	0.354	1.241	0.284	0.716	0.397
1,750	100	60.8	0.00605	0.368	1.272	0.289	0.711	0.406
2,000	112	72.8	0.0051	0.371	1.310	0.284	0.716	0.397
2,250	124	84.8	0.0045	0.381	1.335	0.285	0.715	0.399
2,500	136	96.8	0.00406	0.393	1.370	0.287	0.713	0.401

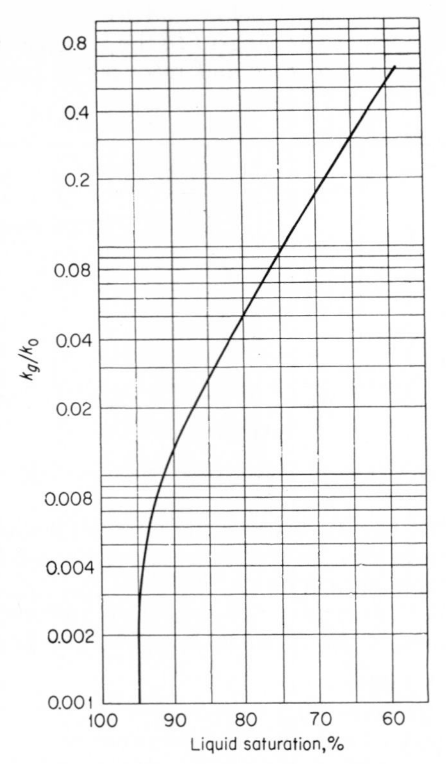

FIG. 11-29. k_g/k_o vs. liquid saturation.

The data of this example have been plotted on Fig. 11-30. Four f_g curves are traced, corresponding to pressures of 500, 1,000, and 1,500 psi and the last for all pressures from 2,000 to 2,500 psi since there is little change of fluid viscosity at the higher pressures.

Four possible connate water saturations were assumed: 0, 0.1, 0.2, and 0.3 which give four loci for the pole on Fig. 11-30. The loci for the poles according to injection pressure are indicated by horizontal straight lines.

A gas drive at 500 psi without gas going into solution would displace 19 per cent of pore space in reservoir oil ($\beta = 1.117$) or 17 per cent in stock-tank oil. When the injection pressure is 750 psi, and without connate water, the displacement is 28.5 per cent of pore space in reservoir oil swollen to a volume of 1.15. The stock-tank oil volume recovered at breakthrough expressed as per cent of pore space is

$$\frac{1}{1.117} - \frac{0.715}{1.150} = 27.7\%$$

Should there be a connate water saturation present, recoveries would be reduced.

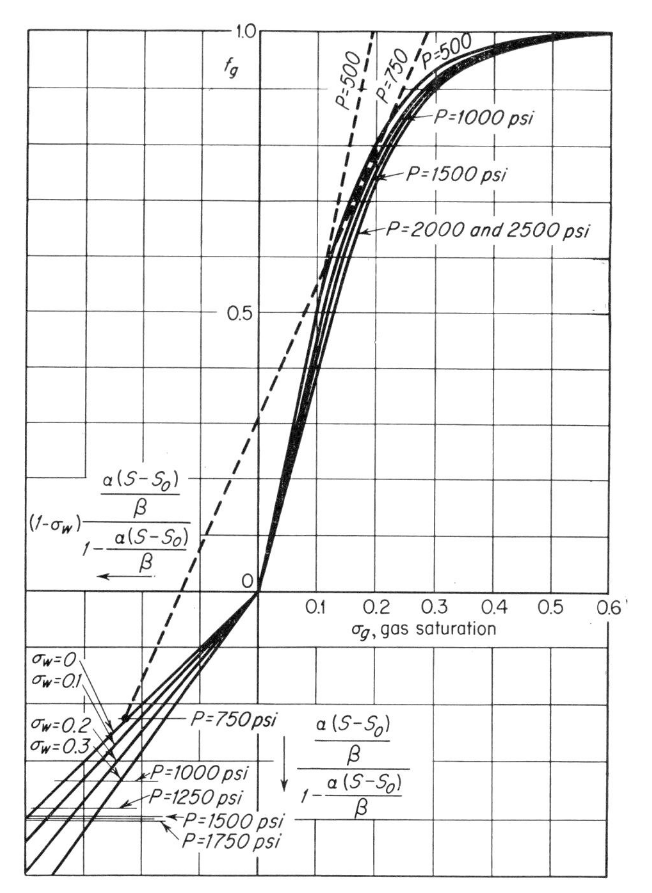

FIG. 11-30. Geometric construction for calculating recovery by condensation and/or vaporization gas drives.

A similar calculation would indicate the recoveries at break-through (connate water absent) shown in Table 11-4.

High-pressure Gas Injection with Highly Soluble Gas and Retrograde Vaporization of Residual Oil (Vaporization Gas Drive). Let v be the fraction of residual oil that vaporizes back of the driving front and d be the reservoir volume of the vapor per unit volume of residual oil. These figures may be determined from a knowledge of injected-gas composition, reservoir-oil composition, injection pressure, and equilibrium vaporization constants.

For the purpose of the present derivation it will be assumed that there is no *pressure* or *fluid* composition gradient back of the front. This is probably approximately so because most of the pressure drop takes place in the oil zone ahead of the front.

TABLE 11-4. RECOVERIES AT BREAK-THROUGH FOR HIGH-PRESSURE GAS INJECTION

Injection pressure, psi	Gas phase created, % pore volume σ_g	β	Stock-tank oil volume recovered, % pore volume $= \frac{1}{1.117} - \frac{1-\sigma_g}{\beta}$
500	19.0	1.117	17.0
750	28.5	1.150	27.7
1,000	30.5	1.180	31.0
1,250	32.0	1.210	33.6
1,500	32.0	1.241	35.1
1,750	32.5	1.272	36.8
2,000	33.3	1.310	39.0
2,250	33.0	1.335	39.6
2,500	33.0	1.370	41.0

By applying the gas balance previously used we have the following terms:

1. Total gas injected $= Q_t\, \Delta\theta$ measured at reservoir conditions.
2. Reservoir volume of injected gas remaining as free gas is

$$Q_t\, \Delta\theta \left[\sigma_{g_f} \left(\frac{\partial f_g}{\partial \sigma_g} \right)_f + 1 - f_{g_f} \right]$$

3. Reservoir volume of gas that goes into solution is

$$Q_t\, \Delta\theta \frac{\alpha(S - S_0)}{\beta} \left[(1 - \sigma_{w_c} - \sigma_{g_f}) \left(\frac{\partial f_g}{\partial \sigma_g} \right)_f - 1 + f_{g_f} \right] (1 - v)$$

4. Reservoir volume of oil that vaporizes back of the front is

$$Q_t\, \Delta\theta \left[(1 - \sigma_{w_c} - \sigma_{g_f}) \left(\frac{\partial f_g}{\partial \sigma_g} \right)_f - 1 + f_{g_f} \right] vd$$

Equating the above terms in a gas balance in the following manner

$$(1) = (2) + (3) + (4)$$

and after simplifications and rearranging, we have

$$f_{g_f} + \frac{\dfrac{\alpha(S - S_0)}{\beta}(1 - v) + vd}{1 - \dfrac{\alpha(S - S_0)}{\beta}(1 - v) - vd} = \left(\frac{\partial f_g}{\partial \sigma_g} \right)_f \left[\sigma_{g_f} + \frac{(1 - \sigma_{w_c}) \left\{ \dfrac{\alpha(S - S_0)}{\beta}(1 - v) + vd \right\}}{1 - \dfrac{\alpha(S - S_0)}{\beta}(1 - v) - vd} \right] \tag{11-73}$$

It may be observed that Eq. (11-73) may be treated in exactly the same manner as Eq. (11-71) and its solution is most readily obtained by graphic means. The quantities to be added to the f_g and σ_g axes in order to determine the pole are explicitly written in the formula. It may readily be inferred that the occurrence of residual oil vaporization back of the front is beneficial to the gas drive because it provides additional gas input volume and reduces the oil viscosity at the front.

The manner in which the product vd occurs in Eq. (11-73) indicates that with a large vaporization factor v, the pole as origin of the tangent to the f_g curve is further removed from the origin; under certain conditions it may approach infinity. The recovery is then obtained by drawing a tangent to the f_g curve at a 45-deg angle. A 45-deg diagonal for the f_g curve is obtained when the physical properties of the driving gas and of the driven oil are identical. For these conditions, the ultimate recovery of the oil in place is 100 per cent.

SELECTED REFERENCES ON FRONTAL DISPLACEMENT

1941

Buckley, S. E., and M. C. Leverett: Mechanism of Fluid Displacement in Sands, *AIME Tech. Pub.* 1337.

1945

Pirson, S. J.: The Engineering Approach to Oil Reservoir Controls, *Oil Weekly*, Dec. 31, pp. 22ff.

1950

Whorton, L. P., and W. F. Kieschnick, Jr.: Preliminary Report on Oil Recovery by High Pressure Gas Injection, *Petroleum Engr.*, April, pp. B-54ff.

1951

Felsenthal, M., and S. T. Yuster: A Study of the Effect of Viscosity on Oil Recovery by Water Flooding, *AIME Tech. Paper* 163-G.

Leibrock, R. M., et al.: Results of Gas Injection in the Cedar Lake Field, *Trans. AIME Petroleum Div.*, pp. 357ff.

Terwilliger, P. L., et al.: An Experimental and Theoretical Investigation of Gravity Drainage Performance, *Trans. AIME Petroleum Div.*, pp. 285ff.

1952

Kern, L. R.: Displacement Mechanism in Multi-Well System, *Trans. AIME Petroleum Div.*, vol. 195, pp. 39ff.

Welge, H. J.: A Simplified Method of Computing Oil Recovery by Gas and Water Drive, *Trans. AIME Petroleum Div.*, vol. 195, pp. 91ff.

1953

Anders, E. L., Jr.: Mile-six Pool; An Evaluation of Recovery Efficiency, *Trans. AIME Petroleum Div.*, pp. 279ff.

Griffith, B. L., and V. M. Hollrah: High-pressure Gas Injection in Block 31 Devonian Reservoir, Crane County, Texas, *Producers Monthly*, February, pp. 26ff.; *World Oil*, July 1, 1952, pp. 163ff.

Jones-Parra, J., and J. C. Calhoun, Jr.: Computation of a Linear Flood by the Stabilized Zone Method, *Trans. AIME Petroleum Div. Tech. Note* 193, pp. 335ff.

Rapoport, L. A., and W. J. Leas: Properties of Linear Water Floods, *Trans. AIME Petroleum Div.*, pp. 139ff.

Slobod, R. L., and H. A. Koch, Jr.: High-pressure Gas-injection Mechanism of Recovery Increase, *API Paper* 901-28-B.

1954

Hollrah, V. M., et al.: Five Years of High-pressure Gas Injection in the Block 31 Field, *World Oil*, vol. 139, pp. 192ff., July.

Levine, J. S.: Displacement Experiments in a Consolidated Porous System, *Trans. AIME Petroleum Div.*, March, pp. 21ff.

Nielsen, R. F.: Fluid Displacement in Linear Floods, series of five articles, *Oil Gas J.*, July 12, p. 120; July 19, p. 119.

Offeringa, J., and C. Van der Pool: Displacement of Oil from Porous Media by Miscible Fluids, *J. Petroleum Technol.*, vol. 6, pp. 37ff., December.

Root, P. J., and J. C. Calhoun, Jr.: Displacement of Gas by Water from Unconsolidated Sands, *Producers Monthly*, vol. 18, pp. 18–21, August.

1955

Craig, F. F., Jr., et al.: Oil Recovery Performance of Pattern Gas or Water Injection Operations from Model Tests, *J. Petroleum Technol.*, vol. 7, pp. 7ff., January.

Croes, G. A., and N. Schwarz: Dimensionally Scaled Experiments and the Theories on the Water-drive Process, *J. Petroleum Technol.*, vol. 7, pp. 35ff., March.

Hock, R. L., and E. C. Sincox: Use of Light Hydrocarbons for Better Oil Recovery in North Louisiana, Interstate Oil Compact Commission, Denver Meeting, June 18.

Rapoport, L. A.: Scaling Laws for Use in Design and Operations of Water–Oil Flow Models, *J. Petroleum Technol.*, vol. 7, pp. 143ff., September.

Warren, J. E., and J. C. Calhoun, Jr.: A Study of Water Flood Efficiency in Oil-wet Systems, *J. Petroleum Technol.*, vol. 7, pp. 22ff., February.

1956

Bail, P. T.: The Calculation of Water Flood Performance for the Bradford Third Sand from Relative Permeability and Capillary Pressure Data, *Producers Monthly*, vol. 20, no. 9, pp. 20ff.

Craig, F. F., Jr., and T. M. Geffen: The Determination of Partial Pressure Maintenance Performance by Laboratory Flow Tests, *J. Petroleum Technol.*, vol. 8, pp. 42ff., February.

Craig, F. F., et al.: A Laboratory Study of Gravity Segregation in Frontal Drives, *AIME Tech. Paper* 676G.

Hadley, G. F., and L. L. Handy: A Theoretical and Experimental Study of the Steady State Capillary End Effect, *AIME Tech. Paper* 707G.

Hall, H. N., and T. M. Geffen: A Laboratory Study of Solvent Flooding, *AIME Tech. Paper* 711G.

Jenks, L. H., et al.: A Field Test of the Gas-driven Liquid Propane Method of Oil Recovery, *AIME Tech. Paper* 713G.

Koch, H. A., Jr., and R. L. Slobod: Miscible Slug Process, *AIME Tech. Paper* 714G.

Kyte, J. R., et al.: Mechanism of Water Flooding in the Presence of Free Gas, *J. Petroleum Technol.*, vol. 8, pp. 215ff., September.

Moore, T. F., and R. L. Slobod: The Effect of Viscosity and Capillarity on the Displacement of Oil by Water, *Producers Monthly*, vol. 20, no. 10, pp. 20ff.

Richardson, J. G., and F. M. Perkins, Jr.: A Laboratory Investigation of the Effect of Rate on Recovery of Oil by Water Flooding, *AIME Tech. Paper* 4491.

Rapoport, L. A., et al.: Flow Model Studies of Five-spot Water-flood Performance, *AIME Tech. Paper* 677G.

Stone, H. L., and J. S. Crump: The Effect of Gas Composition upon Oil Recovery by Gas Drive, *J. Petroleum Technol.*, vol. 8, pp. 105ff., May.

Templeton, C. C., and S. S. Rushing, Jr.: Oil Water Displacements in Microscopic Capillaries, *J. Petroleum Technol.*, vol. 8, pp. 211ff , September.

CHAPTER 12

OIL PRODUCTION BY WATER DRIVE

When water encroaches into an oil reservoir either naturally or artificially, oil is displaced ahead of the advancing water in the form of a front, provided the fluid saturation conditions are satisfactory. Natural water encroachment in sufficient quantity may occur only when the reservoir is embedded into an aquifer of sufficient extent to provide volumetric replacement by water of the oil withdrawn. Oil replacement by water from the aquifer may occur under the influence of various factors operating singly or in combination: by volumetric water expansion as a result of field-pressure decline, by hydraulic flow as a result of water infiltration at the outcrops of the reservoir rock, or by artificial injection of water into the oil-bearing horizon. Water injection may be resorted to as a supplement to bottom or edge-water drive; it may be applied as peripheral water injection, as a center-line drive, or as a pattern flood. The pressure behavior of the reservoir under water drive is dependent upon the rate of oil withdrawal and upon the rate of water encroachment. When exact volumetric balance exists between water influx and fluid withdrawals, field pressure is maintained. Ultimate oil recovery is greatly dependent upon the pressure behavior of the field, and one of the first tasks in the study of a water-drive field is the determination of its natural rate of water encroachment. This may be done by various methods based on past performance history in the form of statistical data.

Oil withdrawal from a water-drive field is done from wells located in advance of the water front in order to avoid water break-through, water coning, and the like.

Oil-withdrawal rates in a water-drive field have a large effect on recovery, and it appears that an optimum production rate exists which is the rate required to create an optimum amount of free gas saturation uniformly distributed in the oil zone in advance of the water front.

RECOGNITION AND EVALUATION OF WATER DRIVE

The prediction of the water-encroachment rate may be based upon the application of Darcy's law to the field as a whole, according to which the instantaneous water influx into the field is proportional to the differential pressure existing between the edge-water pressure and the field pressure and to the area exposed to water encroachment on the field's boundary.

This method was suggested by Schilthuis (1946), according to which the cumulative water encroachment W may be calculated from

$$W = C_s \int_0^\Theta \Delta P \, d\Theta \tag{12-1}$$

where C_s is a proportionality constant which includes the formation permeability, the water viscosity, and the area of encroachment on the field's boundary.

ΔP is the differential pressure which exists at any time (Θ) between edge-water pressure (substantially equal to the original reservoir pressure) and the prevailing field pressure.

Another formula for the cumulative water encroachment, known as the simplified Hurst formula, is as follows:

$$W = C_h \int_0^\Theta \frac{\Delta P}{\log \Theta} \, d\Theta \tag{12-2}$$

where C_h is a different constant from that in (12-1). This formula is similar to the previous one but for the logarithm of time (Θ) factor, which is introduced because of the gradually lengthening travel path of the encroaching water during the span of the production process. This, in effect, takes care, to a certain measure, of the expanding radius of the pressure sink created in the aquifer by virtue of oil production from the oil reservoir; since the influx of water is inversely proportional to the logarithm of the pressure sink's radius, it is natural to include an empirical correction to the influx which is inversely proportional to total time since the initiation of production.

Hurst (1943) has proposed a more complex solution to the problem which takes into account the transient nature of water influx from an infinite aquifer.

Van Everdingen and Hurst (1949) proposed a more complete solution to the transient influx which also takes into account the possibility of a finite aquifer.

A statistical study of production data in conjunction with the material-balance equation has been suggested by Woods and Muskat (1945) for the simultaneous determination of the following three unknowns: the original stock-tank oil in place N, the relative gas-cap size m, and the cumulative water influx W. However, these writers concluded, as might be expected, that this approach leads to unsatisfactory results by virtue of the indeterminate nature of the material-balance equation, especially under conditions of active water drive when small observational errors lead to disproportionate relative effects on the results (Chap. 10). In particular, it appears advisable to determine independently the value of the relative gas-cap size m, such as by a study of coregraphs, formation testing records, electric and radioactivity logs, or drilling mud logs.

Water-influx Determination by the Schilthuis Method. Let us consider the material-balance equation

$$N = \frac{n[\beta + \alpha(r_n - S)] - (W - w)}{m\beta_0(\alpha/\alpha_0 - 1) + \alpha(S_0 - S) - (\beta_0 - \beta)} \tag{12-3}$$

and assume that all physical properties of the reservoir fluids are known (β,S,α), that the production statistics are well kept and up to date (n,r_n,w), and that a reasonable evaluation of the gas-cap volume ratio (m) could be made from geological, geophysical, and drilling information. Hence the only two unknowns in the equation are N, the original stock-tank oil in place, and W, the cumulative water encroachment.

The first step is to ascertain if water encroachment exists. To this end let us first assume it to be nonexistent ($W = 0$). However, in the eventuality that this assumption is untrue, the calculations of the original oil in place (N_1, N_2, N_3, etc.) from the material-balance equation corresponding to various known cumulative productions (n_1, n_2, n_3, etc.) will be found to increase with time; for example, $N_1 < N_2 < N_3 \cdots$, since the numerator of Eq. (12-3) is deprived of a negative term and becomes larger than it should be at each new production increment.

The next step in the calculations consists in introducing the water-encroachment term: $W = C_s\int_0^\Theta \Delta P\, d\Theta$. This integration must forcibly be made numerically for specific time increments. Hence the integration is replaced by a summation: $W = C_s\Sigma\, \Delta P\, \Delta\Theta$ where the differential time ($\Delta\Theta$) is chosen sufficiently small so that no appreciable error is introduced.

The material-balance equation may now be written more simply

$$N = f(n,w) - \frac{C_s\Sigma\, \Delta P\, \Delta\Theta}{\text{den.}} \tag{12-4}$$

where

$$f(n,w) = \frac{n[\beta + \alpha(r_n - S)] + w}{m\beta_0\,(\alpha/\alpha_0 - 1) + \alpha(S_0 - S) - (\beta_0 - \beta)} \tag{12-5}$$

and where den. stands for the value of the denominator of the expression of N in (12-3). It is given by

$$\text{den.} = m\beta_0\,(\alpha/\alpha_0 - 1) + \alpha(S_0 - S) - (\beta_0 - \beta) \tag{12-6}$$

The known production steps, with corresponding pressures and times, are tabulated as follows:

Time	Cumulative production	Pressure
0	0	P_0
Θ_1	n_1	P_1
Θ_2	n_2	P_2
Θ_3	n_3	P_3
Θ_i	n_i	P_i
Θ_j	n_j	P_j

With the introduction of the proper water-encroachment term, the calculated values of the original oil in place N must remain constant. Hence the following relations must be verified:

$$N = f(n_1,w_1) - \frac{C_s\left(P_0 - \frac{P_0 + P_1}{2}\right)\Theta_1}{\text{den. } 1}$$

$$N = f(n_2,w_2) - \frac{C_s\left[\left(P_0 - \frac{P_0 + P_1}{2}\right)\Theta_1 + \left(P_0 - \frac{P_1 + P_2}{2}\right)(\Theta_2 - \Theta_1)\right]}{\text{den. } 2}$$

$$N = f(n_3,w_3) - \frac{\left\{C_s\left[\left(P_0 - \frac{P_0 + P_1}{2}\right)\Theta_1 + \left(P_0 - \frac{P_1 + P_2}{2}\right)(\Theta_2 - \Theta_1) + \left(P_0 - \frac{P_2 + P_3}{2}\right)(\Theta_3 - \Theta_2)\right]\right\}}{\text{den. } 3} \tag{12-7}$$

. . . .

The system of Eqs. (12-7) assumes that the water-encroachment performance is similar, during a specific time increment, to the influx which would take place under a constant pressure differential between the original bottom-hole pressure P_0 and the average field pressure $(P_i + P_j)/2$ during the time interval $(\Theta_j - \Theta_i)$.

From the system of Eqs. (12-7) it is possible to calculate a most probable value for the water-encroachment coefficient (C_s) by the well-known methods of averages, or of least squares. An example will illustrate the method more clearly, as applied to the Schuler field, Arkansas.

The production data are available from the literature (Kaveler, 1943) and are recorded in Table 12-1.

It is observed from column 3 that the original stock-tank oil in place (N) is constantly on the increase when the water influx is neglected. Accordingly, we set up the following system of equations which includes the unknown water-encroachment factor C_s:

$$\begin{aligned} N &= 109{,}000{,}000 - 80{,}000C_s \\ N &= 112{,}000{,}000 - 93{,}000C_s \\ N &= 115{,}000{,}000 - 120{,}000C_s \end{aligned} \tag{12-8}$$

Adding the three equations (12-8) term by term, we obtain

$$3N = 336{,}000{,}000 - 293{,}000 \times C_s \tag{12-9}$$

Multiplying each equation in (12-8) by the coefficient of C_s in each and adding term by term, we obtain

$$293N = 29{,}450 \times 10^6 - 32{,}940 \times 10^3 C_s \tag{12-10}$$

The solution of the two simultaneous equations (12-9) and (12-10) yields

$N = 97{,}900{,}000$ bbl
$C_s = 144$ bbl per month per psi pressure differential

The uncertainties which enter into the use of the material-balance equation in the calculations of the initial stock-tank oil in place N and of

TABLE 12-1. CALCULATION OF THE WATER-ENCROACHMENT RATE IN THE SCHULER FIELD, ARKANSAS

Time Θ, months	Average field pressure P, psi	Calculated original residual oil in place neglecting water drive N, bbls	Time increment $\Delta\Theta$, months	Average pressure during production interval, $\frac{P_i + P_j}{2}$	Water driving pressure, $P_0 - \frac{P_i + P_j}{2} (\Delta P)$	Den.	$\frac{\Sigma \Delta P \Delta \Theta}{\text{den.}}$
(1)	(2)	(3)	(4)	(5)	(6)	(7)	(8)
0	3,520						
44	1,552	109,000,000	4	1,588.5	1,931.5	0.570	80,000
50	1,500	112,000,000	6	1,526.0	1,994.0	0.614	93,000
59	1,480	115,000,000	9	1,490.0	2,030.0	0.629	120,000

the cumulative water influx W result most likely from our ignorance of the mechanism of gas vaporization within the reservoir oil (whether by equilibrium or differential vaporization, or a composite of the two), and of the amount of vaporization hysteresis. Cook (1943) has suggested such a composite equation, but, in view of our ignorance on the relative importance of both vaporization processes, this expression is of difficult application. Hence the degree of approximation involved in the use of laboratory equilibrium data in the study of reservoir problems is unknown.

In the case of water-drive fields, the calculation of the original oil in place N is most difficult to perform with a reasonable degree of accuracy. However, two approaches to improve the results of the calculations are available:

1. The original oil in place is determined from geologic data by volumetric calculations, using quantitative information provided by geological and geophysical maps, drilling and core-analysis information, electric and radioactive well logs, etc. (Chaps. 2, 5, and 9). The material balance may then be used for the calculation of cumulative water influx (W) and

for the prediction of future pressure variations vs. cumulative production (n).

2. The cumulative water influx W and its rate of encroachment $dW/d\Theta$ are calculated independently from the pressure history of the reservoir and its physical characteristics such as permeability, porosity, and saturation. The material-balance equation may then be used to calculate the original oil in place (N). This is the method suggested by Hurst (1943).

Water-influx Calculation by the Hurst Method. Hurst's approach (1943) consists in considering the connate water, in an active water-drive field, as a diffusible fluid, slightly compressible, to which Darcy's law is applicable. Connate water is therefore viewed as a fluid of variable density δ, which can be expressed by

$$\delta = \delta_0 e^{-c_w(P_0 - P)} \tag{12-11}$$

where δ_0 = water density at original pressure P_0
c_w = water compressibility factor
P = field pressure

Applying the equation of continuity $\nabla\ \delta\bar{v} = -\phi(\partial\delta/\partial\Theta)$ in two dimensions, we obtain

$$\frac{\partial}{\partial x}(\delta u) + \frac{\partial}{\partial y}(\delta v) = -\phi\frac{\partial\delta}{\partial\Theta} \tag{12-12}$$

in which u and v are, respectively, the linear velocities in the x and y directions. Θ is the time variable, ϕ is the reservoir porosity, and $\bar{v}$ is the velocity vector. By Darcy's law we have

$$\begin{aligned} u &= -\frac{K}{\mu_w}\frac{\partial P}{\partial x} \\ v &= -\frac{K}{\mu_w}\frac{\partial P}{\partial y} \end{aligned} \tag{12-13}$$

It will be assumed that the viscosity of water μ_w does not change with pressure.

We have immediately, by substitution of expression (12-11) in the differentiations of (12-12),

$$\begin{aligned} \frac{\partial}{\partial x}(\delta u) &= -\frac{\delta c_w K}{\mu_w}\left(\frac{\partial P}{\partial x}\right)^2 - \frac{\delta K}{\mu_w}\frac{\partial^2 P}{\partial x^2} \\ \frac{\partial}{\partial y}(\delta v) &= -\frac{\delta c_w K}{\mu_w}\left(\frac{\partial P}{\partial y}\right)^2 - \frac{\delta K}{\mu_w}\frac{\partial^2 P}{\partial y^2} \\ \frac{\partial\delta}{\partial\Theta} &= -\delta c_w\frac{\partial P}{\partial\Theta} \end{aligned} \tag{12-14}$$

By substitution of (12-14) in (12-12) and neglect of the terms containing the squares of the pressure gradient and the compressibility coefficient c_w, we obtain

$$\frac{\partial^2 P}{\partial x^2} + \frac{\partial^2 P}{\partial y^2} = \frac{\mu_w \phi c_w}{K} \frac{\partial P}{\partial \Theta} \tag{12-15}$$

which may be written

$$\nabla^2 P = \frac{1}{\boldsymbol{\alpha}^2} \frac{\partial P}{\partial \Theta} \tag{12-16}$$

where

$$\boldsymbol{\alpha}^2 = \frac{K}{\mu_w \phi c_w} \tag{12-17}$$

$\boldsymbol{\alpha}^2$ is called the diffusivity constant of the water into a reservoir of permeability K and porosity ϕ, the water having the characteristic viscosity μ_w and compressibility c_w.

Hurst makes the following assumptions for the solution of the water diffusivity equation:

1. Gravitational forces have negligible effects in restraining or promoting water encroachment.
2. The pressure variation at the periphery of the field may be represented by a stepwise variation as a function of time, provided that the step intervals are not taken to be too large. The edge-water pressure is assumed to stay constant on plateaus for the duration of an interval.
3. The water encroachment is taking place radially into the field from a circular reservoir of infinite horizontal extent.
4. When a constant terminal pressure solution for the radial equation is known, it is possible to obtain the water pressure P at a distance r and at time Θ by a superposition of the step solutions.

Without discussion of details of the mathematical arguments, Hurst's final formulas are Eqs. (12-18) and (12-19). The total water influx (W) is obtained by

$$W = \frac{2\pi \times 144 \times K\boldsymbol{\sigma}H}{5.62\mu} \frac{R^2}{\boldsymbol{\alpha}^2} \int_0^\Theta \frac{dP}{d\Theta'} G \frac{\boldsymbol{\alpha}^2(\Theta - \Theta')}{R^2} d\Theta' \tag{12-18}$$

where $\boldsymbol{\sigma}$ = fractional periphery of field through which water encroaches

R = average field radius, ft

H = reservoir thickness, ft

$\frac{dP}{d\Theta'}$ = time slope of pressure-history curve

$G \frac{\boldsymbol{\alpha}^2(\Theta - \Theta')}{R^2}$ = solution step functions which are read directly from charts (Figs. 12-1a and b)

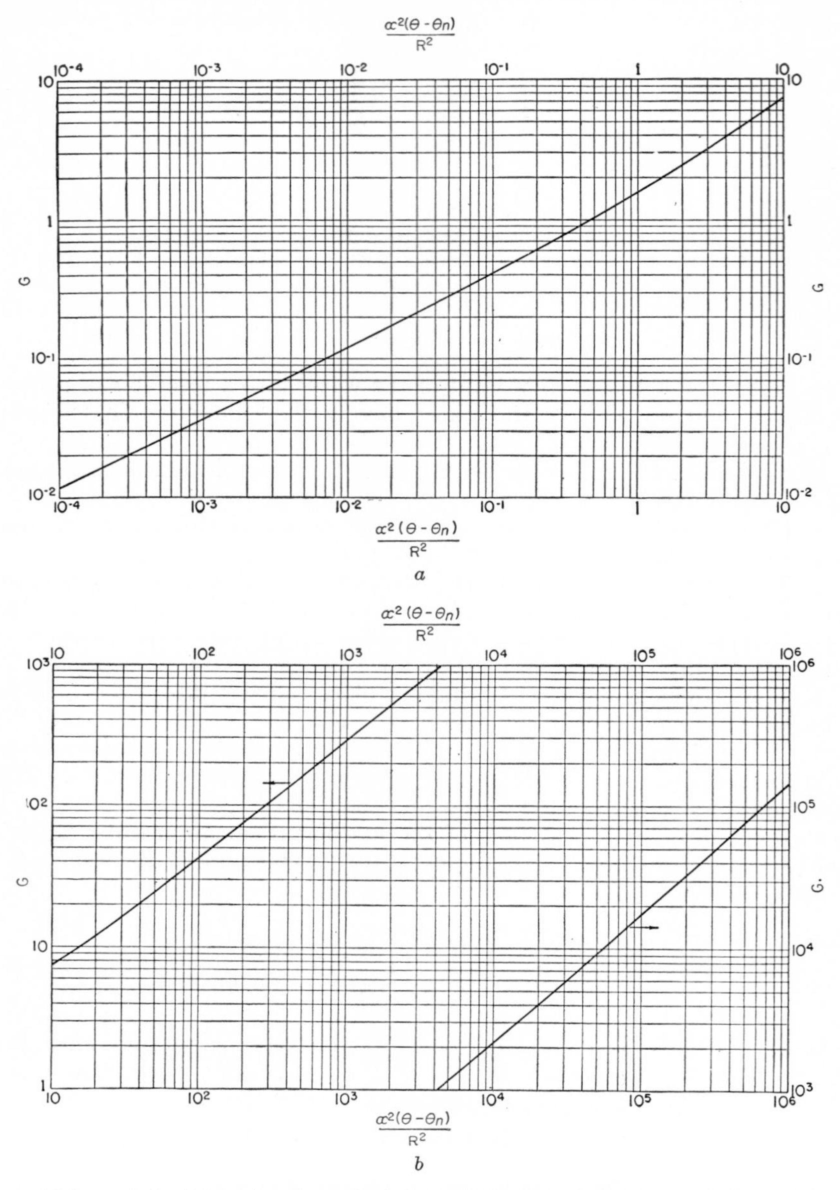

FIG. 12-1*a* and *b*. *G* function for calculation of the cumulative water influx. (*After Hurst, courtesy AIME.*)

The rate of water influx $dW/d\Theta$ is obtained from the following relation:

$$\frac{dW}{d\Theta} = \frac{2\pi \times 144 \times K\sigma H}{5.62\mu} \int_0^{\Theta} \frac{dP}{d\Theta'} G' \frac{\alpha^2(\Theta - \Theta')}{R^2} d\Theta' \qquad (12\text{-}19)$$

where G' is the derivative of the G step function, which can also be read from charts (Fig. 12-2).

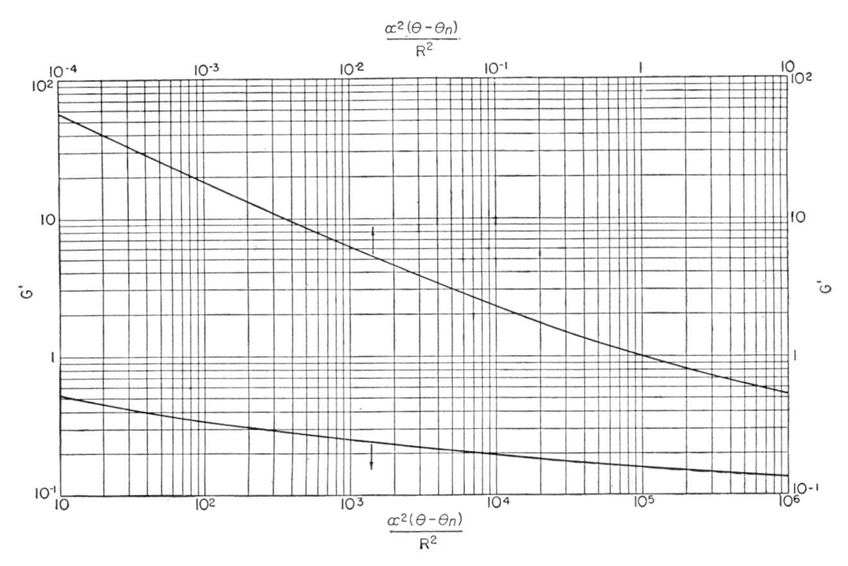

Fig. 12-2. G' function for calculation of the rate of water influx. (*After Hurst, courtesy AIME.*)

Table 12-2. Pressure-time Data

Θ_n, days	$\alpha^2\Theta/R^2$	P_n, reservoir pressure, psi	$P_n - P_{n+1}$, psi
0	0	4,225	25
184	3.75	4,200	55
366	7.47	4,145	95
550	11.22	4,050	150
731	14.91	3,900	140
915	18.67	3,760	140
1,096	22.36	3,620	140
1,280	26.11	3,480	140
1,461	29.80	3,340	190
1,645	33.56	3,150	127
1,766	36.03	3,023	

Calculations of the total water influx are simplified by the introduction of a new step function ($\bar{G}$), which is the integral of G over cumulative production:

$$\bar{G} = \int_0^n G(n)\, dn \tag{12-20}$$

the values of which are read from Fig. 12-3.

In practice the integrations are carried out numerically, and the known pressure history of the field is divided into time sections. One difficulty resides in determining the value of the fractional influx periphery (σ), but an estimate may be had from geological considerations.

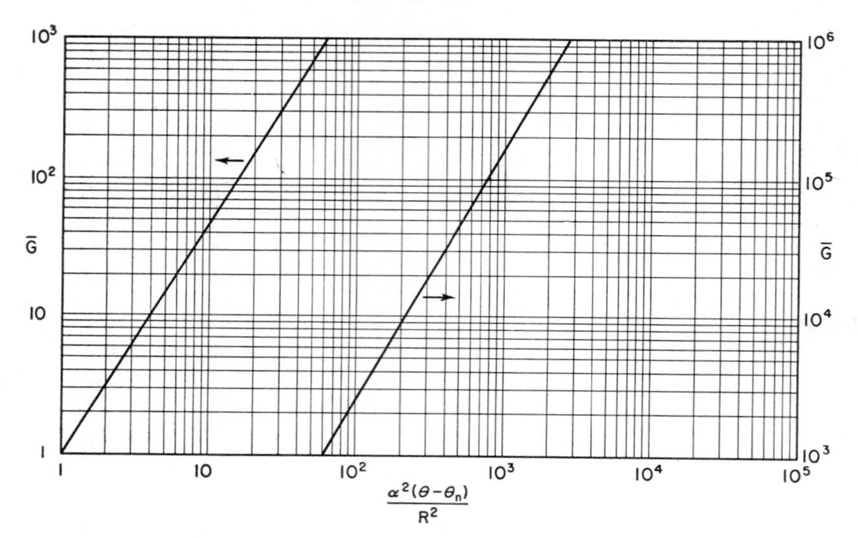

FIG. 12-3. $\bar{G}$ function for determination of the integrated average value of G. (*After Hurst, courtesy AIME.*)

An example of calculation, given by Hurst (1943), will illustrate the method more clearly:

The field and encroaching water have the following characteristics:

$K = 200$ md

$\mu = 22{,}700$, fpd system

$\phi = 0.28$

$c = 2.5 \times 10^{-8}$ cu ft per cu ft per lb per sq ft

$$\alpha^2 = \frac{K}{\mu c_w \phi} = 1.26 \times 10^6 \text{ sq ft per day}$$

$R = 7{,}850$ ft

Pressure-time data are given in Table 12-2, and sample calculations are given in Table 12-3.

TABLE 12-3. SAMPLE CUMULATIVE WATER-INFLUX CALCULATION

(Time, Θ = 1,645 days)

$\alpha^2\Theta_n/R^2$	$\frac{\alpha^2(\Theta - \Theta_n)}{R^2}$	$\alpha^2(\Theta_{n+1} - \Theta_n)/R^2$	$\bar{G}[\alpha^2(\Theta - \Theta_n)/R^2] - \bar{G}[\alpha^2(\Theta - \Theta_{n+1})/R^2]$	$\frac{\bar{G}[\alpha^2(\Theta - \Theta_n)/R^2] - \bar{G}[\alpha^2(\Theta - \Theta_{n+1})/R^2]}{\alpha^2(\Theta_{n+1} - \Theta_n)/R^2} \times (P_n - P_{n+1})$
0.00	33.56	3.75	65	17.35 × 25 = 433 bbl
3.75	29.81	3.72	55	14.80 × 55 = 814 bbl
7.47	26.09	3.75	53	14.15 × 95 = 1,348 bbl
11.22	22.34	3.69	47	12.71 × 150 = 1,905 bbl
14.91	18.65	3.76	40	10.62 × 140 = 1,490 bbl
18.67	14.89	3.69	33	8.95 × 140 = 1,252 bbl
22.36	11.20	3.75	25.2	6.72 × 140 = 940 bbl
26.11	7.45	3.69	18.4	4.98 × 140 = 698 bbl
29.80	3.76	3.76	8.4	2.23 × 190 = 424 bbl
33.56				$W_{1,645}$ = 9,304 bbl

Water-influx Calculations by the van Everdingen and Hurst Method. The solution of the diffusivity equation given by van Everdingen and Hurst (1949) and discussed in Chap. 8 as applied to a single fluid-phase transient flow into a well bore is also applicable to the determination of the rate of and cumulative water encroachment into an oil field, for an oil reservoir embedded into an aquifer of large extent may be considered as a large well, the radius of which is the equivalent field radius. The aquifer may be considered as the reservoir from which fluid is withdrawn and from which water is expulsed into the oil field by virtue of its expansibility. Because of the length of time involved and of the large physical size of the geologic features, dimensionless time is larger than 100 and the simplified solution of the diffusivity equation is generally not applicable; hence, full use must be made of the exact theoretical solution of the diffusivity equation.

The practical solution applicable to water encroachment calculations is written as follows:

$$W = Q(\bar{t}_{i+1}) = 2\pi\phi c_{ew} h_e R_b{}^2 \left[\sum_{j=0}^{i+1} \Delta P \, Q(\bar{t}_{i+1} - \bar{t}_j) \right] \qquad (12\text{-}21)$$

where $\bar{t}$ is dimensionless time and is expressed by

$$\bar{t} = \frac{K}{\phi \mu_w c_{ew}} \frac{1}{R_b{}^2} \theta \qquad (12\text{-}22)$$

Subscript $i + 1$ indicates the time at which the cumulative influx is to be evaluated, whereas j varies between 0 and $i + 1$.

The above formulas are written in the conventional units which define the darcy unit of permeability, namely, seconds for time, centimeters for length, and atmospheres for pressure. Other symbols have the following meaning:

c_{ew} = effective water compressibility taking into account rock expansion into pore space because of geostatic compression of the reservoir rock

R_b = equivalent field radius expressed in centimeters, $\pi R_b{}^2 = A$, the area of the field

$Q(\bar{t}_{j+1} - \bar{t}_j)$ = cumulative water encroachment per cm of formation which enters the reservoir under a pressure differential of 1 atm during a time difference between ultimate dimensionless time $\bar{t}_{j+1}$ and any particular dimensionless time $\bar{t}_j$; values of $Q(\bar{t})$ are read directly from Table 12-4 by interpolation or from suitable plots thereof

ΔP = pressure differential, atm, by which field pressure drops over an increment of time $\Delta\theta$

K = permeability, darcys

ϕ = porosity as fraction

μ_w = viscosity of water, cps

h_e = effective-pay thickness, cm

TABLE 12-4. RADIAL FLOW, CONSTANT TERMINAL PRESSURE, AND CONSTANT TERMINAL RATE CASES FOR INFINITE RESERVOIRS
(After van Everdingen and Hurst, courtesy AIME.)

$\bar{t}$	$Q(\bar{t})$	$P(\bar{t})$	$\bar{t}$	$Q(\bar{t})$	$P(\bar{t})$
$1.0(10)^{-2}$	0.112	0.112	$3.0(10)^{2}$	$10.58(10)^{1}$	3.263
$5.0(10)^{-2}$	0.278	0.229	$4.0(10)^{2}$	$13.48(10)^{1}$	3.406
			$5.0(10)^{2}$	$16.24(10)^{1}$	3.516
$1.0(10)^{-1}$	0.404	0.315	$6.0(10)^{2}$	$18.97(10)^{1}$	3.608
$1.5(10)^{-1}$	0.520	0.376	$7.0(10)^{2}$	$21.60(10)^{1}$	3.684
$2.0(10)^{-1}$	0.606	0.424	$8.0(10)^{2}$	$24.23(10)^{1}$	3.750
$2.5(10)^{-1}$	0.689	0.469	$9.0(10)^{2}$	$26.77(10)^{1}$	3.809
$3.0(10)^{-1}$	0.758	0.503			
$4.0(10)^{-1}$	0.898	0.564	$1.0(10)^{3}$	$29.31(10)^{1}$	3.860
$5.0(10)^{-1}$	1.020	0.616	$1.5(10)^{3}$	$4.136(10)^{2}$	
$6.0(10)^{-1}$	1.140	0.659	$2.0(10)^{3}$	$5.315(10)^{2}$	
$7.0(10)^{-1}$	1.251	0.702	$2.5(10)^{3}$	$6.466(10)^{2}$	
$8.0(10)^{-1}$	1.359	0.735	$3.0(10)^{3}$	$7.590(10)^{2}$	
$9.0(10)^{-1}$	1.469	0.772	$4.0(10)^{3}$	$9.757(10)^{2}$	
			$5.0(10)^{3}$	$11.88(10)^{2}$	
1.0	1.570	0.802	$6.0(10)^{3}$	$13.95(10)^{2}$	
1.5	2.032	0.927	$7.0(10)^{3}$	$15.99(10)^{2}$	
2.0	2.442	1.020	$8.0(10)^{3}$	$18.00(10)^{2}$	
2.5	2.838	1.101	$9.0(10)^{3}$	$19.99(10)^{2}$	
3.0	3.209	1.169			
4.0	3.897	1.275	$1.0(10)^{4}$	$21.96(10)^{2}$	
5.0	4.541	1.362	$1.5(10)^{4}$	$3.146(10)^{3}$	
6.0	5.148	1.436	$2.0(10)^{4}$	$4.079(10)^{3}$	
7.0	5.749	1.500	$2.5(10)^{4}$	$4.994(10)^{3}$	
8.0	6.314	1.556	$3.0(10)^{4}$	$5.891(10)^{3}$	
9.0	6.861	1.604	$4.0(10)^{4}$	$7.634(10)^{3}$	
			$5.0(10)^{4}$	$9.342(10)^{3}$	
$1.0(10)^{1}$	7.417	1.651	$6.0(10)^{4}$	$11.03(10)^{3}$	
$1.5(10)^{1}$	9.965	1.829	$7.0(10)^{4}$	$12.69(10)^{3}$	
$2.0(10)^{1}$	$1.229(10)^{1}$	1.960	$8.0(10)^{4}$	$14.33(10)^{3}$	
$2.5(10)^{1}$	$1.455(10)^{1}$	2.067	$9.0(10)^{4}$	$15.95(10)^{3}$	
$3.0(10)^{1}$	$1.681(10)^{1}$	2.147			
$4.0(10)^{1}$	$2.088(10)^{1}$	2.282	$1.0(10)^{5}$	$17.56(10)^{3}$	
$5.0(10)^{1}$	$2.482(10)^{1}$	2.388	$1.5(10)^{5}$	$2.538(10)^{4}$	
$6.0(10)^{1}$	$2.860(10)^{1}$	2.476	$2.0(10)^{5}$	$3.308(10)^{4}$	
$7.0(10)^{1}$	$3.228(10)^{1}$	2.550	$2.5(10)^{5}$	$4.066(10)^{4}$	
$8.0(10)^{1}$	$3.599(10)^{1}$	2.615	$3.0(10)^{5}$	$4.817(10)^{4}$	
$9.0(10)^{1}$	$3.942(10)^{1}$	2.672	$4.0(10)^{5}$	$6.267(10)^{4}$	
			$5.0(10)^{5}$	$7.699(10)^{4}$	
$1.0(10)^{2}$	$4.301(10)^{1}$	2.723	$6.0(10)^{5}$	$9.113(10)^{4}$	
$1.5(10)^{2}$	$5.980(10)^{1}$	2.921	$7.0(10)^{5}$	$10.51(10)^{4}$	
$2.0(10)^{2}$	$7.586(10)^{1}$	3.064	$8.0(10)^{5}$	$11.89(10)^{4}$	
$2.5(10)^{2}$	$9.120(10)^{1}$	3.173	$9.0(10)^{5}$	$13.26(10)^{4}$	

TABLE 12-4. RADIAL FLOW, CONSTANT TERMINAL PRESSURE, AND CONSTANT TERMINAL RATE CASES FOR INFINITE RESERVOIRS (*Continued*)

$\bar{t}$	$Q(\bar{t})$	$P(\bar{t})$	$\bar{t}$	$Q(\bar{t})$	$P(\bar{t})$
$1.0(10)^6$	$14.62(10)^4$		$2.0(10)^9$	$1.880(10)^8$	
$1.5(10)^6$	$2.126(10)^5$		$2.5(10)^9$	$2.328(10)^8$	
$2.0(10)^6$	$2.781(10)^5$		$3.0(10)^9$	$2.771(10)^8$	
$2.5(10)^6$	$3.427(10)^5$		$4.0(10)^9$	$3.645(10)^8$	
$3.0(10)^6$	$4.064(10)^5$		$5.0(10)^9$	$4.510(10)^8$	
$4.0(10)^6$	$5.313(10)^5$		$6.0(10)^9$	$5.368(10)^8$	
$5.0(10)^6$	$6.544(10)^5$		$7.0(10)^9$	$6.220(10)^8$	
$6.0(10)^6$	$7.761(10)^5$		$8.0(10)^9$	$7.066(10)^8$	
$7.0(10)^6$	$8.965(10)^5$		$9.0(10)^9$	$7.909(10)^8$	
$8.0(10)^6$	$10.16(10)^5$				
$9.0(10)^6$	$11.34(10)^5$		$1.0(10)^{10}$	$8.747(10)^8$	
			$1.5(10)^{10}$	$1.288(10)^9$	
$1.0(10)^7$	$12.52(10)^5$		$2.0(10)^{10}$	$1.697(10)^9$	
$1.5(10)^7$	$1.828(10)^6$		$2.5(10)^{10}$	$2.103(10)^9$	
$2.0(10)^7$	$2.398(10)^6$		$3.0(10)^{10}$	$2.505(10)^9$	
$2.5(10)^7$	$2.961(10)^6$		$4.0(10)^{10}$	$3.299(10)^9$	
$3.0(10)^7$	$3.517(10)^6$		$5.0(10)^{10}$	$4.087(10)^9$	
$4.0(10)^7$	$4.610(10)^6$		$6.0(10)^{10}$	$4.868(10)^9$	
$5.0(10)^7$	$5.689(10)^6$		$7.0(10)^{10}$	$5.643(10)^9$	
$6.0(10)^7$	$6.758(10)^6$		$8.0(10)^{10}$	$6.414(10)^9$	
$7.0(10)^7$	$7.816(10)^6$		$9.0(10)^{10}$	$7.183(10)^9$	
$8.0(10)^7$	$8.866(10)^6$				
$9.0(10)^7$	$9.911(10)^6$		$1.0(10)^{11}$	$7.948(10)^9$	
			$1.5(10)^{11}$	$1.17(10)^{10}$	
$1.0(10)^8$	$10.95(10)^6$		$2.0(10)^{11}$	$1.55(10)^{10}$	
$1.5(10)^8$	$1.604(10)^7$		$2.5(10)^{11}$	$1.92(10)^{10}$	
$2.0(10)^8$	$2.108(10)^7$		$3.0(10)^{11}$	$2.29(10)^{10}$	
$2.5(10)^8$	$2.607(10)^7$		$4.0(10)^{11}$	$3.02(10)^{10}$	
$3.0(10)^8$	$3.100(10)^7$		$5.0(10)^{11}$	$3.75(10)^{10}$	
$4.0(10)^8$	$4.071(10)^7$		$6.0(10)^{11}$	$4.47(10)^{10}$	
$5.0(10)^8$	$5.032(10)^7$		$7.0(10)^{11}$	$5.19(10)^{10}$	
$6.0(10)^8$	$5.984(10)^7$		$8.0(10)^{11}$	$5.89(10)^{10}$	
$7.0(10)^8$	$6.928(10)^7$		$9.0(10)^{11}$	$6.58(10)^{10}$	
$8.0(10)^8$	$7.865(10)^7$				
$9.0(10)^8$	$8.797(10)^7$		$1.0(10)^{12}$	$7.28(10)^{10}$	
			$1.5(10)^{12}$	$1.08(10)^{11}$	
$1.0(10)^9$	$9.725(10)^7$		$2.0(10)^{12}$	$1.42(10)^{11}$	
$1.5(10)^9$	$1.429(10)^8$				

From the theoretical solution it appears that one should be in a position to calculate water influx from a knowledge of the geometry of the reservoir, of its physical properties, and of the physical properties of water. However, this is generally not possible in practice because of difficulties in determining representative values for permeability and effective pay. Core-analysis values of permeability are often too high because laboratory measurements are made on dried cores with air flow; even when reasonable Klinkenberg and saturation corrections are applied, values for permeability must be further adjusted downward because sampling of cores is rarely representative of reservoir rock. Other causes of errors in evaluating a representative field-wide permeability value result from geostatic pressure and hydration of clays. Effective pay is another value entering the computations which is generally determined optimistically.

The safest technique to use in forecasting future performance of water-drive fields is to determine the rate of water influx statistically from past performance data. To this end the cumulative water influx will be written

$$W = C_v \sum_{j=0}^{i+1} \Delta_j^{j+1} P \, Q(\bar{t}_{i+1} - \bar{t}_j) \tag{12-23}$$

where $C_v = 2\pi\phi c_{ew} h_e R_b^2$ will be considered as a gross approximation leading to an order of magnitude only.

The material-balance equation which permits us to solve simultaneously for oil in place N and the constant C_v is written as follows:

$$N = \frac{n[\beta + \alpha(r_n - S)] + w - C_v \sum_{0}^{i+1} \Delta_j^{j+1} P \, Q(\bar{t}_{i+1} - \bar{t}_j)}{\alpha(S_0 - S) - (\beta_0 - \beta)} \tag{12-24}$$

For a field producing oil from an undersaturated reservoir,

$$N = \frac{n\beta + w - C_v \sum_{0}^{i+1} \Delta_j^{j+1} P \, Q(\bar{t}_{j+1} - \bar{t}_j)}{\beta - \beta_0} \tag{12-25}$$

The evaluation of dimensionless time by Eq. (12-22) is also uncertain and its analytic expression must be considered as approximate only. However, with the value of C_v determined from statistical considerations, it is possible to adjust K and h_e in a reasonable manner and thereby recalculate more dependable dimensionless time values.

A difficulty which is encountered in the above determination results from the necessity of starting with a preassumed time conversion of the future performance. It should be more satisfactory in most cases to calculate water influx on the basis of pressure decline as a function of time.

However, such a solution is not available and accordingly the van Everdingen and Hurst water-influx calculation may not be used for the study of water-drive fields wherein the field pressure drops below the bubble point.

The van Everdingen and Hurst theory provides also for the determination of pressure decrements above the bubble point by

$$\Delta P = C'_v q(\Theta) \sum_{0}^{i+1} P(\bar{t}_{j+i} - \bar{t}_j) \tag{12-26}$$

where

$$C'_v = \frac{\mu}{2\pi K h_e} \tag{12-27}$$

$q(\Theta)$ being a constant production rate in cubic centimeters per second.

The technique for determining C'_v in (12-26) may, in all respects, be identical to that previously studied for the Schilthuis method of water-influx calculation when a dependable value for N is known from volumetric studies. However, van Everdingen suggests the determination of both N and C_v by a method of least squares from a set of equations in N and C_v obtained from the material-balance equation (12-25) in which some time conversion factors for (12-22) are assumed in a reasonable range. The combinations of N and C_v values so obtained which renders the standard deviation a minimum are chosen as the most probable answers, respectively, for the original stock-tank oil in place (N) and the quantity of water (C_v) which enters the oil reservoir per unit value of $\Sigma\ \Delta P\ Q(\bar{t})$.

Example of Application. A small undersaturated oil reservoir has the following characteristics:

Areal extent	220 acres
Gross pay thickness h	31 ft
Porosity ϕ	0.17
Connate water σ_w	0.10
Reservoir volume factor β_o	1.010
Volumetric oil in place	6.1×10^6 bbl
Permeability	
By cores	204 md
By PI tests	121 md
Radius of the reservoir R_b	1,540 ft
Bubble-point pressure	1,618 psi
Oil viscosity μ_o	3.5 cps
Water viscosity μ_w	0.65 cps
Effective water compressibility	$c_{ew} = 3.76 \times 10^{-6}$ per psi
Effective oil compressibility	$c_o = 12.4 \times 10^{-6}$ per psi

Statistical information on production is available for three years as follows:

Date	Pressure P, psi	Cumulative oil production n, bbl	Cumulative water production w, bbl	Calculated cumulative water encroachment W, bbl
11/3/48	302	205,400	6,500	115,600
11/3/49	494	347,200	11,400	279,300
10/29/50	170	508,900	13,900	423,200

Calculate the probable value of C_v, the rate of water encroachment in the van Everdingen and Hurst formula.

It is assumed, for this example, that the oil originally in place calculated by volumetric method is correct. This is at times the case when production data are very good; generally it is not correct and a determination of N is also required, as was outlined in the example worked out by the Schilthuis method.

In the present example, volumetric water encroachment may be calculated at the dates given, from the simplified material-balance equation (12-25) valid above the bubble-point pressure. The results are indicated in the last column of the above table.

$$\bar{t} = \frac{K_{\text{darcys}}}{\phi \mu_w c_w R_b{}^2} \theta_{\text{sec}} = \frac{0.121}{0.17 \times 0.65 \times 4 \times 10^{-5} \times (1{,}540 \times 30.5)^2} \theta_{\text{sec}}$$

$$\bar{t} = \frac{0.121 \times 24 \times 3{,}600}{0.17 \times 0.65 \times 4 \times 10^{-5} \times (1{,}540 \times 30.5)^2} \theta_{\text{days}} = 1.08\theta_{\text{days}}$$

For complete circle of encroachment,

$$Q(\theta)_{\text{cc}} = 2\pi\phi c_w h R_b{}^2 \{\Sigma\, \Delta P_{\text{atm}} [Q(\bar{t}_{366} - \bar{t}_j)]\}$$

For cumulative encroachment,

$$Q(\theta)_{\text{bbl}} = \frac{2\pi \times 0.17 \times 4 \times 10^{-5} \times 31 \times 30.5(1{,}540 \times 30.5)^2}{5.61 \times (30.5)^3 14.7}$$

$$\{\Sigma\, \Delta P_{\text{psi}} [Q(\bar{t}_{366} - \bar{t}_j)]\}$$

$$= 38.0 \Sigma\, (\Delta P)_{\text{psi}}\, Q(\bar{t})$$

The values of the coefficient C_v are obtained by dividing the cumulative water encroachment obtained from material-balance calculations in Tables 12-5, 12-6, and 12-7 by the cumulative values $\Sigma\ \Delta P\ Q(\bar{t} - \bar{t}_i)$. The values obtained are 1.36, 1.21, and 1.17. The expected value was of the order of 38.0, as computed from the reservoir size and fluid properties. The discrepancy may be attributed to several reasons:

1. Water does not encroach over the full perimeter of the field. In this case it is estimated that only one-third of the boundary is affected by water influx.

2. Effective-pay thickness may be less than estimated from core analysis; actually this is a most common occurrence and it is perhaps safe to consider in the absence of a pressure build-up test and micrologs that only 50 per cent of the estimated gross pay contributes to fluid flow. Furthermore, it is probable that formation thickness responsible for fluid flow in the aquifer is less than in the oil zone.

3. Actual permeability is probably less than the average computed from core analysis, probably even less than obtained by productivity index tests. If the affected perimeter exposed to water influx is one-third of the total circumference and if effective pay is 50 per cent of the reported value, effective permeability to water influx would be of the order of 23 md instead of 121 md.

Using these new values for permeability and effective pay, a new dimensionless time may be computed and a new and better value for C_v may be obtained. By proceeding in this manner by successive approximations, constant values of C_v will be obtained over the past history of the field,

TABLE 12-5. WATER ENCROACHMENT AFTER ONE YEAR

θ_{days}	$\bar{t} = 1.08T_d$	ΔP	$\bar{t}_{366} - \bar{t}_j$	$Q(\bar{t} - \bar{t}_j)$	$\Delta P\ Q(\bar{t} - \bar{t}_j)$
0	0	58	396	134	7,800
30	32.4	85	363.6	120	10,200
61	66.0	85	330	110	9,350
92	100.0	35	296	105	3,680
121	131.0	75	265	91	6,810
152	164.0	88	232	85	7,500
182	197.0	72	199	75	5,400
213	230.0	138	166	65	9,000
243	263.0	182	133	55	10,000
274	296.0	200	100	43	8,600
305	330.0	160	66	31	4,950
336	362.0	75	34	18	1,350
Total...	...	...	...	...	84,600

The computed value of C_v is obtained from $\dfrac{115{,}600}{84{,}600} = 1.36.$

values which may then be used safely to project the performance into the future.

A similar technique to the above may be resorted to for the calculation of the appropriate value of C'_v to be used for the calculation of cumulative pressure decline by formula (12-26).

TABLE 12-6. WATER ENCROACHMENT AFTER TWO YEARS

θ_{days}	$\bar{t} = 1.08\theta$	ΔP_{psi}	$\bar{t}_{731} - \bar{t}_j$	$Q(\bar{t}_{731} - \bar{t}_j)$	$\Delta P\, Q(\bar{t}_{731} - \bar{t}_j)$
0	0	58	790	238	13,800
30	32.4	85	767.6	234	19,900
61	66	85	724	222	18,900
92	100	35	690	214	7,500
121	131	75	659	206	15,500
152	164	88	626	197	17,300
182	197	72	593	188	13,500
213	230	138	560	178	24,600
243	263	182	527	169	30,700
274	296	200	494	162	38,400
305	330	160	460	152	24,400
335	362	75	428	143	10,700
366	396	30	394	133	4,000
396	427	10	363	125	1,250
427	461	5	329	114	570
458	494	3	296	105	410
486	525	−25	265	95	−2,380
517	559	−13	231	85	−1,100
547	591	−8	199	76	−600
578	624	−32	166	65	−2,080
608	656	−35	134	54	−1,900
639	690	−31	100	43	−1,330
670	724	−31	66	31	−960
700	756	−35	34	17	−600
731	790	0	0	0	
Total	. . .	. . .	. . .	. . .	230,480

$$\text{Therefore } C_v = \frac{279{,}300}{230{,}480} = 1.21.$$

TABLE 12-7. WATER ENCROACHMENT AFTER THREE YEARS

θ_{days}	$\bar{t} = 1.08\theta$	ΔP_{psi}	$\bar{t}_{1,096} - \bar{t}_j$	$Q(\bar{t}_{1,096} - \bar{t}_j)$	$\Delta P\, Q(\bar{t}_{1,096} - \bar{t}_j)$
0	0	58	1,183	340	19,700
30	32.4	85	1,151	330	28,000
61	66	85	1,117	321	27,200
92	100	35	1,083	316	11,100
121	131	75	1,052	306	22,950
152	164	88	1,019	296	26,050
182	197	72	986	291	20,950
213	230	138	953	286	39,500
243	263	182	920	273	49,600
274	296	200	887	260	52,000
305	330	160	853	255	42,400
335	362	75	821	247	18,500
366	396	30	787	239	7,200
396	427	10	756	230	2,300
427	461	5	722	222	1,110
458	496	5	689	214	650
486	525	−25	658	206	−5,150
517	559	−13	624	197	−2,560
547	591	−8	592	188	−1,500
578	624	−32	559	180	−5,760
608	656	−35	527	171	−6,000
639	690	−31	493	161	−5,000
670	724	−31	459	152	−4,710
700	756	−35	427	143	−5,000
731	790	0	393	133	0
	822	7	361	124	870
	856	5	327	114	570
	889	5	294	104	520
	920	80	263	95	7,600
	953	69	230	85	5,860
	985	121	198	75	9,070
	1,019	20	164	64	1,280
	1,050	10	133	58	580
	1,083	0	100	43	0
	1,119	5	64	30	150
	1,150	2	33	18	40
1,096	1,183	0	0	0	
Total	...	...	...	...	360,070

Therefore $C_v = \dfrac{423{,}200}{360{,}070} = 1.17.$

PREDICTION OF WATER-DRIVE PERFORMANCE ABOVE THE BUBBLE-POINT PRESSURE

In a water-drive field, the oil-production rate is paramount as a factor which influences the pressure behavior of the field. It is therefore necessary to be able to forecast in a reasonable manner the expected future production rate. Most generally a constant field-wide oil-production rate Q_o is assumed to prevail until abandonment. In a high-relief structure, however, and where well allowables are fixed, the field-wide production rate may decline because the water-oil contact progressively drowns the edge wells.

For simplification a constant value of Q_o is postulated throughout the future history of the field in the derivation of the following performance equations.

Prediction by Schilthuis' Method. The material balance above the bubble-point pressure may be written:

$$\beta_{i+1} N c_{oe}(P_0 - P_{i+1}) = n_{i+1}\beta_{i+1} + w_{i+1} - C_s \sum_0^{i+1} \Delta P \, \Delta\theta \quad (12\text{-}28)$$

where the symbols have the usual significance: $i + 1$ is a time index, i being the preceding time to $i + 1$, which is considered as present time; c_{oe} is the effective oil compressibility which includes the effect of connate water and geostatic compression of the reservoir rock. ΔP is the differential pressure between the original field and aquifer pressure and the present mean field pressure:

$$\Delta P = P_0 - \frac{P_i + P_{i+1}}{2}$$

Let
$$\begin{aligned} n_{i+1} &= n_i + \Delta_i^{i+1} n \\ \Delta_i^{i+1} n &= Q_o \, \Delta_i^{i+1}\theta \\ w_{i+1} &= w_i + \Delta_i^{i+1} w = w_i + C_1 \, \Delta_i^{i+1}\theta \\ W_{i+1} &= C_s \sum_0^{i+1} \Delta P \, \Delta\theta \end{aligned}$$

Substituting in (12-27) and solving for $\Delta\theta$,

$$\Delta\theta = \frac{\beta_{i+1} N c_{oe}(P_0 - P_{i+1}) - n_i\beta_{i+1} - w_i + W_i}{\beta_{i+1} Q_o + C_1 - C_s \, \Delta P} \quad (12\text{-}29)$$

Calculations of future performance are made by assuming successive pressure decrements $P_0, P_1, P_2, P_3, \ldots, P_i, P_{i+1}$. Completion of the calculations is obtained when the water-oil contact reaches the top of the structure. This may be accomplished only by making a displacement efficiency calculation and determining at each step the structural position of the water-oil contact.

A tabulation may readily be devised by which the calculations are conveniently recorded.

It is observed that a field pressure P_{i+1} is maintained when field production rate is such that

$$Q_o = C_1 + C_s \, \Delta P \tag{12-30}$$

Future Prediction of Performance by the Simplified Hurst Method. It may readily be established that the performance equation is

$$\Delta\theta = \frac{\beta_{i+1} N c_{oe}(P_0 - P_{i+1}) - n_i\beta_{i+1} - w_i + W_i}{\beta_{i+1}Q_o + C_1 - C_h \, (\Delta P/\log \theta_i)} \tag{12-31}$$

where the symbols have the same significance as previously; the only difference is the rate of water influx C_h which is determined from past performance history with the introduction of a logarithmic term ($\log \theta$) which, in a certain measure, takes care of the transient nature of the water influx and implies its gradual decrease with time.

Prediction by the van Everdingen and Hurst Transient Water-influx Formulas. Field performance behavior above the bubble point entails predicting pressure variations and water influx. Inasmuch as volume withdrawal of fluids from the oil field is substantially equal to the volumetric water influx at all times, it is possible to predict as a first step the future field-pressure behavior by means of Eq. (12-26) and then to calculate the water influx by Eq. (12-23).

In order to determine the future field-pressure behavior, it is necessary to know the expected withdrawal rates. These may be constant with future time or they may be assumed to vary according to a definite schedule. The value of C'_v which may be considered as the pressure change per unit value of production $\Sigma \, \Delta\bar{t} \, P(t)$ and which is given approximately by

$$C'_v = \frac{\mu}{2\pi K h_e} \tag{12-32}$$

must have been adjusted to past performance history.

Inasmuch as the past performance production rate may have been variable, the value of the constant C'_v must be found from a more general formula than (12-26)

$$\Delta P = C'_v \sum_{j=0}^{i+1} (q_{j+1} - q_j) P(\bar{t}_{j+1} - \bar{t}_j) \tag{12-33}$$

Knowing the value of C'_v, the future pressure behavior vs. time is calculated by Eq. (12-33) with the appropriate substitution of the production-rate schedule for $q_{j+1} - q_j$. For an infinite aquifer, the $P(\bar{t})$ values are read from Table 12-4.

Once the pressure behavior vs. time is known for the future, the water-influx behavior may be determined from the water-influx formula (12-23).

The usefulness of the transient water-influx calculation has been greatly impaired with the realization that the optimum manner of producing a water-drive field is no longer by maintaining its pressure above the bubble point but rather at a producing rate such that the field pressure will remain below the bubble point in order to maintain a free-gas phase uniformly distributed throughout the oil reservoir that will reduce the residual trapped oil saturation back of the flood front.

Under such conditions the fluid volume withdrawal from the oil zone no longer is identical to water influx, and one of the requirements for the exact application of the transient water-influx theory disappears. Under these circumstances it is felt that the use of the van Everdingen and Hurst theory is no longer valid and that simpler means of water-influx calculation such as by the Schilthuis or the Hurst simplified methods are justified.

GENERALIZED METHOD OF WATER-DRIVE PERFORMANCE CALCULATIONS

Before water-drive performance calculations may be attempted, it is presumed that the reservoir engineer has ascertained, first, that water encroachment exists and, second, what its magnitude is.

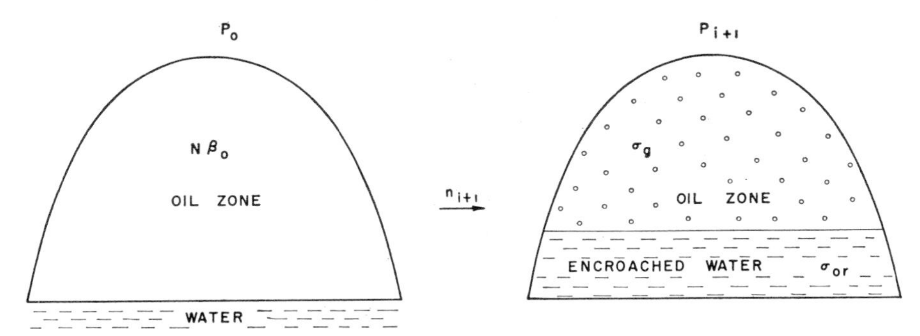

FIG. 12-4. Schematic representation of fluid-saturation distribution in a water-drive field.

By contrast with depletion gas drive where the reservoir fluids are presumed uniformly distributed, water drive implies fluid separation in the reservoir into two zones, the boundary between zones being constantly moving (Fig. 12-4). This boundary is not extremely sharp; i.e., one does not pass from 100 per cent water on one side to 100 per cent oil on the other side. While there is a large and abrupt change in fluid saturation at the boundary or flood front, the displacement by water is by no means complete, and residual oil and gas in varying amounts remain in the flooded-out sections of the field, depending on field pressure and rate of water encroachment.

The pressure, gas-oil ratio, and productivity behavior of a water-drive field are controlled mainly by the withdrawal rate at the wells. Depending on this rate, since most water-drive fields are discovered at a prevailing field pressure larger than the bubble-point pressure of the reservoir oil, the field behavior may be such that its pressure remains above the bubble point or just at the bubble point, or goes below the bubble point, and perhaps eventually goes back up to it or even above it when the withdrawal rates are reduced with time.

The complete study of a water-drive field, therefore, entails more than a mere pressure and gas-oil-ratio prediction vs. time or a mere displacement efficiency calculation; it actually requires simultaneous calculations of both, keeping track of the amount and position of the reservoir fluids and of their effectiveness in expulsing the remaining oil from the reservoir.

Performance Equation in Finite Form. In the derivation of a generalized water-drive theory it is postulated that water influx into the oil reservoir may be calculated by means of the simplest approach, namely, Schilthuis' method. If this is deemed inappropriate, the theory may readily be modified to include the Hurst simplified method.

The material-balance equation with the water-drive term is, at a time $i + 1$,

$$1 = \frac{n_{i+1}\left(\frac{\beta}{\alpha} - S\right)_{i+1} + \sum_{0}^{i+1} \Delta n\, R_{av} - \frac{1}{\alpha_{i+1}} \sum_{0}^{i+1} \frac{C_s\, \Delta P - C_1}{N}\, \Delta\theta}{\left(\frac{\beta}{\alpha} - S\right)_{i+1} - \left(\frac{\beta_0}{\alpha_{i+1}} - S_0\right)} \tag{12-34}$$

where n = cumulative fractional oil produced, expressed as a fraction of original stock-tank oil in place, N

Δn, $\Delta\theta$ = variations in n and time within the pressure interval between P_i and P_{i+1}

R_{av} = average gas-oil ratio (vol/vol) between P_i and P_{i+1}

$\Delta P = P_{aq} - \frac{P_i + P_{i+1}}{2}$ (where P_{aq} = aquifer pressure or original field pressure)

ΔP = pressure differential responsible for water encroachment

C_s = Schilthuis' rate of water encroachment, bbl/month/psi

C_1 = rate of water production, bbl/month; however, it could also represent net rate of water injection into aquifer in which case it would have a negative sign

The following substitutions are made in the material-balance equation (12-34):

$$n_{i+1} = n_i + \Delta_i^{i+1} n$$

$$G_{i+1} = \sum_{0}^{i+1} \Delta n\, R_{av} = G_i + \Delta_i^{i+1} n\, R_{av}$$

$$D_{i+1} = \left(\frac{\beta}{\alpha} - S\right)_{i+1} - \left(\frac{\beta_0}{\alpha_{i+1}} - S_0\right)$$

Let Q_o be the allowable producing rate from the field, or the producing capacity of the field as controlled by the prevailing well productivity index and thickness of the oil column, in barrels of stock-tank oil per month.

$$\Delta_i^{i+1} n = \frac{Q_o}{N}\, \Delta_i^{i+1} \theta$$

The material-balance equation becomes, after substitution and rearrangement,

$$1 = \frac{\left\{\begin{aligned}&n_i\left(\frac{\beta}{\alpha} - S\right)_{i+1} + \Delta_i^{i+1}n\,R_{\text{av}} + \Delta_i^{i+1}n\left(\frac{\beta}{\alpha} - S\right)_{i+1} \\ &+ G_i - \frac{1}{\alpha_{i+1}}\left(\sum_0^i \frac{C_s\,\Delta P - C_1}{N}\Delta\theta + \frac{C_s\,\Delta P - C_1}{N}\Delta_i^{i+1}\theta\right)\end{aligned}\right\}}{D_{i+1}} \tag{12-35}$$

Now substitute $\Delta_i^{i+1}n$ by its value as a function of $\Delta_i^{i+1}\theta$ and let

$$\sum_0^i \frac{C_s\,\Delta P - C_1}{N}\Delta\theta = \frac{W_i - w_i}{N}$$

Solving for $\Delta_i^{i+1}\theta$,

$$\Delta_i^{i+1}\theta = \frac{D_{i+1} + \dfrac{1}{\alpha_{i+1}}\dfrac{W_i - w_i}{N} - n_i\left(\dfrac{\beta}{\alpha} - S\right)_{i+1} - G_i}{\dfrac{Q_o}{N}\left[\left(\dfrac{\beta}{\alpha} - S\right)_{i+1} + R_{\text{av}}\right] - \dfrac{C_s\,\Delta P - C_1}{\alpha_{i+1}N}} \tag{12-36}$$

In the calculations of water-drive performance by Eq. (12-36), extremely great simplifications are introduced when making the following assumption. Inasmuch as the average gas-oil ratio R_{av} is controlled by the prevailing average field pressure and was determined in a previously solved depletion-drive problem, the solution of the water-drive problem may be done directly without trial-and-error procedure by solving by means of Eq. (12-36) for the interval of time $\Delta_i^{i+1}\theta$ required for the field pressure to drop from a value of P_i to P_{i+1}. The validity of this assumption will be examined later.

If an infinite time is obtained in this calculation by means of Eq. (12-36), it is an indication that the field pressure is maintained by the encroachment of water. This occurs when the denominator of $\Delta\theta$ vanishes. If a negative answer is obtained, it is an indication that the pressure is being increased by water encroachment. Pressure increments should then be assumed.

Verification that the calculations are correct may then be made by computing the water-drive and depletion-drive indices, the sum of which must be equal to unity.

$$\text{DDI} = \frac{ND_{i+1}}{n_{i+1}\left(\dfrac{\beta}{\alpha} - S\right)_{i+1} + G_{i+1}}$$

$$\text{WDI} = \frac{\dfrac{1}{\alpha_{i+1}}(W_{i+1} - w_{i+1})}{n_{i+1}\left(\dfrac{\beta}{\alpha} - S\right)_{i+1} + G_{i+1}} \tag{12-37}$$

The above calculations are limited in their scope in that they do not permit the calculations of the displacement efficiency of the water drive. In order to arrive at the expected recovery as a function of production rate, it is necessary to make a *volumetric fluid inventory* at all times which is compatible with the material-balance equation and the frontal-drive displacement efficiency. The procedure for achieving this is as follows:

1. Plot a graph of structural acre-feet (V) and structure cross section in acres (A) vs. height in feet above the oil-water contact.

2. Assume a certain reasonable displacement efficiency by the water-drive front (or a certain value for the residual oil and gas saturation behind the front). A guide to this value may be obtained from frontal-drive construction (the Buckley-Leverett theory with simplification by the tangent to the f_w curve) (Chap. 11).

3. From the cumulative net water encroachment ($W_{i+1} - w_{i+1}$) determine the height of the oil-water contact from the graph of V vs. height. Also read A and compute the value of q_t in barrels per day per acre to be used in the f_w curve calculations.

4. Procedure (3) is carried out until water has filled up the reservoir and risen to the crest of the structure and the oil field is abandoned. It is noted that the value of q_t is variable throughout the life of the field and therefore the displacement efficiency will also be variable with time. A satisfactory termination to the problem is obtained only when the overall recoveries by material-balance calculation and displacement-efficiency calculations are substantially identical.

The complete solution of the problem includes:

1. Material-balance tabulation
2. Plot of pressure decline, gas-oil ratio, and production rate vs. time
3. f_w diagram and displacement-efficiency calculations at various pressures
4. Diagrams representing fluid inventory at various pressures in a unit reservoir volume

PERFORMANCE EQUATION IN THE FINITE DIFFERENCE FORM

A somewhat more convenient solution of the water-drive performance problem is obtained when using the material balance in differential form. Writing the material balance in finite form at two successive pressures, including the net water-influx term,

$$\left(\frac{\beta}{\alpha} - S\right)_i - \left(\frac{\beta_0}{\alpha_i} - S_0\right) = n_i\left(\frac{\beta}{\alpha} - S\right)_i + \sum_0^i \Delta n\, R_{\text{av}} - \frac{W_i - w_i}{N\alpha_i} \qquad (12\text{-}38)$$

$$\left(\frac{\beta}{\alpha} - S\right)_{i+1} - \left(\frac{\beta_0}{\alpha_{i+1}} - S_0\right) = n_{i+1}\left(\frac{\beta}{\alpha} - S\right)_{i+1} + \sum_0^{i+1} \Delta n\, R_{\text{av}} - \frac{W_{i+1} - w_{i+1}}{N\alpha_{i+1}} \qquad (12\text{-}39)$$

Subtracting (12-38) from (12-39) and introducing the following functions,

$$\Delta_i^{i+1}\left(\frac{\beta}{\alpha} - S\right) = \left(\frac{\beta}{\alpha} - S\right)_{i+1} - \left(\frac{\beta}{\alpha} - S\right)_i \tag{12-40}$$

$$\Delta_i^{i+1}\left(\frac{1}{\alpha}\right) = \frac{1}{\alpha_{i+1}} - \frac{1}{\alpha_i} \tag{12-41}$$

we obtain

$$\Delta_i^{i+1}\left(\frac{\beta}{\alpha} - S\right) - \beta_0\,\Delta_i^{i+1}\left(\frac{1}{\alpha}\right) = n_i\,\Delta_i^{i+1}\left(\frac{\beta}{\alpha} - S\right) + \Delta_i^{i+1}n\left(\frac{\beta}{\alpha} - S\right)_{i+1} + \Delta_i^{i+1}n\,R_{\text{av}} - \frac{\Delta_i^{i+1}(W - w)}{N\alpha_{i+1}} - \frac{W_i - w_i}{N}\,\Delta_i^{i+1}\left(\frac{1}{\alpha}\right) \tag{12-42}$$

But by Schilthuis' formula

$$\Delta_i^{i+1}(W - w) = (C_s\,\Delta P - C_1)\,\Delta_i^{i+1}\theta \tag{12-43}$$

Also let

$$\Delta_i^{i+1}n = \frac{Q_o}{N}\,(\Delta_i^{i+1}\theta) \tag{12-44}$$

After substitution of (12-43) and (12-44) in (12-42) and solving for $\Delta\theta$, we obtain

$$\Delta_i^{i+1}\theta = \frac{(1 - n_i)\,\Delta_i^{i+1}\left(\frac{\beta}{\alpha} - S\right) - \beta_0\,\Delta_i^{i+1}\left(\frac{1}{\alpha}\right) + \frac{W_i - w_i}{N}\,\Delta_i^{i+1}\left(\frac{1}{\alpha}\right)}{\frac{Q_o}{N}\left[\left(\frac{\beta}{\alpha} - S\right)_{i+1} + R_{\text{av}}\right] - \frac{C_s\,\Delta P - C_1}{N\alpha_{i+1}}} \tag{12-45}$$

Compared to (12-36) it is seen that formula (12-45) is simpler and entails a lesser number of computations in calculating water-drive performance.

Discussion of Performance Equations (12-36) and (12-45). Examining, first, Eq. (12-36) it is observed that the numerator and denominator are made up of terms which have the following significance:

D_{i+1} = volumetric gas expansion provided by pressure reduction which is effective in displacing oil by depletion gas drive

$\frac{1}{\alpha_{i+1}}\frac{W_i - w_i}{N}$ = cumulative effective fractional water encroachment expressed in equivalent gas volume at standard conditions

$n_i\left(\frac{\beta}{\alpha} - S\right)_i + G_i$ = cumulative effective reservoir voidage expressed in equivalent gas volume at standard conditions

$\frac{Q_o}{N}\left[\left(\frac{\beta}{\alpha} - S\right) + R_{av}\right]$ = rate of effective fractional reservoir voidage expressed in gas volume at standard conditions

$\frac{1}{\alpha}\frac{C_s\,\Delta P - C_1}{N}$ = rate of effective water encroachment expressed in equivalent gas volume at standard conditions

Examining Eq. (12-45) gives the following significance of the terms in the numerator:

$(1 - n_i)\,\Delta_i^{i+1}\left(\frac{\beta}{\alpha} - S\right) - \beta_0\,\Delta_i^{i+1}\frac{1}{\alpha}$ = incremental expansion of oil and gas remaining in reservoir as a result of depletion drive; contributes to the production of oil by this mechanism

$\frac{W_i - w_i}{N}\,\Delta_i^{i+1}\left(\frac{1}{\alpha}\right)$ = contribution to production resulting from cumulative water encroachment

The denominators of both formulas (12-36) and (12-45) are identical. It is observed that should the denominator of either formula be zero, the time required for the field pressure to drop from P_i to P_{i+1} is infinite. Expressed in another manner, the field pressure would be maintained indefinitely. It is well known that this occurs often in practice when reservoir withdrawals and net water encroachment exactly compensate one another.

Solving for Q_o when the denominator vanishes, we find

$$Q_o = \frac{C_s\,\Delta P - C_1}{\left[\left(\frac{\beta}{\alpha} - S\right) + R\right]\alpha} \tag{12-46}$$

where the subscripts are dropped since the various functions pertain to a single pressure, namely, that which is maintained.

Conversely, it may be desired to write Eq. (12-46) so as to determine the field pressure required to maintain a certain field-wide rate of production:

$$\Delta P = \frac{C_1}{C_s} + \frac{Q_o}{C_s}\,\alpha\left[\left(\frac{\beta}{\alpha} - S\right) + R\right] \tag{12-47}$$

where ΔP is the pressure difference between aquifer and reservoir.

It is to be noted that C_1 may express the net water injection, in which case it has a negative sign, and the required pressure differential ΔP is thereby lessened by water injection in the reservoir.

A common belief is that water-drive fields should be operated at a producing rate such that the bubble-point pressure is maintained throughout the reservoir history. Regardless of the merit of this contention, this rate may readily be found from (12-46).

At the bubble point, we have

$$\beta = \beta_0 \qquad \alpha = \alpha_0 \qquad S = S_0 \qquad R = S_0$$

Substituting in (12-46),

$$Q_o = \frac{C_s \, \Delta P - C_1}{\beta_0} \tag{12-48}$$

where ΔP is pressure difference between the aquifer and bubble-point pressures.

Driving Indices. The driving indices in a combination type drive field, such as a water-drive field, are a measure of the effectiveness of each displacing mechanism in expulsing the oil from the reservoir. In this instance the oil is partly driven out by gas expansion or depletion and partly by water encroachment. There are two indices, the depletion-drive index (DDI) and the water-drive index (WDI). It is also desirable to express these fractions for the pressure decrement involved rather than on an over-all basis as given by (12-37).

Formula (12-45) may be rewritten as follows:

$$\frac{Q_o}{N} \Delta\theta \left[\left(\frac{\beta}{\alpha} - S \right) + R_{\text{av}} \right] - \frac{(C_s \, \Delta P - C_1)}{N\alpha_{i+1}} \Delta\theta$$

$$= (1 - n_i) \, \Delta_i^{i+1} \left(\frac{\beta}{\alpha} - S \right) - \beta_0 \, \Delta_i^{i+1} \frac{1}{\alpha} + \frac{W_i - w_i}{N} \Delta_i^{i+1} \left(\frac{1}{\alpha} \right) \tag{12-49}$$

But

$$\frac{Q_o}{N} \Delta\theta = \Delta_i^{i+1} n$$

$$(C_s \, \Delta P - C_1) \, \Delta\theta = \Delta_i^{i+1} (W - w)$$

$$\frac{\Delta_i^{i+1}(W - w)}{N\alpha_{i+1}} + \frac{W_i - w_i}{N} \Delta_i^{i+1} \left(\frac{1}{\alpha} \right) = \Delta_i^{i+1} \left(\frac{W - w}{N\alpha} \right)$$

By substitution in (12-49), we obtain

$$\Delta_i^{i+1} n \left[\left(\frac{\beta}{\alpha} - S \right) + R_{av} \right] = (1 - n_i) \Delta_i^{i+1} \left(\frac{\beta}{\alpha} - S \right) - \beta_0 \Delta_i^{i+1} \frac{1}{\alpha} + \Delta_i^{i+1} \left(\frac{W - w}{N\alpha} \right)$$

or

$$1 = \frac{(1 - n_i) \Delta_i^{i+1} \left(\frac{\beta}{\alpha} - S \right) - \beta_0 \Delta_i^{i+1} \frac{1}{\alpha}}{\Delta_i^{i+1} n \left[\left(\frac{\beta}{\alpha} - S \right) + R_{av} \right]} + \frac{\Delta_i^{i+1} \left(\frac{W - w}{N\alpha} \right)}{\Delta_i^{i+1} n \left[\left(\frac{\beta}{\alpha} - S \right) + R_{av} \right]} \tag{12-50}$$

In formula (12-50), the denominator of each fraction represents the total volumetric withdrawal in the pressure interval P_i to P_{i+1}. The numerators are, respectively, the withdrawals by depletion and by water drive. Hence, the driving indices on a differential basis in the pressure interval are

$$\text{DDI} = \frac{(1 - n_i) \Delta_i^{i+1} \left(\frac{\beta}{\alpha} - S \right) - \beta_0 \Delta_i^{i+1} \frac{1}{\alpha}}{\Delta_i^{i+1} n \left[\left(\frac{\beta}{\alpha} - S \right) + R_{av} \right]}$$

$$\text{WDI} = \frac{\Delta_i^{i+1} \left(\frac{W - w}{N\alpha} \right)}{\Delta_i^{i+1} n \left[\left(\frac{\beta}{\alpha} - S \right) + R_{av} \right]} \tag{12-51}$$

When reservoir withdrawal rates are smaller than net water encroachment rates, the reservoir pressure tends to build up and the free-gas phase may eventually dissolve completely.

The bubble-point pressure of the reservoir oil which has been subjected to a certain degree of gas depletion is, however, not identical to the original one. To calculate this new saturation pressure it is necessary to know the minimum pressure reached (P_{min}) and the corresponding free-gas saturation (σ_{gm}). When all the gas is put back in solution in the reservoir oil, this free-gas saturation disappears and the volume of gas redissolved, measured at standard conditions, and per unit stock-tank oil, is given by

$$\Delta S = \frac{\sigma_{gm}}{\alpha_m} \frac{\beta_m}{(1 - \sigma_{gm} - \sigma_w)} \tag{12-52}$$

where the subscript m indicates that the property function is measured at the minimum reservoir pressure reached. The value of ΔS so obtained is added graphically to the plot of solution gas S vs. pressure P and the pressure point so determined on the solubility curve is the new bubble-point pressure.

Above this bubble-point pressure, Eq. (12-45) simplifies to

$$\Delta_i^{i+1}\theta = \frac{(1 - n_i)\,\Delta_i^{i+1}\beta}{\frac{Q_o}{N}\beta_{i+1} - \frac{C_s\,\Delta P - C_1}{N}} \tag{12-53}$$

because $\Delta \frac{1}{\alpha} = 0$, $S = R$, and $1/\alpha$ cancel from numerator and denominator.

However, we have

$$\Delta_i^{i+1}\beta = -c_{oe}\beta\,\Delta_i^{i+1}P \tag{12-54}$$

where c_{oe} is the effective oil compressibility above the bubble-point pressure and $\Delta_i^{i+1}P$ is the increase in field pressure not to be confused with $\Delta P = P_{\text{aq}} - (P_i + P_{i+1})/2$.

Substituting (12-54) in (12-53) and changing the sign,

$$\Delta_i^{i+1}\theta = \frac{\beta c_{oe}(1 - n_i)\,\Delta_i^{i+1}P}{\frac{C_s\,\Delta P - C_1}{N} - \frac{Q_o}{N}\beta_{i+1}} \tag{12-55}$$

which is the practical equation to calculate field performance above the bubble-point pressure.

The derivation of Eq. (12-55) assumes also that the trapped gas saturation within the flooded-out section of the reservoir is redissolved in the residual oil.

Hypothetical Problem on Water Drive. An oil field, the structure contour map of which is given in Fig. 12-5, contains undersaturated oil when discovered at an original pressure of 2,000 psia; the physical properties are those of the depletion-drive problem in Chap. 10.

Additional fluid properties are as follows:

Oil API gravity = 36
Reservoir-oil specific gravity = 0.85
Reservoir-water specific gravity = 1.05
Water viscosity = 0.8 cps at reservoir conditions

The reservoir-rock properties are also those specified in the depletion-drive problem. (No allowance is made for changes in k_o/k_w owing to the presence of gas.) The reservoir is contained in an aquifer of infinite extent and it is estimated that the cumulative water influx W in barrels may be calculated on a monthly basis from $W = C_s\Sigma\,(\Delta P)\,(\Delta\theta)$, where $C_s = 120$ bbl per psi per month and ΔP is the pressure differential between reservoir and aquifer in pounds per square inch. $\Delta\theta$ = time interval in months.

It is desired to compute the performance of this field under various assumed rates of production. Before water encroachment becomes significant, it is, of course, necessary for the field to be initially produced by fluid expansion but also possibly by depletion drive in order to create the required pressure differential between field and aquifer. During that time, depletion, if present, is assumed to take place according to the manner predicted in the depletion-drive problem, especially with regard to development of a gas phase, increase in oil viscosity, etc.

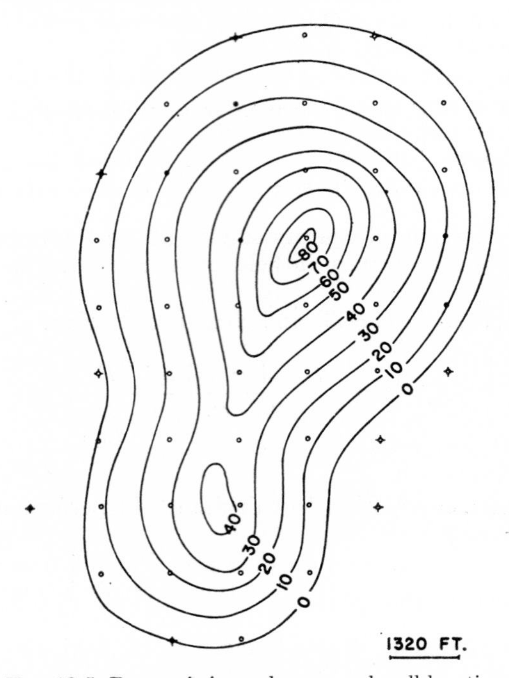

FIG. 12-5. Reservoir isopach map and well locations.

The gravitational segregation of gas into a gas cap is assumed nonexistent.

The field production rates at which it is desired to make performance predictions correspond to the following allowable rates:

100 bbl per day per well
80 bbl per day per well
60 bbl per day per well

The oil originally in place is assumed to be 44.941×10^6 bbl stock-tank oil. A uniform specific $(PI)_0 = 0.01$ is assumed to prevail throughout the field. Because of the high specific productivity index (PI) of the wells, they are able to produce their allowable up to the time that the oil-water contact reaches the roof on the structure.

Assume all wells completed simultaneously. All wells have the same productivity index regardless of location on structure and of the water level. As the water level rises, wells are plugged back so as to maintain a negligible water-oil ratio. An equivalent and feasible assumption is that all produced water is returned to the reservoir below the water table. Producing pressure gradients are assumed small enough to prevent water coning at the wells. Under the prevailing proration rules, no allowable production may be transferred from drowned-out wells. Hence, field-wide production rate will decline as the level of water-oil contact is raised.

For each assumed production rate, calculate:

1. The volumetric inventory of the reservoir and the pressure performance vs. time by means of an iterative tabulation analysis; in effect this is a solution of the material-balance equation.

2. The displacement efficiency of the water drive, assuming complete uniformity in the reservoir rock and a bottom drive (vertical water drive)

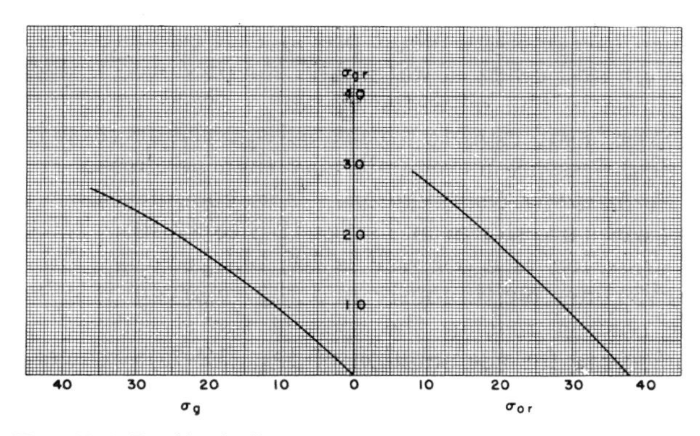

FIG. 12-6. Residual oil and gas saturations after water flood.

and taking into account the rate of advance of the flood front and the development of a free-gas phase uniformly distributed throughout the oil zone. The rate of advance of water is not constant since the cross section of the structure constantly decreases. The displacement efficiency of the water drive is accordingly variable. The beneficial effect of the development of a free-gas saturation on the displacement efficiency by water drive is to be evaluated by the data of Fig. 12-6.

Additional observations:

a. At a certain time during the life of the field, it will be observed that pressure is maintained. This will occur when the fluid withdrawals and expansion are volumetrically balanced by water influx. This requires an adequate producing capacity for the field; if that is not sufficient because of pressure depletion, or reduction in the number of producing wells, the water encroachment will rebuild the field pressure. The pressure at which field pressure will build up may be computed by means of formula (12-47).

b. The method of water-drive performance calculation presumes that a depletion-drive calculation has already been performed. Even when water encroachment is in effect, it is nevertheless assumed that oil is carried to the wells by a depletion mechanism and that no oil bank is formed by the advancing water front. This occurs when the producing rate is such that a uniform gas phase develops within the oil zone; this condition generally leads to maximum recovery by water displacement at a certain producing rate which may be called the *optimum rate.*

c. Difficulties in the calculation are encountered when the field pressure tends to stabilize. If a constant production rate could be expected throughout the life of the field, this difficulty would not exist because the pressure would not increase with time. With a declining production rate, however, a minimum will be observed in the pressure curve vs. time. One may proceed as follows: Determine approximately the field pressure at which it will stabilize for a constant value of production rate Q_o field-wide that will prevail near the singularity. Assume a reasonable interval of time $\Delta\theta$ during which this pressure might prevail and calculate the incremental oil production Δn and influx of water ΔW, the produced water Δw, and the corresponding rise in the oil-water contact. Field productivity will be lost when this rise is sufficient to cause a substantial decrease in production rate Q_o, and field-pressure increments may then be chosen.

Results of Performance Computations. The computation results for the three required cases are shown in Tables 12-8 to 12-10.

When the proration rate per well is 100 bbl per day (Table 12-8), the field pressure declines continuously and the reservoir is exhausted when the oil-water contact reaches the apex of the structure. Columns (1) to (18) inclusive are for the solution of Eq. (12-45). Once $\Delta\theta$ is known in column (18), Δn is calculated in column (19). Driving indices are calculated in column (20) for DDI and in column (24) for WDI. Cumulative water encroachment is required in column (8) and is obtained from the increments of water encroachment in column (21).

Fluid inventories, which evaluate the residual gas and oil trapped behind the flood front from Fig. 12-6, are made at all pressure-decline steps. The reservoir volume (in acre-feet) filled up by the encroaching water is computed from the displacement efficiency of the water drive in column (31). From this volume and the graph of Fig. 12-7, the height h to which the oil-water contact has risen from the beginning of production is read and recorded in column (32). The area A of this interface in acres is also read from Fig. 12-7 and recorded in column (35). Knowing h, it is possible to determine the number of wells x_o that will continue to produce oil from the structure map of Fig. 12-5 which shows well locations. The allowable production rate Q_o is then readily determined and recorded in column (34). In column (36) is recorded the rate of water influx per unit area of the oil-water interface. This rate is computed in barrels per day per acre and is to be used in the water fractional-flow formula to calculate the displacement efficiency of the water drive. This displacement efficiency is obtained by the tangent method to the f_w curve. In view of the slow rate of water encroachment and the flatness of the capillary-pressure

TABLE 12-8. ANALYSIS OF WATER-DRIVE FIELD PERFORMANCE

$N = 44.941 \times 10^6$ stock-tank oil
$P_{aq} = 2{,}000$ psia
$q_o = 100$ bbl/day/well
$C_s = 120$ bbl/psi/month
$C_1 = 0$

Pressure P, psia (1)	Δn from (19) (2)	$n = \Sigma(2)$ (3)	$1 - n = 1 - (3)$ (4)	$\Delta\left(\frac{\beta}{\alpha} - S\right)$ (5)	$(4)_i \times (5)$ (6)	$\beta_0 \Delta \frac{1}{\alpha}$ (7)	$\frac{W - w}{N} = \Sigma(21)$ (8)	$\Delta \frac{1}{\alpha}$ (9)	$(8)_i \times (9)$ (10)	(6) + (7) + (10) (11)	$\left(\frac{\beta}{\alpha} - S\right) +$ R_{av} from depletion drive (12)
1,500	0	0	1	...	...	...	0	...	...	...	...
1,400	0.0332	0.0332	0.9668	−11.2	−11.2	−13.98	0.0182	−11.25	0	2.78	154.3
1,300	0.0516	0.0848	0.9152	−10.4	−10.02	−13.64	0.0528	−11.00	−0.20	3.42	139.4
1,200	0.0858	0.1706	0.8294	−10.0	−9.152	−13.28	0.1188	−10.70	−0.565	3.563	120.1
1,100	0.1125	0.2831	0.7169	−9.0	−7.46	−12.85	0.2288	−10.35	−1.23	4.16	125.7
1,000	0.0768	0.3499	0.6501	−8.7	−6.23	−12.41	0.3330	−10.00	−2.288	3.892	161.9
900	0.0328	0.3827	0.6173	−7.7	−5.01	−12.11	0.3883	−9.75	−3.22	3.88	239.4
800	0.0202	0.4029	0.5971	−6.1	−3.77	−11.69	0.4392	−9.40	−3.65	4.27	357.0
700	0.0107	0.4136	0.5864	−6.5	−3.88	−11.30	0.4707	−9.10	−3.99	3.43	479.6
600	0.00702	0.4206	0.5794	−5.7	−3.34	−10.88	0.4907	−8.75	−4.12	3.42	606.4
500	0.0062	0.4268	0.5732	−4.8	−2.78	−10.69	0.5164	−8.60	−4.22	3.69	746.4
400	0.0048	0.4316	0.5684	−4.0	−2.29	−9.99	0.5392	−8.05	−4.16	3.54	875.6
300	0.0046	0.4362	0.5638	−2.9	−1.64	−9.55	0.5669	−7.70	−4.15	3.76	940.4
200	0.0048	0.4410	0.5590	−1.6	−0.901	−9.06	0.6145	−7.30	−4.14	4.019	970.3
150	0.00261	0.4436	0.5564	−0.8	−0.447	−4.85	0.6525	−3.90	−2.39	2.013	931.5
100	...	...	...	+0.5	...	−4.22	...	−3.40	...	...	876.3

TABLE 12-8. ANALYSIS OF WATER-DRIVE FIELD PERFORMANCE (*Continued*)

$\frac{Q}{N}(12)$ (13)	$\Delta P =$ 2,000 − P_{av} (14)	$\frac{1}{\alpha}$ (15)	$\frac{C_s(14)(15)}{N}$ (16)	(13) − (16) (17)	$\Delta\theta = \frac{(11)}{(17)}$, month (18)	$\Delta n =$ (18) $\frac{Q_o}{N}$ (19)	DDI = $\frac{(6) - (7)}{(19)(12)}$ (20)	$\frac{\Delta(W - w)}{N} = \frac{C_s(14)(18)}{N}$ (21)	$\frac{W - w}{N}\frac{1}{\alpha} =$ $(8)_{i+1}(15)$ (22)	Δ(22) (23)	WDI = $\frac{(23)}{(19)(12)}$ (24)
...	...	135.10	...	...	...	...	...	0	0	...	...
0.413	550	123.85	0.189	0.224	12.4	0.0332	0.542	0.0182	2.255	2.255	0.442
0.372	650	112.85	0.195	0.177	19.3	0.0516	0.503	0.0336	5.96	3.705	0.515
0.312	750	102.15	0.204	0.108	33.0	0.0858	0.398	0.0660	12.30	6.34	0.614
0.294	850	91.80	0.208	0.086	48.3	0.1125	0.381	0.1100	21.00	8.70	0.615
0.302	950	81.80	0.2075	0.0945	41.2	0.0768	0.497	0.1042	27.00	6.00	0.483
0.399	1,050	72.05	0.202	0.197	19.7	0.0328	0.902	0.0553	28.00	1.00	0.127
0.473	1,150	62.65	0.192	0.281	15.2	0.0202	1.095	0.0509	27.50	−0.50	−0.069
0.542	1,250	53.55	0.179	0.363	9.45	0.0107	1.448	0.0315	25.20	−2.30	−0.448
0.617	1,350	44.80	0.1615	0.4555	7.52	0.00702	1.770	0.0200	22.00	−3.20	−0.752
0.696	1,450	36.20	0.140	0.556	6.65	0.0062	1.710	0.0257	18.70	−3.30	−0.713
0.758	1,550	28.15	0.1165	0.6415	5.52	0.0048	1.840	0.0228	15.20	−3.50	−0.835
0.690	1,650	20.45	0.0905	0.5995	6.28	0.0046	1.820	0.0277	11.55	−3.65	−0.843
0.454	1,750	13.15	0.0617	0.3923	10.20	0.0048	1.750	0.0476	8.08	−3.47	−0.745
0.311	1,825	9.25	0.0528	0.2582	7.80	0.00261	1.810	0.0380	6.03	−2.05	−0.843
...	1,850	5.85	...	...	...	...	...	...	...	...	...

TABLE 12-8. ANALYSIS OF WATER-DRIVE FIELD PERFORMANCE (*Continued*)

(20) + (24) = 1 (25)	$(W - w)_{i+1} = (8)_{i+1}N$ ($\times 10^3$ bbl) (26)	σ_g from depletion drive (27)	σ_{gr} (28)	σ_{or} (29)	$1 - \sigma_w - \sigma_{gr} - \sigma_{or}$ (30)	$V = \frac{(26)}{7{,}758\phi(30)}$ acre-ft (31)	h, ft (32)	x_o, number of oil wells (33)	$Q_o = (33)\ q_o \times 30$ bbl/month (34)	A, acres (35)	$q_t = \frac{Q_o\beta}{30A}$, bbl/acre/day (36)
. . .	. . .	0	0	0.38	0.42	0	0	40	120,000	1,560	
0.984	820	0.024	0.024	0.360	0.416	1,260	0.6	40	120,000	1,490	
1.018	2,370	0.057	0.05	0.335	0.415	3,070	2.2	39	117,000	1,460	
1.012	5,350	0.079	0.075	0.310	0.415	6,930	5.0	35	105,000	1,300	
0.996	10,300	0.115	0.105	0.285	0.41	13,500	10.5	28	84,000	1,220	
0.980	14,820	0.145	0.130	0.26	0.41	18,600	15.0	25	75,000	1,000	2.95
1.029	17,450	0.169	0.15	0.24	0.41	22,900	19.5	20	60,000	925	
1.026	19,750	0.190	0.165	0.225	0.41	25,900	23.5	17	51,000	830	
1.000	21,200	0.205	0.175	0.21	0.405	28,100	27.0	14	42,000	700	
1.018	22,100	0.219	0.185	0.20	0.415	28,600	28.0	14	42,000	650	
0.997	23,200	0.232	0.19	0.195	0.415	30,100	30.5	13	39,000	560	
1.005	24,200	0.246	0.20	0.185	0.415	31,400	33.0	11	33,000	440	
0.977	25,500	0.256	0.205	0.18	0.415	33,000	37.0	7	21,000	340	
1.005	27,600	0.271	0.215	0.165	0.42	35,800	49.0	5	15,000	160	
0.957	29,300	0.287	0.225	0.155	0.42	37,500	84.0	0	0	0	
. . .	. . .	0.330	0.25	0.13	0.42	(fill-up)					

TABLE 12-9A. ANALYSIS OF WATER-DRIVE FIELD PERFORMANCE

$N = 44.941 \times 10^6$ bbl stock-tank oil
$P_{aq} = 2{,}000$ psia
$q_o = 80$ bbl/day/well
$C_s = 120$ bbl/psi/month
$C_1 = 0$

P, psia (1)	Δn from (19) (2)	$n = \Sigma(2)$ (3)	$1 - n$ (4)	$\Delta\left(\frac{\beta}{\alpha} - S\right)$ (5)	$(4)_i(5)$ (6)	$\beta_0 \Delta \frac{1}{\alpha}$ (7)	$\frac{W - w}{N} = \Sigma(21)$ (8)	$\Delta \frac{1}{\alpha}$ (9)	$(8)_i(9)$ (10)	(6) − (7) + (10) (11)	$\left(\frac{\beta}{\alpha} - S\right) + R$ (12)
1,500	0	0	1	...	...	...	0	...	...	...	...
1,400	0.0423	0.0423	0.9577	−11.2	−11.2	−13.98	0.0290	−11.25	0	2.78	154.3
1,300	0.0711	0.1134	0.8866	−10.4	−9.96	−13.64	0.0868	−11.00	−0.319	3.361	139.4
1,275	0.029	0.1424	0.8576	−2.5	−2.216	−3.11	0.1163	−2.50	−0.217	0.577	132.4
1,250	0.0682	0.2106	0.7894	−2.5	−2.14	−3.48	0.1911	−2.80	−0.326	−1.014	131.0
1,275	0.148	0.3586	0.6414	+2.5	+1.97	+3.48	0.3781	+2.80	+0.530	−0.98	132.4
1,300	0.0373	0.3959	0.6041	+2.5	+1.60	+3.11	0.4291	+2.50	+0.946	−0.564	139.4
1,400 (new BPP)	0.0972	0.4931	0.5069	+10.4	+6.28	+13.64	0.5793	+11.00	+4.72	−3.64	154.3

TABLE 12-9A. ANALYSIS OF WATER-DRIVE FIELD PERFORMANCE (*Continued*)

$\frac{Q_o}{N}$ (12) (13)	$\Delta P =$ 2,000 − P_{av} (14)	$\frac{1}{\alpha}$ (15)	$\frac{C_s(14)(15)}{N}$ (16)	(13) − (16) (17)	$\Delta\theta = \frac{(11)}{(17)}$ (18)	$\Delta n =$ (18) $\frac{Q_o}{N}$ (19)	DDI = $\frac{(6)-(7)}{(19)(12)}$ (20)	$\frac{\Delta(W-w)}{N} = \frac{C_s(14)(18)}{N}$ (21)	$\frac{W-w}{N}\frac{1}{\alpha} =$ $(8)_{i+1}(15)$ (22)	Δ(22) (23)	WDI = $\frac{(23)}{(19)(12)}$ (24)
...	...	135.10	...	...	...	...	...	...	0	...	...
0.329	550	123.85	0.189	0.140	19.8	0.0423	0.425	0.0290	3.590	3.590	0.588
0.297	650	112.85	0.196	0.101	33.3	0.0711	0.368	0.0578	9.800	6.210	0.626
0.247	712.5	110.3	0.210	0.037	15.5	0.029	0.232	0.0295	12.850	3.050	0.794
0.237	732.5	107.5	0.210	0.027	37.6	0.0682	0.151	0.0748	20.500	7.650	0.858
0.204	732.5	110.3	0.216	−0.012	81.5	0.148	−0.072	0.1870	41.500	21.200	1.080
0.194	712.5	112.85	0.215	−0.021	26.8	0.0373	−0.291	0.0510	48.300	6.800	1.305
0.173	650	123.85	0.215	−0.042	86.7	0.0972	−0.491	0.1502	71.700	23.400	1.570

(20) + (24) = 1 (25)	$(W-w)_{i+1} =$ $(8)_{i+1}N$ (26)	σ_g from depletion drive (27)	σ_{gr} (28)	σ_{or} (29)	$1 - \sigma_w - \sigma_{gr} - \sigma_{or}$ (30)	$V = \frac{(26)}{7{,}758\phi(30)}$ acre-ft (31)	h, ft (32)	x_o (33)	Q_o, bbl/month (34)	A, acres (35)	q_t = bbl/acre/day (36)
...	...	0	0	0.38	0.42	0	0	40	96,000	1,560	
1.013	1,300	0.014	0.014	0.365	0.42	1,660	1.0	40	96,000	1,480	
0.994	3,910	0.057	0.050	0.335	0.415	5,040	3.8	35	84,000	1,460	
1.026	5,250	0.065	0.060	0.325	0.415	6,780	5.0	34	81,600	1,300	
1.009	8,600	0.068	0.065	0.32	0.415	11,000	8.5	29	69,600	1,170	
1.008	16,900	0.065	0.060	0.325	0.415	21,800	18.5	26	62,500	940	
1.014	19,300	0.057	0.050	0.335	0.415	25,000	22.0	21	50,500	870	
1.079	26,000	0.014	0.014	0.365	0.42	33,300	37.5	11	26,400	330	

Table 12-9B. Analysis of Water-drive Performance above the Bubble-point Pressure

P (1)	$1 - n$ (2)	$\Delta_i^{i+1} P$ (3)	$c_{oe}\beta(2)_i(3)$ ($\times 10^{-3}$ bbl) (4)	β (5)	$\frac{Q_o}{N} \times (5)$ (6)	$\Delta P = 2{,}000 - P_{av}$ (7)	$\frac{C_s\,\Delta P - C_1}{N}$ (8)	(8) − (6) (9)	$\Delta\theta = (4)/(9)$, month (10)	$\Delta n = \frac{Q_o}{N} \times (10)$ (11)
1,400	0.5068	...	...	...	...	...	...	...	...	...
1,600	0.5061	200	0.81	1.2275	0.721	500	1.330	0.609	1.33	0.00078
1,700	0.5050	100	0.405	1.2265	0.72	350	0.935	0.215	1.88	0.0011
1,800	0.5025	100	0.404	1.2255	0.59	250	0.667	0.077	5.25	0.00252
1,850	0.4917	50	0.201	1.2250	0.46	175	0.467	0.007	28.8	0.0108
1,850	0.4805	0	...	...	...	150	0.400	...	Assume 30	0.0112
1,875 (?)	...	...	...	...	...	...	...	...	133	0.0284

$n = \Sigma(11)$ (12)	$\Delta(W - w) = (8) \times (10)N$ ($\times 10^3$ bbl) (13)	$(W - w) = \Sigma(13)$ ($\times 10^3$ bbl) (14)	σ_{or} (15)	$1 - \sigma_w - \sigma_{or}$ (16)	$V = \frac{(14)}{7{,}758\phi(16)}$ (17)	h, ft (18)	x_o (19)	Q_o (20)	A (21)	q_t (22)
0.4931	...	26,000	...	...	...	...	11	26,400		
0.4939	79.8	26,080	38	42	33,400	37.6	11	26,400	330	
0.4950	79	26,160	38	42	33,500	37.8	9	21,600	320	
0.4975	157	26,317	38	42	34,000	40	7	16,800	290	
0.5083	604	26,921	38	42	34,400	42	7	16,800	250	
0.5195	540	27,461	38	42	35,000	44	6	14,400	220	
0.5479	...	...	...	...	...	...	4 av	9,600		

TABLE 12-10A. ANALYSIS OF WATER-DRIVE FIELD PERFORMANCE

$N = 44.941 \times 10^6$ bbl stock-tank oil
$P_{aq} = 2{,}000$ psia
$q_o = 60$ bbl/day/well
$C_s = 120$ bbl/psi/month
$C_1 = 0$

P, psia (1)	Δn from (19) (2)	$n = \Sigma(2)$ (3)	$1 - n$ (4)	$\Delta\left(\frac{\beta}{\alpha} - S\right)$ (5)	$(4)_i(5)$ (6)	$\beta_0 \Delta \frac{1}{\alpha}$ (7)	$\frac{W - w}{N} = \Sigma(21)$ (8)	$\Delta \frac{1}{\alpha}$ (9)	$(8)_i(9)$ (10)	(6) − (7) + (10) (11)	$\left(\frac{\beta}{\alpha} - S\right) + R$ (12)
1,500	0	0	1	...	...	...	0	...	...	...	...
1,400	0.0768	0.0768	0.9232	−11.2	−11.2	−13.98	0.0705	−11.25	0	2.78	154.3
1,350	0.1900	0.2668	0.7332	−5.1	−4.71	−7.02	0.2905	−5.65	−0.398	1.912	147.0
1,400	0.0376	0.3044	0.6956	5.1	+3.74	7.02	0.3508	5.65	1.64	−1.64	154.3
1,457 (new BPP)	0.0294	0.3338	0.6662	6.3	+4.38	7.91	0.3957	6.35	2.23	−1.30	163.0

TABLE 12-10A. ANALYSIS OF WATER-DRIVE FIELD PERFORMANCE (*Continued*)

$\frac{Q_o}{N}$ (12) (13)	$\Delta P = 2{,}000 - P_{av}$ (14)	$\frac{1}{\alpha}$ (15)	$\frac{C_s(14)(15)}{N}$ (16)	(13) − (16) (17)	$\Delta\theta = \frac{(11)}{(17)}$ (18)	$\Delta n = (18)\frac{Q_o}{N}$ (19)	DDI = $\frac{(6)-(7)}{(19)(12)}$ (20)	$\frac{\Delta(W-w)}{N} = \frac{C_s(14)(18)}{N}$ (21)	$\frac{W-w}{N}\frac{1}{\alpha} = (8)_{i+1}(15)$ (22)	Δ(22) (23)	WDI = $\frac{(23)}{(19)(12)}$ (24)
...	...	135.10	...	...	...	...	...	...	0	...	...
0.247	550	123.85	0.189	0.058	47.9	0.0768	0.234	0.0705	8.73	8.73	0.736
0.212	625	118.20	0.1975	0.0145	132	0.1900	0.0829	0.2200	34.30	25.55	0.909
0.1605	625	123.85	0.206	−0.0455	36.1	0.0376	−0.57	0.0603	43.5	9.2	1.59
0.1565	572.5	130.20	0.199	−0.0425	30.6	0.0294	−0.731	0.0449	51.6	8.1	1.69

(20) + (24) = 1 (25)	$(W-w)_{i+1} = (8)_{i+1}N$ ($\times 10^3$ bbl) (26)	σ_g (27)	σ_{gr} (28)	σ_{or} (29)	$1 - \sigma_w - \sigma_{gr} - \sigma_{or}$ (30)	$V = \frac{(26)}{7{,}758\phi(30)}$ acre-ft (31)	h, ft (32)	x_o (33)	Q_o, bbl/month (34)	A, acres (35)	q_t, bbl/acre/day (36)
...	...	0	0	0.38	0.42	0	0	40	72,000	1,560	
0.980	3,170	0.014	0.014	0.365	0.42	4,050	3	36	64,800	1,390	
0.992	13,100	0.035	0.030	0.35	0.42	16,700	13	26	46,800	1,100	
1.020	15,800	0.035	0.030	0.35	0.42	20,500	16.5	24	43,200	975	
0.959	17,800	0	0	0.38	0.42	22,800	19.5	21	37,800	920	

TABLE 12-10B. ANALYSIS OF WATER-DRIVE FIELD PERFORMANCE ABOVE THE BUBBLE-POINT PRESSURE

P (1)	$1 - n$ (2)	$\Delta_i^{i+1}P$ (3)	$c_{oe}\beta(2)_i(3)$ ($\times 10^{-3}$ bbl) (4)	β_{i+1} (5)	$\frac{Q_o}{N}(5)$ (6)	$\Delta P = 2{,}000 - P_{av}$ (7)	$\frac{C_s\,\Delta P - C_1}{N}$ (8)	(8) − (6) (9)	$\Delta\theta = (4)/(9)$, month (10)	$\Delta n = \frac{Q_o}{N}(10)$ (11)
1,457	0.6662	...	...	...	...	...	...	...	...	...
1,500	0.6654	43	0.344	1.2355	1.035	521.5	1.390	0.355	0.97	0.815
1,600	0.6640	100	0.532	1.2350	0.989	450	1.200	0.313	1.73	1.38
1,650	0.64635	50	0.265	1.2345	0.988	375	1.000	0.012	22.05	1.765
1,650	0.62355	0	...	...	...	350	1.000	...	Assume 30	22.8
1,700	0.6193	50	0.250	1.2340	0.840	325	0.880	0.040	6.25	4.25
1,700	0.5989	0	...	...	...	300	0.800	...	Assume 30	20.4
1,700	0.5689	...	...	...	...	300	0.800	...	Assume 50	30
1,750	...	50	0.227	1.2335	0.593	275	0.735	0.142	1.6	...
1,750	0.5441	0	...	...	...	275	7.350	...	Assume 50	24.8
1,800	...	...	...	...	...	...	...	...	189	53
(?)										

$n = \Sigma(11)$ (12)	$\Delta(W - w) = (8)(10)N$ ($\times 10^{-3}$ bbl) (13)	$(W - w) = \Sigma(13)$ ($\times 10^{-3}$ bbl) (14)	σ_{or} (15)	$1 - \sigma_w - \sigma_{or}$ (16)	$V = \frac{(14)}{7{,}758\phi(16)}$ acre-ft (17)	h, ft (18)	x_o (19)	Q_o (20)	A (21)	q_t (22)
0.3338	...	17,800	...	...	...	...	21	37,800		
0.3346	60.7	17,860	38	42	22,900	20	20	36,000	895	
0.3360	94	17,954	38	42	23,000	20	20	36,000	895	
0.35365	992	18,946	38	42	24,200	21	19	34,200	890	
0.37645	935	19,881	38	42	25,400	23	17	30,600	850	
0.3807	247	20,128	38	42	25,800	23.5	17	30,600	840	
0.4011	1,080	21,208	38	42	27,300	25.5	15	27,000	735	
0.4311	1,800	24,008	38	42	30,800	31	12	21,600	505	
...	...	...	...	...	...	...	10	18,000		
0.4559	700	24,708	38	42	32,800	37				
0.5089	...	...	...	...	...	...	7 av	12,600		

curve in the case at hand, the length of the transition zone between oil and water (stabilized zone) is very short and is thus negligible for practical purposes. The determination of saturation gradient above the oil-water contact is therefore not necessary. The calculation of the dis-

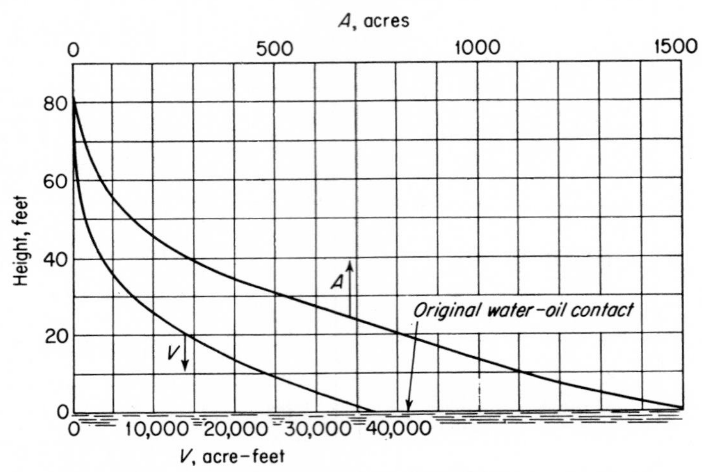

FIG. 12-7. Structure volume and cross-sectional area vs. height.

placement efficiency by water drive is recorded in Table 12-11 and the graphic determination of the recovery is made in Fig. 12-8. These calculations are made for the case when a gas phase is not present in the oil zone. When a gas phase is present, the same f_w curve applies but a part

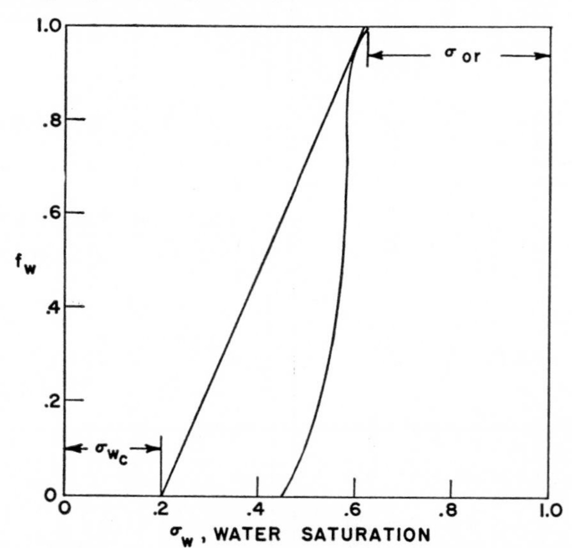

FIG. 12-8. Water flood displacement-efficiency calculation.

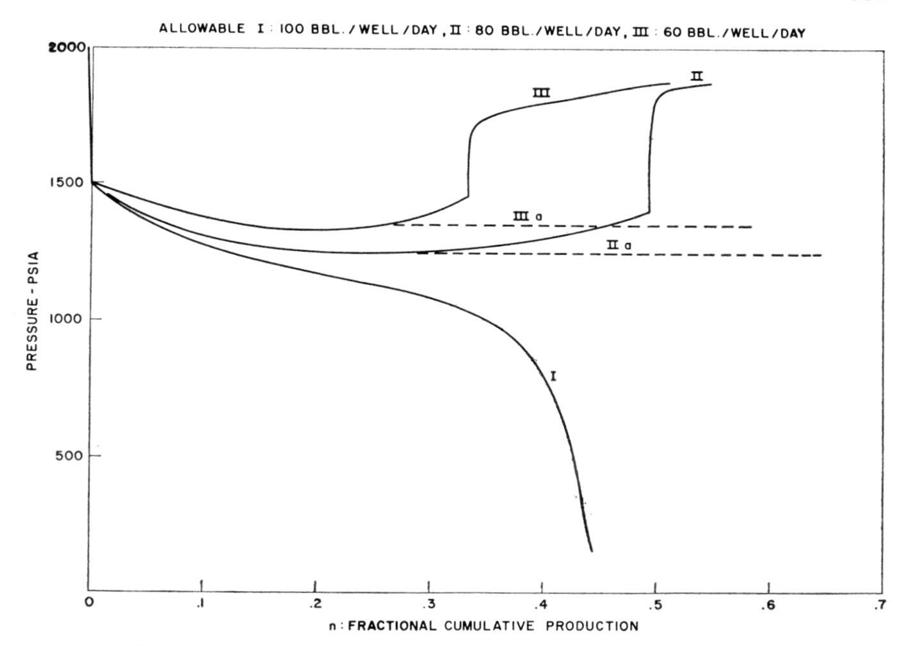

FIG. 12-9. Water-drive performance vs. cumulative fractional production for three well allowables.

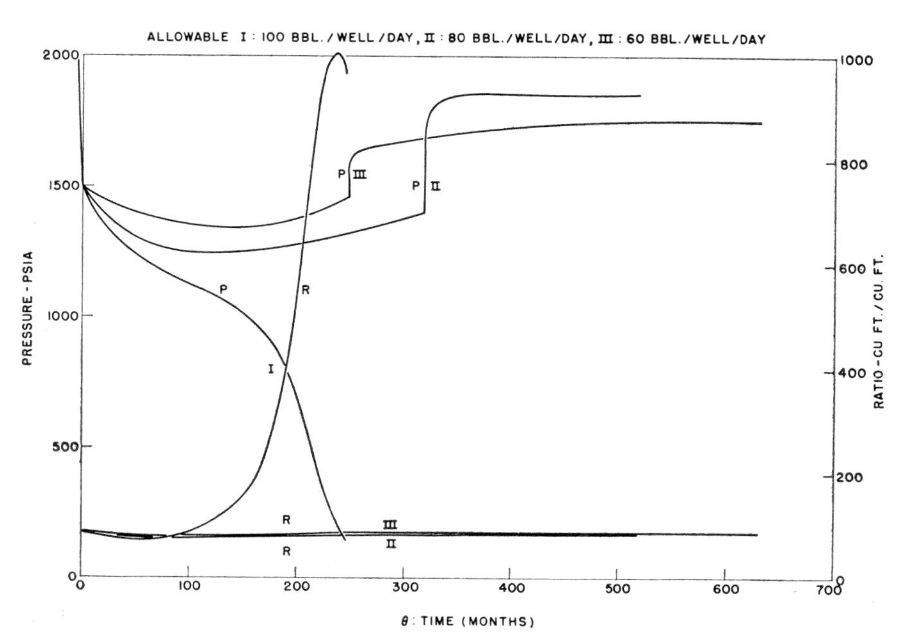

FIG. 12-10. Water-drive performance vs. time for three well allowables.

TABLE 12-11. WATER FLOOD DISPLACEMENT-EFFICIENCY CALCULATIONS

For conditions of Case 1, at 1,000 psia

$$\mu_w = 0.9 \text{ centipoise at } 97°\text{F} \qquad \Delta\vartheta = 0.2$$

$$\mu_o = 1.33 \text{ centipoises} \qquad \sin\alpha = 1.0$$

Fractional-flow formula in practical units, neglecting capillary-pressure gradient, is

$$f_w = \frac{1 - 21{,}238 \dfrac{K_o}{q_t \mu_o} \Delta\vartheta \sin\alpha}{1 + \dfrac{K_o}{K_w}\dfrac{\mu_w}{\mu_o}}$$

where $q_t = \dfrac{Q_o \beta}{A \times 30}$ bbl/acre/day: $\beta = 1.18$

$Q_o = 75{,}000$ bbl/month

$A = 1{,}000$ acres

σ_w	k_o	k_w	$\dfrac{k_o}{k_w}$	$\dfrac{k_o}{k_w}\dfrac{\mu_w}{\mu_o}$	$1 + \dfrac{k_o \mu_w}{k_w \mu_o}$	$\dfrac{1}{1 + \dfrac{k_o}{k_w}\dfrac{\mu_w}{\mu_o}}$
20	1	0				
30	0.7	0.001	700			
40	0.41	0.005	82	55.5	56.5	0.0177
45	0.29	0.01	29	19.5	20.5	0.049
50	0.17	0.015	11.3	7.65	8.65	0.116
55	0.07	0.027	2.6	1.75	2.75	0.363
60	0.01	0.05	0.2	0.135	1.135	0.88
62	0	0.07	0	0	1	1

The f_w curve is plotted on Fig. 12-8 for the case where Q_o is infinite and the residual oil is 38 per cent. It is observed that when the rate of flow is 75,000 STO bbl per month, the residual oil remains unchanged and it is safe to postulate it will be the same at all practical producing rates.

of the gas phase is nonmovable and is trapped by the advancing water. The amount of gas phase developed is obtained at a given pressure from the corresponding depletion-drive calculation at the same prevailing field pressure (Chap. 10). The residual gas and oil saturations are then evaluated from Fig. 12-6 at each step. Performance curves are obtained from Tables 12-8 to 12-10 and are plotted for comparison purposes on Figs. 12-9 and 12-10.

The fluid-saturation distribution may then be obtained for each increment of water influx and it may be represented within a unit reservoir volume as shown in Figs. 12-11 to 12-13 for the various cases studied here. The reservoir-volume fractions are obtained from column (31) by dividing the figure by the total reservoir volume, namely, 37,500 acre-feet. Figures 12-11 to 12-13 are accordingly an inventory of the reservoir fluids according to various production techniques. Figure 12-11 is for the fastest production rate, q_o = 100 bbl per day per well, and it shows that the gas phase continuously increases as well as the trapped gas saturation. However,

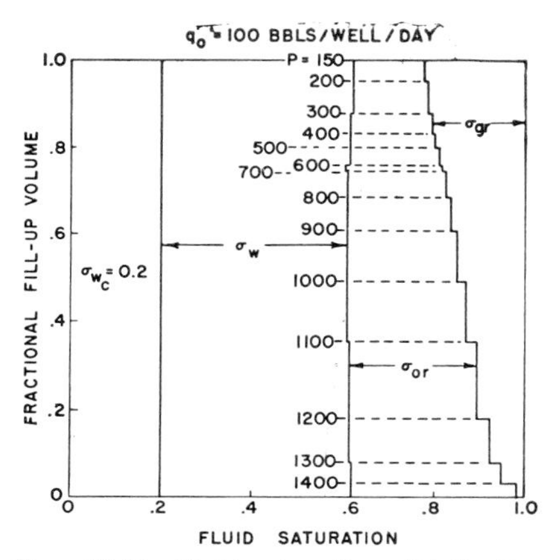

Fig. 12-11. Fluid-saturation distribution on a unit reservoir pore-volume basis.

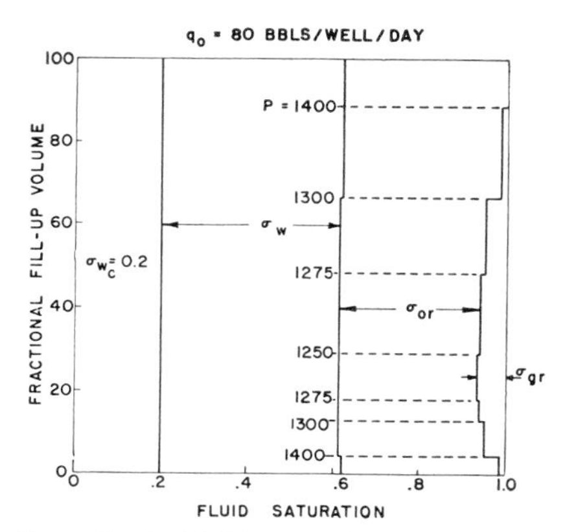

Fig. 12-12. Fluid-saturation distribution on a unit reservoir pore-volume basis.

the over-all recovery (n = 0.4436) by this rate is the least in the three cases considered, even though the residual oil appears less. This is because of the shrinkage of the residual oil with large pressure drop below the bubble point. It is more efficient to trap reservoir oil with an optimum amount of gas in solution, as it represents a lesser volume of stock-tank oil.

Figure 12-12 is for the medium production rate of 80 bbl per day per well. In this case a substantial gas phase develops when the field pressure reaches 1,250 psia, which is 250 psi below the bubble point. However, because of the decrease in withdrawals attendant to the reduced number of producing wells as the oil-water contact rises, this gas phase disappears by redissolving because of the increasing pressure until the new bubble-point pressure of 1,400 psia is reached. Some production is still obtained when the field pressure is maintained above this new saturation pressure because the withdrawal rates are less than net water influx rate. At reservoir fill-up, the over-all recovery is 0.5479 of the original oil in place, substantially larger than at the faster rate of 100 bbl per well per day.

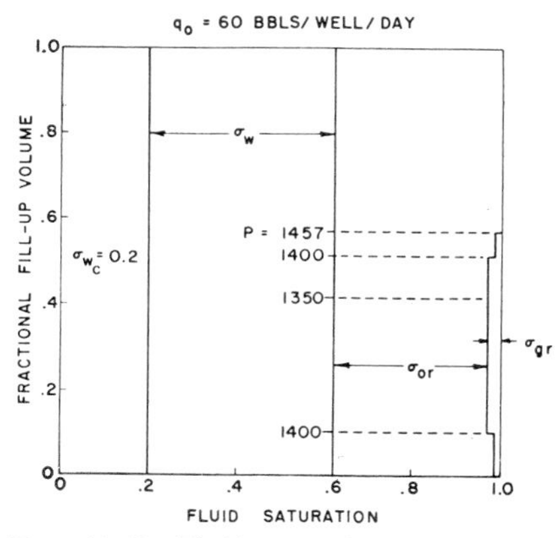

Fig. 12-13. Fluid-saturation distribution on a unit reservoir pore-volume basis.

Of interest is the recovery which would have been obtained by adjusting withdrawal rates to such a point as to maintain the field pressure of 1,250 psia by giving higher allowable to wells higher on structure or, if this is not permitted by conservation authorities, by withdrawing water from the aquifer so as to permit maintenance of 1,250 psia field pressure until abandonment. When 1,250 psia is reached, the recovery has been 0.2106 and 26,500 acre-ft remain unswept by the water drive from which, flooding at constant pressure with the presence of a gas phase, would be recovered

$$\frac{26{,}500 \times 7{,}758 \times 0.24 \times 0.4}{1.211 \times 45 \times 10^6} = 0.433$$

making a total of 0.6436 of the original oil or an additional recovery of $(0.6436 - 0.5479) \times 45 \times 10^6 = 4{,}300{,}000$ bbl stock-tank oil over the recovery under proration schedules. Unwise proration limitations may therefore be detrimental to recovery by water drive and lead to underground waste. Flexible allowable production schedules of sufficient magnitude originally in water-drive fields of the structural type studied here appear to be advisable from a conservation standpoint.

Figure 12-13 is for the lowest production rate of 60 bbl per day per well. It is observed that field pressure drops slightly below the bubble point to 1,350 psia and is rebuilt to a new saturation pressure of 1,457 psia with a substantial amount of the production occurring above this pressure. Because of the development of a small gas phase, the ultimate recovery is only 0.5089. If the producing rate had been adjusted to maintain 1,350 psia once this pressure had been reached, the ultimate production would have been 0.5848.

It is of interest to compare the above recoveries with the expected results by maintaining the original bubble-point pressure of 1,500 psia while production proceeds and without the development of a gas phase. The rate that will maintain this pressure is obtained for Eq. (12-48) and is 48,500 bbl per month field-wide. Recovery is then 0.525 of original oil.

While the most efficient rate (MER) of a water-drive field is generally considered to be the rate that will maintain a field pressure equal to the original saturation pressure, it is observed that such a rate may cause considerable underground waste in the form of residual oil which very likely can never be recovered economically by any secondary or tertiary recovery process.

Validity of the Basic Postulate. The basic postulate made in the water-drive calculations presented here is that at any prevailing field pressure during the water-drive operation, the oil and gas saturations within the oil zone are identical to those prevailing during straight depletion drive at the same pressure. This postulate implies that the mechanism by which the oil is transported to the wells is the same as in the depletion-drive process even though the oil zone is constantly shrinking in volume. The calculations are made as if at each successive step a new reservoir of lesser volume were subjected to the process of depletion, for the trapped oil and gas behind the flood front are ineffective in maintaining pressure or contributing to

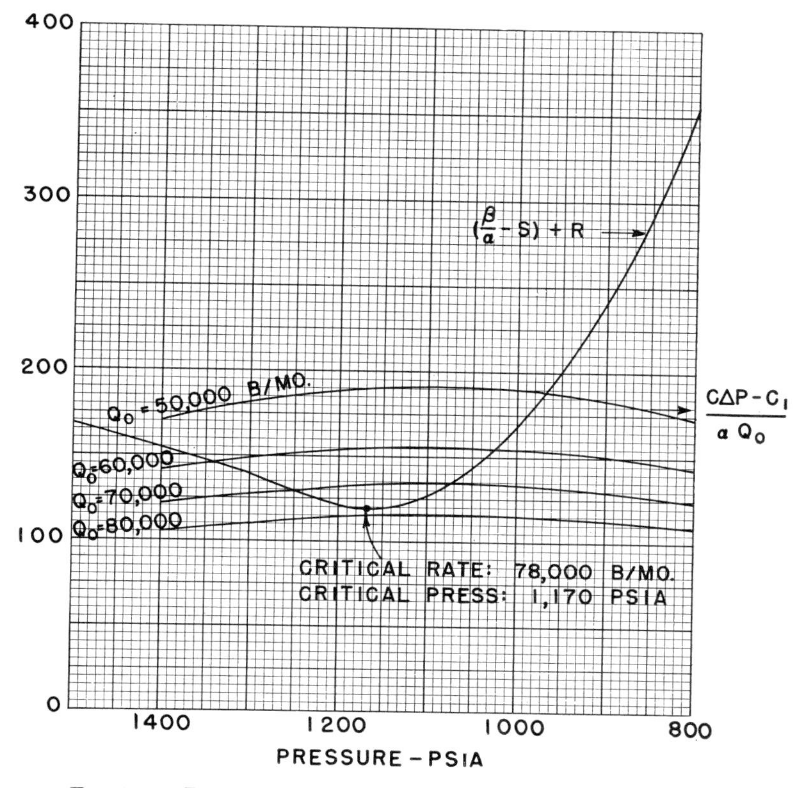

FIG. 12-14. Determination of field-wide critical-oil-production rate.

the depletion process. Water drive is therefore viewed as a particular case of depletion drive where the latter takes place within a shrinking oil column. An alternative method of making such calculations is to do just that and to calculate at each step the prevailing fluid saturation in the shrinking oil column. In so doing the displacement efficiency of the water drive comes into the computations in such a manner that slight errors in the residual oil and gas computed have unduly large effects on the answer. It is felt that the basic postulate made here is better than the results obtained on the basis of a shrinking oil column.

Development of a Free-gas Phase. The development of a free-gas phase by permitting the field pressure to drop below the bubble point results in increased oil recovery by water drive only in water-wet reservoir rocks, for in an oil-wet system no additional oil is displaced by water in the presence of a nonmovable gas phase. In addition pore texture and structure may be such that the replacement of oil by gas is not always favorable even in water-wet reservoirs; basic flow tests must be made on actual and representative reservoir-rock samples in order to determine if fluid-replacement characteristics are suitable.

SELECTED REFERENCES ON OIL PRODUCTION BY WATER DRIVE

1936

Schilthuis, R. J.: Active Oil and Reservoir Energy, *Trans. AIME*, vol. 118, pp. 33ff.

1940

Jacob, C. E.: The Flow of Water in an Elastic Artesian Aquifer, *Trans. Am. Geophys. Union*, vol. 21, pp. 574ff.

1941

De Golyer, E.: Production under Effective Water Drive as a Standard for Conservation Practice, *AIME Tech. Pub.* 1340.

1942

Bruce, W. A.: Pressure Prediction for Oil Reservoirs, *AIME Tech. Pub.* 1454.

Old, R. E., Jr.: Analysis of Reservoir Performance, *AIME Tech. Pub.* 1529.

1943

Bruce, W. A.: An Electrical Device for Analyzing Oil-reservoir Behavior, *AIME Tech. Pub.* 1550.

Cook, A. B.: Derivation and Application of Material Balance Equations, *U.S. Bur. Mines Rept. Invest.* 3720.

Horner, W. L., and D. R. Snow: Water Injection for Maintaining Reservoir Pressure and Increasing Natural Drive, *Oil Gas J.*, Nov. 11, pp. 226ff.

Hurst, W.: Water Influx into a Reservoir and Its Application to the Equation of Volumetric Balance, *Trans. AIME*, vol. 151, pp. 57ff.

1944

Bruce, W. A.: A Study of the Smackover Limestone Formation and the Reservoir Behavior of Its Oil and Condensate Pools, *AIME Tech. Pub.* 1728.

1945

Elliott, G. R.: Behavior and Control of Natural Water-drive Reservoirs, *AIME Tech. Pub.* 1880.

Pirson, S. J.: The Engineering Approach to Oil Reservoir Controls, *Oil Weekly*, Dec. 31, pp. 22ff.

Woods, R. W., and M. Muskat: An Analysis of Material Balance Calculations, *AIME Tech. Pub.* 1780.

1946

Muskat, M.: The Performance of Bottom Water-drive Reservoirs, *AIME Tech. Pub.* 2060.

Werner, P. W.: Notes on Flow-time Effects in the Great Artesian Aquifers of the Earth, *Trans. Am. Geophys. Union*, vol. 27, no. 5, pp. 687ff.

1947

Schaefer, H.: Extending the Application of Electric Analogy in Oil-reservoir Studies, *AIME Tech. Pub.* 2125.

1949

Brownscombe, E. R., and F. Collins: Estimation of Reserves and Water Drive from Pressure and Production History, *AIME Tech. Pub.* 2589.

Evans, R. L., and R. P. Roe: Increased Oil Recovery from Injection Operations, *Oil Gas J.*, Sept. 28, pp. 68ff.

Horner, W. L.: Increased Oil Recovery by Means of Water Injection Pressure Maintenance, *Producers Monthly*, December, pp. 15ff.

Van Everdingen, A. F., and W. Hurst: The Application of the Laplace Transformation to Flow Problems in Reservoirs, *AIME Tech. Pub.* 2732.

1950

Brownscombe, E. R., and F. Collins: Pressure Distribution in Unsaturated Oil Reserves, *AIME Tech. Note* 61, October.

Trube, A. S., and S. N. DeWitt: High Pressure Water Injection for Maintaining Reservoir Pressures, New Hope Field, Franklin County, Texas, *Trans. AIME Petroleum Div.*, vol. 189, pp. 325ff.

1951

Akins, D. W., Jr.: Primary High Pressure Water Flooding in the Pettit Lime Haynesville Field, *Trans. AIME Petroleum Div.*, vol. 192, pp. 239ff.

Bell, John S., and J. M. Shepherd: Pressure Behavior in the Woodbine Sand, *AIME Tech. Pub.* 3000.

Holmgren, C. R., and R. A. Morse: Effect of Free Gas Saturation on Oil Recovery by Water-flooding, *Trans. AIME Petroleum Div.*, vol. 192, pp. 135ff.

Muskat, M.: The Effect of Withdrawal Rate on the Uniformity of Edgewater Intrusion, *Trans. AIME Petroleum Div.*, vol. 192, pp. 327ff.

1952

Geffen, T. M., et al.: Efficiency of Gas Displacement from Porous Media by Liquid Flooding, *Trans. AIME Petroleum Div.*, vol. 195, pp. 29ff.

Moore, W. D., and L. G. Truby, Jr.: The Pressure Performance of Five Fields Completed in a Common Aquifer, *Trans. AIME Petroleum Div.*, vol. 195, pp. 297ff.

1953

Van Everdingen, A. F., et al.: Application of the Material Balance Equation to a Partial Water-drive Reservoir, *Trans. AIME Petroleum Div.*, vol. 198, pp. 51ff.

1954

Dyes, A. B.: Production of Water-driven Reservoirs below Their Bubble Point, *J. Petroleum Technol.*, vol. 6, no. 10, pp. 31ff.

Stewart, F. M., et al.: Comparison of Methods for Analyzing a Water Drive Field, Torchlight Tensleep Reservoir, Wyoming, *J. Petroleum Technol.*, vol. 6, no. 9, pp. 105ff.

1955

McDowell, J. M.: Performance of Water Drive Reservoirs, Including Pressure Maintenance, as Determined by the Reservoir Analyzer, *J. Petroleum Technol.*, vol. 7, no. 4, pp. 73ff.

Mortada, M.: A Practical Method of Treating Oilfield Interference in Water-drive Reservoirs, *Trans. AIME Petroleum Div.*, vol. 204, pp. 217ff.

1956

Brown, W. O.: The Mobility of Connate Water during a Water Flood, *AIME Tech. Paper* 694G.

Hutchinson, T. S.: An Extended Analysis of Bottom Water Drive Reservoir Performance, *AIME Tech. Paper* 689G.

Woody, L. D., and W. D. Moore: Performance Calculations for Reservoirs with Natural or Artificial Water Drives, *AIME Tech. Paper* 692G.

CHAPTER 13

OIL PRODUCTION BY SEGREGATION DRIVE

In high-relief geologic structures suitable to act as reservoirs for oil and gas it is not uncommon to discover the reservoir in a state of segregation, i.e., an oil zone overlain by a gas cap. When no original gas cap exists and when the gross vertical permeability of the reservoir rock is sufficiently large, a secondary gas cap may develop as a result of oil production and pressure decline. This development takes place by active counterflow of oil and gas within the oil zone under the influence of gravity forces and the buoyancy of the gas phase with respect to oil. Should vertical permeability be substantially negligible owing to the presence of shale stringers or other impermeable zones, active counterflow of oil and gas may be suppressed to a large extent; yet passive segregation of oil and gas may still exist by natural expansion of a preexisting gas cap or through injection of gas at the crest of the structural accumulation. In essence, the process of oil production by segregation is one in which the force of gravity is made use of to its fullest extent; it is often called oil recovery by *gravity drainage*.

The production of oil from a reservoir by segregation drive always implies the preexistence or the development of an expanding gas cap with or without field-wide pressure decline wherein complete or partial segregation of the oil and gas takes place into two separate and distinct zones, namely, the oil zone and the gas cap. When there is no original gas cap, the process leads to what is called a "secondary gas-cap development."

In the simplest case, no water encroachment or water injection is postulated.

The development of a gas cap and its expansion may occur according to two distinct processes:

1. By expansion of a preexisting gas cap with or without gas injection into it, or by inducing a gas cap through gas injection at the crest of the structure. The amount of gas so injected may be a constant or a variable fraction of the produced gas; it may also be a larger amount than the gas produced with the oil. This process implies that there is no gas moving into the gas cap from the oil zone under the buoyancy effect of the differential gravity pull on gas and oil. This is generally the case in formations of low specific vertical permeability or in laminated lenticular or interbedded sands and shales. This production process is called "segregation drive without counterflow."

2. By counterflow of oil and gas within the oil zone under the influence of the buoyancy effect of gravity owing to the difference in density between oil and gas. An original gas cap may or may not exist. This process generally requires a reservoir rock of high specific permeability or the presence of vertical fractures or vuggy channels. Active counterflow of oil and gas may take place perpendicular to bedding surfaces in homogeneous reservoir rocks or in nonhomogeneous rocks when fractures, solution channels, and vugs are present. Segregation takes place more readily parallel to bedding when reservoir rocks are structurally deformed. This production process is called "segregation drive with counterflow."

In all cases the gas cap acts as a *frontal drive* maintaining at all times a gas-oil contact surface between the oil and gas zones.

SEGREGATION DRIVE WITHOUT COUNTERFLOW

Various cases may be considered in the production of oil by segregation drive without counterflow. They are enumerated here, together with some of their characteristics:

1. Production of oil from the oil zone alone without production of gas-cap gas, gas saturation in the oil zone being determined uniquely by the prevailing field pressure. The existence of an original gas cap is postulated here. Calculations may be made with or without taking into account the release of gas from solution in the residual oil. Various cases may be considered, depending on whether or not gas is considered to be released from solution in the residual oil. A special operation obtains with production of oil from the oil zone and gas production from an original gas cap, gas saturation in the oil zone being determined uniquely by the prevailing field pressure. Release of gas from solution in the residual-oil saturation may or may not be taken into account. A particular case of this operation results when gas-cap gas production is so adjusted at all times as to prevent its expansion. Since there is no residual-oil saturation, release of gas from solution in it need not be considered.

2. Production of oil from the oil zone alone without production of gas-cap gas but with a constant fraction I of the produced gas being returned to the gas cap, the oil saturation in the oil zone being determined uniquely by the prevailing field pressure.

Various special cases may be considered:

a. Production of oil from the oil zone alone without production of gas-cap gas, with gas injection into the gas cap, but taking into account the release of gas from solution in the residual-oil saturation in the expanded section of the gas cap, the gas-oil ratio being uniquely determined by the prevailing field pressure.

b. Production of oil from the oil zone alone in a field with an original gas cap with or without gas injection, but where the oil saturation in the shrinking oil zone is calculated taking into account the oil displacement efficiency of the expanding gas cap. No gas-cap gas production.

c. Production of oil from the oil zone alone in a field with an original gas cap, with or without gas injection, but where the oil saturation in the shrinking oil zone is calculated taking into account the oil displacement efficiency of the expanding gas cap but considering that gas comes out of solution from the residual-oil saturation in the expanded section of the gas cap. No gas-cap gas production.

Case 1. Segregation Drive under a Naturally Expanding Original Gas Cap (without Gas Vaporization from Residual-oil Saturation). It is postulated that well operations are such that oil may be produced from the oil zone alone without gas coning. The productivity of the individual wells therefore depends upon the prevailing field pressure and the height of the oil column at each well. As each or both of these elements decline in value, well productivity declines, the field-wide production rate also declines, and the rate of advance of the expanding gas front is reduced. This results in a greater displacement efficiency by the frontal gas drive. This factor, however, is generally of minor importance in the over-all recovery process but its effect may be gauged by means of the frontal-drive theory. Oil production terminates when the expanding gas cap achieves structural fill-up. The abandonment pressure of the oil production is therefore greatly dependent upon the size of the original gas cap.

Since the gas-cap gas remains segregated and does not diffuse through the oil zone, it may be postulated that the prevailing field pressure determines the gas saturation in the oil column and that the latter is, at each pressure, that which prevails in the simple depletion drive without dispersed gas injection. At least, it is safe to presume that this condition prevails until the "critical gas saturation" to external gas drive is established. (This critical gas saturation is determined by the tangent drawn from the equilibrium gas saturation σ_{ge} to the f_g curve calculated for the prevailing field conditions of reservoir rock and fluid properties.) As the field pressure declines and the gas phase develops within the oil column, the displacement efficiency of the advancing gas front is continuously reduced since the displaced reservoir oil is the mean gas saturation $\bar{\sigma}_g$ minus the gas saturation that prevails in the oil zone σ_g. When the critical gas saturation is reached, the calculations should then proceed on the basis of gas-cap gas diffusion through the oil zone, the volume of which now remains stationary.

The calculation of the performance of a naturally expanding gas-cap drive may be performed on the basis of two assumptions:

1. The simplifying assumption that no gas is released from solution in the residual-oil saturation in the expanded section of the gas cap
2. The more realistic assumption that gas is released from solution from said residual oil

The calculations under the first assumption are much simpler.

The general technique of calculation of performance of a naturally expanding gas-cap drive under the first assumption will now be considered.

Performance Equations in Finite Form. On a *finite form* basis, the equation of the process during the gas-cap expansion stage is

$$\frac{n_{i+1}\left(\frac{\beta}{\alpha} - S\right)_{i+1} + \sum_{0}^{i+1} \Delta n\, R_{\text{av}}}{m\beta_0\left(\frac{1}{\alpha_0} - \frac{1}{\alpha_{i+1}}\right) + \left(\frac{\beta}{\alpha} - S\right)_{i+1} - \left(\frac{\beta_0}{\alpha_{i+1}} - S_0\right)} = 1 \qquad (13\text{-}1)$$

which is the material-balance equation written in a different form from the usual presentation. The equations for the gas-oil ratio and fluid saturation in the oil zone need not be considered at this stage since the prevailing field pressure uniquely determines them according to a previously carried-out depletion-drive calculation. The increments of production may then be calculated directly by substituting in Eq. (13-1):

$$n_{i+1} = n_i + \Delta_i^{i+1} n$$

$$D_{i+1} = \left(\frac{\beta}{\alpha} - S\right)_{i+1} - \left(\frac{\beta_0}{\alpha_{i+1}} - S_0\right)$$

$$G_{i+1} = \sum_{0}^{i+1} \Delta n\, R_{\text{av}} = G_i + \Delta_i^{i+1} n\, R_{\text{av}}$$

where G is the cumulative volume of gas produced.

The material balance becomes, after solving for $\Delta_i^{i+1}n$,

$$\Delta_i^{i+1} n = \frac{D_{i+1} + m\beta_0\left(\frac{1}{\alpha_0} - \frac{1}{\alpha_{i+1}}\right) - n_i\left(\frac{\beta}{\alpha} - S\right)_{i+1} - G_i}{\left(\frac{\beta}{\alpha} - S\right)_{i+1} + R_{\text{av}}} \qquad (13\text{-}2)$$

If a constant rate of production Q_o in barrels of stock-tank oil per day is allowed from the field, the increment of time $\Delta_i^{i+1}\theta$ in days required to produce it is obtained from

$$\Delta_i^{i+1}\theta = \frac{D_{i+1} + m\beta_0\left(\frac{1}{\alpha_0} - \frac{1}{\alpha_{i+1}}\right) - n_i\left(\frac{\beta}{\alpha} - S\right)_{i+1} - G_i}{\frac{Q_o}{N}\left[\left(\frac{\beta}{\alpha} - S\right)_{i+1} + R_{\text{av}}\right]} \qquad (13\text{-}3)$$

The above calculations are carried out in a straightforward manner, i.e., without trial and error, for a predetermined series of pressure decrements until the critical gas saturation σ_{gc} is reached in the oil zone at which pressure the gas-cap diffusion stage begins. At this point the oil-zone production must be treated as a depletion drive with dispersed gas injection, the source of the gas being the free gas in the gas cap. The gas saturation in the oil zone is no longer controlled by the prevailing field pressure and it must be determined on a trial-and-error basis. The oil zone is no longer shrinking and the fluid saturations are calculated using the oil-zone volume that prevails at σ_{gc} as that of a constant-volume reservoir. The simultaneous equations of the gas-diffusion stage are

$$\Delta_i^{i+1} n = \frac{D_{i+1} + m\beta_0 \left(\dfrac{1}{\alpha_0} - \dfrac{1}{\alpha_{i+1}} \right) - n_i \left(\dfrac{\beta}{\alpha} - S \right)_{i+1} - G_i}{\left(\dfrac{\beta}{\alpha} - S \right)_{i+1} + R_{\text{av}}}$$

$$R = S + \frac{\beta}{\alpha} \frac{k_g}{k_o} \frac{\mu_o}{\mu_g} \tag{13-4}$$

$$\sigma_l = \sigma_w + (1 - \sigma_w) \left[\frac{(1 - n)\beta}{(1 - n_c)\beta_0} - \sigma_{gc} \right]$$

For predetermined pressure decrements during the gas-diffusion stage, certain corresponding production increments Δn are assumed by a trial-and-error technique until all equations (13-4) are verified at each step.

The driving indices of the process on a finite basis are

$$\text{DDI} = \frac{N \left[\left(\dfrac{\beta}{\alpha} - S \right) - \left(\dfrac{\beta_0}{\alpha} - S_0 \right) \right]}{n \left(\dfrac{\beta}{\alpha} - S \right) + G} \tag{13-5}$$

$$\text{SDI} = \frac{mN\beta_0 \left(\dfrac{1}{\alpha_0} - \dfrac{1}{\alpha} \right)}{n \left(\dfrac{\beta}{\alpha} - S \right) + G}$$

These indices are a measure of the degree of effectiveness to which each process is present in the recovery operation, and during each pressure decrement.

Driving indices are merely another way of expressing the material-balance equation and therefore their sum must be equal to unity.

Performance Equations in Finite Difference Form. On a finite *difference form* basis, the process performance is described somewhat more simply:

1. Gas-cap expansion stage. At each pressure decrement, the prevailing gas saturation σ_g in the oil column is that of the simple depletion drive, and the gas-oil ratio R is also obtained directly from said calculations.

Increments of oil production Δn are calculated from Eq. (13-6):

$$\Delta_i^{i+1} n = \frac{(1 - n_i)\, \Delta_i^{i+1} \left(\dfrac{\beta}{\alpha} - S \right) - (1 + m)\beta_0\, \Delta_i^{i+1} \dfrac{1}{\alpha}}{\left(\dfrac{\beta}{\alpha} - S \right)_{i+1} + R_{\text{av}}} \tag{13-6}$$

The residual-oil saturations σ_{or} behind the advancing gas front at each pressure decrement step are calculated by means of the f_g diagrams. The volumetric expansion of the gas cap is calculated from $mN(\beta_o/\alpha_o)\ \Delta\alpha$ from which the level of the gas-oil contact is determined from a plot of the reservoir volume vs. structural height. The calculations are carried out until the critical gas saturation σ_{gc} is reached in the oil column.

2. Gas-cap diffusion stage. From the critical gas saturation on, the oil-zone production must be treated as a depletion drive with dispersed gas injection, the source of the gas being the free gas in the gas cap. The gas saturation in the oil zone is no longer controlled by the prevailing field pressure and it must be determined on a trial-and-error basis. The oil-zone volume is no longer shrinking and the fluid saturations are calculated using the oil-zone volume that prevails at σ_{gc} as that of a constant-volume reservoir. The equations of the gas-cap diffusion stage are

$$\Delta_i^{i+1} n = \frac{(1 - n_i)\ \Delta_i^{i+1}\left(\frac{\beta}{\alpha} - S\right) - (1 + m)\beta_0\ \Delta_i^{i+1}\frac{1}{\alpha}}{\left(\frac{\beta}{\alpha} - S\right)_{i+1} + R_{\text{av}}}$$

$$R = S + \frac{\beta}{\alpha}\frac{k_g}{k_o}\frac{\mu_o}{\mu_g} \qquad (13\text{-}7)$$

$$\sigma_l = \sigma_w + (1 - \sigma_w)\left[\frac{(1 - n)\beta}{\beta_c(1 - n_c)} - \sigma_{gc}\right]$$

The driving indices on a finite difference basis are written as follows:

$$\text{DDI} = \frac{(1 - n_i)\ \Delta_i^{i+1}\left(\frac{\beta}{\alpha} - S\right) - \beta_0\ \Delta_i^{i+1}\frac{1}{\alpha}}{\Delta_i^{i+1} n\left[\left(\frac{\beta}{\alpha} - S\right)_{i+1} + R_{\text{av}}\right]}$$

$$\text{SDI} = \frac{-m\beta_0\ \Delta_i^{i+1}\left(\frac{1}{\alpha}\right)}{\Delta_i^{i+1} n\left[\left(\frac{\beta}{\alpha} - S\right)_{i+1} + R_{\text{av}}\right]} \qquad (13\text{-}8)$$

Driving indices on a finite difference basis gauge the production behavior within a particular interval of pressure decline, whereas on a finite basis they pertain to the integrated operation since the beginning of production. Again the sum of the indices must be equal to unity.

The following problem illustrates the computation technique.

Hypothetical Problem on Gas-cap Expansion Drive without the Counter-flow of Gas and Oil. An oil field, the structure contour map of which is given in Fig. 13-1, contains saturated oil when discovered at an original pressure of 1,500 psia. The physical properties of the oil and of the reservoir rock are the same as those of the depletion-drive problem of Chap. 10. The field is assumed to have no water encroachment and to produce no water. The pre-existing gas cap has been determined, by core and well-log analysis, to extend from the 40-ft contour to the crest of the structure. The field production rate at which it is desired to make performance predictions is 120,000 bbl of stock-tank oil per month corresponding to an allowable rate of 100 bbl of stock-tank oil per day per well.

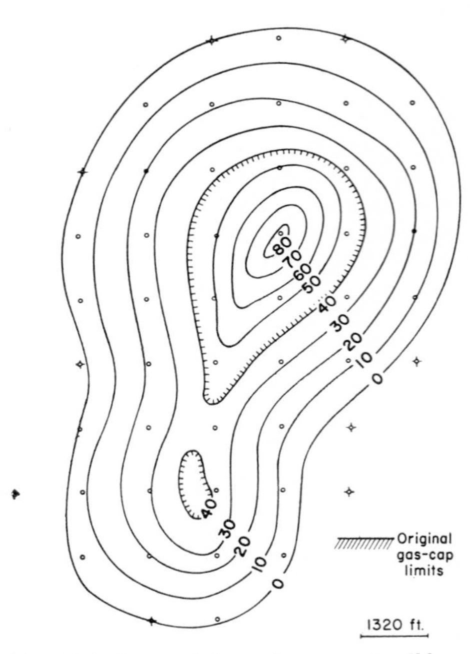

FIG. 13-1. Reservoir isopach map and well locations, showing initial gas-cap extent.

The 40 producing wells (locations of which are shown in Fig. 13-1) are completed at the base of the structure in just enough pay interval to permit the allowable production. Reduction in well productivity will occur because of pressure decline and because of possible cement squeezing of the upper perforations as the gas cap reaches them. No difficulties with the gas coning are anticipated and the base of the expanding gas cap is assumed uniformly flat. Reservoir volume and structure cross-sectional area are represented in Fig. 13-2. Calculate:

1. The original oil in place.
2. The volumetric inventory of the reservoir as well as the pressure and gas-oil-ratio performance vs. cumulative production; in effect, this is a solution of the material-balance equation.
3. The displacement efficiency of the expanding gas cap, taking into account the development of a dispersed gas phase and the gas cap's expansion into a partially gas-saturated oil zone. Determine the position of the gas-oil contact at various pressures and represent schematically the fluid distribution in the reservoir. The k_g/k_o curve used in the depletion-drive problem is assumed to hold. The rate of advance of the gas-oil contact is not constant since the cross section of the structure constantly increases. The displacement efficiency of the gas-cap expansion drive is accordingly variable but the variations are of such small magnitude as to be considered negligible.
4. Draw schematically the fluid-saturation distribution in a unit reservoir volume at various pressures, together with the position of the gas-

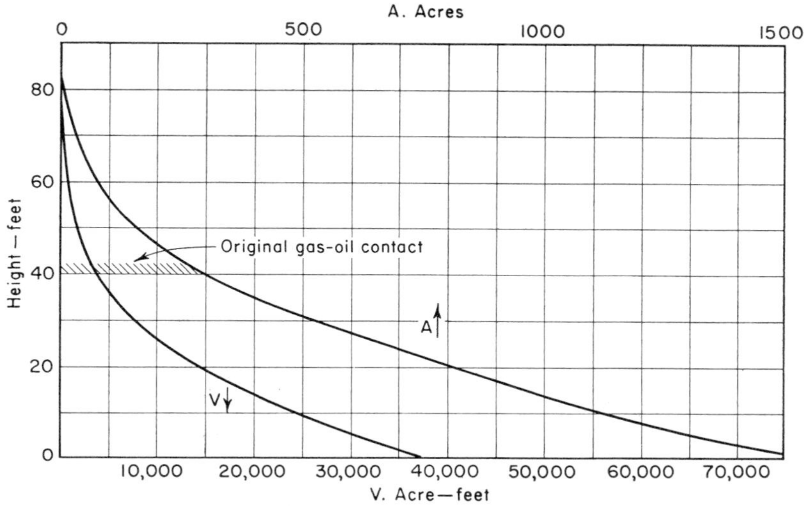

FIG. 13-2. Structure volume and cross-sectional area vs. height, showing initial gas-cap size.

oil contact. The recoveries calculated in steps 2 and 3 must check satisfactorily with the schematic representation.

Gas-cap volume = 3,865.6 acre-ft

$$m = \frac{3.865.6}{33,606.4} = 0.115$$

$m + 1 = 1.115$ $\qquad \phi = 0.24$

$(m + 1)\beta_0 = 1.384$ $\qquad \sigma_w = 0.2$

Oil-zone volume = 33,606.6 acre-ft

$$\text{Oil in place} = 7,758 \times 33,606.6 \times \frac{0.80 \times 0.24}{1.241} = 40,300,000 \text{ bbl STO}$$

The performance calculations of the gas-cap expansion drive are made in Table 13-1. Columns (1) to (11) inclusive are a solution of the differential material-balance calculation wherein it is assumed that at each field pressure the prevailing gas saturation in the oil column and the corresponding gas-oil ratio are those of the depletion-drive problem. The calculations of Δn are therefore straightforward without trial and error.

The displacement efficiency of the expanding gas cap is calculated by means of an f_g diagram (Fig. 13-3) which is drawn for the conditions prevailing at 1,000 psia from the data of Table 13-2. For these calculations it is necessary to know the rate of advance q_t of the gas cap, which is determined by making an inventory of the reservoir fluids at all pressure steps. To this end the expansion of the gas cap at each pressure decrement is calculated, and when the displacement at a previous step is known, the

Table 13-1. Segregation Drive (without Counterflow)

Naturally expanding gas cap ($I = 0$)

P, psia (1)	Δn from (11) (2)	$n = \Sigma \Delta n$ (3)	$1 - n$ (4)	$\Delta\left(\frac{\beta}{\alpha} - S\right)$ (5)	$(4)_i \times (5)$ (6)	$\Delta\left(\frac{1}{\alpha}\right)$ (7)	$(m + 1)\beta_0(7)$ (8)	(6) − (8) (9)	$\left(\frac{\beta}{\alpha} - S\right) +$ $R_{av}(1 - I)$ from DD (10)	$\Delta n = \frac{(9)}{(10)}$ (11)	$-\beta_0 \Delta \frac{1}{\alpha}$ (12)	(6) + (12) (13)
1,500	0	0	1.0	...	...	...	...	...	...	...	...	...
1,400	0.0283	0.0283	0.9717	−11.2	−11.20	−11.25	−15.57	4.37	154.3	0.0283	13.96	2.76
1,300	0.0367	0.0650	0.9350	−10.4	−10.11	−11.00	−15.22	5.11	139.4	0.0367	13.65	3.54
1,200	0.0455	0.1105	0.8895	−10.0	−9.35	−10.70	−14.81	5.46	120.1	0.0455	13.28	3.93
1,100	0.0502	0.1607	0.8393	−9.0	−8.01	−10.35	−14.32	6.31	125.7	0.0502	12.84	4.83
1,000	0.0404	0.2011	0.7989	−8.7	−7.30	−10.00	−13.84	6.54	161.9	0.0404	12.41	5.11
900	0.0306	0.2317	0.7683	−7.7	−6.15	−9.75	−13.49	7.34	239.4	0.0306	12.10	5.95
800	0.0233	0.2550	0.7450	−6.1	−4.69	−9.40	−13.01	8.32	357.0	0.0233	11.67	6.98
700	0.0162	0.2712	0.7288	−6.5	−4.84	−9.10	−12.59	7.75	479.6	0.0162	11.29	6.45
600	0.0131	0.2843	0.7157	−5.7	−4.15	−8.75	−12.11	7.95	606.4	0.0131	10.86	6.71
500	0.0113	0.2956	0.7044	−4.8	−3.44	−8.60	−11.90	8.46	746.4	0.0113	10.67	7.23
400	0.0095	0.3051	0.6949	−4.0	−2.82	−8.05	−11.14	8.33	875.6	0.0095	9.99	7.17
300	0.0092	0.3143	0.6857	−2.9	−2.02	−7.70	−10.66	8.65	940.4	0.0092	9.56	7.54
260		0.3180										
200	0.0092	0.3241	0.6759	−1.6	−0.503	−7.30	−10.10	9.597	970.3	0.0098	9.06	8.56

TABLE 13-1. SEGREGATION DRIVE (WITHOUT COUNTERFLOW) (*Continued*)

$\Delta_i^{i+1}n \left[\left(\frac{\beta}{\alpha} - S\right) + R_{av}\right]$ (14)	DDI = $\frac{(13)}{(14)}$ (15)	$m(12)$ (16)	$\Delta n\, R_{av} I$ (17)	(16) + (17) (18)	SDI = $\frac{(18)}{(14)}$ (19)	(15) + (19) = 1 (20)	$\Delta\, \alpha$ (21)	$mN \frac{\beta_0}{\alpha_0}$ (21) ($\times 10^{-4}$ bbl) (22)	σ_g (23)	σ_g' (24)	$\Delta_i^{i+1}n$ $NR_{av}I$, bbl (25)	$\sum_0^{i+1}$ (25), bbl (26)
...	...	...	...	...	...	...	...	...	0	0.80	...	...
4.37	0.632	1.605	...	1.605	0.368	1.000	0.0007	54.3	0.014	0.72	...	...
5.11	0.692	1.570	...	1.570	0.308	1.000	0.00079	61.3	0.057	0.72	...	...
5.47	0.720	1.527	...	1.527	0.280	1.000	0.00091	70.6	0.079	0.72	...	...
6.32	0.765	1.475	...	1.475	0.234	0.999	0.00108	83.8	0.115	0.72	...	...
6.54	0.782	1.428	...	1.428	0.218	1.000	0.00131	101.7	0.145	0.72	...	...
7.22	0.825	1.391	...	1.391	0.193	1.018	0.00168	130.4	0.169	0.72	...	...
8.32	0.839	1.341	...	1.341	0.149	0.988	0.00207	160.7	0.190	0.72	...	...
7.78	0.829	1.298	...	1.298	0.167	0.996	0.0027	209.6	0.205	0.72	...	...
7.95	0.845	1.250	...	1.250	0.157	1.002	0.00365	283.3	0.219	0.72	...	...
8.44	0.857	1.225	...	1.225	0.145	1.002	0.0053	411.4	0.232	0.72	...	...
8.32	0.861	1.114	...	1.114	0.137	0.998	0.0079	613.2	0.246	0.72	...	...
8.65	0.871	1.100	...	1.100	0.127	0.998	0.0134	1040.0	0.256	0.72	...	...
9.51	0.900	1.040	...	1.040	0.109	1.009	0.0271	2110.0	0.271	0.72	...	...

TABLE 13-1. SEGREGATION DRIVE (WITHOUT COUNTERFLOW) (*Continued*)

$(25)_{i+1}\alpha_{i+1}$, bbl (27)	$(26)_i\,\Delta_i^{i+1}\alpha$, bbl (28)	(22) + (27) + (28) ($\times 10^{-4}$ bbl) (29)	$\frac{(29)}{7{,}758\phi\sigma_g'}$, acre-ft (30)	h, ft (31)	x_o (32)	$Q_o = x_o \cdot q_o$, bbl/day (33)	A, acres (34)	$\Delta\theta = \frac{N\,\Delta n}{Q_o}$, days (35)	$q_t = \frac{(29)}{A\,\Delta\theta}$, bbl/day/acre (36)	$\sum_0^{ab}(25) = \text{ultimately } \frac{N\beta_0}{\alpha_{ab}}$ $\left[\frac{\sigma_g'}{1-\sigma_w}\right.$ (37)	$\left. - m\left(\frac{\alpha_{ab}}{\alpha_0} - 1\right)\right]$ (38)
...	...	...	...	40	40	4,000	284.8				
...	...	54.3	405	38.5	40	4,000	318	285	5.99		
...	...	61.3	457	37.0	40	4,000	363	370	4.56		
...	...	70.6	526	35.6	40	4,000	394	458	3.91		
...	...	83.8	625	33.5	40	4,000	425	506	3.90		
...	...	101.7	958	32.8	40	4,000	465	407	5.37		
...	...	130.4	972	30.6	40	4,000	528	308	8.01		
...	...	160.7	1,198	28.5	40	4,000	580	235	11.8		
...	...	209.6	1,563	26.0	40	4,000	650	163	19.8		
...	...	283.3	2,113	23.0	40	4,000	632	132	34.0		
...	...	411.4	3,068	18.8	40	4,000	857	114	42.1		0.8
...	...	613.2	4,573	13.7	40	4,000	1,005	95.7	63.8		0.8
...	...	1,040.0	7,756	7.0	40	4,000	1,240	92.7	90.5	0.644	0.8
...	...	2,110.0	15,750	...	40	4,000	...	...	...	1.065	0.8

TABLE 13-2. GAS-DRIVE DISPLACEMENT-EFFICIENCY CALCULATIONS

Example calculation for conditions of Case 1 at 1,000 psia.

$\mu_g = 0.0144 \qquad \vartheta_g = 0.058 \times 10^{-3} \times P = 0.058$

$\mu_o = 1.33$ cps $\qquad \Delta\vartheta = -0.85 + 0.058 = -0.792;\ \beta = 1.180$

$\mu_g/\mu_o = 0.01083 \qquad \sin\alpha = -1.0$

$K = 0.4$ darcy

Fractional-flow formula in practical units, neglecting capillary-pressure gradient, is

$$f_g = \frac{1 - 21{,}238 \dfrac{K_o}{q_t\mu_o} \cdot \Delta\vartheta \sin\alpha}{1 + \dfrac{k_o}{k_g}\dfrac{\mu_g}{\mu_o}}$$

where $q_t = 10$ bbl per day per acre of gas-cap expansion and $\Delta\vartheta$ is now differential specific gravity.

σ_g (1)	$\frac{k_g}{k_o}$ (2)	$\frac{k_o}{k_g}\frac{\mu_g}{\mu_o}$ (3)	$1 + \frac{k_o}{k_g}\frac{\mu_g}{\mu_o}$ (4)	$\frac{1}{(4)}$ (5)	k_o (6)	$21{,}238 \frac{K_o\,\Delta\vartheta}{q_t\,\mu_o}$ (7)	$f_g = [1 - (7)]\cdot(5)$ (8)
45	14.0	0.000775	1.000775	0.9995	0.100	127.000	Negative
50	...	...	1.00	1.00	0.060	76.000	Negative
55	...	...	1.00	1.00	0.035	4.400	Negative
60	...	...	1.00	1.00	0.020	2.540	Negative
65	...	...	1.00	1.00	0.005	0.634	0.366
70	...	...	1.00	1.00	0.001	0.125	0.875
75	...	...	1.00	1.00	0.000	0.000	1.000
80	...	...	1.00	1.00	0.000	0.000	1.000

reservoir volume swept by the expanding gas cap is determined. When this volume is known, the level of the gas-oil contact is determined from Fig. 13-2 and is recorded in the tabulation. For certain structural reservoir considerations, this level will determine the number of producing oil wells (x_o) and the field-wide rate of production of barrels of stock-tank oil per day (Q_o). Knowing the area of the oil-gas contact A in acres, the value of q_t in barrels per acre per day at reservoir conditions is calculated. An f_g diagram should

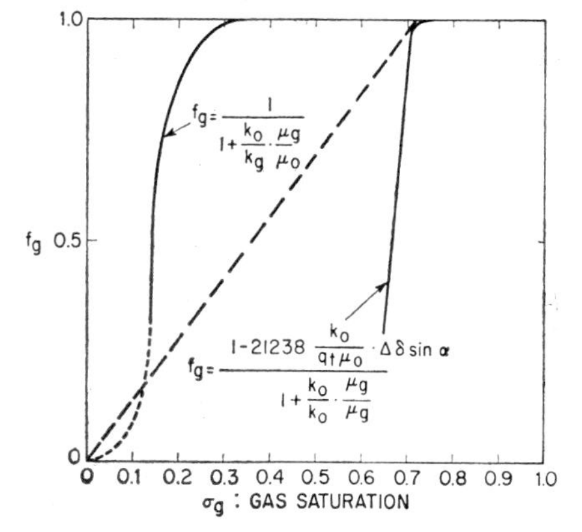

FIG. 13-3. Displacement-efficiency calculation by frontal gas drive.

be made at every pressure step, but generally there will be little variation in the displacement efficiency once the withdrawal conditions are set. The factor which most affects the displacement efficiency by frontal gas drive is the formation dip and direction of displacement. In the problem at hand, a gas saturation of 72 per cent in the expanded section of the gas cap prevails throughout the operation.

The fluid-saturation distribution within the reservoir at various stages of production is represented in Fig. 13-4 on a unit reservoir volume basis,

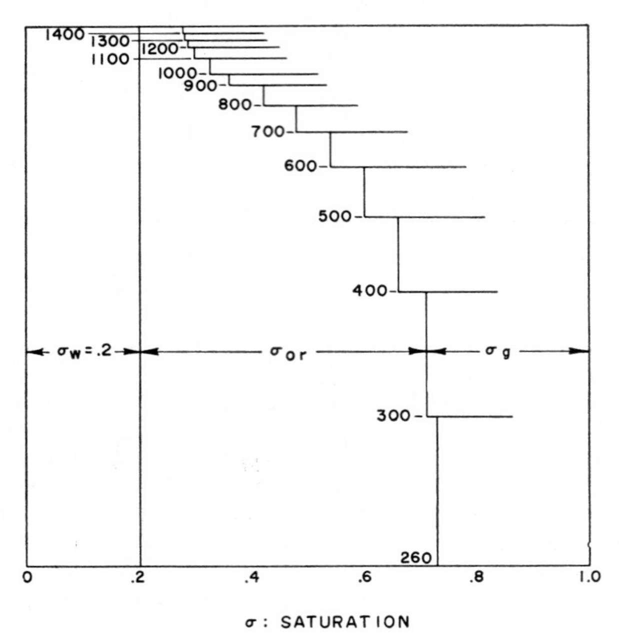

Fig. 13-4. Fluid-saturation distribution in unit reservoir rock volume for naturally expanding gas cap. (Semiquantitative only.)

whereas the performance curve of this operation is compared to straight depletion in Fig. 13-5.

Gas Vaporization from Residual-oil Saturation. A special case may be considered when the residual-oil saturation in the expanded zone of the gas cap is relatively high as is often the case when producing from a low-relief structure or from a stratigraphic trap. In such a case the displacement efficiency of the expanding gas cap is low.

As the field pressure declines, gas is liberated from solution in the residual-oil saturation and it contributes to a faster expansion of the gas cap. Hence it is actually a detrimental factor to oil recovery, because the faster a frontal gas drive, the less the displacement efficiency.

The volumetric gas-cap increase could be evaluated stepwise from the

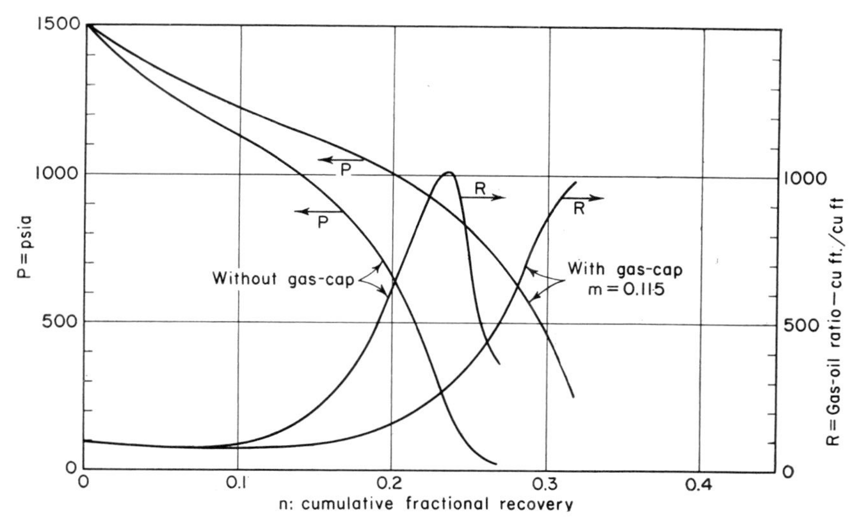

FIG. 13-5. Performance of a naturally expanding gas-cap drive.

volumes of the expanded section of the gas cap, the pressure decrement, and the solubility characteristics of gas in oil.

Segregation Drive with Free-gas Production from a Preexisting and Naturally Expanding Gas Cap. Production of free gas from the gas cap is often required because of the competitive situation existing between the owners of the oil and gas rights in a reservoir, especially when the reservoir has a large original gas cap and more particularly in a monoclinal reservoir structure of low relief. Under such conditions the wells completed in the gas cap are often assigned fixed volumetric rates of gas production per day, whereas the oil wells completed in the oil zone are assigned fixed rates of stock-tank oil production per day.

On a monthly basis let

q_o = allowable production of stock-tank oil per well in barrels
q_g = allowable production of gas per well in barrels and measured at standard conditions

It is convenient to make the performance prediction on a time basis by calculating increments of oil and gas production. The number of producing oil and gas wells may vary at all times because of the variation in height of the gas-oil contact.

At any one time let

x_o = number of oil wells
x_g = number of gas wells

It may readily be shown that the time increment required for field pressure to drop from P_i to P_{i+1} is given by

$$\Delta_i^{i+1}\theta = \frac{(1 - n_i)\,\Delta_i^{i+1}\left(\frac{\beta}{\alpha} - S\right) - (m + 1)\beta_0\,\Delta_i^{i+1}\frac{1}{\alpha}}{\frac{1}{N}\left\{x_o q_o\left[\left(\frac{\beta}{\alpha} - S\right)_{i+1} + R_{av}\right] + x_g q_g\right\}} \tag{13-9}$$

It is postulated again that the prevailing field pressure determines the flowing gas-oil ratio R of the oil wells.

The performance of the field can readily be computed by means of the above equation and the position of the oil-gas contact may be determined by computing the expansion of the gas cap. Computations are greatly simplified by neglecting the release of solution gas in the residual-oil saturation. In fact this assumption is always verified if gas withdrawals from the gas cap are so selected as to prevent its expansion as field pressure declines.

It can readily be computed that the required increments of gas production necessary to keep the gas cap from expanding are given by

$$\Delta\theta x_g q_g = mN\beta_0\frac{\Delta_i^{i+1}\alpha}{\alpha_0\alpha_{av}} \tag{13-10}$$

The performance equation becomes

$$\Delta_i^{i+1}\theta = \frac{(1 - n_i)\,\Delta_i^{i+1}\left(\frac{\beta}{\alpha} - S\right) - (m + 1)\beta_0\,\Delta_i^{i+1}\frac{1}{\alpha}}{\frac{1}{N}\left\{x_o q_o\left[\left(\frac{\beta}{\alpha} - S\right)_{i+1} + R_{av}\right] + mN\beta_0\frac{\Delta_i^{i+1}\alpha}{\alpha_0\alpha_{av}}\right\}} \tag{13-11}$$

when the gas withdrawal from the gas cap is so adjusted as to prevent its expansion.

Case 2. Segregation Drive under an Expanding Gas Cap as a Result of Gas Injection (without Gas Vaporization from Residual-oil Saturation). It is assumed that the reservoir conditions postulated for Case 1 also prevail here. An original gas cap (m) may exist or it may be induced by gas injection through structurally high wells such that the injected gas will remain segregated over the oil zone and will not diffuse through it as is the case in a dispersed-gas-drive operation.

Oil is withdrawn selectively from the oil column from structurally low levels and the gas-oil contact is presumed to move downward in such a manner as to keep a horizontal interface throughout the life of the operation. The prevailing fluid-saturation distribution in this operation is shown in Fig. 13-6.

Should field pressure decline and a free-gas phase develop within the oil zone in such a measure as to reach the critical gas saturation, gas-cap gas would start to diffuse through the oil zone. As in the preceding case, two stages of calculation are possible. In a well-planned gas-cap injection operation, the diffusion stage should not be permitted because of its low displacement efficiency. Such a stage will therefore no longer be considered.

For the purpose of simplification, it is stated that a constant fraction I of the gas produced with the oil is injected into the expanding gas cap. It is obvious that no gas should be produced from the gas cap for a successful gas-cap injection operation.

The performance equations of this process may be written immediately both in the finite and in the differential forms.

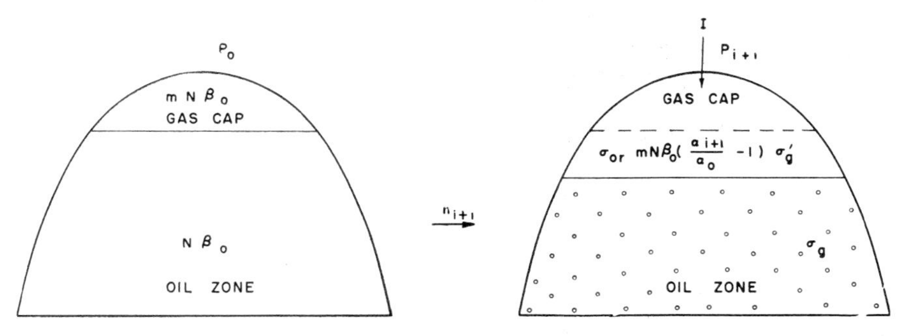

FIG. 13-6. Schematic representation of prevailing fluid distribution in a reservoir under segregation drive without counterflow of oil and gas.

Finite Form of the Performance Equations. In the simple case where no water drive exists and no gas-oil counterflow takes place within the oil column, the material-balance equation may be written:

$$\frac{n_{i+1}\left(\frac{\beta}{\alpha} - S\right)_{i+1} + \sum_{0}^{i+1} \Delta n\, R_{\text{av}}(1 - I)}{m\beta_0\left(\frac{1}{\alpha_0} - \frac{1}{\alpha_{i+1}}\right) + \left(\frac{\beta}{\alpha} - S\right)_{i+1} - \left(\frac{\beta_0}{\alpha_{i+1}} - S_0\right)} = 1 \tag{13-12}$$

m is the ratio of the volume originally occupied by the gas cap to that originally occupied by the oil zone.

Let

$$n_{i+1} = n_i + \Delta_i^{i+1} n$$

$$D_{i+1} = \left(\frac{\beta}{\alpha} - S\right)_{i+1} - \left(\frac{\beta_0}{\alpha_{i+1}} - S_0\right)$$

$$G_{i+1} = \sum_{0}^{i+1} \Delta n\, R_{\text{av}} = G_i + \Delta_i^{i+1} n\, R_{\text{av}}$$

then the material-balance equation may be rewritten:

$$\frac{n_i\left(\frac{\beta}{\alpha} - S\right)_{i+1} + \Delta_i^{i+1}n\left(\frac{\beta}{\alpha} - S\right)_{i+1} + G_{i+1}(1 - I) + \Delta_i^{i+1}n\,R_{av}}{m\beta_0\left(\frac{1}{\alpha_0} - \frac{1}{\alpha_{i+1}}\right) + D_{i+1}} = 1 \tag{13-13}$$

Now let $\Delta_i^{i+1}n = \frac{Q_o}{N}\Delta_i^{i+1}\theta$ and substitute.

Solving for $\Delta_i^{i+1}\theta$,

$$\Delta_i^{i+1}\theta = \frac{D_{i+1} + m\beta_0\left(\frac{1}{\alpha_0} - \frac{1}{\alpha_{i+1}}\right) - n_i\left(\frac{\beta}{\alpha} - S\right)_{i+1} - G_i(1 - I)}{\frac{Q_o}{N}\left[\left(\frac{\beta}{\alpha} - S\right)_{i+1} + R_{av}(1 - I)\right]} \tag{13-14}$$

Discussing Eq. (13-14), it is observed that pressure in the oil zone is maintained when the denominator is zero or when

$$I = 1 + \frac{(\beta/\alpha - S)}{R} \tag{13-15}$$

Since the gas-oil ratio R can be obtained as a function of pressure from a previous depletion-drive calculation and $(\beta/\alpha - S)_{i+1}$ is also a function of pressure, it is possible to determine the field pressure to be maintained at which the injection requirements will be a minimum.

From Eq. (13-15) a curve of gas injection requirement vs. field pressure may be drawn, and if a specific value of I is assigned, it is possible to foresee whether the field pressure will be maintained, increased, or decreased.

A tabulation may be devised for the purpose of making the above performance computations. In addition it is necessary to verify if they have been made correctly at each step; this is provided by the driving indices:

$$\text{DDI} = \frac{N\left[\left(\frac{\beta}{\alpha} - S\right) - \left(\frac{\beta_0}{\alpha} - S_0\right)\right] - GI}{n\left(\frac{\beta}{\alpha} - S\right) + G}$$

$$\text{SDI} = \frac{mN\beta_0\left(\frac{1}{\alpha_0} - \frac{1}{\alpha}\right) + GI}{n\left(\frac{\beta}{\alpha} - S\right) + G} \tag{13-16}$$

On a finite basis the driving indices pertain to the whole of the production interval. Their sum must be equal to unity.

Finite Difference Form of the Performance Equations. The increment of production (Δn) obtained through gas-cap injection in a preexisting gas cap (m) is immediately written by analogy:

$$\Delta_i^{i+1} n = \frac{(1 - n_i)\, \Delta_i^{i+1} \left(\frac{\beta}{\alpha} - S\right) - (1 + m)\beta_0\, \Delta_i^{i+1} \frac{1}{\alpha}}{\left(\frac{\beta}{\alpha} - S\right)_{i+1} + (1 - I)R_{\text{av}}} \tag{13-17}$$

The other performance equations are unchanged, namely, for the gas-oil-ratio and fluid-saturation equations.

The driving indices on a differential basis are written as follows:

$$\text{DDI} = \frac{(1 - n_i)\, \Delta_i^{i+1} \left(\frac{\beta}{\alpha} - S\right) - \beta_0\, \Delta_i^{i+1} \frac{1}{\alpha}}{\Delta_i^{i+1} n \left[\left(\frac{\beta}{\alpha} - S\right) + R_{\text{av}}\right]}$$

$$\text{SDI} = \frac{-m\beta_0\, \Delta_i^{i+1} \frac{1}{\alpha} + \Delta_i^{i+1} n\, R_{\text{av}} \cdot I}{\Delta_i^{i+1} n \left[\left(\frac{\beta}{\alpha} - S\right) + R_{\text{av}}\right]} \tag{13-18}$$

On a differential basis the driving indices pertain to a particular interval of pressure decline. Their sum must be equal to unity.

It has been postulated in both previous derivations that the amount of gas released from solution from the residual-oil saturation in the expanded section of the gas cap contributes nothing to its expansion. This is obviously not so when there is a large residual-oil saturation and a large pressure decline.

It is observed that a particular field pressure will be maintained when the denominator of Δn is zero. This leads again to Eq. (13-15).

A special case of gas-cap injection is that of *full pressure maintenance,* namely, when field pressure is maintained by gas-cap injection at the original bubble-point pressure P_0 of the reservoir oil. Under these conditions, the injection requirements I are such that $R = S_0$ and $S = S_0$. Also $\beta = \beta_0$, $\alpha = \alpha_0$.

Therefore

$$I = \frac{\beta_0}{\alpha_0 S_0} \tag{13-19}$$

The termination of the gas-cap injection problem is arrived at by verification of the displacement efficiency by the frontal-drive theory (Buckley-Leverett theory with simplifying modifications) of the expanding gas cap in conjunction with the material-balance tabulation and the structural volume of the reservoir. A satisfactory termination and solution to the problem is obtained only when the recoveries calculated by material-balance calculation and by frontal drive are identical at the time the expanding gas cap has completely swept the reservoir.

In order to arrive at the expected recovery as a function of the assigned production rate, it is necessary to make a *volumetric fluid inventory* at all times which is compatible with the material-balance equation and the frontal-drive displacement efficiency. The procedure for achieving this is as follows:

1. Plot a graph of structural acre-feet (V) and structure cross section in acres (A) vs. heights (h) in feet below the original gas-oil contact (Fig. 13-2).
2. Assume a certain reasonable displacement efficiency for the gas-cap drive (or a certain reasonable value) for the residual-oil saturation behind the front. A guide to this value is obtained by the simplified frontal-drive theory.
3. From the cumulative net gas injection and gas-cap expansion, determine the level of the gas-oil contact below the original level from the graph of V vs. height. Also read A and compute the value of q_t in barrels per day per acre to be used in the f_g calculation.
4. Step 3 is repeated for each pressure decrement until the gas-oil contact has reached the base of the structure and the oil field is abandoned. It will be noticed that the value of q_t is variable throughout the life of the field and therefore the displacement efficiency is also variable with time.

The complete solution of the problem includes:

1. Material-balance tabulation
2. Plot of pressure decline, gas-oil ratio, and production rate vs. time
3. f_g diagram and displacement-efficiency calculation at various pressures
4. Diagrams representing fluid inventory at various pressures in a unit reservoir volume

Hypothetical Problem on Induced Gas-cap Expansion Drive without Counterflow of Oil and Gas. The reservoir structure of Fig. 13-1 is again considered and the same reservoir rock and fluid properties prevail. The wells located structurally high in the reservoir are presumed recompleted so as to permit gas injection into the preexisting gas cap.

Various cases were considered wherein the fraction I of the produced gas injected is, respectively, 0.25, 0.5, 0.75, and 1.92. The last figure is the gas-injection requirement to maintain the field pressure at the original bubble-point pressure of 1,500 psia as calculated from Eq. (13-19).

An example of a performance calculation is given in Table 13-3. Figures 13-7*a*, 13-7*b*, and 13-7*c* represent the reservoir behavior and inventory on a unit reservoir volume basis. The residual oil which is represented in these diagrams is that which occurs at the prevailing reservoir conditions at a particular pressure. It is more specifically a function of the residual-oil

TABLE 13-3. SEGREGATION DRIVE (WITHOUT COUNTERFLOW)

($I = 0.50$)

P, psia (1)	Δn from (11) (2)	$n = \Sigma \Delta n$ (3)	$1 - n$ (4)	$\Delta\left(\frac{\beta}{\alpha} - S\right)$ (5)	$(4)_i \times (5)$ (6)	$\Delta\left(\frac{1}{\alpha}\right)$ (7)	$(m + 1)\beta_o(7)$ (8)	(6) − (8) (9)	$\left(\frac{\beta}{\alpha} - S\right) + R_{av}(1 - I)$ from DD (10)	$\Delta n = \frac{(9)}{(10)}$ (11)	$-\beta_0 \Delta \frac{1}{\alpha}$ (12)	(6) + (12) (13)
1,500	0	0	1.0	. . .	. . .	. . .	. . .	. . .	. . .	. . .	. . .	. . .
1,400	0.03911	0.03911	0.9609	−11.2	−11.2	−11.25	−15.57	4.37	111.75	0.0391	13.96	2.76
1,300	0.05277	0.09188	0.90812	−10.4	−9.993	−11.00	−15.22	5.23	99.1	0.05277	13.65	3.66
1,200	0.06592	0.1578	0.8422	−10.0	−9.081	−10.70	−14.81	5.73	86.925	0.06592	13.28	4.20
1,100	0.08145	0.23925	0.76075	−9.0	−7.58	−10.35	−14.32	6.74	82.75	0.08145	12.84	5.26
1,000	0.07484	0.31409	0.68591	−8.7	−6.619	−10.00	−13.84	7.22	96.475	0.07484	12.41	5.79
900	0.06248	0.37657	0.62343	−7.7	−5.282	−9.75	−13.49	8.21	131.4	0.06248	12.10	6.82
800	0.04922	0.42579	0.57421	−6.1	−3.803	−9.40	−13.01	9.21	187.125	0.04922	11.67	7.87
700	0.03613	0.46192	0.53808	−6.5	−3.732	−9.10	−12.59	8.86	245.2	0.03613	11.29	7.56
648		0.4790										
600	0.02957	0.49149	0.50851	−5.7	−3.067	−8.75	−12.11	9.04	305.72	0.02957	10.86	7.79

TABLE 13-3. SEGREGATION DRIVE (WITHOUT COUNTERFLOW) (*Continued*)

$\Delta_i^{i+1}n \left[\left(\frac{\beta}{\alpha} - S\right) + R_{av}\right]$ (14)	DDI $= \frac{(13)}{(14)}$ (15)	$m(12)$ (16)	$\Delta n\, R_{av} I$ (17)	(16) + (17) (18)	SDI = $\frac{(18)}{(14)}$ (19)	(15) + (19) = 1 (20)	$\Delta\alpha$ (21)	$mN \frac{\beta_0}{\alpha_0}$ (21) ($\times 10^{-4}$ bbl) (22)	σ_g (23)	σ_g' (24)	$\Delta_i^{i+1}n\, NR_{av}I$ ($\times 10^{-6}$ bbl) (25)	$\sum_0^i$ (25), bbl (26)
...	...	...	...	...	...	...	...	...	...	0.80	...	...
6.035	0.457	1.605	1.664	3.269	0.5417	0.9987	0.0007	54.3	0.014	0.72	67.06	0
7.356	0.497	1.570	2.127	3.697	0.5026	0.9996	0.00079	61.3	0.057	0.72	85.70	67.06
8.24	0.5097	1.527	2.514	4.041	0.4903	1.000	0.00091	70.6	0.079	0.72	101.26	152.76
10.24	0.5137	1.477	3.498	4.975	0.4858	0.9995	0.00108	83.8	0.115	0.72	140.96	254.02
12.11	0.4781	1.427	4.893	6.32	0.5219	1.000	0.00131	101.7	0.145	0.72	197.17	394.98
15.01	0.4544	1.392	6.748	8.14	0.5423	0.9967	0.00168	130.4	0.169	0.72	271.94	592.15
17.57	0.4479	1.342	8.359	9.701	0.5521	1.000	0.00207	160.7	0.190	0.72	336.86	864.1
17.33	0.4632	1.298	8.469	9.767	0.5636	0.9998	0.0027	209.6	0.205	0.72	341.29	1,200.95
17.93	0.4345	1.249	8.889	10.138	0.5654	0.9999	0.00365	283.3	0.219	0.72	358.22	1,542.24

Table 13-3. Segregation Drive (without Counterflow) (*Continued*)

$(25)_{i+1}\alpha_{i+1}$ ($\times 10^{-4}$ bbl) (27)	$(26)_{i+1}\Delta_i^{i+1}\alpha$ ($\times 10^{-4}$ bbl) (28)	(22) + (27) + (28) ($\times 10^{-4}$ bbl) (29)	$\frac{(29)}{7{,}758\phi\sigma_g'}$, acre-ft (30)	h, ft (31)	x_o (32)	$Q_o = x_0 \cdot q_o$ (33)	A, acres (34)	$\Delta\theta = \frac{N\,\Delta n}{Q_o}$, days (35)	$q_t = \frac{(29)}{A\,\Delta\theta}$, bbl/day/acre (36)	$\sum_0^{ab}(25)$ = ultimately $\frac{N\beta_0}{\alpha_{ab}}\left[\frac{\sigma_g'}{1-\sigma_w} - m\left(\frac{\alpha_{ab}}{\alpha_0} - 1\right)\right]$, bbl (37)
. . .	. . .	. . .	. . .	40	40	4,000	284.8			
54.39	0	108.64	810.4	37	40	4,000	360	394	7.66	
76.27	5.30	142.87	1,065.7	34.4	40	4,000	430	531	6.25	
99.34	13.90	183.84	1,371.3	31.2	40	4,000	510	664	5.52	
153.51	27.43	264.74	1,974.8	27.5	40	4,000	610	820	5.29	
240.55	51.74	393.99	2,938.9	23	40	4,000	730	754	7.16	
377.45	99.48	607.33	4,530.3	18	40	4,000	875	629.5	11.03	
537.29	178.87	876.86	6,540.8	11.3	40	4,000	1,085	495.9	16.30	
636.51	324.27	1,170.38	8,730.2	4.6	40	4,000	1,350	364.0	23.82	
798.83	562.90	1,645.03	12,270.8	. . .	40	4,000				

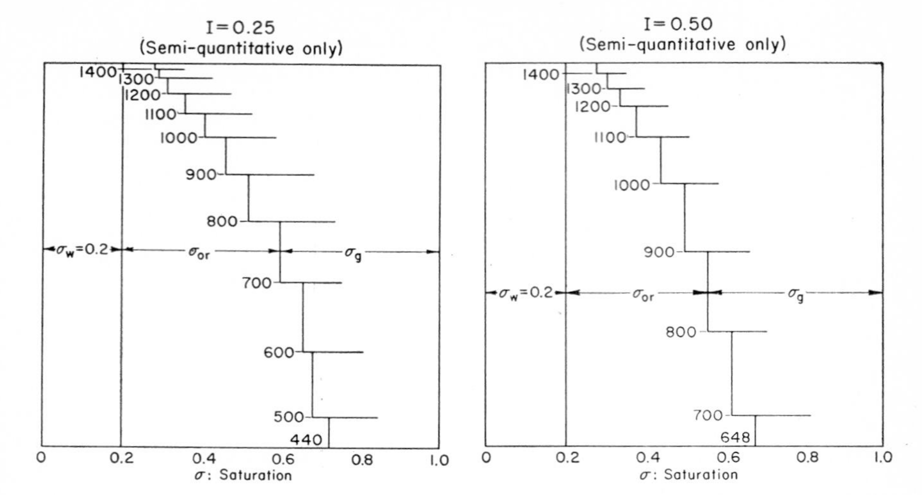

FIG. 13-7*a*. Fluid-saturation distribution in unit reservoir rock volume for gas-cap injection.

FIG. 13-7*b*. Fluid-saturation distribution in unit reservoir rock volume for gas-cap injection.

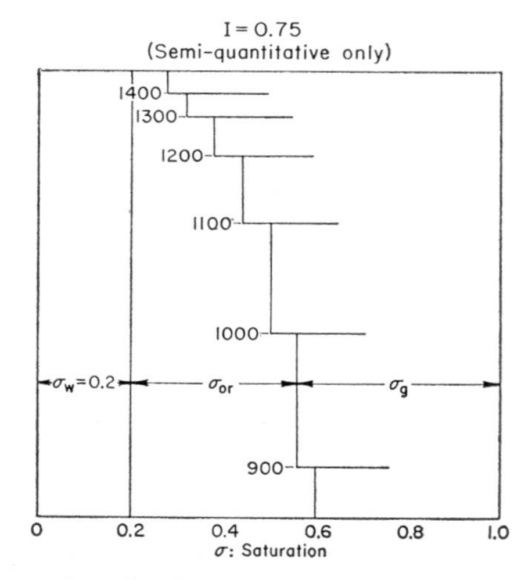

FIG. 13-7*c*. Fluid-saturation distribution in unit reservoir rock volume for gas-cap injection.

viscosity, the prevailing free-gas saturation in the oil zone, and the velocity of expansion of the gas cap. Release of gas from solution in the residual oil and the resulting shrinkage of the latter is not taken into account in the diagrams; however, this is necessary in order to verify the material balance and the performance calculations of Table 13-3. Table 13-4 gives a comparative summary of the results according to the various operational procedures.

TABLE 13-4. COMPARATIVE SUMMARY OF SEGREGATION-DRIVE RECOVERY

Injected gas, I	Ultimate oil recovery, n	Terminal pressure at abandonment, P	Maximum gas-oil ratio, R_{max}, vol/vol
0	0.318	260	980
0.25	0.382	440	930
0.50	0.479	648	570
0.75	0.620	844	365
1.92	0.900	1,500	87.4

The comparative performance curves (pressure decline and gas-oil ratio) are given in Fig. 13-8.

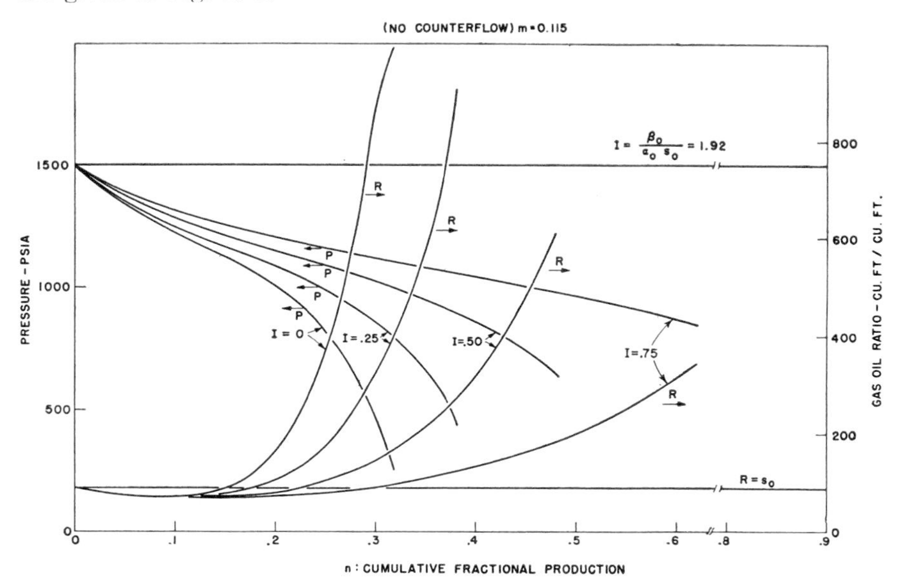

FIG. 13-8. Comparative performance of an artificially induced gas-cap expansion drive for various gas-injection ratios (without counterflow).

SEGREGATION DRIVE WITH COUNTERFLOW

The development and expansion of a gas cap over an oil zone may take place as a result of counterflow of oil and gas within the oil zone. The existence of such a process of *active fluid segregation* requires that certain conditions be satisfied:

1. Field-wide pressure decline must take place so that gas will come out of solution from the reservoir oil and will form bubbles of gas which may ultimately coalesce and form continuous vertical communication channels through which upward gas flow may take place under the influence of the buoyancy effect of gravity owing to the difference in density between oil and gas under reservoir conditions. The physical conditions of this process are schematically represented in Fig. 13-9.

2. Upward gas flow takes place under a very low flow potential gradient. Any application of pressure into the expanding gas cap such as by gas

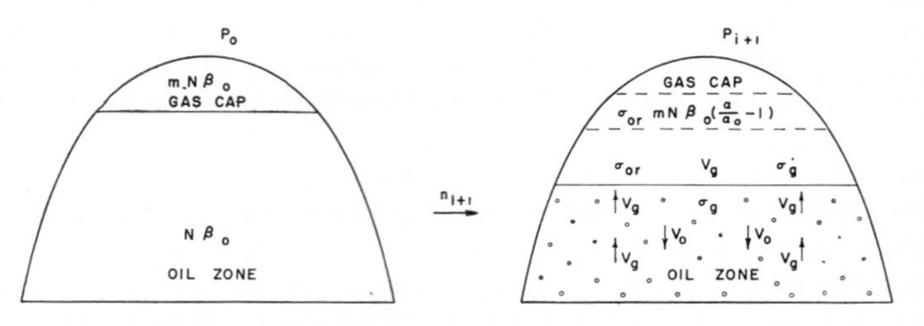

Fig. 13-9. Schematic representation of prevailing fluid distribution and movement in a reservoir under segregation drive with counterflow of oil and gas.

injection would reverse this gradient and counterflow would cease. Therefore the use or existence of counterflow in a recovery operation precludes the injection of gas into the gas cap, but the injection of gas in a dispersed manner into the oil zone below is not excluded.

3. The movement of gas to the gas cap by active segregation is controlled by the fluid which has the smallest mobility ratio, that is, K_o/μ_o or K_g/μ_g, because volumetrically there must be as much gas going up as there is oil going down at any one point within the oil column, except in the immediate vicinity of a well bore where the horizontal component of the gas-flow velocity vector is predominant. Writing the flow-velocity expressions for the two fluids in the porous medium,

$$\begin{aligned} \downarrow \; v_o \text{ cm/sec} &= \frac{1}{\phi}\frac{K_o}{\mu_o}\frac{\vartheta_o - \vartheta_g}{1{,}033}\sin\alpha \\ \uparrow \; v_g \text{ cm/sec} &= \frac{1}{\phi}\frac{K_g}{\mu_g}\frac{\vartheta_o - \vartheta_g}{1{,}033}\sin\alpha \end{aligned} \tag{13-20}$$

When the *maximum* rate of segregation is achieved, the two expressions are equal and we have immediately

$$\frac{K_o}{\mu_o} = \frac{K_g}{\mu_g} \tag{13-21}$$

If the producing reservoir rock may be assumed to be uniform and isotropic with respect to permeability and relative permeability, a simple expression for the prevailing production gas-oil ratio is obtained. Since $\frac{K_g}{K_o}\frac{\mu_o}{\mu_g} = 1$, we have

$$R = S + \frac{\beta}{\alpha} \tag{13-22}$$

This gas-oil ratio prevails when the maximum rate of segregation is achieved and as long as no free gas is produced from the gas cap. When field pressure is very low, the value of R may therefore become much smaller than the minimum values of R obtained in depletion drive. This is a method of recognizing the existence of active segregation drive from production data.

When conditions for the maximum rate of segregation are not fulfilled, the usual relationship for the producing gas-oil ratio prevails.

4. The volume of gas segregated into a gas cap may be calculated at each decrement of pressure. It is of course a function of time, and the production process by segregation is accordingly *rate-sensitive*. An approximation to the volume of gas segregated may be obtained by application of Darcy's law:

$$\Delta_i^{i+1} V_g = 21{,}238A \left(\frac{K_g}{\mu_g} \text{ or } \frac{K_o}{\mu_o}\right) \Delta\vartheta \sin\alpha\, \Delta\theta \tag{13-23}$$

where V_g = reservoir volume of gas segregated in barrels
A = area of gas-oil interface between gas cap and oil zone, acres
K_g, K_o = effective permeabilities to gas and oil, darcys
α = angle of dip in direction of active segregation
$\Delta\theta$ = time interval, days

A choice for K_g/μ_g or K_o/μ_o is provided in Eq. (13-23); whichever of the two values is the smaller should be chosen because the maximum rate of segregation does not always prevail and it is obvious that one fluid may not move up faster or slower at any one point than the other moves down. However, the prevailing value of K_g/K_o in the oil zone still determines the producing gas-oil ratio.

When the mobilities of gas and oil are equal, the *maximum rate of segregation* is achieved. Since the gas-cap displacement efficiency in a segregation drive is relatively independent of production rate, the field-wide production rate at which maximum segregation occurs may be considered as the *engineering most efficient rate* for the field when operated by this process.

5. The cumulative amount of gas V_g measured at reservoir conditions of pressure and temperature segregated into the gas cap should be verified by means of a *gas balance* which takes into account the position of the various fluids in the reservoir. The gas balance is also necessary in order to reduce the problem of gas segregation to a single degree of freedom. The derivation of the gas balance is as follows:

Total gas evolved from solution $= (N - n)(S_0 - S) + nS_0$
$= N(S_0 - S) + nS$

Total gas production $= nr_n$

Total gas segregated to gas cap $= \dfrac{1}{\alpha} V_g$

Total free gas remaining in oil zone $=$ (oil-zone volume) $\dfrac{\sigma_g}{\alpha}$

Oil-zone volume $= N\beta_0 - \left[V_g + mN\beta_0\left(\dfrac{\alpha}{\alpha_0} - 1\right)\right]\dfrac{1}{\sigma_g'}$

where σ_g' is free-gas saturation in the gas cap.

The gas balance is obtained by equating the total gas evolved from solution to the sum of the produced and free-gas volumes:

$$nr_n + \frac{1}{\alpha}\left[V_g + \frac{\sigma_g}{\sigma_g'}\left\{N\beta_0\sigma_g' - \left[V_g + mN\beta_0\left(\frac{\alpha}{\alpha_0} - 1\right)\right]\right\}\right] = N(S_0 - S) + nS \quad (13\text{-}24)$$

or

$$\frac{n}{N} r_n + \frac{1}{\alpha}\left[\frac{V_g}{N} + \frac{\sigma_g}{\sigma_g'}\left\{N\beta_0\sigma_g' - \left[\frac{V_g}{N} + m\beta_0\left(\frac{\alpha}{\alpha_0} - 1\right)\right]\right\}\right] = (S_0 - S) + \frac{n}{N} S \quad (13\text{-}25)$$

Using n as a fraction of the oil originally in place, a convenient form of the gas balance is

$$nr_n = S_0 - (1 - n)S - \frac{1}{\alpha}\left[\frac{V_g}{N} + \frac{\sigma_g}{\sigma_g'}\left\{\beta_0\sigma_g' - \left[\frac{V_g}{N} + m\beta_0\left(\frac{\alpha}{\alpha_0} - 1\right)\right]\right\}\right] \quad (13\text{-}26)$$

where r_n is always less than original solution gas.

The gas balance provides a means by which the cumulative volumetric flow of gas to the gas cap V_g may be evaluated.

Performance Equation in Finite Form. Summarizing, the equations of segregation drive with counterflow in *finite form* are as follows:

$$N = \frac{n[\beta + \alpha(r_n - S)]}{m\beta_0\left(\dfrac{\alpha}{\alpha_0} - 1\right) + \alpha(S_0 - S) - (\beta_0 - \beta)}$$

$$R = S + \frac{\beta}{\alpha}\frac{k_g}{k_o}\frac{\mu_o}{\mu_g} \quad (13\text{-}27)$$

$$nr_n = \Sigma\, \Delta n\, R_{av} = G$$

$$\sigma_l = \sigma_w + (1 - \sigma_w)\frac{(1 - n)\beta - \left[\dfrac{V_g}{N} + m\beta_0\left(\dfrac{\alpha}{\alpha_0} - 1\right)\right]\dfrac{\sigma_{or}}{\sigma_g'}}{\beta_0 - \left[\dfrac{V_g}{N} + m\beta_0\left(\dfrac{\alpha}{\alpha_0} - 1\right)\right]\dfrac{1}{\sigma_g'}}$$

The oil-zone saturation σ_l must take into account the shrinking oil zone from its original volume $N\beta_0$ by a term

$$\frac{N}{\sigma_g'}\left[\frac{V_g}{N} + m\beta_0\left(\frac{\alpha}{\alpha_0} - 1\right)\right]$$

where σ_g' is the gas saturation in the expanded section of the gas cap. Because of the high displacement efficiency of this process, it is postulated that gas released from solution in the residual-oil saturation σ_{or} in the expanded section of the gas cap contributes only a negligible amount to its expansion.

The cumulative volume of the segregated gas may be determined from summation of increments calculated from Eq. (13-23) or from the gas balance [Eq. (13-26)].

The driving indices of the process are immediately available from

$$\text{DDI} = \frac{N\left[\left(\frac{\beta}{\alpha} - S\right) - \left(\frac{\beta_0}{\alpha} - S_0\right)\right] - \frac{V_g}{\alpha}}{n\left(\frac{\beta}{\alpha} - S\right) + G}$$

$$\text{SDI} = \frac{mN\beta_0\left(\frac{1}{\alpha_0} - \frac{1}{\alpha}\right) + \frac{V_g}{\alpha}}{n\left(\frac{\beta}{\alpha} - S\right) + G} \qquad (13\text{-}28)$$

Performance Equations in Finite Difference Form. On a finite *difference basis*, the equations of the process may be written:

$$\Delta_i^{i+1} n = \frac{(1 - n_i)\,\Delta_i^{i+1}\left(\frac{\beta}{\alpha} - S\right) - (1 + m)\beta_0\,\Delta_i^{i+1}\frac{1}{\alpha}}{\left(\frac{\beta}{\alpha} - S\right)_{i+1} + R_{\text{av}}}$$

$$R = S + \frac{\beta}{\alpha}\frac{k_g}{k_o}\frac{\mu_o}{\mu_g} \qquad (13\text{-}29)$$

$$\sigma_l = \sigma_w + (1 - \sigma_w)\frac{(1 - n)\beta - \left[\frac{V_g}{N} + m\beta_0\left(\frac{\alpha}{\alpha_0} - 1\right)\right]\frac{\sigma_{or}}{\sigma_g'}}{\beta_0 - \left[\frac{V_g}{N} + m\beta_0\left(\frac{\alpha}{\alpha_0} - 1\right)\right]\frac{1}{\sigma_g'}}$$

The value of V_g is determined as in the finite form. Driving indices are

$$\text{DDI} = \frac{(1 - n_i)\,\Delta_i^{i+1}\left(\frac{\beta}{\alpha} - S\right) - \beta_0\,\Delta_i^{i+1}\frac{1}{\alpha} - \Delta_i^{i+1}\left(\frac{V_g}{\alpha N}\right)}{\Delta_i^{i+1}n\left[\left(\frac{\beta}{\alpha} - S\right)_{i+1} + R_{\text{av}}\right]}$$

$$\text{SDI} = \frac{-m\beta_0\,\Delta_i^{i+1}\frac{1}{\alpha} + \Delta_i^{i+1}\left(\frac{V_g}{\alpha N}\right)}{\Delta_i^{i+1}n\left[\left(\frac{\beta}{\alpha} - S\right)_{i+1} + R_{\text{av}}\right]} \tag{13-30}$$

In either the finite or the differential form of the performance equations, the sum of the driving indices must be equal to unity.

Procedure for Calculating Field Performance by Segregation Drive with Counterflow. Since this is a rate-sensitive process, production rate field-wide must be specified; let it be Q_o stock-tank oil barrels per day.

1. Assume a pressure decrement from P_i to P_{i+1}. Since no fluid is injected into the reservoir, production must necessarily result in a continuous pressure decline (no pressure stabilization is possible).
2. Assume a corresponding gas saturation σ_g in the oil zone. This value should be smaller than the value of σ_g at the same pressure in the depletion-drive problem. This determines k_g/k_o and R.
3. Calculate $\Delta_i^{i+1}n$ on a finite or differential basis. If there is a dispersed gas injection into the oil zone, the denominator of $\Delta_i^{i+1}n$ is $\left(\frac{\beta}{\alpha} - S\right)_{i+1} + R_{\text{av}}(1 - I)$
4. Determine the increment of time from

$$\Delta_i^{i+1}\theta = \frac{N}{Q_o} \cdot \Delta_i^{i+1}n$$

5. Calculate the increment ΔV_g of gas which moves to the gas cap from

$$\Delta_i^{i+1}V_g = 21{,}238A\left[\frac{K_g}{\mu_g} \text{ or } \frac{K_o}{\mu_o}\right]\Delta\vartheta \sin\alpha \cdot \Delta\theta$$

where A is the oil-gas interface in acres and $\Delta\theta$ in days.

6. Calculate the cumulative volume V_g from

$$V_g = \alpha_{i+1}\sum_0^{i+1}\frac{\Delta V_g}{\alpha_{\text{av}}}$$

7. Verify the value of V_g by the gas balance using a value for the gas saturation in the gas cap σ_g' determined by frontal gas-drive theory.

If the value of V_g so determined does not check, assume a different value of σ_g in the oil zone, and repeat the calculations until a satisfactory check is obtained.

8. A further verification of the correctness of the answer is obtained by calculating the driving indices and observing that their sum equals one.

9. Determine the position of the gas-oil contact at each step.

10. The problem is terminated when the gas-oil contact reaches the base of the structure, at which time considerable *gas* pressure may exist in the structure, and the reservoir may yet have economic value as a gas field.

Hypothetical Problem on Oil Production by Segregation Drive with Counterflow. The reservoir structure of Fig. 13-1 is again used and production is obtained from the wells shown in completion intervals at the base of the structure. No difficulty with gas coning is anticipated and oil production will be obtained in this manner until the gas-oil contact reaches the base of the structure. The allowable production is 100 bbl stock-tank oil per day per well or 4,000 bbl stock-tank oil per day field-wide.

The tabulation and results from the performance calculations are shown in Table 13-5. In making these calculations it is presumed that the displacement efficiency of the expanding gas cap is constant and equal to $\sigma_g' = 72$ per cent. Results show that the end of oil production occurs

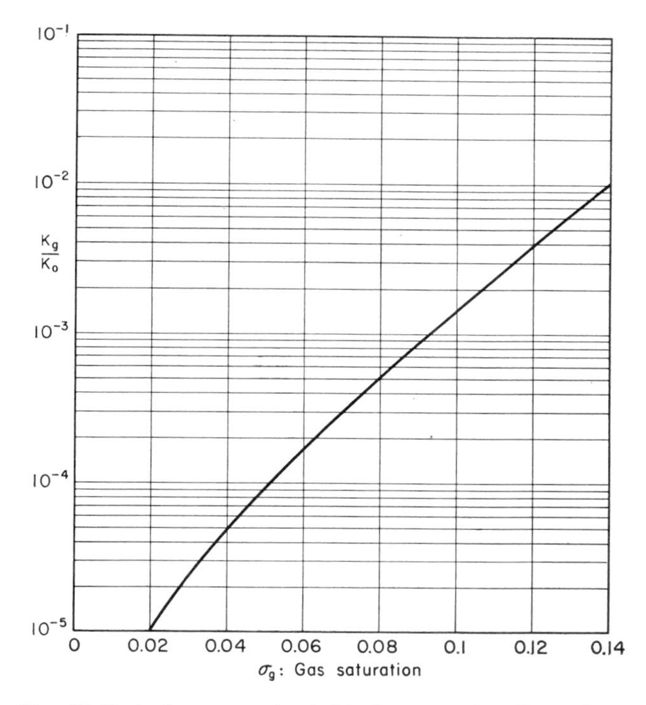

FIG. 13-10. k_g/k_o curve extended to low gas-saturation values.

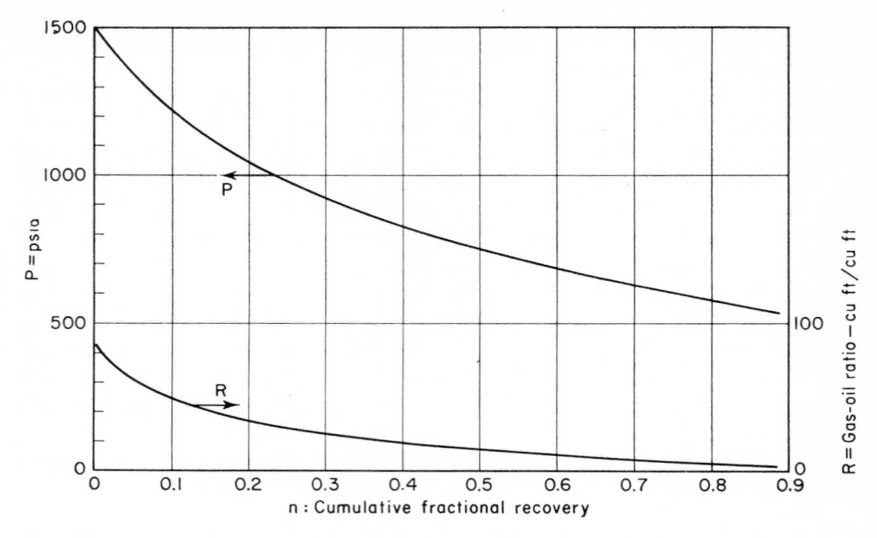

FIG. 13-11. Segregation-drive performance with counterflow of oil and gas.

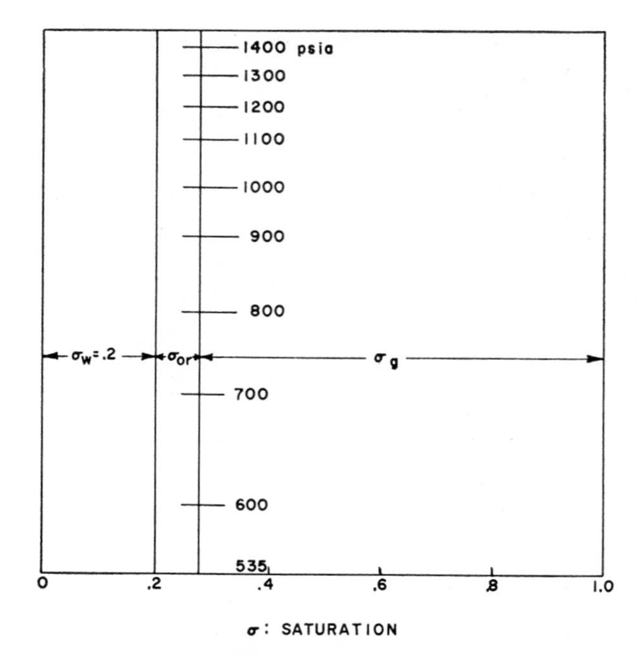

FIG. 13-12. Fluid-saturation distribution in unit reservoir volume for segregation drive with counterflow of oil and gas.

when 89 per cent of the original oil in place is recovered in 24.6 years, at which time field pressure is 535 psia. A considerable amount of gas is still present as gas reserve.

In order to perform the calculations, it was necessary to extend the gas-oil relative-permeability relationship beyond the usual range, i.e., in the zero to 10 per cent gas saturation range. This was done empirically and the resulting extended k_g/k_o curve is shown in Fig. 13-10. The performance curves of the segregation drive with counterflow are shown in Fig. 13-11, where it is observed that the producing gas-oil ratio declines continuously throughout the production history of the field. The ultimate recovery by this process compares very favorably with the bubble-point-pressure maintenance operation by gas injection previously discussed, but active segregation drive has the added advantage of not requiring any expenditure for crestal gas injection. Whenever feasible, it may be the most economical and most efficient oil recovery process in the hands of the reservoir engineer.

Figure 13-12 depicts the fluid-saturation distribution that prevails during this operation in a unit-reservoir-rock volume.

TABLE 13-5. SEGREGATION DRIVE (WITH COUNTERFLOW)

Material balance (finite difference form)

P, psia	σ_g assumed	$\frac{k_g}{k_o}$ ($\times 10^6$)	$\frac{\mu_o}{\mu_g}$	$\frac{\beta}{\alpha}$	(3) ·(4) ·(5)	S	R_{inst} = (7) + (6)	R_{av}	$\frac{\beta}{\alpha} - S$	(9) + (10)	$n_i = \Sigma(18)$	$1 - n_i$	$\Delta\left(\frac{\beta}{\alpha} - S\right)$	(13)i ·(14)	$(1+m)\beta_0 \Delta \frac{1}{\alpha}$	(15) − (16)	Δn = (17)/(11)
(1)	(2)	(3)	(4)	(5)	(6)	(7)	(8)	(9)	(10)	(11)	(12)	(13)	(14)	(15)	(16)	(17)	(18)
1,500	...	...	...	...	...	87.4	87.4	...	80.4	...	0	1.000	...	...	...	...	0
1,400	0.014	5	77.85	151.0	0.0590	82.8	82.9	85.1	69.2	154.3	0.0283	0.9717	−11.2	−11.2	−15.57	4.37	0.0283
1,300	0.0175	7.6	81.17	137.2	0.0844	78.4	78.5	80.7	58.8	139.5	0.0649	0.9351	−10.4	−10.11	−15.22	5.11	0.0366
1,200	0.0145	5.4	84.67	123.9	0.0562	74.1	74.2	76.4	48.8	125.2	0.1085	0.8915	−10.0	−9.35	−14.81	5.46	0.0436
1,100	0.011	3.4	88.44	108.5	0.0329	69.7	69.8	72.0	39.8	111.8	0.1649	0.8351	−9.0	−8.02	−14.32	6.30	0.0564
1,000	0.009	2.0	92.36	96.7	0.0179	65.6	65.6	67.6	31.1	98.7	0.2316	0.7684	−8.7	−7.26	−13.84	6.58	0.0667
900	0.0065	1.2	98.56	84.2	0.0100	60.8	60.8	63.2	23.4	86.6	0.3190	0.6810	−7.7	−5.92	−13.49	7.57	0.0874
800	0.0065	1.2	106.72	72.4	0.0093	55.1	55.1	58.0	17.3	75.3	0.4367	0.5633	−6.1	−4.15	−13.01	8.86	0.1177
700	0.004	0.6	116.15	61.3	0.0043	50.5	50.5	52.8	10.8	63.6	0.5771	0.4229	−6.5	−3.66	−12.59	8.93	0.1404
600	0.002	0.4	129.60	50.7	0.0026	45.6	45.6	48.0	5.1	53.1	0.7598	0.2402	−5.7	−2.41	−12.11	9.70	0.1827
535	0.0046	0.11	140.98	44.9	0.0007	42.0	42.0	43.8	2.9	46.7	0.8906	0.1094	−2.2	−5.3	−6.64	6.11	0.1308

TABLE 13-5. SEGREGATION DRIVE (WITH COUNTERFLOW) (*Continued*)

Volumetric gas-cap expansion												Liquid saturation $\sigma_l = \sigma_w + (1 - \sigma_w) \dfrac{(1-n)\beta - \left[\frac{V_g}{N} + m\beta_0\left(\frac{\alpha}{\alpha_0} - 1\right)\right]\frac{\sigma_{or}}{\sigma_g'}}{\beta_0 - \frac{1}{\sigma_g'}\left[\frac{V_g}{N} + m\beta_0\left(\frac{\alpha}{\alpha_0} - 1\right)\right]}$				
$\Delta\theta = \frac{N\,\Delta n}{Q_o}$, days	$\frac{K_g}{\mu_g}$ or $\frac{K_o}{\mu_o}$ $(\times 10^5)$	$\frac{\Delta\vartheta \sin\alpha}{\phi}$	21,238 (20)(21) $(\times 10^{-6}$ bbl/day)	$\frac{(22)}{\alpha}\phi$ (30)(19) $(\times 10^{-6}$ bbl)	$\Sigma(23)$ $(\times 10^{-6}$ bbl)	$V_g = \alpha(24)$ $(10^{-6}$ bbl)	$\left(\frac{\alpha}{\alpha_0} - 1\right)$	$mN\beta_0\left(\frac{\alpha}{\alpha_0} - 1\right)$ $(\times 10^{-6}$ bbl)	(25) + (27) $(\times 10^{-6}$ bbl)	$\frac{(28)}{\sigma_g'}$ $(\times 10^{-6}$ bbl)	A, acres	$\frac{(29)}{N}\sigma_{or}$	$(1 - n)\beta$	(32) − (31)	$\beta_0 - \frac{(29)}{N}$	$\sigma_l = \sigma_w + (1 - \sigma_w)\frac{(33)}{(34)}$
(19)	(20)	(21)	(22)	(23)	(24)	(25)	(26)	(27)	(28)	(29)	(30)	(31)	(32)	(33)	(34)	(35)
. . .	. . .	. . .	. . .	. . .	. . .	. . .	. . .	. . .	. . .	. . .	284.5					
285.12	12.6	3.2	8.30	86.6	86.6	0.700	0.094	0.544	1.244	1.85	342	0.00265	1.195	1.19235	1.208	1.0
369	18.0	3.23	1.630	183.92	270.01	2.170	0.201	1.156	3.559	4.943	465	0.00981	1.138	1.12883	1.118	1.007
439	13.2	3.25	1.837	187.61	457.62	4.489	0.324	1.863	6.352	8.822	565	0.01679	1.074	1.05721	1.031	1.020
568	8.7	3.3	1.963	180.16	637.78	6.945	0.470	2.703	9.648	13.400	675	0.02722	0.99544	0.96822	0.901	1.060
672	5.2	3.3	1.658	135.62	773.40	9.435	0.646	3.715	13.150	18.264	780	0.03791	0.90671	0.8688	0.767	1.106
881	3.3	3.33	1.6085	115.89	889.29	12.343	0.873	5.021	17.364	24.117	890	0.05078	0.75941	0.74463	0.606	1.183
1,186	3.4	3.33	2.546	159.48	1,048.77	16.728	1.152	6.626	23.354	32.436	1,040	0.0648	0.65061	0.58213	0.385	1.410
1,415	1.8	3.38	1.907	102.12	1,150.89	21.464	1.517	8.725	30.189	41.929	1,200					
1,841	1.3	3.4	2.080	93.18	1,244.07	27.743	2.009	11.555	39.298	54.581	1,410					
1,318	0.5	3.42	0.4903	19.61	1,263.68	31.592	2.374	13.654	45.246	62.842	1,560					
8,974 days 24.6 years																

TABLE 13-5. SEGREGATION DRIVE (WITH COUNTERFLOW) (*Continued*)

Gas balance: $nr_n = S_0 - (1-n)S - \frac{1}{\alpha}\left[\frac{V_g}{N} + \frac{\sigma_g}{\sigma'_g}\left\{\beta_0\sigma'_g - \frac{1}{N}\left[V_g + mN\beta_0\left(\frac{\alpha}{\alpha 0} - 1\right)\right]\right\}\right]$									DDI = $\dfrac{(1-n_i)\,\Delta\left(\frac{\beta}{\alpha} - S\right) - \beta_0\,\Delta\frac{1}{\alpha} - \Delta\left(\frac{1}{\alpha}\frac{V_g}{N}\right)}{\Delta n\left[\left(\frac{\beta}{\alpha} - S\right) + R_{av}\right]}$					SDI = $\dfrac{-m\beta_0\Delta\frac{1}{\alpha} + \Delta\left(\frac{1}{\alpha}\frac{V_g}{N}\right)}{\Delta n\left[\left(\frac{\beta}{\alpha} - S\right) + R_{av}\right]}$	
$\Delta n\, R_{av} =$ (18)·(9) (36)	$nr_n =$ Σ(36) (37)	$S_0 -$ $(1-n)S$ (38)	$\frac{V_g}{N} =$ (25)/N (39)	$\beta_0\sigma'_g - \frac{(28)}{N}$ (40)	$\frac{\sigma_g}{\sigma'_g}$ (40) (41)	(39) + (41) (42)	$\frac{1}{\alpha}$ (42) (43)	Verification (37) = (38) − (43) (44)	(15) − $\beta_0\,\Delta\frac{1}{\alpha}$ (45)	$\frac{\Delta(24)}{N}$ (46)	(45) − (46) (47)	DDI = (47)/ (17) (48)	$-m\beta_0\,\Delta\frac{1}{\alpha}$ (49)	SDI = $\frac{(49) + (46)}{(17)}$ (50)	Verification (48) + (50) = 1.0 (51)
2.41	2.41	6.9	0.0175	0.8600	0.0167	0.0342	4.23	2.41 = 2.67	2.75	2.15	0.60	0.137	1.61	0.867	1.004
2.95	5.36	14.1	0.0596	0.8052	0.0197	0.07925	8.938	5.36 = 5.162	3.54	4.55	−1.01	−0.200	1.57	1.175	0.975
3.33	8.69	21.3	0.1114	0.7359	0.0148	0.1262	12.89	8.69 = 8.41	3.93	4.65	−0.72	−0.132	1.53	1.13	0.998
4.06	12.75	29.2	0.1723	0.6541	0.0100	0.1823	16.74	12.75 = 12.46	4.82	4.47	0.35	0.0555	1.48	0.945	1.0005
4.51	17.26	37.0	0.2341	0.5672	0.0071	0.2412	19.73	17.26 = 17.27	5.15	3.37	1.78	0.270	1.43	0.730	1.000
5.52	22.78	46.0	0.3063	0.4626	0.0042	0.3105	22.37	22.78 = 23.68	6.18	2.87	3.31	0.437	1.39	0.563	1.000
6.83	29.61	56.4	0.4150	0.3140	0.0028	0.4179	26.18	29.61 = 30.22	7.52	3.95	3.57	0.403	1.34	0.598	1.001
7.41	37.02	66.0	0.5326	0.1444	0.0008	0.5334	28.56	37.02 = 37.44	7.63	2.53	5.10	0.570	1.30	0.430	1.000
8.77	45.79	76.4	0.6844	−0.0816	−0.0002	0.6882	30.83	45.79 = 45.57	8.45	2.31	6.14	0.632	1.25	0.368	1.000
5.73	51.52	82.8	0.7839	−2.2920	−0.00019	0.782	31.28	51.52 = 51.52	5.43	0.485	4.945	0.810	1.215	0.278	1.088

SELECTED REFERENCES ON OIL PRODUCTION BY SEGREGATION DRIVE

1943

Stahl, R. F., et al.: Gravitational Drainage of Liquids from Unconsolidated Wilcox Sand, *Trans. AIME*, vol. 151, pp. 138ff.

1945

Pirson, S. J.: The Engineering Approach to Oil Reservoir Controls, *Oil Weekly*, Dec. 31, pp. 22ff.

1946

Amorocho, J.: A Study of Gravitational Drainage in Sands, Pennsylvania State University, M.Sc. Thesis (Unpublished).

1948

Cardwell, W. T., Jr., and R. L. Parsons: Gravity Drainage Theory, *AIME Tech. Pub.* 2464.

Gibson, H. S.: The Production of Oil from the Fields of Southwestern Iran, *J. Inst. Petroleum*, vol. 34, no. 294, pp. 374ff.

1951

Terwilliger, P. L., et al.: An Experimental and Theoretical Investigation of Gravity Drainage Performance, *Trans. AIME Petroleum Div.*, vol. 192, pp. 285ff.

1953

Anders, E. L.: Mile Six Pool—An Evaluation of Reservoir Efficiency, *J. Petroleum Technol.*, vol. 5, no. 11, pp. 279ff.

Klotz, J. A.: The Gravity Drainage Mechanism, *J. Petroleum Technol.*, vol. 5, no. 4, pp. 19ff.

McCord, D. R.: Performance Predictions Incorporating Gravity Drainage and Gas Cap Pressure Maintenance, LL-370 Area, Bolivar Coastal Field, *J. Petroleum Technol.*, vol. 5, no. 9, pp. 231ff.

1954

Chatas, A. T.: The Stock Tank Volume of Residual Oil in Expanding Gas Cap Drive Reservoirs, *5th Venezuelan Eng. Congr.*, Jan. 12.

Justus, J. B., et al.: Pressure Maintenance by Gas Injection in the Brookhaven Field, Mississippi, *J. Petroleum Technol.*, pp. 97ff., April.

Levine, J. S.: Displacement Experiments in a Consolidated Porous System, *Trans. AIME Petroleum Div.*, vol. 201, pp. 57ff.

1955

Stewart, F. M., et al.: Pressure Maintenance by Inert Gas Injection in the High Relief Elk Basin Field, *AIME Tech. Pub.* 4008.

1956

Stamm, H. E., III, et al.: Calculation of the Depletion History and Future Performance of a Gas-cap-drive Reservoir, *AIME Tech. Paper* 671G.

CHAPTER 14

A UNIVERSAL THEORY OF RESERVOIR ENGINEERING

The preceding chapters have shown the existence of three fundamental processes by which oil may be recovered from a naturally occurring reservoir, namely, by *depletion drive*, by *water drive*, and by *segregation drive*. It was also shown how two of the processes may operate in combination: *depletion–water drive*, and *depletion–segregation drive*. In such combined operations, each process may be more or less operative in recovering oil from the reservoir and the degree of effectiveness of each process is gauged by means of *driving indices*. In the most general case all recovery processes may be operative simultaneously to give a combined *depletion–water–segregation drive*. The study of such a complex operation is the basis of a *unified theory of reservoir engineering*.

REVIEW

Oil-reservoir engineering is the art and science dealing with the *forecast* and *control* of the performance of oil and gas production from naturally occurring reservoir rocks in place, with or without the application of an external or artificial source of energy. As a forecaster, the reservoir engineer predicts the performance of field production and the expected recovery under postulated conditions. Such conditions include anticipated possible production rates as well as certain limiting gas-oil ratios or water-oil ratios. In their effort, reservoir engineers use tools which are mainly mathematical in nature.

Reservoir performance of an oil field is characterized by certain *essential* elements: pressure decline, gas-oil ratio, water-oil ratio, productivity index, production rate, driving index, etc. These elements may be expressed as a function of cumulative production [either on a fractional or volumetric (barrel) basis] or as a function of time. Certain derived elements of the performance prediction are of interest for economic, business, and management reasons; they are cumulative oil, gas, and water production vs. time, as well as ultimate recovery and reserves. Production of oil or gas from a natural reservoir involves displacing it from the pore space of rocks which act as the petrologic reservoir within the earth. In recovering oil from porous rocks, there are two fundamentally different displacing mechanisms:

1. Depletion drive
2. Frontal drive

There are two main types of frontal drives:

1. Water drive
2. Gas drive

In each of the frontal drives, gravity may or may not play a predominant part in influencing displacement efficiency and ultimate recovery. It may be so important in certain frontal-drive operations as to overshadow the influence of other factors; it is then called *gravity drainage*.

Depletion Drive. Depletion drive is the oil recovery mechanism wherein the displacement of oil from its reservoir rock is achieved by the expansion of the very gas it holds in solution under pressure. When pressure is reduced on the reservoir oil through the process of drilling, gas comes out of solution and expulses oil from the rock openings. Both oil and gas flow simultaneously through the rocks and their relative flow ability is characterized by the relative permeability of the rock to each phase. These flow properties are paramount in controlling the recovery efficiency by depletion and one of the main tasks of the reservoir engineer in studying this recovery process is determining the appropriate k_g/k_o relationship that will prevail throughout the life of the field.

The tools or mathematical equations which describe this type of reservoir behavior and which are used for depletion-drive performance forecast when expressed in finite difference form are the following:

Material-balance equation:

$$\Delta n = \frac{(1 - n_i)\,\Delta\left(\frac{\beta}{\alpha} - S\right) - \beta_0\,\Delta\frac{1}{\alpha}}{\left(\frac{\beta}{\alpha} - S\right)_{i+1} + R_{\text{av}}}$$

Instantaneous gas-oil-ratio equation:

$$R = S + \frac{\beta}{\alpha}\frac{k_g}{k_o}\frac{\mu_o}{\mu_g} \tag{14-1}$$

Liquid saturation equation:

$$\sigma_l = \sigma_w + (1 - \sigma_w)\frac{(1 - n)\beta}{\beta_0}$$

Depletion drive is characterized by the existence of a relatively uniform fluid-saturation distribution within the pore spaces of the reservoir rock. The solution of the above equations is a trial-and-error technique whereby a reasonable value for $\Delta_i^{i+1}n$ is first postulated to correspond to an assumed pressure-decline increment (P_i to P_{i+1}). If the calculated value does not check satisfactorily with the postulated value, the calculated Δn is now used as the postulated answer in a new trial. Generally a satisfactory answer is obtained in no more than three trials. The technique has the advantage of convergence and is highly adaptable to high-speed mechanical and electronic computers.

Special cases of depletion drive obtain when attempts are made at increasing recovery through the medium of *dispersed* gas injection. Two cases are possible, depending on whether the injected gas is uniformly dispersed throughout the reservoir rock (conformance factor $e = 1.0$) or the injected gas affects only part of the reservoir rock volume ($e < 1.0$).

In the case of uniform dispersion of the injected gas, the depletion-drive-performance equations remain unchanged except for the inclusion of a multiplier $(1 - I)$ to R_{av} in the denominator of Δn, I being the constant fraction of the produced gas which is continuously injected.

In the case of nonuniform dispersion of the injected gas, it is necessary to evaluate on a reasonable basis the fraction e or conformable section of the reservoir which is affected by gas injection. This may be done in a certain measure through pore-size distribution studies in large cores or better by fitting an appropriate value of e to a past performance history. The depletion-performance equations now become:

$$\Delta n = \frac{(1 - n_i)\,\Delta\left(\frac{\beta}{\alpha} - S\right) - \beta_0\,\Delta\frac{1}{\alpha}}{\left(\frac{\beta}{\alpha} - S\right)_{i+1} + R_{e,\text{av}}(1 - I)} \qquad (14\text{-}2)$$

$$R_e = S + \frac{\beta}{\alpha}\left(\frac{k_g}{k_o}\right)_e \frac{\mu_o}{\mu_g}$$

$$\sigma_{le} = \sigma_w + (1 - \sigma_w)\,\frac{(e - n_e)\beta}{e\beta_0}$$

The subscript e indicates that the subject function is to be evaluated in the conformable section of the reservoir.

A special case of depletion with gas injection obtains when pressure is maintained (pressure maintenance operation); this occurs when $I = 1 + \frac{\beta/\alpha - S}{R}$.

Typical performance and recovery predictions have been made in Chap. 10 for various postulated conditions wherein the influence of a single variable is illustrated, i.e., viscosity, gas in solution, formation-water saturation, etc. In the main, depletion drive is a relatively inefficient oil displacement mechanism; its influence should be reduced as much as possible when the possibility of economic use of other recovery mechanisms exists. In a combination-type drive, the influence of depletion may be gauged by means of the driving indices, and efforts should be made to reduce the depletion-drive index to as small a fraction as possible.

Frontal Drive. Frontal drive is the mechanism wherein the displacement of oil from its reservoir rock is achieved by an external driving fluid, either water or gas, and where a sharp saturation discontinuity exists between the driven and the driving fluid at a well-defined line of demarcation or front.

The tools, or mathematical equations which are used for frontal-drive-performance calculations and recovery forecast, are the following:

Fractional-flow equation:

$$f_D = \frac{1 - \dfrac{K_o}{q_t \mu_o}\left(\dfrac{\partial P_c}{\partial u} + g\,\Delta\vartheta \sin\alpha\right)}{1 + \dfrac{k_o}{k_D}\dfrac{\mu_D}{\mu_o}} \tag{14-3}$$

Rate of advance of a region of constant saturation:

$$\left(\frac{du}{d\theta}\right)_{\sigma_D} = \frac{q_t}{\phi}\left(\frac{\partial f_D}{\partial \sigma_D}\right)_\theta$$

where D represents any displacing fluid, water or gas.

$$q_t = q_o + q_D$$

$$\Delta\vartheta = \vartheta_D - \vartheta_o$$

$$P_c = P_D - P_o$$

It is seen that Eqs. (14-3) contain all the factors which have an effect on recovery by water or gas drive: effective and relative permeability, K_o, k_o/k_D; oil and relative viscosity, μ_o, μ_D/μ_o; rate of drive, q_t; capillary-pressure gradient $(\partial P_c/\partial u)$; gravity, g; fluid density difference, $\Delta\vartheta$; structural dip, α; and direction of drive with respect to dip, u.

Except for depletion drive in volumetric reservoirs, it is seldom that any of the above mechanisms operate singly. Various types of combination drive operations are possible.

Combination Depletion-Water Drive. This type of drive is one in which both depletion and water displacement are partially to totally effective in producing oil. The contribution of each mechanism depends greatly on the rate of field-wide oil production Q_o, as compared with the rate of water influx C into the field.

The water-influx rate C, generally expressed in barrels per month per pounds per square inch pressure drop between field and aquifer, must be determined statistically from a knowledge of an adequate past performance history by means of a generalized water-encroachment formula of the type:

$$W_{i+1} = C \sum_{0}^{i+1} P(\theta)\,\Delta\theta \tag{14-4}$$

where $P(\theta)$ is a time function which may have the following forms:

Schilthuis: $$P(\theta) = \Delta P$$

Hurst (simplified): $$P(\theta) = \frac{\Delta P}{\log \theta}$$

Hurst and van Everdingen: $$P(\theta) = P(\bar{\theta})$$

where $\bar{\theta}$ is dimensionless time obtained from

$$\bar{\theta} = \frac{K}{\phi \mu_w c_w} \frac{1}{R_b^2} \theta$$

Performance is calculated on a time basis for preassigned and expected field-wide production rate Q_o:

$$\Delta\theta = \frac{(1 - n_i)\,\Delta\left(\frac{\beta}{\alpha} - S\right) - \beta_0\,\Delta\frac{1}{\alpha} + \frac{W_i - w_i}{N}\,\Delta\frac{1}{\alpha}}{\frac{Q_o}{N}\left[\left(\frac{\beta}{\alpha} - S\right)_{i+1} + R_{\text{av}}\right] - \frac{C\,\Delta P - C_1}{N\alpha_{i+1}}} \tag{14-5}$$

Depending on which water-encroachment formula is selected, the values of C will be numerically different.

It should be noted that C_1 may include the contribution of artificial water injection or of water disposal by injection into the aquifer.

The simultaneous solution of the depletion equations and of the water-encroachment formula determines performance and recovery of a water-drive–depletion-drive combination operation. The calculations are based on a presumably valid postulate that the prevailing field pressure determines the fluid-saturation conditions in the oil zone, and that these conditions are those of simple depletion. Oil production is presumably obtained from the oil zone alone.

A characteristic of this type of operation is that field pressure is stabilized when reservoir withdrawal rate and net water influx are equal:

$$\frac{C\,\Delta P - C_1}{\alpha} = Q_o\left[\left(\frac{\beta}{\alpha} - S\right) + R_{\text{av}}\right] \tag{14-6}$$

In this equation the subscripts are dropped because pressure is constant.

The field producing rate Q_o is a function of the field pressure, of the effective pay h_e, and of the specific productivity index of the wells.

The driving index concept is useful in gauging the degree of effectiveness of each mechanism in recovering oil. The driving index may be defined as the volume ratio of the reservoir-fluid withdrawals contributed by a particular mechanism to the total reservoir-fluid withdrawals contributed by all mechanisms:

Depletion-drive index (finite basis):

$$\mathrm{DDI} = \frac{N\left[\left(\frac{\beta}{\alpha} - S\right) - \left(\frac{\beta_0}{\alpha} - S_0\right)\right]}{n\left(\frac{\beta}{\alpha} - S\right) + G}$$

Water-drive index (finite basis):

$$\mathrm{WDI} = \frac{\frac{1}{\alpha}(W - w)}{n\left(\frac{\beta}{\alpha} - S\right) + G} \tag{14-7}$$

All subscripts are dropped because all functions and variables are evaluated at the same time. G represents the cumulative volume of gas produced, measured at standard conditions up to a particular pressure.

On a finite difference basis, the driving indices are

$$\mathrm{DDI} = \frac{(1 - n_i)\,\Delta\left(\frac{\beta}{\alpha} - S\right) - \beta_0\,\Delta\frac{1}{\alpha}}{\Delta n\left[\left(\frac{\beta}{\alpha} - S\right)_{i+1} + R_{\mathrm{av}}\right]}$$

$$\mathrm{WDI} = \frac{\Delta\left(\frac{W - w}{N\alpha}\right)}{\Delta n\left[\left(\frac{\beta}{\alpha} - S\right)_{i+1} + R_{\mathrm{av}}\right]} \tag{14-8}$$

Over-all recovery by both processes for a combination depletion–water-drive reservoir is a function of the degree of effectiveness of all processes, i.e., of their respective driving indices, but also of the rate of advance of the water front because the displacement efficiency of a water drive is rate-sensitive. A displacement-efficiency calculation should therefore be performed at each pressure decrement. The over-all recovery r by both processes may then be computed from

$$r = \sum_{0}^{i+1} [(\mathrm{DDI})r_d + (\mathrm{WDI})r_w] \tag{14-9}$$

where r_d = recovery by depletion for a specific pressure decrement
r_w = recovery by water drive for the same specific pressure decrement
DDI = depletion-drive index on a finite difference basis over the same pressure decrement
WDI = corresponding water-drive index on a finite difference basis

Theoretical and laboratory studies have shown that maximum recovery from a water-drive field is obtained when field pressure is adjusted by field-wide fluid withdrawals so as to maintain within the overlying oil zone a gas saturation such as to favor optimum replacement of residual reservoir oil by a dispersed and immovable gas phase. This optimum behavior entails operating at a production rate such that field pressure drops below the bubble-point pressure in order to cause the development of a free-gas phase. Techniques by which optimum pressure and production rate may be determined under specific conditions have been discussed in Chap. 12. The reservoir-rock flow characteristics determine whether or not an effective free-gas phase may be created within the oil zone; it appears that the latter may not exceed the equilibrium gas saturation, for then segregation by gas and oil counterflow becomes predominant.

The operating conditions favoring maximum physical recovery may be termed *engineering most efficient rate*. Such conditions may not necessarily correspond to the *economic most efficient rate* which entails considering market, operating cost, and political expediency conditions.

Combination Depletion–Segregation Drive. This type of drive is one in which both depletion and frontal displacement of oil by gas drive take place simultaneously.

Two types of segregation drives are possible: one where the frontal gas drive is by a naturally or artificially expanding gas cap and without gas and oil counterflow; in the other the expansion of the gas cap results altogether from counterflow of gas and oil within the oil zone under the influence of gravity.

Segregation Drive without Counterflow. The performance and recovery by gas-cap expansion without counterflow of oil and gas in the oil zone may be solved by means of modified equations of depletion drive. A preexisting gas cap expanding naturally because of field-pressure decline may provide the frontal drive or an artificial gas cap may be induced by injecting a certain fraction I of the produced gas at structurally high positions or into a preexisting gas cap. Gas injection in effect precludes the occurrence of gas and oil counterflow in the oil column since the injection pressure reverses the vertical gas-flow potential gradient necessary for its movement by buoyancy to the gas cap.

The simultaneous equations which describe this process on a differential basis are as follows:

$$\Delta n = \frac{(1 - n_i)\,\Delta\left(\frac{\beta}{\alpha} - S\right) - (1 + m)\beta_0\,\Delta\frac{1}{\alpha}}{\left(\frac{\beta}{\alpha} - S\right)_{i+1} + (1 - I)R_{\text{av}}} \tag{14-10}$$

$$R = S + \frac{\beta}{\alpha}\frac{k_g}{k_o}\frac{\mu_o}{\mu_g}$$

$$\sigma_l = \sigma_w + (1 - \sigma_w)\frac{(1 - n)\beta}{\beta_0}$$

where m is the original gas-cap volume relative to the oil zone and I is the injected fraction of the produced gas.

The injection ratio necessary to maintain a certain pressure or to operate a partial pressure maintenance is

$$I = 1 + \frac{(\beta/\alpha - S)}{R}$$

Since pressure is maintained, no subscripts are needed to the various functions. It is noted that the gas-injection requirement to maintain pressure is independent of the field producing rate.

The injection ratio necessary to maintain the field at the bubble-point pressure through gas-cap injection is given by $I = \beta_0/\alpha_0 S_0$.

The driving indices on a finite basis of this combination drive process are

Depletion-drive index:

$$\text{DDI} = \frac{N\left[\left(\frac{\beta}{\alpha} - S\right) - \left(\frac{\beta_0}{\alpha} - S_0\right)\right] - GI}{n\left(\frac{\beta}{\alpha} - S\right) + G}$$

Segregation-drive index: (14-11)

$$\text{SDI} = \frac{mN\beta_0\left(\frac{1}{\alpha_0} - \frac{1}{\alpha}\right) + GI}{n\left(\frac{\beta}{\alpha} - S\right) + G}$$

The driving indices on a finite difference basis are given by

$$\text{DDI} = \frac{(1 - n_i)\,\Delta\left(\frac{\beta}{\alpha} - S\right) - \beta_0\,\Delta\frac{1}{\alpha}}{\Delta n\left[\left(\frac{\beta}{\alpha} - S\right)_{i+1} + R_{\text{av}}\right]}$$

(14-12)

$$\text{SDI} = \frac{-m\beta_0\,\Delta\left(\frac{1}{\alpha}\right) + \Delta n\,R_{\text{av}}I}{\Delta n\left[\left(\frac{\beta}{\alpha} - S\right)_{i+1} + R_{\text{av}}\right]}$$

Over-all recovery by both processes for a combination depletion–segregation-drive reservoir is a function of the degree of effectiveness of all processes, i.e., of their respective driving indices, but also of the rate of advance of the expanding gas-cap front, for the displacement efficiency of a frontal gas drive is rate-sensitive. This displacement-efficiency calculation should therefore be made at each pressure decrement. The over-all recovery r by both processes may then be computed from

$$r = \sum_{0}^{i+1} [(\text{DDI})r_d + (\text{SDI})r_s] \tag{14-13}$$

where r_s is the recovery by segregation drive at a specific step. The driving indices and the recovery factors are written for a specific pressure decrement and the summation extends over the duration of the operation until ultimate abandonment pressure P_{i+1} is reached. This abandonment pressure is determined by reservoir fill-up, i.e., when the gas front has expanded to the producing wells.

This oil-recovery process does not appear to possess a well-defined physical most efficient rate at which recovery will be maximum unless it be at the original bubble-point pressure because no dispersed gas phase develops then and no tendency for gas diffusion into the oil zone exists. Although the displacement efficiency is affected by the rate of withdrawal, when the economic most efficient rate is considered, additional increased physical efficiency seems to be a minor consideration in view of the major purchasing gas requirements needed to maintain the high field pressures required in bubble-point pressure maintenance.

Segregation Drive with Counterflow. Segregation drive with counterflow is the oil-recovery process whereby oil is expulsed from its rock container by the expansion of a naturally developing gas cap generated by the accumulation of gas flowing upward through the oil column under the action of the buoyancy force existing between two fluids of different density, namely, reservoir oil and gas.

For this process to operate, a gas phase must be developed and maintained within the oil column in order that gas permeability may exist for its upward flow. This gas phase is produced by simple depletion, which process must first exist alone before segregation drive may take over later. No gas-cap injection may take place; otherwise active segregation would be prevented. The equations of depletion drive will therefore control the process in the early stage of operation. An original gas cap may exist at the start, and the performance equations that describe this process are written as follows on a finite difference basis:

$$\Delta n = \frac{(1 - n_i)\,\Delta\left(\dfrac{\beta}{\alpha} - S\right) - (1 + m)\beta_0\,\Delta\dfrac{1}{\alpha}}{\left(\dfrac{\beta}{\alpha} - S\right)_{i+1} + R_{\text{av}}}$$

$$R = S + \frac{\beta}{\alpha}\frac{k_g}{k_o}\frac{\mu_o}{\mu_g}$$

$$\sigma_l = \sigma_w + (1 - \sigma_w)\,\frac{(1 - n)\beta - \left[\dfrac{V_g}{N} + m\beta_0\left(\dfrac{\alpha}{\alpha_0} - 1\right)\right]\dfrac{\sigma_{or}}{\sigma_g'}}{\beta_0 - \left[\dfrac{V_g}{N} + m\beta_0\left(\dfrac{\alpha}{\alpha_0} - 1\right)\right]\dfrac{1}{\sigma_g'}} \tag{14-14}$$

$$\Delta V_g = A \left[\frac{K_g}{\mu_g} \text{ or } \frac{K_o}{\mu_o} \right] \frac{\Delta\vartheta \sin \alpha}{1{,}033} \Delta\theta$$

$$nr_n = S_0 - (1 - n)S - \frac{1}{\alpha}\left(\frac{V_g}{N} + \frac{\sigma_g}{\sigma_g'}\left\{\beta_0\sigma_g' - \left[\frac{V_g}{N} + m\beta_0\left(\frac{\alpha}{\alpha_0} - 1\right)\right]\right\}\right)$$

In the process of active reservoir oil and gas segregation, over-all field pressure no longer controls fluid-saturation distribution within the oil zone and it is necessary to calculate the liquid saturation resulting from oil replenishment because of gravity drainage and counterflow of oil and gas. This modification is introduced in the saturation equation. Solution to this problem requires calculating the volumetric segregated gas V_g which contributes to the expansion of the gas cap. For verification purposes, a gas-balance equation is also introduced.

A characteristic of segregation drive with counterflow is the constantly declining pressure and gas-oil ratio (the latter being always less than the original solution gas) and the very high recovery. It is naturally postulated that all the producing oil wells are completed within the oil column and the flowing gas-oil ratio is determined by the prevailing fluid saturation therein.

The driving indices on a finite basis are written:

$$\text{DDI} = \frac{N\left[\left(\frac{\beta}{\alpha} - S\right) - \left(\frac{\beta_0}{\alpha} - S_0\right)\right] - \frac{V_g}{\alpha}}{n\left(\frac{\beta}{\alpha} - S\right) + G}$$

$$\text{SDI} = \frac{mN\beta_0\left(\frac{1}{\alpha_0} - \frac{1}{\alpha}\right) + \frac{V_g}{\alpha}}{n\left(\frac{\beta}{\alpha} - S\right) + G} \tag{14-15}$$

and on a finite difference basis:

$$\text{DDI} = \frac{(1 - n_i)\,\Delta\left(\frac{\beta}{\alpha} - S\right) - \beta_0\,\Delta\frac{1}{\alpha} - \Delta\left(\frac{V_g}{\alpha N}\right)}{\Delta n\left[\left(\frac{\beta}{\alpha} - S\right)_{i+1} + R_{\text{av}}\right]}$$

$$\text{SDI} = \frac{-m\beta_0\,\Delta\frac{1}{\alpha} + \Delta\left(\frac{V_g}{\alpha N}\right)}{\Delta n\left[\left(\frac{\beta}{\alpha} - S\right)_{i+1} + R_{\text{av}}\right]} \tag{14-16}$$

The recovery equation of this process is

$$r = \sum_{0}^{i+1} [(\text{DDI})r_d + (\text{SDI})r_s] \tag{14-17}$$

where r_s is the recovery by segregation. r_s has very high value approaching 1 − irreducible oil saturation in this process since the value $q_t = q_o - q_g$ at the gas-oil interface is essentially nil. Segregation drive is therefore a process capable of yielding maximum oil recovery. This is obtained when DDI = 0 and when the proper balance is maintained between the rate of production Q_o and the rate at which gas segregates into the gas cap. To a determined field pressure and production rate corresponds a definite gas saturation in the oil column. However, the free-gas phase is not critical and has little effect on the displacement efficiency of the expanding gas cap because of its small magnitude.

The maximum segregation rate at which this operation may be carried out is obtained when $K_g/\mu_g = K_o/\mu_o$. This condition is satisfied at a specific fluid saturation in the oil zone which in turn corresponds to a specific field-wide production rate. The latter, however, may be determined only by trying out various values for Q_o that will bracket the maximum segregation rate.

Combined Depletion–Water–Segregation Drive. In the most general case of oil field production, all three fundamental oil-recovery processes may be operative simultaneously. Two cases must be distinguished, depending on whether or not gas is injected at the crest of the structure into the expanding gas cap. An original gas cap is not likely to be present owing to the water drive; for the sake of generality, however, one is postulated.

Combined Depletion–Water–Segregation Drive without Counterflow (Fig. 14-1). In this instance, gas injection into the gas cap prevents active segregation of gas and oil in the oil column. The equations of the process may be written immediately on a differential basis. Pressure performance

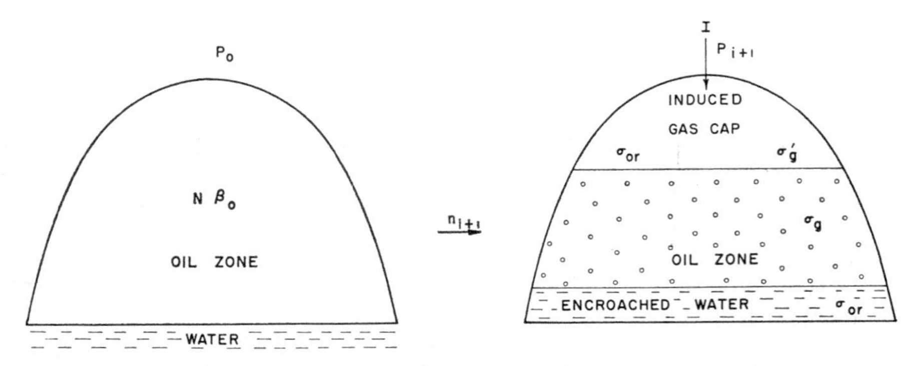

FIG. 14-1. Schematic representation of prevailing fluid distribution in a reservoir under the combined depletion–water–segregation drives (without oil and gas counterflow) simultaneously operative.

is first calculated on the basis of a simple depletion drive:

$$\Delta n = \frac{(1 - n_i)\,\Delta\left(\frac{\beta}{\alpha} - S\right) - \beta_0\,\Delta\frac{1}{\alpha}}{\left(\frac{\beta}{\alpha} - S\right)_{i+1} + R_{\text{av}}} \tag{14-18}$$

$$R = S + \frac{\beta}{\alpha}\frac{k_g}{k_o}\frac{\mu_o}{\mu_g}$$

$$\sigma_l = \sigma_w + (1 - \sigma_w)\frac{(1 - n)\beta}{\beta_0}$$

Then the time interval necessary to produce a fraction of oil based on a preassigned field-wide production rate Q_o is calculated by

$$\Delta\theta = \frac{(1 - n_i)\,\Delta\left(\frac{\beta}{\alpha} - S\right) - (1 + m)\beta_0\,\Delta\frac{1}{\alpha} + \left(\frac{W_i - w_i}{N}\right)\Delta\frac{1}{\alpha}}{\frac{Q_o}{N}\left[\left(\frac{\beta}{\alpha} - S\right)_{i+1} + R_{\text{av}}(1 - I)\right] - \frac{C\,\Delta P - C_1}{N\alpha_{i+1}}} \tag{14-18a}$$

in which the net volumetric water encroachment is evaluated from

$$W_i - w_i = C\sum_0^i \Delta P\,\Delta\theta - C_1\sum_0^i \Delta\theta \tag{14-18b}$$

The driving indices of the combined process of a finite basis are

$$\text{DDI} = \frac{N\left[\left(\frac{\beta}{\alpha} - S\right) - \left(\frac{\beta_0}{\alpha} - S_0\right)\right] - GI}{n\left(\frac{\beta}{\alpha} - S\right) + G}$$

$$\text{WDI} = \frac{\frac{1}{\alpha}(W - w)}{n\left(\frac{\beta}{\alpha} - S\right) + G} \tag{14-19}$$

$$\text{SDI} = \frac{m\beta_0 N\left(\frac{1}{\alpha_0} - \frac{1}{\alpha}\right) + GI}{n\left(\frac{\beta}{\alpha} - S\right) + G}$$

On a finite difference basis the driving indices are written:

$$\mathrm{DDI} = \frac{(1 - n_i)\,\Delta\left(\dfrac{\beta}{\alpha} - S\right) - \beta_0\,\Delta\dfrac{1}{\alpha}}{\Delta n\left[\left(\dfrac{\beta}{\alpha} - S\right) + R_{\mathrm{av}}\right]}$$

$$\mathrm{WDI} = \frac{\Delta\left(\dfrac{W - w}{n\alpha}\right)}{\Delta n\left[\left(\dfrac{\beta}{\alpha} - S\right) + R_{\mathrm{av}}\right]} \qquad (14\text{-}20)$$

$$\mathrm{SDI} = \frac{-m\beta_0\,\Delta\dfrac{1}{\alpha} + \Delta n\,R_{\mathrm{av}}I}{\Delta n\left[\left(\dfrac{\beta}{\alpha} - S\right) + R_{\mathrm{av}}\right]}$$

Over-all recovery:

$$r = \sum_{0}^{i+1}\left[(\mathrm{DDI})r_d + (\mathrm{WDI})r_w + (\mathrm{SDI})r_s\right]$$

The above performance equations are written on the assumption that the wells are completed solely in the oil zone and that producing conditions at the wells are controlled solely by saturation conditions in said oil zone. In this particular case, field pressure determines saturation conditions in the oil zone since no segregation is postulated.

Combined Depletion–Water–Segregation Drive with Counterflow (*Fig.* 14-2). In this instance, there may not be any gas injection into the gas cap, and the latter expands solely by virtue of gas migration by counterflow under the influence of gravity. The equations of the process may be written im-

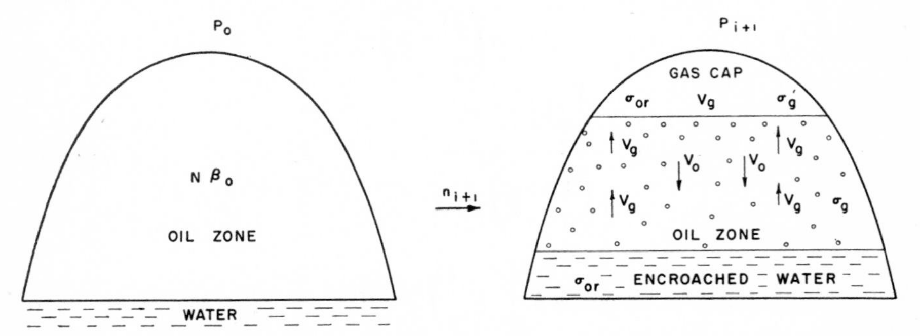

FIG. 14-2. Schematic representation of prevailing fluid distribution and movement in a reservoir under the combined depletion–water–segregation drives (with counterflow of oil and gas) simultaneously active.

mediately on a finite difference basis:

$$\Delta\theta = \frac{(1 - n_i)\,\Delta\left(\frac{\beta}{\alpha} - S\right) - (1 + m)\beta_0\,\Delta\frac{1}{\alpha} + \left(\frac{W_i - w_i}{N}\right)\Delta\frac{1}{\alpha}}{\frac{Q_o}{N}\left[\left(\frac{\beta}{\alpha} - S\right)_{i+1} + R_{\text{av}}\right] - \frac{C\,\Delta P - C_1}{N\alpha_{i+1}}}$$

$$R = S + \frac{\beta}{\alpha}\frac{k_g}{k_o}\frac{\mu_o}{\mu_g}$$

$$\sigma_l = \sigma_w + (1 - \sigma_w)\frac{(1 - n)\beta - \left[\frac{V_g}{N} + m\beta_0\left(\frac{\alpha}{\alpha_0} - 1\right)\right]\frac{\sigma_{or}}{\sigma_g'}}{\beta_0 - \left[\frac{V_g}{N} + m\beta_0\left(\frac{\alpha}{\alpha_0} - 1\right)\right]\frac{1}{\sigma_g'}} \tag{14-21}$$

$$\Delta V_g = A\left(\frac{K_g}{\mu_g}\text{ or }\frac{K_o}{\mu_o}\right)\frac{\Delta\vartheta}{1{,}033}\sin\alpha\,\Delta\theta$$

$$nr_n = S_0 - (1 - n)S - \frac{1}{\alpha}\left[\frac{V_g}{N} + \frac{\sigma_g}{\sigma_g'}\left\{\beta_0\sigma_g' - \left[\frac{V_g}{N} + m\beta_0\left(\frac{\alpha}{\alpha_0} - 1\right)\right]\right\}\right]$$

in which the net volumetric water encroachment is calculated by

$$W_i - w_i = C\sum_0^i \Delta P\,\Delta\theta - C_1\sum_0^i \Delta\theta \tag{14-21a}$$

The driving indices of the combined process on a finite basis are

$$\text{DDI} = \frac{N\left[\left(\frac{\beta}{\alpha} - S\right) - \left(\frac{\beta_0}{\alpha} - S_0\right)\right] - \frac{V_g}{\alpha}}{n\left(\frac{\beta}{\alpha} - S\right) + G}$$

$$\text{WDI} = \frac{\frac{1}{\alpha}(W - w)}{n\left(\frac{\beta}{\alpha} - S\right) + G} \tag{14-22}$$

$$\text{SDI} = \frac{mN\beta_0\left(\frac{1}{\alpha_0} - \frac{1}{\alpha}\right) + \frac{V_g}{\alpha}}{n\left(\frac{\beta}{\alpha} - S\right) + G}$$

On a finite difference basis, the driving indices are written:

$$\text{DDI} = \frac{(1 - n_i)\,\Delta\left(\frac{\beta}{\alpha} - S\right) - \beta_0\,\Delta\frac{1}{\alpha}}{\Delta n\left[\left(\frac{\beta}{\alpha} - S\right)_{i+1} + R_{\text{av}}\right]}$$

$$\text{WDI} = \frac{\Delta\left(\frac{W - w}{N\alpha}\right)}{\Delta n\left[\left(\frac{\beta}{\alpha} - S\right)_{i+1} + R_{\text{av}}\right]} \qquad (14\text{-}23)$$

$$\text{SDI} = \frac{-m\beta_0\,\Delta\frac{1}{\alpha} + \Delta\left(\frac{V_g}{\alpha N}\right)}{\Delta n\left[\left(\frac{\beta}{\alpha} - S\right)_{i+1} + R_{\text{av}}\right]}$$

The above equations are written on the assumption that the wells are completed solely in the oil zone and that producing conditions at the wells are controlled by saturation conditions in said oil zone. In this particular case, field pressure no longer determines saturation conditions in the oil zone since oil replenishment takes place in it as a result of oil and gas counterflow in the oil column.

Over-all recovery:

$$r = \sum_{0}^{i+1} [(\text{DDI})r_d + (\text{WDI})r_w + (\text{SDI})r_s] \qquad (14\text{-}24)$$

The sets of equations developed in this section constitute the *universal theory of oil-reservoir engineering;* the last set of equations may, in fact, be considered as being fully general if it were not for the fact that gas injection is absent from it. It is believed that the two sets of equations are more appropriate, for they are incompatible; i.e., when *gas-cap injection* is resorted to, gravity segregation of oil and gas is almost impossible. However, it is still possible under conditions of *dispersed gas injection*, a case which has not been specifically considered in combination with water and segregation drives.

From the generalized set of equations, one may revert to simpler combinations of drive by merely dropping the terms not applicable to the conditions at hand.

ULTIMATE OIL RECOVERY FROM COMBINATION DRIVE FIELDS

The preceding discussion has shown that field-wide oil recovery should be rate-sensitive when frontal-drive mechanisms are operative in recovering oil from reservoir rocks. Qualitatively, the recovery by each of the mechanisms can be represented as a function of field-wide production rate Q_o as shown in Fig. 14-3.

Depletion drive is substantially a non-rate-sensitive recovery process and its recovery value r_d is a constant regardless of the value of Q_o. There may be some conditions of rock texture, however, which may cause variations of r_d vs. field-wide withdrawal rate, such as complex pore structure, fracture porosity, etc. For this discussion r_d is assumed to remain constant with Q_o.

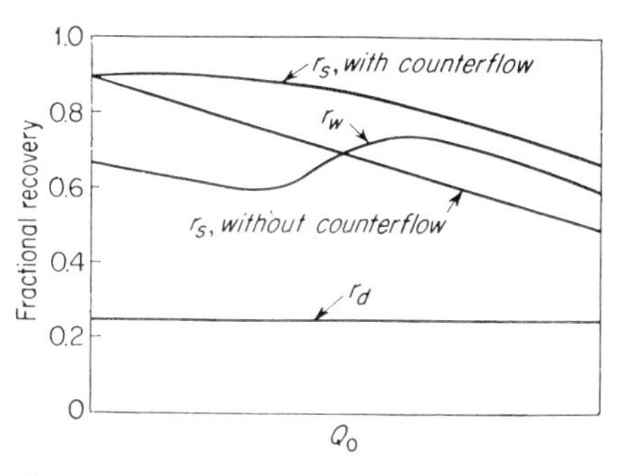

FIG. 14-3. Probable trend of oil recovery by three independent driving mechanisms as a function of the field-wide oil-producing rate.

If a *water drive* is superimposed on the field, occurring either naturally by encroachment from an aquifer or artificially by water injection, water-drive recovery r_w may remain fairly constant until such a rate of production is reached which permits field pressure to drop below the bubble-point pressure of the oil. This is substantially so when the water drive is horizontal, but for an up-dip water drive, recovery may be somewhat higher at very low withdrawal rates when field pressure remains above the bubble point. When field production rates are such that a free-gas phase develops within the oil zone, the displacement efficiency of the water drive increases until an optimum field-wide production rate which may be determined analytically is reached; thereafter for greater production rates, recovery by water drive decreases again.

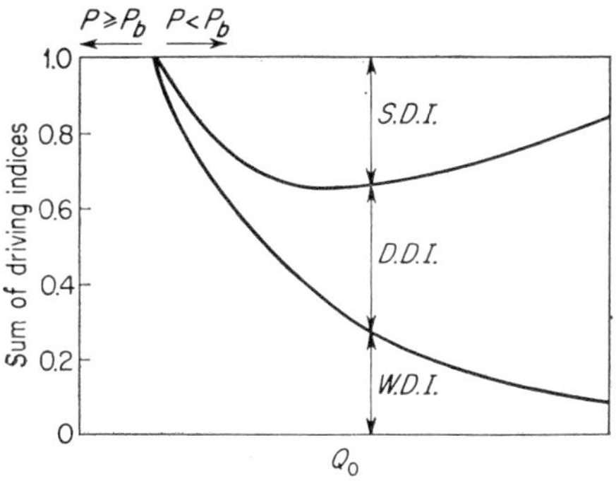

FIG. 14-4. Probable trend of variations in driving indices as a function of the field-wide oil-producing rate.

If *segregation drive* is superimposed on a simple depletion performance, two situations are possible. Without counterflow of gas and oil, the recovery r_s decreases constantly with increasing withdrawal rates. If gas and oil counterflow is possible, while a high oil recovery is obtained at low field-wide production rates, somewhat higher oil recovery is possible at higher production rates until an optimum gas phase is developed in the oil column which permits the maximum rate of oil and gas counterflow. Thereafter, oil-recovery efficiency by segregation with counterflow decreases.

In the general case where all three recovery processes are in operation simultaneously, and since each takes on a relative degree of importance as measured by the driving indices (Fig. 14-4) as a function of withdrawal rates, the over-all oil ultimate recovery, which is the weighted average of the recoveries by the individual processes, is also a function of field withdrawal rate. In most cases it is a curve of the type shown in Fig. 14-5. This curve indicates a maximum at a certain field production rate Q_o which may well be called the *engineering most efficient rate* for the field. Since gross returns are proportional to the recovery curve, when subtracting operating cost per barrel recovered, a net return curve is obtained as a function of Q_o and it determines the *economic most efficient rate*.

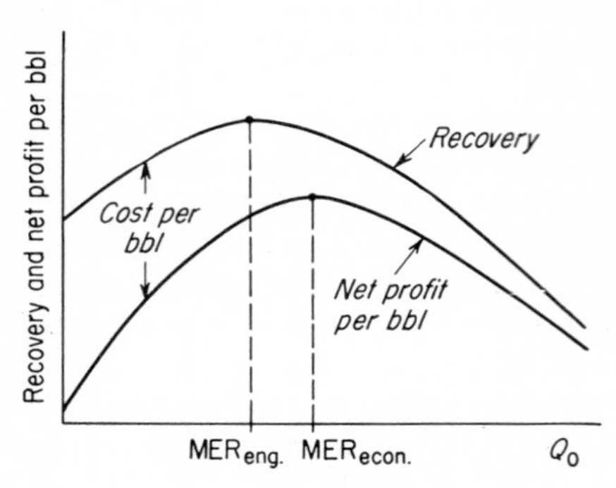

Fig. 14-5. Probable trend of field-wide oil recovery and of oil production cost as a function of the field-wide oil-producing rate.

Improved over-all recoveries may also be secured at higher field production rates through the medium of gas injection and artificial water drive. It is obvious that in order to obtain the benefit of higher recovery through planned and engineered field-wide operations, it is necessary that the field be *operated as a unit* according to a master plan, the execution of which must be in experienced and authoritative hands.

UNITIZATION

Unitization, or pooling of interest among the various owners of a field, is actually a technique of allocating in advance the returns from anticipated oil production issuing from a common source of supply, namely, the geologic entity which constitutes the oil reservoir. Prior to 1930, allocation from a common source of supply was universally done by jungle practice, i.e., by the "rule of capture." Such practice is still in effect in various states. But since 1930 official regulatory bodies in the main oil-producing states have issued proration rules which allocate the state's allowable production among the main producing fields. In many instances the allocation is made on a well basis.

Unitization of leases over a common reservoir and proration or allocation of market demand to the various pools go hand in hand.

In effect, unitization of oil and gas rights is an operation by which royalty owners and operators in a common reservoir exchange limited property rights for an equivalent undivided interest in a larger property, namely, the *unit*. The original leases or royalties no longer exist.

The purposes for which unitization agreements are entered into are multiple and varied:

1. To reduce cost of production and of lease equipment and to eliminate unnecessary wells without reducing ultimate recovery. This is generally the primary incentive.

2. To eliminate *injurious* competition among the operators and prevent a return to the application of the rule of capture.

3. To promote conservation of a natural resource and increase recovery through favoring the best recovery mechanism on a field-wide basis. This finds its best example of application when there is a large gas cap through shutting-in of large gas-oil-ratio wells.

4. To promote the application of external oil production stimulation means which permit higher recovery such as by gas injection (in dispersed or in segregated manner) or by water injection (water flooding). This is a most important aspect of unitization and, in fact, it is the only reason that may legally be advanced to permit a pooling of interest and elimination of competition. Unitization is a prerequisite to the field-wide application of stimulation or of secondary recovery techniques because through injection of gas or water, migration of oil across property lines takes place because of disturbances introduced thereby in the normal drainage pattern of wells under competitive production.

The crux of a unitization agreement is the determination of the participating interest fraction in the unit. In advance of the establishment of a unit, current production and gross income necessarily existed; the *equity* of each producer and royalty owner in the common supply is in fact his fair share of the current gross income derived from production under competitive methods. Gross income is specifically indicated because of possible differences in crude values. Factors which may enter into the determination of equity are:

1. Productive acreage.

2. Acre-feet of effective reservoir; effective pay is, however, an interpretive element.

3. Recoverable oil in place exclusive of oil that may be recovered by migration from adjoining properties.

4. Producible reserves including oil that may be recovered by migration under normal competitive production practice. Recovery of oil by drainage of adjacent properties is, however, difficult to evaluate objectively; it is mostly a matter of opinion.

5. Value of future reserves, including those that may be obtained by stimulation and secondary recovery means. The question of overhead cost enters this factor and it is a variable with all operators.

6. Present worth of future earnings.

7. Current production or allowable. This is not a fair measure of reserves or oil in place, but it is a measure of current income.

8. Cumulative production; this factor may be affected by migration and early development of a lease.

9. Number of wells; this is a measure of the investment on which return is expected.

10. Bottom-hole pressure; this may be a measure of the state of depletion of a property.

11. Well productivity; this factor is another measure of current income.

12. Ownership of oil in place; this is actually the net acre-feet $\times (1 - \sigma_w)$. It is not a good element in a participation formula because it does not include oil that may be recovered by migration from other parts of the pool.

13. Acre-feet times porosity.

14. Acre-feet times permeability.

15. Present-day value of ultimate production or of reserves.

16. Adjusted acre-feet; this concept comes about in the unitization of two-phase reservoirs where it is necessary to establish relative values between oil and gas phases on an acre-foot basis. This requires that recovery factors for each zone be established and that a dollar value be agreed upon for oil, gas, and condensate. In some units, gas in place has been given arbitrarily one-fifth the value of oil in place. In others, where gas is rich in distillate, gas and oil are given the same value per unit reservoir volume.

Reserves, migration, and present worth are mostly a matter of interpretation, and it is difficult to arrive at irrefutable proof of evaluation; therefore they are a stumbling block in the unitization agreements and they are often left out of the mechanics of unitization proceedings when the primary purpose is to devise a *participation formula* by which the equity of each operator may readily be established.

The best participation formula is the simplest one that may be devised and that does not include interpretive elements; it should also ensure equal treatment to all operators. A common formula determines participation in a unit on the basis of 50 per cent on oil in place and 50 per cent on current production. Oil in place is a measure of reserves, whereas current production is a measure of earning power, which two factors are of paramount importance in considering equity.

In a large field where oil will be moved over long distances across the reservoir (such as in the Sacroc Unit, Scurry County, Texas) more weight is given to reserves than to current production, such as 75 per cent on acre-feet and 25 per cent on production averaged over a stipulated base period. The Fullerton formula is 50 per cent on production and 50 per cent on oil in place times bottom-hole pressure.

A participating formula which has been used in the Levelland field, West Texas, is 0.375 on acreage, 0.50 on current production, and 0.125 on the number of wells.

When depleted fields are unitized for the purpose of secondary recovery by water flooding, past cumulative production often enters the formula, as it is believed to be a measure of recoverable oil by artificial water drive.

While there are several types of units formed for special purposes, such as *spacing units* for observance of spacing regulations and *exploration units* for wildcat drilling and subsequent orderly field development, we are mainly concerned with *producing units*.

A recent development in designing a participating formula is the *split-formula*. It was originally used in semidepleted fields, but now it is used in newly discovered flush fields. This formula recognizes that the share of oil production to which each owner is entitled is not necessarily the same during the period of primary production as during the period of stimulated or secondary recovery. The formula provides that, until a certain stipulated date or until a certain field-wide cumulative production has been obtained, the sharing of interest will be according to a certain pattern; beyond this point a different basis is used for the remainder of the life of the field. A basic principle in the establishment of a participating formula is the recognition that the allocation of production should be made equal to the contribution which each lease makes to the unit as a whole. It should also be cognizant of the production mechanism that prevails in the reservoir and of the degree of depletion that has already set in when unitization goes into effect.

Unitization Regulations. Unitization regulations are variable in each oil-producing state because one of the requirements before a producing unit may be formed is to ascertain that immunity from state antitrust laws exists.

A number of oil-producing states have definite unitization statutes:

Texas. The law is very specific in its requirements:

1. A unit agreement between operators is required before stimulation or secondary recovery operations may be applied to a reservoir.

2. The sole purpose for which unit operation is permitted is to prevent waste, to promote conservation of all natural resources, and to protect the rights of all interested parties. A unit may not be formed to reduce operating cost and to prevent competition; it must be shown that a real increase in oil recovery is to be obtained.

3. It must be shown that the increased cost of operation under unit agreement will be less than the value of additional oil recovered.

4. The area of the unit must be that defined by the drilling development; it may not be smaller or larger.

5. All interested parties must be given an equal opportunity to participate in the unit agreement. Participation must be on a voluntary basis.

6. Permission for unit operation is granted only after a public hearing before the state regulatory body, the Texas Railroad Commission.

Oklahoma. Unit operation may be formed only if at least 63 per cent of the working interest approves as well as 63 per cent of the royalty interest, exclusive of royalty interest held by lessee. Then minority interest is compelled to participate.

Arkansas. Unit operation is permitted only if at least 75 per cent of all interested parties approve.

Louisiana. While voluntary oil- and gas-operating units are permitted, the state may compell the unitization of any recycling distillate fields on its own motion and assign participation in absence of agreement between interested parties.

In *Colorado, New Mexico, Montana,* and *Wyoming,* unitization of oil and gas pools is permitted for conservation purposes through the medium of selective production, while injection of gas or water is not always permitted.

Ten other oil states have unitization statutes, while *California, Missouri, Utah,* and *Virginia* have no unitization laws whatsoever.

PRORATION AND CONSERVATION

It may be said that conservation of a wasting resource, and of oil in particular, is not its hoarding but it is the intelligent production of this resource with the minimum amount of waste as well as its intelligent use. Unitization contributes to the elimination of *physical waste* underground by promoting the efficient recovery of crude oil and gas condensate, as well as aboveground by reducing gas flaring. However, waste of a depleting resource occurs also when it is produced at a rate greater than market demand. In this eventuality prices of the natural resource are depressed and marginal production must be abandoned; this is *economic waste*. It befalls the producing oil states to determine periodically the current market demand for crude oil, to recommend a national production ceiling, and to allocate such production between the various states. The machinery through which this is accomplished is the Interstate Oil Compact Commission which meets quarterly and has a permanent committee studying the supply and demand problems and makes recommendations for approval by oil-state governors.

Within an oil state itself, the allocation of state quota among pools and wells is made through the medium of *proration*. The machinery of state proration differs with each state.

In *Texas*, an allowable per well is fixed generally at one barrel per day per acre drained, but the total monthly allowable is limited by controlling the number of monthly producing days. Stimulation and secondary recovery projects are not as yet limited in production.

Allocation of state quotas between fields is based on the determination of the most efficient rate for each field through the medium of yearly most efficient rate (MER) hearings conducted by the Texas Railroad Commission; at such meetings a serious effort is made to determine the proper most efficient rate for each pool in the state.

In *Oklahoma*, production allowable per well is varied on a barrel per day basis according to state quota. Stimulation and secondary recovery projects are not limited in production.

When a new field is brought in, it is given a preference or discovery allowable of 150 bbl per day. This is to remain in effect for 60 days or for such period as may be required to test the well properly, after which time the operator requests from the Oklahoma Corporation Commission to be granted an allowable which in his judgment is a safe producing rate for the well and field. The Commission generally permits the requested rate unless it is unreasonably high. In effect, the most efficient rate in a field is set by the original discoverers in cooperation with later operators.

In *Louisiana*, a depth schedule allowable method is used to determine the field allowable. The greater the depth of production, the greater the allowable; this recognizes the need for return on investment, but not engineering merit, as a measure to increase recovery and to promote conservation.

In *New Mexico*, a technique of most efficient rate determination similar to that of Louisiana is in favor.

In *Mississippi*, the most efficient rate of a pool is set by the Conservation Commission of that state based on recommendations from operators in that pool.

While proration is a state machinery which, in the main, prevents economic waste from flush fields, it treats them more or less equally on a well basis and pays little or no attention to the fact that oil fields, especially if they produce by the water- or segregation-drive mechanisms, should be operated at withdrawal rates specific to each in order to ensure maximum recovery and prevent *underground waste.* State conservation authorities should be more cognizant of this fact in order to promote real conservation of oil and gas resources.

SELECTED REFERENCES ON COMBINATION DRIVE FIELDS, UNITIZATION, AND CONSERVATION AND ON OIL PRODUCTION IN COMBINATION DRIVE FIELDS

Combination Drive Fields

1945

Pirson, S. J.: The Engineering Approach to Oil Reservoir Controls, *Oil Weekly,* Dec. 31, pp. 22ff.

1951

Clark, N. J.: A Review of Reservoir Engineering, *World Oil,* May, pp. 157ff., June, pp. 184ff.

1955

Wooddy, L. D., Jr., and R. Moscrip, III: Performance Calculations for Combination Drive Reservoirs, *AIME Tech. Pub.* 4253.

Unitization

1916

McMurray, W. F., and J. O. Lewis: Underground Wastes in Oil and Gas Fields and Methods of Prevention, *U. S. Bur. Mines Tech. Paper* 130.

1924

Doherty, H. L.: Suggestions for Conservation of Petroleum by Control of Production, *Trans. AIME,* vol. 7.

1930

Swigart, T. E.: Engineering and Economic Aspects of Unit Operation, *Oil Weekly,* Nov. 21 and 28.

1943

Kaveler, H. H.: Engineering Features of the Shuler Field and Unit Operation, *AIME Tech. Pub.* 1605.

1948

Elkins, L. F., et al.: Lance Creek Sundance Reservoir Performance–A Unitized Pressure-maintenance Project, *AIME Tech. Pub.* 2401.

Hardwicke, R. E.: Anti-trust Laws, et al. vs. Unit Operation of Oil and Gas Pools, *AIME,* New York.

Horner, W. L., and E. G. Trostel: Benton Field Unit, *Oil Gas J.,* Mar. 4, pp. 77ff.

1949

Swedenborg, E. A.: Production of Oil under Unitization in Wertz Dome Field, Wyoming, *AIME Tech. Pub.* 2588.

Welsh, J. R., et al.: A Study of Oil and Gas Conservation in the Picton Field, *AIME Tech. Pub.* 2564.

1951

Tarner, J., et al.: The Shuler Jones Sand Pool: Nine Years of Unitized Pressure-maintenance Operations, *Trans. AIME Petroleum Div.*, vol. 192, pp. 121ff.

1953

Miller, E. B., Jr.: Unit Agreements and Methods of Participation, *Oil Gas J.*, May 25, pp. 184ff.

Petroleum Conservation

1951

Buckley, S. E.: "Petroleum Conservation," 304 pp., E. J. Storm Printing Company, Dallas, Tex.

ABBREVIATIONS AND SYMBOLS

atm	Atmospheric pressure = 14.7 psia
bbl	Barrel = 42 gallons = 5.61 cu ft
M	Mobility ratio = K_o/μ_o
Mcf	One thousand cubic feet of gas
MER	Most efficient rate
NTP	Normal temperature (60°F) and base pressure (14.4 psia)
psi	Pressure in pounds per square inch, gauge
psia	Pressure in pounds per square inch, absolute
ϕ	Porosity as a decimal or fraction of rock volume
φ	Fluidity or reciprocal of viscosity
σ_o	Oil saturation as a decimal or fraction of pore space
σ_{or}	Residual oil saturation as a decimal or fraction of pore space
σ_w	Water saturation as a decimal or fraction of pore space
σ_{wc}	Connate water saturation as a decimal or fraction of pore space
σ_{wi}	Invaded-zone water saturation as a decimal or fraction of pore space
σ_{wt}	Total water saturation as a decimal or fraction of pore space
σ_g	Gas saturation as a decimal or fraction of pore space
σ_D	Displacing fluid saturation as a decimal or fraction of pore space
K	Absolute or specific permeability, darcys
K_a	Absolute or specific air permeability, darcys
K_∞	Klinkenberg or equivalent liquid permeability, darcys
K_o	Effective permeability to oil, darcys
K_w	Effective permeability to water, darcys
K_g	Effective permeability to gas, darcys
k_o	Relative permeability to oil as a fraction of 1
k_w	Relative permeability to water as a fraction of 1
k_g	Relative permeability to gas as a fraction of 1
δ	Fluid density, mass per unit volume; also specific gravity
δ_o	Oil density, mass per unit volume; also oil specific gravity
δ_w	Water density, mass per unit volume; also water specific gravity
δ_g	Gas density, mass per unit volume; also gas specific gravity
r	Radial distance
r_w	Well radius
r_e	Extreme drainage radius
h	Formation thickness, ft
h_e	Effective-pay thickness, ft; also completion interval, ft
H	Flow potential = $z + 2.31P/\delta$, ft
H_o	Flow potential in oil phase, ft
H_w	Flow potential in water phase, ft
H_g	Flow potential in gas phase, ft
R	Resistivity or specific electric resistance of formation in ohm-meters

R_o Resistivity of a porous rock saturated 100 per cent in conductive fluid, ohm-meters
R_a Apparent resistivity, ohm-meters
R_{mc} Mud-cake resistivity, ohm-meters
R_i Resistivity of invaded zone, ohm-meters
R_m Mud resistivity, ohm-meters
R_{wc} Resistivity of connate water, ohm-meters
R_{mf} Mud-filtrate resistivity, ohm-meters
R_t True resistivity of uninvaded formations, ohm-meters
R_{xo} Flushed-zone resistivity, ohm-meters
g Acceleration of gravity = 980 cm per sec per sec
$\mathbf{R}$ Gas constant
R Instantaneous gas-oil ratio, cu ft per bbl STO
R_{av} Average gas-oil ratio (instantaneous) over a production interval
P_0 Original bottom-hole pressure, psia, psi, or atm
P Bottom-hole pressure at any time during production, psia, psi, or atm
P_a Atmospheric pressure = 14.4 psia
P_b Bubble-point pressure (or saturation pressure), psia, psi, or atm
P_w Bottom-hole pressure at the well while producing, psi or atm
P_e Field pressure at external drainage radius r_e, psi or atm
P_m Mean pressure $= \dfrac{P_w + P_e}{2}$, psi or atm
P_c Capillary pressure, psi or atm
P_o Pressure in oil phase, psi or atm
P_g Pressure in gas phase, psi or atm
P_w Pressure in water phase, psi or atm
T_f Formation temperature, °R = 460 + t_f
t_f Formation temperature, °F
T_a Normal atmospheric temperature = 60°F, or 520°R
D Depth of well penetration, ft
D_i Diameter of invasion, hole diameter
d Hole diameter, in.
D Displacing fluid
Θ Time
θ Angle of contact
S_0 Original solution gas in stock-tank oil (dimensionless), cu ft at NTP per cu ft of stock-tank oil
S Solution gas in stock-tank oil (dimensionless), cu ft at NTP per cu ft of stock-tank oil
c Fluid compressibility, per psi or per atm
c_o Oil compressibility, per psi or per atm
c_w Water compressibility, per psi or per atm
c_r Rock compressibility, per psi or per atm
α_0 Reservoir volume of 1 cu ft of gas at NTP when placed under initial reservoir conditions, cu ft
α Gas reservoir volume factor or volume of 1 cu ft of gas at NTP when placed under prevailing reservoir conditions, cu ft

α Formation dip angle

α^2 Diffusivity constant $= \dfrac{K}{\mu\phi c}$

β_0 Original oil-reservoir volume factor, at P_0 (dimensionless)

β Oil-reservoir volume factor, at P (dimensionless)

β_b Oil-reservoir volume factor at bubble-point pressure (dimensionless)

Z_0 Original gas compressibility factor at P_0 (dimensionless)

Z Gas compressibility factor at P (dimensionless)

z Coordinate perpendicular to stratification

x,y Coordinate parallel to stratification

γ Surface tension, dynes per cm

μ_o Viscosity of oil, centipoises

μ_w Viscosity of water, centipoises

μ_g Viscosity of gas, centipoises

V_o Reservoir volume saturated with oil, acre-ft

V_g Reservoir volume of gas in the gas cap, acre-ft

m Ratio of gas-cap volume to reservoir volume saturated with oil

W Cumulative water encroachment, cu ft or bbl

w Cumulative water production, cu ft or bbl

N Original stock-tank oil volume in place, cu ft or bbl

$\mathbf{n}$ Cumulative stock oil production, cu ft or bbl

n Cumulative fractional oil production, fraction

f_D Fraction of displacing fluid in two flowing fluid phases within the reservoir rock

f_w Fraction of water in total oil-water flow within the reservoir

f_g Fraction of gas in total oil-gas flow within the reservoir

Q_t Total fluid flow through any cross-sectional area (cc per sec or bbl per day)

q_t Total fluid flow or throughput in the reservoir per unit area, cc per sec per sq cm or bbl per acre per day

q_o Oil-flow rate in the reservoir per unit area, cc per sec per sq cm or bbl per acre per day; also allowable STO production rate per well, bbl per day

q_w Water-flow rate in the reservoir per unit area, cc per sec per sq cm or bbl per acre per day

q_g Gas-flow rate in the reservoir per unit area, cc per sec per sq cm or bbl per acre per day; also gas-production rate per well, cu ft per day

Q_o Oil-flow rate field-wide or through any cross-sectional area, cc per sec or bbl per day

Q_g Gas-flow rate field-wide or through any cross-sectional area, cc per sec or bbl per day

Q_w Water-flow rate field-wide or through any cross-sectional area, cc per sec or bbl per day

r_n Net cumulative gas-oil ratio: (dimensionless), cu ft per cu ft

ω Angular velocity

NAME INDEX

SUBJECT INDEX